Applied
General Statistics

Applied
General Statistics

Frederick E. Croxton, Ph.D.

Professor Emeritus of Statistics, Columbia University

Dudley J. Cowden, Ph.D.

Professor of Economic Statistics
School of Business Administration
University of North Carolina

and

Sidney Klein, Ph.D.

Associate Professor of Economics
Rutgers—The State University

Third Edition

PRENTICE-HALL, INC.

Englewood Cliffs, N. J.

THIRD EDITION

Library of Congress Catalog Card Number: 67-15187

Current Printing (last digit):
10 9 8 7 6 5 4 3 2 1

Printed in the United States of America

PRENTICE-HALL INTERNATIONAL, INC., *London*
PRENTICE-HALL OF AUSTRALIA, PTY. LTD., *Sydney*
PRENTICE-HALL OF CANADA, LTD., *Toronto*
PRENTICE-HALL OF INDIA (PRIVATE) LTD., *New Delhi*
PRENTICE-HALL OF JAPAN, INC., *Tokyo*

Preface

In this, the third edition of *Applied General Statistics*, the primary objective is the same as that of previous editions: to describe as briefly, yet, as clearly as possible, the more commonly used statistical methods and to illustrate their applications in many fields.

The scope is substantially the same as that of the preceding edition despite the shortening of the book by almost 100 pages. All those illustrative examples which required such treatment have been changed or up-dated and, as before, are based on real rather than hypothetical data. However, neither the order of topics nor the symbols have been changed. In this edition the lists of symbols, which formerly preceded each chapter that used symbols, have been brought together as Appendix A. The forthcoming fifth edition of *Workbook in Applied General Statistics* will conform to this edition in regard to both order of topics and symbols.

This third edition of *Applied General Statistics* was prepared by Sidney Klein.

I am indebted to Professor Sir Ronald A. Fisher, Cambridge, to Dr. Frank Yates, Rothamsted, and to Messrs. Oliver and Boyd Ltd., Edinburgh, for permission to reprint portions of Tables III and IV from their book *Statistical Tables for Biological, Agricultural, and Medical Research*. I am similarly indebted to Professor Egon S. Pearson and to the Biometrika Trustees for permission to reprint the tables or portions of tables from *Biometrika* and from E. S. Pearson and H. O. Hartley's *Biometrika Tables for Statisticians*, Volume 1, which are shown here in Appendices I, J, M, O, and P, as well as in Charts 25.6 and 25.7. Other persons and organizations who supplied data or gave permission to reprint material are acknowledged at the appropriate locations.

Many people and organizations contributed directly or indirectly to the production of this revision; unfortunately space does not permit acknowledgment of every individual contribution. The administration, faculty, and/or staff of Rutgers—The State University; Columbia University; the University of California at Los Angeles; National Chengchi University, Taipei, Taiwan, Republic of China; The Council for International Economic Cooperation and Development, Republic of China; the University of Hong Kong; and The Asia Foundation, U.S.A. provided much moral support and excellent facilities as needed when I taught under their auspices or served as Director of Studies, Economics Training Program, CIECD. Special thanks are extended to Robert C. Walters, Senior Editor of Prentice-Hall, Inc., whose careful and cooperative production-editorial supervision was most helpful and most necessary in the absence of the writer from the United States.

Various portions of the manuscript reflect the contributions of Professor Alfred J. Kana of Seton Hall University. Mrs. Helen Chanin and Miss Ruby Ying Chu assisted greatly by typing parts of the manuscript. Spencer R. Klein contributed much clerical work. Last but by no means least, I should like to acknowledge my indebtedness to my wife, Eleanor Klein, who computed, typed, drew charts, and edited as required.

SIDNEY KLEIN

University of Hong Kong
Hong Kong, B. C. C.

Contents

(For a short course in statistical methods, the chapters or sections which are starred in this table of contents may be omitted without destroying the continuity of treatment.)

Applied
General Statistics

CHAPTER 1

Introduction

STATISTICAL DATA AND STATISTICAL METHODS

The term *statistics* is used in either of two senses. In common parlance it is generally employed synonymously with the word *data*. Thus someone may say that he has seen "statistics of industrial accidents in the United States." It would be conducive to greater precision of meaning if we were not to use *statistics* in this sense, but rather to say "data (or figures) of industrial accidents in the United States."

"Statistics" also refers to the statistical principles and methods which have been developed for handling numerical data and which form the subject matter of this text. Statistical methods, or statistics, range from the most elementary descriptive devices, which may be understood by anyone, to those extremely complicated mathematical procedures which are comprehended by only the most expert theoreticians. It is the purpose of this volume not to enter into the highly mathematical and theoretical aspects of the subject but rather to treat of its more elementary and more frequently used phases.

Statistics may be defined as *the collection, presentation, analysis, and interpretation of numerical data.* The facts which are dealt with must be capable of numerical expression. We can make little use statistically of the information that dwellings are built of brick, stone, wood, and other materials; however, if we are able to determine *how many* or *what proportion* of, dwellings are constructed of each type of material, we have numerical data suitable for statistical analysis.

Statistics should not be thought of as a subject correlative with physics, chemistry, economics, and sociology. Statistics is not a science; it is a scientific method. The methods and procedures which we are about to examine constitute a useful and often indispensable tool for the research worker. Without an adequate understanding of statistics, the investigator in the social sciences may frequently be like the blind man groping in a dark closet for a black cat that isn't there. The methods of statistics

1

are useful in an ever-widening range of human activities, in any field of thought in which numerical data may be had.

The derivation of the word "statistics" suggests its origin. The administration of states required the collection and analysis of data of population and wealth for purposes of war and finance. Gradually data of more diverse nature were obtained for the general uses of government. Certain phases of statistics were developed by students of games of chance. Insurance and biology, as well as other natural sciences, were fertile fields for the application and development of statistical methods. Today there is hardly a phase of endeavor which does not find statistical devices at least occasionally useful. Economics, sociology, anthropology, business, agriculture, psychology, and education—all lean heavily upon statistics. The medical research worker often must rely upon statistics to determine the significance of his results. The lawyer, especially if he is in corporation practice, may frequently find statistical devices of definite use. It should, of course, be added that the musician, the artist, the actor, and the writer of fiction would rarely have occasion to employ statistics, but even here the analysis of certain data of sales, box-office receipts, and trends of popular taste might prove useful.

In defining statistics it was pointed out that the numerical data are collected, presented, analyzed, and interpreted. Let us briefly examine each of these four procedures.

Collection. Statistical data may be obtained from existing published or unpublished sources, such as government agencies, trade associations, research bureaus, magazines, newspapers, individual research workers, and elsewhere. On the other hand, the investigator may collect his own information, going perhaps from house to house or from firm to firm to obtain the data. The first-hand collection of statistical data is one of the most difficult and important tasks which a statistician must face. The soundness of his procedure determines in an overwhelming degree the usefulness of the data which he obtains.

The following chapter treats of these two methods of obtaining data. It should be emphasized, however, that the investigator who has experience and good common sense is at a distinct advantage if original data must be collected. There is much which may be taught about this phase of statistics, but there is much more which can be learned only through experience. Although a person may never collect statistical data for his own use and may always use published sources, it is essential that he have a working knowledge of the processes of collection and that he be able to evaluate the reliability of the data he proposes to use. Untrustworthy data do not constitute a satisfactory base upon which to rest a conclusion.

It is to be regretted that many people have a tendency to accept statistical data without question. To them, any statement which is presented in numerical terms is correct and its authenticity is automatically established. Shortly after the retirement of a clerical employee of a rail-road, it was announced in the press that during his 43 years of employment he had commuted a total of 1,200,000,000 miles. Most readers of the statement probably accepted it without question. As a matter of fact, in order for the figure to be correct the employee would have had to travel approximately 3,200 miles each and every hour of every day during the entire 43 years!

Presentation. Either for one's own use or for the use of others, the data must be presented in some suitable form. Usually the figures are arranged in tables or represented by graphic devices as described in Chapters 3 to 6.

Analysis. In the process of analysis, data must be classified into useful and logical categories. The possible categories must be considered when plans are made for collecting the data, and the data must be classified as they are tabulated and before they can be shown graphically. Thus the process of analysis is partially concurrent with collection and presentation.

There are four important bases of classification of statistical data: (1) qualitative, (2) quantitative, (3) chronological, and (4) geographical, each of which will be examined in turn.

Qualitative. When, for example, employees are classified as union or non-union, we have a qualitative differentiation. The distinction is one of kind rather than of amount. Individuals may be classified concerning marital status, as single, married, widowed, divorced, and separated. Farm operators may be classified as full owners, part owners, managers, and tenants. Natural rubber may be designated as plantation or wild, according to its source.

Quantitative. When items vary in respect to some measurable characteristic, a quantitative classification is appropriate. Families may be classified according to the number of children. Manufacturing concerns may be classified according to the number of workers employed, and also according to the value of goods produced. Individuals may be classified according to the amount of income tax paid.

Most quantitative distributions are *frequency distributions.* The data of Table 8.3 show a frequency distribution of grades received by 409 of the liberal arts graduates of Rutgers—The State University. A number of other frequency distributions are shown in Chapters 8, 9, and 10.

Sometimes, qualitatively classified data may be reclassified on a quantitative basis by making very slight changes. The assets of a bank may be listed in respect to degree of liquidity (cash, due from banks, United States securities, marketable securities, call loans, eligible paper, other loans, real estate loans, real estate, and furniture and fixtures). Although these categories differ from one another in a more or less unassignable quantitative fashion, the classification is actually made upon a qualitative basis. If we should reclassify the bank assets according to the length of time required to convert each into cash, the classification would be quantitative. In general the assets would be in the same order as before, but a few specific items among the less liquid qualitative groups (for example, certain real estate and real estate loans) would be convertible into cash in a relatively short time.

Chronological. Chronological data or *time series* show figures concerning a particular phenomenon at various specified times. For example, the closing price of a certain stock may be shown for each day over a period of months or years; the birth rate in the United States may be listed for each of a number of years; production of coal may be shown monthly for a span of years. The analysis of time series, involving a consideration of trend, cyclical, periodic (seasonal), and irregular movements, will be discussed in Chapters 11 to 16.

In a certain sense, time series are somewhat akin to quantitative distributions in that each succeeding year or month of a series is one year or one month further removed from some earlier point of reference. However, periods of time—or, rather, the events occurring within these periods—differ qualitatively from each other also. The essential arrangement of the figures in a time sequence is inherent in the nature of the data under consideration.

Occasionally a time series may be converted into a frequency distribution. If a railroad company has kept records of the number of railroad ties replaced each year, the data constitute a time series. When the same information is used in conjunction with the dates of installation, the life of the various ties may be expressed as a frequency distribution, showing perhaps:

Length of life	Number of ties
4 but under 5 years	2
5 but under 6 years	5
6 but under 7 years	17
etc.	etc.

Geographical. The geographical distribution is essentially a type of qualitative distribution, but is generally considered as a distinct classification. When the population is shown for each of the states in the United States, we have data which are classified geographically. Although there is a qualitative difference between any two states, the distinction that is being made is not so much one of kind as of location. Geographically classified data are shown in Table 3.1 and in Charts 6.19–6.22.

Sometimes a geographical distribution may be put into the form of a frequency distribution. Thus, if we had data of the yield of corn per acre in each county of Iowa, we would have a geographical series. These data may be put into the form of a frequency distribution by stating the number of counties having yields per acre of "10 and under 15 bushels," "15 and under 20 bushels," and so forth.

The presentation of classified data in tabular and graphic form is but one elementary step in the analysis of statistical data. Many other processes are described in the following pages of this book. Statistical investigation frequently endeavors to ascertain what is typical in a given situation. Hence all types of occurrences must be considered, both the usual and the unusual.

In forming an opinion, most individuals are apt to be unduly influenced by unusual occurrences and to disregard the ordinary happenings. In any sort of investigation, statistical or otherwise, the unusual cases must not exert undue influence. Many people are of the opinion that to break a mirror brings bad luck. Having broken a mirror, a person is apt to be on the lookout for the expected "bad luck" and to attribute any untoward event to the breaking of the mirror. If nothing happens after the mirror has been broken, there is nothing to remember and this result (perhaps the usual result) is disregarded. If bad luck occurs, it is so unusual that it is remembered, and consequently the belief is reinforced. The scientific procedure would include all happenings following the breaking of the mirror, and would compare the "resulting" bad luck to the amount of bad luck occurring when a mirror has not been broken.

Statistics, then, must include in its analysis all sorts of happenings. If we are studying the duration of cases of pneumonia, we may study what is typical by determining the average length and possibly also the divergence below and above this average. When considering a time series showing steel-mill activity, we may give attention to the typical seasonal pattern of the series, to the growth factor (trend) present, and to the cyclical behavior. Sometimes it is found that two sets of statistical data tend to be associated. In Chapter 19 it is pointed out that there is an association between temperature and the rapidity with which crickets chirp. If the temperature increases, the crickets chirp faster; if the temperature decreases, the crickets chirp more slowly. The relationship can be expressed mathematically and we can estimate the rapidity of crickets' chirps from the temperature; or, conversely we can make a good estimate of the temperature based upon the rapidity of chirps.

Occasionally a statistical investigation may be exhaustive and include all possible occurrences. More frequently, however, it is necessary to study a smaller group or sample. If we desire to study the expenditures of lawyers for life insurance, it would hardly be possible to include all lawyers in the United States. Resort must be had to a sample; and it is essential that the sample be as nearly representative as possible of the entire group, so that we may be able to make a reasonable inference as to the results to be expected for an entire population. The problem of selecting a sample is discussed in the following chapter. In Chapters 24, 25, and 26 an attempt is made to determine how much reliance may be placed in the results obtained from samples.

Sometimes the statistician is faced with the task of forecasting. He may be required to prognosticate the sales of automobile tires a year hence, or to forecast the population some years in advance. Several years ago a student appeared in a summer session class of one of the writers and in a private talk announced that he had come to the course for a single purpose: to get a formula which would enable him to forecast the price of cotton. It was important to him and to his employers to have some advance information on cotton prices, since the concern purchased enormous quantities of cotton. Regrettably, the young man had to be disillusioned. To our knowledge, there are no magic formulae for forecasting. This does not mean that forecasting is impossible; rather it means that forecasting is a complicated process of which a formula is but a small part. And forecasting is uncertain and dangerous. To attempt to say what will happen in the future requires a thorough grasp of the subject to be forecast, up-to-the-minute knowledge of developments in allied fields, and recognition of the limitations of any mechanical forecasting device. Further comments concerning forecasting are to be found in Chapter 22.

Interpretation. The final step in an investigation consists of interpreting the data which have been obtained. What are the conclusions growing out of the analysis? What do the figures tell us that is new or that reinforces or casts doubt upon previous hypotheses? The results must be interpreted in the light of the limitations of the original material. Too exact conclusions must not be drawn from data which themselves are but approximations. It is essential, however, that the investigator discover and clarify all the useful and applicable meaning which is present in his data.

A FEW IMPROPRIETIES

The research worker must be constantly on the alert to avoid any misuses of his material. Illogical and careless reasoning or improper use of data will destroy the value of a study which may be technically acceptable in its earlier phases. A few examples of fallacious procedures may clarify this point. In later chapters of the book, other fallacies are occasionally mentioned in connection with the methods to which they apply.

Bias. The presence of bias on the part of an investigator is, obviously, sufficient to discredit the entire undertaking. Bias may be conscious or deliberate; in such a case it is synonymous with falsification. One well publicized example of this type of statistical impropriety concerns a railroad train crew in Communist China which one year apparently made very long safe runs—without major overhauls and with very low fuel consumption.   It was later discovered that numerous accidents had occurred and that secret repairs and refueling had taken place.[1]

On the other hand, an unconscious bias may be operative and this, perhaps, is a more dangerous form since the analyst himself may not be aware of it.   It seems to be a universal principle that individuals interpret and remember facts in the light most favorable to themselves.   *Rashomon*, a Japanese literary classic that has been translated into many languages, is based on this understandably human trait.   It is for this reason that there are so many law suits which involve sharply different versions of the same incident which are based on honest differences of opinion.

As will be seen in the following chapter, statistical data cannot be picked out of thin air as the conjurer appears to produce coins at his finger tips.   The process is one requiring care and attention to details.   The data, when obtained, should be of value and not be casually disregarded. Note what a reviewer said of a certain author:

> Blank is thorough and undaunted.   Have statistics on any subject been collected before?   He has collected more and better ones.   If it is by its intrinsic nature unchartable, he has charted it none the less. . . . Chronology itself fares badly in his hands at times.   If his examples require to be a century or two misplaced, Blank can forget even his statistics and his charts in the good cause of logic.

Omission of important factor.   One year, a certain manufacturing company felt called upon to prove that all-metal tops did not result in hotter car interiors.   They suggested a test involving three steps:

1. Take a piece of top fabric about 8 inches square.   Place a piece of lining material of similar size beneath the fabric, and a thermometer beneath the lining material.

2. Take a piece of highly finished steel about 8 inches square.   Place similar sized pieces of $\frac{1}{4}$-inch felt and lining material beneath the metal, and a thermometer beneath the lining material.

3. Place each of the above assemblies on a board at room temperature. Carry the entire apparatus out into hot sunshine, leave it exposed for about 10 minutes, and then read the temperature of the two thermometers.

The difficulty with the above experiment is that the reader is asked, in step 2, to use a piece of *highly finished* steel.   Automobile tops are painted and therefore absorb more heat than does *highly finished* steel. The obvious fallacy in the test vitiates the experiment, although the additional insulation may actually make the metal-top car cooler than the fabric-top car.

---

[1] See Sidney Klein, "A Note on Statistical Techniques in Communist China," *The American Statistician*, June 1959, pp. 18–21, *passim*.

Carelessness. We cannot go through life without making mistakes, but carelessness should be reduced to a minimum. The wife of one of the authors wrote to a large department store to ask the size of a cedarized storage chest. The reply said, "This merchandise is available in the $3'' \times 1'' \times 1\frac{1}{2}''$ size."

Many of us have received sealed envelopes minus enclosures, or postal cards blank on the message side, and have, perchance, been guilty of sending the grocer's bill back to the grocer minus the check or with the check unsigned.

A chain store advertised a kind of meat at 49 cents per pound. In one of its stores there were nine portions, all wrapped in transparent material and labelled as to price per pound (49¢), weight, and price for the piece. Three of the portions were marked as follows: 3 lb. $9\frac{3}{4}$ oz., \$2.92; 4 lb. $15\frac{3}{4}$ oz., \$4.05; 4 lb. $12\frac{1}{4}$ oz., \$3.86. Division of these prices by their weights will show that the charge was at the rate of 81 cents per pound, a price much higher than that current at the time for that particular kind of meat. Several months later similar mispricings were observed in the same store for still other kinds of meat, so possibly this illustration should be listed under a heading other than "carelessness."

Non-sequitur. A weekly news magazine, the circulation of which had been growing in a healthy fashion, undertook to demonstrate for a particular year that its readers greatly exceeded its circulation. After showing figures of its circulation, the magazine stated: "And each of these subscribers represents 3.26 cover-to-cover readers, according to former Deputy Police Commissioner ———, who counted and identified [sic] 216,948 fingerprints on copies his operatives had picked up at random from subscribers' homes in seven different cities or towns." How could the investigator *know* the fingerprints belonged to cover-to-cover readers? Or, did he find each fingerprint on *every* page and, if so, does that prove each page was read? Do you ever actually read a magazine from cover to cover?

Non-comparable data. One year, newspapers carried reports of a meeting of the American College of Osteopathic Obstetricians at which a doctor was reported, by a metropolitan paper, to have stated that the maternal death rate among mothers treated by osteopathic physicians was less than half that among cases handled by the medical profession. The higher rate in the latter instance was said to be due to excessive use of anaesthetics, interruption of labor, and undue reliance on mechanical devices. A survey of 14,000 osteopathic delivery cases was said to show a maternal death rate of 2.8 per thousand cases. This figure was compared with the nation's average of more than 6 per thousand. It should be obvious that the average rate for the entire country is not representative of the rate for cases attended by the medical profession, since many maternity cases are not attended by physicians.

The makers of a small, inexpensive car had been stressing the fact that the introduction of their car had converted many used-car buyers into new-car owners. Concerning costs of operation, they pointed out that "owners report up to thirty-five miles to the gallon of gasoline, which compared with the average mileage obtained with a used car . . . is a saving of great importance to persons in the low-income group." The comparison of *maximum* mileage for one type of car with *average* mileage for other types of used cars is certainly unjustified.

Confusion of association and causation. Sometimes factors which are associated are erroneously regarded as being causally related. A southern meteorologist discovered that the fall price of corn is inversely related to the severity of hay fever cases. This does not imply that the low price of corn causes hay fever to be severe, nor does it imply that severe cases of hay fever bring about a drop in the price of corn. The price of corn is generally low when the corn crop has been large. When the weather conditions have been favorable for a bumper corn crop, they have also been favorable for a bumper crop of ragweed. Thus the fall price of corn and the suffering of hay fever patients may each be traced (at least partly) to the weather, but are not directly dependent upon each other. A further discussion of association and causation is given in Chapter 19.

Another instance of the confusion of association with causation occurred in a statement by a research organization which, having studied annual data, said, "When farm income goes up, factory payrolls invariably follow, but they do not lead the procession. One is cause, the other effect." If such a procession does exist, it can hardly be shown by annual data. If factory payrolls *follow* farm income, we should show that fact by plotting monthly data as is done for other series in Chart 22.9 and Chart 22.10. As to the causal relationship, it is fairly obvious that, while an increase (or decrease) in farm income does have a corresponding effect upon factory payrolls, the payrolls in turn have a reciprocal effect upon farm income. Furthermore, both are dependent upon any other factors which tend to affect the pattern of general business.

Insufficient data. Insufficient data result in a high degree of uncertainty respecting any conclusion which may be made from them. A very small sample may lead us to a correct conclusion, but we cannot place a high degree of assurance in our conclusion. When a medical worker is developing a new treatment, he does not announce its efficacy after trying it out on a few individuals. He must have enough data so that he can be relatively sure of results. If two or three subjects respond favorably, he cannot be safe in claiming that the occurrences were not due to chance. The favorable responses of these few might have come without the treatment, or in spite of it! Of course, there must be a "control" group to show how the subjects would respond without any treatment, or with the usual treatment. Moreover, both the control group and the treated group must be sufficiently large to warrant a conclusion. A discussion of the reliability of values computed from samples is given in Chapters 24–26.

Unrepresentative data. Conclusions may be based upon data which are numerically sufficient, but which are not representative. A small sample *may* be representative; on the other hand, a large sample *may not* be representative.

A classic example of a conclusion based upon unrepresentative data, one long-dwelt upon in the literature, is the forecast of the 1936 presidential election as made by the *Literary Digest*. More than 10,000,000 straw ballots were sent out by the *Digest*. Of these, 2,376,523 were returned and they indicated that 370 electoral votes would be cast for Landon and 161 for Roosevelt. The final election results were 523 electoral votes for Roosevelt and 8 for Landon. The difficulty was that the mailing lists used as a basis for the poll were relatively heavily weighted with persons in the upper economic brackets and thus were not representative of the entire voting population.

Concealed classification. Conclusions drawn from statistical data may sometimes be invalid because of the presence of a concealed classification which is overlooked. One such concealed classification was found to be present in a study of suicides. The data seemed to show that suicides were more likely to occur among certain religious groups than among others. Upon further consideration it was apparent that the matter of the urban or rural occurrence of the suicides had been overlooked. The conclusion should have been—not that suicides tended to tie up with given religious groups—but that suicides were more common in urban territories and that these religious groups were also more numerous in the cities.

Failure to define units. In a pamphlet given to each motorist with his renewal of an automobile vehicle or driver's license, a state automobile commissioner called attention to the fact that 26 years earlier the "mileage death rate" had been 23.6 while in the year just ended there had been a "mileage death rate" of 4.2. There was no explanation of whether this was the number of deaths per mile—or per thousand miles—of highway in the state, or the number of deaths per hundred, per thousand, or per million miles of vehicle travel during the year. Certainly it was not deaths per mile of vehicle travel, although at a quick reading that was what it seemed to be. Inquiry revealed that the ratio was the number of highway fatalities per hundred million miles of vehicle travel. The mileage was obtained by multiplying the number of gallons of gasoline sold in the state during the year by 13.12, the average mileage per gallon of gasoline. Incidentally, one may well wonder about the accuracy of this average and how it was obtained. Gasoline sales were, of course, available from state tax records.

In some developing countries, failures by the Central Government to define units clearly have resulted in different methods yielding widely varying results being used in the same activity. In Communist China, for example, over a period of years, at least three different methods were employed concurrently in the collectives and communes to determine the ratios of collective and commune "accumulation" and consumption to total collective and commune income. One of the authors once applied these three methods to the accounts of a specific commune and found alternative "accumulation" ratios of 27 per cent, 40 per cent, and 48 per cent.[2]

Misleading totals. Those of us who read the sport pages of the newspaper are likely to have noticed a statement each autumn to the effect that a certain number of thousand—or million—fans had watched the home team play during the baseball season just ended. For example, it was stated that 1,538,007 fans attended the home games of the New York Yankees during a particular baseball season. This figure was arrived at by adding the number of persons attending each home game. It does not, as is too often carelessly said or intimidated, represent 1,538,007 fans, but rather the specified number of admissions, many individuals having attended more than one game.

A somewhat similar meaningless, but impressive-sounding, total was present in a statement made by a horticultural concern that had recently acquired another similar company, which itself represented a recent merger of two other concerns. The statement was to the effect that their combined horticultural experience now totalled 295 years. This figure was obtained by adding the ages of the three companies.

Poorly designed experiment. For an experiment to be valid, it must be so designed[3] that the results which are arrived at cannot be attributed to factors other than those which are under consideration. The illustration which follows will be mentioned again, in another connection, at the end of Chapter 25. Many years ago when fluorescent lighting was first introduced, some people believed that persons who were exposed to the radiation of the lights would become sterile. A railroad had already installed fluorescent lights and, hoping to counteract this belief, undertook an experiment in which one group of rats was subjected to incandescent light, while another group was subjected to fluorescent

---

[2] Sidney Klein, "Some Aspects of Chinese Communist Statistics," paper delivered before Assn. for Asian Studies, Chicago, March 29, 1961, pp. 11–14, unpublished.

[3] A discussion of experimental design will be found in C. C. Li, *Introduction to Experimental Statistics*. McGraw-Hill Book Company, New York, 1964. See also D. J. Finney, *An Introduction to the Theory of Experimental Design*, The University of Chicago Press, 1960.

light. After a period of time the first group had the usual number of offspring, while the second group had none! A skeptical executive asked that the second group of rats be re-examined with care, and it was discovered that all of the rats of that group were of the same sex. It is elementary that the two groups should have had the same sex composition.

RESEARCH METHODS

It must not be assumed that the statistical method is the only method to use in research; neither should this method be considered the best attack for every problem. Just as the carpenter has a number of tools, each appropriate for a different sort of operation, so the researcher can avail himself of various techniques which are the tools of his trade and each of which is appropriate to a specific type of situation. If an amateur carpenter uses a screwdriver in lieu of a chisel, the results are not likely to be either workmanlike or satisfactory. Similarly, it is important that the investigator consider his problem carefully at the outset and make use of the technique or techniques which are appropriate to it. Just as the carpenter needs to use more than one tool in completing a piece of work, so the research worker must often make use of, not one, but several methods. [4]

When we desire a great deal of information concerning each individual or occurrence to be studied, much of our data may be non-quantitative by its very nature. In such an event we employ the *case study* method of investigation, the purpose of which is to consider in detail the characteristics peculiar to the individual case and to generalize from a number of such detailed studies. Some of the information obtained in a study of case histories (such as wages, number of offspring, and so forth) may be statistical, and when many cases are included, statistical summaries may be made of the non-quantitative information obtained.

If interest centers in changes in behavior or attitudes, the *panel* technique may be used. This consists of interviewing the same group of people on two or more occasions. The panel procedure may obtain data of a quantitative nature when information concerning, for example, consumption habits and family budgets is obtained; as for case studies, statistical analyses may be made of non-quantitative information, such as opinions on public questions, if the panels are large enough.

[4] For examples of the use of quantitative analysis in fields generally concerned with qualitative matters, see S. Brinegar, "Mark Twain and the Quintus Curtius Snodgrass Letters: A Statistical Test of Authorship," *Journal of The American Statistical Association*, March 1963, pp. 85–96; and F. Mosteller and D. L. Wallace, "Inference in an Authorship Problem," *Journal of the American Statistical Association*, June 1963, pp. 275–309. Various methods are described in R. Ferber and P. J. Verdoorn, *Research Methods in Economics and Business*, The Macmillan Company, New York, 1962 and H. Hyman, *Survey Design and Analysis*, The Free Press of Glencoe, 1955. Researchers will also find useful M. G. Kendall and W. R. Buckland, *A Dictionary of Statistical Terms*, International Statistical Institute, Unesco, 1959.

Sometimes a problem may be attacked by the historical approach. Although the *historical method* is largely descriptive and non-quantitative, we may find statistical aspects when we consider growth or decline of imports, exports, population, and other series.

Again, the appropriate procedure may be to make use of the *experimental method*, in which we allow only the factor we are studying to vary, and attempt to control as many as possible of the other factors. For example, if we wished to study the effect of car weight upon tire mileage, we should control road conditions, speed, temperature, size of tire, quality of rubber and of cord, inflation of tire, and many other factors.

In the social sciences, the experimental method can rarely be applied and certain aspects of the statistical method are used in lieu of it. We cannot, for example, ascertain the effect of different sorts of diets upon length of life, by forcing groups of people to live upon prescribed diets and by actually making all other phases of their lives identical. Instead, we must find groups of people on different diets, and then we must measure the importance of, and control statistically, as set forth in Chapter 21, as many as possible of the other phases of their lives, since we cannot control them experimentally. The experimental and statistical methods are not antithetical, but under practical conditions the statistical method supplements the experimental method. If an experiment could be so designed that *all* variables were *completely* controlled, statistics might not be needed. At best we can usually control but a few of the more important factors, and thus it is necessary to evaluate statistically the importance of a host of other minor disturbing factors (sometimes designated as "chance"), as described in Chapters 24–26.

Some problems may be approached by the *deductive method* rather than by the *inductive method*. When a hypothesis has been set up deductively and when quantitative data are available, statistics may enable an inductive test to be made of the hypothesis, and this test may serve to support or to discredit the hypothesis. Conversely, relationships arrived at statistically (as, for example, the rather close negative association found in some states concerning the size of farms and the value of land per acre) may suggest causal connections which may be worked out deductively. Again we have two methods which are not antagonistic, but complementary.

The complementary nature of these methods of research is also reflected in *operations research*. This relatively new field is the application of quantitative methods to specific management problems which revolve around the use of men and machines within an organization. The objective is to optimize the solutions to the problems. *In operations research* (sometimes called *management science*) the principles of such social sciences as economics and sociology and the principles of such physical sciences as physics and chemistry are frequently combined. Of particular importance in *operations research* is the mathematical technique of *linear programming* in which the inputs, the outputs, and the objectives are completely quantified.

The spirit of inquiry—controlled directed skepticism—is the essence of the statistical method. Even where they cannot arrive at "the" answer to a problem, if nothing else, statistically trained individuals know enough to ask the right questions. Application of the spirit of the statistical method as well as specific statistical techniques helps reduce the marketability of timeworn cliches about statistics, i.e., inaccuracies being classifiable as "lies, darn lies, and statistics," "figures don't lie but liars figure," etc.

In both free enterprise and in planned economies, in developed and in underdeveloped countries, the value of statistical training is reflected in the high incomes paid those who have it. In the United States, in the fields of biology, demography, economics, education, engineering, health and medicine, insurance, market research, psychology, and sociology, statistics-trained individuals are being actively sought by government agencies, by private enterprise, and by academic institutions. In the late 1960's, a number of mathematical statisticians were earning over $20,000 per annum. In the years since then, undoubtedly such salaries have been increased.

CHAPTER 2

Statistical Data

When a research worker undertakes the study of a topic, he may be able to choose between collecting the data himself or obtaining the needed figures from already available published or unpublished compilations. If an individual or organization has prepared reliable data which are pertinent to the problem, it is vastly less expensive to make use of the existing information. Although to collect one's own data is more costly, that procedure may enable the investigator to obtain exactly the information which is needed to answer the specific questions that are under consideration.

Not all readers will be faced with the problem of collecting original statistical data; many will find it possible to refer to existing sources for information. However, the data from such sources may be evaluated and more intelligent use may be made of them if the research worker has some knowledge of the procedure and pitfalls involved in collecting, editing, and marshalling statistical data.

A widely cited illustration is to the point: Harold Cox, when a young man in India, quoted some Indian statistics to a judge. The judge replied, "Cox, when you are a bit older, you will not quote Indian statistics with that assurance. The government are very keen on amassing statistics—they collect them, add them, raise them to the nth power, take the cube root and prepare wonderful diagrams. But what you must never forget is that every one of those figures comes in the first instance from the *chowty dar* (village watchman), who just puts down what he damn pleases."[1] It should be added that this story refers to the India of a day long past. Today India has many able statisticians and an active statistical society. One hopes that the *chowty dar* no longer functions as the source of local statistical information.[2]

---

[1] The earliest use known to have been made of this story is in Sir Josiah Stamp, *Some Economic Factors in Modern Life*, P. S. King and Son, London, 1929, pp. 258–259.

[2] For a short critical review of statistics in major underdeveloped areas see Sidney Klein, "Recent Economic Experience in India and Communist China: Another Interpretation," *American Economic Review*, May 1965, pp. 31–39.

The process of collecting statistical data will be examined first. Later in the chapter, attention will be directed toward the use of statistical sources.

COLLECTING STATISTICAL DATA

Method of collection. Statistical data are frequently obtained by a process in which the desired information is obtained from the householder, business man, or other informant, either by having an enumerator visit the informant, ask the necessary questions, and enter the replies on a *schedule*, or by mailing to the informant a list of questions (sometimes called a *questionnaire*) which he may answer at his convenience. The data collected at each population census are obtained by the enumeration process, the enumerators undertaking to visit every place of abode in the United States. Sometimes information is obtained by registration, which means that the information is reported to the proper authority when, or shortly after, an event occurs. Thus births and deaths must be registered. In many states automobile accidents must be reported to the commissioner of motor vehicles.

In general outline the problems of obtaining data by mailing questionnaires, by enumeration, and by registration are similar. Under a system of registration there is, of course, the difficulty that many persons will neglect to register. Constant vigilance and frequent checkups are necessary on the part of the registrar. Registration, however, is usually with a properly designated government official, and there is ordinarily legal compulsion that the data be supplied. Since most statistical information is obtained by enumeration or by mailing questionnaires, the balance of this section will be devoted to the procedure for collecting data by these methods.

Outline of procedure. The steps in a statistical investigation, which involves the collection of data, may be designated as follows:

1. Planning the study.
2. Devising the questions and making the schedule.
3. Selecting the type of sample, if the enumeration is not to be a complete one.
4. Using the schedules to obtain the information.
5. Editing the schedules.
6. Organizing the data.
7. Making finished tables and charts.
8. Analyzing the findings.

The steps will usually be taken in the order shown, except that the decision concerning the type of sample to be used may be included as part of the first step. We shall discuss each of the eight steps in turn.

1. Planning the study. If a topic is to be studied statistically, it behooves the investigator to become familiar, at the outset, with what has already been done by others. He may find that someone else has already examined the same topic and that his questions have already been answered. He may wish to design his study so that it can be compared with those which have preceded his. He will doubtless profit by the experience and the mistakes of others. He may find that the difficulties involved in the investigation of his topic are so great that they are insurmountable; the cost may be too great, or it may appear that informants do not wish to divulge the type of information which is needed.

Having studied what others have done, the investigator is ready to consider the general aspects of what he would like to know. If an employment and unemployment study is projected, there are many inquiries concerning each individual which are pertinent. The following suggests some of the more important ones:

> Does the individual have any dependents? How many?
> Is the person male or female?
> What is his or her marital status?
> How old is the person?
> What is his formal education?
> Does he own property?
> What is his usual occupation? In what industry?
> What type of work is he doing at present? (If the study is a detailed one, consideration may be given to listing the job experience of the individual for a number of years, together with the wages received.)
> Is he employed full time? Part time? Is he entirely unemployed?
> If the individual is working part time or is totally unemployed, what is the reason?
> If he is totally unemployed, how long has he been so? Also, is he able to work and willing to work; or, alternately, is he actively looking for work?

The reader will doubtless think of other questions of importance, but these suffice to indicate the nature of this preliminary step. Usually we cannot undertake to obtain answers to all the questions which are important. It may be too expensive to make so comprehensive an inquiry. There may be some questions (such as the one concerning property ownership or a query in regard to wages) which informants will often decline to answer. The most important and practicable questions are therefore selected to form the basis of the inquiry. It is these which will be incorporated into the schedule.

There are several matters of general importance which are often considered in connection with laying out the general plan. One of these has to do with the extensiveness of the study. Will it include the entire community or merely a sample? If funds and enumerators are available, we may make a complete enumeration; often we must be satisfied with a sample. We shall discuss the selection of the sample after we have completed consideration of the schedule.

Another problem concerns whether the schedule is to be sent out by mail (in which case it must be very simple and self-explanatory) or whether enumerators are to be used. If use is to be made of paid enumerators, it is necessary to locate qualified persons. However, it is often true that funds are not available to hire enumerators. In fact, it is sometimes the case that, valuable as the results of an investigation might be, they are not worth what it would cost to employ enumerators! Studies nave been made using, as unpaid enumerators, policemen, college students, postmen, truant officers, and even school children.

A third matter has to do with the place where the informants will be interviewed. For an employment-unemployment study we could send enumerators to interview people at their work, in the streets, or at home. It is obvious that the last of the three is preferable. For the unemployment study we should also consider whether or not to enumerate all the people in a household, irrespective of age, sex, desire for work, and mental or physical condition. To list everyone would give a complete picture, but it also involves much work. When making an employment study, we may not be interested in housewives who seek no work outside the home. We may be interested in elderly men, in an attempt to learn what proportion of the population is retired or is considered too old or infirm to work. Since young children are not ordinarily part of the labor force, it may be desirable to exclude all persons below (say) 14 or 16 years of age. For the purpose of the following illustration, we shall consider that all persons over 14 years of age were enumerated.

2. Devising the questions and making the schedule. It has already been pointed out that not all the questions which we would like to have answered can be included in the schedule. Having selected those topics which we wish to include in our inquiry, we must formulate each question so that it may be readily and accurately answered, and then we must draft the schedule form. The schedule form shown on page 35 is one that might be used in a community study of employment and unemployment. This schedule would, of course, be supplemented by a sheet or booklet of instructions to the enumerators. The instructions would explain what is meant by "household" and by "family," since both terms are used, whether age was to be "to nearest birthday" (the so-called "insurance method") or "to last birthday" (the so-called "census method"), the meaning of the terms "occupation" and "industry," and so on.

A very simple schedule is shown on page 19. This was a postcard to be returned to the *Country Gentleman* magazine. This form is of interest, not only because of its simplicity, but also because the Curtis Publishing

---

1. How is your mail delivered?   R.F.D. or Star route........
   At Post Office........   Door-to-door delivery........

2. What is the occupation of the
   head of your household?..

3. What is his (or her) kind of business?..

4. Do you live on a farm or ranch?   Yes........   No........

5. If you do *not* live on a farm or ranch, does anyone in your household___
   a. Own or rent farm land?   Yes........   No........
   b. Operate or work on a farm?   Yes........   No........

6. If you are not a farmer, what is your interest in *Country Gentleman?*
   ....

Post-card Questionnaire Used by the Curtis Publishing Company.

Company sent a "shiny new dime" as a "token of appreciation" to those cooperating. The company states that a postcard questionnaire, such as the one shown, will bring in a return of about 20 per cent when no coin is sent. When a dime was sent, a return of 65 per cent was obtained. It was also found that by using a quarter instead of a dime, the return could be brought up to about 70 per cent.

One year, one of the authors supervised a study of the contribution of Rutgers—The State University (of New Jersey) to the economy of the City of New Brunswick and devised a schedule containing 155 questions some of which had as many as 9 alternate responses. These were 9 mimeographed pages of questions plus 2 pages of instructions and other prose. About 42 per cent of the faculty, 25 per cent of the staff, and 15 per cent of the students who received the questionnaire filled it out in accordance with the instructions given and returned it for recording.[3]

The construction of statistical schedules is something which is learned most satisfactorily by actually making and using them. Nevertheless, there are some cautions which are helpful:

(a) *Clarity is essential.* The entire schedule, as well as each question, should be as simple and as clear as possible. This is particularly true of schedules sent to, or left with, persons to be filled out at their convenience. An ambiguous question or a question that invites an ambiguous answer produces useless data and involves waste of time and money.

---

[3] *The Contribution of Rutgers—The State University to the Economy of the City of New Brunswick During the Calendar Year 1959*, The Bureau of Economic Research, Rutgers—The State University, April 25, 1961, pp. 1–41, *passim*, unpublished.

One organization, in making a study, queried some hundreds of parents: "Is your child's outlook on life broader or narrower than yours was at the same age?" The investigator presumably expected the replies to read "Broader" or "Narrower." Replies actually received, however, were frequently "Yes," "No," "I doubt it," and "I hope so"—none of which had any meaning. Furthermore, the question is so worded as not to allow for the fact that there may be two or more children in the family.

The inquiry concerning marital status when put "Married or Single?" is open to two objections: (1) Either a "Yes" or a "No" answer is meaningless; (2) not all persons are included in these two categories. One good way of asking this question is to say:

> Check whether:
> Single————————
> Married————————
> Widowed————————
> Divorced————————
> Separated————————

To clarify the meaning of "single," the term "never married" is sometimes used.

The investigator should not be satisfied merely with wording his questions so that they can be understood; he should draft them so carefully that they cannot be misunderstood.

(b) *Not all questions can be accurately answered.* No matter how clearly a question is stated, there are some sorts of queries which are apt to elicit unsatisfactory returns. Some census returns have shown some peculiar irregularities in the distribution of the population by single years of age. Beginning with age 25 and continuing through age 70, there have been definite concentrations of persons on every age ending in 0 or 5, except for age 55. For example, there have been *more* people who were reported to be 25 than either 24 or 26 years of age. There have also been secondary concentrations upon some ages which are multiples of 2, most noticeable when these even years of age are not adjacent to a multiple of five. Thus, there have been concentrations at 28, 32, 38, 42, and so on, through 62. Furthermore, there seem to have been too many males reported as 21.

The rounding of ages is not peculiar to the United States Census; it may be expected to occur in any inquiry where age is not obtained from birth certificates or some other accurate record of date of birth. Some of the factors believed to lead to reporting ages in round numbers are: (1) The information concerning an individual is not necessarily furnished to the enumerator by the person himself; it is often given by a relative, friend, rooming-house keeper, or other person, and some of these informants cannot have exact information. (2) When ages are intentionally misstated, as they occasionally are, there is reason for believing that they are often rounded. (3) Some persons are careless, or occasionally a person may always think in terms of round numbers. Rounding is most noticeable for those classes of the population in which the proportion of illiterates is greatest. (4) A few persons do not know their exact ages. (5) There may be carelessness on the part of enumerators. Some improvement in the accuracy of reporting ages may be had by asking date of birth instead of, or in addition to, age. It should be recognized, however, that the posing of a more exact question does not produce better data when exact knowledge is lacking, as in the case of a landlady reporting for her roomers. Furthermore, the matter of the expense involved in asking this additional question might more than offset the expected increase in accuracy. When age is of primary importance, as in the case of application for insurance, date of birth is usually asked and may be verified by documentary evidence.

Another interesting example of thinking in terms of round numbers occurred in the case of a contest sponsored by a motion picture theater. An irregular-shaped glass jar was filled with cranberries, and six prizes were offered to the patrons who guessed most nearly the correct number of cranberries in the jar. An analysis of the 1,996 guesses showed that there were 1,465 which ended in 0 or 5.

(c) *Certain types of questions should be avoided.* When the prosecuting attorney asked the alleged wife beater, "Have you stopped beating your wife?" he attempted to put the defendant, whether he replied "Yes" or "No," in the position of admitting that he had beaten his wife. In a scientific investigation we should scrupulously avoid such leading questions. When asking the reason for unemployment in an unemployment survey, made during a recession, an enumerator would be suggesting the answer if he said, "I suppose you are unemployed because of the recession?" Rather, he should inquire, "What is the reason you are unemployed?"

Questions which are unduly inquisitive or which are liable to offend should likewise be avoided. In a study of social workers, each married woman was asked whether or not she lived with her husband. The inquiry was injudicious, aroused resentment, and would hardly have been productive of useful data if it had been answered by all the persons queried. Questions concerning personal matters (such as income) should be handled with tact—perhaps asked at the close of the interview after the cooperation of the informant has been obtained. Sometimes it is better not to ask such a question but to infer the general income level from knowing if there is a dishwashing machine in the home; if the home is owned, and its apparent value; the individual's occupation; make of car(s) driven, if any; servants employed, if any; and so forth. One

Census of Population asked the amount of income for a twenty per cent sample of the population and, although this question—like all Census queries—was authorized by law, a special confidential form requiring no postage was provided for those who preferred to send this information directly to the Bureau of the Census. In one survey informants were asked: How much cash do you customarily carry on your person? How much cash do you ordinarily keep around the house? Many refusals to answer may be expected for such questions.

(d) *Answers should be objective and capable of tabulation.* When factual studies are being made, questions should be so designed that objective answers will be forthcoming. Instead of asking the condition of a building and allowing the enumerator to state the condition in his own words, a study made by the United States Department of Commerce asked if a structure was in good condition, needed minor repairs, needed structural repairs, or was unfit for use. Although the answers to these questions are not completely objective, at least they are capable of being readily tabulated.

(e) *Instructions and definitions should be concise.* The enumerator and informant should never be in doubt as to what information is desired and what terms or units are to be used. When inquiring as to the employment status of an individual, the inquiry must refer to some specific time. Thus, the Census of Population has asked information as of the week preceding the visit of the enumerator.

If information is desired as to the exact situation of a part-time worker, it must be made clear whether the desired answer should be: (1) hours per day; (2) hours (or days) per week; or (3) fraction of usual full time.

The units used in a study should be clearly understood by both the enumerator and the informant. If we are collecting data from farmers and orchardists on apple production, we should specify whether we want data in terms of bushels or boxes of fruit. If we desire information as to the number of rooms in houses, it should be noted whether or not bathrooms, kitchenettes, powder rooms, dressing rooms, and the like are to be counted as rooms.

(f) *Arrangement of questions should be carefully planned.* Not only must the questions be well arranged on the schedule form to allow proper space for answers, but the order of the questions should be such as to facilitate the answering of each question in turn. If a logical flow of thought is involved, it should be followed in the arrangement of questions. Questions should not skip back and forth from one topic to another.

After a schedule has been drafted, the desirable procedure is to try it out with a group, discover its shortcomings, and then revise it in the light of the tryout. If there is not time for a tryout, ask some competent investigators to go over it and make suggestions for its improvement. When the final form of the schedule has been decided upon, careful instructions for filling it out should be prepared. If the schedules are to be mailed to the persons furnishing information, these directions should be as clear and consise as possible. If enumerators are used, the instructions to the enumerators should be complete in order to cover as many as possible of the situations which may occur in their work.

3. Selecting the type of sample. The United States Census of Population is a complete enumeration of the inhabitants of the United States. That is to say, it is as complete as it is possible to make it. A very few people, such as tramps, fugitives from justice, and dwellers in extremely remote places, may not be included, but the intent is to include everyone, and no one is knowingly omitted. Similarly, the Census of Agriculture undertakes to include all farms in the United States as well as certain specialized operations such as greenhouses, nurseries, poultry yards, and apiaries.

Sometimes a partial enumeration is used instead of a complete enumeration. Occasionally, only the larger units may be included. For example, one biennial Census of Manufactures included only those establishments with annual products valued at $5,000 or more. The enumerations were incomplete in regard to number of establishments included, but included a high proportion of the total number of wage earners in manufacturing and of the total value of manufactured products. Later all establishments employing one or more persons were included. Still later an Annual Survey of Manufactures was instituted; the annual survey used a sample, employing a combination of the procedures described in the following paragraphs.

It may be too expensive or too time-consuming to attempt either a complete or a nearly complete coverage in a statistical study. Furthermore, to arrive at valid conclusions, it may not be *necessary* to enumerate all or nearly all of a population. We may study a sample drawn from the larger population and, if that sample is adequately representative of the population, we should be able to arrive at valid conclusions. There are various ways in which a sample may be selected from a population. No matter which of these is employed, it must be remembered that the cardinal purpose is to obtain a representative sample, that is, one which contains all elements in the same proportion as in the population from which it is drawn. In short, it is *not* merely a matter of grabbing *any* 2, 5, 10, or 20 per cent sample of a population, but of selecting that sample in such a way that it will be as representative as possible.

(a) *Random sample.* If a sample is drawn in such a way that each time an item is selected, each item in the population (or universe) has an equal chance of being drawn, the sample is said to be a *random* one. Under these conditions, each combination of a specified number of items will have the same probability of being selected. This is sometimes referred to as *unrestricted* or *simple* random sampling to differentiate it from sampling procedures which combine random sampling with other requirements, for example, the initial division of a non-homogeneous population into appropriate homogeneous sub-groups.

When populations are homogeneous, in regard to the characteristic in which we are interested, random samples may be expected to produce satisfactory results. If, for example, a large receptacle contains a population of thousands of marbles, $\frac{1}{3}$ of which are white, $\frac{1}{3}$ black, and $\frac{1}{3}$ red, and if those marbles are identical in size, shape, density, and all other characteristics except color, we have a homogeneous population. If the marbles can be thoroughly mixed, between each draw of a marble, by rotating the receptacle, or otherwise, randomness is not too difficult to achieve. Under the conditions indicated, it is more likely that a sample of marbles will show the three colors in the same proportion that they exist in the population than that these colors will be present in some other proportion. This does not mean that every sample will show the proportion in the population; but if many samples are drawn they will tend to do so. Furthermore, wide disagreements will rarely occur.

In the illustration just given, randomness was not difficult to attain. Suppose that a population consists of equal proportions of four sizes of bolts and that all were made from the same material. In such a situation, mixing the bolts in a container will not help us to obtain a random sample of the various sizes, since smaller objects tend to gravitate to the bottom. Satisfactory mixing might possibly be obtained on a horizontal surface, but here one would have to be careful not to select the larger bolts because they are more prominent. A somewhat similar problem is met in sampling shipments of grain and of coal. For grain, the lack of homogeneity is recognized and samples are sometimes taken by plunging a tube vertically into the grain in several locations. This procedure is similar to stratified sampling described in section (d).

Sometimes items cannot be physically mixed, yet a random sample is desired. Mixing may be impossible because the items are bulky, immovable, or fragile, or because they may be households or individual persons. Again, mixing may be possible but may not assure randomization, since the individual selecting items from the mixed population may not pick the items at random. Randomization is sometimes achieved by assigning numbers to the items in the population and drawing the sample or samples by reference to a table of random numbers.[4] This may be referred to as "mechanical randomization," the term being also applied to the use of coins or dice.

---

[4] For example, the table given in R. A. Fisher and F. Yates, *Statistical Tables for Biological, Agricultural and Medical Research*, Hafner Publishing Company, Inc., New York, 1949, pp. 104–109.

When samples are taken from each batch of screws, nails, bolts, brick, wire, or other products of a factory, physical mixing may not be necessary since the items may be selected from time to time from the production stream. Such a method of selection is not exactly random and may, in fact, contain a bias if the machine, die, drill, jig, or other device used in producing the items tends to wear or get out of adjustment during the production of a batch. Selecting items from a production stream is somewhat akin to the method next described.

(b) *Systematic sample.* When a sample is obtained by drawing every, say, tenth item on a list or in a file, the sample is a systematic one. The first item should be selected at random. Such a sample is sometimes drawn from an alphabetical list of names or from cards filed in alphabetical, numerical, or other order. Certain population information called for on the schedule used in one Census of Population and Housing was obtained for but 20 per cent of the persons listed. To obtain this sample, every fifth line on a schedule was labeled "Sample line . . . ask ques. below." Five forms of the schedule were printed, each with a different arrangement of sample lines.

It is important that the basic list, from which a systematic sample is chosen, is actually the population which one desires to study. The failure of the *Literary Digest* to forecast correctly the 1936 presidential election was due to the fact that its apparently systematic sample of more than 2,300,000 ballots was not selected from an appropriate basic list. The voters were selected from lists of automobile owners and telephone subscribers, which, even more so in 1936 than would be true today, failed to include enough of those persons in the lower income groups. A similarly incomplete list was used as the basis from which to draw a sample for an unemployment study in a New England city during the depression of the 1930's. The sample was selected from the subscribers for electricity, gas, and water. The list did not include the poorest families.

No general statement can be made to the effect that more reliable or less reliable results may be had from a systematic sample than from a random sample of the same size. The conditions under which systematic selection is to be preferred to random sampling, or vice versa, are too involved to be discussed here, but one caution should be mentioned. The sampling intervals (every 5th item, every 10th item, on a list) must not coincide with any constantly recurring characteristics in the listing of the items.[5]

(c) *Cluster sample.* Before proceeding to describe a cluster sample, it

---

[5] For advanced work, see M. N. Murthy, "Some Recent Advances in Sampling Theory," *Journal of the American Statistical Association*, September 1963, pp. 735–755. See also A. M. Mood and F. A. Graybill, *Introduction to the Theory of Statistics*, second edition, McGraw-Hill Book Company, New York, 1965, *passim.*

will be useful to introduce the term *sampling unit*. The sampling unit is the basic entity in any sample and may be a marble, a bolt, an individual, a manufacturing concern, a farm, a household, a geographic area, and so forth. In the case of the marbles, the units were simple and differed from each other only in regard to color. Other units may be complex and may differ from each other in many respects. For example, manufacturing concerns differ in regard to nature of products, capital invested, number of employees, and in many other ways. When our units are people, we find that they differ in respect to sex, age, race, occupation, employment status, economic status, religion, and so forth. About all that they may have in common is that they are human beings and live in the same community. Such differences are important and need to be kept in mind when a sample is selected. The more unlike the sampling units, the more difficult is the problem of selecting a representative sample.

The cluster sample is sometimes referred to as an *area* sample because it is frequently applied on a geographical basis. Essentially it consists of a random selection of groups of units. For example, on a geographical basis, we might select blocks of a city or counties of continental United States. As a non-geographical illustration, the bolts of four sizes, previously mentioned, might be spread out on a horizontal surface marked into squares of equal size and a random sample of the squares taken. The blocks, counties, or squares constitute the clusters,[6] and within each group all of the units present may be included. *Multi-stage sampling* involves samples of the units from the groups, or samples of sub-groups from the groups (for example, townships from the counties in the cluster), or both. Multi-stage sampling may also include other types of samples in one or more of the steps.

(d) *Stratified sample.* When a population is known to be heterogeneous, and when that heterogeneity has a bearing on the characteristic being studied, the population may be divided into strata and random samples of units drawn from each stratum. The purchaser of a box of berries recognizes the existence of heterogeneity, and thus of strata, when she turns out the contents to examine the bottom as well as the top layers. Frequently, the number of units selected from each stratum is proportional to the number of units in that stratum in the population. An interesting application of the stratified sample was made in the study of the effects of strategic bombing on Japanese morale made many years ago by the United States Strategic Bombing Survey.[7] One important provision in the selection of this sample was that interviewers could make no substitutions for persons designated on the sampling lists. Substi-

---

[6] The clusters are sometimes called "primary sampling units" and the items in the clusters termed "elementary sampling units."

[7] For a discussion, see Hyman, *op. cit.*, pp. 158–159, *passim*.

tutions for persons not at home, or otherwise not readily available, is a dangerous source of error in any type of sample.

Note that stratified sampling cannot be used unless some information concerning the population and its strata is available. An extremely important point, which is often overlooked, is that the strata must be ones which are related to the topic being studied. If we are making a health study of male students in a college, we might recognize such strata as those who do or do not live at home; those who are totally, partially, or not at all self-supporting; those who do or do not take regular exercise; those who do or do not smoke; and so forth. However, there are other strata which clearly have no bearing on the problem. To take an extreme illustration, we might recognize such strata as those who habitually wear caps or hats, those who prefer single- or double-breasted coats, or any other categories which are not related to health. Another important consideration is that stratified sampling is most advantageous when the strata differ from each other as much as the population will allow, but there should be homogeneity within each stratum.

Many public opinion and market research organizations make use of the principle of stratified sampling. Sometimes enumerators may be told to work within a given city block (a geographical stratum) and talk with a given number of people selected at random. The selection, too often, is not a random one, consisting as it does of those who are at home, those willing to be interviewed, and those who, by their appearance, look as if they would be willing to talk.

For a non-homogeneous population, a properly stratified sample may be expected to yield more reliable[8] results than a random sample of the same size. From this it follows that the same reliability may be had from a smaller stratified sample. There is some danger that investigators, having an excessive feeling of security in the stratified sample, may use samples that are too small to give statistically reliable results. This can be guarded against by an intelligent use of the method and of the reliability formulas. Although both proper stratification and size of sample are important, a large sample cannot compensate for poor stratification. Of course, a stratified sample taken from a homogeneous population is no more reliable than a random sample of the same size.

---

[8] In this text we shall consider (in Chapters 24, 25, and 26) the error formulas for random samples only. An understanding of the behavior of random samples is a necessary groundwork for evaluating samples obtained by more complex procedures. Error formulas may be found in many texts on statistical inference, sampling techniques, and sample survey methods. For still more advanced techniques see W. A. Ericson, "Optimum Stratified Sampling Using Prior Information," *Journal of the American Statistical Association*, September 1965, pp. 750–771; and D. Singh and B. D. Singh, "Double Sampling for Stratification on Successive Occasions," *ibid.*, pp. 784–792.

(e) *Sequential sampling.*[9] Sequential sampling has been used most widely in connection with quality-control schemes having to do with raw material or a manufactured product, but it is gradually coming to have other applications.[10] It involves testing a relatively small number of items which may lead to a decision to accept or reject the lot from which the sample came. If the first sample leads to no clear decision, it is enlarged (possibly one item at a time) until a decision can be made.

(f) *Other types of samples.* The five types of samples previously described are sometimes referred to as "probability samples," since it is possible to ascertain the probability that an individual item will be included in the sample. Other sampling schemes, differing from those already described, also exist. They are not considered desirable procedures since they involve subjective factors, or their reliability cannot be ascertained satisfactorily, or both. Among these are: (1) the *purposive sample*, in which one sets out to make a sample agree with the population in regard to certain characteristics—for example, average income and size of family; (2) the *quota sample*,[11] in which interviewers, working in a certain area, are instructed to talk with individuals having particular characteristics. (If interviewers are told to talk with 10 native-white males, 4 Negro males, and 3 foreign-born males, it is more than likely that the foreign born who are interviewed will be those who are able to speak English well enough to be conversed with satisfactorily. This would introduce a bias into most studies, since the population actually studied would not be the population which was intended to be studied.); (3) the *random point* sample, which consists of locating many points at random on a map and enumerating a predetermined number of sampling units nearest to each point. (This procedure is occasionally used for sampling farms, but through its use large farms are more likely to be included than are small farms.)

When deciding which sampling plan to use, the investigator must consider the efficiency of the scheme. It has already been noted that a stratified sample yields more reliable results (that is, its sampling error is smaller) than does a random sample of the same size. Cluster sampling may be expected to yield less reliable results than random sampling for

---

[9] A complete explanation of sequential analysis is given by the originator, Abraham Wald, in his book, *Sequential Analysis*, John Wiley and Sons, Inc., New York, 1947. Numerous applications of sequential sampling in commercial research are described in the many books available which deal with market research.

[10] See F. J. Anscombe, "Sequential Medical Trials," *Journal of the American Statistical Association*, June 1963, pp. 365–383, and P. Armitage, "Some Comments on Anscombe's Paper," *ibid.*, pp. 384–387. See also Mood and Graybill, *op. cit.*, pp. 383–402.

[11] A good, albeit non-recent discussion of quota sampling may be found in F. Mosteller and others, *The Pre-Election Polls of 1948*, Social Science Research Council, New York, 1949, pp. 83–91 and 94–96. The danger of using a quota sample is well illustrated on page 95.

samples of the same size. The efficiency of a sample scheme refers to the reliability in relation to unit cost. Thus, a geographic cluster sample with groups of units in, say, 20 locations in a large state may have a lower cost per sampling unit than a random sample of the same size with the units scattered here and there about the state. The difference in unit cost may be so great that the cluster sample may be made enough larger than the random sample so that the cluster sample will yield more reliable results than could be had from a random sample for the same expenditure.

A sample may be selected by use of a combination of the methods previously discussed. Here is the procedure which has been followed by the American Institute of Public Opinion:[12]

> The regular sample for the national surveys of the American Institute of Public Opinion is a sample of the adult population. Provision is made for selecting from the regular sample a sample of an approximation of the voting population when such is desired. The design provides stratification by seven regions (groups of states), and within each region stratification by geographical distribution, three rural-urban strata, the census economic areas, and the size of the locality finally selected. A systematic sample of localities was drawn within each stratum from a random start with probability of selection proportional to size. Within large urban communities sampling units[13] (small clusters of blocks) were drawn at random with probability proportional to size. In smaller communities and rural regions sampling areas were drawn with equal probability.
>
> Interviewers are assigned selected areas, and required to work within the boundaries of such areas. Each national survey uses about 150 sampling points, with equal numbers of interviews assigned to each point. A staff of over 1,000 interviewers is maintained.

Sometimes a sample is taken in a more or less haphazard fashion. Or, the investigator may include the data which are convenient or readily available, after which he will trustingly announce that the sample so taken is doubtless representative of the population which he is studying. For example, one researcher, who had ascertained that just under 2,500,000 children, eligible to be enrolled in high school, were not enrolled, desired to estimate how many of these 2,500,000 left school because of economic pressure. He managed to locate 16 acceptable studies concerning the reasons why students left school. These studies each included 53 to 274 children, a total of 2,525. The studies were made in schools in 13 different states. Negroes were studied in one instance. There were no figures from New York, Massachusetts, Illinois, Michigan, Wisconsin, Texas, and certain other populous states. Yet, because the geographical distribution was diverse and because large-city, small-city, and rural children were included, the investigator concluded: "The sample seems

---

[12] By correspondence from Dr. George H. Gallup, Director of the American Institute of Public Opinion.

[13] These are apparently "primary sampling units." See footnote 6.

sufficiently representative of the various elements of the population to serve as the basis for estimation of the whole group." This may or may not have been true. The sample was neither random, stratified, systematic, nor cluster; it merely included what was available.

As will be shown in Chapters 24, 25, and 26, for random samples, the larger the sample, the more confidence we can place in conclusions drawn from the sample. It will also be shown that the greater the diversity there is in the population, the less reliability we can repose in samples of the same size. Mere size, of course, does not assure representativeness in a sample. A small random or stratified sample is apt to be much superior to a larger but badly selected sample. Sometimes a test of stability is made to determine when a sample is large enough. For example, a sample of 1,000 may be selected from a group of voters, and 57.3 per cent of the sample may indicate that they intend to vote for a certain candidate. Another 1,000 may be chosen, and the two groups combined may show 56.9 per cent. Adding another 1,000 may change the percentage to 56.8, and still another 1,000 (4,000 in all) may leave the proportion unchanged, at 56.8. From this test, 3,000 or 4,000 would seem to be an adequate sample from the standpoint of size. However, the test of stability tests only stability and not representativeness. The fact that a percentage persists essentially unchanged means merely that we are continuing to get about the same result as before. Conceivably, the first sample of 1,000 could have been decidedly unrepresentative (say, from only the poorer sections of the voting population), and each succeeding sample similarly unrepresentative.

Mention has already been made of the possibility of bias being present in a sample. When a sample is being selected, it is important that bias be avoided. *Bias* does not mean the personal bias of the investigator which leads him deliberately to select his sample in order to show the results he desires. That is intellectual dishonesty. Neither does it mean that the persons answering the questions on the schedule are biased. The avoidance of bias involves, first, that there shall be no selective factor present in the drawing of the sample, and, second, that there shall be no selective factor present when schedules are returned from those persons included in the sample. In the case of the *Literary Digest* 1936 straw vote, a selective factor was present because the basic lists from which the sample was selected did not include the lower economic levels of the population. Sometimes the basic list may be complete, but the method of selecting the sample may introduce bias. Thus, a selection from an alphabetical list of names may be unsatisfactory because of nationality differences in the alphabetical distribution of family names. Such a bias may arise if sections of the list are chosen; it is not likely if (say) every tenth name is taken.

The second type of selective factor is frequently encountered if the mailed-questionnaire method of collection is used. When schedules are sent out by mail, an investigator never expects that all of them will be returned. Since only part of the inquiries are answered, how can he be sure that those who did answer are representative of all those to whom schedules were sent? Often he cannot be sure; sometimes it is obvious that they are not representative. An alumni association sent out 363 inquiries to graduates, asking each to report (anonymously) his income for the preceding year. Replies were received from 133. It is quite likely that a selective factor was present in these returns. Alumni who were out of work or who had very low incomes probably did not reply. This assumption is borne out by the data, which showed an almost complete absence of incomes below $1,500, although the study was made in a depression year. Conclusions based upon biased samples are, obviously, not only useless but misleading.

4. Using the schedules to obtain the information. When agents or enumerators take the schedules to the persons who are to furnish the information, the enumerators may explain the purpose of the investigation and solicit cooperation. Each question can be clearly explained as it is asked. Obviously, enumerators must be carefully instructed before they begin their work. Occasionally they are required to study the schedule and printed instructions, and then to take an examination. Enumerators should be persons of unquestioned integrity and should also be patient, polite, and tactful. Many a person resents being bothered to supply statistical (or other) information; some persons are reluctant; some refuse. The enumerator should plan his interviews to consume as little time as possible, and should bend every effort to get the desired information if it is feasible to do so. In some instances the work of the enumerator may be facilitated if a letter of explanation precedes the visit. Sometimes enumerators conduct interviews and fill in the schedules afterward. This is done on the theory that people feel more free to talk if the remarks are not being written down at the time. It is believed, however, that this is an undesirable procedure, especially when there are a number of facts to be remembered and later recorded. Enumerators should carry credentials in order that the persons visited may be satisfied as to the official connection of the visitor. Even though an enumerator makes his request for information as tactfully as possible, he may sometimes meet with a refusal. Frequently another visitor with a different approach may have better luck. It is sometimes a good plan to have one especially qualified worker who will follow up the more difficult cases. Occasionally an enumerator may encounter a person who is too willing to cooperate and who wants to talk at great length about the study. In such a situation good terminal facilities are an asset.

Sending schedules by mail rather than using enumerators is, at the outset, a less expensive method of collecting data. There is also the added advantage that the person supplying the information can fill out the form at his convenience, instead of being disturbed by the enumerator perhaps at a busy or inconvenient time. Furthermore on a mail questionnaire (provided, of course, that the informant is sure his identity is unknown), confidential information may be given which the informant would hesitate to divulge to an enumerator. On the other hand, a large proportion of persons fail to reply to a mail inquiry and considerable follow-up work may be necessary. There is also great danger that the informant will not understand the questions, or will knowingly or otherwise make incorrect answers. Not only must clear, concise directions be sent with the schedule, but also a brief letter explaining the purpose of the inquiry and requesting cooperation. A modest gift (such as the coin sent by the Curtis Publishing Company) may insure a high proportion of returns. In any event, an addressed and stamped (or business reply) envelope should be included. An air mail business reply envelope (or card) is occasionally used by investigators with the hope that it will result in more and quicker responses. When follow-up work is necessary, the persons who have not yet returned their forms may be sent courteous personal letters reminding them of the inquiry and again requesting cooperation. When appropriate, the follow-up may be by means of air mail letters, special delivery letters, registered letters (to be sure the communication has been delivered), telegrams, or telephone calls. Of course, the investigator should not make a nuisance of himself; he should not be too insistent. When only part of the schedules are finally received, it is necessary to examine the situation carefully to be sure that no selective factor has been present. Or, if a selective factor appears to be present, it may be necessary to conduct a supplementary investigation to remedy the situation.

5. Editing the schedules. After the filled-out schedules are received, a certain amount of preparatory work is necessary before the data are in shape to be tabulated. The editorial tasks are varied. In the case of a small study, one editor may do the entire work. In a larger study, different phases of the editing may be portioned out among a number of editors.

(a) *Computing.* It is usually better not to ask enumerators or persons supplying information to make any computations. Thus, if information has been obtained concerning the number of rooms in a home and the number of members in the household, the editor may compute the ratio of persons per room, to give some idea of crowding. If data have been collected concerning the time lost through non-compensated accidents and also of daily wages for each of a number of workers, the editor may compute for each case the income lost because of accidents.

(b) *Coding.* Tabulation is frequently facilitated by coding. When machine tabulation (to be discussed shortly) is used, all entries on a schedule are reduced to a numerical code. Even when tabulation is manual, it may still be easier to look for a code mark—letters, numbers, or a combination of letters and numbers—instead of attempting to read the original entry. The work of the tabulator may be further facilitated by the fact that the editor writes, or should write, legibly and uses a distinctive color, often red.

The unemployment schedule is shown edited according to a numerical code on page 35. Every entry is numerically coded, except those already expressed as numbers, in order to facilitate tabulation by mechanical means. Note that question 7 was self-coded. A simple code scheme for questions 5 and 6 might appear as follows:

10. Professional
20. Clerical (not otherwise specified)
30. Domestic and personal service
40. Government employees (other than teachers)

Trade and Transportation

50. Retail and wholesale trade
51. Telephone and telegraph
52. Railway, express, gas, electric light
53. Water transportation
54. Bank and brokerage
55. Insurance and real estate
56. Other

Manufacturing and Mechanical Pursuits

60. Building trades, contractors
61. Building trades, wage earners
62. Clay, glass, and stone products
63. Food and kindred products
64. Iron, steel, and their products
65. Metal products, other than iron and steel
66. Paper, printing, and publishing
67. Wearing apparel and textiles
68. Automobiles, parts, and tires
69. Lumber and furniture
70. Airplanes
71. Other manufacturing and mechanical pursuits

75. Labor (not otherwise specified)
80. Self-employed (other than 10 or 60)
90. Miscellaneous employments not classified above
00. Not reported

(c) *Deciphering.* The handwriting of an enumerator or of an informant may occasionally be difficult to read. This is especially true when an enumerator makes entries on a schedule while he is outdoors in the rain or snow. Deciphering such copy is the editor's task; he not only saves time for the tabulator, but also insures accurate results. If entries are literally unreadable, the schedule may have to be referred back to the enumerator or the person who sent in the information.

(d) *Checking.* The editor may look over the schedules for inconsistencies. Entries of age and date of birth may disagree. Something is probably awry if an individual reported as aged 8 is also shown to be married. Similarly, a mistake has probably (though not necessarily) been made if a woman is reported working full time as a blacksmith. Such entries must be verified if they are to be used.

(e) *Examining for completeness.* The editor must also scrutinize the schedule to see if any entries are missing or incomplete. If the missing information is important, the schedule must be referred back to the enumerator or to the informant. Otherwise, the editor writes "N.R." (not reported) or the corresponding numerical code in place of the missing information.

6. Organizing the data. After the schedules have been edited, the data must be organized before finished tables and charts can be made. They are three methods that may be used:

(1) *The score or tally sheet.* For purposes of illustration, let us consider a score sheet to show, by industry, for male heads of households the number of hours worked during the week ending March 20, 19—. The score sheet is shown on page 37 and represents the data from all of the edited cards for male heads of households from one area of the community. The numerical coding of the industry groups is not necessary for hand tabulation (which includes both scoring and hand sorting, described in the next subsection), but it saves space in the tally sheet to use the code numbers instead of the full industry designation. Numerical coding is necessary when mechanical tabulation is employed.

Observe that the score marks are arranged in groups of five, four vertical and a diagonal. This facilitates counting. The second set of score marks is for checking purposes. Since the tally sheet is for but one area, it is necessary to combine the results from a number of such tally sheets to arrive at the figures for the entire community. The resulting table might appear as in Table 2.1.

The score sheet is a useful device for organizing information from a small study. However, if there are many schedules to be scored or if it is desired to subdivide classifications, the score sheet becomes cumbersome. For example, if we wish to use the same categories of hours as shown on the score sheet but to show also males and females and at the same time distinguish between those who are heads of households and those who are not, we might have two major categories "head of household" and "not head of household." Each of these would be divided into "male" and "female," and each of these four categories further subdivided into the classes shown in the tally sheet on page 37. This would call for $4 \times 6 = 24$ columns and would result in a very sizeable tally

Name _John Doe_   Area _103_   Household _0682_

Address _100 Nonest Street_   Card _01_ Enumerator _A. Jones_

1. Relation to head of household _Head_ ① 2. Age _33_ 3. Sex _M_ ①

4. Years of school _6_ ①

5. Regular employment:
   ⑥① Occupation _Bricklayer_
      Industry _Building Houses_

6. Present employment:
   ⑥① Occupation _Bricklayer_
      Industry _Building Houses_

7. Circle one number to indicate what this person was primarily doing during the week ending March 20, 19—.
   - 01 Working for compensation in money or "kind."
   - 02 Self-employed.
   - Has a job or is self-employed, but not at work because_____
     - 03 On vacation.
     - 04 Bad weather.
     - 05 Labor dispute.
     - 06 Layoff of 30 days or less.
     - 07 Own sickness.
     - 08 Other_____
   - 09 Not at work, new job to begin within 30 days.
   - 10 Not at work, looking for work.
   - 11 Casual worker, no regular job.
   - 12 Attending school.
   - 13 In the armed forces.
   - 14 Keeping house (not as employee).
   - 15 Unpaid worker on family farm or in family business.
   - 16 Volunteer worker, not on family farm or in family business.
   - 17 Retired.
   - 18 Physically or mentally unable to work.
   - 19 Inmate of institution.
   - 20 Other_____

8. If this person worked at all last week, for compensation, or on family farm or in family business, or as a self-employed person, how many hours did he or she work? _30_ hours.

9. If this person was looking for work, how many weeks has he or she been seeking employment?_____ weeks.

Remarks_____

Urbantown Employment-Unem· ᵼᵥyment Study, 19—.

Edited Urbantown Employment-Unemployment Schedule.

sheet.   It could, of course, be broken down into several score sheets, but it would be even better to use a different method of organizing the data.

(2) *Hand sorting.*   When a study does not involve too large a number of schedules, and when the schedules are small enough and on card-board or heavy paper, so that they can be handled readily, the data may be organized by a process of manual sorting.   If we wished to obtain the information mentioned in the preceding paragraph, we might: (1) sort the cards into four piles—male heads of households, female heads of households, male non-heads, and female non-heads; (2) sort each of the four piles into the 27 industry categories, giving a maximum of 108 piles; and (3) sort each of these piles into the hours-of-work categories shown on page 37.   The cards in each pile would then be counted to obtain the desired figures.

(3) *Mechanical tabulation.*   Mechanical tabulation involves the same basic procedure as hand sorting, but it is much faster.   Mechanical sorting and tabulating (counting and totaling) devices enable the work of organizing the information of a statistical study to be done most expe-ditiously, provided, of course, that the study is extensive enough to warrant the use of such equipment.   The use of mechanical tabulating equipment is recommended when there is a large number of schedules to be analyzed or when there are numerous entries on each schedule.   The process consists essentially of the following steps:

(a) Transforming all entries on the schedule into numerical terms, using appropriate codes.

(b) Recording these entries on a punch card by punching holes to represent the code numbers.

(c) Sorting the cards and assembling the data by the use of machines.

On page 39 there is shown a blank punch card and also an enlarged portion of a card, punched to represent the data of the edited schedule on page 35.   The first entry on the card (103) identifies the area from which the schedule came.   The next entry, using four columns, identifies the household and enables the cards for each household to be brought together, if desired.   The following two columns indicate the number of the card within the household, since there may be several cards for a household.   The first nine numbers taken together make it possible to bring together any schedule and the punch card made from it, if desired. The next column shows by a "1" that the individual was the head of a household; a "2" would indicate that he was not a head.   Age is shown in the two following columns.   In the next column, "1" indicates that the respondent was male; for a female, "2" is punched.   The next column indicates years of school by these numbers: *1*, 0–6 years; *2*, 7–12 years; *3*, 13–16 years; *4*, 17 or more; *0*, not reported.   The industry code, which has already been given, occupies the next four columns, two columns for

AREA........../..........

SCORED BY *Jane Smith*
CHECKED BY *William Jones*

INDUSTRY AND HOURS WORKED
MALE HEADS OF HOUSEHOLDS

INDUSTRY GROUP	35 HOURS OR MORE	28 BUT LESS THAN 35 HOURS	21 BUT LESS THAN 28 HOURS	14 BUT LESS THAN 21 HOURS	7 BUT LESS THAN 14 HOURS	LESS THAN 7 HOURS
10	(7)					
20	(2)			(1)		
30	(12)	(2)	(2)			(1)
40	(27)	(2)		(1)		
50	(16)	(1)	(2)	(2)	(2)	
51	(3)					
52	(32)	(2)	(2)	(2)		(1)
53	(6)		(2)			
54	(3)					
55	(5)	(1)				
56	(2)					
60	(4)	(2)				
61	(25)	(5)	(2)	(3)	(2)	
62						
63	(8)	(1)	(3)			
64	(17)	(5)	(3)	(4)	(2)	(2)
65	(4)		(1)		(1)	
66	(3)	(2)	(1)			
67	(5)			(3)		
68	(12)	(3)	(2)			
69	(4)	(1)				
70	(6)		(2)			
71	(1)		(1)			
75						
80	(17)	(3)	(2)	(1)	(2)	
90	(2)					
00						

Industry and Hours Worked, Male Heads of Household.

regular employment and two for present employment. Two more columns take care of the answers to the self-coding Question 7. Question 8 calls for a numerical answer, which occupies the next two columns. The last three columns take care of the numerical answers to Question 9. Note that it was necessary to use only part of the punch card for this schedule.

After the cards have been prepared, they are verified. This is accomplished by reading each punched card against the schedule represented by it. The cards are examined by placing them over a source of light

TABLE 2.1

Hours Worked by Male Heads of Households in Urbantown During Week Ending March 20, 19—, by Industry Group

Industry group	35 hours or more	28 but less than 35 hours	21 but less than 28 hours	14 but less than 21 hours	7 but less than 14 hours	Less than 7 hours	Total
Professional	247	16	12	1	2	...	278
Clerical (not otherwise specified)	10	5	4	13			32
Domestic and personal service	386	125	44	11	6	9	581
Government employees (other than teachers)	1,563	232	48	25	11	15	1,894
Trade and transportation	6,339	532	269	166	49	34	7,389
Retail and wholesale trade	2,207	65	103	33	25	9	2,442
Telephone and telegraph	120	3	20	6	2	...	151
Railway, express, gas, electric light	3,119	408	66	94	11	20	3,718
Water transportation	308	12	71	16	5	...	412
Bank and brokerage	239	8	5	6	1	2	261
Insurance and real estate	245	20	4	9	5	3	286
Other	101	16		2			119
Manufacturing and mechanical pursuits	8,468	1,054	693	268	85	73	10,646
Building trades, contractors	557	27	4	2		1	591
Building trades, wage earners	1,223	311	108	67	31	8	1,748
Clay, glass, and stone products	251	30	15	21			317
Food and kindred products	1,243	47	124	8	2	3	1,427
Iron, steel, and their products	2,205	308	211	53	26	47	2,850
Metal products, other than iron and steel	213	25	76	8	13	5	340
Paper, printing, and publishing	220	41	37				298
Wearing apparel and textiles	304	13	21	62	4	7	411
Automobiles, parts, and tires	1,083	102	41	25	1	1	1,253
Lumber and furniture	298	100	8	2	5	3	416
Airplanes	703	33	36	17	1	2	792
Other	168	17	12	3	2	1	203
Labor (not otherwise specified)	12	7	3	3	6	4	35
Self-employed	1,530	88	49	18	23	11	1,719
Miscellaneous	63	10	7	2			82
Not reported	1		1	1		...	3
Total, male heads of households	18,619	2,069	1,130	508	182	151	22,659

The data shown in this table are for illustrative purposes. They do not represent an actual enumeration.

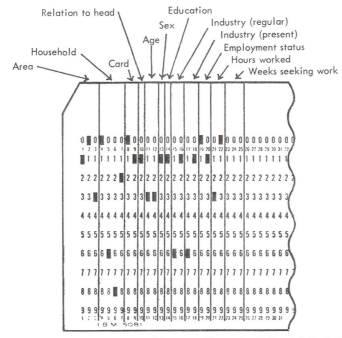

A Punch Card.

or over a black background. Alternatively, a special machine called a "verifier" may be used. The verifier resembles the card-punch machine, but it does not punch the cards.

Following verification, the cards are sorted and tabulated by machine. Electronic statistical machines perform these operations. They sort, count, total, and print the results. The machines also check cards for

A Portion of a Punch Card, Showing How the Edited Schedule on Page 35 Would Be Recorded.

consistency of information [See paragraph (d) under "Editing."] based on pre-established criteria.

A simple device, useful for many studies, is known as Keysort[14] and employs cards having holes around the edges. Information is recorded by notching away the portion of the card between the hole and the edge as shown:

Notched and unnotched cards are separated by means of a large sorting needle.

In recent years, automatic data processing equipment has come into wide use by large business firms and by government agencies. These high-speed machines are capable of not only performing extremely complex mathematical operations in a small fraction of a second but can also store the data and the instructions for processing them. Automatic data processing equipment is used by businesses to make up payrolls, keep detailed records concerning assets and liabilities and especially inventories, and to prepare analyses of the consequences of various alternative projected operations.

7. Presentation and analysis. After the information on the schedules has been organized by manual or mechanical means, the finished statistical tables and charts may be drawn up. Statistical tables are discussed in Chapter 3. Graphic presentation is considered in Chapters 4, 5, and 6. The analysis of statistical data is treated in Chapters 7 through 26.

USING EXISTING SOURCES

Primary versus secondary sources. As pointed out at the beginning of this chapter, statistical data may already exist which are suitable for use in a projected study. The data may or may not have been published. They may have been collected by an individual, a business firm, a research organization, a trade association, a local, state, or federal government office, a newspaper or magazine, and so forth. Some publications, such as the volumes of the *United States Census of Population and Housing*, contain only data which were collected by the issuing organization. Such sources are designated as *primary*. Other publications bring together data some or all of which were originally compiled by organizations other than the one responsible for the publication. These are referred to as *secondary* sources. The *Survey of Current Business*, published monthly by

---

[14] The Keysort is sold by the Royal McBee Company, 295 Madison Ave., New York, N. Y.

the Office of Business Economics of the U. S. Department of Commerce, is a secondary source, as it includes data from many governmental and non-governmental sources. Obviously it is preferable to make use of a primary source whenever possible, but it may often be more convenient to make use of a secondary source. One invaluable secondary source of data is the *Statistical Abstract of the United States*, issued annually by the U. S. Bureau of the Census.

The reasons for preferring a primary source are:

(1) The secondary source may contain mistakes due to errors in transcription made when the figures were copied from the primary source.

(2) The primary source frequently includes definitions of terms and units used. This is an important consideration, since intelligent use can hardly be made of data unless the user knows exactly what is meant by each term or unit employed by the collecting agency. When data are taken from several sources, it is particularly important that definitions of terms and units be scrutinized. The term "family" may sometimes have the limited meaning of father, mother, and offspring; sometimes it may be used more or less synonymously with "household." The term "exports" may sometimes refer to gross exports (including re-exports); sometimes, to exports of United States merchandise only. Although a measured bushel is 2,150.4 cubic inches, a bushel does not represent the same number of pounds for all commodities. For example, a bushel of green peanuts in the shell weighs 22 pounds, a bushel of oats weighs 32 pounds, and a bushel of apples weighs 45 pounds; but a bushel of wheat, beans, peas, or potatoes weighs 60 pounds. The *Statistical Abstract of the United States*, although a secondary source, includes the necessary definitions of units.

(3) The primary source often includes a copy of the schedule and a description of the procedure used in selecting the sample and in collecting the data; the reader is thus enabled to ascertain how much confidence may be reposed in the findings of the study.

(4) A primary source usually shows the data in greater detail. A secondary source often omits part of the information or combines categories, such as showing counties instead of townships, or states instead of counties.

Suitability of data. The analyst should not make use of data, from either a primary or a secondary source, without assuring himself as to the reliability, accuracy, and applicability of the data. There are numerous points worthy of consideration here:

(1) If the enumeration was based on a sample, was the sample representative?

(2) Was the schedule well designed? Were any leading questions or ambiguous questions included?

(3) Was the collecting agency unbiased, or did it "have an axe to grind"? It is well to remember that bias may enter either consciously or unconsciously.

(4) Was a selective factor introduced because of careless enumeration? For example, in an unemployment study, canvassers might be careless about following up their calls at houses where no one was at home, and thus perhaps the data would show a smaller number of employed persons than actually existed.

(5) Were the enumerators capable and properly trained? Incom petent or poorly trained enumerators cannot be depended upon to produce useful results.

(6) Was the editing carefully and conscientiously done? Careless coding or computing on the part of editors may render of little value the findings of an otherwise valuable study.

(7) Was the tabulating (tally sheets, sorting, or mechanical tabulations) performed with care and accurately checked?

(8) In view of the definitions used, the area studied, and the methods of procedure, are the data applicable to the problem that is under investigation?

It is not always possible to ascertain the quality of work which was done by enumerators, editors, and tabulators. As just noted, primary sources are apt to reproduce a copy of the schedule used and give a more or less adequate description of the methods and procedures followed. Additional information may frequently be had by correspondence.

When using data over a period of years from a given source, we must be sure that definitions of terms have not changed or, if they have changed, to make due allowance for the change if it is possible to do so. For example, a new definition of the urban population was first used for the 1950 Census of Population. We shall not take the space to give the old and new definitions[15] in this text, but the object of the change was to include, as urban, more of the large and densely settled, unincorporated places, such as fringe areas around cities and unincorporated places of 2,500 or more inhabitants outside of an urban fringe. Data for 1950 were tabulated on the basis of both the old and the new definitions and showed an urban population of 88,927,464 using the old definition and 96,467,686 on the basis of the new definition. For preceding censuses, data are available only upon the basis of the old definition.

Newspapers are not ordinarily good sources of statistical data, particularly when the figures are in a news item. One reason for this is that newspaper copy is prepared and printed so rapidly that the material

---

[15] The new definition and the nature of the change are given in U. S. Bureau of the Census, *U. S. Census of Population: 1950*, Vol. II, *Characteristics of the Population*, Part 1, U. S. Summary, pp. 9–10.

cannot be as carefully proofread as can the contents of magazines and books. In addition, many figures quoted in news items are taken from speeches or statements from individuals who are themselves sources of dubious reliability. As an example consider this statement, made in a news item in one of the country's leading newspapers: "The estimated . . . (Australian) wool clip is 3,740,000 bales, the largest on record. Competent observers consider destruction of the rabbits (which ate grass intended for sheep) has added 25,000,000 bales to the clip." There is no way of ascertaining, from the news item, which figure is correct. However, the first figure is approximately right, the second figure being grossly incorrect.

Comparability of data from different sources. When data are to be drawn from two or more sources, the reliability of each source must be considered and, in addition, the user must be sure that the data from the different sources are comparable. Let us list some of the reasons for lack of comparability:

(1) Different definitions of terms may have been used. Coal production is given by the United States Bureau of Mines in *short* tons of 2,000 pounds, while at one time exports of coal were shown by the Bureau of Foreign and Domestic Commerce in *long* tons of 2,240 pounds. Short tons are now used by both bureaus. United States stocks of raw and refined sugar are reported by the Department of Agriculture in *short* tons; Cuban stocks of raw sugar are given by the *Weekly Statistical Sugar Trade Journal* in *Spanish* tons. A Spanish ton contains 2,271.64 English pounds. As if these three sorts of tons were not sufficiently confusing, it is necessary to be aware of two other "tons" used in shipping. These are the *gross* ton and the *net* (or registered) ton, each of which represents 100 cubic feet. Gross tonnage is the capacity of the hull plus the enclosed spaces above deck available for cargo, stores, passengers, and crew; whereas net tonnage is the gross tonnage less the space occupied by propelling machinery, fuel, crew quarters, master's cabin, and navigation spaces—in other words, approximately the space available for cargo and passengers.

Because of different accounting systems, the term "profit" may have different meanings in different industries. Profit for a railroad may be quite different from profit for a department store. In a certain industry, carried on almost solely by partnerships, an investigator found that many firms showed little or no profit and that great differences were present among firms. The partners were frequently paying themselves generous salaries, and therefore a new term, "profit plus partners' salaries," was used for the study! Ages may be reported as of the last birthday; as of the nearest birthday; or, in Asian fashion, as of the next birthday. Comparability of age data is thus affected by the bases of reporting.

(2) Different methods of computation or estimation may have been

employed. For example, between March 10, 1966 and April 7, 1966, burglaries and robberies in New York City nearly doubled, according to the New York City Police Commissioner. However, the "increase" was due "only" to a change in reporting methods. In a number of cases, felonies had previously been reported as misdemeanors.[16]

(3) The samples may have been so chosen that the results are not comparable. Or, perchance, one study may have been based on a sample whereas the other was a complete enumeration. It is, of course, possible so to choose a sample that the results of a study may be forced to fit a preconceived idea.

(4) Different standards of accuracy may have prevailed with respect to enumeration, editing, and tabulating.

(5) The sources may not be comparable in respect to areas included, or in respect to the period of time to which they refer. When the chronological difference is not too great, comparisons may sometimes be made or adjustments effected.

Whether an investigator is using primary or secondary sources, it is necessary to keep on the lookout for obvious mistakes and misprints. For example, one year, a secondary source stated that in Continental United States potential water power amounting to 38,110,000 horse power was available 90 per cent of the time, while potential water power of 9,166,000 horse power was available 50 per cent of the time. It is clear that there must be a greater potential horse power available for 50 per cent of the time than for 90 per cent of the time. Data were given for each state and, if these details are added, it appears that 59,166,000 horse power of potential water power were available 50 per cent of the time. Obviously this was a typographical mistake which occurred in printing the publication, or possibly was carried over from the primary source. Such an apparent contradiction would be observed at once by the experienced user of figures.

---

[16] United Press, "New York Learns Truth on Crime," *Pacific Stars and Stripes*, April 8, 1966, p. 3.

CHAPTER 3

Statistical Tables

METHODS OF PRESENTATION

Four methods of statistical presentation are available. Data may be (1) incorporated in a paragraph of text, (2) put into tabular form, (3) placed in a semi-tabular arrangement, or (4) expressed graphically.

Text presentation. Combining figures and text is not a particularly effective device, since it is necessary to read, or at least scan, all of the paragraph before one can grasp the meaning of the entire set of figures. Most persons cannot easily comprehend the data when set forth in this manner, and it is especially difficult for the reader to single out individual figures. There is the advantage, however, that the writer can direct attention to, and thus emphasize, certain figures and can also call attention to comparisons of importance. Following is an example of text presentation:

The 1960 Census of Population of the United States enumerated 870,467 males and 883,480 females in Colorado. This state, the most populous in the Mountain Division, had 665,149 males and 659,940 females in 1950. Next in population to Colorado, at the time of both the 1960 Census and the 1950 Census, was Arizona. In 1960, it had 654,928 males and 647,223 females; at the 1950 enumeration, it had 379,059 males and 370,528 females. Utah, in 1960 was fourth among the Mountain States, while in 1950 it was third. In 1960, it had 444,926 males and 445,703 females, while in 1950 it had 347,636 males and 341,226 females. New Mexico, which was fourth among the Mountain States in 1950, displaced Utah in third place in 1960. In 1960, it had 479,770 males and 471,253 females, whereas in 1950 it had 347,544 males and 333,643 females. Montana, Idaho, Wyoming, and Nevada were fifth, sixth, seventh, and eighth place respectively in both 1960 and 1950. In 1960, Montana had 343,743 males and 331,024 females; in 1950, it had 309,423 males and 281,603 females. Idaho, which had 338,421 males and 328,770 females in 1960, had 303,237 males and 285,400 females a decade earlier. Wyoming, next to the smallest of the Mountain States with respect to population, had 169,015 males and 161,051 females in 1960, whereas in 1950 the population was 154,853 males and 135,676 females. Least populous of the eight Mountain States was Nevada

45

which had 147,521 males and 137,757 females in 1960. Ten years before, it had 85,017 males and 75,066 females.

Tabular presentation. The same data that were included in the preceding text statement are shown in Tables 3.1 and 3.3. In addition, for each state the tables show the sex ratio; the latter to be described in Chapter 7. This method of setting forth statistical data is usually superior to the use of text. A table with its title should be fully self-explanatory, although it may frequently be accompanied by a paragraph of interpretation or a paragraph directing attention to important figures.

TABLE 3.1

Number of Inhabitants in the States of the Mountain Division,
by Sex, 1950 and 1960

State	Male		Female		Males per 100 females, 1960
	1960	1950	1960	1950	
Colorado......	870,467	665,149	883,480	659,940	98.5
Arizona.......	654,928	379,059	647,223	370,528	101.2
Utah..........	444,924	347,636	445,703	341,226	99.8
New Mexico...	479,770	347,554	471,253	333,643	101.8
Montana......	343,743	309,423	331,024	281,603	103.8
Idaho.........	338,421	303,237	328,770	285,400	102.9
Wyoming......	169,015	154,853	161,051	135,676	104.9
Nevada........	147,521	85,017	137,757	75,066	107.1

Population data for 1960 from U. S. Bureau of the Census, *U. S. Census of Population: 1960,* Vol. I, *Characteristics of the Population,* p. xiii, Table A in the part for each state; 1950 data from U. S. Bureau of the Census, *U. S. Census of Population: 1950,* Vol. II, *Characteristics of the Population,* Table 13 in the part for each state. Males/100 females from U. S. Department of Commerce, *Statistical Abstract of the United States, 1964,* U. S. G. P. O., Washington, D. C., 1964, p. 21.

It is readily seen that the table is much briefer than the text statement, since the row and column headings eliminate the necessity of repeating explanatory matter. As no text appears with the figures, the presentation is more concise. The logical arrangement of items in the stub (the left-hand column and its heading) and box head (the headings of the other columns) makes a table clear and easy to read. The use of columns and rows for the figures facilitates comparisons.

In Table 3.2 the various parts of a table have been slightly separated and labeled for identification. A table will have at least the four essentials: title, stub, box head, and body. There may also be present a prefatory note (see Table 3.5) and one or more footnotes, as in Table 3.2. If the figures in the table are not original, a source note is also included, sometimes with the prefatory note but usually below the table and below the footnotes to the table, if any are present.

Semi-tabular presentation. When only a few figures are to be used in a discussion, the text may be broken and the data listed as follows:

The number of motor vehicle factory sales by United States plants, was

6,933,240 in 1962,
7,637,728 in 1963,
7,751,822 in 1964.

TABLE 3.2

Population and Area of the United States, Territories, Posses-}Title
sions, and Other Holdings, 1960

	Population		Gross
Region	Number	Per cent of total	area in square miles
Total....................	183,285,009	100.00	3,628,150
Continental United States......	178,464,236	97.37	3,022,387
Hawaii.......................	632,772	0.35	6,424
Alaska.......................	226,167	0.12	586,400
Possessions:			
Puerto Rico................	2,349,544	1.28	3,435
Guam.....................	67,044	0.04	206
Virgin Islands of the U. S....	32,099	0.02	133
American Samoa............	20,051	0.01	76
Midway Islands.............	2,356	**	2
Wake Island...............	1,097	**	3
Other islands*.............	504	**	37
Canal Zone†.................	42,122	0.02	553
Corn Islands#................	1,872	**	4
Trust Territory of the Pacific Islands.....................	70,724	0.04	8,484
Population abroad‡...........	1,374,421	0.75	...

Box head
Stub
Body

* For a list of the islands, banks, reefs, and cays included in this category, see the source given below.   For some islands the area was not available.
† Under jurisdiction of the United States by Treaty with the Republic of Panama.
# Leased from the Republic of Nicaragua.
‡ Excludes citizens abroad on private business, travel, etc.,who were enumerated at their usual place of residence.
** Less than one-hundredth of one per cent.

Foot-
notes

Source note { Data from U. S. Bureau of the Census, *U. S. Census of Population: 1960*, Vol. I, *Characteristics of the Population*, Part A, *Number of Inhabitants*, Table 1, pp. 1–3.

This method is not often used, but it is serviceable in that the figures are made to stand out from the text as they would not do if worked into one or two sentences.   Incidentally, the figures can be more readily compared than if they were in the text.

Graphic presentation.   Graphic devices are extremely useful and effective for quickly presenting a limited amount of information.   The three following chapters deal with curves, bar charts, maps, and other statistical diagrams.

LEADING CONSIDERATIONS

Types of tables.   From the point of view of usage, there are two types of tables.   In the first place there are *general* or *reference* tables, which are used as a repository of information.   These are frequently very extensive and cover many pages.   Such tables give detailed information arranged for ready reference.   In a general table no attempt is made to arrange the entries so that emphasis will be placed on certain items, nor is there usually any reason for arranging columns and rows in order to bring out comparisons desired by the investigator.   The primary, and usually sole, purpose of a reference table is to present the data in such a manner that individual items may be found readily by a reader.   Reference or general tables are often placed in an appendix or a separate part of a published report.

In the second place there are *summary* or *text* tables, which are usually relatively small in size and which are designed to set forth one finding or a few closely related findings as effectively as possible.   While the reference table may be rather complicated, with subheadings and sub-subheadings in stub and caption, the summary table should be relatively simple in construction.   It frequently accompanies a text discussion and hence is also referred to as a *text* table.   If a reader is expected to divert his attention from a running discourse to a table, it is essential that the table be not too formidable, but simple and easy to understand.   Too many readers have a tendency to skip all the tables in a report.   This tendency can be combatted successfully only by making tables appear so simple as to be interesting and by introducing graphs that are attractive and not unduly complicated.   Because of the purpose which a summary table is to serve, the items shown therein will be arranged to place emphasis where desired, and the columns and rows will be so placed as to facilitate the comparisons of paramount importance.

A summary table is almost invariably the result of boiling down information contained in one or more reference tables, although upon occasion a summary table may be based, in whole or in part, upon one or more other summary tables.   Still more rarely, a summary table may be constructed directly from data contained in schedule forms.   The methods which can be used in deriving one table from one or more others are:

1. Data which are not important for the problem in hand may be omitted.   Thus, although there are about twenty states which produce sizeable amounts of bituminous coal, it might suffice to show separate data for only the ten or twelve leading states.

2. Detailed data may be combined into groups.   For example, data shown by states may be grouped into geographical divisions.   Again, data shown by individual industries may be combined into broader industrial groups.   For example, the manufacture of brick, tile, and terra cotta products; of cement, glass, and pottery; and the quarrying of

marble, granite, slate, and like products may be combined into the major category "clay, stone, and glass products."

3. The arrangement of data may be altered. Thus an alphabetical arrangement of cities may be replaced by an arrangement according to size of municipality.

4. Averages, ratios, percentages, or other computed measures may be substituted for, or given in addition to, the original absolute figures. A column of percentages is shown in Table 3.4. It will be observed that these figures facilitate the interpretation of the data upon which they are based.

Comparisons. While the arrangement into columns and rows makes it easy to compare the data, such treatment does not automatically focus attention upon the comparisons that are important. This may be effected by placing the figures to be compared in contiguous columns or rows. Thus it may be seen that Table 3.1 facilitates the comparison of data obtained at the two censuses for either males or females, while Table 3.3 makes it easy to compare the number of males and females enumerated at either census.

TABLE 3.3

Number of Inhabitants in the States of the Mountain Division, by Sex, 1950 and 1960

State	1960		1950		1960
	Male	Female	Male	Female	Males/100 females
Colorado.......	870,467	883,480	665,149	659,940	98.5
Arizona........	654,928	647,223	379,059	370,528	101.5
Utah..........	444,924	445,703	347,636	341,226	99.8
New Mexico...	479,770	471,253	347,554	333,643	101.8
Montana......	343,743	331,024	309,423	281,603	103.8
Idaho.........	338,421	328,770	303,237	285,400	102.9
Wyoming......	169,015	161,051	154,853	135,676	104.9
Nevada.......	147,521	137,757	85,017	75,066	107.1

Population data for 1960 from U. S. Bureau of the Census, *U. S. Census of Population: 1960*, Vol. I, *Characteristics of the Population*, p. xiii, Table A in the part for each state; 1950 data from U. S. Bureau of the Census, *U. S. Census of Population: 1950*, Vol. II, *Characteristics of the Population*, Table 13 in the part for each state. Males/100 females from U. S. Department of Commerce, *Statistical Abstract of the United States, 1964*, U. S. G. P. O., Washington, D. C., 1964, p. 21.

Each of these tables is well constructed, but each focuses attention upon a different comparison. One of the most important considerations in table construction is that figures which are to be compared must be placed in immediate juxtaposition. It should be remembered that two or more series of figures are more easily compared when placed in adjacent columns than when placed in adjacent rows, and that figures of a series are more easily compared with each other when arranged in a column than when placed in a row.

Comparisons may be greatly facilitated by the use of ratios, percentages, averages, or other computed relationships. Ratios are shown

TABLE 3.4

Composition of the Urban Population of the United States by Region, 1960

Region	Total urban population	Within urbanized areas	
		Number	Per cent
Northeast...................	35,840,140	30,611,324	85.4
North Central..............	35,481,254	26,550,170	74.8
South......................	32,160,250	21,501,114	66.9
West......................	21,787,106	17,185,879	78.9
Total.................	125,268,750	95,848,487	76.5

Data from U. S. Bureau of the Census, *U. S. Census of Population: 1960*, Vol. I, *Characteristics of the Population*, Part A, *Number of Inhabitants*, Table 17, pp. 1–26.

in Table 7.4; percentages, which are really a form of ratio (see Chapter 7), are included in Tables 3.2 and 3.4. Ratios and percentages are particularly useful when the absolute figures to be compared are large. Note that in Tables 3.2 and 3.4 rather large population figures can be compared readily by the use of percentages. When tables show monthly fluctuations and both maxima and minima are noted, the additional entry "minimum as percentage of maximum" is useful for purposes of comparison. See, for example, the second edition of this text, page 58. Averages are shown in Tables 14.1, 14.3, and 14.7.

Emphasis. The proper placing of an item in a table enables it to be given suitable emphasis. Since Occidentals read from left to right and from top to bottom, it follows that the most prominent position in the stub is at the top, and in the box head the most prominent position is at the left; likewise, the position of least prominence is at the bottom of the stub and at the right of the box head. Notice that, by following this principle in Table 3.3, males were emphasized rather than females, and 1960 was placed in a more prominent position than 1950.

Totals are generally placed in either the most prominent or the least prominent position, depending upon whether or not it is desired to give emphasis to them. When "total" is shown at the top in the stub, a line should be placed below the first row of figures, as in Table 3.2. If the total entry is at the bottom of the stub, the figures are set off by a line drawn above them, as in Table 3.4. An alternative procedure consists of using a space instead of a line to set off the totals as in Table 3.5. Whatever its position, the word "total" in the stub should be indented if possible.

Individual figures, or columns or rows of figures, may also be emphasized by the use of boldface type, as in Table 3.5. When monthly fluctuations of employment, sales, or other factors are shown, the maximum figure may be set in boldface and the minimum may be put in italic type. In general, italics are used to indicate an exception rather than for emphasis. Thus, in some issues of *Agricultural Statistics*, the

TABLE 3.5

*Foreign Visitors to the United States From Oversea Countries,**
1963–1964

(Thousands of travelers)

Oversea area and year	Total	Business	Pleasure	Transit	Student
Total from oversea countries:					
1964	1,098	150	807	110	31
1963	847	122	613	84	28
Europe and Mediterranean:					
1964	527	93	376	54	4
1963	398	75	278	40	5
West Indies, Central and South America:					
1964	414	21	346	35	12
1963	332	20	273	28	11
Other oversea areas:					
1964	157	36	85	21	15
1963	117	27	62	16	12

* Excludes visitors from Canada and Mexico; excludes foreign government personnel and foreign businessmen employed in the United States.

Data from U. S. Department of Justice, Immigration and Naturalization Service, as quoted in *Survey of Current Business*, June 1965, Vol. 45, No. 6, p. 28.

figures in italics are census returns, whereas all other figures are compilations or estimates made by the U. S. Department of Agriculture. Italics are also sometimes used to show deficits, items to be subtracted in arriving at a total, and items to be omitted from a total.

Arrangement of items in stub and caption. Considering the basic nature of statistical data which may be encountered, it was noted (page 3) that data may refer to geographical, chronological, qualitative, or quantitative classifications. We are now interested in the methods which may be employed in arranging the items in the stub or the box head of a table. The method of arrangement will be determined partly by the nature of the data (whether basically geographical, chronological, qualitative, or quantitative), and partly by a consideration of whether the data are to appear in a reference table or in a summary table. A number of different methods of arrangement may be employed.

Alphabetical. This method of arrangement is admirably adapted for use in a general table, because it enables individual items to be located with ease. It is, obviously, not a useful method for text tables. It can be used only with series which are classified geographically or qualitatively.

Geographical. The geographical method of arrangement may be employed for series classified geographically, but it is applicable only when an established usage has been set up and should be used only when the statistician is sure that his readers are familiar with the classification.

The customary order of the geographic divisions of the United States and of the various states may be seen in many tables in the United States summary, in Volume I of the 1960 *United States Census of Population*. Although the Census makes frequent use of the geographical method of arrangement for the states, it almost invariably lists the counties of a state alphabetically. For ease of reference, in a general table, the geographical arrangement is hardly so satisfactory as the alphabetical. Although it may be argued that the geographical arrangement often places together contiguous, and therefore comparable, areas, it must be obvious that the geographical arrangement does not always do so. It is not usually a good method of arrangement for a summary table, since this arrangement does not place important items in prominent positions.

Magnitude. A very satisfactory method of arranging items in a summary table consists of listing them according to size, usually with the largest item first, but sometimes with the order reversed. The states shown in the stub of Table 3.3 are given in order of magnitude in 1950. When the largest item is placed first, the most important items (numerically) are placed in the most prominent positions. Arrangement of items according to size is not useful in a general table because it does not facilitate the finding of individual items as does the alphabetical arrangement. Data classified geographically or qualitatively may be arranged according to magnitude. So also may data classified chronologically, but they lose their chronological sequence when arranged by magnitude.

Historical. Data classified on a chronological basis would generally be arranged chronologically or historically. When years are listed, either the most recent or the earliest date may be shown first. The months, however, are customarily listed with January first. When the historical arrangement is called for, it may be used in either general or text tables. The historical arrangement is used in the stub of various tables in Chapter 12.

Customary. Certain data that are basically *qualitative* are generally arranged according to customary classes. Exports and imports are often grouped into five categories: crude materials, crude foodstuffs, manufactured foodstuffs, semi-manufactures, and finished manufactures. The population of the United States, when divided into groups upon a so-called "race-nativity" basis, is frequently subdivided into the following classes: native White, foreign-born White, Negro, Indian, Japanese, Chinese, and "all other." These are ordinarily listed in the order given. When an "all other" group appears in a table, it is ordinarily placed at the bottom in the stub, or at the right in the box head. Good statistical practice dictates that an "all other," "miscellaneous," or "not reported" group should include relatively small numbers; otherwise, the adequacy of the classification or the accuracy of the collection of the data may be questioned. Arrangement by customary classes is appropriate for either a text or a reference table. *Quantitative* data may be arranged into classes as shown in the stub of Table 8.6. Such arrangements usually begin with the class of smallest numerical value and may be used in either a text or a reference table.

Progressive. The items are listed in such a way that the final figure develops logically from those given before. One example of the progressive arrangement was shown in the box head of a table which presented monthly data of the number of strikes in the United States during a year. The progressive headings in the box head were:

Continued from preceding month	Beginning in month	In progress during month	Ended in month	In effect at end of month

The progressive arrangement is suitable for either text or reference tables.

Numerical. The wards of cities are usually designated as Ward 1, Ward 2, and so forth. When data for such subdivisions are shown, a numerical arrangement is generally followed. The precincts and districts of counties are sometimes numbered; the departments of a factory and salesmen's territories or sales areas may also be identified by numerical designations. This method may appear in either a text or a reference table. The numbers assigned to the categories are frequently only labels serving to identify some underlying arrangement. For example, in a shoe factory, Department 1 was the cutting department; Department 2, the fitting department; Department 3, the lasting department; and so forth.

In using the various methods of arrangement, remember that in a reference table, the items should be arranged for greatest ease of reference, whereas in a text table the arrangement should be designed to emphasize the important items and to stress the proper comparisons.

DETAILS OF TABLE CONSTRUCTION

Title and identification. A title should accompany every table and is customarily placed above the table. The title should be clearly worded and should state briefly what data are shown in the table. A title should be so worded as to mention the more important considerations first, placing toward the end any statement concerning how the items are arranged and what period of time is covered. In general the title states, in order: what, where, how classified, and when. Illustrations of titles are shown in the various tables of this chapter. It will be noted that, when a title necessitates the use of several lines, an inverted-pyramid arrangement is used.

If a title is long, it may be advantageous to place a "catch title" above the main title or, occasionally, to substitute the catch title for the full title. This shorter title undertakes merely to state the general nature of the data in the table. For Table 7.1 a catch title might read "New Construction in U.S. in 1963 and 1964."

When more than one table is included in a study, it is desirable to number the tables consecutively in order that each one may be identified by number rather than by title.

Prefatory note and footnotes. A prefatory note, one or more footnotes, and a source note may be appended to a table. A prefatory note is placed just below the title and in smaller or less prominent type. The prefatory note provides an explanation concerning the entire table or a substantial part of it, as in Table 3.5.

Explanations concerning individual figures, or a column or row of figures, should be given in footnotes. Footnotes keyed to stub entries and column headings may be referred to by means of numbers; however, footnotes keyed to figures should be identified by a symbol (*, †, #, ‡, etc.), as in Table 3.2, or by a letter, but preferably not by a number. In this book, symbols have been used for keying footnotes to figures, stub entries, column headings, and titles of tables.

Source notes. As previously indicated, the source note may appear below the title or below the footnotes. The latter practice has been generally followed in this text. The data set forth in a table will not often be material which the investigator has collected. Usually the figures will have been taken from one or more published or unpublished sources. The source note should be complete, giving author, title, volume, page, publisher, and date. Not only is it courteous to mention the source of data quoted, but such information gives the reader some idea of the reliability of the data and makes it possible for him to refer to the original source to verify quoted figures or to obtain additional information.

Sometimes data are taken from a secondary source instead of a primary source because the secondary source may be more convenient. In such a case it may be advisable to mention both sources; for example, "Source: National Board of Fire Underwriters as quoted in *Statistical Abstract of the United States*, 1964, p. 482." See Table 3.5.

Data for a table may sometimes be taken from two or more different sources. When this is done, care must be exercised to see that the data are comparable. The importance of comparability of data was discussed in Chapter 2; it is not necessary to say more on that topic at this point.

When apparent mistakes are found in a source, it is well to call attention to the fact. The *Monthly Labor Review* once reprinted a table from *The Oriental Economist* showing that total payrolls in 10 industries in Japan in one year were 647,340,199 yen, but pointed out in a footnote that, if the figures given for each of the 10 industries are added, the result is 647,430,199 yen.

Percentages.   When percentages are used in a table, the stub or the caption entry should indicate clearly to what figures the percentages relate.   Thus, the term "per cent" alone should be avoided; rather say, "per cent of total," "per cent of increase or decrease," and so forth. Sometimes tables are divided into a "number" section (showing absolute figures) and a "per cent" section, as in Table 8.6.   This table and Table 7.2 illustrate the use of adequate headings referring to percentages.

When individual percentages are written correct to tenths of one per cent, as is customary, the total will occasionally be slightly over or below 100.0 because of the accumulation of positive or negative remainders when rounding.   If the percentages had been entered in hundredths or thousandths of a per cent, the total would have been closer to 100.0. Although a "per cent of total" column may add to slightly more or less than 100.0, the total is shown as 100.0, since that is what the individual percentages would yield if carried out far enough.   If a total adds to less than 99.8 or more than 100.2, it is advisable to re-check the calculations for mistakes.

Rounding numbers.   In order to avoid confusion and to facilitate comparisons, numbers of many digits may be rounded.   Numbers may also be rounded because the compiler feels that they are accurate, not to the final digit, but only in terms of (say) thousands or millions.   The production figures shown in Table 17.2 were rounded (but no digits dropped) to call attention to the fact that they were estimates.

When numbers are rounded, a statement to that effect should be made in a prefatory note or in the stub or the box head.   The wording may be "millions of . . . ," "000,000 omitted," and like expressions.   Tables 3.6, 7.1, and 7.2 contain rounded numbers, and mention of that fact is made in a prefatory note or in the appropriate box head.

If a series of figures is to be expressed in thousands of dollars, for example, the rounding is to the *nearest* thousand.   Thus $2,648,302 would become $2,648 (thousand) and $7,226,782 would become $7,227 (thousand).   If the heading "thousands of dollars" appears in the box head (or stub) of a table or as a prefatory note, the dollar mark is not needed.

No serious error is ordinarily introduced by rounding.   If each of a series of numbers is rounded, some will be raised and some will be lowered, but the errors so introduced tend to offset each other.   Furthermore, it may be felt that to show all the digits of a large number is to give the appearance of spurious accuracy.   For example, the population of the United States was ascertained to be 179,323,175, persons in 1960, but the figure could hardly be accurate to units or even to hundreds.   However, it may be maintained that the figure 179,323,175 is the one obtained by the best methods available and is therefore probably more accurate than any rounded figure.   Irrespective of the merits of these two points of view, six (or fewer) significant figures may often be accurate enough for the comparisons desired. Further mention of rounding (and of significant digits) is made on pages 124–125 and in Appendix T.

When computed values, such as totals, percentages, and averages, are to be shown in tables of rounded figures, these values should, if possible, be calculated from the original figures before rounding.

Totals. We have previously noted that totals, when of major importance, may be placed at the top in the stub and at the left in the caption. When it is not desired to emphasize totals, they may be placed at the bottom in the stub and at the right in the caption.

Table 3.5 carries both total columns and a total row. An arrangement such as this results in a single number which is sometimes termed a "grand total" or a "checked grand total." The fact that the figures yield the same sum when added vertically and horizontally is not a positive check, since two or more compensating errors may have been made. That, however, does not often happen. We do have definite proof either that no errors were made or that more than one was made.

Units. The units of measurement of the figures in a column or a row of a table may often be self-explanatory. When this is not true, the nature of the unit should be made clear in the stub or the box head, as in Table 7.2. If the explanation applies to all figures in the table, it may appear as a prefatory note. Data of monetary units are usually self-descriptive, because of the use of the dollar sign. Note, in Table 3.6, that this sign appears for only the first entry in a column.

Size and shape of table. In general, a table should be designed so that it will be neither very long and narrow nor very short and wide. A table must also be adjusted to the space in which it is to appear. Usually this limitation takes the form of a page of a book or a report. Of course, a table need not occupy the entire length or width of a page. If the table is too large for the allotted space, it may be recast into several smaller tables. Reduction of type size may permit a table to be included on a page, but reduction should not be made at the expense of legibility. If the use of a folded page is not desirable, the table may be arranged to occupy two facing pages. Because of the difficulty of aligning pages perfectly in binding, the stub is often repeated on the second page. When reference tables are continued over several pages, they may be split either vertically or horizontally. In either case, complete stub and caption entries should appear on each page, the title should be repeated on each page, and footnotes may appear at the bottom of the appropriate page or may be accumulated at the end of the table.

The horizontal dimension of a table may be determined by allowing for:

(1) Width of stub, determined by longest entry. (A very long entry may be put on two or more lines to save space; see the stub of Table 3.5.)

(2) Width of each column, determined by largest number or by entry

TABLE 3.6

Stock Market Customer Credit, January–December 1964*

(millions)

Month	Total securities other than U. S. Government	Net debit balances with N. Y. Stock Exchange firms secured by—		Bank loans to other than brokers and dealers for purchasing and carrying—	
		U. S. Government securities	Other securities	U. S. Government securities	Other securities
January.......	$7,250	$22	$5,524	$108	$1,726
February......	7,120	21	5,384	97	1,736
March........	7,141	21	5,366	97	1,775
April.........	7,314	21	5,510	101	1,804
May..........	7,277	19	5,439	96	1,838
June.........	7,229	18	5,370	94	1,859
July..........	7,160	25	5,289	70	1,871
August........	7,096	21	5,187	69	1,909
September.....	7,142	19	5,221	81	1,921
October........	7,101	20	5,185	69	1,916
November.....	7,108	20	5,160	64	1,948
December.....	7,053	21	5,079	72	1,974

* Data in first three columns are for end of month; others for last Wednesday.
Data from *Federal Reserve Bulletin*, Washington, D. C., January 1965, p. 143.

in each box head.   (By hyphenating words, an entry in a box head may be compressed horizontally and expanded vertically.)

(3) Ruling.

(4) Margins.

The vertical dimension may be ascertained by considering:

(1) Space needed for title, prefatory note, footnotes, and source note. Since the first line of the title should not exceed the table in width, a long title may require several lines.

(2) Number of lines needed for the heading, in the stub or box head, which requires the most vertical space.

(3) Number of rows in body of table.

(4) Ruling.

(5) Margins.

Ruling.   Most of the tables in this text are shown with single-line ruling and are open at the sides.   Double-line ruling is sometimes used, but double lines seem to make either hand-ruled or printed tables appear somewhat complicated.   Tables are rarely closed at the sides, and should never appear with one side closed and one open.   There seems to be a growing tendency to use text tables without ruling, either vertical or horizontal.

An examination of tables in this book and elsewhere will show that:

(1) No horizontal lines are used in the body of a table except to set off totals and occasionally to separate a table into distinct parts.

(2) Horizontal lines separating major and minor box heads do not continue into the stub heading.

(3) All vertical lines separating box heads appear only between the box heads which they separate; they do not extend above these box heads.

Guiding the eye. Skipping a line every three, four, or five rows, as in Table 3.6, makes it easier for the eye to follow the rows across a table. The use of leaders in the stub of a table is also helpful.

Zeros. It is not customary to show a zero in a table (other than a computation form). When no cases have been found to exist or when the value of an item is zero, the fact may be indicated by means of dots (...) or short dashes(---). When there is no figure for an entry because information is lacking, a footnote should be used to indicate that fact.

Size and style of type. Too much variety in size or style of type (or lettering) is not desirable. In general the title should be most prominent and is usually set in large and small capitals or in boldface type. The items listed in the stub and caption and the figures in the body of the table are usually set in the same size type. Footnotes, prefatory note, and source note are generally set in smaller type than that used in the body of the table.

STATISTICAL REPORTS

When making a statistical report, the method of preparing the tables will be dictated partly by the number of copies of the report required and partly by the cost involved. Tables may be handwritten, typewritten, mimeographed, multigraphed, reproduced by a photostatic or photographic process from handwritten or typed tables, or printed.

There is a distinct disadvantage in the use of the ordinary typewriter for preparing other than relatively simple tables, because of the lack of flexibility of spacing and of size of type. Flexibility is obtained by using two typewriters, one with pica and one with elite type. By using elite type for the stub entries and the body, a certain amount of space may be saved. Somewhat more flexibility in planning a table may be had by using a typewriter with variable spacing and with different kinds and sizes of type.

If only a few copies of a report are required and if the tables are simple, the tables and accompanying text may be typed and carbon copies made. If several dozen copies are needed, the longhand or typed material may be photostated. By this method, reduction or enlarging is possible and copies may be had rather promptly, since no plate need be made. If a larger number of copies is required, resort may be had to mimeographing of multigraphing. Tables may also be reproduced by a photo-offset process, which is quite satisfactory and is often cheaper than printing because typesetting is avoided. Enlarging or reduction is possible; typed material may be reduced so that 4 ordinary $8\frac{1}{2} \times 11$-inch pages (pica type) will appear on one page. It should be noted that the typed copy should be a first-class job if satisfactory reproductions are to be obtained.

CHAPTER 4

Graphic Presentation I:

CURVES USING ARITHMETIC SCALES

THE GRAPHIC METHOD

Attention has already been given to the presentation of statistical data by means of text, tabular, and semi-tabular devices. Ordinarily, statistical data will be presented in the form of either a table or a chart. This chapter and the two which follow are devoted to a discussion of the portrayal of statistical data by graphic devices. As will be readily seen from a perusal of the pages of this book, charts or graphs are more effective in attracting attention than are any of the other methods of presenting data. Readers are therefore not so likely to skip a chart as to skip a table. A simple, attractive, well-constructed graph, showing a limited set of facts, is also easier to understand than is a table.

The outstanding effectiveness of a chart for presenting a limited amount of data makes it a most useful statistical tool. Certain limitations should be noted, however. In the first place, charts cannot show so many sets of facts as may be shown in a table. Numerous columns and rows may appear in a table; but imagine Chart 4.2 with six or eight criss-crossing and intertwining lines, and it is immediately obvious why a chart should show only a limited amount of information. In the second place, although exact values can be given in a table, only approximate values can ordinarily be shown by a chart. In a table we may enter as many digits as are desired, but we can plot only the approximate value on a chart. For example, while the data upon which Chart 4.2 is based could be recorded in a table in terms of exact number of trucks and buses, a chart could show only thousands, or at best hundreds. Thus charts are useful for giving a quick picture of a general situation, but not of details. In the third place, charts require a certain amount of time to

60

construct, since each one is an original drawing.   This difficulty, however, is offset by the added effectiveness which the chart possesses in comparison with a table.[1]

TYPES OF CHARTS

In this text we shall discuss: *curves* or *line diagrams; bar charts,* involving one-dimensional comparisons; *area diagrams,* involving two-dimensional comparisons (including particularly *pie diagrams,* which involve one- or

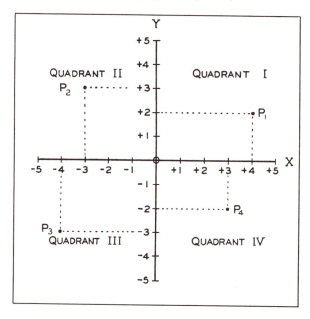

Chart 4.1.   Axes for Curve Plotting.

two-dimensional comparisons, or comparisons of angles); *volume diagrams,* which call for a visualization of the third dimension and three-dimensional comparisons; *pictographs,* which involve aspects of both volume diagrams and bar charts; and *statistical maps.*   Other specialized types of charts and certain charts which are graphic but not statistical (for example, organization and procedure charts) are not treated here, but are discussed

---

[1] William Playfair, who is understood to have "invented outright" the graphic method in the latter part of the 18th century, says: "The advantage proposed by this method, is not that of giving a more accurate statement than by figures, but it is to give a more simple and permanent idea of the gradual progress and comparative amounts, at different periods, by presenting to the eye a figure [chart], the proportions of which correspond with the amount of the sums intended to be expressed." See the article "Playfair and His Charts," by H. Gray Funkhauser and Helen M. Walker, in *Economic History,* February 1935, pp. 103–109.

in books on graphic methods. This chapter will consider only curves using arithmetic scales. In the following chapter attention will be given to curves using a logarithmic vertical scale and an arithmetic horizontal scale. Chapter 6 will include brief discussions of bar charts, area diagrams, volume diagrams, pictographs, and statistical maps.

PLOTTING A CURVE

When statistical data are shown as curves, the points are plotted in reference to a pair of intersecting lines, called *axes* and shown in Chart

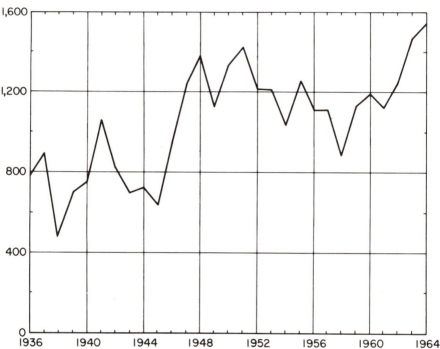

Chart 4.2. Factory Sales of Motor Trucks and Buses by United States Plants, 1963–1964. Data from Automobile Manufacturers Assn., *Automobile Facts and Figures*, 1965, p. 3.

4.1. The horizontal line is known as the "*X*-axis" and the vertical line is designated as the "*Y*-axis." Positive values are shown to the right of zero on the *X*-axis and above the zero on the *Y*-axis; negative values are placed to the left of zero on the *X*-axis and below the zero on the *Y*-axis. The point at which the two axes intersect is zero for both *X* and *Y* and in books on graphic methods. This chapter will consider only curves

"origin."   The positive and negative values on the axes increase as we move away from this origin.

The two axes of Chart 4.1 divide the plotting area into four sections known as "quadrants."   For reference purposes, these quadrants are designated I, II, III, and IV.   Quadrant I accommodates values which are positive on both the X- and Y-axes.   Quadrant II provides for values which are negative on the X-axis and positive on the Y-axis.   Quadrant III takes care of values which are negative on both axes.   Quadrant IV is for values which are positive on the X-axis and negative on the Y-axis.

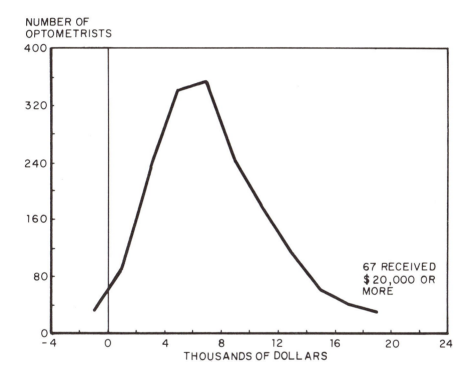

NUMBER OF
OPTOMETRISTS

67 RECEIVED
$20,000 OR
MORE

THOUSANDS OF DOLLARS

Chart 4.3.   Net Income of 1,764 Optometrists.   Data from the American Optometric Association.   The frequencies for the last three plotted classes are estimates.

Any point plotted in one of the quadrants may be located by referring to its abscissa value, which is its horizontal or X distance from zero, and to its ordinate value, which is its vertical or Y distance from zero.   For illustrative purposes four points have been plotted on Chart 4.1, one in each quadrant: P_1 represents $X = +4$, $Y = +2$; P_2 indicates $X = -3$, $Y = +3$; P_3 is $X = -4$, $Y = -3$; P_4 shows $X = +3$, $Y = -2$.

When the axes are used as bases of reference for plotting equations, any or all of the quadrants may be used, since many equations may call for negative values of X or of Y, or of both. At present, however, we are not interested in the graphic representation of equations, but in graphically portraying observed statistical data. When we are dealing with statistical data, it must be obvious that both the X and Y variables are ordinarily positive quantities, and that therefore we shall generally use only the quadrant designated as I. Chart 4.2, showing the factory sales of motor trucks and buses in the United States over a period of years, is an example of a curve lying wholly in quadrant I.

Quadrants II and IV are occasionally used in conjunction with quadrant I. Chart 4.3 shows a curve which makes use of quadrants I and II; the curve of Chart 4.4 lies partly in quadrant I and partly in quadrant IV. Since both X and Y values are negative in quadrant III, that quadrant is very rarely used.

TYPES OF DATA SHOWN BY CURVES

It was noted earlier that statistical data may be classified according to chronological, geographical, quantitative, or qualitative characteristics. Curves are frequently used for picturing time series and for showing frequency distributions (by far the most important sort of quantitatively classified data), although, of course, other types of graphs are also applicable as shown in the following chapters. Qualitatively and, especially, geographically classified data are rarely depicted by curves; instead, bar charts and other devices are used, as will be indicated hereafter.

Time series curves. The method of plotting time series depends upon the type of data to be represented. We may distinguish between *period data* and *point data*. Period data, such as total sales per month, average monthly sales per year, and average prices during the year, refer to a period of time. Point data are those, such as inventory values, price quotations, or temperature readings, which refer to a particular point of time. Whenever chronological data are depicted by means of a curve, the years, months, weeks, days, or other chronological units are shown on the horizontal axis; the other series, which varies with time, is placed on the vertical axis.

Charts 4.2 and 4.18 show period data. When annual data of this type are plotted, the dates on the horizontal scales may be placed below the vertical lines, as in Chart 4.2, or below spaces, as in the right-hand part of Chart 4.18. Either method may be used; one argument for labeling the spaces is that this gives a visual impression of time as having duration. When monthly (and daily, weekly, or quarterly) data are plotted for a number of years, there is no choice but to label the spaces representing each year, since, if the lines were labeled, it would not be immediately obvious to all readers whether the label referred to the space preceding the line, the space following the line, or possibly half of the space on each side.   Each horizontal year-space is divided into 12 parts for the plotting of the monthly figures, and these figures may be plotted at the middle of each of the 12 spaces.   Chart 4.4 illustrates this for period data on a monthly basis.

EXCESS OF ARRIVALS OVER
DEPARTURES IN THOUSANDS

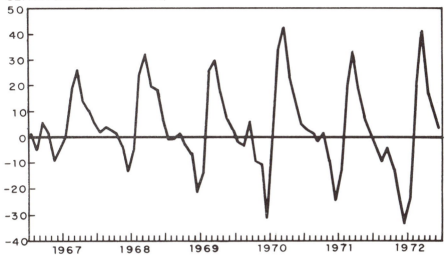

Chart 4.4.   Net Arrivals and Departures of United States Citizens, January 1967–December 1972.   Data hypothetical.

When point data are being represented by a curve, spaces, rather than lines, should be labeled on the horizontal axis and the observations should be plotted within the spaces at the point in time to which the data refer. This latter consideration is more important for annual data than for monthly data.   However, for monthly data we should, ideally, (1) plot beginning-of-the-month data (such as figures of cold-storage holdings as of the first of each month) at the beginning of each space representing a month, (2) plot middle-of-the-month data (for example, payroll data for the payroll nearest the fifteenth of each month) at the middle of each space, and (3) plot end-of-the-month data (such as money in circulation at the end of each month) at the end of each space.   If this procedure is not followed, the appearance of a curve of monthly data is not altered; the curve is merely shifted to the left or to the right.

Curves of frequency distributions.   The curve of Chart 4.3 is a graphic representation of a frequency distribution.   Frequency distributions will not usually continue into the second quadrant as does this one.   In this instance, however, there were some negative incomes.

TABLE 4.1

Frequency Distribution of Grades Received
for the Four-Year Course by 409 Liberal
Arts Students of the 1965 Graduating
Class of Rutgers—The State
University

Grade	Number of students
75.0–76.9	3
77.0–78.9	23
79.0–80.9	52
81.0–82.9	61
83.0–84.9	74
85.0–86.9	61
87.0–88.9	53
89.0–90.9	35
91.0–92.9	23
93.0–94.9	15
95.0–96.9	7
97.0–98.9	2
Total	409

Data from Newark College of Arts and Sciences of Rutgers—The State University.

Table 4.1 shows a frequency distribution[2] of the grades of 409 liberal arts students of the 1965 graduating class of Rutgers—The State University. In order to show the genesis of the frequency distribution curve, the data are first represented by a series of rectangles or bars in the "column diagram" of Chart 4.5. It will be noticed that the grades have been placed along the horizontal axis and the frequencies (number of students) along the vertical axis. There are as many columns in the chart as there were classes in the table, and the height of each column represents the frequency for the corresponding class. This column diagram is transformed into a curve by connecting the midpoint of the top of each rectangle with the midpoint of the top of each adjacent rectangle, as shown by the broken line in Chart 4.5. This is done upon the assumption that the values in a class interval are evenly distributed throughout the class. The mid-value of a class is consequently taken as representing the class.[3] It will be observed that the dotted line cuts off some small triangular pieces of the original rectangles and that it also includes some small triangles not formerly included, but it is obvious that triangle A = triangle A', triangle B = triangle B', and so forth. Sometimes the curve is continued at each end to join the X-axis (indicating a frequency of zero) at the mid-value of the next possible class.

[2] Frequency distributions are discussed in Chapter 8.

[3] This point is discussed at greater length in Chapter 9.

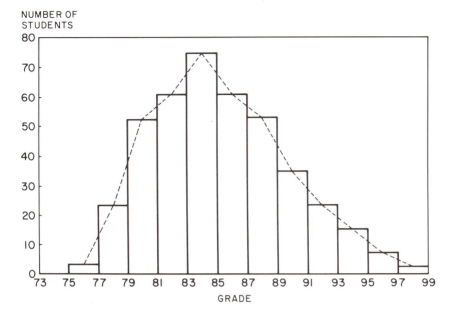

Chart 4.5. Grades Received for the Four-Year Course by 409 Liberal Arts Students of the 1965 Graduating Class of Rutgers—The State University, Shown by a Column Diagram and by a Frequency Curve. Data of Table 4.1.

This procedure results in having the same area under the curve as is included in the rectangles. However, the result may sometimes be a curve which extends beyond zero on the X-axis, and this is apt to be meaningless. In any event the extensions suggest to the reader that items occurred beyond the limits of the observed data. Except for special purposes (see Chart 23.14), it is better not to extend the curve to the X-axis. The frequency distribution may be shown either as a column diagram or as a frequency curve (frequency polygon). The latter is more usual and the curve is plotted directly, as in Chart 4.6, without the intermediate step of constructing columns.

Sometimes frequency distributions are encountered which refer to such information as number of children in a family, number of automobiles parked in a block, or other data which can have only values that are integers (0, 1, 2, 3, etc.). Frequency distributions dealing with variables of this sort, which we shall identify in Chapter 8 as "discrete," are generally shown by a column diagram, rather than by a curve. Chart 23.12, showing the data of Table 23.7, illustrates this point; the separation of the bars serves to emphasize the lack of continuity which is present.

NUMBER OF
STUDENTS

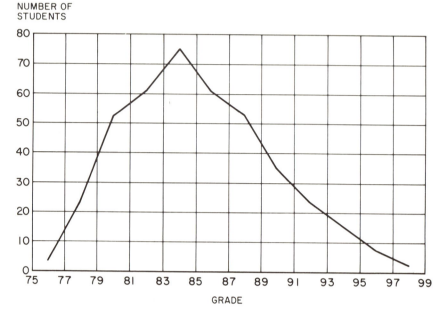

GRADE

Chart 4.6. Grades Received for the Four-Year Course by 409 Liberal
Arts Students of the 1965 Graduating Class of Rutgers—The State University. Data of Table 4.1.

RULES FOR DRAWING CURVES

While statisticians have not agreed upon a standard procedure setting
forth in detail exactly how line diagrams should be constructed, there are
certain rather obvious considerations of importance. The student who
is interested in going into more detail in regard to the technique of chart
construction is referred to a book dealing solely with that topic.[4]

Zero on vertical scale. The inclusion of a zero on the vertical scale
of a curve is perhaps one of the most important rules. Chart makers
all too frequently neglect to observe this principle and the result is always
misleading, since the visual impression is incorrect. In Chart 4.2 factory
sales of motor trucks and buses from 1936 to 1964 were plotted with
reference to a vertical scale beginning with zero. The same series of
data appear in Chart 4.7, but on this chart the vertical scale begins at
400,000. Chart 4.7 gives the reader a visual impression which is quite
contrary to the facts. For example, sales in 1960 appear to have been
about 8 times that for 1938, whereas Chart 4.2 shows clearly that 1960
sales were only about two and one-half times as large as 1938 sales. Very
few readers notice the omission of zero on a vertical scale, and fewer still
are apt to make due allowance for the omission in interpreting a curve.

---

[4] For example, Ely Francis, *Using Charts to Improve Profits*, Prentice-Hall, Inc.,
Englewood Cliffs, N. J., 1962.

THOUSANDS OF
TRUCKS AND BUSES

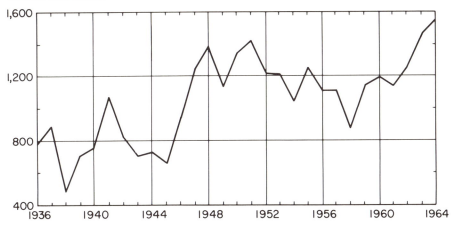

Chart 4.7. Factory Sales of Motor Trucks and Buses by United States Plants, 1936–1964. This chart is incorrectly drawn, since the vertical scale begins with 400 and there is no clear indication of the omission of the zero. Data from source given below Chart 4.2.

It should not be necessary for a reader to refer to a scale in order to make approximate comparisons; the chart should be so drawn that visual comparisons may be made as quickly as possible.

Showing the zero as in Chart 4.2 would sometimes result in placing the curve high up on the grid and might also make the movements of the curve difficult to discern. Therefore, the omission of the zero on the vertical scale of a chart usually occurs because the person constructing

THOUSANDS OF
TRUCKS AND BUSES

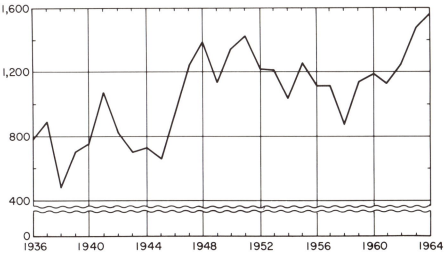

Chart 4.8. Factory Sales of Motor Trucks and Buses by United States Plants, 1936–1964. Data from source given below Chart 4.2.

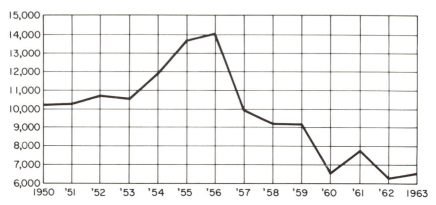

Chart 4.9.   Trend in Still Seizures by United States Federal Agents, 1950–1963.   From Licensed Beverages Industries *Facts Book 1964*, p. 36.   This is one of the three statistical series shown in the original chart; for purposes of clarity the other two have been omitted.   Note the absence of a label for the units on the vertical axis.   From the text accompanying the original source, it is evident that the unit is "number of still seizures."

the chart wishes to emphasize the movements of the curve and feels that the space between the curve and the X-axis is useless.   There are several ways in which it is possible to show the zero (or to indicate clearly its omission), and also to avoid placing the curve high up on the chart. Chart 4.8 shows a method in which a definite break is made across the chart.   Sometimes the parallel lines are serrated (notched) instead of wavy.   They may be drawn freehand or, as in Chart 4.8, by making use of a bread knife as a ruler.   Charts 4.15, 11.1 and 11.3 show other devices which are occasionally used.   Notice that Charts 4.8 and 4.15 show the zero and a scale break, while Charts 11.1 and 11.3 do not show the zero but merely call attention to the fact that the vertical scale is incomplete.

Chart 4.9 appeared in the annual report of a trade association.   Because no warning is given of the omission of the zero on the vertical scale, this chart gives a misleading visual impression of the decrease in still seizures by Federal agents.   Unless the vertical scale is consulted, the reader may conclude that still seizures by Federal agents have nearly ceased.

Occasionally curves will be seen which lack a zero on the vertical scale and which show the growth of sales of a commodity, membership in an organization, circulation of a periodical, or other data.   The omission of the zero makes the growth appear to be much more rapid than it really has been.

Chart 4.10 shows index numbers of the retail prices of food.   This chart is unusual in two respects.   In the first place, it carries a zero for the vertical scale, which, though not wrong, is not necessary when price index numbers are being plotted, because it is hardly conceivable that prices will ever approach zero and because 100 is the base of the index number.   The 100 line should always be emphasized when it is the base, as in this chart.   Similarly the zero line should be emphasized, as in Chart 4.8, when it is the base of the chart.   When charting index numbers, some persons prefer to show the fluctuations above and below 100 in terms of positive and negative values.   In the case of Chart 4.10, 100 would become zero, 105 would become $+5$, and 85 would become -15. The vertical scale of Chart 4.10 would be altered to read $+20$, 0, -20, -40, -60, -80, and -100.   The curve itself would remain unchanged. The second unusual feature of Chart 4.10 is the treatment of the horizontal and vertical guide lines, which results in giving the curve an unusually clear profile.   Notice also that space has been left to add later data.   This practice allows the same original chart to be reproduced time after time by merely extending the curve as new data become available.

Ruling curves.   The curve or curves representing the data should stand out clearly from the background of the chart.   The curve should therefore be ruled more heavily than the coordinates.   (When two or more curves are shown which follow each other closely or which intertwine, it is sometimes necessary to use more lightly ruled lines for some of the curves.   See, for example, Chart 17.3.)   As will be seen from the various curves in this text, the plotted points are not usually shown, since the attempt is to present the general situation rather than the individual readings.

When several curves are drawn on the same axis, it is important for the reader to be able to identify each curve.   Thus we may use solid, dotted,

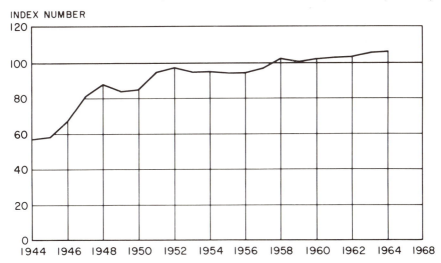

INDEX NUMBER

Chart 4.10.   Consumers Price Index of Food in the United States, 1944–1964.   Data from *Statistical Abstract of the United States, 1964*, p. 356.   1964 index as of March, 1964.

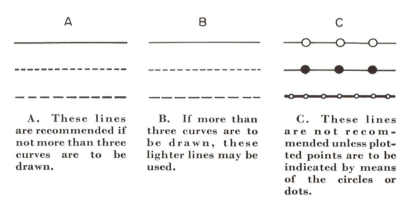

A. These lines are recommended if not more than three curves are to be drawn.

B. If more than three curves are to be drawn, these lighter lines may be used.

C. These lines are not recommended unless plotted points are to be indicated by means of the circles or dots.

and dashed lines, and we may use heavy and light lines.   If a light line is used for a curve, it should ordinarily not be so light as the coordinates. The suggested rulings are listed below as A and B.

When two or more curves appear on a chart, each should be clearly identified.   This may be accomplished by labeling the curves as in Charts 4.13, 4.17, and 17.3.

It is ordinarily well to avoid the use of more than two or three curves on one chart.   Particularly if they cross and re-cross, confusion is likely to result.   When several curves appear on a large wall chart which is to be presented to a group, different colors may occasionally be used, though it is usually better practice to reserve the use of color for those occasions when special emphasis is to be placed on one or two curves.   Black, red, green, light or medium blue, and medium or dark orange are readily distinguished.   If there is a likelihood that the wall chart is to be photostated, photographed, or reproduced for printing, black and red may be used in solid and broken, light and heavy, combinations, since the red line will reproduce as black.   Blue, yellow, and some shades of green photograph either not at all or faintly.   Color is ordinarily too expensive to be used in a book.

Coordinates.   Chart makers emphasize the zero line by making it a little heavier than the other marginal lines.   In similar fashion, a 100 per cent line (or other base with which comparisons are made) may be stressed.   The marginal vertical and horizontal lines may be made slightly heavier than the other coordinate lines.

The coordinate lines should be drawn very lightly.   No more coordinate lines should appear than are necessary to assist in reading the chart. Occasionally all coordinates are omitted, as in Chart 4.4, which uses "tics" in lieu of coordinate lines.   If it is desired to have a closely ruled grid in order to make plotting easy, the chart may be drawn on tracing cloth or tracing paper which has been placed over a grid which has the desired closely spaced coordinate lines.   Alternatively, when a chart is to be reproduced, a closely ruled grid of light blue may be used.   The lines which should appear in the reproduction are ruled in black.   The blue lines of the background do not show up in the reproduction under ordinary conditions. Some of the charts in this text were drawn on such a light blue background.

In order to insure a proper understanding of a chart, the two scales should be clearly labeled. Not only should the nature of the data be indicated, but the units used should also be stated. For example, in Chart 4.3 the horizontal axis shows incomes, the unit being thousands of dollars. Occasionally a curve of a long time series may be rather extended horizontally. In such instances it is sometimes desirable to repeat the vertical scale at the right of the chart.

Chart proportions. It is hardly possible to give an objective rule as to the proper proportions for a curve diagram. It should be noted, however, that bizarre impressions result from over-expanding or over-contracting either scale used for a curve. In Chart 4.11 the vertical scale is exaggerated in relation to the horizontal scale; in Chart 4.12 the horizontal scale is exaggerated. The former gives an impression of large fluctuations; the latter conveys the idea that truck and bus sales have undergone relatively unimportant fluctuations. These two charts indicate distorted results of replotting the data shown properly in Chart 4.2. Rules of thumb are often unsatisfactory because they are apt to be adopted blindly. However, it has been suggested that the proper proportions are those which result in a 45-degree angle for the movements of the curve which are to be emphasized.

Just as it is possible to overemphasize or to minimize fluctuations by poor choice of scales, so it is possible to create misleading impressions in regard to growth. One curve of Chart 5.3 shows automobile registrations in the United States for 1928–1964. Expanding the vertical scale and contracting the horizontal scale would give a visual impression of very rapid growth of United States automobile registrations; contracting the vertical scale and expanding the horizontal scale would make the growth appear to have been very slow.

Although the two preceding paragraphs referred to curves of time series, it should be understood that misleading visual impressions may be given by curves of frequency distributions, and by virtually any other type of chart, if one scale is over-expanded or is unduly contracted in relation to the other scale.

Lettering. All lettering on a chart, including scale labels, scale values, legend, curve labels, and any other words or figures, should be placed horizontally, if possible. Occasionally space limitations may necessitate placing the vertical scale label in a vertical position, but such a limitation is not often present. Needless to say, all lettering should be legible. Freehand words and figures may be made very attractive when executed by a skilled person. The amateur may, however, make excellent formal letters and figures with a little practice by the use of stencil lettering devices available from artists' or draftsmen's supply houses. Nearly all of the charts in this text, except those reproduced from other publications, were lettered by means of such devices.

THOUSANDS OF
TRUCKS AND BUSES

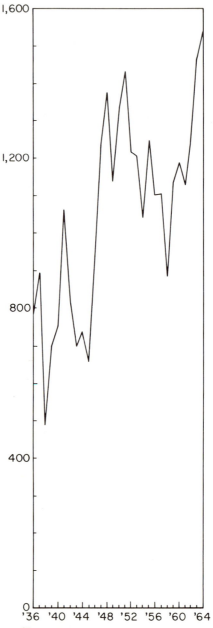

Chart 4.11.   Factory Sales of Motor Trucks and Buses by United States Plants, 1936–1964.   Data from source given below Chart 4.2.

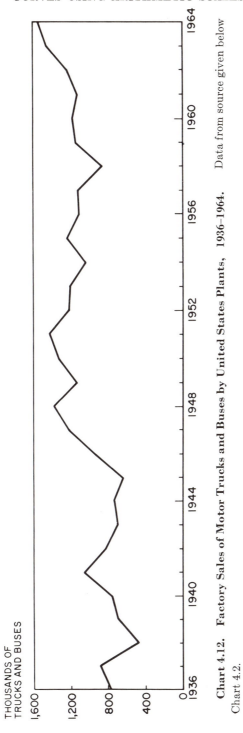

Chart 4.12.   Factory Sales of Motor Trucks and Buses by United States Plants,   1936–1964.   Data from source given below Chart 4.2.

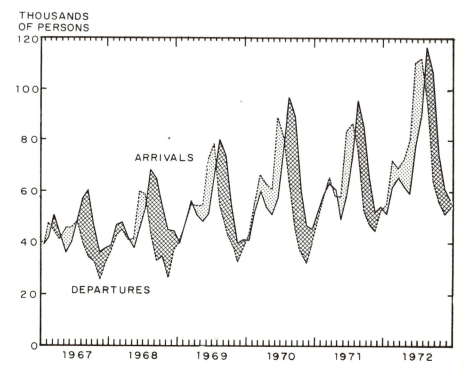

**Chart 4.13.   Arrivals and Departures of United States Citizens, January 1967–
December 1972.**   Hypothetical data as in Chart 4.4.

Title.   Each chart, like each table, should have a title, which should
state clearly and succinctly what the chart purports to show.   The title
of a printed chart may appear either above or below the chart, but
preferably below.   The titles of large wall charts are often placed above
the grid or, sometimes, upon it.

Source.   Again, as in the case of a table, each chart should contain a
source reference to indicate the author, title, volume, page, publisher, and
date of the publication from which the data were taken.   Naturally the
cautions regarding comparability of data taken from the same source or
different sources, mentioned in Chapter 2, apply with full force to the
figures used for making charts.

LINE DIAGRAMS FOR SPECIAL PURPOSES

Net balance charts.   Chart 4.4 shows one method of indicating the
net total of two series.   For each month, departures were subtracted
from arrivals and the result plotted as a positive or negative figure.   The
balance of trade (value of exports minus value of imports) may be shown
in the same manner, as may also profit and loss.   An alternative method

of showing the arrival and departure data is illustrated in Chart 4.13. Here the curves for arrivals and for departures are given; excess of arrivals is indicated by the height of the cross-hatched area, while the excess of departures is shown by the height of the stippled portion.

Silhouette charts. Chart 4.13 (referred to in the preceding paragraph) illustrates not only the showing of net amounts rather than gross amounts, but likewise the practice of shading the area between two curves in order to obtain emphasis. Chart 4.14 is similar to Chart 4.4 in that it shows fluctuations above and below a base line. In Chart 4.14, however, the areas of the curve have been emphasized by filling in with black. The result is a more striking portrayal of the "plus" and "minus" parts of the curve. A chart of this type is even more effective when the "plus" areas are filled in with black and the "minus" areas are filled in with red.

Range charts. Chart 4.15 shows a device by means of which the range of stock prices may be depicted. It will be noticed that the black band expands when the range is greater and contracts when the range is smaller. The white line indicates the closing price. An alternative method of showing the same data is illustrated in Chart 4.16. Here the top of each bar represents the high for the day, while the bottom of each bar represents the low for the day. The line connecting the bars represents the closing price. Charts such as these may be used for showing commodity prices and other sorts of data if it is desired to show a range of variation over a period of time.

Z-charts. The Z-chart consists of three curves on the same axes as shown in Chart 4.17. Usually the chart covers a period of one year, by months. One curve shows the monthly figures, another shows the cumulative figures from the beginning of the year, while the third shows the total for the twelve months ending with each month. This last curve is generally called the *moving annual total* curve; more specifically, it is a 12-month moving total for the twelve months ending with each designated month. Two vertical scales are used with the Z-chart, since, if the monthly data were plotted against the same scale as the other data, the fluctuations of the monthly data would not be apparent. The Z-chart is often used for internal business purposes, showing, for example, data of production and sales. It is, of course, limited to those situations in which the chart maker is interested in visualizing: (1) the figure for a given month, (2) the figure for each month for that part of the calendar (or fiscal) year which has elapsed, and (3) the figure for the twelve months ending with each given month.

Except for special purposes such as this, it is not usually desirable to use two, or more, vertical scales (sometimes referred to as "multiple scales") on a chart of the type described in this chapter. The occur-

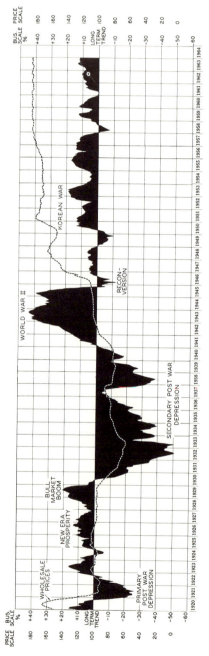

Chart 4.14. A Portion of The Cleveland Trust Company's Chart of American Business Activity Since 1790. From the 35th edition of that chart, issued April 1964, by The Cleveland Trust Company.

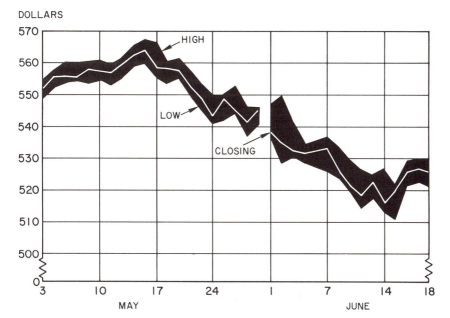

Chart 4.15. High, Low, and Closing Prices of 50 Stocks as Shown by the New York Times Averages, May 3–June 18, 1965. Data from various issues of *The New York Times.*

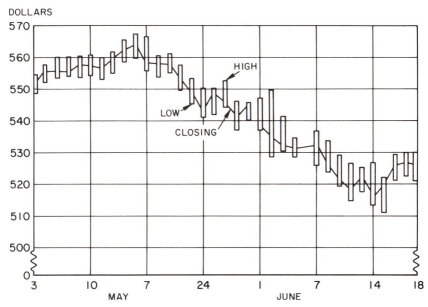

Chart 4.16. High, Low, and Closing Prices of 50 Stocks as Shown by the New York Times Averages, May 3–June 18, 1965. Data from various issues of *The New York Times.*

rences of fluctuations (but not their magnitudes) in two series expressed
in different units may occasionally be compared on a chart having two
different vertical scales.   However, the use of two, or more, different
vertical scales is likely to give false visual impressions of the comparative
magnitudes of changes occurring in the various series.

Varying horizontal-scale charts.   Occasionally it is desired to show
annual data over a number of years, and monthly data for one or two
more recent years.   This may be done as in Chart 4.18, in which the horizontal scale is expanded to show the monthly data in more detail.   Notice
that the two parts of the chart are separated by a break.   Similarly, a
change in horizontal scale may be in order if we wish to show a combination of annual or monthly data with weekly data, or a combination of
annual, monthly, or weekly data with daily data.

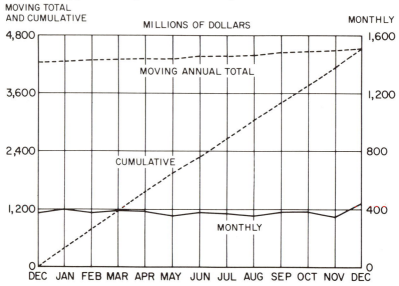

**Chart 4.17.   Total Death Benefit Payments in the United States:
Monthly Cumulative and Moving Annual Total, 1964.**   Data from
Institute of Life Insurance, Division of Statistics and Research.

Multiple-axis charts.   Occasionally it is desirable to compare the
fluctuations of several curves and yet to have each curve stand out
clearly.   A simple method of accomplishing this result is to plot the different curves along different horizontal axes, these different X-axes being
arbitrarily separated by convenient vertical distances.   An illustration
is Chart 14.4, which is also referred to as a "year-over-year chart."
Here the different curves have been brought close together for ease of
comparison, but there is no crossing of the lines.   Although different
horizontal axes are employed, the vertical and horizontal scales remain
the same.   In interpreting such a chart on arithmetic graph paper (as

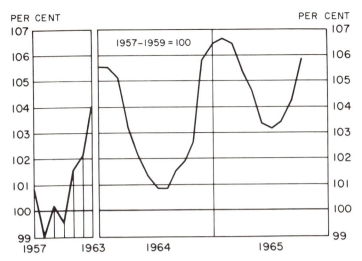

Chart 4.18. Consumer Price Index of Fuel Oil and Coal Annually, 1957–1963, and Monthly, 1964–1965. Data from *Federal Reserve Bulletin*, September 1965, p. 1334, and November 1965, p. 1604.

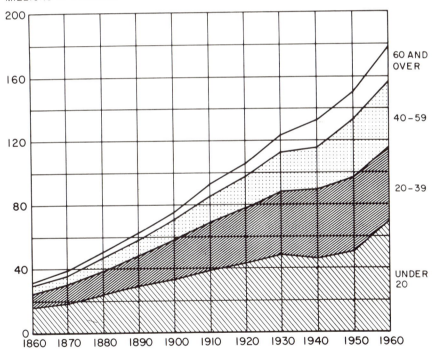

Chart 4.19. Population of the United States in Each Specified Age Group, 1860–1960. Data from U.S. Bureau of the Census, *Fifteenth Census of the United States, 1930*, Population Vol. II, p. 576; *U.S. Census of Population, 1950*, Vol. II, *Characteristics of the Population*, Part I, *U.S. Summary*, p. 1–93 and *Census of Population, 1960*, Vol. I, *Characteristics of the Population*, Part I, *U.S. Summary*, p. 1–199.

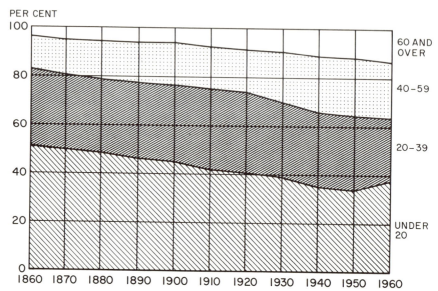

Chart 4.20. Proportion of the Population of the United States in Each Specified Age Group, 1860–1960. Data from sources given below Chart 4.19.

distinguished from semi-logarithmic graph paper described in the following chapter), it should be remembered that the comparison afforded is that of absolute and not of relative changes. It is unlikely that the use of this type of chart will be found desirable for presentation to the general reader, unless the diagram is accompanied by a clear explanation.

Component-part charts. Chart 4.19 shows the number of persons in the United States at each census from 1860 to 1960, in each of four general age groups. The height of each band indicates the number of each age in the country at a given census. It is possible to observe, from this type of chart, whether or not a given group is increasing or decreasing, and whether or not the total of all groups is increasing or decreasing. The *relative* importance of a particular group cannot be visualized from Chart 4.19, but in Chart 4.20 the age groups are shown according to the proportions which they constitute of the total population. Here it may be clearly seen that there has been a decrease in the proportion of younger persons and an increase in the proportion of older persons in the population. When component-part data covering a few years are to be shown graphically, a bar chart such as the upper part of Chart 6.17 or 6.18 may be used. When a number of years are to be shown, the general trend can be more easily pictured by curves.

Frequency distribution and range chart. Sometimes it is advantageous to show a frequency distribution curve for one set of data and to compare with that curve the range of values for another distribution.

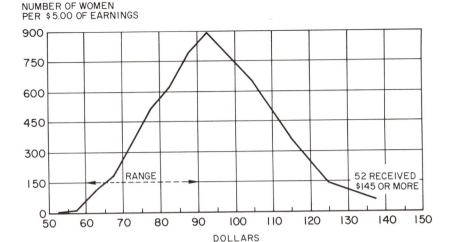

NUMBER OF WOMEN
PER $5.00 OF EARNINGS

Chart 4.21. Weekly Earnings of 7,011 Female Secretaries in Boston, Massachusetts, October, 1964 and Range of Pay for Hypothetical Data. The data of weekly earnings are from Table 8.5 and are "frequency densities," which are explained in the discussion concerning Chart 8.5.

Chart 4.21 shows a frequency distribution of the average weekly earnings of 7,011 female secretaries in Boston in October 1964. A hypothetical range of secretarial salaries for a non-commercial organization is also shown. Alternatively, two frequency distributions could have been shown, as in Chart 8.7.[5]

---

[5] For more advanced charts, see W. C. Guenther and P. O. Thomas, "Some Graphs Useful For Statistical Inference," *Journal of the American Statistical Association,* Vol. 360, No. 309, March 1965, pp. 334–343.

CHAPTER 5

Graphic Presentation II:

THE SEMI-LOGARITHMIC OR RATIO CHART

AMOUNT OF CHANGE VS. RATIO OF CHANGE

When considering the development of a series of statistical data over a period of time, we are sometimes interested in the *amount* of change that has taken place, but more often we wish to know something about the *ratio* of change that has occurred between two dates. Diagrams such as those in Chapter 4 are of the familiar type, having what are termed *arithmetic scales*, and are of use, primarily, for indicating absolute changes in the factor shown on the *Y*-axis. It is the purpose of this discussion to explain a slightly different sort of grid which enables one to visualize the ratio of change in a plotted series.

TABLE 5.1

An Arithmetic Progression

Year (X value)	Y value	Amount of increase
1968	0	. . .
1969	200	200
1970	400	200
1971	600	200
1972	800	200
1973	1,000	200
1974	1,200	200
1975	1,400	200

The ability of the usual type of chart to give a satisfactory visual impression of absolute change, but not of ratio of change, is brought out by Chart 5.1. Curve *A* represents a constant amount of increase of 200 units per year (see Table 5.1), and this, or any other, *arithmetic progression* (constant amount of increase or decrease) will be depicted by a straight line when plotted on the conventional or arithmetic grid. Curve *B*,

84

Y VALUES

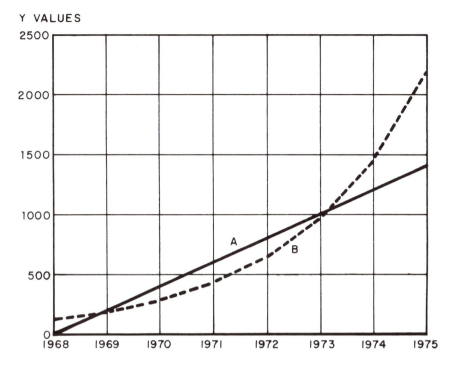

Chart 5.1.   An Arithmetic Progression (A) and a Geometric Progression (B) Plotted on an Arithmetic Grid.   Data of Tables 5.1 and 5.2.

TABLE 5.2

A Geometric Progression

Year (X value)	Y value	Per cent of increase
1968	128	. . .
1969	192	50
1970	288	50
1971	432	50
1972	648	50
1973	972	50
1974	1,458	50
1975	2,187	50

however, is the result of plotting a series of figures which begin with 128 and increase 50 per cent each year (see Table 5.2). It will be noticed that this curve is not a straight line; the curve bends upward more and more sharply as time passes.

A series showing a constant ratio of increase or decrease is known as a *geometric progression*, and any geometric progression will yield a curved line when plotted on an arithmetic grid.[1] An increasing geometric progression is represented by a curve which slopes upward and is concave upward, as in Curve B of Chart 5.1; a decreasing geometric progression is represented by a curve which slopes downward and is concave upward. A serious difficulty in interpreting such curves, however, lies in the fact that the eye cannot discern whether or not a particular curved line does or does not represent a constant ratio of change.   Chart 5.2 depicts a series which is neither an arithmetic nor a geometric progression.   The data of Table 5.3 show that the series increases more rapidly than an

TABLE 5.3

A Series of Increasing Values

Year (X value)	Y value	Amount of increase	Per cent of increase
1968	50	. . .	. . .
1969	80	30	60.0
1970	160	80	100.0
1971	300	140	87.5
1972	550	250	83.3
1973	1,080	530	96.4
1974	1,730	650	60.2
1975	2,500	770	44.5

arithmetic progression, and the eye can grasp this fact because the curve bends upward.   The table also indicates that the ratio of increase of the series is not constant.   Visually, however, this fact is not apparent.   It is not possible for the reader of an arithmetic chart to be sure whether a curved line, such as this, represents a constant ratio of increase, a ratio of increase which is diminishing, or a ratio of increase which is accelerating.   Any series of figures that increases more rapidly th...n an arithmetic progression (for example, 10, 12, 15, 19, 24, 30) slopes upward and is concave upward when plotted on an arithmetic grid; any series of figures that decreases less rapidly than an arithmetic progression (for example, 100, 91, 83, 76, 70, 65) slopes downward and is concave upward when shown on arithmetic coordinates.

Before proceeding to develop the basis for the semi-logarithmic or ratio grid, which will enable us to visualize ratios of change, let us examine further the arithmetic grid.   Chart 5.3 shows the growth of motor vehicle registrations in the United States and in Canada from 1928 to 1964.   We can see from this chart that registrations in the United States were erratic from 1928 to 1935; rose between 1935 and 1941 except for a slight decrease between 1937 and 1938; dropped in 1941–1945; and enjoyed a

---

[1] A curve representing a geometric progression is termed an "exponential curve" and is indicated by the equation $Y = ab^X$. The reader may be familiar with this equation in the form $P_n = P_o(1 + r)^n$, which is the compound interest equation and is discussed in Chapter 9.   A straight line representing an arithmetic progression is indicated by $Y = a + bX$.

sharp upward movement from 1946 to 1964.   Changes in registration in Canada are difficult to see because the scale which must be used to accommodate the United States causes the curve for Canada to fall rather close to the base line.   However, it appears that registrations in Canada were relatively level from 1928 to 1948, and then began to increase steadily thereafter.   It is quite obvious that the *amounts* of increase and decrease each year were greater for the United States than for Canada, but there is no way of knowing from the appearance of the curves which country had the greater *ratios* of increase or decrease from year to year.

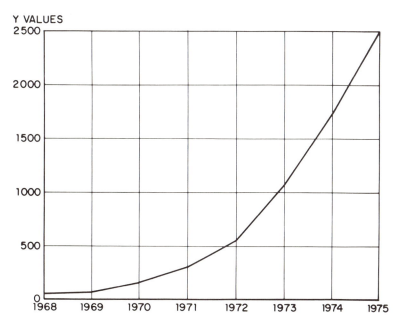

Chart 5.2.   A Series of Figures Increasing by Increasing Amounts.   This series is not a geometric progression, but may give that visual impression.   Data of Table 5.3.

It would not do to replot the data of Chart 5.3 by using one vertical scale for the United States and another for Canada, in order to magnify the movements of the curve for the latter.   The fact that one curve is below another on an arithmetic grid tells us at a glance that the lower curve represents a series of smaller magnitude than does the upper.   If two vertical scales are used, we have really two distinct, non-comparable charts, and no *satisfactory* visual comparisons may be made in respect to (1) the size of the two series plotted, (2) the amount of change which has taken place in one series in comparison with the amount of change in the other, or (3) the ratios of change of the two series.

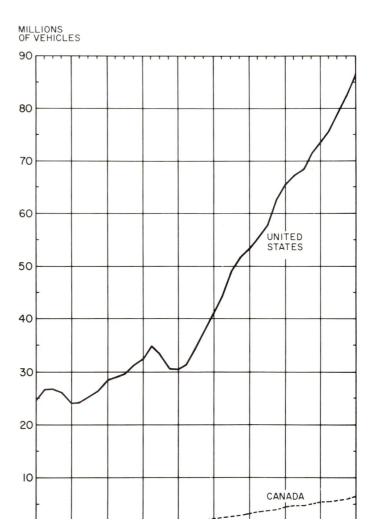

Chart 5.3. Motor Vehicle Registrations in the United States and Canada, 1928–1964. Data from *Historical Statistics of the United States*, p. 564; *Statistical Abstract of the United States*, 1963, p. 564; Automobile Manufacturers Assn., *Automobile Facts and Figures*, 1965, pp. 19, 29; and Dominion Bureau of Statistics, *Canada Year Books*, 1937, p. 668, 1946, p. 663, 1950, p. 755, 1954, p. 252, and 1964, p. 774.

A GRID TO SHOW RATIOS OF CHANGE

From what has already been said it must be obvious that graphic comparisons in respect to ratios of change will be facilitated if we can employ

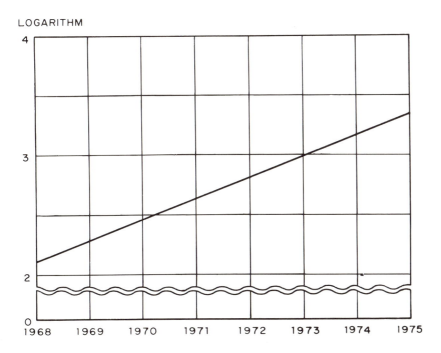

Chart 5.4. Logarithms of a Geometric Progression Plotted on an Arithmetic Grid. Data of Table 5.4.

a sort of grid which will make a constant ratio of increase (or decrease) appear as a straight line. In Table 5.4 the geometric progression of Table 5.2 and Chart 5.1 is again shown, and with it are given the logarithms of the various numbers. Examination of these logarithms reveals that they form an arithmetic progression; therefore, if these logarithms are plotted on an arithmetic grid, a straight line will result, as may be seen in Chart 5.4. This is one way of accomplishing our objective, but it involves the additional step of looking up logarithms before the data can be plotted. However, instead of plotting the logarithms of the values of a series, we may use a grid which is designed with a logarithmic vertical scale, as in Chart 5.5. Here, again, we find that the geometric

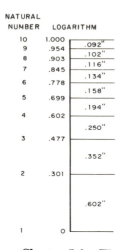

NATURAL
NUMBER   LOGARITHM

10	1.000
9	.954
8	.903
7	.845
6	.778
5	.699
4	.602
3	.477
2	.301
1	0

.092"
.102"
.116"
.134"
.158"
.194"
.250"
.352"
.602"

Chart 5.6. The Logarithmic Scale. The vertical distances are proportional to the differences between the logarithms. Each vertical distance is twice the difference between the logarithms measured in inches.

progression appears as a straight line. A grid of this type is termed *semi-logarithmic* because one scale is logarithmic and the other is arithmetic.

The logarithmic scale. The construction of the logarithmic scale merely involves spacing the vertical-scale values in proportion to the differences between their logarithms. Referring to Chart 5.6, it will be found that the distance from 2 to 3 on the scale is 0.352 inch, and from 3 to 4 is 0.250 inch. We then have:

$$\frac{\log 3 - \log 2}{\log 4 - \log 3} = \frac{0.352 \text{ inch}}{0.250 \text{ inch}},$$

$$\frac{0.477 - 0.301}{0.602 - 0.477} = \frac{0.352 \text{ inch}}{0.250 \text{ inch}},$$

and the proportion is:

$$0.176 : 0.125 : : 0.352 \text{ inch} : 0.250 \text{ inch}.$$

An alternative approach to an understanding of the logarithmic scale does not involve logarithms. Reference to Chart 5.1 will recall that equal distances on the vertical scale of an arithmetic grid represent equal *amounts*. Equal distances measured along a logarithmic scale, however, represent equal *ratios*. On the vertical scale of Chart 5.5 it may be seen that the distance from 100 to 200 is 0.48 inch; likewise the distance from 300 to 600 is 0.48 inch. Measurement will reveal that any two numbers of ratio 1:2 are separated by 0.48 inch on this scale. On this same scale the distance from 200 to 800 is 0.96 inch, and it follows that any two numbers of ratio 1:4 will be separated by 0.96 inch. Thus we see why the semi-logarithmic chart is frequently termed the *ratio chart*.

The vertical scale of Chart 5.5 is divided into two parts which are generally called *cycles*. We therefore refer to the paper on which Chart 5.5 was drawn as "two-cycle semi-logarithmic paper." In labeling the vertical scale of a semi-logarithmic chart, we may begin with any positive value. The figure at the top of the first cycle will be ten times that at the bottom of the cycle; the figure at the top of the second cycle will be ten times the figure at the bottom of the second cycle (the top of the first cycle); and so on.[2] In Chart 5.7 there are illustrated eight different logarithmic scales beginning with 0.1, 1, 2, 5, 10, 17, 25, and 50, respectively. Although it is mathematically permissible to begin a logarithmic

---

[2] A common logarithm is the power to which 10 must be raised to produce a given number. Thus, 100 is 10^2, and the logarithm of 100 is 2.0; 10,000 is 10^4, and the logarithm of 10,000 is 4.0.

TABLE 5.4

A Geometric Progression and Logarithms of the Geometric Progression

Year (X value)	Y value	Logarithm of Y value	Amount of increase of logarithms
1968	128	2.107210	...
1969	192	2.283301	.176091
1970	288	2.459392	.176091
1971	432	2.635484	.176092*
1972	648	2.811575	.176091
1973	972	2.987666	.176091
1974	1,458	3.163758	.176092*
1975	2,187	3.339849	.176091

* These values differ slightly because the logarithms were rounded to the nearest millionth.

Y VALUES

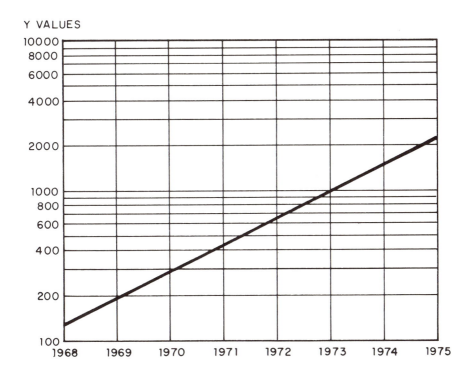

Chart 5.5.   A Geometric Progression Plotted on a Semi-Logarithmic or Ratio Grid.   Data of Table 5.2.   Printed semi-logarithmic forms have more intermediate rulings than shown in this chart.   These closely spaced lines are an aid to plotting but are omitted from most of the charts in this book, since reduction to fit the size of the page would result in bringing these lines very close together.

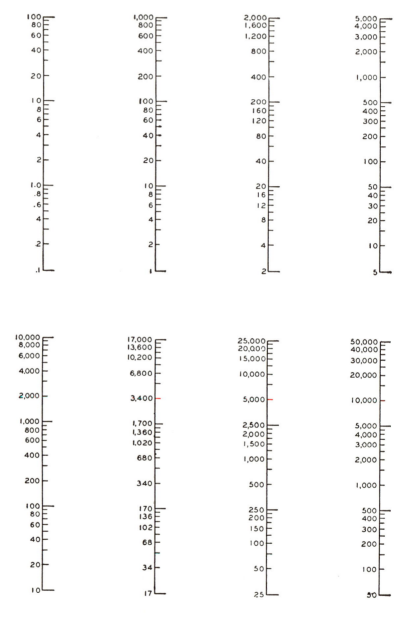

Chart 5.7. Logarithmic Vertical Scales. The scale beginning with 17 would be difficult to use.

scale with any positive value, it is advisable to select a scale which will allow interpolations of intermediate values to be made readily. The scale beginning with 17 would be very difficult to use. If it were desired to have a three-cycle scale beginning with 0.5, the various values of the first scale could be multiplied by 5. Most ready-ruled semi-logarithmic paper carries scale designations along the right edge of the grid. These are multiplying factors and indicate that the value to be written opposite each horizontal line on the left scale must be the value at the bottom of that cycle multiplied by the figure shown opposite that horizontal line on the scale at the right.

If a logarithmic scale were begun with zero, the top of the first cycle would be $10 \times 0 = 0$, and all values on the scale would also be zero. Suppose that the uppermost value of a three-cycle logarithmic scale is 0.01. Then the bottom of the third cycle is $\frac{1}{10}$ of 0.01, or 0.001; the bottom of the second cycle is 0.0001; and the bottom of the first cycle is 0.00001. There can thus be no zero base line, and the semi-logarithmic chart does not permit interpretation of curves in terms of distances above a base line as does the arithmetic chart. Although plotted values may, of course, be read against the vertical logarithmic scale, no visual impression may be had of the absolute magnitudes plotted. The semi-logarithmic chart shows: (1) a constant ratio of change as a straight line; (2) the ratio of increase or decrease by the slope of the line; and (3) the comparison of ratios between two or more lines by means of parallelism of these lines or lack of it.

Whenever a logarithmic scale is employed, enough rulings, or rulings and tics, should be shown so that the reader will be aware that he is not seeing a chart drawn on an arithmetic grid. Since there are other unequally spaced scales in addition to the logarithmic scale (for example, the reciprocal scale), it is sometimes also desirable to state: "ratio chart," "semi-logarithmic chart," or "logarithmic vertical scale."

Note that a logarithmic scale may cover an integral number of cycles, as in Chart 5.5, which has two cycles, and Chart 5.9, which has one cycle. On the other hand we may use part of one cycle, as in Chart 13.1, or we may employ one or more cycles and part of another cycle, as in Chart 11.4B.

Interpretation of curves. Before proceeding with a consideration of applications of the semi-logarithmic chart, attention should be given to Charts 5.8A and 5.8B and the comments below them. When two straight lines are parallel on semi-logarithmic paper (for example, a, a'; d, d'), we know that they have constant ratios of change and also that the ratio between the two has remained constant. Parallelism between curved lines is very difficult to judge with the eye. Reference to the lower sections of Chart 5.8A will show that the curved lines are always the same

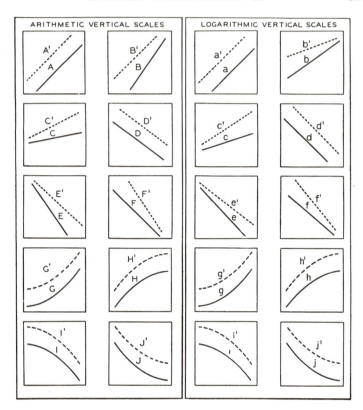

ARITHMETIC VERTICAL SCALES

A, A'—Constant amounts of increase, same for both curves.
B, B'—Different constant amounts of increase, greater for B.
C, C'—Different constant amounts of increase, greater for C'.
D, D'—Constant amounts of decrease, same for both curves.
E, E'—Different constant amounts of decrease, greater for E.
F, F'—Different constant amounts of decrease, greater for F'.
G, G'—Amounts of increase increasing, same for both curves.
H, H'—Amounts of increase decreasing, same for both curves.
I, I'—Amounts of decrease increasing, same for both curves.
J, J'—Amounts of decrease decreasing, same for both curves.

LOGARITHMIC VERTICAL SCALES

a, a'—Constant percentage of increase, same for both curves.
b, b'—Different constant percentages of increase, greater for b.
c, c'—Different constant percentages of increase, greater for c'.
d, d'—Constant percentages of decrease, same for both curves.
e, e'—Different constant percentages of decrease, greater for e.
f, f'—Different constant percentages of decrease, greater for f'.
g, g'—Percentages of increase increasing, same for both curves.
h, h'—Percentages of increase decreasing, same for both curves.
i, i'—Percentages of decrease increasing, same for both curves.
j, j'—Percentages of decrease decreasing, same for both curves.

Chart 5.8A.   Curves on Arithmetic and Semi-Logarithmic Grids.   The two curves in each of the lower eight squares are equidistant vertically from each other.

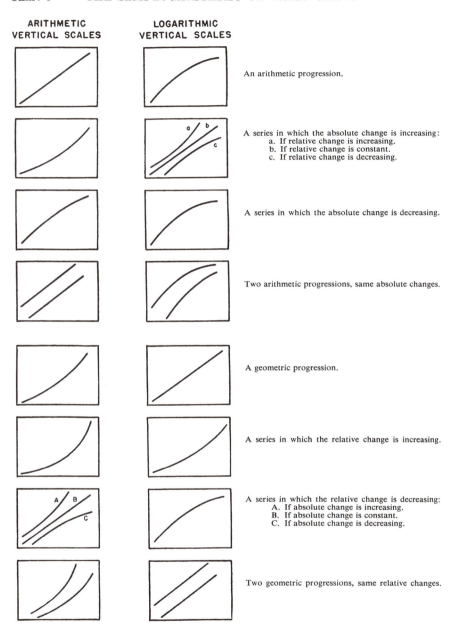

ARITHMETIC
VERTICAL SCALES

LOGARITHMIC
VERTICAL SCALES

An arithmetic progression.

A series in which the absolute change is increasing:
  a. If relative change is increasing.
  b. If relative change is constant.
  c. If relative change is decreasing.

A series in which the absolute change is decreasing.

Two arithmetic progressions, same absolute changes.

A geometric progression.

A series in which the relative change is increasing.

A series in which the relative change is decreasing:
  A. If absolute change is increasing.
  B. If absolute change is constant.
  C. If absolute change is decreasing.

Two geometric progressions, same relative changes.

5.8B.   Comparisons of Series of Various Types Plotted in Relation to Arithmetic and Logarithmic Vertical Scales.   Series plotted as shown on one scale become as indicated on the other.   The above comparisons refer to increasing series only.   It is suggested that the reader sketch some comparisons involving declining series.

vertical distance apart, and thus the two curves in each section are parallel with respect to the *X*-axis.

APPLICATIONS

Comparing ratios of increase or decrease.   Since there is no zero on the vertical scale of the semi-logarithmic chart, and thus no base line, and since equal vertical distances (on the same scale) always represent the same ratio, it is permissible to use two or more different vertical scales in order to bring curves of different magnitude close together for comparison.   This has been done in Chart 5.9, which presents the data of motor vehicle registrations previously shown on an arithmetic grid in

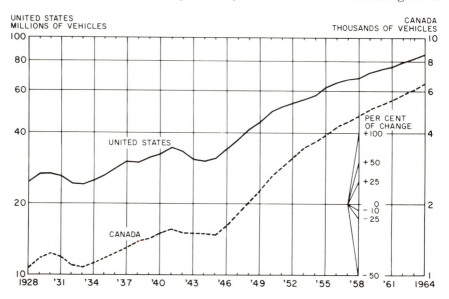

Chart 5.9.   Motor Vehicle Registrations in the United States and Canada, 1928–1964.   Data from sources given below Chart 5.3.

Chart 5.3.   Shifting the vertical scale of a semi-logarithmic chart moves the curve upward or downward, but the slope, which is of paramount importance, is not altered thereby.   When using two logarithmic scales, as in Chart 5.9, it is desirable (though not absolutely necessary) to keep the series of smaller magnitude below that of greater magnitude; likewise, if one or more components are being compared with a total, the curves for the components should be below that for the total.

Chart 5.3 gave us no idea of the *relative* growth of automobile registrations in either the United States or Canada.   Chart 5.9, however, shows relative growth for each series and enables us to compare the ratios of growth of these two series of dissimilar size.   In general, both series have

PER CENT
OF CHANGE

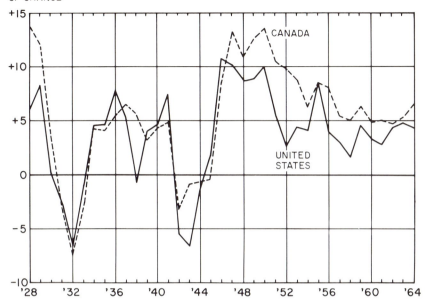

Chart 5.10.   Annual Per Cent of Increase or Decrease in Motor Vehicle Registrations in the United States and Canada, 1928–1964. Data from sources given below Chart 5.3.

shown about the same ratios of increase and decrease throughout the period.   However, the ratio of increase from 1947 to 1964 is seen to be greater for Canada.   The insert on Chart 5.9 makes it possible to estimate the ratio of increase or decrease from any one year to the next for the curves shown.   It does not, however, apply to other charts which have different scales.

An alternative method of showing the relative change in motor vehicle registrations in the United States and Canada consists of calculating the per cent of change for each year and plotting the results on an arithmetic grid.   This has been done in Chart 5.10.

Instead of comparing the percentages of change of two different series over the same period of time, we may be interested in comparing ratios of growth of the same series at different times.   Thus in Chart 5.9 we can see that the per cent of increase of United States automobile registrations was greater from 1954 to 1955 than from 1955 to 1956, and also that the relative decline was greater from 1942 to 1943 than from 1937 to 1938. Similar conclusions may be drawn from Chart 5.10.

It is frequently necessary to compare series which are expressed in different units.   For example, we may compare any two or more of the following: commercial failures, in millions of dollars; volume of trading on

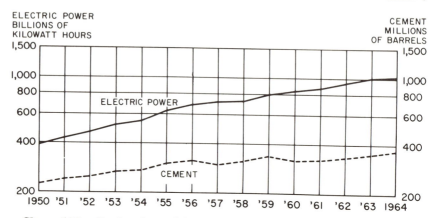

Chart 5.11. Production of Electric Power and of Portland Cement 1950–1964. Data from various issues of *Statistical Abstract of the United States* and from *Survey of Current Business*, May 1965, pp. S-26 and S-38. Cement production for 1951 is estimated.

a stock exchange, in number of shares traded; coal production, in 2,000-pound tons; petroleum production, in 42-gallon barrels; lumber production, in board feet; cement production, in 376-pound barrels; electric power produced, in kilowatt hours; manufactured gas, in cubic feet. It is possible to reduce 376-pound barrels to tons, but it is not possible to change kilowatt hours to board feet, or vice versa.

While one could plot two series expressed in different units on an arithmetic grid, it is not often that such a comparison is useful. Except to ascertain whether the two series fluctuate concurrently, we are not likely to be interested in comparing the changes in electric power production in kilowatt hours with the changes in cement production in barrels. Rather are we apt to want to compare the percentage change in electric power production with the percentage change in cement production. On the semi-logarithmic grid, there is no zero base line; only the slope of a curve has meaning, and we are enabled to make a valid comparison of the relative changes in the two series expressed in such dissimilar units as those just mentioned. Chart 5.11 shows a comparison of the production of electric energy and of portland cement 1950–1964. Among other interesting comparisons may be noted the more rapid ratio of growth in the production of electric power from 1950 to 1957 and the twin peaks in the production of cement in 1956 and 1959.

Comparing fluctuations. Comparison of the fluctuations taking place in two chronological series of different size may be illustrated by reference to Charts 5.3 and 5.9, which show the number of motor vehicle registrations in the United States and in Canada, 1928–1964. Both series are expressed in millions, but United States registrations greatly exceed those of Canada. The result is that when the two series are shown on an arithmetic grid, as in Chart 5.3, the fluctuations of the larger series may be clearly seen but those of the smaller series are not apparent. When the two sets of data are depicted on a semi-logarithmic grid (Chart 5.9), not only can the fluctuations of both series be seen, but their relative severity may be compared.   For example, it is clear from Chart 5.9 that the ratio of increase in Canadian registrations from 1949 to 1952 was greater than the ratio of increase in United States registrations for these same years, and also that the relative decrease from 1941 to 1943 was greater for the United States than for Canada.   These data are illustrative of the principles involved in comparing fluctuations.   In the more usual case, analysts would be more concerned with fluctuations in production and in consumption than in registration data.

Instead of being interested in two series, we may wish to compare the undulations of a single series which fluctuated around relatively small values during one period and around decidedly larger values at another time.   For example, commercial failures numbered about 22,000 annually from 1921 to 1935.   From 1941 to 1950 they numbered about 5,500 annually.   In the 1960's they have averaged about 16,000 annually. The semi-logarithmic chart enables us to study the relative severity of the fluctuations during such different periods.

Showing ratios.   Chart 5.12 shows how ratios may be presented on the semi-logarithmic chart.   The two series plotted are the price per bushel received by farmers for corn, and the price per 100 pounds received by farmers for hogs.   When corn is bringing a price which is low in relation to the price of hogs, farmers will generally find it profitable to feed corn to hogs rather than to sell the corn for cash.   On the other hand, when corn is bringing a price which is high in relation to that of hogs, farmers will tend to sell corn for cash.   If 100 pounds of hogs brings the farmer about 13 times as much as a bushel of corn, it is largely immaterial to the farmer whether he sells his corn for cash or feeds the corn to his hogs.[3]   For this reason the two scales of Chart 5.12 have been placed in a 13-to-1 ratio.[4]   The chart not only shows the fluctuations in the price of hogs and the price of corn, but also makes it easy to see when the price of 100 pounds of hogs is more than, less than, or exactly 13 times the price of a bushel of corn.   When 100 pounds of hogs is selling for more than 13 times as much as a bushel of corn, the curve for hogs is above the curve for corn, hogs are relatively valuable, and farmers tend to feed corn to their hogs.   When 100 pounds of hogs is selling for less than 13 times as much as a bushel of corn, the curve for hogs is below that for corn, corn is relatively valuable, and farmers tend to sell corn for cash.   When the two curves are parallel, the ratio is remaining con-

---

[3] See page 129, where the hog-corn ratio is discussed.

[4] The scale for hog prices is awkward but is unavoidable in this instance.

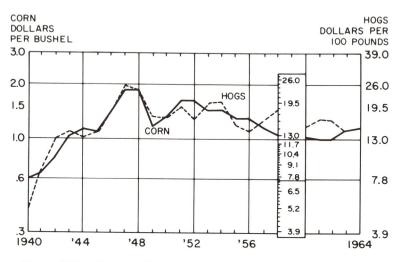

Chart 5.12. Average Farm Prices of Corn, per Bushel, and of Hogs, per Hundred Pounds, 1940–1964. The supplementary scale enables us to read the ratio of hog prices to corn prices for any year. The value 13 is placed opposite the line for corn and the value opposite the hog line gives the ratio of the hog price, per hundred pounds, to the corn price, per bushel. For 1958, the ratio is shown to be slightly below 19, which may be verified by referring to Chart 5.13. The supplementary scale is graduated in the same manner as is the scale at the right of the chart, the figure 13 being placed opposite the corn line because the scale for hog prices has values which are 13 times the corresponding values on the scale for corn prices. Data from Department of Agriculture, *Agricultural Statistics, 1964*, p. 330 and *Statistical Abstract of the United States, 1965*, p. 651.

stant; when the corn-price curve is sloping upward *more* rapidly (or downward *less* rapidly) than the hog-price curve, corn is becoming *more* valuable in relation to hogs; when the corn-price curve is sloping upward *less* rapidly (or downward *more* rapidly) than the hog-price curve, corn is becoming *less* valuable in relation to hogs. The supplementary scale, which is a separate piece of paper and which is shown on the chart, enables the reader to measure the ratio between the two price curves at any time.

Chart 5.13 illustrates another method of showing the relationship between hog and corn prices. Here the ratio of hog prices to corn prices has been computed for each year and plotted on an arithmetic grid. The ratio may be studied without the use of a supplementary scale, but changes in corn prices and in hog prices are not shown.

Interpolation and extrapolation. While an interpolation on an arithmetic chart is an arithmetic interpolation, an interpolation on the semi-logarithmic chart is a logarithmic interpolation. Thus, if we refer

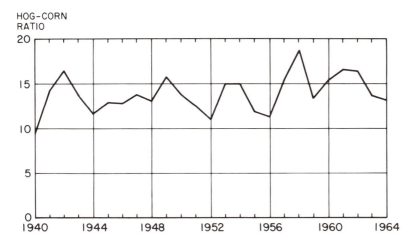

Chart 5.13. Hog-Corn Ratio, 1940–1964. The ratio is obtained by by dividing the average farm price of hogs per hundred pounds by the average price of corn per bushel; the ratio is the number of bushels of corn required to buy a hundred pounds of live hogs at the prices quoted.   Data from sources given below Chart 5.12.

to Chart 5.5 and graphically interpolate for the Y value midway between 1972 and 1973, we obtain about 790, which is approximately the same figure that we get if we use (log 648 + log 972) ÷ 2 and take the anti-logarithm of the result.

Extrapolation consists of extending the curve at one end or the other. When we extend a curve to estimate for later years than those for which we have data, we are forecasting. This application of the semi-loga-rithmic chart is definitely of questionable value if it involves only the extension of a curve which has indicated in the past that the data exhibit a fairly constant rate of increase. Any forecasting procedure which involves merely the continuation of a curve or the automatic application of a formula, without at the same time requiring a careful consideration of underlying and modifying factors, is hardly to be depended upon, particularly if economic conditions are in a state of flux. The curve of Chart 5.14 shows the male population fourteen years old and over of the East South Central Division of the United States from 1800 to 1960. Although the extension of the curve indicates a possible estimate for 1970, it should be realized that any estimate of population in 1970 based *only* on a knowledge of the preceding censuses can have little validity. Ignored have been such considerations as: movements of industry to (or from) the division, possible increase in population in the division because of decentralization of cities located elsewhere, continued movement of

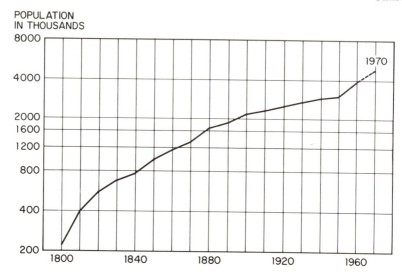

Chart 5.14. Male Population, Fourteen Years Old and Over, of the East South Central Division of the United States, 1800–1960, and a Rough Estimate for 1970. A dubious application of the semi-logarithmic chart. The states included in the East South Central Division are: Alabama, Kentucky, Mississippi, and Tennessee. Data from *U.S. Bureau of the Census, U.S. Census of Population, 1950*, Vol. I, Number of Inhabitants, pp 1–8 and 1–9 and 1960, Vol. I, *Characteristics of the Population*, Part I. U.S. Summary, p. 1–264.

Negroes from the division or a reversal of that movement, and other factors.[5]

Now that the reader is aware of the nature and uses of the semi-logarithmic chart, he may note the occasional presentation of arithmetic charts in books, articles, or reports when semi-logarithmic charts would have been more suitable. The reverse mistake is rarely made. Each type of chart serves a useful, but quite different, purpose. The arithmetic chart should be used when absolute comparisons are desired (Charts 5.10 and 5.13 are absolute comparisons of ratios); the semi-logarithmic chart should be employed when relative comparisons are called for.

CONSTRUCTION OF LOGARITHMIC SCALES

One logarithmic cycle will accommodate a tenfold increase; two cycles make provision for a hundredfold increase. Reference to the various

---

[5] The problems involved in forecasting population are discussed in *"Better Population Forecasting for Areas and Communities,"* by Van Beuren Stanbery, issued by the U. S. Department of Commerce.

charts included in this chapter will show that no vertical logarithmic scale (other than those shown in Chart 5.7) extends over more than two cycles. Two-cycle semi-logarithmic paper will suffice for most series which the chart maker is likely to encounter; rarely will he need paper covering more than three cycles, since it allows for a thousandfold increase. Even in cases where a series of very small magnitude must be compared with one of very large magnitude, a number of cycles is not needed, since it is desirable to use two vertical scales to bring the two curves together for

Scale value	Logarithm	Difference
1	0	
2	0.301030	0.301030
3	0.477121	0.176091
4	0.602060	0.124939
5	0.698970	0.096910
6	0.778151	0.079181
7	0.845098	0.066947
8	0.903090	0.057992
9	0.954243	0.051153
10	1.000000	0.045757
20	1.301030	0.301030
30	1.477121	0.176091
40	1.602060	0.124939
50	1.698970	0.096910
60	1.778151	0.079181
70	1.845098	0.066947
80	1.903090	0.057992
90	1.954243	0.051153
100	2.000000	0.045757

comparison, as in Chart 5.9.   Many sorts of ready-ruled semi-logarithmic paper are available from various sources.   If, however, only two-cycle paper is available and paper having more cycles is needed, it is merely necessary to trim the lower margin from a sheet of two-cycle paper and paste it above another sheet.

At times it may be desirable to use one- or two-cycle paper, but with a larger- or smaller-size cycle than those which are readily available. Using an ordinary sheet of semi-logarithmic paper and placing a sheet of plain paper diagonally on top of it, a logarithmic scale may be expanded. A logarithmic scale may be contracted by placing a sheet of semi-logarithmic paper diagonally on a piece of plain paper and ruling horizontal lines.   Of course, any number of cycles may be derived in this fashion. For illustrations of the methods of scale expansion, scale contraction, and scale variation, see the second edition of this text, pages 114–115.

In case no suitable logarithmic paper and no logarithmic scales of any sort are available, it is possible to construct a logarithmic scale of any desired size by referring to a table of logarithms. With scale values spaced in proportion to the differences between their logarithms, a scale may be constructed in terms of any convenient unit. From the figures shown below it is seen that the distance from 1 to 2 would be 0.301030 units, the distance from 2 to 3 would be 0.176091 units, and so on. Intermediate values are located similarly.

The usefulness of logarithmic scales is not limited to the applications shown in this chapter. In Chapter 23 we shall make use of a horizontal logarithmic scale and an arithmetic vertical scale. In Chapter 20 we shall use logarithmic scales on both the horizontal and vertical axes.

CHAPTER 6

Graphic Presentation III:

OTHER TYPES OF CHARTS

A number of other graphic devices, in addition to curves, are available for presenting statistical information. In this chapter we shall give brief attention to bar charts, pie diagrams, pictographs, and statistical maps.

BASES OF COMPARISON

Chart 6.1 shows how the number of tractors on farms may be compared by means of three types of diagrams: (A), a bar chart involving one-dimensional comparisons; (B) and (C), circles and squares, involving two-dimensional comparisons; and (D), a three-dimensional comparison represented by tractors of varying sizes. Readers of charts obtain most accurate impressions of the magnitudes shown when data are represented by means of bar charts, and least accurate impressions when data are represented by volume diagrams. Area diagrams are more accurately judged than volume diagrams, but less accurately than bar charts.[1] It should also be remembered that volume diagrams shown on the printed page make it necessary for the reader to visualize the third dimension before making his comparison. Another disadvantage of charts using squares, circles, or pictures of different sizes is that the reader may be uncertain whether to compare heights, areas, or volumes. In any event, the basis upon which the diagram was drawn should be indicated. If it is argued that the correct basis of comparing the size of such objects as tractors is the apparent weight of the different tractors, and if the chart maker has drawn the tractors so that the number of tractors in different years is shown by the height or length of the tractors, as is sometimes

---

[1] See "Graphic Comparisons by Bars, Squares, Circles, and Cubes," by Frederick E. Croxton and Harold Stein, *Journal of the American Statistical Association*, March 1932, pp. 54–60.

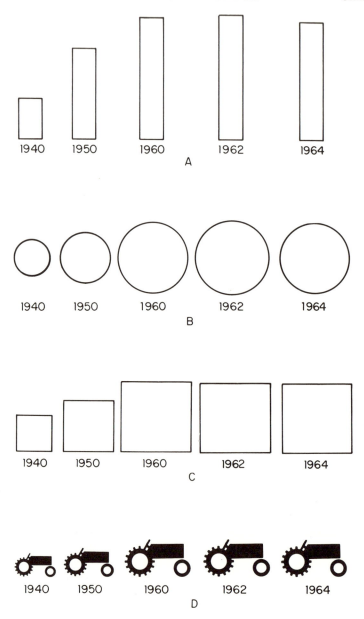

Chart 6.1. Number of Tractors on Farms in the United States, 1940, 1950, 1960, 1962, and 1964. The data are represented by (A) bars, (B) circles, (C) squares, and (D) pictures of tractors. Part A involves linear comparisons; parts B and C require comparisons of areas; part D calls for comparisons of volumes. Data from *Agricultural Statistics, 1962*, p. 520, *1963*, p. 442, *1964*, p. 440. 1964 data are preliminary.

done, then the reader who judges the sizes upon the basis of apparent weight (essentially volume) will get an exaggerated impression of the variation in number of tractors during the different years.

Charts involving volume comparisons appear all too often in newspapers and magazines. Later in this chapter we shall see how it is possible, by means of pictographs, to obtain the attention-getting value of pictures and at the same time get visual impressions as accurate as may be had from bar charts.

BAR CHARTS

The bar chart shown in section A of Chart 6.1 is a simplified form using no scale. In Chart 6.2 the same data are shown by means of a bar chart

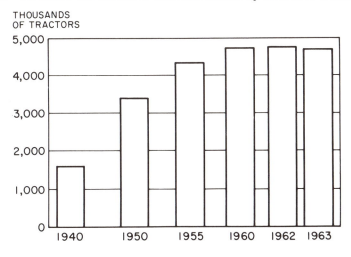

Chart 6.2. Number of Tractors on Farms in the United States, 1940, 1950, 1955, 1960, 1962, and 1964. Data from sources given below Chart 6.1.

which has a scale and which also varies the spacing between the bars in order to call attention to the fact that the time intervals vary. When the chart is expected merely to convey a very general impression, simple bar charts may be drawn without the use of a scale, as in section A of Chart 6.1. However, when two (or more) bar charts using different scales are in juxtaposition and may be compared with each other, the scales should be shown. Another caution concerns the presence of zero on the scale; Chart 6.3, which lacks the zero, shows that the omission of the zero is just as misleading in this type of chart as in the case of arithmetic curves. However, Chart 6.4 is a good example of space being saved without a misleading impression being conveyed. This is accomplished via a scale break.

All of the preceding bar charts showed chronological data, and, following the customary procedure, the bars were arranged vertically. Vertical
bars should also be used for data classified quantitatively, for example,
data of the number of persons in the United States classified by age groups
or according to years of schooling. When making comparisons of data
classified qualitatively or geographically, on the other hand, horizontal
bars are generally used. Chart 6.5 shows such a comparison of the values
of selected new construction activity in the United States in 1964.

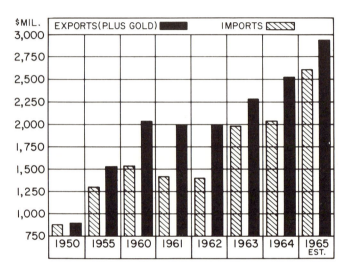

**Chart 6.3. A Bar Chart Lacking a Zero on the Vertical
Scale.** Data show exports (plus gold) and imports of an African
nation, 1950–1965. Data from an advertisement placed by the
Commercial Consul of that nation in 1966.

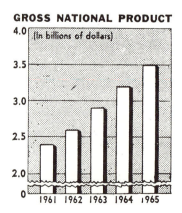

**Chart 6.4. Gross National
Product in Central American
Common Market, 1951–1965.**
Data from International Monetary
Fund and First National City Bank.
The scale break prevents misleading
impressions.

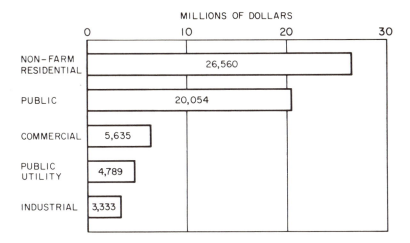

Chart 6.5. Value of Selected New Construction Activity in the United States, 1964. Data from *Federal Reserve Bulletin*, April 1965, p. 597.

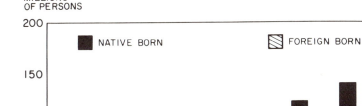

Chart 6.6. Native-Born and Foreign-Born Population of the United States, 1890–1960. The relative growth of the two series is not apparent from this type of chart, but may be shown by means of a semi-logarithmic chart, as described in the preceding chapter. Because of the non-existence of zero on a logarithmic scale, curves would be used instead of bars. Data from *Statistical Abstract of the United States, 1952*, p. 31, *1965*, p. 25, and from *U.S. Census of Population, 1950*, Vol. II, Part 1, Chap. B, pp. 1–87, and Vol. IV, Part 3, Chap. B, pp. 3B-82.

There are no set rules to be observed in drawing bar charts. Certain considerations, however, are helpful.

(1) Individual bars should be neither exceedingly short and wide nor very long and narrow.

(2) Bars should be separated by spaces which are not less than about $\frac{1}{2}$ the width of a bar or greater than about the width of a bar.

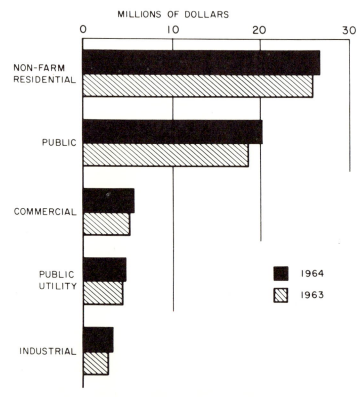

Chart 6.7. Value of Selected New Construction Activity in the United States, 1963 and 1964. Data from source given below Chart 6.5.

(3) A scale is generally useful. It should be about $\frac{1}{4}$ the width of a bar from the top bar (or from the left bar, if the bars are vertical).

(4) Guide lines are an aid in reading the chart. Sometimes the chart is enclosed and the guide lines are extended through the entire chart, as in Chart 6.5; sometimes the chart is not enclosed and the guide lines are cut off, as in Chart 6.7.

When showing a time series graphically, we may use either a bar chart or a curve. A curve facilitates a study of the general change which has taken place in a series, whereas a bar chart enables comparisons of specific years to be made more readily. If the series covers many years, it is

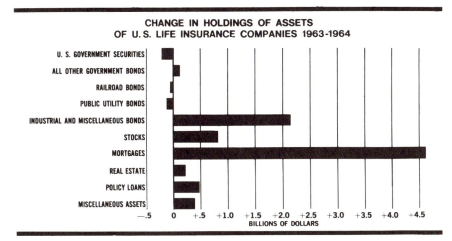

Chart 6.8.   An Illustration of Two-Way Horizontal Bar Charts. From *Life Insurance Fact Book*, 1965, p. 69.

generally not desirable to use a bar chart, which is laborious to construct. When only a few years are shown, as in Chart 6.2, a bar chart is preferable.

Sometimes we wish to compare two sets of data over a period of several years.   This may be done by means of a two-unit bar chart, as shown in Chart 6.6.   Similarly, we may wish to compare several categories for two years; a comparison of this nature is shown in Chart 6.7.

A two-direction bar chart, such as Chart 6.8, may be used to show increases and decreases.   This type of chart is even more effective if increases can be shown in black and decreases in red.   Increases and decreases in a series of data for a number of years may be shown by means of vertical bars above and below a horizontal zero line.

PICTOGRAPHS

In section D of Chart 6.1 the number of tractors on farms at each of certain years was represented by means of pictures of tractors of varying size.   While this sort of chart does not convey a satisfactory comparison to a reader, it does attract attention.   The pictorial effect may be retained and a satisfactory visual comparison afforded by using a number of small pictures, all of the same size, and arranging them so as to form a bar chart.   Such a graph is referred to as a *pictograph*.   Chart 6.9 shows a comparison of tractors on farms by means of this device.   While the diagram is essentially a bar chart, it is more attractive and thus is more likely to be examined by a reader.   No scale is used, but since the pictures are all of the same size and since each represents one million tractors, approximate numerical values may be had from the chart, if they are wanted.   Although a bar chart of a time series generally uses vertical bars, it will be observed that the pictograph shown as Chart 6.9 has hori-

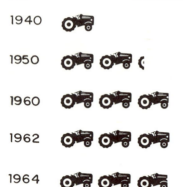

1940

1950

1960

1962

1964

EACH SYMBOL REPRESENTS 1,000,000 TRACTORS.

Chart 6.9.   **Number of Tractors on Farms in the United States, 1940, 1950, 1960, 1962, and 1964.** Data from sources given below Chart 6.1.

zontal bars. Pictographs are often arranged in this way because it seems more suitable to have tractors, people, houses (or whatever is being pictured) standing side by side rather than on top of one another.

Chart 6.10, another example of a pictograph, is an interesting method of showing that campaigns for funds are apt to depend heavily upon relatively few large gifts. Chart 6.11 represents a slightly different application of the pictograph idea. Here, pictures and bars are shown side by side with the bars conveying the quantitative data. It should be apparent that, in making a pictograph, the picture is so chosen as to suggest the nature of the data being shown. Certain basic rules for the use of pictorial devices are shown in Chart 6.12.

COMPONENT-PART CHARTS

The parts of a total may be shown by means of a bar as in Chart 6.13 or by a pie diagram as in Chart 6.14. The bar chart involves a one-dimensional comparison of the lengths of the sections of the bar; whereas the pie diagram involves a two-dimensional comparison of the pie sections, or a one-dimensional comparison of the arcs of the pie sections, or a com-

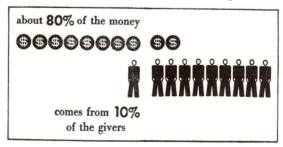

Chart 6.10. A Pictograph Used by Hobart and William Smith College. From *Let's Look at Hobart and William Smith*, p. 14. The original was in two colors.

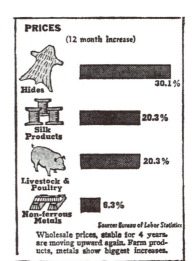

Chart 6.11. Pictures and Bars. From U.S. Bureau of Labor Statistics. Note that the horizontal scale has been omitted.

SYMBOLS SHOULD BE SELF-EXPLANATORY

CHANGES IN NUMBERS ARE SHOWN
BY MORE OR FEWER SYMBOLS

NOT BY LARGER OR SMALLER ONES

EACH SHIP REPRESENTS 5 MILLION TONS

CHARTS GIVE AN OVER-ALL PICTURE

NOT MINUTE DETAILS

4,873,285

11,075,357

20,468,953

PICTOGRAPHS MAKE COMPARISONS

NOT FLAT STATEMENTS

1870

1900

1930

1930

Chart 6.12. The Basic Rules for Drawing Pictographs as Suggested by Modley and Lowenstein. From Rudolph Modley and Dyno Lowenstein, *Pictographs and Graphs*, Harper & Row, New York, 1952, pp. 25 and 26.

parison of the central angles. Accuracy of judgment is about the same whether based on a bar chart or a pie diagram,[2] with the exception that, when depicted by a pie diagram, 25-per-cent (shown by a right angle) and 50-per-cent (shown by a diameter) sections are more accurately gauged. The pictorial value of the pie diagram is perhaps greater than that of the bar chart, and it is increased when the pie diagram is designed to suggest a silver dollar. Chart 6.15 shows an application of this sort. A single component-part bar is occasionally drawn without a scale and is sometimes horizontal. One advantage of the vertical bar over either the horizontal bar or the pie diagram is that the sections of the vertical bar are easier to label.

Several suppliers of graph paper offer sheets showing a circle with the circumference graduated from 0 to 100, thus enabling one to construct pie diagrams readily. If such sheets are not available or if varying sizes of circles are desired, pie diagrams may be made by the use of compasses and a protractor. Since the conventional protractor divides a circle into 360 parts or degrees, the percentages which are to be shown should be multiplied by 3.6. Dividing a circle into percentages is facilitated by use of a protractor[3] calibrated to divide a circle into 100 parts, as shown in Chart 6.16; such a scale may be engraved or otherwise marked on the back of an ordinary protractor.

Chart 6.17 shows how bar charts may be used to compare several sets of component parts and also how the same comparisons may be made by means of pie diagrams. It seems clear that comparisons between the years are made more easily from the bars than from the circles. The guide lines

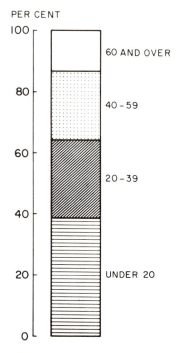

Chart 6.13. Proportion of the Population of the United States in Each Specified Age Group, 1960. Data from U.S. Bureau of the Census, *U.S. Census of Population, 1960*, Vol. I, *Characteristics of the Population*, Part I, *United States Summary*, pp. 1–199.

running from section to section assist in making comparisons from the bar chart: when the lines are parallel, there has been no change; when they diverge, there has been an increase; when they converge, a decrease has occurred.

[2] See Frederick E. Croxton and Roy E. Stryker, "Bar Charts Versus Circle Diagrams," *Journal of the American Statistical Association*, December 1927, pp. 473–482.

[3] See Frederick E. Croxton, "A Percentage Protractor," *Journal of the American Statistical Association*, March 1922, pp. 108–109.

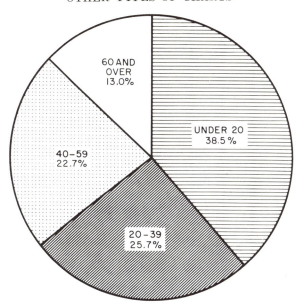

Chart 6.14. Proportion of the Population of the United States in Each Specified Age Group, 1960. Data from sources given below Chart 6.13.

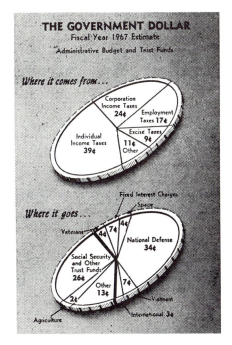

Chart 6.15. Pie Diagrams Used With the President's Budget Message for Fiscal Year 1967.

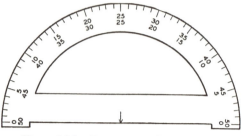

Chart 6.16.   Percentage Protractor.

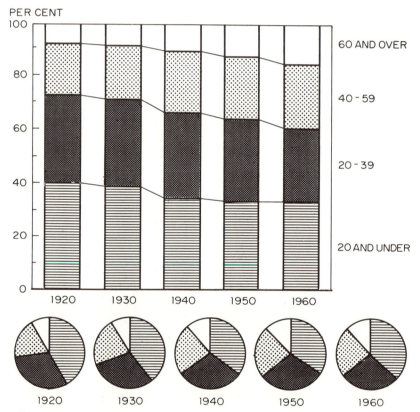

Chart 6.17.   Proportion of the Population of the United States in Each Specified Age Group 1920–1960. Data from sources given below Chart 4.19.

The comparison of component parts in Chart 6.17 is on a relative basis; the proportion of each age group in the population is shown. When we indicate how many of each age group were enumerated, we have diagrams such as are shown in Chart 6.18. The bars and circles vary in size because the total population has increased. In this instance the bar chart is clearly preferable to the pie diagram. When data such as those shown in Charts 6.17 and 6.18 cover a number of years, it is generally preferable to make use of curves, as was done in Charts 4.19 and 4.20. While the bar charts of Charts 6.17 and 6.18 present chronological data, we may also compare component parts for different places or categories.

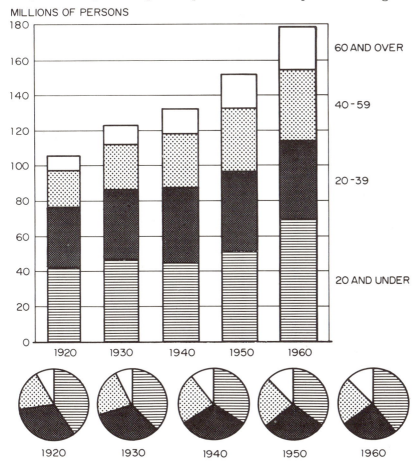

Chart 6.18. Population of the United States in Each Specified Age Group, 1920–1950. Data from sources given below Chart 4.23.

For example, we might compare the proportions of males and females in the urban population with the proportions of males and females in the rural population. One bar, subdivided for males and females, would represent the urban population; the other bar, similarly divided for the sexes, would represent the rural population.

STATISTICAL MAPS

Statistical maps are graphic devices which show quantitative information on a geographical basis. We shall consider hatched or shaded maps, dot maps, and pin maps.

Hatched maps.   Hatched or shaded maps undertake to show for each geographical area under consideration the magnitude of the phenomenon which is being studied.   The variations in magnitude are represented graphically by progressive differences in hatching or shading.   In Chart 6.19 the various hatchings indicate the per cent of farm operators working off their farms in the United States in 1959.   The areas having the highest percentages of all farm operators working off their farms are shown in solid black.   The shading becomes progressively lighter so that the light-

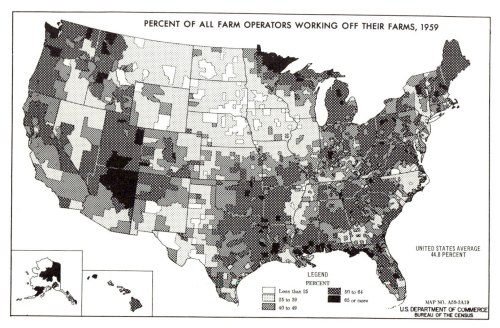

Chart 6.19.   A Hatched Map.

est, which is to say, the non-shaded area, shows the lowest percentage. The outstanding characteristic of maps such as this is that a progressive change in the hatching or shading indicates an increase (or decrease) in the phenomenon being measured.

Sometimes statistical maps are made in colors.   However, the principle of progressive shading cannot be developed satisfactorily by using different colors.   It is possible, of course, to use progressive shades of a single color and thus sometimes to produce a more attractive map than could be done by using black and white.

Dot maps.   The preceding statistical map showed data that applied to entire areas—specifically, the per cent of all farm operators working off their farms—and so hatched or shaded map was appropriate.   When the geographical distribution of *occurrences* is to be shown, the dot map should be used.   Chart 6.20 shows one of the simplest of dot maps. Each dot represents 500 farms, and the concentration in various parts of the country is clearly shown.   In a dot map, the number of units represented by one dot may be large, as in Chart 6.20, so that the number of dots in a region is small enough to be counted, or the number of units represented by one dot may be small, so that the numerous dots give the effect of a gradual change in intensity of shading from light to dark. Which technique to use depends on the purpose of the chart.

A different sort of dot map is shown in Chart 6.21, which uses dots of varying size.   Here, the areas of the circles indicate the amount of change

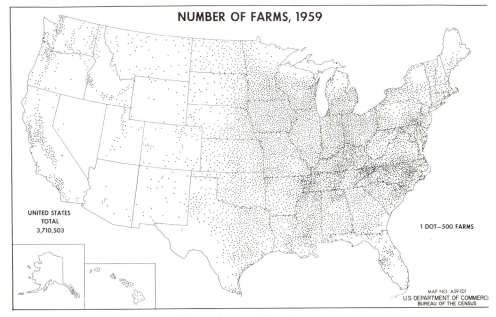

Chart. 6.20.   A Dot Map.

in total population by states, between 1950 and 1960.   While the varying circle sizes indicate the different changes among the states, it is not easy to make accurate comparisons from the circles.   We cannot compare diameters directly.   We must remember that, if one circle has a diameter twice as great as another, then the first circle has an area four times that of the second.

Pin maps.   Pin maps may be thought of as a particularly flexible sort of dot map.   They consist of maps mounted on a backing of cork, cardboard, wallboard, corrugated cardboard, or the like, on which information is recorded by means of pins having (usually) glass heads of different size, color, and shape.   The available pins have heads that range in size from about $\frac{1}{16}$ inch to about $\frac{3}{4}$ inch in diameter.   A large number of colors is available as well as a variety of shapes, such as round-, square-, and triangular-head pins.   Pin maps may be readily altered as the facts change.   Because of this flexibility and the wide variety of pins avail-

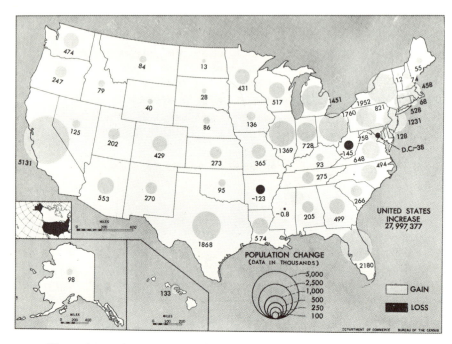

Chart 6.21. Another Kind of Dot Map. Notice that dot size is varied to indicate the amount of change. Shaded dots indicate increase, black dots show decrease.

able, the pin map is frequently employed as a method of presenting geographical data. An extensive pin-map scheme, involving one or more maps mounted on cork and hundreds or thousands of pins, is expensive but may often prove very useful.

Pin maps are frequently used to record the location and result of automobile accidents. By using one or more such maps, it is possible not only to observe the frequency with which accidents occur at various places, but also the nature of each accident (automobile hitting pedestrian, automobile hitting automobile, automobile hitting fixed object, and so forth) and the result of the accident (property damage, occupant injured, occupant killed, pedestrian injured, pedestrian killed, and so on).

One difficulty with the statistical map is that the importance of different regions is not to be judged by their areas. For instance, a hatched map showing income per family in different states would be somewhat misleading because there are many more families in some of the states occupying very small areas than there are in other states occupying very large areas. An interesting device sometimes used for overcoming this difficulty consists of drawing the map in such a way that the area of each state is in proportion to the number of families in that state.

CHAPTER 7

Rates, Ratios, and Percentages

It was pointed out in the chapter dealing with statistical tables that derived figures are useful to assist in summarizing and comparing data. In that chapter specific mention was made of rates,[1] ratios, percentages, and averages. This chapter will discuss rates, ratios, and percentages. Averages and related measures will be examined in later chapters.

To express the ratio which 753 bears to 251, we divide 753 by 251, which gives 3, and we say that 753 is to 251 as 3 is to 1, or more briefly, 753:251::3:1. We have thus indicated the relationship which the first of these two numbers bears to the second as a *ratio to one*. If it suited our purpose better, we could express the relationship as a ratio to any other number. For example, we could use a ratio to ten, saying 753: 251::30:10; we could use a ratio to one hundred and write 753:251:: 300:100. This last ratio, per hundred, is generally referred to as a *percentage*, and we note that 753 is 300 per cent (from *per centum*) of 251. It will thus be seen that percentages, which are used so frequently, are merely special cases of the more general concept of ratios. If, instead of using a ratio per hundred, we find occasion for a ratio per thousand, we may refer to our figures as "per mille."

Ratios are computed in order to expedite comparisons. Not only are large numbers reduced as in Table 3.2, but much is gained by comparing a series of figures with a rounded base of 100 (which can be carried in one's mind) rather than by attempting to compare each individual population figure with the total for the entire United States. Relative change may be visualized more concretely when shown by percentages, as in Table 7.1, or when shown by one of the methods used in Table 7.2.

---

[1] The term *rate* is sometimes used to mean the amount or quantity of one variable considered in relation to one unit of a different variable. Thus, 20 miles per hour is a rate of speed. The relationship that two similar variables bear to each other is often termed a *ratio*. For example, the *current ratio*, which is the ratio of current assets to current liabilities, compares two figures which are both in terms of dollars. General usage does not always observe this distinction between rate and ratio.

TABLE 7.1

*Value of Selected New Construction Activity in the United
States 1963 and 1964*

(Millions of dollars)

Construction type	1963	1964	Per cent increase
Non-farm residential...........	25,843	26,560	2.8
Public.......................	18,679	20,054	7.4
Commercial..................	5,200	5,635	8.4
Public utility.................	4,494	4,789	6.6
Industrial...................	2,962	3,333	12.5

Data from *Federal Reserve Bulletin*, April 1965, p. 597.

TABLE 7.2

*Production of Steel Ingots and Steel for Castings in the United States
1955–1964*

Year	Production (millions of short tons)	Per cent of 1955	Per cent decrease* from 1955	Per cent preceding year	Per cent increase* over preceding year
1955	117.0	100.0	...	...	...
1956	115.2	98.5	− 1.5	98.5	− 1.5
1957	112.7	96.3	− 3.7	97.8	− 2.2
1958	85.3	72.9	−27.1	75.7	−24.3
1959	93.4	79.8	−20.2	109.5	9.5
1960	99.3	84.9	−15.1	106.3	6.3
1961	98.0	83.8	−16.2	98.7	− 1.3
1962	98.3	84.0	−16.0	100.3	0.3
1963	109.3	93.4	− 6.6	111.2	11.2
1964	126.9	108.5	+ 8.5	116.1	16.1

* A plus sign denotes an increase.
Data from various issues of *Statistical Abstract of the United States* and from *Survey of
Current Business*, February 1965, pp. S-32.

CALCULATION

When one or more numbers are being compared to another number, the
figure to which comparisons are made is known as the *base*. A ratio is
found by dividing[2] the figure, which is being compared to the base, by
the base. The figure is then expressed in terms of or in relation to the
base, and ratios of all sorts are therefore sometimes referred to as *relative
numbers* or *relatives*.

At the end of July 1965, total consumer credit outstanding was
$80,686,000. At the end of July 1964, it was $72,456,000. To state
the July 1965 amount outstanding in terms of July 1964, we divide
$80,686,000 by $72,456,000 and obtain 1.1135. This means that the
total consumer credit outstanding in July 1965 was 1.1135 as great as

---

[2] Instructions for operating calculating machines may be obtained from the sales
offices of the calculating machine companies.

in July 1964. In many instances, ratios are most useful when stated as percentages. To change 1.1135, the ratio to 1, to a ratio per hundred, the decimal place is moved two places to the right. The resulting figure, 111.35, indicates that total consumer credit outstanding in July 1965 amounted to 111.35 per cent of the amount outstanding in July 1964.

It should be noted that there are two ways in which we can express the percentage figure just given. Instead of saying that July 1965 consumer credit outstanding was 111.35 per cent *of* July 1964 consumer credit outstanding, we may say that it was 11.35 per cent *greater than* in July 1964. In the first instance, we compared the figures for the two years; in the second, we compared the change which took place[3] with the figure for July 1964.

EFFECT OF CHANGING BASE

Naturally, a different set of figures would be obtained if we compared the July 1964 total consumer credit figure with the July 1965 figure. We are now using July 1965 as the base and the July 1964 figure is divided by that for July 1965. Performing this operation indicates that total consumer credit outstanding in July 1964 was 89.79 per cent that of July 1965, or that the total consumer credit outstanding then was 10.21 per cent less than in July 1965. Observe that, while the July 1965 figure was 11.35 per cent greater than the July 1964 figure with July 1964 as the base, the July 1964 figure was only 10.21 per cent less than the July 1965 figure using July 1965 as the base. The difference, is, of course, due to the fact that the basis of comparison was first in reference to July 1964 and then to July 1965. The difference in results attributable to changing the base can be illustrated in still another way. If a number is increased 100 per cent, the second number need be decreased but 50 per cent to arrive at the original figure. Conversely, if a given number is decreased 50 per cent, the second number must be increased 100 per cent to reproduce the given number.

The failure to realize the effect of this change of base may lead to the drawing of false conclusions. A firm decreased the wages of its employees 15 per cent; later it increased the reduced wages 5 per cent; then it raised these increased figures 5 per cent; and finally it increased these second figures another 5 per cent. Afterwards it announced that the three 5 per cent increases put wages back where they were before the 15 per cent reduction. Calculation will show that the new wages were really 98.4 per cent of the original wages before reduction. If the company

---

[3] Suppose we are comparing two percentages, as 4.0 per cent and 9.0 per cent. We may speak in absolute terms and say that 9.0 per cent is 5.0 per cent more than 4.0 per cent. We may speak in relative terms and say that 9.0 per cent is 125 per cent greater than 4.0 per cent, or that 9.0 per cent is 225 per cent of 4.0 per cent. When comparing percentages, it is advisable to make quite clear whether we are speaking in absolute or relative terms.

had given a single 15 per cent increase of the reduced wages, the new wages would have been but 97.75 per cent of the original wages.

Table 7.3 shows for selected percentages of increase the per cent which the new number must be decreased to reproduce the original number. It

TABLE 7.3

Illustrations of Effect of Shifting Base in Calculating Percentages

Given number	Per cent of increase	New number	Per cent new number must be decreased to yield given number
10	500.00	60.00	83.33
10	200.00	30.00	66.67
10	100.00	20.00	50.00
10	50.00	15.00	33.33
10	33.33	13.33	25.00
10	25.00	12.50	20.00
10	10.00	11.00	9.00
10	5.00	10.50	4.76
10	1.00	10.10	0.99

should be borne in mind that a per-cent-of-increase figure may be indefinitely large; however, a per-cent-of-decrease figure of 100 indicates· a decline to zero, while a per cent of decrease of over 100 indicates a fall to a negative quantity.

RECORDING PERCENTAGES

Generally percentages are recorded to one decimal place. If the percentages are based upon large figures, and particularly if one, or more than one, part of a total is quite small (see Table 3.2), it may be desirable to use more than one decimal. Occasionally only whole percentages are shown, in order that relationships may be grasped readily. Whole percentages will not suffice, however, when the relative variations are extremely small.

Percentages should not be calculated if the absolute numbers are small, especially if the base is appreciably less than 100. A serious difficulty arising out of the use of percentages based on small absolute numbers is discussed on page 134.

When percentages are to be recorded with one decimal, they are rounded to the nearest tenth of one per cent. The following examples will indicate the procedure in rounding percentages (and also in rounding other calculations[4] involving remainders):

(1) \$371.16 ÷ \$679.28 = 0.5464, or 54.64 per cent. The second decimal is less than 5 and therefore this percentage, to the nearest tenth of one per cent, is 54.6.

---

[4] See Appendix T for a more comprehensive discussion of rounding numbers.

(2) 2,319 pounds ÷ 7,532 pounds = 0.3079, or 30.79 per cent. In this instance the second decimal is more than 5 and the percentage should be recorded as 30.8.

(3) 280,511 feet ÷ 11,000,000 feet = 0.025501, or 2.5501 per cent. Here the second decimal is 5, but there is a remainder which results in the 1 in the fourth decimal place. Recorded to the nearest tenth of one per cent, this figure is 2.6.

(4) 1,341 barrels ÷ 6,000 barrels = 0.2235, or 22.35 per cent. Here the nearest tenth is either 22.3 or 22.4. It does not greatly matter whether occasional results such as this are raised in the first decimal place or whether the second decimal is dropped. However, it is better to follow some consistent scheme. Particularly when many computations are being made which are eventually to be added, it is well to employ a method which will cause half of the values with a second decimal of exactly 5 to be raised and half to be lowered. This practice will avoid the accumulation of errors. Probably the most satisfactory scheme is to raise the first decimal when the first decimal is an odd number (67.35 becomes 67.4) and to drop the second decimal when the first decimal is an even number (67.65 becomes 67.6).

Sometimes the consequence of rounding all percentages to one decimal place results in totals of 99.9 or 100.1 and occasionally shows 99.8 or 100.2. Some statisticians adjust one of the percentages in order to produce the correct total, but it seems preferable to let each percentage stand correctly rounded.

TYPES OF COMPARISONS

We have already seen an instance in which the parts of a whole were compared to the total in Table 3.2. Here the percentages were obtained by dividing each item in turn by the total. More expeditiously we may take the reciprocal of the total and multiply the reciprocal by each of the component figures. This is a time-saving device adapted particularly to the calculating machine, and is applicable whenever we are dividing a series of numbers by a constant number.

Various illustrations of comparisons of one figure with another figure are given on later pages in this chapter. For instance, in the paragraph on sex ratios it is noted that each figure for males is divided by the appropriate figure for females, since the sex ratio consists in stating the number of males per 100 females.

Table 7.2 indicates a number of different comparisons which may be made in regard to data arranged chronologically. In column 3, the production of steel ingots and steel for castings for each year is compared with the 1955 production; each figure is divided by that for 1955. Column 4 shows the percentage by which the production for each year exceeded or was less than that for 1955. In column 5, the production each year is related to that of the preceding year; each year's figure is divided by that for the preceding year. Column 6 indicates the per cent of increase or decrease of each year in relation to the preceding year; the numerical increase (or decrease) of each year over the preceding year is divided by the production for the preceding year. In columns 3 and 4, comparisons are made with a fixed base, 1955. In columns 5 and 6, the base is constantly shifting, being always the preceding year.

Another application of percentages is shown in Table 7.1. Here the 1963 figure for each item is the base. The percentage column headed "per cent increase" indicates the relative increase or decrease in the value of each type of new construction from 1963 to 1964.

SOME FREQUENTLY USED RATIOS

The following paragraphs indicate a few interesting applications of ratios and percentages.[5] The reader will doubtless become aware of many others as he reads more or less technical material in magazines, newspapers, books, and advertisements.

Index numbers. Most index numbers are presented in the form of percentages. In the construction of an index number of wholesale prices, for example, the commodities to be included are selected first, and their prices are then combined with due regard to the varying importance of the different commodities. If the index number is a chronological one, as is usually the case, some year may be designated as the base and prices in that year are set equal to 100. The prices for the other years are then expressed in relation to that base year. The United States Bureau of Labor Statistics uses the average of the years 1957–1959 as the base year for its index numbers of approximately 2,200 wholesale prices. Wholesale prices during these three years are therefore represented by 100. The wholesale price index number for December 1963 was 100.3; for January 1964, it was 101.0; for February 1964, it was 100.5; for March 1964, it fell to 100.4. Prices for these months are thus expressed in terms of the average for the thirty-six months of 1957–1959.

Sex ratio. The relationship of the number of males to the number of females in the population is given by the sex ratio, which states the number of males per 100 females. In 1960, there were 88,303,113 males and 91,022,558 females in the United States. Thus, there were 97.0 males per 100 females in this country. The ratio varied among the different age groups. It was lowest for the age group "65 and over," 82.8, and highest for the age group "under 15 years," 103.4. It also varied among

---

[5] See Chapters 17 and 18 for a more complete discussion of index numbers.

the different states. It was lowest in Massachusetts where there were 93.4 males per 100 females and highest in Alaska where there were 132.3 males per 100 females.

Population density. Instead of merely comparing the total population of two communities, it may often be more meaningful to consider the density of the population. We do this by dividing the total population by the area in square miles, and thus determine the number of persons per square mile. For example, in 1960, the population of Montana was 674,767 and the population of New Hampshire was 606,921. If we relate these figures to the land area of each state, we find that New Hampshire had 67.3 persons per square mile, while Montana had but 4.6 persons per square mile. These figures do not mean, of course, that there were 67 or 68 persons on *every* square mile in New Hampshire and 4 or 5 persons on *every* square mile in Montana. They are merely summary figures which indicate that, on the average, there were the indicated number of persons per square mile in each state.

Population density may also be used in making chronological comparisons. As our country has grown older, the population density has increased. In 1800 there were 6.1 persons per square mile in the United States; in 1960 there were 50.5 persons per square mile.

Ratios per capita. Many figures are more meaningful or more useful when expressed on a per capita basis. The Federal debt of the United States reflects not only the level of expenditures in past years and increases in government services, but also the growth of population. For example, on June 30, 1941, the Federal debt was $48,961,000,000; by June 30, 1963, the figure had grown to $305,860,000,000. If these figures are divided by the population at the two periods, it appears that the per capita Federal debt was $367 on June 30, 1941, and $1,616 on June 30, 1963.

The consumption of various commodities is frequently stated on a per capita basis. Thus in 1963 the estimated consumption of beef was 94.8 pounds per capita; the estimated consumption of eggs was 315 per capita; the approximate amount of refined sugar consumed was 97.2 pounds per capita.

Death rates. The crude, gross, or general death rate for a given year is obtained by dividing the number of deaths occurring in a community during that year by the mid-year population of that community, and expressing the result per thousand. In 1963 there were in the United States an estimated 1,813,000 deaths from all causes. The July 1, 1963 population, resident in the United States, was estimated to be 188,531,000. The death rate for 1963 was therefore

$$1{,}813{,}000 \div 188{,}531{,}000 = 0.0096, \text{ or } 9.6 \text{ per thousand.}$$

It will be seen that the accuracy of a death rate depends first upon the degree of completeness of the registrations of deaths, and second upon the accuracy of the mid-year population estimate used as the base. Since population counts are made only once in 10 years, most of the population figures used must be estimates. When the population is estimated for a year falling between two censuses, the estimate is termed an *inter-censal* estimate; when the estimate is for a year after a census, it is termed a *post-censal* estimate. Inter-censal estimates are naturally somewhat more accurate than post-censal estimates. For the years 1961 to 1969 inclusive, death rates must at present be based upon post-censal estimates and are called *preliminary* rates. After the 1970 census results are available, inter-censal estimates may be made for the years 1961–1969, and the death rates may be recomputed upon the basis of these new population estimates. Such rates are called *revised* rates.

When the deaths occurring in a state or city are divided by the population of that community, the resulting crude death rate is subject to certain corrections. For example, in any given year people may die in a community who are residents elsewhere, and also some residents of any large community may die outside of that community. If the non-resident deaths are deducted from those which occurred in the community, the resulting rate is referred to as a *local* rate. If, in addition, the deaths of residents occurring outside of that community are added, the resulting rate is referred to as a *resident* rate. Failure to recognize these important differences may lead to drawing false conclusions. One year it was announced that the death rate for Queens borough of New York City was 6.5 per 1,000, for Bronx 7.8, for Brooklyn 9.3, for Richmond 13.5, and for Manhattan 16.3. The death rate for Queens was lower than for any other such community in the United States, and at least one newspaper promptly announced that Queens was "the healthiest place in the country." It was very quickly pointed out, however, that Queens possessed a very low quota of hospitals and that, therefore, some residents of Queens in need of hospital care would seek it in Manhattan or elsewhere. Hospital cases naturally show a very high death rate, and a crude death rate would not reflect the fact that some persons dying in Manhattan and elsewhere were really residents of Queens.

Death rates for particular classes of the population (males and females, various age groups, and other categories) and for particular diseases or causes are referred to as *specific* death rates. Because the deaths from any one cause are relatively few, cause-specific rates are usually stated per 100,000 of the population. Thus in 1962 the death rate for motor vehicle accidents was 22.0 per 100,000.

An intelligent comparison of the death rates of different communities involves consideration of the fact that the proportions of the sexes may differ and also that there may be differences in the age distributions, in the racial and nativity composition of the inhabitants, in occupations, and in other factors.   A discussion of these differences and the methods of computing *adjusted* and *standardized* death rates is too specialized a topic to be treated in this text.[6]

Birth rates.   Birth rates are usually calculated by dividing the births during a year by the mid-year population for that year.   Just as in the case of death rates, we may have preliminary rates and revised rates.   We may also have gross, local, and resident rates.   Stillbirths are not counted as births, although they have been so counted in the past; this fact should be remembered in making chronological comparisons.   Perhaps it is also worth while calling attention to the fact that the registration of births is not so complete as is the registration of deaths.   A death must be registered before a burial permit may be issued and before interment may be made.   A newborn infant, however, may be absorbed into the family and the community whether or not his birth is registered.

The calculation of birth rates in relation to the total population is not thoroughly satisfactory, since the proportion of "child producers" in the population is not constant either from time to time or from place to place. Refinements in the calculation of birth rates are beyond the scope of this volume.

Crop yields per acre.   Data of the total amount of a crop produced may tell us whether or not there is more of that commodity available in one year than in another.   From such figures, however, we cannot know if an increase may have been due to a more abundant yield, to an increase in acreage, or to both.   In 1962 there were 669,211,000 bushels of soybeans harvested from 27,604,000 acres in the United States; in the following year, 28,628,000 acres yielded 701,465,000 bushels.   Both the acreage harvested and the total yield had risen, resulting in an increase in the yield per acre, which was 24.2 bushels in 1962 and 24.5 bushels in 1963. On a geographical basis, the United States, which produces more soybeans than any other country for which figures are available, is not first in yield per acre.   Italy, producing far less in 1963 than did the United States, had a yield per acre of 26.5 bushels.

Hog-corn ratio.   The hog-corn ratio is the result of dividing the average price per 100 pounds which farmers receive for hogs by the average price per bushel which farmers receive for corn.   For example, if, one day, farmers are receiving $17.80 per 100 pounds for hogs and $1.48 per bushel for corn, the ratio is $17.80 ÷ $1.48 = 12.0.   This ratio may be interpreted to mean that 100 pounds of hogs are 12.0 times as valuable as a bushel of corn, or more simply, that 12.0 bushels of corn

[6] See the numerous studies issued by the National Center For Health Statistics with data taken from the National Vital Statistics System.   Also the *Vital Statistics of the United States* which have been issued annually by the Public Health Service of the U. S. Department of Health, Education, and Welfare.   These deal in detail with birth rates, morbidity rates, case-fatality ratios, marriage rates, divorce rates, fertility rates, stillbirth ratios, and others.   Monthly *Vital Statistics* reports are also available.

are equal in value to 100 pounds of hogs. If, on another day hogs bring $16.40 per 100 pounds and corn yields the farmer $1.68 per bushel, the ratio is then 9.8. Over one 6-year period, the hog-corn ratio averaged about 13.2, falling as low as 9.2 and reaching as high as 19.8. When the ratio is low, it is more profitable for farmers to sell their corn outright than to feed the corn to hogs being fattened for market. When the ratio is high, it becomes more profitable for the farmer to feed corn to his hogs than to sell the corn outright. Since corn is the principal element of cost in producing hogs for market, the ratio is used as an indicator of the desirability of future expansion or contraction of hog production. There is thus a relationship between the hog-corn ratio and the hog production cycle. When the ratio is high, an increase in hog production tends to follow. Such an increase is frequently followed by a decline in hog prices in relation to corn prices, and there then follows a tendency to restrict hog production. Curves showing hog-corn ratios for 1940–1964 are shown in Charts 5.12 and 5.13.

Batting averages. The familiar batting average of the sport pages of the daily paper is a ratio of the hits made by a batter in relation to the total number of times he was at bat. Table 7.4 shows a series of selected batting averages. The figures in the last column of Table 7.4 may be correctly thought of as either ratios to one or as averages of a series of observations each having a value of 1 or 0 (that is, either the batter did or did not make a hit). If a man has been at bat 75 times and has made 25 hits, his batting average would be shown as .333 and is spoken of as "three hundred and thirty-three." If he had made a hit every time he was at bat, his figure would be 1.000, which is referred to as "one thousand." Notice that certain contradictions are involved in some of the terms used to refer to these data. The column of figures is frequently headed "percentage"; the figures are printed as *ratios to one;* the figures are spoken of as *per thousand!*

TABLE 7.4

Individual Batting Averages of 10 Outstanding American League Players,
1965

Player and Club	Games	Times at bat	Hits	Batting average*
Oliva, Minnesota....................	149	576	185	.321
Yastrzemski, Boston................	133	494	154	.312
Davalillo, Cleveland................	142	505	152	.301
Robinson, Baltimore................	144	559	166	.297
Wagner, Cleveland..................	144	517	152	.294
Howard, Washington................	149	516	149	.289
Colavito, Cleveland.................	162	592	170	.287
Hall, Minnesota....................	148	522	149	.285
Buford, Chicago....................	155	586	166	.283
Tresh, N. Y.......................	156	602	168	.279

* This column is headed "PCT" in the original table.
Data from American League of Professional Baseball Clubs.

Airline Accident Ratios.   The safety of air travel may be indicated by means of ratios.   During 1963, scheduled domestic air carriers flew 40,263,000,000 passenger-miles and had a total of 42 accidents in which passenger fatalities totaled 48.   Thus, the airlines averaged one passenger fatality for every 838,812,500 passenger-miles flown.   In 1946, the figure was 80,910,867, and in 1952 it was 282,536,326 passenger-miles per passenger fatality.   As these few data may suggest, although the ratios can and do fluctuate tremendously from year to year because of the relatively small number of accidents and fatalities involved, the trend generally has been toward higher ratios as air travel has become safer. Ratios of the number of fatal accidents per million plane-miles and the number of passenger fatalities per 100 million passenger-miles may also be computed.

The 100 per cent statement.   When banks, insurance companies, and other corporations present financial information to the public, they

TABLE 7.5

Assets of the Pension Trust Fund of Bethlehem Steel Corporation and Subsidiary Companies, 1963 and 1964

Asset	Amount		Per cent of total	
	1963	1964	1963	1964
Cash and Accrued Interest Receivable.	$ 2,419,000	$ 3,004,000	.7	.8
Investments at Cost:				
Short-term Obligations.............	18,352,000	47,677,000	5.0	12.2
U. S. Government Bonds...........	14,916,000	14,916,000	4.1	3.8
Other Bonds, Notes, and Obligations				
Domestic Corporate.............	89,972,000	91,636,000	24.5	23.4
Real Estate Mortgages..........	18,769,000	18,144,000	5.1	4.6
Foreign......................	23,434,000	20,985,000	6.4	5.4
Preferred Stocks.................	7,856,000	3,402,000	2.1	.9
Common Stocks				
Industrial.....................	128,129,000	130,554,000	34.9	33.4
Public Utility.................	36,717,000	32,270,000	10.0	8.3
Bank Finance, and Insurance.....	26,541,000	28,297,000	7.2	7.2
Total......................	$367,105,000	$390,885,000	100.0	100.0

Data from Bethlehem Steel Corporation, *Annual Report, 1964,* p. 20.

find it effective to supplement the dollar figures with percentages.   Thus, a financial statement may show each asset as a percentage of all assets, and each liability as a percentage of all liabilities.   The procedure is particularly effective when the dollar figures are large.   Table 7.5 shows the assets of the Pension Trust Fund of Bethlehem Steel Corporation and subsidiary companies as set forth in an annual report.   The actual figures, even though rounded, are too large for the ordinary reader to grasp and compare, but the percentage data make comparisons less difficult.   In preparing such a percentage statement, it is desirable not to show too many decimal places, else comparisons cannot readily be made.

A statement of the resources of a bank carried all percentages to three decimal places. This was quite unnecessary, particularly since the smallest item, "sundry securities," was 0.035 (0.0349) per cent and could have been shown as 0.03 per cent, and since the second smallest item, "other assets," was 0.039 per cent and could have been shown as 0.04 per cent. For popular presentation, there is some advantage in lumping such small items together in order to center attention upon the more important ones. These two small items, if combined, would have appeared as 0.07 per cent, or as 0.1 per cent with all percentages shown to but one decimal place. However, it may have been desired to emphasize the smallness of either "sundry securities" or "other assets," or both.

Railroad ratios. The efficient operation of railroads necessitates the collection and use of a vast amount of statistical data in connection with which numerous ratios are calculated. The figures which follow are for United States railroads for 1963.

The investment per mile of line is obtained by dividing total investment in road and equipment (including cash, materials, and supplies) by the number of miles of railroad line. This figure was $163,292 per mile, or, allowing for accrued depreciation, $120,153 per mile.

Freight revenue per ton-mile is obtained by dividing total freight revenue by the total number of ton-miles of freight hauled. The freight revenue per ton-mile was 1.310 cents. Similarly, we may compute the passenger revenue per passenger mile, which amounted to 3.178 cents.

The operating ratio is the ratio of operating expenses to operating revenues. Operating expenses were $7,451,608,665, while operating revenues were $9,559,546,424. The operating ratio was 77.95 per cent.

There are a number of other railroad ratios; the meaning of each is rather obvious. Enumerating a few: the gross revenue per ton of freight was $6.14; the haul per ton of freight was 464 miles; the revenue per passenger was $1.90; the average trip per passenger was 59.6 miles; the rate of return on aggregate property investment was 3.10 per cent; the hours worked during the year per railroad employee were 2,413; the percentage of unserviceable freight cars averaged 7.0 during the year; the ton-miles per day per freight car were 113, the mileage per day per freight car was 49.2 miles.[7]

The railroad ratios mentioned above are one type of business ratios. Many sorts of business organizations compute diverse ratios for the better functioning of the enterprise. Discussed in another volume[8] are such

---

[7] For these and other railroad ratios, see *A Yearbook of Railroad Information*, issued annually by the Committee on Public Relations of the Eastern Railroads, New York.

[8] See F. E. Croxton and D. J. Cowden, *Practical Business Statistics*, third edition, Prentice-Hall, Inc., Englewood Cliffs, N. J., 1960, pp. 90–99.

ratios as current ratio (current assets ÷ current liabilities), merchandise turnover (net sales ÷ merchandise inventory), margin of profit (profit ÷ sales), and labor turnover (replacements ÷ number on payroll).

FAULTY USE OF PERCENTAGES

Ratios and percentages are in such general use that it is not surprising to find them occasionally misused. Difficulties encountered in the calculation and use of percentages can generally be traced to one of the following causes: (1) confusion in regard to the base, (2) calculation of percentages based on small absolute numbers, (3) misplaced decimal points, (4) arithmetic mistakes, (5) improper procedure in averaging percentages. These will be discussed in order.

Confusion in regard to base. Over one period of five years, the enrollment in veterinary colleges in the United States declined from 3,160 to 641 students. The decrease was 2,519 students, or 79.7 per cent of the original enrollment, yet the dean of a midwestern veterinary college was quoted as having said that during the period in question the enrollment had decreased 500 per cent! The dean may have actually said that the original registration figure was about 500 per cent of the later figure. A decrease of 500 per cent would mean a negative enrollment four times the size of the earlier registration.

One year a determined effort was made by the United States district attorney to have restaurants in Pittsburgh lower their prices to a certain level. Newspapers announcing the success of the drive stated that Pittsburgh restaurants had cut their prices 50 to 100 per cent. It is, of course, clear that prices cannot be cut 100 per cent, else the servings formerly sold would be given away! The price reductions on a number of dishes were stated. Some food had formerly sold at 15 cents per order. Identical-size servings were sold at 5 cents after the reduction; hence, the reduction amounted to 66.7 per cent of the former selling price.

It is not at all unusual to see an advertisement claiming "prices reduced 100 per cent." Of course, this should mean that goods are being given away. One company even went so far as to advise that their catalog would enable one to "save from 50 to 200 per cent."

Serious confusion in regard to a base seems to be present in a mail-order house guarantee of tires. The concern claims that the guarantee is "without limit as to mileage, months or years of service," and that tires will be repaired free or replaced at a charge "only for the actual amount of mileage you have received." Literally, the base is infinity, and, if the guarantee were to be fully carried out for all tire buyers, the company would quickly have to cease selling tires. In fairness to the concern involved, it should be noted that their adjustment policy is a generous one.

Percentages from small numbers. An extremely old, classic illustration of the undesirability of using percentages based upon small numbers is given by Chaddock.[9]

A short time after Johns Hopkins University had opened certain courses in the University to women, it was reported that $33\frac{1}{3}$ per cent of the women students had married into the faculty of the institution. Of course the important information was the number of women students. There were only three. *When dealing with a small number of cases, the use of percentages alone leads to wrong impressions.* In these cases either percentages should not be used at all or the numbers upon which they are based should accompany the percentages.

Ordinarily, percentages should not be computed unless the base consists of 100 or more cases.

Misplaced decimal points. Mistakes involving misplaced decimal points may lead to gross misinterpretations. They are a common sort of mistake and should be guarded against. Misplaced decimal places involve mistakes of such a rudimentary nature that the reader may feel they are too elementary to be mentioned here. However, a research report from a state university stated that during a year the military forces of the United States had consumed 8.7 per cent of the coffee available during that year. The figures from which the percentage was computed were 24 and 2,756 millions of pounds. The correct figure is 0.87 of one per cent.

A feature writer for a metropolitan newspaper, discussing the Navaho Indians, said, "The known Navaho death rate is 360 per 100,000." Stated in the usual fashion, this would be 3.6 per 1,000 or, roughly, one-third of the rate for the United States, which was 10.6 during the same year. Although the basic data from which the Navaho death rate was computed were of dubious value, it is known that the figure is much larger than that for the entire country. The feature writer not only misplaced a decimal (he had intended to say 3,600 per 100,000, which is 36 per 1,000), but may have made an arithmetic mistake as well.

It is of interest to note that a misplaced decimal always involves a serious misstatement, since the least mistake that can occur results in the incorrect figure being 10 times as large as it should be or one-tenth as large as it should be.

Computers seem most likely to misplace decimals (1) when large absolute numbers are involved or (2) when one of the absolute numbers is very large (or small) in relation to the other, resulting in a very large (or small) ratio. Two illustrations will suffice.

Over a period of years, the resources of a bank grew from $100,000 to $300,000,000. A newspaper stated that the growth was 3,000 per cent. Actually, the second figure is *3,000 times* the first figure, or *300,000 per cent* of it, and the growth was 299,900 per cent.

---

[9] Robert E. Chaddock, *Principles and Methods of Statistics*, Houghton Mifflin Co., Boston, 1925, pp. 13–14.

An advertisement once pointed out that more than 200,000,000 checks a day are paid in the United States, and that about 99.9995 per cent of them are good. Said the advertisement, "Only 1 out of 2,000 is dishonored." The percentage and the ratio are in disagreement. Correspondence revealed that about 1,000 checks per day were bad, so that the ratio should have been "1 out of 200,000."

Arithmetic mistakes. One year, a prominent government official stated, according to newspapers, that Russian Communists dominated 800,000,000 persons, and compared this figure with the United States population of about 150,000,000. The ratio, he is alleged to have said, was 7 to 1. The correct ratio is 5.33 to 1.

Improper averaging of percentages and ratios. The occasional necessity for averaging percentages and ratios calls for mention of a pitfall and for consideration of the proper procedure. Consider the figures of Table 3.1. It is desired to know the average percentage or ratio of males per 100 females for the eight states of the Mountain Division of the United States for 1960. If we add the eight percentages or ratios listed and divide by eight, we get $820.5 \div 8 = 102.5$. This figure, however, does not correctly represent the situation; the eight percentages or ratios were calculated from different bases and therefore should be weighted accordingly. The easiest procedure for obtaining the correct percentage or ratio consists of totaling the male population for the eight states, totaling the female population of the eight states, and dividing the first figure by the second. This yields a figure of 101.2. The same result could also be obtained by averaging the eight figures provided each is weighted according to the base from which it has been calculated. The procedure of multiplying each figure by its base, summing the results, and dividing by the sum of the base figures (or weights) is essentially the same as the method just used. The result, however, is a little less accurate, since each percentage figure or ratio has been rounded. The error involved in rounding a given percentage is magnified when the percentage is multiplied. But since some percentages are understated and some are overstated, there is a *tendency* for these errors to counterbalance. Under certain conditions, it may be appropriate to average percentages without weighting them according to their bases. This is discussed on pages 163 and 164.

CHAPTER 8

The Frequency Distribution

One method of organizing and summarizing statistical data consists in the formation of a frequency distribution. In this device the various items of a series are classified into groups and the number of items falling into each group is stated. A frequency distribution is shown in Table 8.3. Sometimes the user of statistics will find frequency distributions already constructed in the publications to which he may refer; sometimes he will construct his own frequency distribution from unclassified data. We shall begin our discussion of the frequency distribution by first considering the appearance of the raw or unclassified data.

RAW DATA

The unclassified data from which a frequency distribution might be made may appear as do the data of Table 8.1. Here we have the grades received for the four-year course by 409 liberal arts students of the 1965 graduating class of Rutgers—The State University (Newark branch). The arrangement of the grades is random and we have omitted the names in order to save space. Another illustration of raw data, from which a frequency distribution might be constructed, is the payroll of a factory. The employees on the payroll may be listed alphabetically by name; by employee number; by departments, and then by name or number; by seniority; or in some other convenient order. Considering the grades of the students as shown in Table 8.1, it is apparent that very little information is forthcoming unless the figures are rearranged.[1] When the data are listed as in Table 8.1, it is a tedious task to find even the lowest grade and the highest grade. It is even more difficult to ascertain around what value the grades tend to concentrate, or if, indeed, they do show such a concentration. These and other steps in analysis are facilitated by rearranging and summarizing the data.

---

[1] Grades were converted from 1.0, 2.0, 3.0, etc., to 100.0, 90.0, 80.0, etc.

TABLE 8.1

Grades Received for the Four-Year Course by 409 Liberal Arts Students of the 1965 Graduating Class of Rutgers—The State University

86.1	83.2	84.1	91.1	84.3	93.6	79.7	87.4	95.0
83.3	92.9	82.4	82.6	89.8	81.0	89.5	83.1	82.5
81.5	78.0	87.2	89.8	81.3	84.8	91.0	92.2	90.2
89.7	84.0	80.0	84.8	86.3	88.7	84.6	81.3	87.6
85.0	79.4	94.3	83.5	79.8	82.2	87.1	88.8	78.9
78.6	86.8	82.8	80.7	96.5	83.7	77.8	81.2	84.1
88.5	77.7	84.4	90.6	80.2	90.2	98.3	86.1	90.6
80.6	90.2	85.3	79.1	86.6	80.9	86.2	83.0	86.4
83.5	84.3	91.7	84.0	78.1	88.1	79.6	89.8	81.5
94.6	81.3	88.4	81.0	89.6	81.8	83.2	85.2	83.8
81.1	78.6	83.1	92.8	76.9	83.7	92.0	80.6	94.2
86.2	87.9	81.7	83.8	87.4	85.6	91.8	88.7	79.9
79.7	86.3	89.5	80.9	81.3	94.3	86.6	81.0	90.9
88.7	82.3	84.1	87.6	83.3	81.2	80.2	93.0	82.7
78.9	92.2	80.3	86.4	90.5	87.3	84.0	82.4	86.0
82.5	79.8	88.0	78.3	84.6	82.1	88.8	85.4	88.0
87.2	83.0	82.0	93.9	81.5	87.7	79.3	96.2	82.3
90.7	87.0	83.4	91.8	88.2	79.4	85.8	83.6	85.0
80.2	81.4	90.2	84.8	79.7	92.2	77.4	86.5	89.5
84.7	87.7	80.9	86.2	85.0	82.8	87.7	83.1	91.8
87.5	78.7	86.0	79.9	90.7	83.9	79.2	88.4	84.5
82.7	94.2	83.1	88.5	79.5	86.2	93.8	85.1	94.6
84.0	79.6	97.5	80.6	87.9	77.9	84.2	81.3	81.1
88.6	83.2	80.0	83.3	83.1	88.9	78.6	87.6	86.3
79.3	86.6	85.2	89.8	77.4	84.1	83.7	81.2	89.9
91.4	88.0	79.8	78.5	86.8	83.0	88.7	84.3	84.2
89.8	81.9	85.0	84.5	91.5	84.9	82.9	91.8	91.4
85.1	77.9	87.8	76.5	95.2	91.7	78.9	86.6	87.4
83.8	90.3	81.4	86.8	82.5	89.7	84.7	84.0	84.6
81.8	85.3	92.0	82.3	80.1	86.1	87.0	93.9	83.3
96.7	79.9	82.5	84.0	89.5	79.3	79.6	83.4	88.5
82.2	84.2	85.6	84.3	91.4	85.0	89.6	80.5	84.8
86.1	89.0	77.6	90.9	83.4	78.3	81.4	87.4	82.6
87.4	80.7	86.1	80.4	86.6	93.0	86.0	82.7	96.7
79.6	82.4	94.6	86.5	79.2	83.7	91.6	87.9	83.2
90.2	85.0	83.5	91.8	88.5	82.0	90.3	85.3	86.4
86.2	78.8	87.2	83.2	77.7	88.3	78.8	79.8	87.1
81.0	88.5	79.5	90.2	85.2	81.2	84.5	92.5	81.9
86.8	81.1	84.6	86.3	80.9	85.9	87.5	83.1	89.2
81.3	93.5	83.0	76.9	96.0	80.1	81.0	86.6	80.7
85.6	79.4	87.4	83.7	82.8	84.1	90.7	82.3	85.5
92.5	86.4	80.3	85.3	79.8	87.9	81.7	87.7	...
81.4	84.5	83.1	89.4	86.9	79.6	85.0	82.1	...
84.8	82.3	87.8	78.5	83.1	89.3	80.3	90.2	...
87.1	86.3	79.7	86.6	81.0	79.3	87.3	83.0	...
85.9	93.9	82.8	82.6	87.7	86.1	80.7	84.0	...

Data from Registrar's Office, Rutgers—The State University.   Grades were converted from 1.0, 2.0, 3.0, etc., to 100.0, 90.0, 80.0, etc.

THE ARRAY

In Table 8.2, the students' grades have been rearranged in descending order. Such an arrangement (whether ascending or descending) is called an *array*. It arranges the items in order of magnitude. We have not summarized; that will be done when we construct the frequency distribution. A consideration of the array puts us in a position to learn something from the data. First, the array enables us to see at once the range of the grades, which varied from 76.5 to 98.3. Second, it may also be observed that there is a concentration of grades between 83 and 85. This will be more clearly seen when we examine the frequency distribution and consider measures of central tendency. Third, a somewhat more extended examination gives us a rough idea of the distribution of the grades. We may observe, for example, that there are few grades below 78 or above 96. This particular feature of the series will be much more readily studied when we have the frequency distribution. Fourth, it may be noticed that the figures show a fair degree of continuity. If the grades are expressed as whole percentages, all consecutive values from 77 to 98 are represented. If we consider the figures as shown, to one decimal place, we may observe that within the range of 79.0 to 92.0 inclusive, which includes 350 of the 409 students, 118 of the possible 131 values are to be found. If the grades had been for a larger number of students, this tendency would have been more marked.

The array, however, is a cumbersome form of the data. Furthermore, it is troublesome to construct, because of the necessity of rearranging all the items. One fairly satisfactory method of constructing an array consists of recording the figures on small cards and sorting the cards. Of course, if the data are punched on mechanical tabulating cards, the construction of an array is simple.

When studying grades, we may frequently want to make an array. Some institutions publish each year a roll of the graduating class, listing the names and standings of the students in order from highest to lowest.

If we are interested in a campaign to raise funds for a hospital or community chest, it might be very useful (for publicity purposes, for example) to list the individual gifts in descending order. It is obvious, however, that such a listing of 500 or 1,000 contributions would be cumbersome and of limited value. In many instances there is no particular advantage in making an array. It would be a waste of time for a concern to make an array of the amounts paid to its employees each month. There is not much reason why a bank should make an array of the daily balances of its many depositors. On the other hand, a student of vital statistics might find it very valuable in a study of birth rates to array the various cities in ascending or descending order and consider the reasons for the differences.

TABLE 8.2

Array of Grades Received for the Four-Year Course by 409 Liberal Arts Students of the 1965 Graduating Class of Rutgers— The State University

98.3	91.0	88.5	86.8	85.2	84.0	82.7	81.1	79.6
97.5	90.9	88.5	86.8	85.2	84.0	82.7	81.1	79.6
96.7	90.9	88.5	86.6	85.2	83.9	82.6	81.1	79.6
96.7	90.7	88.4	86.6	85.1	83.8	82.6	81.0	79.5
96.5	90.7	88.4	86.6	85.1	83.8	82.6	81.0	79.5
96.2	90.7	88.3	86.6	85.0	83.8	82.5	81.0	79.4
96.0	90.6	88.2	86.6	85.0	83.7	82.5	81.0	79.4
95.2	90.6	88.1	86.6	85.0	83.7	82.5	81.0	79.4
95.0	90.5	88.0	86.6	85.0	83.7	82.5	81.0	79.3
94.6	90.3	88.0	86.5	85.0	83.7	82.4	80.9	79.3
94.6	90.3	88.0	86.5	85.0	83.7	82.4	80.9	79.3
94.6	90.2	87.9	86.4	85.0	83.6	82.4	80.9	79.3
94.3	90.2	87.9	86.4	84.9	83.5	82.3	80.9	79.2
94.3	90.2	87.9	86.4	84.8	83.5	82.3	80.7	79.2
94.2	90.2	87.9	86.4	84.8	83.5	82.3	80.7	79.1
94.2	90.2	87.8	86.3	84.8	83.4	82.3	80.7	78.9
93.9	90.2	87.8	86.3	84.8	83.4	82.3	80.7	78.9
93.9	90.2	87.7	86.3	84.8	83.4	82.2	80.6	78.9
93.9	89.9	87.7	86.3	84.7	83.3	82.2	80.6	78.8
93.8	89.8	87.7	86.3	84.7	83.3	82.1	80.6	78.8
93.6	89.8	87.7	86.2	84.6	83.3	82.1	80.5	78.7
93.5	89.8	87.7	86.2	84.6	83.3	82.0	80.4	78.6
93.0	89.8	87.6	86.2	84.6	83.2	82.0	80.3	78.6
93.0	89.8	87.6	86.2	84.6	83.2	81.9	80.3	78.6
92.9	89.7	87.6	86.2	84.5	83.2	81.9	80.3	78.5
92.8	89.7	87.5	86.1	84.5	83.2	81.8	80.2	78.5
92.5	89.6	87.5	86.1	84.5	83.2	81.8	80.2	78.3
92.5	89.6	87.4	86.1	84.5	83.1	81.7	80.2	78.3
92.2	89.5	87.4	86.1	84.4	83.1	81.7	80.1	78.1
92.2	89.5	87.4	86.1	84.3	83.1	81.5	80.1	78.0
92.2	89.5	87.4	86.1	84.3	83.1	81.5	80.0	77.9
92.0	89.5	87.4	86.0	84.3	83.1	81.5	80.0	77.9
92.0	89.4	87.4	86.0	84.3	83.1	81.4	79.9	77.8
91.8	89.3	87.3	86.0	84.2	83.1	81.4	79.9	77.7
91.8	89.2	87.3	85.9	84.2	83.1	81.4	79.9	77.7
91.8	89.0	87.2	85.9	84.2	83.0	81.4	79.8	77.6
91.8	88.9	87.2	85.8	84.1	83.0	81.3	79.8	77.4
91.8	88.8	87.2	85.6	84.1	83.0	81.3	79.8	77.4
91.7	88.8	87.1	85.6	84.1	83.0	81.3	79.8	76.9
91.7	88.7	87.1	85.6	84.1	83.0	81.3	79.8	76.9
91.6	88.7	87.1	85.5	84.1	82.9	81.3	79.7	76.5
91.5	88.7	87.0	85.4	84.0	82.8	81.3	79.7	...
91.4	88.7	87.0	85.3	84.0	82.8	81.2	79.7	...
91.4	88.6	86.9	85.3	84.0	82.8	81.2	79.7	...
91.4	88.5	86.8	85.3	84.0	82.8	81.2	79.6	...
91.1	88.5	86.8	85.3	84.0	82.7	81.2	79.6	...

THE FREQUENCY DISTRIBUTION

The array of Table 8.2 rearranged the students' grades. The frequency distribution of Table 8.3 summarizes the grades into 12 groups or classes.

TABLE 8.3

Frequency Distribution of Grades Received for the Four-Year Course by 409 Liberal Arts Students of the 1965 Graduating Class of Rutgers—The State University

Grade	Number of students
75.0–76.9	3
77.0–78.9	23
79.0–80.9	52
81.0–82.9	61
83.0–84.9	74
85.0–86.9	61
87.0–88.9	53
89.0–90.9	35
91.0–92.9	23
93.0–94.9	15
95.0–96.9	7
97.0–98.9	2
Total	409

It is obvious that the frequency distribution does not show the details given in the array, but much is gained by the summarization. We can see that the lowest grade is not below 75 and that the highest grade is not quite 99; we cannot ascertain the exact values of the highest and lowest grades as we did from the array. The concentration of grades in the neighborhood of 83–85 is apparent at a glance. If we draw a curve of the frequency distribution, as in Chart 8.1, we can visualize the data readily and we may make comparisons with other series, as discussed in a later section of this chapter. Having classified the data, we are in a position to make rapid computations of certain values (discussed in the following chapters) which will assist us in describing and analyzing the data.

When an array is available, the frequency distribution may be made by merely counting the items. It is not advisable, however, to make an array solely for the purpose of making the frequency distribution, because too great an amount of time is required to construct the array.

If the data are in unorganized form, as in Table 8.1, we may construct a frequency distribution by a scoring device similar to that shown in Chapter 2. Another method of handling the figures consists of making an entry form such as that of Table 8.4. This is less laborious than making an array and has certain advantages over the scoring procedure. The advantages of the entry form are: (1) we can scan the columns to see if any item is incorrectly entered; (2) we can total the items entered and check this total against the total of the unclassified data; (3) if we should decide that we want classes of 1 per cent or 3 per cent instead of 2 per cent, we can re-form our frequency distribution with little effort; (4) as will be shown in the next chapter, the entry form enables us to find out

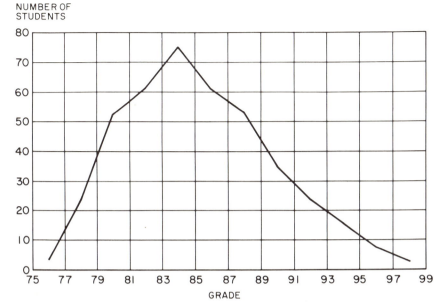

NUMBER OF
STUDENTS

GRADE

Chart 8.1. Grades Received for the Four-Year Course by 409 Liberal Arts Students of the 1965 Graduating Class of Rutgers—The State University. Data of Table 8.3.

how closely the mid-value of a class agrees with the average of the items in that class. If desired, the classes used in the entry form may be narrower than we think we shall want for the frequency distribution. These classes may then be readily combined into wider ones, using whatever interval and whatever class limits seem advisable.

All the class intervals of the frequency distribution of Table 8.3 are 2 per cent. Charting and computations are facilitated when the class intervals are all the same. Whenever possible, therefore, frequency distributions should be constructed with uniform class intervals. This, however, is not always practicable. Table 8.5 shows a frequency distribution which has non-uniform class intervals. In this instance the result is to give more detailed information for the secretaries having lower earnings.

Selecting the number of classes. No hard-and-fast rule can be given as to the number of classes into which a frequency distribution should be divided. If there are too many classes, many of them will contain only a few frequencies and the distribution may show irregularities which are not attributable to the behavior of the variable being measured. If there are too few classes, so many frequencies will be crowded into a class as to cause much information to be lost. The number of classes to use depends partly upon the nature of the data (as will be noted for meal checks in the next section), and partly upon the number of frequencies in the series. The greater the number of fre-

TABLE 8.4

Entry Form for Grades Received for the Four-Year Course by 409 Liberal Arts Students of the 1965 Graduating Class of Rutgers—The State University

75.0–76.9	77.0–78.9	79.0–80.9	81.0–82.9	83.0–84.9	85.0–86.9	87.0–88.9	89.0–90.9	91.0–92.9	93.0–94.9	95.0–96.9	97.0–98.9
76.5	78.6	80.6	81.5	83.3	86.1	88.5	89.7	91.4	94.6	96.7	97.5
76.9	78.9	79.7	81.1	83.5	85.0	88.7	90.7	92.5	94.2	96.5	98.3
76.9	78.0	80.2	82.5	84.7	86.2	87.2	89.8	92.9	93.5	95.2	
	77.7	79.3	82.7	84.0	85.1	87.5	90.2	92.2	93.9	96.0	
	78.6	79.6	81.8	83.8	86.1	88.6	90.2	91.7	94.3	96.2	
	78.7	79.4	82.2	84.8	86.2	87.4	90.3	92.0	94.6	95.0	
	77.9	79.8	81.0	83.2	86.8	87.1	89.0	91.1	93.9	96.7	
	78.8	79.6	81.3	84.0	85.6	87.9	89.5	92.8	93.6		
	77.6	79.9	81.4	84.3	85.9	87.0	90.2	91.8	94.3		
	78.3	80.7	81.3	83.0	86.8	87.7	89.8	91.8	93.0		
	78.5	79.4	82.3	83.2	86.3	88.0	90.6	91.5	93.8		
	78.5	80.0	81.4	84.2	86.6	88.5	89.8	91.4	93.0		
	78.1	80.3	81.9	84.5	85.3	87.2	90.2	92.2	93.9		
	77.4	80.9	82.4	84.1	85.0	88.4	89.4	91.7	94.2		
	77.7	80.0	81.1	84.4	86.4	88.0	89.8	91.0	94.6		
	77.9	79.8	82.3	83.1	86.3	87.8	89.6	92.0			
	78.3	79.5	82.4	84.1	85.3	87.2	90.5	91.8			
	77.8	80.3	82.8	83.4	86.0	87.4	90.7	91.6			
	77.4	79.7	81.7	83.1	85.2	87.8	89.5	92.2			
	78.6	80.7	82.0	83.5	85.0	87.6	90.2	91.8			
	78.9	79.1	81.4	84.6	85.6	88.5	89.7	92.5			
	78.8	80.9	82.5	83.0	86.1	87.4	89.3	91.8			
	78.9	79.9	82.8	83.1	86.4	88.2	89.5	91.4			
		80.6	82.6	84.8	86.2	87.9	89.6				
		80.4	81.0	83.5	86.8	88.5	90.3				
		79.8	82.3	84.0	86.5	87.7	90.7				
		80.2	82.6	83.8	86.3	88.7	89.8				
		79.7	81.3	84.8	85.3	88.1	90.2				
		79.5	81.3	83.3	86.6	87.3	90.2				
		80.1	81.5	84.5	86.3	87.7	90.6				
		79.2	82.5	84.0	86.6	88.9	90.9				
		80.9	82.8	83.3	85.0	88.3	89.5				
		79.8	81.0	83.2	86.8	87.9	89.9				
		80.9	81.0	83.7	86.6	87.1	89.2				
		79.4	82.2	84.3	85.2	88.8					
		79.3	81.8	83.3	86.9	87.7					
		80.1	81.2	84.6	85.6	88.7					
		79.6	82.1	83.1	86.2	87.0					
		79.3	82.8	83.4	86.1	87.5					
		79.7	82.0	83.1	85.0	87.3					
		79.6	81.2	84.8	85.9	87.4					
		80.2	82.9	83.7	86.1	88.8					
		79.3	81.4	83.7	86.2	88.7					
		79.2	81.0	83.9	86.6	88.4					
		79.6	81.7	84.1	85.8	87.6					
		80.3	81.3	83.0	86.0	87.4					
		80.7	81.2	84.9	85.0	87.9					
		80.6	81.0	83.7	86.1	87.7					
		80.5	82.4	84.1	85.2	87.6					
		79.8	81.3	84.6	85.4	88.0					
		79.9	81.2	83.2	86.5	87.4					
		80.7	82.7	84.0	85.1	88.5					
			82.3	84.2	86.6	87.1					
			82.1	83.7	85.3						
			82.5	84.7	86.6						
			81.5	84.5	86.4						
			82.7	83.1	86.0						
			82.3	83.0	85.0						
			81.1	83.6	86.3						
			82.6	83.1	86.4						
			81.9	84.3	85.5						
				84.0							
				83.4							
				83.1							
				83.0							
				84.0							
				84.1							
				83.8							
				84.5							
				84.2							
				84.6							
				83.3							
				84.8							
				83.2							

quencies, the more classes we may have.   The regularity with which the frequencies are distributed within the range of values under consideration is also a determining factor.   The more regular the distribution of the frequencies, the more classes we may use, since data having a high degree of regularity may be divided into a large number of classes without showing unwarranted gaps and irregularities in the frequencies.   In general, it might be said that fewer than 6 or 8 classes should rarely be used, and that more than 16 classes would be useful only for working with extensive data.   For illustrative purposes, 12 classes were used in Table 8.3.   When the number of classes has been determined, the range of values for the entire distribution indicates the class interval to be used.

TABLE 8.5

Average Straight-Time Weekly Earnings of 7,011 Female Secretaries in Boston, Massachusetts, October 1964

Weekly earnings	Number of women	Frequency densities, number of women per $5.00 of earnings
$ 50 but less than $ 55	1	1
55 but less than 60	9	9
60 but less than 65	107	107
65 but less than 70	167	167
70 but less than 75	461	461
75 but less than 80	517	517
80 but less than 85	620	620
85 but less than 90	786	786
90 but less than 100	1,796	898
100 but less than 110	1,297	648.5
110 but less than 120	728	364
120 but less than 130	291	145.5
130 but less than 145	179	59.7
145 or more	52	. . .
Total..........	7,011	. . .

Data from United States Bureau of Labor Statistics, *Occupational Wage Survey*, Boston, Massachusetts, December 1964, p. 7.

Selecting class limits.   It was pointed out in Chapter 4 that the mid-value of each class is used to represent the class.   The mid-values of the classes are made use of not only when charting the frequency distribution, but also in making various computations to be discussed in later chapters.   If the limits of each class are not clearly indicated, the mid-value, which is the average of the upper and lower limits, cannot be properly determined.   The adequacy of the mid-value assumption will be discussed more fully in Chapter 9.   It is important at this point to make clear that, when a frequency distribution is being constructed, the class limits should be so chosen that the mid-value of each class will coincide, so far as possible, with any values around which the data tend to be concentrated.

Suppose that measurements are made of the academic standing of a large group of college freshmen upon a numerical scale ranging from 0 to 100. The data could be expected to be graduated fairly smoothly from, say, 50 to nearly 100. There would be students rating 88.0 and others 89.0; in addition, there would be still others falling between these two values. If a large enough group were to be measured, the minuteness of the variations between 88.0 and 89.0 would be limited only by the accuracy of the measuring instrument (in this case, the grading system). There would not be a series of values around which the frequencies would tend to concentrate, and the problem mentioned at the end of the preceding paragraph would not arise.

On the other hand, consider the meal checks of a cafeteria, many (but not all) of which are a multiple of 5 cents. In this instance, the class intervals should be written 8–12 cents, 13–17 cents, 18–22 cents, and so forth, thus giving mid-values of 10 cents, 15 cents, 20 cents, and so on, which coincide with the concentration points.

The data of freshmen grades and the ratings of the liberal arts graduates are illustrations of what is termed a *continuous* variable, since the values are capable of infinitely small variations from each other. Heights and weights of people are also continuous variables. Length of life is another illustration. The data of cafeteria meal checks are illustrative of a *discrete* or *discontinuous* variable, since the values differ from each other by finite amounts—in this case, one cent. A discrete variable need not show the concentrations which were present in the meal-check data. For example, if many workmen are employed at similar tasks and are paid on a piece-rate basis (that is, upon the basis of amount produced) it is quite possible that there may be individuals receiving $161.21, $161.22, $161.23, and so forth, for a week's work. Although piece rates might be, and often are, in fractions of a cent, the weekly payment must be in terms of whole cents.

The foregoing suggests an important consideration; namely, that we are not so much concerned with the fact that a variable is discrete as we are with the fact that the data may be *broken* and that there are inherent gaps and concentrations in the actual data in hand. Such a situation often occurs when dealing with salaries. One organization with several hundred employees might pay salaries ranging from about $5,200 to more than $40,000 per year. There probably was not an evenly graduated distribution between these limits. The gaps between adjacent values may range from $100 to $5,000, and there may be pronounced concentrations at various customary salaries such as $6,000, $7,000, $7,500, $8,000, $10,000, and so on. The selection of class limits for a distribution of this type presents great difficulty. Often it is not possible to adjust the mid-values to coincide with all concentration points. An approximate adjustment must then suffice.

The fact that we may be dealing with a continuous variable does not warrant us selecting class limits blindly. If data are being collected concerning weights of individuals, reported to the *nearest* pound, persons reported as weighing 142 pounds would vary between 141.5 pounds and 142.5 pounds; as a group, they would average about 142 pounds. Suppose, however, that weight is reported to the *last* full pound. In that event, persons reported as weighing 142 pounds would vary between exactly 142 pounds and just under 143 pounds; as a group, they would average about 142.5 pounds. Let us assume that a frequency distribution with class interval of 3 pounds is to be formed. If weights have been reported to the nearest pound, it is correct to write class intervals "142–144, 145–147, 148–150," and so on, with mid-values of 143, 146, 149, and so forth. If, however, weights have been reported to the last full pound, the above is incorrect, but it is correct to write "142 and under 145, 145 and under 148, 148 and under 151," and so on, with mid-values of 143.5, 146.5, 149.5, and so forth.

Sometimes, when dealing with a continuous variable, the classes are written so that the limits appear to overlap. For example, the data of students' grades could have been classified 76.0–78.0, 78.0–80.0, 80.0–82.0, and so on. When this is done, frequencies which fall on a class limit are divided between the two classes, usually resulting in some fractional frequencies in the distribution.[2] A frequency distribution using these classes may be easily constructed from the array of Table 8.2 or the entry form of Table 8.4. Overlapping class limits are not often used for data of grades.

Curves of frequency distributions. The graphic representation of a frequency distribution was discussed in Chapter 4. Although a frequency distribution may be represented by either a column diagram or a curve, it is usual to employ the latter device. (We shall make use of the column diagram in Chart 8.5 and in Chapter 23.) One advantage of the curve is that two or more curves may readily be drawn on the same axes for purposes of comparison. In any event, the first step in the analysis of a frequency distribution should be the construction of a chart, for it will tell us at a glance with which of the following types of distributions we are dealing.

Chart 8.1, showing the graphic appearance of the data of students' grades, is not symmetrical, but is slightly skewed to the right. (Skewness

---

[2] See F. E. Croxton, *Elementary Statistics with Applications in Medicine and the Biological Sciences*, Dover Publications, Inc., New York, 1959, pp. 41–49.

is discussed in Chapter 10.) Many frequency distribution curves encountered in the social sciences are asymmetrical and frequently are skewed to the right. Only rarely do we find a curve skewed to the left.

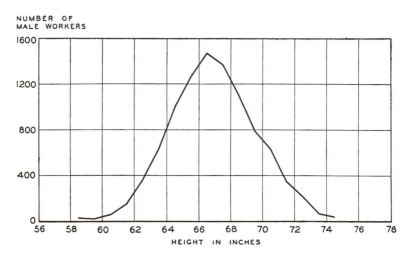

Chart 8.2. Heights of 9,552 Male Industrial Workers. Data from *A Health Study of Ten Thousand Male Industrial Workers*, p. 59. United States Public Health Service, Public Health Bulletin No. 162.

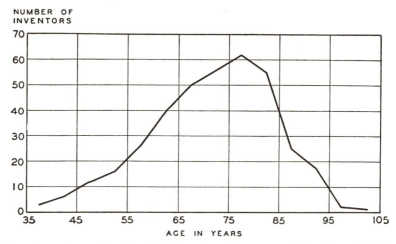

Chart 8.3. Age at Death of 371 American Inventors. Data from "Bio-Social Characteristics of American Inventors," by Sanford Winston, *American Sociological Review*, Vol. 2, No. 6, pp. 837–849.

Biological and anthropometrical series (especially those involving linear measurements, such as height, rather than two- or three-dimension measurements, such as waist circumference or weight) frequently yield curves which are roughly symmetrical. Such a series is shown in Chart 8.2, which pictures the height distribution of a large group of male industrial workers.

A curve which is skewed to the left is shown in Chart 8.3, which depicts the age at death of 371 American inventors. As pointed out in Chapter 10, where the amount of skewness in this series is ascertained, the skewness may be characteristic of the variable or may be due to the fact that nearly one-fifth of the inventors included in the study were born before 1800.

The curve of Chart 8.4 indicates the length of time during which cars were parked in Albuquerque, New Mexico, and shows a great many cars parked for short periods and generally smaller numbers parked for longer lengths of time. Curves having this characteristic "reverse J" shape may be encountered occasionally.

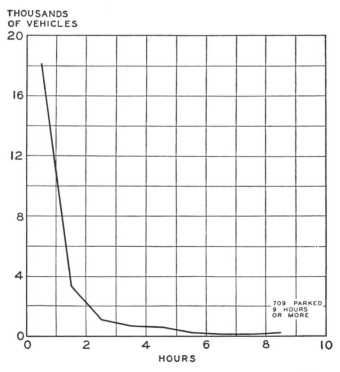

Chart 8.4. Parking Time of Motor Vehicles in Albu-querque, New Mexico. The data are from the Automotive Safety Foundation.

Graphic representation when the class intervals are unequal.
For some frequency distributions, it is not feasible to maintain the same class interval throughout. The distribution of Table 8.5 has eight classes of $5.00, four classes of $10.00, one class of $15.00, and one class of indeterminate width. It would not have been desirable to have used $5.00 class intervals throughout, since that would have necessitated 19 classes to cover the range from $50.00 to $145.00. This would be too many classes to be useful and would provide a more detailed breakdown than needed for the upper ranges of the series. Class intervals of $10.00 throughout would not have been desirable either, since details concerning secretaries having earnings of less than $90.00 per week would have been lost.

To draw a suitable chart of the data of Table 8.5, it is necessary to make adjustments for the varying class intervals. The class "$90.00 but less than $100.00" is twice as wide as the classes which precede it. We do not know how many of the 1,796 secretaries earned $90.00 but less than $95.00 a week and how many earned $95.00 but less than $100.00 a week. We can say, however, that on the average there were 898 secretaries in each of the two halves of the class "$90.00 but less than $100.00." Adjustments of this sort have been made in the last column of Table 8.5, where the frequencies are stated per $5.00 of earnings. These are frequency densities.

The distribution of secretaries' earnings may now be plotted in terms of the frequency densities, as in Chart 8.5. It is not possible to make an estimate of the width of the last class interval in Table 8.5, so no adjustment of the frequencies of that class has been made. Notice on the chart

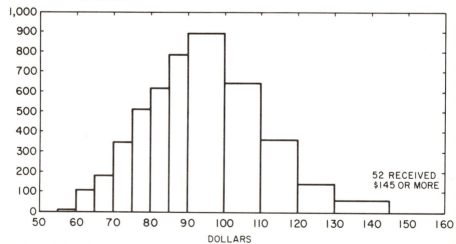

NUMBER OF WOMEN
PER $5.00 OF EARNINGS

Chart 8.5. Frequency Densities of Average Straight-Time Weekly Earnings of 7,011 Female Secretaries in Boston, Massachusetts, October 1964. Data from Table 8.5.

how the reader's attention was called to the presence of these 52 secretaries. Alternatively, the data of frequency densities could have been shown by a curve instead of a column diagram, and this was done in Chart 4.25. However, the column diagram makes it easier for the reader to note the changing class width.

Graphic comparison of frequency distributions.   Table 8.6 shows two frequency distributions, one giving the straight-time weekly earnings of 619 class B switchboard operators, the other presenting the straight-time weekly earnings of 90 general stenographers. Both series are for females only. If the two distributions dealt with approximately the same number of women, we could merely plot two frequency curves on the same grid and study their outlines. The result of doing this for the two series of Table 8.6 is shown in Chart 8.6. The comparison is not particularly illuminating, because of the sharply different absolute data involved. However, if each frequency is expressed as a percentage of the total of which it is a part, we obtain the percentage frequency distributions, which are also given in Table 8.6. Plotting the two percentage frequency distributions, as in Chart 8.7, enables us to make a graphic comparison of the two series, which is no longer complicated because of the different number of items. The relative importance of all of the various classes may now readily be seen.

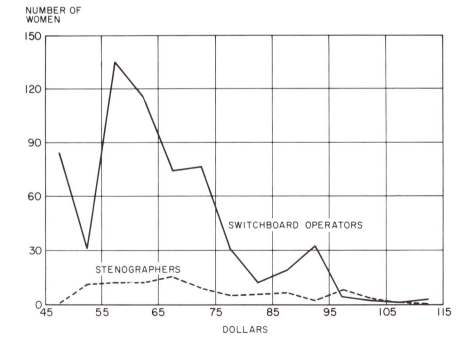

NUMBER OF WOMEN

Chart 8.6. Average Straight-Time Weekly Earnings of 619 Switchboard Operators, Class B in Washington, D.C., and of 90 General Stenographers in Sioux Falls, South Dakota, October 1964.   Data from Table 8.6.

The comparison of the two series of Table 8.6 was facilitated because the class intervals were the same. If two series, expressed in the same units but having different class intervals, are to be compared graphically, we may plot frequency densities per unit (that is, per dollar, per pound, or whatever the unit may be). If the two series also differ appreciably in regard to the number of items involved, the areas under the two curves may be made the same by computing percentage frequencies and expressing the percentage frequencies as frequency densities.

Occasionally we wish the differences between the numbers of items in two series to be apparent, as in Charts 24.1–24.4, and in such a situation we do not use percentage frequencies. Frequency densities would, however, be used when needed, as in Charts 24.1, 24.3, and 24.4A.

TABLE 8.6

Average Straight-Time Weekly Earnings of 619 Switchboard Operators, Class B in Washington, D. C., and of 90 General Stenographers in Sioux Falls, South Dakota, October 1964

Weekly earnings	Number		Per cent of total	
	Switchboard operators	Stenog-raphers	Switchboard operators	Stenog-raphers
$ 45 but less than $ 50	84	0	13.6	0.0
50 but less than 55	31	11	5.0	12.2
55 but less than 60	135	12	21.8	13.3
60 but less than 65	115	12	18.6	13.3
65 but less than 70	73	15	11.8	16.7
70 but less than 75	77	8	12.4	8.9
75 but less than 80	31	5	5.0	5.6
80 but less than 85	13	5	2.1	5.6
85 but less than 90	18	7	2.9	7.8
90 but less than 95	32	3	5.2	3.3
95 but less than 100	4	8	0.6	8.9
100 but less than 105	2	3	0.3	3.3
105 but less than 110	1	1	0.2	1.1
110 but less than 115	3	0	0.5	0.0
Total..............	619	90	100.0	100.0

Data from U. S. Bureau of Labor Statistics, *Occupational Wage Survey*, Washington, D. C.—Maryland—Virginia, December 1964, p. 7, and *Occupational Wage Survey*, Sioux Falls, South Dakota, December 1964, p. 3.

When two frequency distributions are expressed in terms of different units (dollars, pounds, inches, and so on), a direct graphic comparison is not feasible, since there is no simple way in which the X-scales may be adjusted to each other. Certain computed values, to be discussed later, may be used to obtain effective numerical comparison.

Cumulative frequency distributions and the ogive. The data of Table 8.3 show the usual (non-cumulative) form of the frequency distribution and enable us to ascertain the number of students falling in each class. Sometimes, however, it may be useful to know how many or what proportion of students received less than certain stated grades, or to know how many or what proportion of students received specified grades or above. This information may be seen clearly in a cumulative

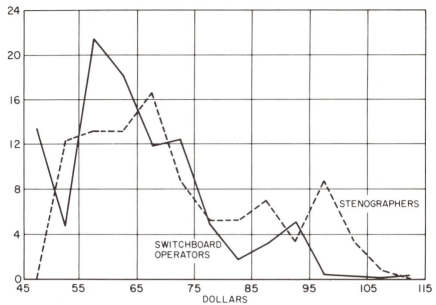

PER CENT
OF WOMEN

Chart 8.7. Percentage Distributions of Average Straight-Time Weekly Earnings of 619 Switchboard Operators, Class B in Washington, D.C. and of 90 General Stenographers in Sioux Falls, South Dakota, October 1964. Data from Table 8.6.

TABLE 8.7

Cumulative Distributions of Grades of the 1965 Liberal Arts Graduates of Rutgers—The State University

Grade	Number of students whose grades		Per cent of students whose grades	
	Fell below the upper limit of each class	Equaled or exceeded the lower limit of each class	Fell below the upper limit of each class	Equaled or exceeded the lower limit of each class
75.0–76.9	3	409	0.7	100.0
77.0–78.9	26	406	6.4	99.3
79.0–80.9	78	383	19.1	93.6
81.0–82.9	139	331	34.0	80.9
83.0–84.9	213	270	52.1	66.0
85.0–86.9	274	196	67.0	47.9
87.0–88.9	327	135	80.0	33.0
89.0–90.9	362	82	88.5	20.0
91.0–92.9	385	47	94.1	11.5
93.0–94.9	400	24	97.8	5.9
95.0–96.9	407	9	99.5	2.2
97.0–98.9	409	2	100.0	0.5

table such as Table 8.7. In this table the frequencies of Table 8.3 have been accumulated upon a "less than" basis and also upon an "or more" basis.

NUMBER OF
STUDENTS

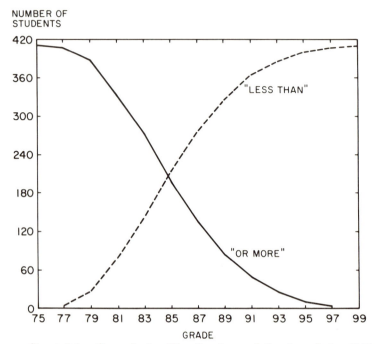

Chart 8.8. Cumulative Distributions of Grades of the 1965
Liberal Arts Graduates of Rutgers—The State University. Data
of Table 8.7.

When cumulative frequency distributions are drawn, the frequencies
are plotted opposite the appropriate class limits, resulting in curves such
as those shown in Chart 8.8. Such curves are called *ogives*.

Cumulative frequency tables and ogives are often used to present data
of wages and of hours of work. With reference to wages, they enable us
to ascertain how many (or what proportion) of a group receive less than a
subsistence level, standard level, or comfort level. Similarly, we can
ascertain the number or proportion receiving a subsistence level or more,
a standard level or more, and a comfort level or more. It is also possible
to ascertain what wage the lowest- (or highest-) paid 10, 25, 50, or other
per cent of the workers are receiving. With respect to hours of work, we
can see quickly the number or proportion working unusually long or short
hours.

If two cumulative frequency distributions are based upon nearly the
same number of items, their ogives may be plotted and compared in
absolute terms. If, however, the two series are based upon different
totals, the comparison must be based upon the percentage frequencies,
just as in the case of comparing two frequency distributions in non-
cumulative form, which was previously discussed.

CHAPTER 9

Measures of Central Tendency

We have seen how to construct a frequency distribution and how to draw a frequency curve. From either the classified data or the chart, it is obvious that there are certain values that are frequently present and others that occur less frequently. Most of the curves that we encounter are of the type that is very roughly "bell-shaped," as shown in Charts 8.1, 8.2, and 8.3. For such series as these charts represent, it is obvious that the more characteristic values are in the *central* part of the distributions. We therefore use the term *measures of central tendency* to identify the values which may be computed in an attempt to characterize this aspect of a frequency distribution. We shall discuss in this chapter the arithmetic mean, the median, the mode, and, briefly, the geometric mean and the harmonic mean.

In the following chapter we shall consider measures of dispersion, which refer to the spread of a distribution; measures of skewness, which measure the direction and amount of asymmetry; and measures of kurtosis, which indicate the degree of "peakedness" of a series.

THE ARITHMETIC MEAN

The arithmetic mean from ungrouped data. The arithmetic mean is in such constant everyday use that nearly all of us are familiar with the concept. Sometimes we refer to the arithmetic mean merely as "the average" or "the mean," but we always use the appropriate adjective when we are speaking of the geometric mean, the harmonic mean, or some other less usual mean.

The arithmetic mean of a series of items is obtained by adding the values of the items and dividing by the number of items. Suppose that, in a certain small city, carrots are selling for 8¢, 10¢, 11¢, and 12¢ a pound. The arithmetic mean of these four figures would be given by

$$\frac{8¢ + 10¢ + 11¢ + 12¢}{4} = \frac{41¢}{4} = 10.25¢.$$

If we let X_1, X_2, X_3, etc., indicate the various values; N, the number of items; and $\bar{X}$, the arithmetic mean, we have

$$\bar{X} = \frac{X_1 + X_2 + X_3 + \cdots + X_N}{N}.$$

Or, more briefly, using the summation symbol Σ, we may say

$$\bar{X} = \frac{\Sigma X}{N}.$$

The foregoing computation of the arithmetic mean involved no consideration of the fact that different quantities of carrots may have been sold at the various prices. When an arithmetic mean is computed in this fashion, it may be referred to as a *simple* arithmetic mean. It is not correct to refer to this mean as an *unweighted* arithmetic mean, since each of the prices was weighted equally. Let us proceed to compute a properly weighted arithmetic mean, considering the fact that there were sold 10,000 pounds of carrots at 8¢, 8,000 pounds at 10¢, 4,000 pounds at 11¢, and 1,000 pounds at 12¢. We now have

$$\bar{X} = \frac{(10,000 \times 8¢) + (8,000 \times 10¢) + (4,000 \times 11¢) + (1,000 \times 12¢)}{23,000}$$

$$= \frac{216,000¢}{23,000} = 9.39¢.$$

If we use the symbols f_1, f_2, f_3, etc., to indicate the numbers or frequencies associated with each value being averaged, we have

$$\bar{X} = \frac{f_1 X_1 + f_2 X_2 + f_3 X_3 + \cdots}{f_1 + f_2 + f_3 + \cdots} = \frac{\Sigma f X}{\Sigma f} = \frac{\Sigma f X}{N}.$$

Ordinarily an arithmetic mean is considered to be a weighted arithmetic mean, as just described, unless otherwise specified.

It should be noted that, although the arithmetic mean price of carrots is 9.39¢ per pound, no carrots were actually sold at this exact price per pound. The arithmetic mean must therefore be thought of as a computed value and not as a value which actually exists.

Properties of the arithmetic mean. One important property of the arithmetic mean is that the algebraic sum of the deviations of the various values from the mean equals zero. This is important, since it will enable us to develop a method for computing $\bar{X}$ which will save an appreciable amount of time when we are dealing with a frequency distribution. Let us consider a series of five values, 6, 8, 9, 11, 14, each one of which occurs but once. Then

$$\overline{X} = \frac{6 + 8 + 9 + 11 + 14}{5} = \frac{48}{5} = 9.6.$$

Now let us compute the deviation of each value from the arithmetic mean, $x_1 = X_1 - \overline{X}$, $x_2 = X_2 - \overline{X}$, $x_3 = X_3 - \overline{X}$, etc.   We have

X	x
6	-3.6
8	-1.6
9	$- .6$
11	$+1.4$
14	$+4.4$

It will be observed that $\Sigma x = 0$; this is always true for any series of values.[1]

If we compute the deviations d of the five items from some designated value which is not the arithmetic mean, the sum of these deviations Σd will not equal zero. If the designated value is less than the arithmetic mean, there will be too many positive deviations and the sum of the deviations will be greater than zero. If the designated value is greater than the arithmetic mean, there will be too many negative deviations and the sum of the deviations will be a negative quantity. Since *each* of the five (N) items has been compared to a designated number which is not the true mean, the sum of the deviations will fail to equal zero by an amount which is exactly five (N) times the amount by which the designated value deviates from the actual arithmetic mean. It is therefore possible to designate some value as an assumed mean $\overline{X}_d$, to determine the deviations from this designated value, and, by adding (algebraically) the necessary correction $\dfrac{\Sigma d}{N}$, to obtain the arithmetic mean.[2]   The process is illustrated in Table 9.1, where $\overline{X}_d$ is taken as 9.   Here it is observed that $\Sigma d = +3$. If we divide this figure by N, we see that $\overline{X}_d$ was too small by 0.6.   This is given by

$$\frac{\Sigma d}{N} = \frac{+3}{5} = +0.6.$$

---

[1] See Appendix S, section 9.1. If $\Sigma x = 0$, it is obvious that $\dfrac{\Sigma x}{N} = 0$. $\dfrac{\Sigma x}{N}$ is referred to as the "first moment about the mean," or merely as the "first moment." In the following chapter we shall have occasion to consider the second moment $\dfrac{\Sigma x^2}{N}$, the third moment $\dfrac{\Sigma x^3}{N}$, and the fourth moment $\dfrac{\Sigma x^4}{N}$.

[2] See Appendix S, section 9.2.

This is the correction to be added to the assumed mean; thus,

$$\bar{X} = \bar{X}_d + \frac{\Sigma d}{N} = 9 + \frac{3}{5} = 9.6,$$

which agrees exactly with $\bar{X}$ computed by adding the values and dividing by 5.

TABLE 9.1

*Calculation of the Arithmetic Mean, $\bar{X}$,
by Use of the Assumed Mean, $\bar{X}_d = 9$*

X	d	
6	−3	$\Sigma d = +3$
8	−1	$\bar{X} = \bar{X}_d + \dfrac{\Sigma d}{N}$
9	0	
11	+2	
14	+5	$= 9 + \dfrac{3}{5} = 9.6.$
	+3	

In the foregoing illustration, $\bar{X}_d$ was less than $\bar{X}$. Suppose we choose $\bar{X}_d$ as 13. The computations are shown in Table 9.2.

TABLE 9.2

*Calculation of the Arithmetic Mean, $\bar{X}$,
by Use of the Assumed Mean, $\bar{X}_d = 13$*

X	d	
6	−7	$\Sigma d = -17$
8	−5	$\bar{X} = \bar{X}_d + \dfrac{\Sigma d}{N}$
9	−4	
11	−2	
14	+1	$= 13 + \dfrac{-17}{5} = 9.6.$
	−17	

In this case, $\bar{X}_d$ was larger than $\bar{X}$, as is indicated by $\dfrac{\Sigma d}{N} = \dfrac{-17}{5} =$ −3.4. The result is, as before, $\bar{X} = 13 - 3.4 = 9.6$.

A second property of the arithmetic mean, which is of importance in connection with later discussions, is that the sum of the *squared* deviations, Σx^2, is *less* when the deviations are taken around $\bar{X}$ than when they are taken around any other value. This is demonstrated in Appendix S, Section 10.1.

The arithmetic mean from grouped data: long method. Table 9.3 shows the frequency distribution of the grades of the students, and it is desired to ascertain the value of $\bar{X}$ for the series. When dealing with a frequency distribution, we do not ordinarily have the original data from which the frequency distribution was made. When we do have the unclassified data (as in Table 8.1), we can obtain the value of the arithmetic mean most accurately by totaling the values and dividing by the number of items. When we have only the frequency distribution, we must compute the mean from the grouped data. Let us proceed to compute $\overline{X}$ for the frequency distribution of Table 9.3, and then compare our result with the arithmetic mean computed from the unclassified data.

In computing the arithmetic mean from a frequency distribution, we take the mid-value (sometimes called the *class mark*) of each class as representative of that class, multiply the various mid-values by their corresponding frequencies, total these products, and divide by the total number of items. Symbolically, if $X_1, X_2, X_3 \cdots$ represent the mid-values and $f_1, f_2, f_3 \cdots$ the frequencies, then

$$\overline{X} = \frac{f_1 X_1 + f_2 X_2 + f_3 X_3 + \cdots}{f_1 + f_2 + f_3 + \cdots} = \frac{\Sigma f X}{\Sigma f} = \frac{\Sigma f X}{N}.$$

The mid-value of a class is obtained by adding the upper and lower *limits* of the class and dividing by 2. For every frequency distribution, we must consider carefully what those limits are. For the distribution of Table 9.3, we might take the limits of the first class as 75.0 and 77.0,

TABLE 9.3

Computation of the Arithmetic Mean for Grades of the 1965 Liberal Arts Graduates of Rutgers— The State University by Use of the Expression

$$\overline{X} = \frac{\Sigma f X}{N}$$

Grade	Number of students f	Mid-value of class X	fX
75.0–76.9	3	75.95	227.85
77.0–78.9	23	77.95	1,792.85
79.0–80.9	52	79.95	4,157.40
81.0–82.9	61	81.95	4,998.95
83.0–84.9	74	83.95	6,212.30
85.0–86.9	61	85.95	5,242.95
87.0–88.9	53	87.95	4,661.35
89.0–90.9	35	89.95	3,148.25
91.0–92.9	23	91.95	2,114.85
93.0–94.9	15	93.95	1,409.25
95.0–96.9	7	95.95	671.65
97.0–98.9	2	97.95	195.90
Total	409	...	34,833.55

$$\overline{X} = \frac{\Sigma f X}{N} = \frac{34,833.55}{409} = 85.17.$$

giving a mid-value of 76.0. This would be correct if the grades had each been rounded to the *last completed* tenth, so that 75.0 included values ranging from exactly 75 to 75.099 $\cdots$, 76.1 included values from exactly 76.1 to 76.199 $\cdots$, and so on, instead of having been rounded to the *nearest* tenth, as was actually done. If rounding had been to the last completed tenth, the class should have been designated "75 and under 77." Since we are dealing with a continuous variable, the *limits* of such a class would be 75 and 77, and the mid-value 76. For the students' grades, rounding was to the nearest tenth, and the lowest value which could fall in the class "75.0–76.9" is 74.95, while the highest value is 76.9499 · · · . Thus, since the variable is continuous, the class limits are 74.95 and 76.95, and the mid-value is 75.95. The mid-values have been entered in Table 9.3 according to this procedure.

When a class is designated (for example) "32.00–33.99," the mid-value is actually 32.995. Many statisticians would, however, state the mid-value as 33.00, since the relative discrepancy is small. In determining the mid-values for a frequency distribution, it is important to know how the readings were rounded. When no information concerning the rounding is given in connection with the frequency distribution, it is probably best to assume that figures were rounded to the nearest unit given. For example, if a one-inch class is written "12.0–12.9 inches," consider the limits as 11.95 and 12.95 inches; if a five-pound class is written "10–14 pounds," consider the limits as 9.5 and 14.5 pounds. However, for discrete data, a $2 class "$10.00–$11.00" has the limits $10.00 and $11.99, and a $10 class "$70–$79" has the limits $70 and $79 if data were given only in whole dollars. A class should not be written "5 pounds but under 10 pounds" unless we mean exactly what we say; namely, that items in this class do not fall below 5 pounds and do not equal 10 pounds. If the classes for the students' grades were written 75.0–77.0, 77.0–79.0, and so on, and if cases falling on a class limit were divided between the two classes, as noted in Chapter 8, the mid-values would be 76.0, 78.0, and so on.

Considering the mid-values for the grades of students as discussed above, and using the expression $\overline{X} = \dfrac{\Sigma f X}{N}$, we find that the arithmetic mean is 85.17, as shown below Table 9.3. From the unclassified data of Table 8.1, let us compute the value of $\overline{X}$ to see how nearly the figure just obtained agrees with that value. If we total all of the individual grades and divide by 409, we have

$$\overline{X} = \frac{34,828.1}{409} = 85.15.$$

The two values for $\overline{X}$ vary slightly. It is unusual for them to be identical, but we can generally count on a difference of not more than a few per cent at most. The value of the arithmetic mean computed from a frequency distribution will generally be in close agreement with the arithmetic mean from the unclassified data if the variable is continuous and the distribution is symmetrical. If (1) the distribution is skewed or if

(2) the variable is discrete (or if the data are broken), or if both (1) and (2) are true, the agreement will be less close. Likewise, close agreement cannot be expected if the data contain irregularities because an unduly small sample was used.

Whenever lack of agreement between the two values for $\overline{X}$ is present, it is due to the inadequacy of the mid-value assumptions. It is almost always true that *none of the mid-values is actually the true concentration point of its class.* For groups to the *left* of the group of maximum frequency, the mid-value of a group is frequently *less* than the mean of that

TABLE 9.4

Comparison of the Class Mid-Values With the Arithmetic Mean for Each Class for the Liberal Arts Students' Grades

Grade	Number of students	Total in grades in each class (from Table 8.4)	Arithmetic mean for each class	Mid-value of each class
75.0–76.9	3	230.3	76.77	75.95
77.0–78.9	23	1,799.9	78.26	77.95
79.0–80.9	52	4,158.2	79.97	79.95
81.0–82.9	61	4,994.1	81.87	81.95
83.0–84.9	74	6,204.5	83.84	83.95
85.0–86.9	61	5,243.3	85.96	85.95
87.0–88.9	53	4,657.2	87.87	87.95
89.0–90.9	35	3,150.0	90.00	89.95
91.0–92.9	23	2,113.1	91.87	91.95
93.0–94.9	15	1,409.4	93.96	93.95
95.0–96.9	7	672.3	96.04	95.95
97.0–98.9	2	195.8	97.90	97.95
Total	409	34,828.1	85.15	...

group; while for groups to the *right* of the group of maximum frequency, the mid-value of a group frequently *exceeds* the mean of that group. Although all the mid-value assumptions are usually incorrect, there is a definite tendency for the errors to offset each other, provided the distribution is approximately symmetrical. For the data of the liberal arts students' grades, we have the unclassified data from which the frequency distribution was made and we can compute the arithmetic mean for each class and compare the class means and class mid-values. This has been done in Table 9.4, where it may be seen that for 3 of the first 5 classes the mid-value of each class is less than the class mean. However, for the last 6 classes, 3 of the mid-values exceed their class means and 3 of the mid-values are less than their class means.

The arithmetic mean from grouped data: short methods. In Tables 9.1 and 9.2 it was shown that we could assume a value $\overline{X}_d$ for the arithmetic mean and, making use of the fact that $\Sigma x = 0$, compute the necessary correction to obtain $\overline{X}$. This method will save us appreciable time in computing the mean from a frequency distribution. The expression for $\bar{X}$ is as before, except that the symbol f is introduced because of the frequencies in the various classes.   Thus,

$$\bar{X} = \bar{X}_d + \frac{\Sigma fd}{N}.$$

The selected value for $\bar{X}_d$ may be the mid-value of any class.   In Table 9.5 $\bar{X}_d$ has been taken as the mid-value of the fifth class, and the computations below the table show that $\bar{X} = 85.17$, the same as found by the longer method of Table 9.3.

TABLE 9.5

Computation of the Arithmetic Mean for Grades of the 1965 Liberal Arts Graduates of Rutgers— The State University by Use of the Expression

$$\bar{X} = \bar{X}_d + \frac{\Sigma fd}{N}$$

Grade	Number of students f	d	fd	
75.0–76.9	3	− 8	− 24	
77.0–78.9	23	− 6	−138	
79.0–80.9	52	− 4	−208	
81.0–82.9	61	− 2	−122	−492
83.0–84.9	74	0		
85.0–86.9	61	+ 2	+122	
87.0–88.9	53	+ 4	+212	
89.0–90.9	35	+ 6	+210	
91.0–92.9	23	+ 8	+184	
93.0–94.9	15	+10	+150	
95.0–96.8	7	+12	+ 84	
97.0–98.9	2	+14	+ 28	+990
Total	409	. . .	. . .	+498

$$\bar{X} = \bar{X}_d + \frac{\Sigma fd}{N} = 83.95 + \frac{498}{409},$$
$$= 83.95 + 1.218,$$
$$= 85.17.$$

It will be observed that all of the classes of Table 9.5 are of the same width.   When this is true, we may further shorten our computation of $\bar{X}$ by taking our deviations from $\bar{X}_d$ in *terms of class intervals, d',* a process sometimes referred to as "coding."   Our correction $\frac{\Sigma fd'}{N}$ will then be in terms of class intervals and must be multiplied by the class interval i before being algebraically added to $\bar{X}_d$.   For the arithmetic mean, then,

$$\bar{X} = \bar{X}_d + \left(\frac{\Sigma fd'}{N}\right) i.$$

The computation of $\bar{X}$ by this expression is shown in Table 9.6 and yields the same result as given in Tables 9.3 and 9.5. This method should always be used when a frequency distribution is made up of equal class intervals. The greater the number of classes and the greater the number of items included in a frequency distribution, the more time is saved by this procedure.

The arithmetic mean from grouped data having unequal class intervals. For a frequency distribution having unequal class intervals, the computation of $\bar{X}$ by the method shown in Table 9.6 would be

TABLE 9.6

Computation of the Arithmetic Mean for Grades of the 1965 Liberal Arts Graduates of Rutgers— The State University by Use of the Expression

$$\bar{X} = \bar{X}_d + \frac{\Sigma fd'}{N} i$$

Grade	Number of students f	d'	fd'	
75.0–76.9	3	−4	− 12	
77.0–78.9	23	−3	− 69	
79.0–80.9	52	−2	−104	
81.0–82.9	61	−1	− 61	−246
83.0–84.9	74	0		
85.0–86.9	61	+1	+ 61	
87.0–88.9	53	+2	+106	
89.0–90.9	35	+3	+105	
91.0–92.9	23	+4	+ 92	
93.0–94.9	15	+5	+ 75	
95.0–96.9	7	+6	+ 42	
97.0–98.9	2	+7	+ 14	+495
Total	409	...	...	+249

$$\bar{X} = \bar{X}_d + \frac{\Sigma fd'}{N} i = 83.95 + \frac{249}{409} 2,$$
$$= 83.95 + 1.218,$$
$$= 85.17.$$

awkward because fractional values of d' would be involved. The appropriate procedure is either that shown in Table 9.3 or that of Table 9.5. When classes vary in width, the distribution is invariably skewed, and we must remember that, as skewness increases, the errors in our mid-value assumptions offset each other less closely. Thus the mean computed from a frequency distribution having unequal class intervals may differ markedly from the mean computed from the unclassified data. Furthermore, as will be discussed at the end of this chapter, the arithmetic mean of a decidedly skewed distribution is of limited usefulness. When a frequency distribution, such as that of Table 8.5, has a class of indeterminate width at one end (or, occasionally, both ends), there is no indication of the value which should be chosen as representative of the class. If it is assumed that the indeterminate group has the same width as the preceding one, the mid-value will usually be too low. The use of such a mid-value may result in offsetting the upward bias of the preceding mid-values, but we can never be sure how much offsetting takes place or that it may not even overbalance the bias. The reason a class is left indeterminate is usually that it contains a few items scattered over a wide range of values.

It should be emphasized that the value of the arithmetic mean computed for a skewed distribution having unequal class intervals is only a reasonably good approximation. It becomes even less accurate when one or two indeterminate classes are present. The difficulty involved in the computation of the mean for such a distribution is completely resolved if a footnote is added to the table giving the total of the unclassified data. If this procedure is followed, a single division suffices to give the value of the arithmetic mean.

Modified forms of the arithmetic mean. Instead of computing the arithmetic mean for all of a series of items, it may occasionally suffice to make an approximation by taking the average of the smallest and largest figures. The result of such a procedure will not differ greatly from the arithmetic mean if we are dealing with a continuous variable (or a discrete variable which does not show gaps) the distribution of which is symmetrical or nearly so. For example, meteorologists have found that it is not ordinarily necessary to take hourly temperatures throughout a day and average these 24 readings to arrive at the daily mean temperature. It ordinarily suffices to average only the maximum and minimum temperatures. These two readings may be obtained from the high and low points shown on the graph traced by a recording thermometer, or they may be had from a thermometer which automatically records the maximum and the minimum temperatures.

It will be recalled that the data of students' grades is skewed to the right. Consequently we should expect the average of the lowest and highest grades to exceed the arithmetic mean computed from all of the grades. Let us determine the average of these two extreme values and see how far it departs from $\overline{X}$. The highest grade shown in Table 8.2 is 98.3, while the lowest grade is 76.5. The average of these two grades is 87.40. The value of $\overline{X}$ computed from the unclassified data was found to be 85.15. Although the discrepancy resulting from averaging the extremes is only 2.25, or 2.6 per cent, we should not use this method as an approximation of $\overline{X}$ unless the distribution is symmetrical or nearly so.

A second modification of the arithmetic mean is one which will be referred to again in connection with the measurement of seasonal movements (Chapter 14). This modification consists essentially either of ignoring certain items on the basis that they are unusual extreme values, perhaps resulting from the introduction of a non-homogeneous or non-comparable factor into the situation, or of dropping one or more of the highest and lowest values in an array so that only the more typical values are averaged.

Suppose that a runner has competed in the 100-yard dash in ten track meets during a season, and that his times were as follows:

10.2, 10.1, 10.0, 10.0, 10.1, 10.0, 9.9, 10.1, 11.4, 10.2 seconds

Now an arithmetic mean of these ten figures is 10.2 seconds, although only three races were run this slow or slower. In the race represented by the ninth figure above, the runner was spiked and limped in to finish an extremely poor last. The figure 11.4 does not indicate his running ability and could quite logically be excluded in arriving at a mean time which represents this runner's ability. If we average the other nine figures, we obtain 10.07 seconds as the arithmetic mean for this runner under normal running conditions. In like fashion, if one race had been run with a strong wind at the runner's back, his time would be abnormally short for the 100 yards and that figure, too, might be omitted.[3] The procedure just described differs from the one followed in measuring seasonal movements in that only the particular values for which a specific reason could be definitely assigned have been eliminated. When measuring seasonal movements, we shall drop one, two, or more items at both ends of an array in order to average the items which seem to cluster around some central value.

Averaging percentages. It was pointed out in Chapter 7 that a series of percentages based on different numbers should ordinarily be averaged by weighting each percentage in proportion to its base. There are conditions, however, under which we might want to ignore the different bases and to average several percentages using a different system of weights. For example, let us assume that a student has taken two comprehensive examinations, each covering one-half of the subject matter of a course. Suppose that the first examination included 100 "true-false" questions, upon which he made 82 per cent, while the second included 150 such questions, upon which he made 88 per cent. Since each percentage represents a level of accomplishment for one-half of the work of a term, a better description of the work of the student for the term would weight the two percentages equally, resulting in an average of

$$\frac{82 + 88}{2} = 85$$

rather than weight the percentages according to the number of questions asked, giving

---

[3] A discussion of this type of modified mean when used in connection with time studies is given in F. E. Croxton and D. J. Cowden, *Practical Business Statistics*, third edition, Prentice-Hall, Inc., Englewood Cliffs, N. J., 1960, pp. 458–463.

$$\frac{(100 \times 82) + (150 \times 88)}{250} = 85.6.$$

If the second examination had been based upon 10 "essay" questions, it is even more apparent that the weighting should not be determined by the number of questions included.

Averaging averages. The general outlines of the problem of averaging averages are the same as those involved in averaging percentages. If we have several averages, each referring to a category, and wish to average these averages in order to arrive at a statement compatible with that referring to the total composed of these categories, it is necessary to weight each average according to the importance of its category. For example, if seven football linemen averaged 210 pounds in weight and four backfield players averaged 186 pounds, we might add the two means and divide by 2, obtaining 198 pounds. That, however, is not the correct arithmetic mean for the weights of the eleven players. We obtain the correct figure from

$$\frac{(7 \times 210) + (4 \times 186)}{11} = \frac{2{,}214}{11} = 201 \text{ pounds.}$$

This is the figure we would get if we added the individual weights for the eleven players and divided by eleven.

As in the case of percentages, there may be some instances in which the importance of each category is dependent upon some factor other than the number of items included in the category. Suppose that 12 tires have been run on a group of test trucks unloaded except for the driver, and have shown an average mileage of 13,618 miles. Suppose that 20 similar tires have been used on a similar group of test trucks each carrying the driver and 2,000 pounds of load, and have shown an average mileage of 12,136 miles. The weighted average of mileage would be

$$\frac{(12 \times 13{,}618) + (20 \times 12{,}136)}{32} = 12{,}692 \text{ miles.}$$

What we have done is to assign $\frac{20}{12} = 1.67$ times as much weight to the second average as to the first. Actually, trucks sometimes travel unloaded, sometimes loaded, sometimes partly loaded, and sometimes overloaded. If the trucks in our illustration travel $\frac{1}{5}$ of their mileage unloaded and $\frac{4}{5}$ of their mileage loaded, we should arrive at our average by

$$\frac{(1 \times 13{,}618) + (4 \times 12{,}136)}{5} = 12{,}432 \text{ miles.}$$

It is the importance of the various load conditions in the use of the truck which should be considered in weighting rather than the number of tires tested.

THE MEDIAN

The median from ungrouped data. The median is usually defined as that *value* which divides a distribution so that an equal number of items is on either side of it.   If we have five items, $5, $6, $7, $8, $10, it is apparent that the value of the median is $7, since there are two items below that value and two items above it.   If we have six items, 2 inches, 5 inches, 6 inches, 7 inches, 9 inches, 12 inches, it is clear that any value greater than 6 inches and less than 7 inches will satisfy our definition.   As a matter of practice, when there are an even number of items, we usually take the value of the median as halfway between the two central items. In this instance the median would be 6.5 inches.

If we are dealing with a series of values such as 12, 13, 14, 15, 15, 17, and 18 pounds, there is no value which is so located that three items are smaller than it and three items are larger than it.   We would, however, designate 15 pounds as the median.   It must be obvious that the definition first given does not hold for situations such as this.   The definition is therefore recast thus: *the median is that value which divides a series so that one-half or more of the items are equal to or less than it and one-half or more of the items are equal to or greater than it.*

From what has already been said, it is obvious that the median cannot readily be located unless the data have been put into an array or, as we shall see shortly, into a frequency distribution.   It will be recalled that no arranging is necessary for computing the mean, since the items of a series may be totaled no matter what their order.

The value of the median of a series may or may not coincide with the value of an existing item.   When there is an odd number of items in an array, the value of the median coincides with that of one of the items; when there is an even number of items in an array, it does not.

An important property of the median, which will be referred to again, is that it is influenced by the position of the items in the array but not by the size of the items.   It has already been observed that the median of $5, $6, $7, $8, $10 is $7.   The two larger items may have any values greater than $7, yet the median remains $7.

Before proceeding to a consideration of the computation of the median for grouped data, let us compute the value of the median for the grades of the 409 liberal arts students arrayed in Table 8.2.   We want to find the value which is so located that 204 items will be on either side of it.

This is, of course, the value of the 205th item,[4] and counting from either end reveals that the value of the median is 84.6. If we had an array of 200 items, we should find the value which divides the distribution so that 100 items fall below and 100 above it. This is obviously the mean of the 100th and 101st items counted from either end of the array.

The median from grouped data. To determine the value of the median of a frequency distribution, we count half of the frequencies from either end of the distribution in order to ascertain the value on either side of which half of the frequencies fall. To determine the value of the median for the grades of the students (Table 9.6), we first compute $\frac{N}{2} = 204.5$. We then proceed to ascertain the value of the median. There are 139 frequencies included in the first four classes of the distribution. The estimated value of the median is therefore obtained by interpolating 65.5 frequencies (204.5 − 139) into the fifth class, assuming that the frequencies in that class are evenly distributed within the class. The median, then, is given by the expression

$$\text{Med} = 82.95 + \frac{65.5}{74} 2 = 82.95 + 1.77 = 84.72.$$

Exactly the same result is obtained if we begin our computations from the other end of the distribution. There are 196 frequencies included in the last seven classes and we proceed to interpolate 8.5 frequencies (204.5 − 196) into the fifth class, *from the upper limit toward the lower limit.* The result is

$$\text{Med} = 84.95 - \frac{8.5}{74} 2 = 84.95 - 0.23 = 84.72.$$

The value of the median is, of course, the same whether we begin our computations from one end or the other.

The value of 84.72 just obtained for the median from the frequency distribution is in very close agreement with that of 84.6 found from the array. Unless the data contain gaps or irregularities, we can expect rather close agreement when dealing with a continuous variable, and likewise for a discrete variable if the data are not broken.

---

[4] For ungrouped data it may seem convenient to find the value of the median by counting $\frac{N+1}{2}$ items, beginning with the highest (or lowest) item in the array. This is not the same as saying that the median is the $\left(\frac{N+1}{2}\right)$th item. Although some persons hold this concept, it is not satisfactory. The concept of the middle item as the median is unsatisfactory when the array consists of an even number of items, and must be abandoned when the median is determined from grouped data.

We have now computed the values of the arithmetic mean and the median for the frequency distribution of the students' grades. The mean was 85.17. The median was 84.72. The mean exceeds the median because the distribution is skewed to the right. If a distribution is exactly symmetrical, the mean and the median are identical. If a distribution is skewed to the left, the mean will be less than the median. This point will be treated more fully at the end of this chapter and in the following chapter. In Chapter 10 we shall see that one way of measuring skewness involves consideration of the values of the mean and the median.

The computation of the median from a frequency distribution of unequal class intervals does not differ from that just described. Neither does the presence of indeterminate groups at either or both ends complicate the procedure.

If an ogive of a distribution is plotted, it is possible to obtain the value of the median graphically, as shown in Chart 9.1. The process is the graphic equivalent of the computations already made and consists of the following steps: (1) Compute $\frac{N}{2}$ and locate this point on the vertical scale. (2) Draw a perpendicular to the Y-axis at this point and extend the perpendicular to intersect the ogive. (3) At the intersection, drop a perpendicular to the X-axis. The intersection gives the value of the median. From Chart 9.1 it is seen that, for the grades of the students, the value of the median, located graphically, is 84.7, which is virtually identical with that computed arithmetically.

The quartiles, quintiles, deciles, and percentiles. The median characterizes a series of values because of its midway position. There are several other measures of the frequency distribution which, taken individually, are not measures of central tendency but, as we shall see later, may be used to assist in measuring dispersion and skewness. They are, however, allied to the median in that they are based upon their position in a series. We shall therefore digress at this point to discuss the *quartiles*, *quintiles*, *deciles*, and *percentiles*.

There are three quartiles, Q_1, Q_2, and Q_3, which divide the distribution into four equal parts. Q_2 is, of course, the median and is generally so designated. To determine the value of Q_1, the first or lower quartile, for the data of the liberal arts students' grades, we count $\frac{N}{4} = \frac{409}{4} = 102.25$ frequencies from the lower limit of the first class. Thus for the value of Q_1 we have

$$Q_1 = 80.95 + \frac{24.25}{61} \, 2 = 81.75.$$

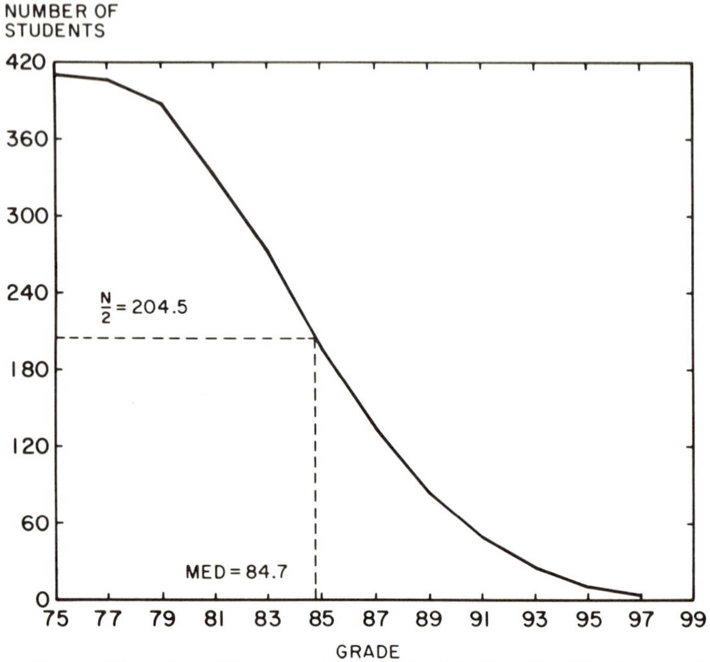

NUMBER OF
STUDENTS

Chart 9.1.   Graphic Location of the Median for Grades of the 1965 Liberal Arts Graduates of Rutgers—The State University. Data of Table 9.6.

The same result may be obtained by counting $\dfrac{3N}{4}$ from the upper limit of the last class.

The value of the third quartile Q_3 may be computed by counting $\dfrac{3N}{4}$ from the lower limit of the first class or, more expeditiously, by counting $\dfrac{N}{4}$ from the upper limit of the last class. Since $\dfrac{N}{4} = 102.25$, and since there are 82 frequencies in the last five classes, we have

$$Q_3 = 88.95 - \frac{20.25}{53}\,2 = 88.19.$$

There are four quintiles, which divide the distribution into five equal parts; nine deciles, which divide the distribution into ten equal parts; and ninety-nine percentiles, which divide the distribution into 100 equal parts.   The procedure for computing these values is similar to that for the median and the quartiles.   For example, we shall compute the value of the 3rd decile, which is also the 30th percentile.   We count $\dfrac{3N}{10} = \dfrac{1{,}227}{10} = 122.7$ from the lower limit of the first class and interpolate.

Since there are 78 frequencies in the first 3 groups, we have

$$80.95 + \frac{44.7}{61} \, 2 = 82.42.$$

Unless a distribution is very extensive, there would be no purpose served in computing very many of the percentiles. Frequent use is made of only a few of them, such as the 99th, 98th, 95th, 90th, 85th, 80th, and so forth.

The terms *quartile, quintile, decile,* and *percentile* are sometimes used in a different sense, to refer to the *part of the distribution* in which an item falls. Thus, if a student is said to be in the upper quartile of his class, he is in the upper 25 per cent. If he is in the upper decile of his class, he is in the upper 10 per cent. It would undoubtedly lead to clarity of expression if we reserved quartiles, quintiles, deciles, and percentiles to mean the *measures* discussed at the opening of this section. To refer to the part of a distribution in which a student falls, we could say "highest quarter" (above Q_3), "second highest quarter" (between Q_2 and Q_3), "third highest quarter" (between Q_1 and Q_2), and "lowest quarter" (below Q_1). Similarly, we could say "fifths" in place of quintiles, "tenths" instead of deciles, and "hundredths" instead of percentiles.

THE MODE

The mode from ungrouped data. The mode of a distribution is the value at the point around which the items tend to be most heavily concentrated. It may be regarded as the most typical of a series of values. For this very reason it is apparent that the occurrence of one or a few extremely high (or low) values has no effect upon the mode.[5] If a series of data is unclassified, not having been either arrayed or put into a frequency distribution, the mode cannot be readily located.

Taking first an extremely simple illustration: If seven men are receiving daily incomes of $35, $42, $49, $49, $49, $56, $70, it is clear that the modal income is $49 per day. If we have a series of values such as

$$21, 35, 42, 49, 63, 70, 77,$$

it is apparent that there is no mode.

---

[5] This is true in respect to the usual method of locating the mode which is described here. If the mode is located by the expression

$$\text{Mode} = \bar{X} - s \, \frac{\sqrt{\beta_1} \, (\beta_2 + 3)}{2(5\beta_2 - 6\beta_1 - 9)},$$

or by determining the X value just below the peak of a fitted curve, the extreme values do have some slight influence. The computation of $s\beta_1$, and β_2 is discussed in the following chapter.

The mode from grouped data. If we examine the array of students' grades shown in Table 8.2, we find that it would be very difficult to determine the single value around which the items tend to concentrate. The mode may be located readily by referring to a frequency distribution such as Table 9.6. Here it is clear that the *modal group* is 83.0–84.9; and if we take the mid-value as representative of the class, we should call 83.95 the mode.

Usually the mid-value is not the best estimate of the mode, since the frequencies in the classes preceding and following the modal class are, as a rule, not equal. It is generally necessary to infer the probable concentration point within the modal class using the expression

$$\text{Mo} = l_1 + \frac{\Delta_1}{\Delta_1 + \Delta_2} \times i,$$

where l_1 = the lower limit of the modal class;

Δ_1 = the difference between the frequency of the modal class and the frequency of the preceding class (sign neglected);

Δ_2 = the difference between the frequency of the modal class and the frequency of the following class (sign neglected);

i = the interval of the modal class.

For the frequency distribution of **grades** of the students,

$$\text{Mo} = 82.95$$
$$+ \frac{74 - 61}{(74 - 61) + (74 - 61)}\, 2,$$
$$= 82.95 + \frac{1}{2}\, 2 = 83.95.$$

In this particular illustration, the modal value computed exactly equals the mid-value, an occurrence not the usual case. This occurs because in the illustration the frequencies in the classes which immediately precede and follow the modal class are equal. Had they been unequal, the modal value computed would have been less than or greater than the mid-value of the class. For example, had the class containing grades of 81.0–82.9 contained 66 rather than 61 frequencies, the modal value computed would have been 83.71. Had the class containing grades of 85.0–86.9 contained 66 rather than 61 frequencies, the modal value computed would have been 84.19.

The interpolation process which we have described may be illustrated graphically as shown in Chart 9.2. To illustrate the roles which Δ_1 and Δ_2 play in the process, we have assumed a frequency of 66 for the class containing grades of 81.0–82.9. It should be realized that we are merely making an estimate of the value of the mode. Nevertheless, it is a useful estimate, and it should be remembered that the mode has two important properties; first, that it represents the most typical value of the distribution and should coincide

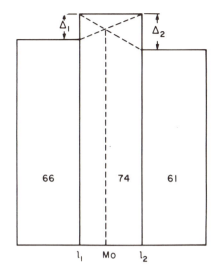

Chart 9.2. Diagrammatic Illustration of the Method of Interpolating for the Value of the Mode. Δ_1 exerts an upward influence, and Δ_2 exerts a downward influence, each in proportion to its magnitude, so that the mode divides the interval of the modal class into two parts proportional to Δ_1 and Δ_2. That is,

$$\frac{Mo - l_1}{l_2 - Mo} = \frac{\Delta_1}{\Delta_2}.$$

Geometrically, the mode may be located by dropping a vertical line from the intersection of the two diagonals as shown on the diagram.

Algebraically the expression

$$Mo = l_1 + \frac{\Delta_1}{\Delta_1 + \Delta_2}i$$

may be developed as follows:
We wish to locate the mode so that

$$\frac{Mo - l_1}{l_2 - Mo} = \frac{\Delta_1}{\Delta_2},$$

$$\Delta_2 Mo - \Delta_2 l_1 = \Delta_1 l_2 - \Delta_1 Mo,$$

$$\Delta_1 Mo + \Delta_2 Mo = \Delta_1 l_2 + \Delta_2 l_1,$$

$$Mo(\Delta_1 + \Delta_2) = \Delta_1 l_2 + \Delta_2 l_1.$$

But $l_2 = l_1 + i.$

$$\therefore \quad Mo = \frac{\Delta_1 l_1 + \Delta_1 i + \Delta_2 l_1}{\Delta_1 + \Delta_2},$$

$$= \frac{\Delta_1 l_1 + \Delta_2 l_1}{\Delta_1 + \Delta_2} + \frac{\Delta_1 i}{\Delta_1 + \Delta_2}$$

$$= l_1 + \frac{\Delta_1}{\Delta_1 + \Delta_2}i.$$

with existing items; second, that the mode (as usually computed) is not affected by the presence of extremely large or small items.

Graphically we may obtain the mode from a column diagram, as in Chart 9.2. We may make a very rough approximation of the mode by reading the value on the X-axis corresponding to the highest point of the frequency curve or corresponding to the steepest portion of the ogive. The curves may be smoothed freehand, since, unless the series has been subjected to a smoothing process, we would obtain a value about the same as the mid-value of the modal group.

Upon occasion, series are encountered which have two modes and are referred to as *bi-modal*. Such a series is pictured in Chart 9.3. Sometimes bimodality is the result of chance; sometimes it results because of the fact that two sets of non-homogeneous data are present. In Chart 9.3 the two concentrations are attributable to the fact that some drivers were on full- (or nearly full-) time work, while others were working only one or two days a week.

CHARACTERISTICS OF THE MEAN, MEDIAN, AND MODE

Before proceeding to a consideration of other measures of central tendency, we shall examine the characteristics of these three relatively simple and very important measures.

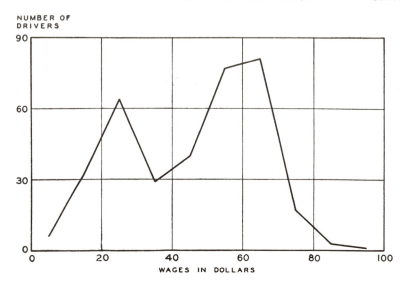

NUMBER OF
DRIVERS

WAGES IN DOLLARS

Chart 9.3. Distribution of Wages Received in Half Month by Drivers in Bituminous Coal Mines, Illinois. Data from United States Bureau of Labor Statistics, *Wages and Hours of Labor in Bituminous-Coal Mining,* Bulletin No. 601, p. 61.

Familiarity of the concept. The arithmetic mean is the most widely used of all the measures of central tendency. As will be pointed out later, it is frequently used under conditions which cause it to be misleading. The median is less well known than the arithmetic mean, but it is based on a simpler concept. Also less well known than the arithmetic mean, the concept of the mode as the most usual or typical of a group of items is probably the simplest of the three.

The concepts of the three measures may be illustrated by means of the three parts of Chart 9.4. The mean is at the point of balance, or center of gravity, such that ΣfX on one side of the mean equals ΣfX on the other side. The median divides the curve into two equal areas. The mode is the value below the peak of the curve.

Algebraic treatment. The arithmetic mean may be treated algebraically:

(a) Since $\bar{X} = \dfrac{\Sigma X}{N}$, it follows that, if any two of the three factors (the total, the arithmetic mean, the number of items) are known, the third may be computed. Thus

$$\bar{X} = \frac{\Sigma X}{N}; \qquad \Sigma X = N\bar{X}; \qquad N = \frac{\Sigma X}{\bar{X}}.$$

(b) Using appropriate weights, a series of arithmetic means may be averaged to yield the arithmetic mean of all the data on which those means were based.

The median does not lend itself to the type of algebraic treatment discussed for the arithmetic mean. Algebraic treatment of the mode, similar to that sketched for the mean, is not possible.

Need for classifying data. The arithmetic mean may be computed from unclassified data, from arrayed data, from the frequency distribution, or (as noted above) merely from a knowledge of the total ΣX and the number of items N. When the arithmetic mean is computed from a frequency distribution, the value of $\overline{X}$ will very closely approximate the value of $\overline{X}$ for the unclassified data. The more nearly symmetrical the distribution, the closer the agreement of these two values.

In order that the value of the median may be computed, the data must be in an array (at least the central items must be arrayed) or in a frequency distribution. The median determined from the frequency distribution will agree approximately with that computed from the array if the distribution of items is regular within the class containing the median.

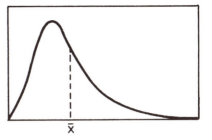

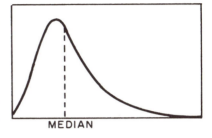

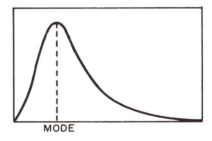

C.   The mode is directly beneath the peak of the curve.

Chart 9.4. Location of the Arithmetic Mean, the Median, and the Mode in a Frequency Distribution Skewed to the Right.

The mode is most readily located from the frequency distribution, and only with some difficulty from an array. One author has pointed out that an array of the cities of the United States according to population of each would show no mode. However, if such data were put into classes, a modal tendency might appear. It should be borne in mind that the process of interpolating for the modal value within the modal group is at best only an approximation. More refined methods of locating the mode involve essentially the smoothing of the data by formula and the determination of the X value of the maximum ordinate.

Effect of unequal class intervals. When classes vary in width, the value of the arithmetic mean may be computed. Such a variation of class intervals is necessitated by the presence of marked skewness (almost invariably to the right, or positive) resulting in a value for $\overline{X}$ which may not be in close agreement with that based on the unclassified data. The value of $\overline{X}$ from such a positively skewed frequency distribution would be expected to exceed the value of $\overline{X}$ from the unclassified data.

The median may ordinarily be determined rather satisfactorily from a frequency distribution having varying class intervals. The upper quartile or one or more of the upper quintiles or deciles might, however, fall in a wide class having few frequencies. The necessary interpolation would in such a case be unreliable.

When the class intervals of a frequency distribution vary in width, the mode may be satisfactorily located if the modal group and those on either side of it are of the same width. Otherwise the determination is apt to be of limited accuracy.

Effect of classses with open end. The presence of a "Less than . . . " class at one end of a frequency distribution and/or an " . . . or more" class at the other end results in an inaccurate determination of $\overline{X}$, since mid-values ordinarily cannot be satisfactorily determined for such classes.

The presence of open-end classes has no effect upon the determination of the median.

Indeterminate groups do not complicate the process of locating the modal value. Occasionally, as when working with an extremely skewed or a reverse J-shaped distribution, the mode is at or near the end of the distribution. Under such conditions there would be no reason for having an indeterminate group at that end of the distribution. Incidentally, in the case of such distributions, the mode is not a measure of *central* tendency.

Effect of skewness. For a symmetrical distribution, the mean, median, and mode are identical. If the symmetrical distribution is altered by merely extending one tail so that the distribution is skewed, there is no necessary change in the value of the mode (as usually computed), but the median is changed in the direction of the skewness. Thus positive skewness (skewness to the right) increases the value of the median. The mean is increased even more, since it is affected not only by the fact that there is now an excess of frequencies on one side of the mode, but also by the amount by which the various excess frequencies deviate from the mode. Although the distribution of grades of the liberal arts students is only slightly skewed, the effect of the presence of skewness is seen when we recall that the mode is 83.95, the median is 84.72, and the mean is 85.17. These values are shown on Chart 10.7.

Effect of extreme values.   When skewness is not general but is due to a few items deviating a great deal from the mode, the median will be only slightly affected.   The arithmetic mean, however, is affected by the value of every item in the series, and the presence of one or a few extremely large (or extremely small) items in a series may result in a mean which is very misleading.   As ordinarily computed, the mode is not at all influenced by the presence of a few unusually high (or low) extreme values.

The foregoing is of such great importance that we shall give further attention to it.   Suppose we have the following series of seven values,

$12, $14, $15, $15, $16, $18, $19,

the mean of which is $15.57, the median $15, and the mode $15.   If an extreme value of $25 is added to these seven, the arithmetic mean becomes $16.75, the median $15.50, while the mode remains $15.   Now if, instead of having added $25 as the eighth item, we add $200, the mean becomes $38.62, but the median is still $15.50 and the mode $15.   The effect upon the median of any added value from $16 to ∞ is the same. The mode was not at all affected by the extreme value, although, if we had added a $16 item, it would have been affected.   This illustrates a different point, also; namely, that the mode is not a useful measure unless it is based upon enough items to show a well-defined concentration.

Because of the effect of extreme values upon the arithmetic mean, it is sometimes a misleading figure to use to describe a distribution.   If we are considering the income of a group of people, and if most of them have moderate incomes but one or a few have extremely high (or low) incomes, the mean will reflect these extremes and to that extent will be atypical rather than typical.   An alumni association once made a study of graduates who had been out of college 20 years.   Among other questions asked was one concerning income during a specific year.[6]   More than 350 questionnaires were sent out; only 133 replies were received.   There is a large probability that these replies were selective and *any* figures derived therefrom would be of doubtful value.   The mean income of the 133 replying was $35,000, but this high average was due to the fact that there were several very large incomes which were definitely extreme values. The median income was $18,750, while the mode was very close to $12,500.   In such a case as this, we should not use the mean alone to describe the distribution.   If only one figure is to be used, it is better to use the median or mode, depending upon which concept is of more importance.   It would be much better, of course, to give all three values, and, if possible, a frequency distribution or a frequency curve.

Sometimes in dealing with a series in which suspected heterogeneity is present, it may be advisable to use the median in lieu of the arithmetic mean.   For example, measurements might have been taken of the weight

---

[6] All figures in current dollars and rounded to nearest $250.

of a number of goldfish, and the figures may reveal the presence of several unusually large specimens. It is suspected that, because of ignorance or carelessness, the enumerator included a few carp with the goldfish. The questionable values could be discarded. However, we are not *sure* that the heavy fish were carp, and perhaps their measurements should not be discarded. The use of the median allows the extreme values to be represented by their position in the series rather than by their size.

Sometimes we have a series in which there are present extremes of which we know the number but not the individual values. In such a situation we can determine the median or the mode, but not the mean.

When we have a series of values extending over a great range, any concept of a measure of central tendency is dubious. Suppose we have the values 4, 6, 2,000, and 2,100. It is obvious that a mean or a median could be computed, but that neither would have any practical meaning.

Effect of irregularity of data. When data are broken or irregular, the value of the mean computed from a frequency distribution may be decidedly different from the value based on the unorganized data.

The same is true in the case of the median if gaps occur among the items falling in the class containing the median. When gaps occur in the vicinity of the median, the median is not a particularly good concept to use, as its value would be erratic if one or two items were added to or subtracted from the series.

If a mode is clearly defined, there are not likely to be gaps near that value. When gaps are present near the mode, it is quite likely that there are too few items in the series for the mode to be either clearly defined or meaningful.

Reliability when based on samples. In Chapter 24 we shall discuss the variation which may be expected in values of the arithmetic mean when based on repeated random samples. This volume will not treat of the sampling variation of medians or modes. However, for samples of the same size from a normal population, the median is subject to greater sampling variation than is the arithmetic mean, and the mode is more variable than the median.

Mathematical properties. The arithmetic mean has two important properties: first, $\Sigma x = 0$; and second, $\Sigma x^2 = $ a minimum. Because of this latter property, the mean is the usual basis of reference for measures of dispersion. The mean is an important function in many processes which will follow in later sections of this book. Among other uses, it is essential for fitting the *normal curve* to observed data.

The sum of the deviations from the median (signs neglected) is a minimum. For this reason, certain measures of dispersion are sometimes based upon the median.

Selection of appropriate measure. Using the foregoing measures as descriptive devices, the statistician may be faced with the problem of deciding which one to use to characterize a given set of data.   In general, the measure of central tendency that he should use depends upon (1) the nature of the distribution of the data and (2) the concept of central tendency which is desired for a particular purpose.

If the distribution is symmetrical, or approximately so, the three measures may be used almost interchangeably.   If a series is skewed, we must bear in mind that the arithmetic mean is frequently not a typical value, and that it may be better to use the mode (which is typical) or the median.   When there are extreme deviations or when there is suspected heterogeneity, we may use the median in place of the mean, or recourse may be had to a modified mean.

If $\bar{X}$ is computed, use may be made of that value to obtain a total. Thus, if adults average 150 pounds in weight, it is safe to load about 20 people in an elevator rated to carry 3,000 pounds.   (The figure of 150 pounds is somewhat high for the average weights of adults, but it is the figure frequently used to compute elevator capacity.   It is obvious that the 20 people referred to should not all be heavy persons.)   If subsequent computations are to be made involving a measure, the mean may be required.   If a curve is to be fitted to a frequency distribution, the mean will probably be used.   If one series of data is eventually to be compared with another in respect to dispersion, the mean may be needed.   This, however, does not mean that the median or the mode should not be used for describing either or both of the series.

The relative standing of a person in a class may be indicated by stating whether his grade is better than the grades of half of the members.   This rating involves the use of the median.   Other statements referring to various proportions of the students may be made by using quartiles, quintiles, deciles, or percentiles.

If we are interested in knowing the typical annual expenditure of motorists for gasoline, we should make use of the mode.

Since the three measures embody different concepts, it may sometimes be advisable to use two or possibly all three.   The use of the mean and the mode, or the mean and the median, gives us an idea of the amount of skewness present, as will be shown in the next chapter.

Sometimes it is necessary to make a quick estimate of the central tendency of a series.   Under such conditions, the mode may be promptly estimated from a frequency distribution, and the median may be quickly approximated from either an array or a frequency distribution.   Of course, if the total and the number of items are given, the arithmetic mean may be computed in a few seconds.

MINOR MEANS

The arithmetic mean, median, and mode are frequently thought of as the more important measures of central tendency, because of their wide usefulness, simplicity, and general applicability. Under certain conditions other measures of central tendency may be useful, and we shall therefore consider the geometric mean and the harmonic mean. As pointed out earlier, the term "mean" is frequently used to designate the arithmetic mean; consequently, when referring to any other mean such as the geometric mean or the harmonic mean, we should always refer to the measure by its complete designation.

The geometric mean.   The geometric mean is defined as "the Nth root of the product of the items." Thus, for the four items 5, 8, 10, 12, the geometric mean is

$$G = \sqrt[4]{5 \times 8 \times 10 \times 12} = \sqrt[4]{4800} = 8.3.$$

It is interesting to note that the arithmetic mean of these four items is 8.75. For any series of positive values (not all the same), the geometric mean is smaller than the arithmetic mean.[7]   If one value of a series equals zero, the geometric mean equals zero and is therefore inappropriate. If one or more values are negative, the geometric mean can sometimes be computed but may be meaningless. These are important drawbacks to its use.

Symbolically, the geometric mean is $\sqrt[N]{X_1 \times X_2 \times X_3 \times \cdots \times X_N}$. The computation is usually carried out by means of logarithms, thus:

$$\log G = \frac{\log X_1 + \log X_2 + \log X_3 + \cdots + \log X_N}{N} = \frac{\Sigma \log X}{N}.$$

The logarithm of the geometric mean is thus the arithmetic mean of the logarithms of the values.

When frequencies are present, each logarithm must be multiplied by the corresponding frequency. Thus

$$\log G = \frac{f_1 \log X_1 + f_2 \log X_2 + f_3 \log X_3 + \cdots}{N} = \frac{\Sigma f \log X}{N}.$$

For a frequency distribution, the geometric mean is usually computed by: (1) ascertaining the logarithm of the mid-value of each class, (2) multiplying each logarithmic mid-value by its proper frequency, (3) summing these products, (4) dividing by the number of items, and (5) taking the anti-logarithm of the result. If a series is symmetrical in a logarithmic sense (see Chapter 23) and the items are evenly distributed within the classes geometrically instead of arithmetically, it is preferable to use the mid-values of the logarithms of the class limits rather than the logarithms of the mid-values of the classes. If the raw data are available, it is, of

---

[7] For a demonstration, see Appendix S, section **9.3.**

course, also advisable to re-form the frequency distribution in order to make the class intervals geometrically equal, if that had not already been done.

It will be recalled that the arithmetic mean is the sum of the values divided by the number, while the geometric mean is the Nth root of the product of the values. As noted before, N times $\overline{X}$ gives ΣX. For the geometric mean, $G^N = X_1 \cdot X_2 \cdot X_3 \cdot$ etc.; that is, the geometric mean raised to the Nth power equals the product of the values. This leads to the rather interesting point that any series of numbers having the same N and the same ΣX have the same arithmetic mean (for example, 1 and 11, 2 and 10, 4 and 8, 5 and 7, -2 and 14 all have an arithmetic mean of 6), and that any series of numbers having the same N and the same *product* have the same geometric mean (for example, 1 and 36, 2 and 18, 4 and 9 all have the geometric mean of 6).

Another property of the geometric mean is that the product of the ratios of the values on one side of the geometric mean to the geometric mean is equal to the product of the ratios of the geometric mean to the values on the other side of the geometric mean. To illustrate, let us take the values 4, 5, 20, 25, the geometric mean of which is $\sqrt[4]{10000} = 10$. The ratios of the values 4 and 5 to the geometric mean are $\frac{4}{10}$ and $\frac{5}{10}$, while the ratios of the geometric mean to the values 20 and 25 are $\frac{10}{20}$ and $\frac{10}{25}$. Thus we have

$$\frac{4}{10} \cdot \frac{5}{10} = \frac{10}{20} \cdot \frac{10}{25},$$

$$\frac{1}{5} = \frac{1}{5}.$$

Similarly, we may reverse the ratios to write

$$\frac{10}{4} \cdot \frac{10}{5} = \frac{20}{10} \cdot \frac{25}{10},$$

$$5 = 5.$$

The following paragraphs discuss certain instances in which the geometric mean is useful.

(1) The geometric mean may be used for averaging ratios. Consider the following data:

Community	Native-born inhabitants	Foreign-born inhabitants	Ratio of foreign-born to native-born (per cent)	Ratio of native-born to foreign-born (per cent)
A..........	8,000	4,000	50	200
B..........	1,500	3,000	200	50

The arithmetic mean of the two ratios of foreign-born to native-born population is 125 per cent. Likewise, the arithmetic mean of the two ratios of native-born to foreign-born population is 125 per cent! These two averages are inconsistent with each other. This incongruous result does not occur if we use the geometric mean, for the geometric mean of each of the two pairs of ratios is $\sqrt{0.50 \cdot 2.00} = 1.0$, or 100 per cent. We could, of course, total or average the foreign-born inhabitants for the two communities, and total or average the native-born inhabitants, thus obtaining two ratios which are consistent. There are 7,000 foreign-born and 9,500 native-born inhabitants, or an average of 3,500 foreign-born and 4,750 native-born inhabitants. The ratio of foreign-born to native-born is

$$\frac{7,000}{9,500} \text{ or } \frac{3,500}{4,750} = 73.7 \text{ per cent,}$$

and the ratio of native-born to foreign-born is

$$\frac{9,500}{7,000} \text{ or } \frac{4,750}{3,500} = 135.7 \text{ per cent.}$$

The product of these two ratios is 1. This arithmetic method, however, does not assign equal weight to the two ratios. Observe that the arithmetic method involves the ratio of the arithmetic means (or totals), whereas the geometric procedure involves the geometric mean of the ratios. We have here two different concepts. Which one to use in a given situation depends upon the purpose. If we wish to establish a typical ratio for a number of communities and wish that ratio to be independent of the number of native-born or foreign-born persons present in the various places (that is, we wish to assign equal weight to each ratio), we may use the geometric mean of the ratios. If we wish to allow the populations to exert an influence, we may determine the ratio of the totals or arithmetic means. The question is not whether to use an arithmetic or a geometric mean of the ratios, but whether to use a ratio based on arithmetic means (or totals) or a geometric mean of ratios.

If the two ratios of foreign-born to native-born are averaged arithmetically but weighted according to the native-born populations, the result is 73.7 per cent. If the two ratios of native-born to foreign-born are averaged arithmetically but weighted according to the foreign-born population, we obtain 135.7 per cent. These figures, of course, agree with those obtained by taking the ratios of the totals.

The geometric mean may be used when we wish to assign equal weight to equal ratios of change. Suppose (a) that two commodities are selling at \$2 and \$10 per unit; (b) that at a later date the first commodity doubles in price while the second one is halved in price, and thus they sell for \$4 and \$5, respectively; and (c) that at a still later date the original price of the first commodity is halved and becomes \$1, while that of the second commodity is doubled and becomes $20. The arithmetic mean under these three situations yields: (a) $6; (b) $4.50; and (c) $10.50. The geometric mean gives: (a) $4.47; (b) $4.47; and (c) $4.47. The assumption used to justify the geometric mean is illustrated by saying that a doubling in price offsets a halving in price, a quadrupling in price offsets a price of one-fourth the original figure, and similarly for any other two ratios whose product is 1. This characteristic will be referred to again concerning a possible use of the geometric mean in connection with price index numbers.

(2) Sometimes a frequency distribution is encountered which is markedly skewed to the right. If, instead of plotting the mid-values of the classes, we use the logarithms of the mid-values (or better, plot the logarithmic mid-values, the geometric mean of each pair of limits, on a logarithmic X-scale) and a symmetrical distribution results, a geometric analysis may be proper. This is discussed more fully in Chapter 23.

(3) Probably the most frequently used application of the geometric principle has to do with the determination of average per cent of change. If a city had a population of 100,000 in a given year and 120,000 ten years later, what was the average annual per cent of change? The change was 20 per cent over the entire period. If we take one-tenth of that figure, or 2 per cent, as the annual per cent of increase and compute a 2 per cent increase each year over the preceding year, the second population figure turns out to be 121,900! Obviously the correct figure is slightly smaller than 2 per cent, since we are actually compounding. We may compute the average annual per cent of change by using

$$P_n = P_o(1 + r)^n,$$

where P_o = population at beginning of period;
  P_n = population at end of period;
  r = relative increase (or decrease) per year, expressed as a decimal;
  n = number of years.

For the data above,

$$120{,}000 = 100{,}000(1 + r)^{10}.$$

Solving this by the use of logarithms gives

$$5.079181 = 5.000000 + 10 \log (1 + r).$$
$$\log (1 + r) = \frac{0.079181}{10},$$
$$= 0.0079181.$$
$$1 + r = 1.0184,$$
$$r = 1.84 \text{ per cent.}$$

The expression $P_n = P_o(1 + r)^n$ is sometimes termed the compound interest formula because of its usefulness in various problems involving compound interest. We have used it above to determine average annual per cent of growth.[8] Knowing values of any three of the four symbols shown, we can solve for the fourth. Thus we may determine:

(a) Average annual per cent of change r.
(b) Population a given number of years later P_n, assuming a constant relative change.
(c) Number of years n until a given population will be attained, again assuming a constant relative change.
(d) Population a given number of years earlier, P_o, if the per cent of change was constant.

It should be noted that the assumption of a constant relative change for population is not valid over extended periods for any except possibly "new" countries.

The harmonic mean. The harmonic mean H is the reciprocal of the arithmetic mean of the reciprocals of the values. The expression is

$$H = \frac{1}{\dfrac{\dfrac{1}{X_1} + \dfrac{1}{X_2} + \dfrac{1}{X_3} + \cdots + \dfrac{1}{X_N}}{N}} = \frac{1}{\dfrac{\Sigma \dfrac{1}{X}}{N}}.$$

For purposes of computation, it is more convenient to use the form

$$H = \frac{N}{\dfrac{1}{X_1} + \dfrac{1}{X_2} + \dfrac{1}{X_3} + \cdots + \dfrac{1}{X_N}} = \frac{N}{\Sigma \dfrac{1}{X}}$$

or

$$\frac{1}{H} = \frac{\dfrac{1}{X_1} + \dfrac{1}{X_2} + \dfrac{1}{X_3} + \cdots + \dfrac{1}{X_N}}{N} = \frac{\Sigma \dfrac{1}{X}}{N}.$$

The harmonic mean of the two values 3 and 12 is

$$\frac{1}{H} = \frac{\dfrac{1}{3} + \dfrac{1}{12}}{2} = \frac{5}{24};$$

$$H = 4.8.$$

---

[8] In the above discussion we found the average per cent of growth between two selected points. Sometimes we wish to find the average per cent of growth which best describes a number of values for different years. Such an average is not dependent upon only the first and last values of a series and is therefore more likely to be a representative figure. A method of fitting a curve to obtain such an average is given in Chapter 13.

For these same values, the arithmetic mean is 7.5, while the geometric mean is $\sqrt{3 \times 12} = 6$.   For any series of values (not all the same or not including zero as one value), the harmonic mean is smaller than either the geometric or the arithmetic mean.[9]

The harmonic mean is so rarely computed for a frequency distribution that we shall merely note the procedure, which consists of multiplying the reciprocal of each mid-value (or mid-value of the reciprocals of the class limits) by its frequency, adding these products, dividing by N, and taking the reciprocal of the result.

While the harmonic mean is not a measure of great importance, it is often confusing and hence we shall give a somewhat extended explanation and indicate several possible applications.

Application (1).   Although oranges are not usually priced in this fashion, let us suppose that two grades of oranges are selling at 10 for $1 and 20 for $1.   The arithmetic mean may be computed as

$$\overline{X} = \frac{10 + 20}{2} = 15.$$

That is, 15 for $1, or $0.067 per orange.   This is the price we must pay per orange *if we spend equal amounts of money for each grade*.   Paying $0.067 for each of 30 oranges, we shall spend $2.00 for the lot.

The harmonic mean gives a different result:

$$H = \frac{2}{\dfrac{1}{10} + \dfrac{1}{20}} = \frac{2}{\dfrac{3}{20}} = \frac{40}{3} = 13\tfrac{1}{3}.$$

That is, $13\tfrac{1}{3}$ for $1, or $0.075 per orange.   This is the price we must pay per orange *if equal numbers of oranges are bought at each price*.   Thus, if we buy 15 oranges at 10 for $1 and 15 oranges at 20 for $1, we shall spend $2.25 for all 30.   Similarly, if we buy 30 oranges at $0.075 each, we shall spend $2.25 for the lot.

The harmonic mean will give the same results as the arithmetic mean if we weight by the quantities bought at each price.   Thus

$$H = \frac{30}{10 \left(\dfrac{1}{10}\right) + 20 \left(\dfrac{1}{20}\right)} = 15 \text{ oranges per } \$1, \text{ or } \$0.067 \text{ per orange,}$$

assuming equal amounts of money spent for each grade.

If prices are quoted in the usual way, as so much per dozen, these oranges are selling at $1.20 per dozen and $0.60 per dozen.   The simple arithmetic mean is:

---

[9] See Appendix S, section 9.4.

$$\bar{X} = \frac{\$1.20 + \$0.60}{2} = \$0.90 \text{ per dozen, or } \$0.075 \text{ per orange.}$$

It is the same as the first harmonic mean, since we are assuming in our computation that equal quantities are to be bought at each price. (Identical results are obtained if the quotations are per orange instead of per dozen oranges.) On the other hand, if we consider that 10 oranges may be bought at $1.20 per dozen and 20 oranges may be bought at $0.60 per dozen, we have

$$\bar{X} = \frac{(\$1.20 \times 10) + (\$0.60 \times 20)}{30} = \$0.80 \text{ per dozen,}$$

or $0.067 per orange.

This result is the same as obtained in our first and third calculations, since we have assumed that equal amounts of money are to be spent for each grade of orange.

In the above illustrations the harmonic mean has furnished no information not already available by use of the arithmetic mean. The harmonic mean may be useful, however, when data are customarily or conveniently given in terms of problems solved per minute, miles covered per hour, units purchased per dollar, and so forth.

The arithmetic mean and the harmonic mean give consistent results if proper consideration is given to (a) how the data are quoted and (b) what weights are to be used. Taking prices as an illustration, the table below sets forth the relationships. Expressions 1, 2, 3, 4 give results consistent with each other. Similarly, expressions I, II, III, IV give consistent results.

If prices are quoted in terms of:	If the assumption is:	
	Equal amounts of money spent for each grade or commodity	Equal number of units of each grade or commodity bought at each price
Price per unit..........	1. $\bar{X}$, weighted by quantities for equal amounts of money (in this case, units per dollar)	I. $\bar{X}$, weighted by number of units (or equally)
	2. H, weighted by dollars (or equally)	II. H, weighted by dollars for equal numbers of units (or price per unit)
Units per dollar........	3. $\bar{X}$, weighted by dollars (or equally)	III. $\bar{X}$, weighted by dollars for equal numbers of units (or price per unit)
	4. H, weighted by quantities for equal amounts of money (in this case, units per dollar)	IV. H, weighted by number of units (or equally)

Consider commodity A as selling at 4 units for \$1, or \$0.25 each, and commodity B as selling at 10 units for \$1, or \$0.10 each.

If equal amounts of money are to be spent for each commodity:

1. $\bar{X} = \dfrac{(0.25 \times 4) + (0.10 \times 10)}{14} = \dfrac{2.00}{14}$

$$= \$0.1429 \text{ per unit, or 7 for \$1.}$$

2. $H = \dfrac{2}{1\left(\dfrac{1}{0.25}\right) + 1\left(\dfrac{1}{0.10}\right)} = \dfrac{2}{7} = \dfrac{1.00}{7}$
$$= \$0.1429 \text{ per unit, or 7 for \$1.}$$

3. $\bar{X} = \dfrac{(4 \times 1) + (10 \times 1)}{2} = \dfrac{14}{2} = 7 \text{ for \$1, or \$0.1429 per unit.}$

4. $H = \dfrac{14}{4\left(\dfrac{1}{4}\right) + 10\left(\dfrac{1}{10}\right)} = \dfrac{14}{2} = 7 \text{ for \$1, or \$0.1429 per unit.}$

If equal numbers of units of each commodity are to be bought at each price:

I. $\bar{X} = \dfrac{(0.25 \times 1) + (0.10 \times 1)}{2} = \dfrac{0.35}{2}$

$$= \$0.175 \text{ per unit, or 5.71 for \$1.}$$

II. $H = \dfrac{0.35}{0.25\left(\dfrac{1}{0.25}\right) + 0.10\left(\dfrac{1}{0.10}\right)} = \dfrac{0.35}{2}$

$$= \$0.175 \text{ per unit, or 5.71 for \$1.}$$

III. $\bar{X} = \dfrac{(4 \times 0.25) + (10 \times 0.10)}{0.35} = \dfrac{2.00}{0.35}$

$$= 5.71 \text{ for \$1, or \$0.175 per unit.}$$

IV. $H = \dfrac{2}{1\left(\dfrac{1}{4}\right) + 1\left(\dfrac{1}{10}\right)} = \dfrac{2}{\dfrac{14}{40}} = \dfrac{80}{14} = 5.71 \text{ for \$1, or \$0.175 per unit.}$

From what has just been said it may be observed that (for either assumption), when averaging fractions (ratios) by the arithmetic or harmonic method, we use the arithmetic mean if weights are in the same terms as the denominator, the harmonic mean if weights are in the same terms as the numerator. Of course, if weights are in the same terms as the numerator, they may be converted into terms of the denominator and the arithmetic mean employed.

Suppose that a transaction consists of 40 handkerchiefs sold at 10 for $1 and 60 handkerchiefs sold at 20 for $1. Now we are not interested in either of the assumptions mentioned above. What we desire is the mean price when 40 handkerchiefs sell at 10 for $1 and 60 sell at 20 for $1. Using the quotations as given (that is, in terms of number of units per dollar), we may use the harmonic mean with quantity weights. Thus

$$H = \frac{100}{40\left(\frac{1}{10}\right) + 60\left(\frac{1}{20}\right)} = \frac{100}{7} = 14\frac{2}{7} \text{ per } \$1, \text{ or } \$0.07 \text{ each.}$$

Still using the quotations in terms of units per dollar, we may obtain the same result by employing the arithmetic mean, if our weights are amounts of money spent for each grade. Thus

$$\bar{X} = \frac{(10 \times 4) + (20 \times 3)}{7} = \frac{100}{7} = 14\frac{2}{7} \text{ per } \$1, \text{ or } \$0.07 \text{ each.}$$

If we shift our quotations to price per unit, we have 40 handkerchiefs sold at $0.10 each and 60 sold at $0.05 each. Now, using the harmonic mean, we weight by amounts of money spent for each grade. Thus

$$H = \frac{7}{4\left(\frac{1}{0.10}\right) + 3\left(\frac{1}{0.05}\right)} = \frac{7}{\frac{10}{0.10}} = \$0.07 \text{ each, or } 14\frac{2}{7} \text{ per } \$1.$$

Finally, using the arithmetic mean of prices per unit and weighting by quantities sold, we have

$$\bar{X} = \frac{(0.10 \times 40) + (0.05 \times 60)}{100} = \frac{7}{100} = \$0.07 \text{ each, or } 14\frac{2}{7} \text{ per } \$1.$$

Application (2). Occasionally a frequency distribution may be encountered which is so skewed to the right that, when plotted in terms of the reciprocals of the class mid-values, it assumes an approximately normal form. In such instances harmonic treatment may be indicated. Such cases are rather unusual, however, and will not be treated in this book.

Application (3). An interesting and apparently valid application of the harmonic mean is given in an article by Holbrook Working.[10] In his study of the factors influencing the price of potatoes, Working uses the harmonic mean, because, as he points out, a low price during part of a season will be compensated only by a disproportionally high price during the remainder of the season. To illustrate, we have selected the monthly prices for one crop year and have shown them in Chart 9.5. When the

---

[10] Holbrook Working, *Factors Determining the Price of Potatoes in St. Paul and Minneapolis*, Technical Bulletin 10, University of Minnesota Agricultural Experiment Station, pp. 9 and 10.

reciprocals or the logarithms are plotted, the curve is straighter than when the arithmetic values are plotted, the reciprocals giving perhaps the most nearly straight line.   This indicates that the harmonic mean is not inappropriate as a measure of the average price of potatoes during a season.

It is sometimes argued that the geometric mean should be used for series of data having a definite lower limit and an indefinite upper limit. One type of such data is price relatives, which, having a base of 100, may fall to 0 but rise to ∞.   The question is not so much one of the existence of such limits as it is one of what values may actually occur and how the limits are approached—arithmetically, geometrically, or reciprocally—whether, if we are dealing with a frequency distribution, the series is approximately symmetrical in terms of X, skewed but approximately symmetrical in terms of log X, or skewed but approximately normal in terms of $\frac{1}{X}$.

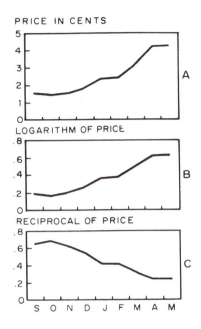

Chart 9.5. Price of Potatoes Per Bushel: A. Price, B. Logarithm of Price, C. Reciprocal of Price. Data from Holbrook Working, *ibid.*, p. 40.

In an arithmetic sense, a price drop of 33.3 per cent is offset by a price rise of 33.3 per cent (of the original base), a decline of 50 per cent is offset by a rise of 50 per cent, and a fall of 90 per cent is offset by a rise of 90 per cent.   Thus

$$\frac{66.7 + 133.3}{2} = 100,$$

$$\frac{50 + 150}{2} = 100,$$

$$\frac{10 + 190}{2} = 100.$$

In a geometric sense, a price drop of 33.3 per cent is offset by a rise of 50 per cent (of the original base), a fall of 50 per cent is offset by a rise of 100 per cent, and a drop of 90 per cent is offset by a rise of 900 per cent.

Thus

$$\sqrt{66.7 \times 150} = 100,$$
$$\sqrt{50 \times 200} = 100,$$
$$\sqrt{10 \times 1000} = 100.$$

In a reciprocal sense, a price drop of 33.3 per cent is offset by a rise of 100 per cent (of the original base), a fall of 50 per cent is offset by a rise to ∞, and a fall of more than 50 per cent cannot be offset by any rise however great. Thus

$$\frac{2}{\dfrac{1}{66.7} + \dfrac{1}{200}} = 100,$$

$$\frac{2}{\dfrac{1}{50} + \dfrac{1}{\infty}} = 100.$$

There are a number of other measures of central tendency which are of mathematical and theoretical rather than of practical interest. One of these is the quadratic mean:

$$\sqrt{\frac{\Sigma X^2}{N}}.$$

This is the square root of the arithmetic mean of the squares of the values. Unless all the values are the same, the quadratic mean exceeds the arithmetic mean. The quadratic mean is mentioned here because the *concept* is important. Although we do not use the term "quadratic" or "mean," we shall shortly compute the quadratic mean of the *deviations* from the arithmetic mean. It will not be a measure of central tendency, but a measure of dispersion; we shall call it the standard deviation, or s, and its expression is

$$s = \sqrt{\frac{\Sigma x^2}{N}}.$$

CHAPTER 10

Dispersion, Skewness, and Kurtosis

In the preceding chapter we considered certain measures which attempted to describe the central tendency of a frequency distribution. There are other aspects of frequency distributions which are also important. First we shall consider the *dispersion*, or spread of the data. Two counties may each show an average yield of wheat of 15 bushels to the acre; but, if the data are considered farm by farm, one county may exhibit extreme values ranging from 10 to 20 bushels per acre, while the other may show yields as low as 5 bushels per acre and as high as 25 bushels per acre. If such a crude measure of dispersion may be used, it is apparent that there is greater uniformity of yield in the first county. Chart 10.1

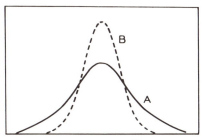

Chart 10.1. Two Frequency Curves Having Different Dispersions.

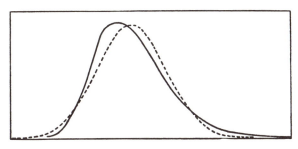

Chart 10.2. A Curve Skewed to the Right (Solid Line) and a Symmetrical Curve (Broken Line).

shows two symmetrical curves which have the same mean but which differ in respect to dispersion.

If a frequency curve or frequency distribution is not symmetrical, it is said to be *skewed*, or *asymmetrical*. Most frequency distributions exhibit

189

more or less skewness.   Chart 10.2 shows two curves, one of which is symmetrical and one of which is skewed.   The skewed curve is skewed to the right—the direction in which the excess tail appears.

Curves of frequency distributions may be symmetrical but may differ from each other in regard to the amount of *kurtosis* present.   The basis of reference is the normal or mesokurtic curve discussed in Chapter 23.   A leptokurtic curve has a narrower central portion and higher tails than does the normal curve.   A comparison of these two is shown in Chart 10.3. Chart 10.4 shows a platykurtic curve and a normal curve.   As may be seen, the platykurtic curve has a broader central portion and lower tails.

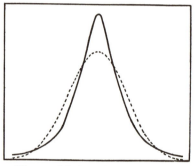

Chart 10.3. A Leptokurtic Curve (Solid Line) and a Normal or Mesokurtic Curve (Broken Line).

MEASURES OF ABSOLUTE DISPERSION

The mean annual temperature at Lexington, Kentucky is 55.2 degrees. The mean annual temperature at San Francisco, California is 55.7 degrees, which is very little different from the temperature at Lexington.   These two figures do not, however, suffice to characterize this aspect of the climatic conditions of the two cities.   The temperature at Lexington has been known to fall as low as −20 degrees

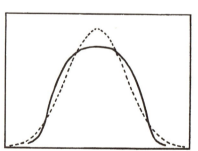

Chart 10.4.   A Platykurtic Curve (Solid Line) and a Normal or Mesokurtic Curve (Broken Line).

and to rise as high as 108 degrees.   In San Francisco the lowest recorded temperature is 20 degrees and the highest is 104 degrees.   It is quite apparent that there is greater variability of temperature at Lexington than at San Francisco.

Let us consider a second illustration. A buyer for a large department store has been offered two types of electric lights for use in the store.   The salesmen each claim about the same average length of life for their bulbs.   The buyer obtains from a testing laboratory test data for 40-watt lamps of the two makes and finds that the average life of each of the two kinds of bulbs is about 1,000 hours.   Examining the data further, however, shows that in one batch of bulbs a lamp burned out at 325 hours while one lasted 1,570 hours.   In the other batch one lamp lasted but 105 hours, while one did not burn out until the expiration of 2,910 hours.   This limited information indicates a greater degree of uniformity among lamps of the first batch.

The range.   The measurement of dispersion may be made in a crude form by referring to the lowest and the highest values, as was done in the preceding paragraphs.   This is a very simple and easy-to-understand measure.   The range gives a comprehensive value for the data in that it includes the limits within which all of the items occurred.   However, the range has certain disadvantages.   It fails to give any consideration to the arrangement of the values between the two extreme values.[1]   Furthermore, the range is misleading if either of the extreme values is an unusual occurrence.

Referring to the liberal arts students' grades in Table 10.3, it is observed that the range is 74.95 (the lower limit of the first class) to 98.95 (the upper limit of the last class).   If we have the array to refer to, as in Table 8.2, the range may be given a little more accurately as 76.5 to 98.3.   The range from the frequency distribution merely tells us that no one in the class received a grade below 74.95 or above 98.95.   The range is usually stated as the difference between the two extreme values.   For the students, $98.95 - 74.95 = 24.00$.   However, if only this single figure is given, we do not know whether the range is from 0 to 24, or from 70 to 94, or what the limits may be.

The 10–90 percentile range.   Sometimes we are interested in knowing the range within which a certain proportion of the items fall.   One such range, which is occasionally used in educational measurement, is the 10–90 percentile range.   This measure excludes the lowest 10 per cent and the highest 10 per cent, giving the two values between which the central 80 per cent of the items occur.   Of course, the 10th percentile is the 1st decile, and the 90th percentile is the 9th decile.   The measure is usually referred to, however, as the 10–90 percentile range, rather than the 1–9 decile range, since the former carries more clearly the idea of the central 80 per cent.

The 10–90 percentile range is not affected by extreme values as is the range.   However, this measure has a very serious shortcoming in that it does not make use of the values of all the items.   As a result, the values below the 10th percentile (or above the 90th percentile) could be massed closely together or spread out widely; the effect upon the 10–90 percentile range would be the same.   Also, the values between the 10th percentile and the 90th percentile could be arranged in any conceivable manner so long as they are somewhere between the 10th and 90th percentiles.

The quartile deviation.   In Chapter 9 mention was made of Q_1 and Q_3, the lower and the upper quartiles.   A measure of dispersion

---

[1] It must be obvious that when $N = 2$, this difficulty does not exist.   It is of minor importance for small samples drawn from a normal population.

based upon these values is termed the *quartile deviation,* or the *semi-inter-quartile range.* It is given by

$$Q = \frac{Q_3 - Q_1}{2}.$$

If a series is symmetrical, it is clear that Q_1 and Q_3 are equidistant from the median. Therefore, if we measure $\pm Q$ from the median, we include 50 per cent of the items of the series, for we have measured back to Q_1 and Q_3. If a series is skewed, as is usually true, we may take $\pm Q$ around the median, and, while we shall not arrive at either Q_1 or Q_3, we may expect to include approximately 50 per cent of the items unless the skewness is great.

The quartile deviation, like the 10–90 percentile range, is not affected by extreme values and also fails to consider the values of all the items.

The average deviation. The *average deviation,* or the *mean deviation,* as it is sometimes called, is usually measured in relation to the arithmetic mean. The average deviation is obtained by taking the sum of the deviations of the items from the arithmetic mean, without regard to signs, and dividing by the number of items. It will be recalled that $\Sigma x = 0$ and it is for this reason that the signs of the various x values are neglected. Thus,

$$AD = \frac{\Sigma |x|}{N},$$

or, for a frequency distribution,

$$AD = \frac{\Sigma f |x|}{N},$$

where | | means that the signs are neglected. Because the sum of the deviations (signs neglected) is a minimum when taken around the median, the mean deviation is sometimes computed in relation to the median. In practice, however, the mean is generally used and, if the series is symmetrical, the resulting AD is the same. Since AD is of limited usefulness compared to the measure of dispersion next discussed, the computation of AD is not shown here. The determination of AD for a frequency distribution is illustrated in the first edition of this book on pages 236 and 239.

If a distribution is normal, 57.5 per cent of the items are included within the range of $\overline{X} \pm AD$. If the distribution is moderately skewed, this will be found to be approximately true.

The standard deviation, ungrouped data. Instead of merely neglecting the signs of the deviations from the arithmetic mean, we may square the deviations, thereby making all of them positive. Thus, we may have a measure

$$s^2 = \frac{\Sigma x^2}{N},$$

the *variance* or mean square deviation.   (At a later point we shall use the term *variation* to refer to Σx^2.) s^2 is also known as the second moment, π_2, of the distribution, since the deviations have been raised to the second power.   We shall make use of the variance in later sections of the book.

At this point we are interested in the square root of this measure,

$$s = \sqrt{\frac{\Sigma x^2}{N}},$$

TABLE 10.1

Computation of Standard Deviation for Scores of 15 Persons in Recalling Trade Names of Advertised Products by Use of the Expression

$$s = \sqrt{\frac{\Sigma x^2}{N}}$$

Subject	Score X	x	x^2
1	12	−20.87	435.56
2	21	−11.87	140.90
3	21	−11.87	140.90
4	23	− 9.87	97.42
5	27	− 5.87	34.46
6	28	− 4.87	23.72
7	30	− 2.87	8.24
8	34	1.13	1.28
9	37	4.13	17.06
10	39	6.13	37.58
11	39	6.13	37.58
12	39	6.13	37.58
13	40	7.13	50.84
14	49	16.13	260.18
15	54	21.13	446.48
Total	493	...	1,769.78

Data from S. M. Newhall and M. H. Heim, "Memory Value of Absolute Size in Magazine Advertising," *Journal of Applied Psychology*, Vol. 13, pp. 62–75.   The above data were for advertisements of 150 square inches each, and each was observed for 5 seconds.   The maximum possible score was 81.

$$\bar{X} = \frac{493}{15} = 32.87.$$

$$s = \sqrt{\frac{\Sigma x^2}{N}} = \sqrt{\frac{1,769.78}{15}} = \sqrt{117.98} = 10.9.$$

which is termed the *standard deviation* or, occasionally, the root-mean-square deviation.   It has been pointed out previously that Σx^2 is a minimum when taken around the arithmetic mean.[2]   Therefore, the standard deviation is always computed in reference to the arithmetic mean.   As the above expression indicates, the steps involved in computing s are:

---

[2] For a demonstration, see Appendix S, section 10.1.

(1) Determine the deviation x of each item from $\overline{X}$;
(2) Square these deviations;
(3) Total them;
(4) Divide this sum by N;
(5) Take the square root.

The computation of s for a series of ungrouped data is shown in Table 10.1. This procedure involves the computation of x for every item, and would be a rather laborious procedure if there were an appreciably larger number of items. The value of s may be obtained, without computing each x, by means of the expression[3]

$$s = \sqrt{\frac{\Sigma X^2}{N} - \left(\frac{\Sigma X}{N}\right)^2}.$$

The computation of s by this shorter method is illustrated in Table 10.2. Notice that the correction $\left(\dfrac{\Sigma X}{N}\right)^2$ is subtracted. This is always true. The sum of the squared deviations is least when taken around $\overline{X}$. We, however, took our deviations around some other value (0, in this instance), and these squared deviations are therefore too large.

Referring to Table 10.1, it will be observed that the value of $\overline{X}$ was rounded to two decimals, and thus each value of x and x^2 is an approximation. If $\overline{X}$ and x are shown to sufficient digits, results by the two methods will be the same. Here, both methods yield 10.9.

At this point it may be well to note that s measures the dispersion *in the sample*. In Chapter 24 we shall discuss σ, the population standard deviation, and $\hat{\sigma}$, an estimate of the population standard deviation based upon a sample.

The standard deviation, grouped data. Before considering the properties of s, let us see how to compute s for a frequency distribution. Since frequencies are present,

$$s = \sqrt{\frac{\Sigma f x^2}{N}},$$

where x now represents the deviation of a class mid-value from the mean. Table 10.3 illustrates the computation of s for the liberal arts students' grades. It is fairly obvious that this method, involving the determination of a number of x values, is cumbersome.

A short method for s is available which allows us to take the mid-value of any class as the assumed mean, work with deviations around this value, and make the necessary correction. The expression is

$$s = \sqrt{\frac{\Sigma f d^2}{N} - \left(\frac{\Sigma f d}{N}\right)^2}.$$

---

[3] For proof of this expression, see Appendix S, section 10.2.

TABLE 10.2

Computation of Standard Devia-
tion for Scores of 15 Persons in
Recalling Trade Names of
Advertised Products by
Use of the Expres-
sion

$$s = \sqrt{\frac{\Sigma X^2}{N} - \left(\frac{\Sigma X}{N}\right)^2}$$

Subject	Score X	X^2
1	12	144
2	21	441
3	21	441
4	23	529
5	27	729
6	28	784
7	30	900
8	34	1,156
9	37	1,369
10	39	1,521
11	39	1,521
12	39	1,521
13	40	1,600
14	49	2,401
15	54	2,916
Total	493	17,973

Data from same source as Table 10.1.

$$s = \sqrt{\frac{\Sigma X^2}{N} - \left(\frac{\Sigma X}{N}\right)^2} = \sqrt{\frac{17,973}{15} - \left(\frac{493}{15}\right)^2}$$
$$= \sqrt{1,198.20 - 1,080.22} = \sqrt{117.98}$$
$$= 10.9.$$

To further shorten the process, the deviations are taken in terms of classes, giving[4]

$$s = i\sqrt{\frac{\Sigma f(d')^2}{N} - \left(\frac{\Sigma fd'}{N}\right)^2},$$

where d' indicates the deviation of a class mid-value from the assumed mean in terms of classes and i is the class interval. It is of interest to note that the correction factor $\left(\frac{\Sigma fd'}{N}\right)^2$ is the square of the correction factor used in computing the arithmetic mean by the short method. The computation of s by this shorter procedure is shown in Table 10.4.

Properties of the standard deviation. Of the various measures of absolute dispersion which have been mentioned, the standard deviation (and its square, the variance) is by far the most important. It will be used in connection with various statistical methods described hereafter.

---

[4] For demonstration, see Appendix S, section 10.2.

TABLE 10.3

Computation of the Standard Deviation for Grades of the 1965 Liberal Arts Graduates of Rutgers—The State University by Use of the Expression

$$s = \sqrt{\frac{\Sigma f x^2}{N}}$$

Grade	Number of students f	Mid-values of classes X	$x = X - \bar{X}$	x^2	fx^2
75.0–76.9	3	75.95	− 9.22	85.0084	255.0252
77.0–78.9	23	77.95	− 7.22	52.1284	1,198.9532
79.0–80.9	52	79.95	− 5.22	27.2484	1,416.9168
81.0–82.9	61	81.95	− 3.22	10.3684	632.4724
83.0–84.9	74	83.95	− 1.22	1.4884	110.1416
85.0–86.9	61	85.95	+ 0.78	0.6084	37.1124
87.0–88.9	53	87.95	+ 2.78	7.7284	409.6052
89.0–90.9	35	89.95	+ 4.78	22.8484	799.6940
91.0–92.9	23	91.95	+ 6.78	45.9684	1,057.2732
93.0–94.9	15	93.95	+ 8.78	77.0884	1,156.3260
95.0–96.9	7	95.95	+10.78	116.2084	813.4588
97.0–98.9	2	97.95	+12.78	163.3284	326.6568
Total	409	. . .	. . .	. . .	8,213.6356

$$s = \sqrt{\frac{\Sigma f x^2}{N}} = \sqrt{\frac{8,213.6356}{409}} = \sqrt{20.0822} = 4.48.$$

$$\bar{X} = 85.17.$$

One important consideration is that it is one of the factors involved in the equation for the normal curve and for various skewed curves, discussed in Chapter 23. It is also used in testing the reliability of certain statistical measures, in correlation, and in connection with business cycle analysis.

The standard deviation is the most frequently used measure of the spread of a series of data. If $\pm s$ is measured from the arithmetic mean of a normal distribution, 68.27 per cent of the items are included; within the range of $\bar{X} \pm 2s$, 95.45 per cent are included; and within $\bar{X} \pm 3s$, 99.73 per cent,[5] or nearly all, of the items are included. Chart 10.5 illustrates what has just been said. The percentages just given refer to a normal curve. If the distribution is skewed, these percentages will be only approximately realized. For the students' grades (Table 10.4), $\bar{X} \pm s$ is 85.17 $\pm$ 4.48 = 80.69 and 89.65. To ascertain the proportion of students in Table 10.4 who fall between 80.69 and 89.65, we first determine the number occurring between 80.69 and 80.95 (the upper limit of the third class), which is 6.8; then we include all of the frequencies in the next four classes, after which we compute the number between 88.95 (the lower limit of the eighth class) and 89.65, which is 12.3. The total is

---

[5] See Appendix E, which gives the areas in one-half of the central portion of the normal curve. More exactly, 68.27 is twice 34.13447; 95.45 is twice 47.72499; 99.73 is twice 49.86501.

TABLE 10.4

***Computation of the Standard Deviation for Grades
of the 1965 Liberal Arts Graduates of Rutgers—The
State University by Use of the Expression***

$$s = i \sqrt{\frac{\Sigma f(d')^2}{N} - \left(\frac{\Sigma fd'}{N}\right)^2}$$

Grade	Number of students f	d'	fd'	$f(d')^2$
75.0–76.9	3	−4	− 12	48
77.0–78.9	23	−3	− 69	207
79.0–80.9	52	−2	−104	208
81.0–82.9	61	−1	− 61	61
83.0–84.9	74	0		
85.0–86.9	61	+1	+ 61	61
87.0–88.9	53	+2	+106	212
89.0–90.9	35	+3	+105	315
91.0–92.9	23	+4	+ 92	368
93.0–94.9	15	+5	+ 75	375
95.0–96.9	7	+6	+ 42	252
97.0–98.9	2	+7	+ 14	98
Total	409	...	+249	2,205

$$s = i \sqrt{\frac{\Sigma f(d')^2}{N} - \left(\frac{\Sigma fd'}{N}\right)^2} = 2 \sqrt{\frac{2,205}{409} - \left(\frac{249}{409}\right)^2},$$

$$= 2 \sqrt{5.020561} = 2(2.241),$$

$$= 4.48.$$

268.1 or 65.6 per cent.   Within $\overline{X} \pm 2s$ (that is, from 76.21 to 94.13), we find 392.0, or 95.8 per cent of the grades.   Within $\overline{X} \pm 3s$(71.73 to 98.61), 99.92 per cent of the grades are included.

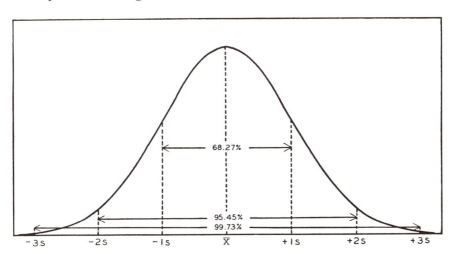

Chart 10.5.   Proportion of Items Included within ±1s, ±2s, and ±3s of the Arithmetic Mean in a Normal Curve.

In dealing with the normal curve in later chapters, we shall not confine ourselves to the proportionate areas included within $\pm s$, $\pm 2s$, and $\pm 3s$ of the mean, but shall consider any desired multiples of s. For example, we shall later be interested in knowing that 95 per cent of the items may be found within $\overline{X} \pm 1.96s$ and that 99 per cent may occur within $\overline{X} \pm 2.58s$. Actually, we shall be more interested in the proportions occurring *beyond* the limits mentioned, that is, 5 per cent and 1 per cent.

Before leaving the topic of absolute dispersion, it may be of interest to point out that, for any series of values, no matter how they are distributed, it may be shown by Tchebycheff's inequality, that the proportion of the values lying within the limits of $\overline{X} \pm Ms$ (where the value of M is greater than one) will be more than $1 - \dfrac{1}{M^2}$, and that the proportion falling beyond the limits of $\overline{X} \pm Ms$ will be less than $\dfrac{1}{M^2}$. If a distribution is unimodal, and if the difference between the mode and the mean does not exceed s, the Camp-Meidell inequality states that more than $1 - \dfrac{1}{2.25M^2}$ of the values are within $\overline{X} \pm Ms$ and that less than $\dfrac{1}{2.25M^2}$ of the values lie beyond $\overline{X} \pm Ms$.

The greater the dispersion of a series, the greater the value of s. As a measure of uniformity of the characteristic measured, the smaller the value of s, the greater the uniformity. To avoid this inverse relationship, a modification referred to as a *measure of precision* is sometimes used, especially with reference to the precision of a series of physical measurements. This measure is

$$h^2 = \frac{1}{2s^2}.$$

It is not often used in statistical work in the social sciences.

MEASURES OF RELATIVE DISPERSION

In the preceding paragraphs we have discussed measures of absolute dispersion, all of which are expressed in terms of the units of the problem, which may be dollars, pounds, inches, percentages, and so forth. When we wish to compare the dispersions of two or more series, it may or may not be desirable to use such a measure. The comparison of dispersions of two or more series resolves itself into three possible situations:

(1) The series to be compared may be expressed in the same units, and the means may be the same, or nearly the same, in size. The grades of the liberal arts students showed a mean of 85.17 and a standard deviation of 4.48. If another graduating class showed $\overline{X} = 85.05$ and $s = 4.25$, it is clear that the second class would exhibit less dispersion.

(2) The series to be compared may be expressed in the same units, but the arithmetic means may differ. Some years ago a tire company developed a new type of cord for automobile tires. The new cord was superior to ordinary cord in that it could stretch more and had a longer flex life. Tests made on cord as received from the cotton mill and prior to fabrication into tires showed for the flex life of the new cord

$$\overline{X} = 138.64 \text{ minutes, and } s = 15.27 \text{ minutes;}$$

while for regular cord the figures were

$$\overline{X} = 87.66 \text{ minutes, and } s = 14.12 \text{ minutes.}$$

If we compare the two s values, it appears that the new cord is more variable in respect to flex life than is regular cord. However, it must be noted that the average flex life of the new cord is much greater than that of regular cord. Taking this factor into consideration, we may set up a measure of *relative dispersion*,

$$V = \frac{s}{\overline{X}}.$$

This is the coefficient of variation and is usually expressed as a percentage. For the new cord

$$V = \frac{15.27}{138.64} = 0.1101, \text{ or } 11.0 \text{ per cent;}$$

while for regular cord

$$V = \frac{14.12}{87.66} = 0.1611, \text{ or } 16.1 \text{ per cent.}$$

It is thus apparent that the relative variation in flex life is much less for the new cord than for regular cord.

Chart 10.6 also illustrates the comparison of dispersions of two series having different mean values. Section A shows the curves of two distributions having the same absolute dispersions but different relative dispersions. In section B are curves of two distributions having quite different absolute dispersions but the same relative dispersions. If the zero is shown on the horizontal scale, as in Chart 10.6, a very rough visual impression may be had of the relative dispersion of a series. For this reason some statisticians think it is desirable to show the zero on the horizontal scale. This does not seem to be a very important matter, however, since relative dispersion can at best be visualized only approximately. Occasionally frequency distributions are formed with class intervals expressed, not in terms of original units, but as percentages of the mean, the interval being some convenient figure, such as 10 per cent of the mean. If two such distributions are plotted on one chart, it is easy to compare visually their relative dispersions.

(3) The series to be compared may be expressed in different units. In such a case the standard deviations cannot be directly compared. A study of a large number of male industrial workers[6] revealed an average pulse rate of 81.1 beats per minute and a standard deviation of about 12.2 beats per minute. Measurements of height showed $\overline{X} = 66.9$ inches and $s = 2.7$ inches. The measurements of height included a small number of men not measured as to pulse rate. Let us disregard this difficulty for the purposes of our illustration. Are the industrial workers more variable in respect to pulse rate or height? It is obvious that the two standard deviations, being in different units, cannot be compared. Computing the two coefficients of variation shows, for pulse rate,

$$V = \frac{12.2}{81.1} = 0.149, \text{ or } 14.9 \text{ per cent,}$$

and, for height,

$$V = \frac{2.7}{66.9} = 0.040, \text{ or } 4.0 \text{ per cent.}$$

It is clear that, for this group of men, pulse rate is subject to greater dispersion than is height.

Somewhat akin to our measurement of relative dispersion is the possibility of expressing a given value in terms of its divergence from the mean and also in terms of the dispersion of the series. Such a procedure is not especially useful when we are considering only one value or comparing two values from the same series. Its usefulness becomes apparent when we want to compare two values from different series and when those two series (1) differ in respect to $\overline{X}$ or s, or both, or (2) are expressed in different units. Suppose that a certain student has made a grade of 180 on an intelligence test, and that his group showed $\overline{X} = 160$ and $s = 15$. This same student made a grade of 86 in history, and the group showed $\overline{X} = 70$ and $s = 12$. We are interested in knowing whether his relative standing is higher in the intelligence test or in history. In the intelligence test he was 20 points above the mean, and in history he was 16 points above the mean. These deviations, however, are not comparable, but may be rendered so by dividing by their respective standard deviations. Thus,

$$\text{Intelligence test:} \quad \frac{X - \overline{X}}{s} = \frac{180 - 160}{15} = \frac{+20}{15} = +1.33;$$

$$\text{History:} \quad \frac{X - \overline{X}}{s} = \frac{86 - 70}{12} = \frac{+16}{12} = +1.33.$$

---

[6] Based on data in *A Health Study of Ten Thousand Male Industrial Workers*, pp. **45** and 59, United States Public Health Service, Public Health Bulletin, 162.

FREQUENCIES

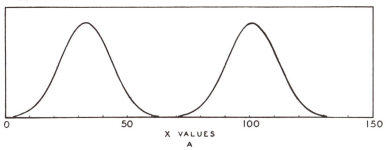

0   50   100   150
X VALUES
A

FREQUENCIES

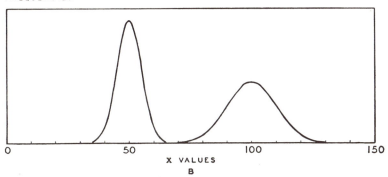

0   50   100   150
X VALUES
B

Chart 10.6. Comparisons of Dispersions of Series Having Different Arithmetic Means. A. Same absolute dispersion, different relative dispersion: left-hand curve, $\bar{X} = 33$, $s = 10$, $V = 30.3$ per cent; right-hand curve, $\bar{X} = 101$, $s = 10$, $V = 9.9$ per cent. B. Different absolute dispersion, same relative dispersion: left-hand curve, $\bar{X} = 50$, $s = 5$, $V = 10$ per cent; right-hand curve, $\bar{X} = 100$, $s = 10$, $V = 10$ per cent. (Sections A and B have different vertical scales since they are not intended to be compared. However, if the vertical scale of section B is expanded 50 per cent, all curves will have the same area.)

It is apparent that the student shows the same relative standing in history and on the intelligence test, being $+1.33s$ above the mean in each. The usefulness of this device is by no means limited to the educational field. It is, however, often used with test data and is then referred to as a "standard score."

SKEWNESS

When a series is not symmetrical, it is said to be asymmetrical or *skewed*. In Chart 10.2 a skewed curve was shown in relation to a symmetrical one. The curve of the liberal arts students' grades (Chart 10.7) is also skewed. Measures of skewness indicate not only the amount of skewness but also the direction. A series is said to be skewed in the direction of the extreme values, or, speaking in terms of the curve, in the direction of the excess tail. Thus the two curves referred to above are both skewed positively, or to the right. Most skewed curves encountered in the social sciences are skewed to the right. Only rarely do we

201

find curves skewed to the left, as in Chart 10.8, and even more rarely do we find data *characteristically* skewed to the left.

Many series, however, are characteristically skewed to the right. Examples are frequency distributions of wages or salaries, use of electricity (see Chart 23.13), weights of adult male human beings, and numerous other variables. Distributions of grades are apt to be moderately skewed to the right, or nearly symmetrical. In the case of the students' grades, the skewness is partly due to the fact that we are considering only those men who had survived the previous three years, during which some of the less able had been dropped. The distribution of ages at death of the American inventors in Chart 10.8 may be characteristically skewed to the left, since younger men do not often have enough inventions to their credit to be classified as "inventors," or the skewness may be due to the fact that a time factor is present—almost one-fifth of the inventors included in this study were born before 1800.

Pearsonian measure of skewness. It was pointed out in the preceding chapter that the mode is not influenced by the presence of extreme values, the median is influenced by their position only, and the arithmetic mean is influenced by the size of the extremes. Consequently we could make use of the mode and the mean to measure skewness. We might say, then, that skewness = mean − mode. But there are some shortcomings of such a measure. In the first place, being a measure of absolute skewness, it would be in terms of the units of the problem. Furthermore, it would have much different meaning for a series of small dispersion than for a widely dispersed series. Statisticians almost never use a measure of absolute skewness, preferring a measure of relative skewness. The measure just mentioned may be put into relative terms and the two difficulties overcome by dividing by s. Now

$$\text{Skewness} = \frac{\overline{X} - \text{Mo}}{s}.$$

This gives us a relative measure with positive sign when skewness is to the right, and with negative sign when skewness is to the left. There is, however, another important difficulty growing out of the fact that the mode for most frequency distributions is only an approximation. The median may be more satisfactorily located, and therefore we use the measure[7]

$$\text{Sk} = \frac{3(\overline{X} - \text{Med})}{s}.$$

---

[7] The presence of the 3 in the expression is explained as follows: Karl Pearson showed empirically that, in moderately skewed distributions of a continuous variable, the median tends to fall about $\frac{2}{3}$ of the distance from the mode toward the mean. Consequently he wrote $\text{Mo} = \overline{X} - 3 (\overline{X} - \text{Med})$ and, substituting this expression for the mode in the measure of skewness, obtained

$$\text{Sk} = \frac{\overline{X} - [\overline{X} - 3(\overline{X} - \text{Med})]}{s} = \frac{3(\overline{X} - \text{Med})}{s}.$$

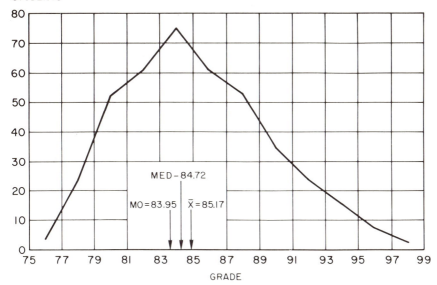

Chart 10.7. Location of Arithmetic Mean, Median, and Mode for Grades of the 1952 Graduating Class of the United States Merchant Marine Academy.

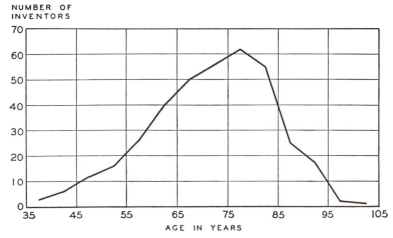

Chart 10.8. Age at Death of 371 American Inventors. Data from "Bio-Social Characteristics of American Inventors," by Sanford Winston, *American Sociological Review*, Vol. 2, No. 6, pp. 837–849.

In the preceding chapter it was found that $\bar{X} = 85.17$ and Med $= 84.72$ for the liberal arts students' grades. In this chapter the value of s was ascertained to be 4.48. The skewness, then, is

$$\text{Sk} = \frac{3(85.17 - 84.72)}{4.48} = +0.301.$$

TABLE 10.5

Computation of Various Measures for Age at Death of 371 American Inventors

Age at death in years	f	d'	fd'	$f(d')^2$	$f(d')^3$
35 and under 40	3	−6	−18	108	−648
40 and under 45	6	−5	−30	150	−750
45 and under 50	12	−4	−48	192	−768
50 and under 55	16	−3	−48	144	−432
55 and under 60	26	−2	−52	104	−208
60 and under 65	40	−1	−40	40	− 40
65 and under 70	50	0	0	0	0
70 and under 75	56	1	56	56	56
75 and under 80	62	2	124	248	496
80 and under 85	55	3	165	495	1,485
85 and under 90	25	4	100	400	1,600
90 and under 95	17	5	85	425	2,125
95 and under 100	2	6	12	72	432
100 and over*	1	7	7	49	343
Total..........	371	...	+313	2,483	+3,691

* This class assumed to have its mid-value at 102.5.

Data from Sanford Winston, "Bio-social Characteristics of American Inventors," *American Sociological Review*, Vol. 2, No. 6, p. 848, and by correspondence.

$$\frac{N}{2} = 185.5.$$

$$\text{Med} = 70 + \frac{32.5}{56} \times 5 = 72.90 \text{ years.} \qquad \bar{X} = 67.5 + \frac{313}{371} \times 5 = 71.72 \text{ years}$$

$$s = 5 \sqrt{\frac{2,483}{371} - \left(\frac{313}{371}\right)^2} = 12.23 \text{ years.}$$

$$\nu_1 = \frac{\Sigma fd'}{N} = \frac{+313}{371} = 0.843666.$$

$$\nu_2 = \frac{\Sigma f(d')^2}{N} = \frac{2,483}{371} = 6.692722.$$

$$\nu_3 = \frac{\Sigma f(d')^3}{N} = \frac{+3,691}{371} = 9.948787.$$

$\pi_1 = 0.$

$\pi_2 = \nu_2 - \nu_1^2 = 6.692722 - (0.843666)^2 = 5.980950.$

$\pi_3 = \nu_3 - 3\nu_1\nu_2 + 2\nu_1^3 = +9.948787 - 3(0.843666)(6.692722) + 2(0.843666)^3$

$\qquad = -5.789483.$

This may be considered as a moderate degree of skewness, since the measure varies within the limits[8] of ±3. It should be added that values as large as ±1 are rather unusual.

For the data of age at death of the American inventors, it is shown under Table 10.5 that $\bar{X} = 71.72$ years, while Med = 72.90 years and $s = 12.23$ years. The Pearsonian measure of skewness is

---

[8] Harold Hotelling and Leonard M. Solomons ("The Limits of a Measure of Skewness," *Annals of Mathematical Statistics*, May 1932, pp. 141–142) have shown that $\dfrac{\bar{X} - \text{Med}}{s}$ lies between ±1.

$$\text{Sk} = \frac{3(71.72 - 72.90)}{12.23} = -0.29.$$

Measures of skewness based on quartiles and percentiles.
Skewness may also be measured by means of the quartile measure of skewness,

$$\frac{(Q_3 - \text{Med}) - (\text{Med} - Q_1)}{Q_3 - Q_1} = \frac{Q_1 + Q_3 - 2\text{Med}}{Q_3 - Q_1},$$

and by use of an expression employing the 10th and 90th percentiles,

$$\frac{(P_{90} - \text{Med}) - (\text{Med} - P_{10})}{P_{90} - P_{10}} = \frac{P_{10} + P_{90} - 2\text{Med}}{P_{90} - P_{10}}.$$

Since these measures suffer from shortcomings similar to those previously mentioned for measures of dispersion based on quartiles and percentiles, they are not altogether satisfactory measures of skewness, and no further consideration will be given to them here.

Measure of skewness based on the third moment. We have seen that the most satisfactory measure of dispersion is the standard deviation, which is based upon the second moment about the mean

$$\pi_2 = \frac{\Sigma x^2}{N}, \text{ and } s = \sqrt{\pi_2} = \sqrt{\frac{\Sigma x^2}{N}}.$$

A measure of skewness may be obtained by making use of the third moment about the mean,

$$\pi_3 = \frac{\Sigma x^3}{N}.$$

It will be recalled that the first moment about the mean,

$$\pi_1 = \frac{\Sigma x}{N},$$

is always zero. However, the third moment about the mean is not zero unless the distribution is symmetrical about the mean. Cubing a deviation does not change its sign. It does, however, have a disproportionately large effect on large deviations. As illustrations, consider the two sets of data given in Tables 10.6 and 10.7, the first of which is symmetrical around a mean of 6, while the second is not symmetrical around a mean of 6. Both sets of data have

$$\pi_1 = \frac{\Sigma x}{N} = 0,$$

and the data of Table 10.6 have

$$\pi_3 = \frac{\Sigma x^3}{N} = 0.$$

But the figures in Table 10.7 show

$$\pi_3 = \frac{\Sigma x^3}{N} = +6.$$

TABLE 10.6	TABLE 10.7
Computation of First and Third Moments of a Symmetrical Series	*Computation of First and Third Moments of an Asymmetrical Series*

X	x	x³	X	x	x³
2	−4	−64	3	−3	−27
4	−2	− 8	4	−2	− 8
6	0	0	6	0	0
8	+2	+ 8	7	+1	+ 1
10	+4	+64	10	+4	+64
	0	0		0	+30

$$\pi_1 = \frac{\Sigma x}{N} = \frac{0}{5} = 0.$$

$$\pi_3 = \frac{\Sigma x^3}{N} = \frac{0}{5} = 0.$$

$$\pi_1 = \frac{\Sigma x}{N} = \frac{0}{5} = 0.$$

$$\pi_3 = \frac{\Sigma x^3}{N} = \frac{+30}{5} = +6.$$

To compute the third moment of a frequency distribution,

$$\pi_3 = \frac{\Sigma f x^3}{N},$$

taking the actual deviations from the arithmetic mean, cubing them, multiplying by the frequencies, summing, and dividing by N, would be laborious. As shown in Appendix S, section 10.2, the second moment, s^2 or π_2, can be obtained by a short process. In terms of class intervals squared,

$$\pi_2 = \frac{\Sigma f(d')^2}{N} - \left(\frac{\Sigma f d'}{N}\right)^2.$$

The value of the third moment (in terms of class intervals raised to the third power) is given by[9]

$$\pi_3 = \frac{\Sigma f(d')^3}{N} - 3\frac{\Sigma f d'}{N}\frac{\Sigma f(d')^2}{N} + 2\left(\frac{\Sigma f d'}{N}\right)^3.$$

Or, letting $\nu_1 = \dfrac{\Sigma f d'}{N}$, $\nu_2 = \dfrac{\Sigma f(d')^2}{N}$, and $\nu_3 = \dfrac{\Sigma f(d')^3}{N}$,

$$\pi_2 = \nu_2 - \nu_1^2,$$

and

$$\pi_3 = \nu_3 - 3\nu_1\nu_2 + 2\nu_1^3.$$

[9] See Appendix S, section 10.3.

Obviously, π_3 is a measure of absolute skewness.   The measure of relative skewness is

$$\beta_1 = \frac{\pi_3^2}{\pi_2^3},$$

where both numerator and denominator are in terms of class intervals raised to the sixth power. Skewness is also sometimes measured by α_3, where[10]

$$\alpha_3 = \sqrt{\beta_1} = \frac{\pi_3}{\sqrt{\pi_2^3}}.$$

TABLE 10.8

Computation of the First Three Moments for Grades of the 1965 Liberal Arts Graduates of Rutgers—The State University

Grade	Number of students	d'	fd'	$f(d')^2$	$f(d')^3$
75.0–76.9	3	−4	− 12	48	−192
77.0–78.9	23	−3	− 69	207	−621
79.0–80.9	52	−2	−104	208	−416
81.0–82.9	61	−1	− 61	61	− 61
83.0–84.9	74	0			
85.0–86.9	61	+1	+ 61	61	61
87.0–88.9	53	+2	+106	212	424
89.0–90.9	35	+3	+105	315	945
91.0–92.9	23	+4	+ 92	368	1,472
93.0–94.9	15	+5	+ 75	375	1,875
95.0–96.9	7	+6	+ 42	252	1,512
97.0–98.9	2	+7	+ 14	98	686
Total	409	...	+249	2,205	+5,685

$$\nu_1 = \frac{\Sigma fd'}{N} = \frac{+249}{409} = +0.608802.$$

$$\nu_2 = \frac{\Sigma f(d')^2}{N} = \frac{2,205}{409} = 5.391198.$$

$$\nu_3 = \frac{\Sigma f(d')^3}{N} = \frac{+5,685}{409} = +13.899756.$$

$\pi_1 = 0.$
$\pi_2 = \nu_2 - \nu_1^2 = 5.391198 - (0.608802)^2 = 5.020558.$
$\pi_3 = \nu_3 - 3\nu_1\nu_2 + 2\nu_1^3.$
$\quad = 13.899756 - 3(0.608802)(5.391198) + 2(0.608802)^3,$
$\quad = 4.504532.$

---

[10] No previous mention has been made of α_1 or α_2.   For any series of figures,

$$\alpha_1 = \frac{\pi_1}{\sqrt{\pi_2}} = 0;$$

$$\alpha_2 = \frac{\pi_2}{\sqrt{\pi_2^2}} = 1.$$

α_3 may be given the sign accompanying π_3. We shall make use of α_3 in fitting a skewed curve in Chapter 23.

The values of the second and third moments for the data of liberal arts students' grades are shown below Table 10.8   From these we obtain

$$\beta_1 = \frac{\pi_3^2}{\pi_2^3} = \frac{(4.504532)^2}{(5.020558)^3} = 0.16.$$

Similarly, the second and third moments for the age at death of the American inventors have been computed in Table 10.5.   From these we obtain

$$\beta_1 = \frac{(-5.789483)^2}{(5.980950)^3} = 0.16.$$

Since $\pi_3 = 0$ when no skewness is present, it follows that a perfectly symmetrical series will have $\beta_1 = 0$.   The greater the value of β_1, the more skewness there is in a series.   At this point we are not in a position to say whether either of the two values just given for β_1 is *significantly* greater than zero.   We shall consider this problem in Chapter 26.

KURTOSIS

Chart 10.9 shows a *leptokurtic* distribution.   A *platykurtic* distribution is shown in Chart 10.10.   The normal curve is designated as *mesokurtic*.[11] The degree of kurtosis present in a series may be measured by making use of the fourth moment,

$$\pi_4 = \frac{\Sigma x^4}{N},$$

or, for a frequency distribution,

$$\pi_4 = \frac{\Sigma f x^4}{N}.$$

By a procedure similar to that given in Appendix S, section 10.3, it may be shown that

$$\pi_4 = \frac{\Sigma f(d')^4}{N} - 4\frac{\Sigma fd'}{N}\frac{\Sigma f(d')^3}{N} + 6\left(\frac{\Sigma fd'}{N}\right)^2\frac{\Sigma f(d')^2}{N} - 3\left(\frac{\Sigma fd'}{N}\right)^4.$$

---

[11] *Kurtic* = humpbacked; thus, humped or unimodal. *Lepto* = slender, narrow *Platy* = broad, wide, flat.   *Meso* = in the middle, intermediate.

or letting

$$\nu_4 = \frac{\Sigma f(d')^4}{N}$$

$$\pi_4 = \nu_4 - 4\nu_1\nu_3 + 6\nu_1^2\nu_2 - 3\nu_1^4.$$

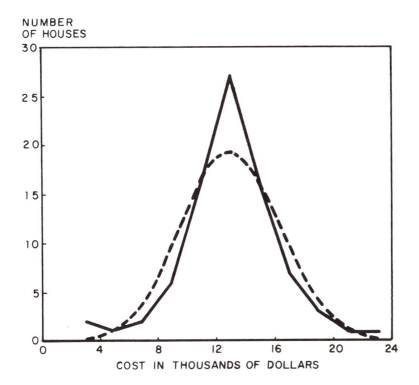

NUMBER
OF HOUSES

Chart 10.9.   Cost of New Five-Room House and Lot to Purchaser, (Solid Line) and Normal Curve (Broken Line) Having Same N, $\overline{X}$, and s, Cleveland.   Based on data of Table 10.9.

Now π_4 gives an absolute expression for kurtosis.   This may be put into relative terms by dividing by π_2^2.   The measure is known as β_2 or α_4, and

$$\beta_2 = \alpha_4 = \frac{\pi_4}{\pi_2^2},$$

where both numerator and denominator are in terms of class intervals raised to the fourth power.   This expression has a value of 3.0 for the normal curve. For a platykurtic curve, $\beta_2 < 3.0$. For a leptokurtic curve, $\beta_2 > 3.0$.

The leptokurtic curve of Chart 10.9 is shown in comparison with a normal curve having the same N, $\overline{X}$, and s. In Table 10.9 the moments of this distribution have been computed and $\beta_2 = 4.46$.

The platykurtic curve in Chart 10.10 is also shown in relation to a normal curve having the same N, $\overline{X}$, and s. The moments of the platykurtic series are shown in Table 10.10, and from these β_2 is found to be 2.22.

TABLE 10.9

Computation of First Four Moments and of β_2 for Cost of New 5-Room Wood House and Lot to Purchaser, Cleveland

Cost (mid-values)	f	d'	fd'	$f(d')^2$	$f(d')^3$	$f(d')^4$
\$ 3,000	2	−5	−10	50	−250	1,250
5,000	1	−4	− 4	16	− 64	256
7,000	2	−3	− 6	18	− 54	162
9,000	6	−2	−12	24	− 48	96
11,000	16	−1	−16	16	− 16	16
13,000	27	0	0	0	0	0
15,000	16	1	16	16	16	16
17,000	7	2	14	28	56	112
19,000	3	3	9	27	81	243
21,000	1	4	4	16	64	256
23,000	1	5	5	25	125	625
Total	82	. . .	0	236	− 90	3,032

Data from Frank R. Garfield and William M. Hood, "Construction Costs and Real Property Values," *Journal of the American Statistical Association*, Vol. 32, No. 200, p. 647. Costs expressed in current dollars.

$$\nu_1 = \frac{\Sigma fd'}{N} = \frac{0}{82} = 0.$$

$$\nu_2 = \frac{\Sigma f(d')^2}{N} = \frac{236}{82} = 2.878049.$$

$$\nu_3 = \frac{\Sigma f(d')^3}{N} = \frac{-90}{82} = -1.097561.$$

$$\nu_4 = \frac{\Sigma f(d')^4}{N} = \frac{3,032}{82} = 36.975601.$$

$\pi_1 = 0.$

$\pi_2 = \nu_2 - \nu_1^2 = 2.878049.$

$\pi_3 = \nu_3 - 3\nu_1\nu_2 + 2\nu_1^3 = -1.097561.$

$\pi_4 = \nu_4 - 4\nu_1\nu_3 + 6\nu_1^2\nu_2 - 3\nu_1^4 = 36.975601.$

$$\beta_2 = \frac{\pi_4}{\pi_2^2} = \frac{36.975601}{(2.878049)^2} = 4.46.$$

NOTE: The assumed mean (\$13,000) and the mean coincide, resulting in a value of 0 for ν_1. There are therefore no differences between the ν and π values, since $\nu_1^2 = 0$, $\nu_1\nu_2 = 0$, $\nu_1^3 = 0$, $\nu_1\nu_3 = 0$, etc.

When a deviation is raised to a fourth or a second power, its sign becomes positive.   The fourth power increases extreme deviations disprotortionately in comparison with raising them to the second power.   Con-

TABLE 10.10

Computation of First Four Moments and of β_2 for Length of Life of a Group of Electric Lamps

Length of life in hours (mid-values)	Percentage frequencies f	d'	fd'	$f(d')^2$	$f(d')^3$	$f(d')^4$
50	1.0	-9	-9.0	81.0	-729.0	6,561.0
150	1.5	-8	-12.0	96.0	-768.0	6,144.0
250	3.1	-7	-21.7	151.9	$-1,063.3$	7,443.1
350	4.4	-6	-26.4	158.4	-950.4	5,702.4
450	5.0	-5	-25.0	125.0	-625.0	3,125.0
550	5.7	-4	-22.8	91.2	-364.8	1,459.2
650	6.6	-3	-19.8	59.4	-178.2	534.6
750	7.3	-2	-14.6	29.2	-58.4	116.8
850	7.6	-1	-7.6	7.6	-7.6	7.6
950	7.8	0	0	0	0	0
1050	7.8	1	7.8	7.8	7.8	7.8
1150	7.6	2	15.2	30.4	60.8	121.6
1250	7.3	3	21.9	65.7	197.1	591.3
1350	6.6	4	26.4	105.6	422.4	1,689.6
1450	5.7	5	28.5	142.5	712.5	3,562.5
1550	5.0	6	30.0	180.0	1,080.0	6,480.0
1650	4.4	7	30.8	215.6	1,509.2	10,564.4
1750	3.1	8	24.8	198.4	1,587.2	12,697.6
1850	1.5	9	13.5	121.5	1,093.5	9,841.5
1950	1.0	10	10.0	100.0	1,000.0	10,000.0
Total	100.0	...	$+50.0$	1,967.2	$+2,925.8$	86,650.0

Data from Robley Winfrey and Edwin B. Kurtz, *Life Characteristics of Physical Property*, Bulletin 103, Iowa Engineering Experiment Station, p. 58, Property Group 28–2.

$$\nu_1 = \frac{\Sigma fd'}{N} = \frac{+50}{100.0} = +0.50.$$

$$\nu_2 = \frac{\Sigma f(d')^2}{N} = \frac{1,967.2}{100.0} = 19.672.$$

$$\nu_3 = \frac{\Sigma f(d')^3}{N} = \frac{+2,925.8}{100.0} = +29.258.$$

$$\nu_4 = \frac{\Sigma f(d')^4}{N} = \frac{86,650.0}{100.0} = 866.500.$$

$\pi_1 = 0.$

$\pi_2 = \nu_2 - \nu_1^2 = 19.672 - (0.50)^2 = 19.422.$

$\pi_3 = \nu_3 - 3\nu_1\nu_2 + 2\nu_1^3 = 29.258 - 3(0.50)(19.672) + 2(0.50)^3 = 0.$

$\pi_4 = \nu_4 - 4\nu_1\nu_3 + 6\nu_1^2\nu_2 - 3\nu_1^4$

$\quad = 866.500 - 4(0.50)(29.258) + 6(0.50)^2(19.672) - 3(0.50)^4$

$\quad = 837.3045.$

$$\beta_2 = \frac{\pi_4}{\pi_2^2} = \frac{837.3045}{(19.422)^2} = 2.22.$$

sequently the narrower the shoulders of a distribution and the longer the tails, the greater will be π_4 in relation to π_2^2.

In Chapter 26 we shall consider a method of ascertaining whether a value of β_2 is significantly less than or greater than 3.0.

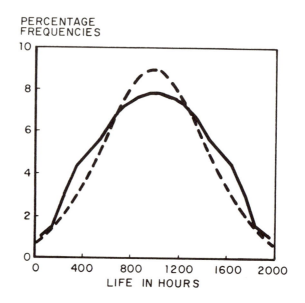

Chart 10.10. Length of Life of a Group of Electric Lamps (Solid Line) and Normal Curve (Broken Line) Having Same N, $\overline{X}$, and s. Based on data of Table 10.10. The tails of the normal curve are not shown. The left tail would cross the Y axis.

CORRECTION OF THE MOMENTS FOR GROUPING ERROR

In computing the mean, π_2 (or s), π_3, and π_4 for frequency distributions, we made use of the mid-values of the classes as representative values. We saw, in the previous chapter, that the mid-values were incorrect assumptions but that the errors present tend to offset each other when we compute the arithmetic mean. This offsetting is also present when the third moment is computed. It will be remembered that the mid-values of the classes preceding the modal class tend to be too small, while the mid-values of the classes following the modal class tend to be too large. The result is that the various x values tend to be slightly larger (in absolute value) than they should be, and no offsetting occurs when they are squared or raised to the fourth power. Consequently the value of π_2 (and s) and the value of π_4 are apt to be slightly larger than the values computed from the same data ungrouped. Sheppard's corrections attempt to offset this upward bias. The corrected moments are indicated by μ and are:[12]

$$\mu_1 = \pi_1 = 0,$$

$$\mu_2 = \pi_2 - \tfrac{1}{12},$$

$$\mu_3 = \pi_3,$$

$$\mu_4 = \pi_4 - \tfrac{1}{2}\pi_2 + \tfrac{7}{240},$$

where all computations are in terms of class intervals.

If we were to use the class means instead of the class mid-values, the arithmetic mean could be computed accurately. However, if class means were used, the values of π_2 (s^2) and π_4 would still be smaller than if computed from the same data ungrouped.

Sheppard's corrections may be applied when we are dealing with a continuous variable which, graphically, approaches the X-axis asymptotically at both ends of the distribution. This latter characteristic is often referred to as "high contact with the X-axis." If these conditions do not obtain, Sheppard's corrections should not be used, as the corrections may over-correct.[13] Neither is there justification for applying Sheppard's corrections if the original observations have not been made with reasonable accuracy.

When Sheppard's corrections are appropriate, the β's and α's may be computed from the μ's as follows:

$$\alpha_1 = \frac{\mu_1}{\sqrt{\mu_2}} = 0.$$

$$\alpha_2 = \frac{\mu_2}{\sqrt{\mu_2^2}} = 1.0.$$

$$\beta_1 = \frac{\mu_3^2}{\mu_2^3}. \qquad \alpha_3 = \frac{\mu_3}{\sqrt{\mu_2^3}} = \sqrt{\beta_1}.$$

$$\beta_2 = \frac{\mu_4}{\mu_2^2}. \qquad \alpha_4 = \frac{\mu_4}{\sqrt{\mu_2^4}} = \frac{\mu_4}{\mu_2^2} = \beta_2.$$

---

[12] For an illustration of the application of Sheppard's correction see the second edition of this text, pp. 237–238.

[13] See footnote 8 in Chapter 23. Consult also W. A. Shewhart, *Economic Control of Quality of Manufactured Product*, D. Van Nostrand Co., Princeton, N. J., 1931, pp. 78–79.

CHAPTER 11

Introduction to Time Series

Time series have already been seen in graphic form in Chapters 4, 5, and 6. The various charts of chronological data which were included in those chapters undertook merely to present the series, not to analyze them. In this and the following five chapters, we shall examine procedures for resolving time series into their more important components. The statistical methods which are used for analyzing time series are quite distinct from, but closely related to, the methods employed in frequency distribution analysis. Although economists have been largely responsible for the development of the techniques of time series analysis, the study of time series is of interest to workers in many other fields, for example, businessmen, sociologists, biologists, geologists, public health workers, and others.

MOVEMENTS IN TIME SERIES

The time series movements which will occupy our attention are secular trend, periodic, cyclical, and irregular. One or two of these movements may overshadow the others in some series. Ordinarily, all four of these movements will be present in a time series and, when present, are coexistent. We shall consider each of the four movents in turn.

Secular trend. Over a period of a dozen or more years, a time series is very likely to show a tendency to increase or to decrease. Chart 11.1, which presents monthly data of deposits in New York State savings banks from January 1946 to December 1964, shows a pronounced upward trend. This series provides an interesting illustration because the trend is unusually predominant; virtually no other movements are discernible.

Another series having an upward trend appears in Chart 11.2, which shows consumption (and consumption per adult) of distilled spirits in the United States, 1945–1963. One of the underlying factors causing an upward trend for this and many other series is the growth of population, and Chart 11.2 has been constructed with a logarithmic vertical scale in order that per adult figures might also be shown. The per adult consumption trend falls off somewhat in relation to the trend of total con-

214

sumption after 1952.   Per capita sales of many products and services have grown, among other reasons, because of a continuing improvement in the purchasing power available to the bulk of the population of the United States since the end of World War II.

BILLIONS OF
DOLLARS

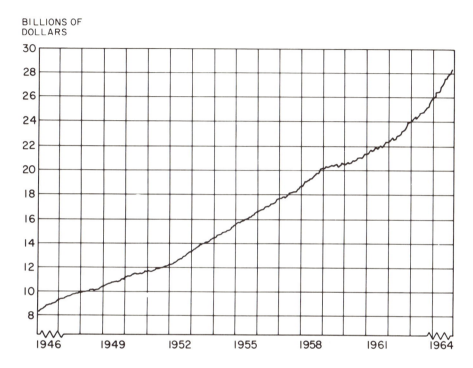

Chart 11.1.   Deposits in New York State Savings Banks, January 1946–December 1964.   Data from various issues of *Survey of Current Business*.

As this may suggest, many specific factors may be responsible for the growth in a time series.   The natural sciences have been applied to industry and to agriculture so as to increase their output enormously. Not always keeping pace with these technological changes, but induced by them, have been changes in business organization and methods. The growth of the corporation has permitted the accumulation of sufficient capital for specialization and mass production.   Scientific management, personnel management, and quality control have also played important parts in increasing the productivity of industry.   Automation will, undoubtedly, continue to increase industrial productivity.   Improved methods of marketing and better shipping facilities have made commodities available at times and places where they were not to be had earlier.

Not all chronological series show upward trends.   Some, like the crude death rate, shown in Chart 11.3, exhibit a generally downward trend. This particular declining trend is attributable to better and more widely available medical knowledge and, in a large sense, reflects again a higher level of living.   An economic series may have a downward trend because a better or cheaper substitute became available.   Thus, synthetic fibers,

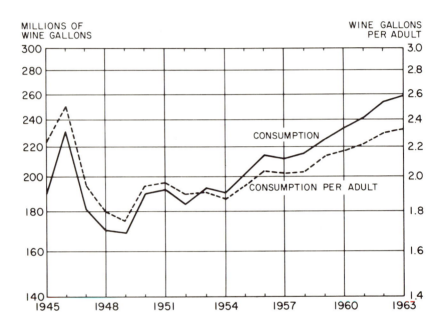

Chart 11.2.   Consumption and Consumption Per Adult of Distilled Spirits in the United States, 1945–1963.   Data from Licensed Beverage Industry, *Facts Book, 1964,* p. 56.

such as orlon and nylon, have partially replaced natural fibers for some uses, and synthetic detergents are being used in place of many types of soap.   More spectacular, though far beyond the memory of all of us, was the development of the railroads, which forced into obsolescence most of the canals in this country.   Now the railroads find themselves hard pressed by competition from trucks, buses, and airplanes.

Improvements in the productive process are apt to be rapid at first, and demand may be brisk.   However, as time goes on, it is often true that further technical and managerial improvements have less and less effect on output, while at the same time the market does not continue to expand as rapidly as before.   Growth may also be retarded because of the increasing difficulty of obtaining raw material, such as minerals which

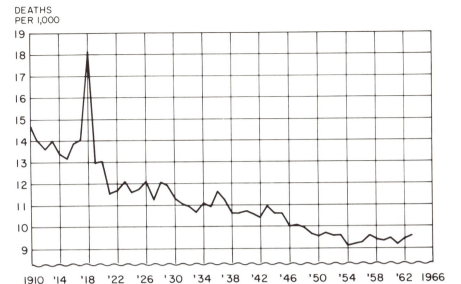

DEATHS
PER 1,000

Chart 11.3. **Crude Death Rate in the Registration Area of the United States, 1900–1966.** Data from various issues of *Statistical Abstract of the United States*. Figure for 1963 is provisional.

must be obtained from smaller deposits and lower-grade ores. We cannot undertake a complete listing of the factors, including financial ones, which often combine to slow up the growth of production in an industry. Whatever the particular causes may be in a given industry, many authorities believe that not only does relative growth tend to decline, but eventually further expansion will be physically impossible. One writer has characterized the tendency we have described as a "law of growth," which is said to apply to all industries. This law embraces four stages: (1) period of experimentation, during which the amount of growth is small; (2) period of growth into the social fabric; (3) period during which growth is retarded as a saturation point is approached; (4) period of stability. Charts 13.10 and 13.11 indicate that the domestic production of ice cream behaves in this manner. From the first of these charts it is seen that, over the period 1929–1961, the annual *amount* of growth was initially small but gradually increased; from the second chart it is clear that the annual *percentage* of growth has gradually declined.

As previously suggested, sometimes the competition faced by an industry is so keen, or its source of supply so limited, that it experiences a transition from growth to decline. An example of such an industry is anthracite coal mining. Another example of growth and decline is the number of farms in the United States from 1790–1966, partially illustrated in Chart 11.4.

217

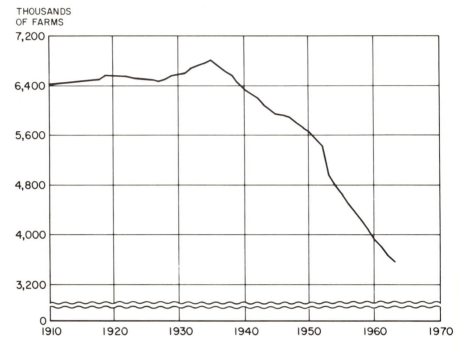

THOUSANDS
OF FARMS

Chart 11.4. Number of Farms in the United States, 1910–1963. Data from
U.S. Department of Commerce, *Historical Statistics of the United States, Colonial
Times to 1957*, p. 278; U.S. Department of Agriculture, *Agricultural Statistics, 1964*,
p. 481.

We may study the trend of a time series because we are interested in
the trend itself, or we may wish to eliminate the trend statistically in
order to throw into relief one or more other movements in the series.
The statistical problem consists, first, of deciding the type of trend which
will fit the data adequately and which is a logical description of the data,
and, second, of fitting the trend of the type selected.

Periodic movements. A *periodic* movement is one which recurs,
with some degree of regularity, within a definite period. The most frequently studied periodic movement is that which occurs within a year and
which is known as *seasonal variation*, or merely *seasonal*. Chart 11.5
shows the monthly farm production of milk from January 1953 through
December 1964. The seasonal movement in this chart is quite marked
in relation to the other movements. Notice that the seasonal variation
of milk production is much the same from year to year. This is true, too,
for the data of consumption of newsprint by United States publishers, the
typical seasonal for which is shown in Chart 11.6. In Chapter 14 we
shall see how to ascertain the seasonal pattern when that pattern is constant or approximately so. However, many series show a seasonal pat-

MILLIONS
OF POUNDS

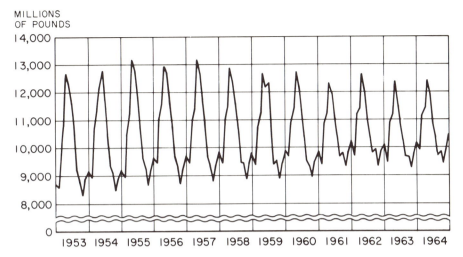

Chart 11.5. Milk Production on Farms in the United States, January 1953–December 1964. Data from various issues of *Survey of Current Business.*

PER CENT

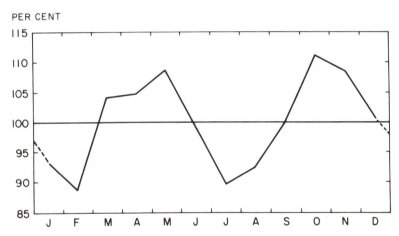

Chart 11.6. Seasonal Index of Consumption of Newsprint by United States Publishers, 1955–1963. Data of Table 14.7.

tern that is gradually changing with the passage of time. The amount of advertising space in newspapers is such a series, and we shall determine the seasonal pattern for data of United States newspaper advertising in Chapter 15.

Climatic conditions, including variations in rainfall, snow and ice, sunshine, humidity, heat, and wind, produce variations in demand which are often reflected in variations in production. Climatic conditions also directly affect production in some industries, for example, agriculture and outdoor construction.   Although nature is primarily responsible for most of the seasonal variations exhibited by time series, there are other factors, too.   The custom of giving gifts at Christmas causes a marked peak in retail (especially department store) sales in December.   Other such peaks may be expected to appear if advertisers are successful in promoting widespread gift-giving on let us say, Groundhog Day, or Sadie Hawkins Day.   Peaks of retail activity before Easter and Thanksgiving are indirectly attributable to the seasons, since those holidays owe their origin in part to weather conditions.   However, the urge to change the style of one's clothing or automobile in the spring or fall is also partly the result of ostentation.

The seasonal movement of automobile sales (and the production of automobiles and parts as well) is not only due to climatic changes but is also the result of certain man-made decisions.   One year, in an attempt to spur a sluggish economy, the automobile show, which would normally have been held in January, was moved ahead to November.   With new models being brought out several months earlier than previously, there was, of course, a sudden shift in the seasonal pattern.   New models of the various makes of cars are not now introduced at exactly the same time, but nearly all appear within a month or two of each other.   The introduction of new models, particularly if they embody style or mechanical changes, continues to have a pronounced effect on the seasonal movement of automobile sales.

We may be interested in seasonal variation either because we wish statistically to eliminate seasonal from a time series or because we are interested in the seasonal movement itself.   In Chapter 16 attention will be given to deseasonalizing time series data for the purpose of making the other movements (particularly cyclical) more readily discernible.

Interest in the seasonal movement itself may have any one of several objectives.   First, it may be that we wish to "iron out" the seasonal so that the intra-year fluctuation will be less pronounced.   Thus, attempts were made to build up the winter demand for ice cream by advertising: "Ice cream is one of your best foods.   Eat a plate a day."   On the production side, hens have been stimulated to lay in the off (winter) season by increasing the length of their day with artificial light.

Second, a manufacturing establishment may wish to decrease the seasonal nature of its activities by producing commodities with complementary seasonals.   Thus, one concern makes sleds and garden cultivators.   On a much larger scale is the objective of an under-water cable from Britain to France linking the electric power systems of these two countries.   A large proportion of French electrical power comes from hydroelectric plants that suffer from water shortages in the late summer when Britain's coal-burning generators are working below capacity.   On the other hand, during most of the winter, when Britain's generators are overloaded, France has surplus water to operate its hydroelectric plants.

Third, one may be interested in a seasonal movement in order to take advantage of it. Thus, the housewife tries to buy fruit for canning or preserving at the peak of the season when the price is low and when quality may be high.

Although we shall not attempt to deal with them in this book, there are also periodic movements which may be characterized as intra-month, intra-week, and intra-day. As an example of an intra-month movement, consider a commercial bank which may show peak activity around the first and fifteenth of each month. If the bank is in an area where weekly factory payrolls must be prepared, its business may show a characteristic intra-week movement, too, which will depend upon the day (or days) of the week on which the factories pay their employees. When monthly and weekly peaks coincide, the staff of the bank may indeed be busy. An interesting intra-week periodic is that observed by Sears Roebuck and Company in regard to the number of cash sales per pound of mail. During a normal week the figures are: Monday 30, Tuesday 37, Wednesday 35, Thursday 32, and Friday 31. The business of a restaurant supplies an illustration of an intra-day movement. With three peaks each weekday, the manager must plan ahead and have enough food and enough help for these relatively short, busy times. The power cable from Britain to France, which was just mentioned, dovetails dissimilar intra-day demands for electricity in the two countries. Although no one has yet devised an efficient method of storing power, as such, it is possible to accumulate water behind a dam. If, during the dry season or any other time of the year when the dams are not full, France uses British power any time during a 24-hour period, some French water is being stored behind French dams to help either country meet peak-load demands.

Cyclical movements. Cyclical movements are fluctuations which differ from periodic movements in that they are of longer duration than a year and also in that they do not ordinarily exhibit regular periodicity. Business cycles are not random movements because the position of business at a given point in a cycle is affected by the activity in previous months and, in turn, affects business in the immediate future. In other words, the transition from a low point to a high point, or vice versa, is a progressive development. Cycles appear to operate somewhat on the principle of a pendulum. Just as a pendulum is pulled by gravity toward a vertical position, but tends constantly to move past its position of equilibrium, so it is said that business is drawn toward an equilibrium by the forces of demand and supply, and so also do the errors in one direction tend to progress into errors in the opposite direction. Such an explanation of business cycles is known as the "self-generative theory," usually associated with the name of Wesley C. Mitchell. But just as the mechanism impelling a pendulum must be wound up occasionally, so it is possible that economic activity would attain equilibrium were it not for other propulsions of varying degrees of intensity. It is possible to speak of cycles in general business or of cycles in particular industries, such as residential construction, cattle raising, or textile production. Rarely, cycles in a specific industry or business may appear to be inherently periodic, but they are, in any event, modified by the position of the cycle in general business. Furthermore, since all industries are so interdependent, a revival or recession in a key industry or industry group soon transmits its effect to other branches of activity.

It appears that cyclical movements of general activity may be generated by a concurrence of the same cyclical phase in the activity of several important industries; or they might be generated by interferences from outside the business world. These interferences might be occasional events of considerable magnitude, such as a war, a discovery, unusual weather, or some political event; or they might be the simultaneous occurrence of several minor events, each reinforcing the effect of the other.

When cycles appear to have a rough regularity, this regularity may possibly be explained by the periodicity of certain of the extraneous events which, some authorities believe, are in part responsible. Cycles in weather have been suggested. It is more likely, however, that what regularity can be observed is due to the fairly constant length of time it takes the business world to respond to stimuli. For instance, the time it takes for erecting a building or for foreclosing a mortgage, or even to decide to go into bankruptcy, is not utterly irregular. Perhaps greater regularity would be observable were it not for the irregularity of accidental occurrences.

There are some who reject the concept of self-generating cycles, believing that cycles are brought about largely by external influences. Even these observers, however, are interested in noting whether production and consumption are increasing or decreasing, and especially in discovering practical measures for stabilization. Whether self-generated or caused by external factors, it is clear, from Chart 16.6, that there have been cyclical fluctuations in United States newspaper advertising, and that the cycles have not been of the same length. Chart 16.6 also illustrates a difficulty frequently encountered in the study of time series. It has to do with the decision concerning what is a cycle. Does the curve of Chart 16.6 show about two large cycles or several smaller ones? A decision may be influenced by the trend used for the series. As will be seen later, the trend employed was a straight line fitted to the years 1932–1960 and extended through 1964. Had we concerned ourselves with a shorter period of time, for example, 1946–1964, and made use of a trend for only those years, a large number of cycles would have appeared for the nineteen-year period.

Irregular variations. The irregular variations in a time series are sometimes divided into two categories: *episodic* and *accidental*. When episodic movements occur in a time series, they may be readily identifiable in the chart of the series if they are due to specific events, such as earthquakes, conflagrations, strikes, early or late melting of ice on the Great Lakes, severe storms, or other occurrences. An episodic movement which was important enough to be reflected in annual data appears in Chart 11.3. The very high death rate in 1918 was the result of an epidemic of influenza which caused many deaths among civilian and military personnel.

As mentioned before, an episode may be important enough to generate, or assist in generating, a cyclical fluctuation. Occasionally it may be difficult to distinguish between an episodic movement and a cycle.

Accidental movements are minor fluctuations not attributable to specific episodes and too small to merit individual consideration. These accidental fluctuations may sometimes be of a random nature. The irregular variations (accidental and episodic combined) for United States newspaper advertising are shown in Charts 16.7 and 16.8.

Other movements. The four movements which have been mentioned are the most prominent ones ordinarily found in time series. Sometimes investigators find "long cycles," which are of much longer duration than the usual business cycle and which may last roughly 50 years. Both types of cycles may be present simultaneously and superimposed on each other. Occasionally, students of time series claim the existence of more than two cyclical components in a time series. Intermediate between the long cycle and the business cycle, a movement called "secondary trend" is sometimes found. In this text we shall give no further attention to long cycles or secondary trends but shall concentrate our attention on the four movements first mentioned.

A GRAPHIC PREVIEW

The nature of the four leading movements in a time series may be understood more clearly if we look at some of the charts of data of United States newspaper advertising, which will be considered in more detail later. The lighter broken line of Chart 16.4 shows the original data in terms of millions of lines. This curve includes all of the movements: trend, seasonal, cyclical, and irregular. Chart 11.7 shows the seasonal variation present in the series, and the solid line of Chart 16.4 shows the appearance of the data after they have been adjusted for seasonal variation. The cyclical movements are indicated in Chart 16.6. No chart of the irregular movements is included here, but, as noted before, they may be seen in Charts 16.7 and 16.8.

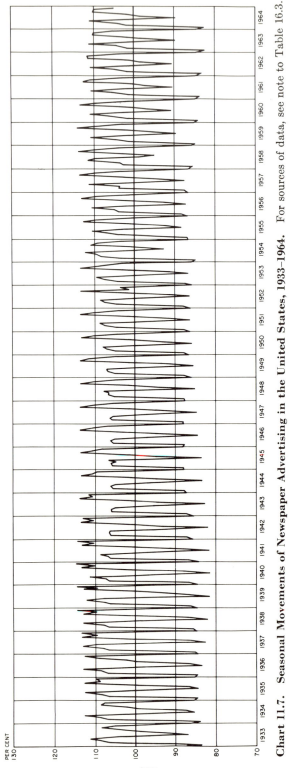

Chart 11.7. Seasonal Movements of Newspaper Advertising in the United States, 1933–1964. For sources of data, see note to Table 16.3.

224

PRELIMINARY TREATMENT OF DATA

Some variations in time series are due to the terms in which the data are expressed, and at times it may be advisable to make certain adjustments before undertaking to analyze a time series.

Calendar variation.   Usually, though not always, there are 365 days in a year.   Although there are 12 months in each year, the months vary in length from 28 to 31 days.   To make matters more complicated, the different months do not start on the same day of the week, nor does the same month in successive years so start.   Another difficulty has to do with the number of working days in a month.   Not only do the number of Saturdays and Sundays vary among months, but February, with 28 or 29 days, has Washington's Birthday and Lincoln's Birthday, while March, with 31 days, may include no holidays.   February may include as few as 18 working days, while March may have as many as 23.   The fluctuation of Easter between March and April also introduces an element of confusion.

Although it seems impossible to divide the year into quarters containing the same number of whole weeks, nevertheless some business firms have tried to minimize the difficulty.   A few firms keep records by 4-week periods.   There are 13 such periods in a year, but quarterly data cannot be kept by this system.   A few other firms keep records by quarters, each quarter being composed of three months—the first two months of four weeks each and the third of five weeks.   Of course, neither of these plans is satisfactory so long as the first of a given calendar month may occur in either of two artificial months.   And under any plan, the unsystematic occurrence of holidays results in a different number of working days in successive artificial months.   Movements have been launched to change the calendar to remedy these defects.   One plan suggests identical quarters; each quarter would contain, not identical months, but three monthly patterns of thirty or thirty-one days each, these three patterns being repeated so as to occur four times a year.   An extra day, however, known as Year Day, would occur at the middle of the year.

The statistician is sometimes confronted with the problem of adjusting a time series for either the number of calendar days in a month or for the number of working days in a month.   If monthly data of the residential consumption of water are to be adjusted for calendar variation, the appropriate adjustment would doubtless be on the basis of calendar days rather than working days.   This adjustment is accomplished by dividing each monthly figure by the number of days in the month, giving consumption per day.   If it is desired to retain the figures in their original magnitude, the consumption per day may be multiplied by the average number of days per month, which is $365 \div 12 = 30.4167$ for a 365-day year. For monthly production data, the adjustment for calendar variation would involve consideration of the number of working days rather than calendar days in each month.[1]

It would be entirely inappropriate to adjust some time series for calendar variation. Clearly it would be spurious to do so for executive, administrative, and supervisory salary expenses of most corporations, since such salaries are usually paid on a monthly basis irrespective of the number of days or working days in a month. For data requiring adjustment, it is frequently a difficult statistical problem to decide whether to adjust for working days or merely for calendar days. For some commodities it can logically be maintained that holidays within a month, far from decreasing consumer purchases during that month, may actually increase them. If the holiday occurs on the last day of the month and the stores are closed, however, it might decrease sales. In organizations which receive orders through the mail from a considerable distance, sales may be decreased by holidays occurring during the last few days of the preceding month. Just what is the logical adjustment to make is often very difficult to determine and requires familiarity with the business or industry in question. In case of doubt it is always possible to determine experimentally what method gives the smoothest results after the adjustment is made. Such a test provides no conclusive evidence but is only presumptive.

Population changes. It has already been noted that one element in an upward trend may be the increase in population. Data may be adjusted for population change by dividing the original figures by the population figures, thus expressing the data on a per capita basis. This is what was done in Chart 11.2. Alternatively, the population figures may be put in relative terms with the population for a selected census year, say 1960, set equal to 1.00, or 100 per cent. If the original data are then divided by the population relatives, the resulting figures will be in terms of a fixed (1960) population.

Price changes. Interest often centers in physical volume changes rather than changes which have occurred in terms of dollars. Series such as sales, earnings, cost of materials, and others which are originally expressed in dollars must be *deflated* in order to be expressed in terms which are independent of price changes. Deflation is accomplished by dividing the dollar series by an appropriate price index series. Table 11.1 shows the average weekly wages paid to production workers in manufacturing industries in each year from 1959 to 1964. To the right of the column of weekly wages is given the Consumers' Price Index for the same years. Now, if weekly wages in dollars for each year are divided

---

[1] For detailed instructions on the procedure, see the second edition of this text, pp. 255–256.

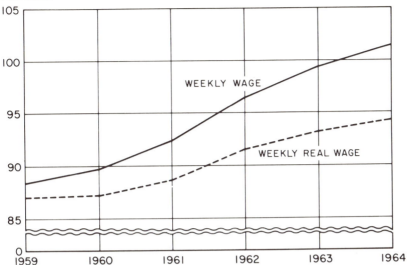

DOLLARS
PER WEEK

Chart 11.8. Average Gross Weekly Earnings of Production Workers in Manufacturing Industries, 1959–1964. Data of Table 11.1. Real wages are in terms of the Consumers Price Index, which has 1957 − 1959 = 100.

by the corresponding price index (expressed as a decimal), the result is a series of weekly wage figures adjusted for changes in prices. These are shown in Column (4) and are referred to as *real wages* or, specifically, wages in terms of 1957–1959 dollars. Chart 11.11 shows curves of weekly dollar wages and weekly real wages. Even though prices rose during 1959–1964, weekly real wages showed a steady increase. Note that the figures shown in Table 11.1 and Chart 11.8 have to do with average weekly wages and that the Consumers' Price Index was used as a deflator. An index of wholesale commodity prices, for example, would have been entirely unsuitable. Unless a deflator is used that pertains to the data

TABLE 11.1

Average Gross Weekly Earnings of Production Workers in Manufacturing Industries and Consumers' Price Index, 1959–1964

Year (1)	Weekly earnings (2)	Price index (1957–1959 = 100) (3)	Weekly real wages [Col. (2) ÷ Col. (3)] (4)
1959	$ 88.26	101.5	$87.0
1960	89.72	103.1	87.1
1961	92.34	104.2	88.6
1962	96.56	105.4	91.6
1963	99.38	106.7	93.1
1964	101.40	107.8	94.1

Data from *Statistical Abstract of the United States, 1964*, pp. 236, 356.

being deflated, a satisfactory adjustment for price changes will not be obtained.

Securing comparability. Statisticians for trade associations experience considerable difficulty in obtaining prompt reports from all members. For instance, 93 firms might report on time one month and 96 the next—the latter not necessarily, however, including all the 93 firms. To be strictly accurate, a new time series should be constructed each month *for the entire period* including all of, and only, those firms which reported promptly for the month in question. Thus, a complete time series one month would be computed for the 93 firms, and the next month for 96. This is a very laborious procedure. An easier procedure is to make a preliminary estimate by computing the percentage of the preceding period for only those firms which reported promptly for the current month, and to multiply the figure for the preceding month (which now includes all firms) by this percentage. A revised figure can be computed when all the reports have been obtained. If an industry is expanding and new firms are appearing, it is, of course, desirable to include them. Increased employment and production may result from increased activity of existing firms or the appearance of new ones. Similarly, firms may cease to exist and must be dropped from a reporting list.

Another source of incomparability may be the fact that the unit of reporting has changed. If it is merely a question of changing from a pound basis to a ton basis, this is a simple matter. Where the product has changed in kind, however, it is difficult to find a satisfactory solution. How, for instance, can we compare the physical production of radios between 1935 and 1967? Not only was there a difference in the proportion of radios of different grades sold in the two years, but radios that were the same with respect to price, weight, number of tubes, or any other readily measurable characteristic were still vastly different in their capacity to render utility to the consumer.

CHAPTER 12

Analysis of Time Series:

SECULAR TREND I—THE STRAIGHT LINE

There are two important reasons for attempting to describe the trend of a series by means of a curve. First, it may be desired to measure the deviations from the trend. These deviations consist of cyclical, seasonal, and irregular movements. Frequently, obtaining these deviations is but one step in attempting to isolate cycles in order to study them. Second, it may be desired to study the trend itself, in order to note the effect of factors bearing on the trend, to compare one trend with another, to discover what effect trend movements have on cyclical fluctuations, or to attempt to forecast the future behavior of the trend.

The purpose for which measurements are made partly determines the methods adopted. If the object is solely to isolate cycles, it seems reasonable to suppose that the trend line chosen should pass through the cycles in such a way as approximately to allow a balancing between the positive and negative phases of each cycle. Whether a curve is deemed to have accomplished this object depends, of course, upon our conception of what constitutes a cycle in each case. If, on the other hand, the object is to make comparisons, generalizations, or forecasts, the curve should be not only logical, but also of such a nature that it can readily be expressed by a mathematical formula. By means of such a formula a person can, for instance, say that at a given time a series shows a certain ratio, or a certain amount, of growth per annum, and that, if this tendency continues, the trend will reach a certain value at some specified time in the future. Fitting a trend by a mathematical formula does not, however, remove the subjective element from trend fitting. The statistician can vary the behavior of the curve by selection of the type of formula he employs, or the years to which he fits the curve. It remains true, therefore, that the statistician decides in advance, *upon as objective and logical a basis as possible*, what he thinks the trend ought to look like, and then selects the mathematical method that will closely approximate this result.

TREND FITTED BY INSPECTION

The simplest method of describing a trend graphically is by inspection. If the trend is a straight line, it may be drawn with the aid of a transparent ruler or a tightly stretched piece of string. If the trend is nonlinear, it may be drawn freehand or use may be made of a spline, an adjustable curve ruler, or a French curve.[1]

MILLIONS
OF LINES

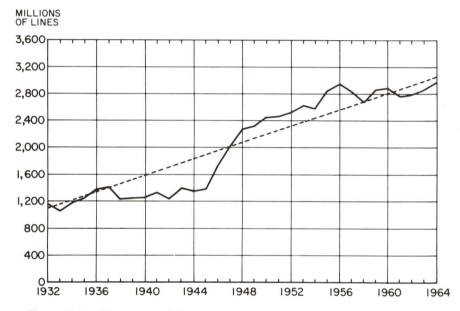

Chart 12.1. Newspaper Advertising in the United States, 1932–1964, and Straight-Line Trend Fitted by Inspection to the Years 1932–1960. Advertising-lineage data from Table 12.2. See notes following the title of Chart 12.3.

Chart 12.1 shows a fit of a straight-line trend, by inspection, to newspaper advertising in the United States for 1932–1960. Whenever a curve is fitted to a set of data, a *criterion of fit* is involved. The trend of Chart 12.1 was drawn through the curve in such a manner that cyclical portions above and below the trend line were judged, by inspection, to be about equal. The trend line also passes through the approximate average (determined by inspection) of the advertising lineage data at the middle year, 1946. This highly subjective method is open to the objection that may be made to all subjective methods: one determines what answer he wants and then proceeds to determine it. However, as has already been

---

[1] These three devices are available from firms selling artists' and draftsmen's supplies.

mentioned, very nearly the same result may be obtained by careful selection from among the numerous available mathematical procedures.

LEAST-SQUARES FIT OF STRAIGHT LINE

A mathematical equation not only allows us to draw the trend of a time series but provides, also, in the trend equation, a concise definition of that trend. If the trend itself is to be studied, or is to be extended beyond the observed data, it is particularly desirable that the trend be described by an objectively determined equation.

The straight line. The simplest type of curve is the straight line, which is described by an equation of the type $Y_c = a + bX$, in which X is the independent variable and Y_c the trend value of the dependent variable.[2] Since their values must be determined for each of the series being analyzed, a and b are referred to as *unknowns*. They are also called *constants*, since, once their values are determined, they do not change.

To take the simplest case, suppose that $a = 0$ and $b = 1$. The equation then becomes: $Y_c = X$; and this means that with each increase of one unit of the independent variable, the dependent variable also increases one unit. This equation is plotted in the upper left section of Chart 12.2. Incidentally, it should be observed that all four quadrants are shown in this chart. Before attempting to plot a curve, it is well to draw up a table of X and Y_c values, as shown on the chart, in which are recorded the computed values of Y that correspond to selected values of X. As a matter of fact, only two points are needed to plot this or any straight line, and most accurate results are obtained by using two X values a considerable distance from each other.

Other straight-line equations and their curves are shown in the other sections of Chart 12.2, an inspection of which yields the following information: a is the value of Y when X is 0 (the Y value at the X origin), or, as it is frequently termed, the Y *intercept;* while b indicates the steepness, or *slope*, of the line. When b is positive, the slope is upward; when b is negative, the slope is downward.

Although the straight-line trend of Chart 12.1 was obtained by inspection and not mathematically fitted to the data, we can nevertheless determine its approximate equation. If the origin be taken at 1932, it will be seen that the curve has a Y_c value of 1,100, so $a = 1,100$. To determine b, we merely need to ascertain the value of the trend for 1960, which is 2,800, take the difference between that value and the trend value for 1932, and divide by the number of elapsed years, 28. This gives

$$\frac{2,800 - 1,100}{28} = 60.71,$$

---

[2] The symbol Y will be used to designate an observed value of the dependent variable, while Y_c indicates a value that has been computed, usually from a mathematical equation.

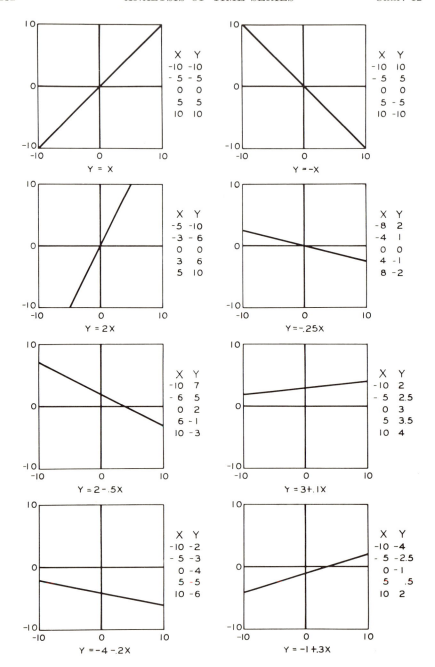

Chart 12.2.   Straight-Line Equations and Curves.

which is the value of b, the amount of increase in the trend each year. The equation, then, is

$$Y_c = 1,100 + 60.71X.$$
Origin, 1932. X units, one year.

Trend equations for time series must always be accompanied by a statement concerning the origin and the X units.   We must specify the X units, since, as we shall see later, they may be one year, one-half year, or one month.   The origin must be indicated because series of data by years, months, or other chronological units do not have a zero useful for fitting purposes.   Consequently, the statistician can select the X-origin where he pleases, and we shall see later that it will be advantageous to choose that origin at the middle of the chronological series whenever possible.

If we rewrite the equation for the trend of Chart 12.1, with 1946 as the origin, we have

$$Y_c = 1,949.9 + 60.71X.$$
Origin, 1946. X units, one year.

Note that the value of b is the same as before.   The new a value may be obtained either by reading the trend value for 1946 or by adding 14 times the b value to the former a value.   The value of b is multiplied by 14 because 1946 is 14 years removed from 1932.

Method of least squares.   The method of least squares provides a convenient device for obtaining an objective fit of a straight-line trend line to a series of data.   It can also be applied to a number of more complex trend types, some of which will be discussed in Chapter 13.   The method of least squares accomplishes two objectives:

1. *The sum of the vertical deviations of the observed values from the fitted straight line equals zero.*   If a vertical line were to be drawn, in Chart 12.3, from each Y value for 1932–1960 to the trend line, the vertical lines extending upward from the trend line would exactly balance those extending downward.   This trend is not the only straight line from which the algebraic sum of the deviations equals zero; as a matter of fact, any straight line (other than vertical) which passes through $\bar{X}$, $\bar{Y}$ fulfills this requirement.

2. *The sum of the squares of all these deviations is less than the sum of the squared vertical deviations from any other straight line.*   It is because of this second characteristic that the method of fitting is called the method

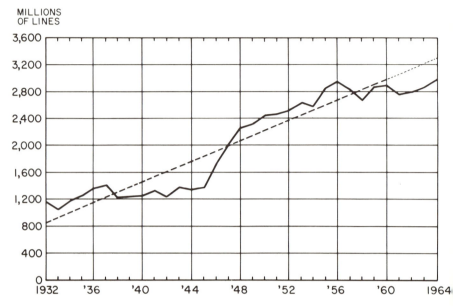

MILLIONS
OF LINES

Chart 12.3. Newspaper Advertising in the United States, 1932–1964 and Trend as Shown by a Straight Line Fitted by the Method of Least Squares to the Years 1932–1960. Data of Table 12.2. Note that two trends, one for the first part of the series, and one for the latter part (See pp. 245–246) might have been used.

of least squares.[3] When a curve is fitted to meet this second requirement, the first requirement is automatically satisfied.[4]

In a sense, a trend line fitted by the method of least squares is analogous to the arithmetic mean, since the arithmetic mean is a *single value*, rather than a series of values, summarizing a set of data and possessing the two characteristics just mentioned.

---

[3] It can be demonstrated that the greatest probability of obtaining deviations which are distributed normally (see Chapter 23) around some computed value or series of values is obtained when the sum of the squared deviations is at a minimum (see Appendix S, section 12.1). If it is believed that deviations from the appropriate norm are chance errors, it follows that the method of least squares is the appropriate method of fitting. The method is also convenient algebraically, as the student can observe in connection with correlation analysis and analysis of variance. Time series fluctuations around a trend line are not, however, independent accidental occurrences, and it is to be doubted that there is any special reason for using the method of least squares in trend fitting, other than its convenience. Certain of the trends explained in this volume are, in fact, fitted by other methods. Some statisticians even argue that the least-squares criterion is not appropriate for time series trends, since time series are sometimes characterized by extreme deviations not in accordance with the normal law. The method of least squares, of course, is particularly influenced by extreme deviations because of the squaring process.

[4] The mean of the Y_c values is the same as the mean of the Y values. This is demonstrated in Appendix S, section 19.1. Before reading that explanation, however, the reader should peruse the next section of this chapter.

The normal equations. It has already been noted that the equation for a straight line involves the two constants a and b. For a fitted straight line, the values of a and b must be determined from the observed data; consequently, two *normal equations* must be obtained and solved simultaneously. These normal equations are:

$$\text{I.} \quad \Sigma Y = Na + b\Sigma X,$$
$$\text{II.} \quad \Sigma XY = a\Sigma X + b\Sigma X^2.$$

Without attempting a derivation[5] of these normal equations at this point, we shall make use of a set of simple illustrative data to see how these

TABLE 12.1

Determination of Normal Equations and of Sums for Fit of Straight Line, by Method of Least Squares, to Illustrative Data, X and Y

X	Y	Observation equation $Y = a + bX$	Coefficient of a	Determination of first normal equation — Observation equation multiplied by coefficient of a Col. (3) × Col. (4)	Coefficient of b	Determination of second normal equation — Observation equation multiplied by coefficient of b Col. (3) × Col. (6)	XY	X²
(1)	(2)	(3)	(4)	(5)	(6)	(7)	(8)	(9)
0	2	$2 = a$	1	$2 = a$	0	...	0	0
1	1	$1 = a + b$	1	$1 = a + b$	1	$1 = a + b$	1	1
2	3	$3 = a + 2b$	1	$3 = a + 2b$	2	$6 = 2a + 4b$	6	4
3	2	$2 = a + 3b$	1	$2 = a + 3b$	3	$6 = 3a + 9b$	6	9
4	4	$4 = a + 4b$	1	$4 = a + 4b$	4	$16 = 4a + 16b$	16	16
5	3	$3 = a + 5b$	1	$3 = a + 5b$	5	$15 = 5a + 25b$	15	25
6	5	$5 = a + 6b$	1	$5 = a + 6b$	6	$30 = 6a + 36b$	30	36
21	20	...	...	$20 = 7a + 21b$	...	$74 = 21a + 91b$	74	91

two equations are arrived at. The data are shown in Columns 1 and 2 of Table 12.1, and in Chart 12.4, where it may be seen that there are seven pairs of X, Y values. We shall therefore first write down seven *observation equations*, from which we shall obtain the two normal equations. Column 3 of Table 12.1 shows the seven observation equations. Since the observed data do not fall on a straight line, the seven observation equations are not all consistent with each other. It is the purpose of the two normal equations to enable us to arrive at a sort of average solution of these observation equations.

The first normal equation is obtained by multiplying each observation equation by the coefficient of a in that equation and adding. The coefficients of a, which are 1, are shown in Column 4 of Table 12.1. Column

[5] For a derivation of the two normal equations, see Appendix S, section 12.2.

5 shows the observation equations again (unchanged, since the coefficients of a were all 1) and their sum, which is the first normal equation.

To get the second normal equation, each observation equation is multiplied by the coefficient of b in that equation and the sum obtained. The coefficients of b are shown in Column 6 of Table 12.1 and the results of the multiplications are given in Column 7. The total of Column 7 is the second normal equation.

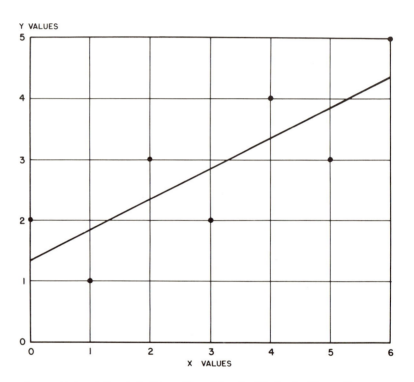

Chart 12.4. A Straight Line, Fitted by the Method of Least Squares, to a Set of Illustrative Values. Data of Table 12.1.

The two normal equations may now be set down:

$$\text{I. } 20 = 7a + 21b.$$
$$\text{II. } 74 = 21a + 91b.$$

To solve these simultaneously, we multiply normal equation I by 3 and subtract it from normal equation II, thus eliminating a and obtaining one equation with one unknown, b:

$$\text{II. } 74 = 21a + 91b,$$
$$(\text{I} \times 3). \ 60 = 21a + 63b,$$
$$14 = 28b,$$
$$b = 0.5.$$

To get the value of a, we substitute the value of b in either normal equation I or II. Using normal equation I:

$$20 = 7a + 21(0.5),$$
$$= 7a + 10.5.$$
$$7a = 9.5,$$
$$a = 1.357.$$

As a check, the values of a and b may be substituted in normal equation II, as follows:

$$74 = 21(1.357) + 91(0.5),$$
$$= 28.5 + 45.5,$$
$$= 74.0.$$

The equation of the fitted straight line (which is shown on Chart 12.4) may now be written:

$$Y_c = 1.36 + 0.5X.$$

Notice that it was not necessary, in this case, to state the origin or the X units, since the X values were not dates.

The foregoing illustration was a specific instance involving but seven pairs of values. To be more general, let us write the observation equations for N pairs of values as follows:

$$Y_1 = a + bX_1,$$
$$Y_2 = a + bX_2,$$
$$Y_3 = a + bX_3,$$
$$\cdot \qquad \cdot \qquad \cdot$$
$$\cdot \qquad \cdot \qquad \cdot$$
$$\cdot \qquad \cdot \qquad \cdot$$
$$Y_N = a + bX_N.$$

If, now, we multiply each of these observation equations by the coefficient of a (which is 1), they are unchanged and their sum is

$$\text{I. } \Sigma Y = Na + b\Sigma X.$$

This is the first normal equation. To get the second normal equation, we multiply each observation equation by the coefficient of b in that equation and add, obtaining:

$$X_1Y_1 = aX_1 + bX_1^2,$$
$$X_2Y_2 = aX_2 + bX_2^2,$$
$$X_3Y_3 = aX_3 + bX_3^2,$$
$$\cdot \qquad \cdot \qquad \cdot$$
$$\cdot \qquad \cdot \qquad \cdot$$
$$\cdot \qquad \cdot \qquad \cdot$$
$$\underline{X_NY_N = aX_N + bX_N^2,}$$

II. $\Sigma XY = a\Sigma X + b\Sigma X^2.$

Note that we write $a\Sigma X$ and $b\Sigma X^2$, rather than ΣaX and ΣbX^2, because a and b are constants.

We are now in a position to use the two normal equations to determine a straight-line trend. We shall not find it necessary to set up any more observation equations; only the normal equations will be needed. For the illustrative data of Table 12.1, *only the sums of Columns 1, 2, 8, and 9 and the value of N are used*, giving, for the two normal equations:

I. $20 = 7a + 21b,$

II. $74 = 21a + 91b,$

which is the same as the two equations shown at the bottom of Columns 5 and 7 of the table.

We shall make use of two, or more, normal equations not only to fit trend lines by the method of least squares in this chapter and in Chapter 13, but we shall also employ them in Chapters 19, 20, and 21 when dealing with linear, non-linear, and multiple correlation and in Chapter 22, as well, where we correlate time series.

Odd number of years. The data of Table 12.2 and the solid curve of Chart 12.3 show the amount of advertising in newspapers in the United States in millions of lines for 1932–1964. We shall fit a straight line to the data for 1932–1960 and extend that trend line through 1964. The two normal equations

I. $\Sigma Y = Na + b\Sigma X,$

II. $\Sigma XY = a\Sigma X + b\Sigma X^2,$

will be used to determine the values of a and b for the straight-line trend. However, it is possible to simplify them in such a manner that simultaneous solution of the two equations will not be necessary. Owing to the fact that years constitute the X variable, we must select an origin for

TABLE 12.2

Computation of Values for Fit of Straight Line to Data of Newspaper Advertising in the United States 1932–1960

(Millions of lines)

Year	X	Y	XY		Trend values Y_c
1932	−14	1,164.8	−16,307.2		857.4
1933	−13	1,065.5	−13,851.5		933.7
1934	−12	1,178.9	−14,146.8		1,010.0
1935	−11	1,246.0	−13,706.0		1,086.2
1936	−10	1,380.0	−13,800.0		1,162.5
1937	− 9	1,409.8	−12,688.2		1,238.8
1938	− 8	1,225.4	− 9,803.2		1,315.0
1939	− 7	1,243.6	− 8,705.2		1,391.3
1940	− 6	1,268.6	− 7,611.6		1,467.6
1941	− 5	1,313.2	− 6,566.0		1,543.9
1942	− 4	1,241.8	− 4,967.2		1,620.1
1943	− 3	1,396.4	− 4,189.2		1,696.4
1944	− 2	1,361.3	− 2,722.6		1,772.7
1945	− 1	1,391.6	− 1,391.6	−130,456.3	1,848.9
1946	0	1,729.7	0		1,925.2
1947	1	2,008.6	2,008.6		2,001.5
1948	2	2,263.3	4,526.6		2,077.7
1949	3	2,302.1	6,906.3		2,154.0
1950	4	2,440.2	9,760.8		2,230.3
1951	5	2,478.3	12,391.5		2,306.6
1952	6	2,505.4	15,032.4		2,382.8
1953	7	2,610.5	18,273.5		2,459.1
1954	8	2,581.3	20,650.4		2,535.4
1955	9	2,843.5	25,591.5		2,611.6
1956	10	2,911.0	29,110.0		2,687.9
1957	11	2,829.1	31,120.1		2,764.2
1958	12	2,685.6	32,227.2		2,840.4
1959	13	2,865.3	37,248.9		2,916.7
1960	14	2,888.6	40,440.4	285,288.2	2,993.0
1961	15*	2,777.0*	. . .		3,069.3
1962	16*	2,798.3*	. . .		3,145.5
1963	17*	2,858.6*	. . .		3,221.8
1964	18*	2,973.4*	. . .		3,298.1
Total	0	55,829.4		154,831.9	. . .

* Not used for computing trend.
Data from various issues of the *Survey of Current Business*.

that variable.   Now, we can choose any year we wish, and in Table 12.2 it may be seen that the X origin was taken at 1946.   By taking the origin at 1946, the middle year, we have caused the sum of the X values to equal zero, with the result that the two normal equations may now be written:

$$\text{I.} \quad \Sigma Y = Na,$$
$$\text{II.} \quad \Sigma XY = b\Sigma X^2.$$

Now, normal equation I gives the value of a and normal equation II yields the value of b. Table 12.2 shows the computation of ΣY and of ΣXY. N is obtained by counting the number of years or by subtracting the first year from the last and adding one. The value of ΣX^2 could have been computed in Table 12.2. However, this is never necessary for a time series problem, since the sums of the squares of a series of natural numbers $(1, 2, 3, \cdots)$ may be read from Appendix B or computed by means of the formula given in that appendix. The sum of the squares of the first 14 natural numbers is seen to be 1,015 in Appendix B, so, for the newspaper advertising data, $\Sigma X^2 = 2(1{,}015) = 2{,}030$. We may now substitute in the two normal equations, obtaining

$$\text{I. } a = \frac{\Sigma Y}{N} = \frac{55{,}829.4}{29} = 1{,}925.2 \text{ and}$$

$$\text{II. } b = \frac{\Sigma XY}{\Sigma X^2} = \frac{154{,}831.9}{2{,}030} = 76.2719.$$

The trend equation is

$$Y_c = 1{,}925.2 + 76.27X.$$
Origin, 1946. X units, 1 year.

The trend values for each year are shown in the last column of Table 12.2. An individual trend value is obtained by substituting the appropriate X value (with sign) in the trend equation. When trend values for all of the years are wanted, they may be obtained most expeditiously by placing the a value of 1,925.2 million lines opposite 1946 and repeatedly adding the value of b for the years 1947–1964. For 1945 to 1932, the value of b is repeatedly subtracted from the 1946 trend value.[6] The trend of the series is shown in Chart 12.3. Since two points determine a straight line, it was drawn by plotting the trend values for 1932 and for 1960 and connecting these points. Selecting the two points well toward the ends of the X series results in greater mechanical accuracy in drawing the trend line. The trend has been extended through 1964 although the observed values for 1961–1964 were not used to obtain the trend. This is a customary procedure, since it is not practical or desirable to recompute a new trend each year. Furthermore, it is not desirable to have too many high or low values at the ends of a series. At a later point in this chapter, it will be explained that, particularly for short series, a trend should be fitted to data which begin and end with approximately the

---

[6] The repeated additions may be made on a calculating machine or, by adding and subtotaling each time, on an adding machine. The repeated subtractions may be done similarly. If an adding machine which has no subtraction key is to be used, it is best to compute first the trend value for the first year and then obtain the others by repeated addition.

same stage of a cycle.   Since the trend for newspaper advertising was fitted to a period of 29 years, this consideration is of minor importance. The effect of excluding some of the early years or of including the data for 1961–1964 will be commented upon toward the end of this chapter.

Chart 12.1 showed a straight-line trend fitted by inspection which was found to have the equation

$$Y_c = 1,949.9 + 60.71X,$$

with origin at 1946 and X units 1 year.   The least-squares trend equation was

$$Y_c = 1,925.2 + 76.27X,$$

with the same origin and X units.   Note that the two equations differ by only 1.3 per cent in regard to their a values, but that b for the inspection trend is smaller.   It is not to be expected that the two should agree. It has already been noted that the criteria of fit for the two methods are different.   Furthermore, the criterion of equal areas for the inspection fit is not applied mathematically, but visually, and is therefore subject to errors of judgment.

Even number of years.   It may have occurred to the reader that the time-saving device of taking the origin at the middle year might fail us when it becomes necessary to deal with an even number of years.   As a

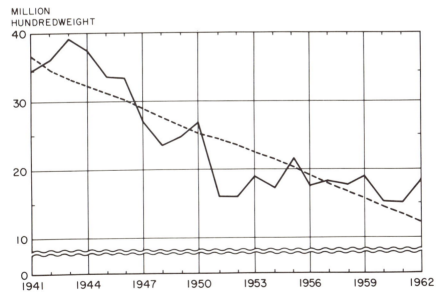

Chart 12.5.   Production of Sweet Potatoes in the United States, 1941–1962, and Trend as Shown by a Straight Line Fitted by the Method of Least Squares.   Data of Table 12.3.

matter of fact, we can continue to use the short forms of the normal equations but we shall (1) take the origin between the two middle years and (2) state the X values in terms of half-years. This has been done in Table 12.3, in which the computations are performed for fitting a straight-line trend to the production of sweet potatoes in the United States for 1941–1962. The data are shown graphically in Chart 12.5.

In Table 12.3 the origin was taken between 1951 and 1952. From this origin it is one-half year ($X = 1$) to the middle of 1952 and one-half

TABLE 12.3

Computation of Values for Fit of Straight Line to Data of Production of Sweet Potatoes in the United States, 1941–1962

(Million hundredweight)

Year	X	Y	XY		Trend values
1941	−21	34.4	−722.4		35.6
1942	−19	36.0	−684.0		34.5
1943	−17	39.1	−664.7		33.4
1944	−15	37.5	−562.5		32.3
1945	−13	33.7	−438.1		31.2
1946	−11	33.5	−368.5		30.1
1947	− 9	27.3	−245.7		29.0
1948	− 7	23.7	−165.9		27.9
1949	− 5	24.8	−124.0		26.8
1950	− 3	27.3	− 81.9		25.7
1951	− 1	16.0	− 16.0	−4,073.7	24.6
1952	1	16.0	16.0		23.5
1953	3	19.0	57.0		22.4
1954	5	17.2	86.0		21.3
1955	7	21.6	151.2		20.2
1956	9	17.4	156.6		19.1
1957	11	18.1	199.1		18.0
1958	13	17.6	228.8		16.9
1959	15	18.9	283.5		15.8
1960	17	15.4	261.8		14.7
1961	19	15.2	288.8		13.6
1962	21	18.5	388.5	2,117.3	12.5
Total	0	528.2		−1,956.4	. . .

Data from U. S. Department of Agriculture, *Agricultural Statistics*, 1963, p. 248, and *Historical Statistics of the United States*, p. 303.

year ($X = -1$) to the middle of 1951. There is, of course, an interval of two half-year periods between any two adjacent years; therefore, 1950 is shown as -3, 1953 as 3, and so on. As before, the value of ΣX^2 need not be obtained by squaring and summing the X values. The sum of the squares of a series of odd natural numbers (1, 3, 5, · · ·) may be read from Appendix C or computed by means of the formula given in that appendix. From Appendix C the sum of squares of the first 11 odd natural numbers is seen to be 1,771, so $\Sigma X^2 = 2(1,771) = 3,542$.   We may now solve the two normal equations for a and b:

$$\text{I. } a = \frac{\Sigma Y}{N} = \frac{528.2}{22} = 24.0.$$

$$\text{II. } b = \frac{\Sigma XY}{\Sigma X^2} = \frac{-1,956.4}{3,542} = -0.55.$$

And the trend equation is

$$Y_c = 24.0 - 0.55X.$$
Origin, 1951–1952. X units, $\frac{1}{2}$ year.

This trend is shown on Chart 12.5 by a broken line.

Note that the trend for sweet potato production has a downward slope. The sign of b in the trend equation is obtained as a result of the computation of ΣXY, being negative when this sum is negative and positive when this sum is positive.

ADAPTING EQUATIONS TO A MONTHLY BASIS

In the preceding illustrations, trend lines were fitted to annual, rather than to monthly, data.   The process of fitting a straight-line trend to monthly data is no different from that of fitting to annual data, but there are 12 times as many observed values to be considered and, because the X values become larger, the labor is multiplied by more than 12.   It is therefore advisable to fit a straight-line trend to annual data and then to transform the trend to a monthly basis.   The result is ordinarily the same as if the trend had been fitted to the monthly data.   In some cases, it is preferable to obtain the trend from annual data, since the presence of a very violent seasonal movement may distort a trend fitted to monthly data.

Annual totals—X units, one year.   The trend for the annual data of newspaper advertising for 1932–1960 was found to be $Y_c = 1,925.2 + 76.27X$ with origin at 1946 and with X units of one year.   The basic data were in terms of millions of lines of advertising per year; each figure, therefore, was a total for the year to which it referred.

The value obtained for a (to four digits) was 1,925.2 millions of lines, and $a = \dfrac{\Sigma Y}{N} = 1,925.2$ was the arithmetic mean of the 29 figures for the years 1932–1960.   Since the figure 1,925.2 was the a value for annual totals, the a value in monthly terms would be one-twelfth of it, or 160.4333 millions of lines.

From the annual data, b was found to be 76.27 millions of lines.   Now this is the annual increase in the amount of newspaper advertising for an entire year.   If we divide by 12, we obtain the *monthly trend increment* in the yearly totals.   Since we still have yearly totals, we must divide again by 12 to reduce the figures to millions of lines *per month*. We perform both of these operations at once by dividing by 144, giving a monthly *b* value of 76.27 ÷ 144 = 0.5297 millions of lines. The equation in monthly terms is

$$Y_c = 160.4333 + 0.5297X.$$
Origin, June–July 1946. *X* units, 1 month.

Our adjustment is not quite completed. Owing to the fact that there are an even number of months in a year, the equation just obtained has an origin which falls between the two middle months and is therefore out of step with the original monthly data by one-half month.[7] Consequently, we must shift the origin from a point between two months to any convenient month. Let us shift it to July 1946. This merely calls for increasing the value of *a* by one-half of the monthly *b* value, or (0.5 × 0.5297) = 0.2649. The value of *b* remains unchanged. The new equation, then, is

$$Y_c = 160.6982 + 0.5297X.$$
Origin, July 1946. *X* units, 1 month.

We shall record only four digits when we use this equation to obtain monthly trend values in Table 16.3.

Annual totals—X units, one-half year. When a straight-line trend was fitted to the production of sweet potatoes for 1941–1962, the resulting equation had *X* units of ½ year because the data covered an even number of years.[8] It would not be particularly meaningful to reduce the annual trend equation for sweet potato production to a monthly basis, because sweet potato production does not take place every month in the year. Neither is an illustration necessary here, since the procedure is exactly the same as that just described except for the fact that *b* is divided by 6 × 12 = 72 instead of by 144. This is so because the *b* value in the annual trend equation refers to the increase taking place in the trend during each six-month period.

Monthly averages—X units, one year. If a straight-line trend has been fitted to annual data which are monthly averages for each of an odd number of years, it is merely necessary to divide the annual *b* by 12 and shift the origin so that it will be compatible with monthly data. Suppose

---

[7] This will always be true, irrespective of whether the original data were first-of-the-month, middle-of-the-month, end-of-the-month, or any other sort. It would not occur if a 13-month year were used.

[8] An annual trend equation, such as that for the production of sweet potatoes, could be shifted so that the *X* units would be 1 year instead of one-half year. This merely requires doubling the value of *b*. However, it would also be necessary to shift the origin so that it would fall on a year instead of between two years.

that a trend for the years 1942–1966 has been obtained for the production of a manufactured commodity, the annual trend equation being

$$Y_c = 2,430 + 24.0X.$$
Origin, 1954. X units, 1 year.

Since the original data were monthly averages for each year, the value of a does not need to be adjusted. The value of b represents the annual increase and must be divided by 12 to obtain the monthly trend increment. The monthly trend equation then is

$$Y_c = 2,430 + 2.0X.$$
Origin, June–July 1954. X units, 1 month.

To complete the adjustment, we must shift the origin of the equation so that it will coincide with a month instead of falling between two months. If the origin is shifted to June 1954, it is merely necessary to decrease the value of a by one-half of the value of the monthly b, giving

$$Y_c = 2,429 + 2.0X.$$
Origin, June 1954. X units, 1 month.

Monthly averages—X units, one-half year. The procedure is the same as that just described except that the semiannual b is divided by 6.

The foregoing discussion of the procedure for shifting annual straight-line trend equations to a monthly basis may be summarized for purposes of reference as follows:

X unit in annual equation	Type of data			
	Monthly averages		Annual totals	
	a	b	a	b
One year	No change	Divide by 12	Divide by 12	Divide by 144
One-half year	No change	Divide by 6	Divide by 12	Divide by 72

Under all circumstances, the origin must be shifted so that it falls on a month instead of between two months.

SELECTING THE PERIOD FOR TREND ANALYSIS

In general, it is desirable to use as long a period as possible when a trend is to be determined. This practice results in a more reliable statement of the trend and one which is less affected by one or two large cyclical movements.

If the nature of the trend of a series has changed, it may be necessary to use two trends. It may or may not be possible to splice the two trends together.   The depression of the 1930's was so severe that, for some series, it now seems to have been more in the nature of a readjustment.   Consequently, one may occasionally use one trend for the years before the readjustment but a different one for the years following the readjustment.   It would have been possible to fit two trends to the data of newspaper advertising, shown in Chart 12.3, but we chose to show those data in terms of a single trend covering a longer period of time.

It is important that the first few and the last few years of a series be given special consideration before a decision is made concerning the period to be used.   If the data cover only ten or fifteen years, this is of particular importance; for longer periods, it is less important.   The first year should not be one of depression and the last year one of prosperity, since that will cause an upward trend to be too steep; b will be too large. Conversely, if the first year was one of prosperity while the last year was one of depression, the slope, if upward, would not be steep enough; b would be too small.   To avoid the introduction of such extraneous factors in the slope, the first and last years should be on opposite sides of the cycle (not on opposite sides of the trend) and about the same distance above, or below, the trend.   Thus, in Chart 12.6 $CD = C'D'$ and a trend fitted to data extending from D to D' will have the correct slope.

Not only should the slope be correct, but the *level* of a trend should also be suitable.   If a trend were fitted to the data of Chart 12.6 running from D to D', the level of the trend would be too high.   The trend should be fitted to a period running from B to B'.   This would result in a proper level for the trend, since the areas ABE and $A'B'E'$ are each one-fourth of a cycle.   The first and last years should not both be low points of particularly deep depressions, since they would then lower the level of the trend; a would be too small.   Conversely, the end years should not both

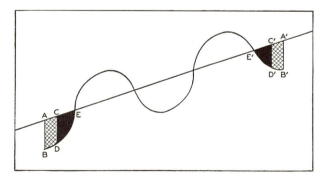

Chart 12.6.   Cycles and Appropriate Trend.

be high points of marked prosperity, since they would then raise the level of the trend unduly.

The trend for newspaper advertising was fitted to the years 1932–1960. Although, as may be seen in Chart 12.3, the series does not begin and end with the same phase of a cycle, the trend is satisfactory because the period covered is relatively long. What changes would occur in the trend equation if some of the early years had been omitted or some of the later years included? The equation obtained earlier for the period 1932–1960 was

$$Y_c = 1,925.2 + 76.27X,$$

with origin at 1946 and X units 1 year. Continuing to use the same origin and X units, the reader can verify, by computations based upon Table 12.2, that if the first four years were omitted, the trend equation for 1936–1960 would be

$$Y_c = 1,877.0 + 85.00X.$$

In view of the rules laid down in the preceding paragraphs, 1936–1960 may be more appropriate than 1932–1960 as the period for which a trend should be determined. However, owing to the length of the series, the results differ little; the 1936–1960 equation, if drawn on Chart 12.3, could be distinguished from the 1932–1960 trend only toward the ends.

If the last four years were to be added, the trend equation for 1932–1964 would be

$$Y_c = 1,897.8 + 69.82X.$$

This equation, too, if drawn on Chart 12.3, could be distinguished from the 1932–1960 trend only toward the ends.

SELECTING THE TYPE OF TREND

Since the discussion, so far, has been limited to trends fitted by inspection and to straight lines fitted by the method of least squares, there is not much that can be said at this point concerning the selection of the type of trend. We shall be in a better position to consider which one of a number of possible trend types is most appropriate after some additional types have been described in the following chapter.

As a first step, the original data should always be plotted and examined. It may even be worth while to sketch in a tentative trend by inspection. In some instances a trend fitted by inspection may suffice; but when the trend itself is to be studied, or extended, a mathematical equation should be used. If examination of the charted data indicates that the trend is not linear, one of the trend types described in Chapter 13 may be appropriate. The trend type chosen should be one which is logical in relation to the series which it undertakes to describe and in relation to the forces affecting that series. It is for this reason that a straight line, which indicates a constant *amount* of increase or decrease, cannot be expected to constitute an appropriate trend of a series over an extended period of time.

CHAPTER 13

Analysis of Time Series:

SECULAR TREND II—NON-LINEAR TRENDS

Chapter 12 discussed only the simplest type of trend equation, the straight line. It was noted that, for short periods of time, a straight line may provide a reasonably good description of the trend of a series, but that for longer periods a curved line of some sort may be called for. This chapter will describe the properties of several non-linear equation types, will explain how to fit them, and will give some indication of how to proceed in choosing among the various trend types.

SIMPLE POLYNOMIALS

This family of curves has as its most elementary representative the straight line, which, it will be remembered, has two constants. The straight line and four other polynomials are shown below:

First-degree (straight line).. $Y_c = a + bX$.

Second-degree............. $Y_c = a + bX + cX^2$.

Third-degree.............. $Y_c = a + bX + cX^2 + dX^3$.

Fourth-degree............. $Y_c = a + bX + cX^2 + dX^3 + eX^4$.

Fifth-degree..... .... $Y_c = a + bX + cX^2 + dX^3 + eX^4 + fX^5$.

When a third constant is added to the equation for the straight line, the second-degree curve, which has one bend, is obtained. Because of the bend in the second-degree curve, the slope of the curve is continually changing. If a sufficient number of X values are included, the second-degree curve will have a positive slope in one portion and a negative slope in another. This may be observed in Chart 13.1, which shows eight second-degree curves.

Each constant added to the second-degree equation may introduce an additional bend in the curve. Thus, a third-degree curve may have two

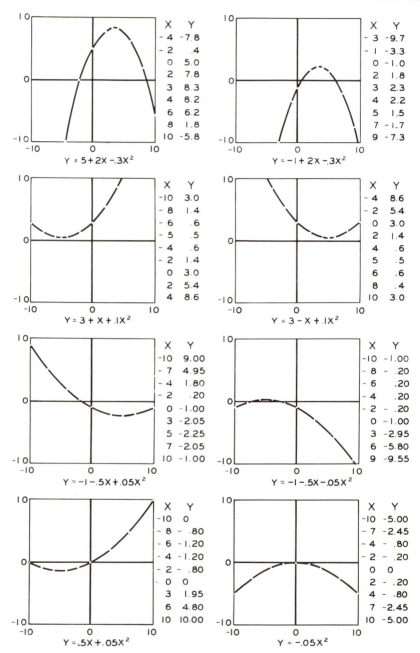

Chart 13.1.   Second-Degree Equations and Curves.

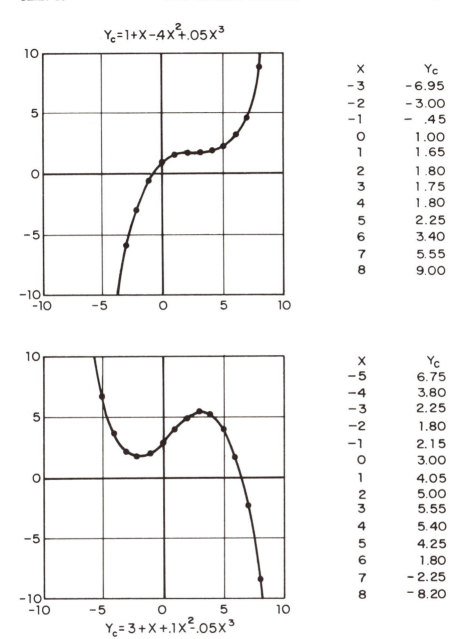

$$Y_c = 1 + X - .4X^2 + .05X^3$$

X	Y_c
-3	-6.95
-2	-3.00
-1	- .45
0	1.00
1	1.65
2	1.80
3	1.75
4	1.80
5	2.25
6	3.40
7	5.55
8	9.00

X	Y_c
-5	6.75
-4	3.80
-3	2.25
-2	1.80
-1	2.15
0	3.00
1	4.05
2	5.00
3	5.55
4	5.40
5	4.25
6	1.80
7	- 2.25
8	- 8.20

$$Y_c = 3 + X + .1X^2 - .05X^3$$

Chart 13.2. Third-Degree Equations and Curves.

bends, as shown in Chart 13.2. The lower of the two curves in Chart 13.2 shows clearly the fact that the slope of a third-degree curve may change twice from positive to negative or from negative to positive. Since such a change in the direction of slope may occur three times in a fourth-degree curve and four times in a fifth-degree curve, it follows that fourth- and fifth-degree curves hardly coincide with the concept of secular trend which is of interest to us. Consequently, we shall give no further attention to fourth- and fifth-degree curves, but shall describe the process of fitting the second-degree curve in some detail and briefly consider the third-degree curve.

Second-degree curve. The second-degree curve is only a little more complicated than a straight line, since it involves merely the addition of cX^2 to the equation for a straight line, giving

$$Y_c = a + bX + cX^2.$$

The eight second-degree equations, which have been plotted in Chart 13.1, give some idea of the flexibility of this equation type. Portions of such a curve fitted to a time series may slope upward or downward (or upward in one portion and downward in another) and may be concave upward or concave downward. While a straight-line indicates a constant amount of increase or decrease, a second-degree curve involves increasing or decreasing amounts of increase or decrease. More specifically: the second differences of the values obtained from the expression $Y_c = a + bX + cX^2$ are constant.[1]

Fitting the second-degree curve. Since there are three constants or unknowns in the second-degree curve, the following three normal equations are required:

$$\text{I.} \quad \Sigma Y = Na + b\Sigma X + c\Sigma X^2.$$
$$\text{II.} \quad \Sigma XY = a\Sigma X + b\Sigma X^2 + c\Sigma X^3.$$
$$\text{III.} \quad \Sigma X^2Y = a\Sigma X^2 + b\Sigma X^3 + c\Sigma X^4.$$

However, we are dealing with a time series, and the origin may be taken at the middle year (or other time unit), or between the two middle years,

---

[1] This may be seen by considering the Y_c values for section 2 of Chart 13.1, for which the equation is $Y_c = -1 + 2X - 0.3X^2$:

X	Y_c	First difference	Second difference	X	Y_c	First difference	Second difference
-3	-9.7			2	1.8	-1.1	-0.6
-2	-6.2	-3.5		3	2.3	-0.5	-0.6
-1	-3.3	-2.9	-0.6	4	2.2	0.1	-0.6
0	-1.0	-2.3	-0.6	5	1.5	0.7	-0.6
1	0.7	-1.7	-0.6	6	0.2	1.3	-0.6

as before, with the result that the summations of all odd powers of X are zero.   Therefore, the three normal equations become

I. $\Sigma Y = Na + c\Sigma X^2$.

II. $\Sigma XY = b\Sigma X^2$.

III. $\Sigma X^2 Y = a\Sigma X^2 + c\Sigma X^4$.

Notice that, instead of having to solve three equations simultaneously, the value of b is obtained from Equation II, while the values of a and c

MILLIONS OF
SHORT TONS

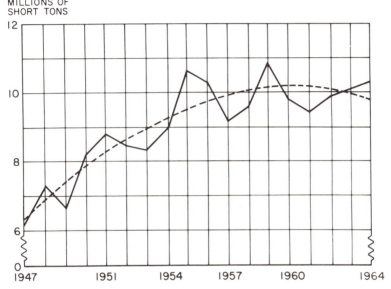

Chart 13.3.   United States Production of Crude Gypsum, 1947–1964, and Trend as Shown by a Second-Degree Curve.   Data of Table 13.1.

are gotten by solving Equations I and III simultaneously.   The use of the middle year as the origin has enabled us to save much labor.

Table 13.1 and Chart 13.3 show the production of crude gypsum in the United States for the years 1947 to 1964 inclusive.   The trend of the series is not linear, and these data will form the basis of our illustration of a fit of a second-degree curve.   The three normal equations call for the numerical values of N, ΣY, ΣXY, and $\Sigma X^2 Y$, which may be obtained from Table 13.1, and the values of ΣX^2 and ΣX^4 (for the first nine odd natural numbers), which may be read from Appendix C.   Substituting in the three normal equations gives

I. $163,178 = 18a + 1,938c$.

II. $207,396 = 1,938b$.

III. $16,734,682 = 1,938a + 374,034c$.

TABLE 13.1

Computation of Values for Fit of Second-Degree Curve to Production of Crude Gypsum in the United States, 1947–1964

(Thousands of short tons)

Year	X	Production Y	XY	X²Y	X²	a + bX	cX²	Trend value Y_c
1947	−17	6,208	−105,536	1,794,112	289	7,789.3	−1,457.7	6,332
1948	−15	7,255	−108,825	1,632,375	225	8,003.3	−1,134.9	6,868
1949	−13	6,608	− 85,904	1,116,752	169	8,217.3	− 852.4	7,365
1950	−11	8,193	− 90,123	991,353	121	8,431.4	− 610.3	7,821
1951	− 9	8,666	− 77,994	701,946	81	8,645.4	− 408.6	8,237
1952	− 7	8,415	− 58,905	412,335	49	8,859.4	− 247.2	8,612
1953	− 5	8,293	− 41,465	207,325	25	9,073.4	− 126.1	8,947
1954	− 3	8,996	− 26,988	80,964	9	9,287.5	− 45.4	9,242
1955	− 1	10,684	− 10,684	10,684	1	9,501.5	− 5.0	9,497
1956	1	10,316	10,316	10,316	1	9,715.5	− 5.0	9,711
1957	3	9,195	27,585	82,755	9	9,929.6	− 45.4	9,884
1958	5	9,600	48,000	240,000	25	10,143.6	− 126.1	10,018
1959	7	10,900	76,300	534,100	49	10,357.6	− 247.2	10,110
1960	9	9,825	88,425	795,825	81	10,571.7	− 408.6	10,163
1961	11	9,500	104,500	1,149,500	121	10,785.7	− 610.3	10,175
1962	13	9,969	129,597	1,684,761	169	10,999.7	− 852.4	10,147
1963	15	10,169	152,535	2,288,025	225	11,213.7	−1,134.9	10,079
1964	17	10,386	176,562	3,001,554	289	11,427.8	−1,457.7	9,970
Total	0	163,178	+207,396	16,734,682	1,938	...	...	...

Data from *Historical Statistics of the United States*, p. 364, *Statistical Abstract of the United States, 1964*, p. 727, *1962*, p. 712, and from various issues of *Survey of Current Business*.

The value of b is given by the second normal equation:

$$1,938b = 207,396;$$
$$b = 107.015.$$

Next, the values of a and c are obtained by solving normal Equations I and III simultaneously. The steps are:

1. Multiply normal Equation I by 193 and subtract normal Equation III from this new form of normal Equation I, thus obtaining[2] the value of a.

$$(\text{I} \times 193). \quad 31,493,354 = 3,474a + 374,034c.$$
$$\text{III.} \quad \underline{16,734,682 = 1,938a + 374,034c.}$$
$$14,758,672 = 1,536a$$
$$a = 9,608.51041.$$

---

[2] The multiplying factor 193 was obtained by dividing the coefficient of c in normal Equation III by the coefficient of c in normal Equation I. That is, $\Sigma X^4 \div \Sigma X^2 = 374,034 \div 1,938 = 193$. When solving two equations simultaneously, either unknown may be eliminated by multiplying one of the equations by the quotient of the coefficients of the unknown which is to be eliminated and subtracting one equation from the other.

2. Substitute the value of a in normal Equation I to obtain the value of c.

$$\text{I. } 163,178 = 18(9,608.51041) + 1,938c.$$
$$1,938c = -9,775.1874.$$
$$c = -5.04395634.$$

3. Substitute, in normal Equation III, the values obtained for a and c. This serves as a check of the computations in steps 1 and 2.

$$\text{III. } 16,734,682 = 1,938(9,608.51041) + 374,034(-5.04395634),$$
$$= 16,734,682.$$

The second-degree trend equation may now be written:

$$Y_c = 9,608.51 + 107.015X - 5.0440X^2.$$
$$\text{Origin, 1955–1956.} \quad X \text{ units, } \tfrac{1}{2} \text{ year.}$$

The computation of the trend values is shown in the last four columns of Table 13.1. The trend, shown in Chart 13.3, is the result of plotting these trend values. Note that the production of crude gypsum seems to show four and one-half cycles during the years covered.

THIRD-DEGREE CURVE

By adding one more constant to the equation for a second-degree curve, we are enabled to put one more bend into the curve. While a straight line has only one slope, a second-degree curve (Chart 13.1) slopes in a positive direction at one stage and in a negative direction at another, and a third-degree curve (Chart 13.2) may include three directions of slope.

Four normal equations are required for a third-degree curve:

$$\text{I.} \quad \Sigma Y = Na + b\Sigma X + c\Sigma X^2 + d\Sigma X^3.$$
$$\text{II.} \quad \Sigma XY = a\Sigma X + b\Sigma X^2 + c\Sigma X^3 + d\Sigma X^4.$$
$$\text{III.} \quad \Sigma X^2Y = a\Sigma X^2 + b\Sigma X^3 + c\Sigma X^4 + d\Sigma X^5.$$
$$\text{IV.} \quad \Sigma X^3Y = a\Sigma X^3 + b\Sigma X^4 + c\Sigma X^5 + d\Sigma X^6.$$

Again, if the X origin is taken at the middle of the period, the odd powers of X will total zero, leaving these equations:

$$\text{I.} \quad \Sigma Y = Na + c\Sigma X^2.$$
$$\text{II.} \quad \Sigma XY = b\Sigma X^2 + d\Sigma X^4.$$
$$\text{III.} \quad \Sigma X^2Y = a\Sigma X^2 + c\Sigma X^4.$$
$$\text{IV.} \quad \Sigma X^3Y = b\Sigma X^4 + d\Sigma X^6.$$

With the equations in this form, we do not have to solve four simultaneous equations, although that would have been necessary if the origin had been taken anywhere other than at the middle of the period. The values of a and c are obtained by solving Equations I and III simultaneously;

simultaneous solution of Equations II and IV gives the values of b and d. Only one column of figures, in addition to those shown in Table 13.1, must be computed; it is a column headed X^3Y, the total of which gives ΣX^3Y. Note that Equations I and III are exactly the same as for the second-degree curve. Consequently, for a given set of data, the values of a and c will be the same for a second-degree curve and for a third-degree curve.[3]

USE OF LOGARITHMS

Straight line fitted to logarithms. A glance at Chart 13.4 makes it quite apparent that a curve of the type $Y_c = a + bX$ would not be a satisfactory description of the trend of the production of asphalt for the period shown. A second-degree curve might be used, but a more logical trend equation is available. A second-degree curve fitted to this series would behave in such a fashion that the amount of increase each year would be increasing by a constant amount; this is the same thing as saying that the

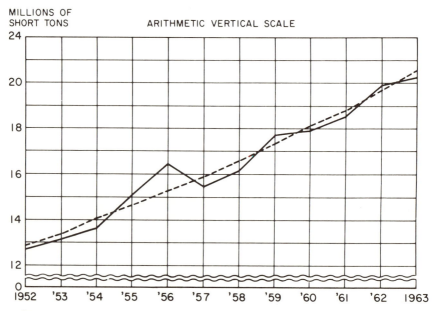

Chart 13.4. United States Production of Asphalt from Petroleum, 1952–1963, and Trend as Shown by a Straight Line Fitted to the Logarithms of the Data. Note that this chart has an arithmetic vertical scale and that the trend line is slightly curved. Data of Table 13.2.

---

[3] See R. A. Fisher, *Statistical Methods for Research Workers*, thirteenth edition, Hafner Publishing Co., New York, 1958, Chaps. V and VI. See also R. A. Fisher and F. Yates, *Statistical Tables for Biological, Agricultural and Medical Research*, third edition, Hafner Publishing Co., New York, 1949, pp. 23–25 and 70–80. For a discussion of orthogonal polynomials, see the second edition of this text, pp. 289–290.

second difference of the trend values is a constant, but with the additional provisos (1) that the trend is upward and (2) that the second differences are positive. Now, a curve of the type $Y_c = ab^x$ indicates a constant ratio of change, and, if such a curve were to be fitted to the data of Chart 13.4, it is clear that the ratio would be greater than 1.0 rather than less than 1.0. That is to say, the series is increasing. The data of asphalt production have been plotted on semi-logarithmic paper in Chart 13.5, and it appears that the trend, which was not linear in Chart 13.4, is now linear. This indicates the suitability of the equation type $Y_c = ab^x$, the exponential curve.

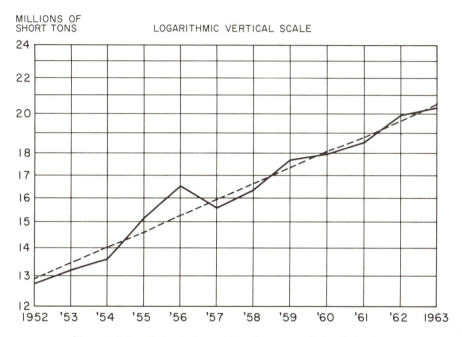

MILLIONS OF SHORT TONS   LOGARITHMIC VERTICAL SCALE

Chart 13.5. United States Production of Asphalt from Petroleum, 1952–1963, and Trend as Shown by a Straight Line Fitted to the Logarithms of the Data. Note that this chart has a logarithmic vertical scale and that the trend is linear. Data of Table 13.2.

It is not possible to fit the exponential curve directly to the Y values by least squares; we can, however, make a least-squares fit to the logarithms of the original data, and this results in minimizing the squared deviations of the logarithms of the observed values from the logarithmic trend values. Putting the exponential equation in logarithmic form gives

$$\log Y_c = \log a + X \log b,$$

which is a straight line in terms of X and log Y. The normal equations are

I. $\Sigma \log Y = N \log a + \log b\Sigma X$.

II. $\Sigma X\log Y = \log a\Sigma X + \log b\Sigma X^2$.

Since the X origin may be taken at the middle of the period, $\Sigma X = 0$; so these equations may be written

I. $\Sigma \log Y = N \log a$.

II. $\Sigma X\log Y = \log b\Sigma X^2$.

TABLE 13.2

Computation of Values for Fit of Straight Line to Logarithms of United States Production of Asphalt from Petroleum 1952–1963

(Thousands of short tons)

Year	X	Production Y	Log Y	X log Y	Trend values Log Y_c	Y_c
1952	−11	12,784	4.106667	−45.173337	4.110353	12,893
1953	− 9	13,165	4.119421	−37.074789	4.128751	13,451
1954	− 7	13,620	4.134177	−28.939239	4.147150	14,033
1955	− 5	15,113	4.179350	−20.896750	4.165548	14,640
1956	− 3	16,479	4.216931	−12.650793	4.183947	15,274
1957	− 1	15,579	4.192539	− 4.192539	4.202346	15,935
1958	1	16,251	4.210880	4.210880	4.220744	16,624
1959	3	17,753	4.249272	12.747816	4.239143	17,344
1960	5	17,940	4.253822	21.269110	4.257541	18,094
1961	7	18,513	4.267476	29.872332	4.275940	18,877
1962	9	19,923	4.299354	38.694186	4.294338	19,694
1963	11	20,354	4.308650	47.395150	4.312737	20,547
Total	0	...	50.538539	+5.262027	...	...

Data from various issues of *Statistical Abstract of the United States*.

Using the summations shown in Table 13.2 and getting ΣX^2 from Appendix C, we have

I. $50.538539 = 12 \log a$,
    $\log a = 4.211545$.

II. $5.262027 = 572 \log b$,
    $\log b = 0.00919935$.

The trend equation in logarithmic form is

$\log Y_c = 4.211545 + 0.00919935X$.
Origin, 1957–1958. X units, $\frac{1}{2}$ year.

To obtain a and b, we look up the anti-logarithms of log a and log b and we can then write the trend equation in natural form:

$$Y_c = (16{,}275.9)(1.0214)^X.$$
Origin, 1957–1958. X units, $\frac{1}{2}$ year.

The log Y_c values and the Y_c values for each year are shown in the last two columns of Table 13.2. The Y_c trend values are shown on both Charts 13.4 and 13.5. To draw the trend on Chart 13.5, it was merely necessary to obtain the Y_c values for 1952 and for 1963, to plot these two values, and to connect them with a straight line. Drawing the trend on Chart 13.4 requires plotting all, or nearly all, of the trend values.

The trend equation, written in the form

$$Y_c = (16{,}275.9)(1.0214)^X,$$

tells us that 16,275.9 thousand short tons was the trend value for a point midway between 1957 and 1958, and that, during the period under consideration, the production of asphalt had an annual growth of 2.14 per cent. Incidentally, 16,275.9 thousand short tons is the geometric mean of the Y values. Since the geometric mean is always a little smaller than

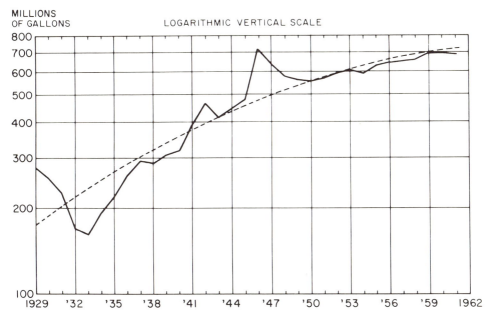

Chart 13.6. Domestic Production of Ice Cream, 1929–1961, and Trend as Shown by a Second-Degree Curve Fitted to the Logarithms of the Data. Data of Table 13.3.

the arithmetic mean, and since the sum of the squares of the deviations of the logarithms (rather than of the original data) is at a minimum for this trend, it follows that the sum of the deviations above the trend line of Chart 13.4 is slightly larger than the sum of those below it. This constitutes a minor shortcoming of this type of trend. However, the measured deviations on either side of the trend line in Chart 13.5 do cancel. In addition, there is some merit in the fact that the use of logarithms equalizes the importance of fluctuations in regard to their *relative*, rather than in regard to their *absolute*, deviations from the trend. This is particularly pertinent when there are small cyclical variations about the lower portion of the trend and larger (that is, larger absolutely) cyclical variations about the upper part of the trend. In such a situation, the trend line is more likely to pass through all of the cycles rather than through only the larger ones. This point may more than offset the technical disadvantage of fitting to the logarithms.

Second-degree curve fitted to logarithms. Sometimes data are encountered which, when plotted on semi-logarithmic paper, continue to show curvature, being concave either upward or downward. Chart 13.6 and Table 13.3 show such a series, the domestic production of ice cream for 1929–1961, which is concave downward, indicating that the ratio of increase has been decreasing. We may fit a second-degree curve to the logarithms of the Y values, using

$$\log Y_c = \log a + X \log b + X^2 \log c.$$

Taking the X origin at the middle of the period, the three normal equations are

I. $\Sigma \log Y = N \log a + \log c\Sigma X^2.$
II. $\Sigma X \log Y = \log b\Sigma X^2.$
III. $\Sigma X^2 \log Y = \log a\Sigma X^2 + \log c\Sigma X^4.$

From Appendix B we ascertain that $\Sigma X^2 = 2(1{,}496) = 2{,}992$ and $\Sigma X^4 = 2(234{,}848) = 487{,}696$. All of the other values may be had from Table 13.3, and we solve the normal equations as follows:

II. $\Sigma X \log Y = \log b\Sigma X^2.$
    $57.402463 = 2{,}992 \log b.$
      $\log b = 0.0191854.$

I. $\Sigma \log Y = N \log a + \log c\Sigma X^2.$
III. $\Sigma X^2 \log Y = \log a\Sigma X^2 + \log c\Sigma X^4.$

I. $86.539428 = 33 \log a + 2{,}992 \log c.$
III. $7{,}751.942035 = 2{,}992 \log a + 487{,}696 \log c.$

$(\text{I} \times 90.666667).$ $7{,}846.241501 = 2{,}992 \log a + 271{,}274.67 \log c.$
III. $\underline{7{,}751.942035 = 2{,}992 \log a + 487{,}696 \quad\, \log c.}$
       $94.299466 = \qquad\qquad\quad\; - 216{,}421.33 \log c.$
         $\log c = -0.000435722.$

TABLE 13.3

Computation of Values for Fit of Second-Degree Curve to Logarithms of Ice Cream Production in the United States, 1929–1961

(Millions of gallons)

| Year | Production Y | Log Y | X | X log Y | X^2 | X^2 log Y | Computation of trend values | | | |
							log a + X log b	X^2 log c	Log Y_c	Y_c
1929	277.2	2.442793	−16	−39.084688	256	625.355008	2.3549456	−0.111544832	2.243401	175.1
1930	255.4	2.407221	−15	−36.108315	225	541.624725	2.3741310	−0.098037450	2.276094	188.8
1931	226.4	2.354876	−14	−32.968264	196	461.555696	2.3933164	−0.085401512	2.307915	203.2
1932	168.0	2.225309	−13	−28.929017	169	376.077221	2.4125018	−0.073637018	2.338865	218.2
1933	161.8	2.208979	−12	−26.507748	144	318.092976	2.4316872	−0.062743968	2.368943	233.9
1934	191.6	2.282396	−11	−25.106356	121	276.169916	2.4508726	−0.052722362	2.398150	250.1
1935	219.1	2.340642	−10	−23.406420	100	234.064200	2.4700580	−0.043572200	2.426486	267.0
1936	258.6	2.412629	−9	−21.713661	81	195.422949	2.4892434	−0.035293482	2.453950	284.4
1937	291.1	2.464042	−8	−19.712336	64	157.698688	2.5084288	−0.027886208	2.480543	302.4
1938	286.4	2.456973	−7	−17.198811	49	120.391677	2.5276142	−0.021350378	2.506264	320.8
1939	305.8	2.485437	−6	−14.912622	36	89.475732	2.5467996	−0.015685992	2.531114	339.7
1940	318.1	2.502564	−5	−12.512820	25	62.564100	2.5659850	−0.010893050	2.555092	359.0
1941	390.3	2.591399	−4	−10.365596	16	41.462384	2.5851704	−0.006971552	2.578199	378.6
1942	464.2	2.666705	−3	−8.000115	9	24.000345	2.6043558	−0.003921498	2.600434	398.5
1943	411.6	2.614475	−2	−5.228950	4	10.457900	2.6235412	−0.001742888	2.621798	418.6
1944	444.9	2.648262	−1	−2.648262	1	2.648262	2.6427266	−0.000435722	2.642291	438.8
1945	477.2	2.678700	0	0	0	0	2.6619120	0	2.661912	459.1
1946	713.8	2.853577	1	2.853577	1	2.853577	2.6810974	−0.000435722	2.680662	479.4
1947	631.0	2.800029	2	5.600058	4	11.200116	2.7002828	−0.001742888	2.698540	499.5
1948	576.5	2.760799	3	8.282397	9	24.847191	2.7194682	−0.003921498	2.715547	519.5
1949	558.1	2.746712	4	10.986848	16	43.947392	2.7386536	−0.006971552	2.731682	539.1
1950	554.4	2.743823	5	13.719115	25	68.595575	2.7578390	−0.010893050	2.746946	558.4
1951	568.8	2.754960	6	16.529760	36	99.178560	2.7770244	−0.015685992	2.761338	577.2
1952	592.7	2.772835	7	19.409845	49	135.868915	2.7962098	−0.021350378	2.774859	595.5
1953	605.1	2.781827	8	22.254616	64	178.036928	2.8153952	−0.027886208	2.787509	613.1
1954	596.8	2.775829	9	24.982461	81	224.842149	2.8345806	−0.035293482	2.799287	629.9
1955	628.5	2.798305	10	27.983050	100	279.830500	2.8537660	−0.043572200	2.810194	645.9
1956	641.3	2.807061	11	30.877671	121	339.654381	2.8729514	−0.052722362	2.820229	661.0
1957	649.9	2.812847	12	33.754164	144	405.049968	2.8921368	−0.062743968	2.829393	675.1
1958	658.0	2.818226	13	36.636938	169	476.280194	2.9113222	−0.073637018	2.837685	688.2
1959	697.9	2.843793	14	39.813102	196	557.383428	2.9305076	−0.085401512	2.845106	700.0
1960	697.6	2.843606	15	42.654090	225	639.811350	2.9496930	−0.098037450	2.851656	710.7
1961	694.7	2.841797	16	45.468752	256	727.500032	2.9688784	−0.111544832	2.857334	720.0
Total	...	86.539428	0	57.402463	2,992	7,751.942035			...	...

Data from *Historical Statistics of United States, Colonial Times to 1957*, p. 292; *Agricultural Statistics*, 1961, p. 400 and 1963, p. 397.

I. $86.539428 = 33 \log a + (2,992)(-0.000435722)$.
　$33 \log a = 87.843108$.
　　$\log a = 2.661912$.

Check, using III.　$7,751.942035 = (2,992)(2.661912)$
$$+ (487,696)(-0.000435722),$$
$$= 7,751.940827.$$

Trend equation: $\text{Log } Y_c = 2.661912 + 0.0191854X - 0.000435722X^2$.
Origin, 1945.　X units, 1 year.

The procedure for computing the trend values is indicated in Table 13.3. The trend is shown graphically in Chart 13.6. A Gompertz curve has also been fitted to the data (see Charts 13.10 and 13.11).

ASYMPTOTIC GROWTH CURVES

The straight line $Y_c = a + bX$, which was discussed in the preceding chapter, describes a constant amount of increase or decrease. The exponential curve, $Y_c = ab^X$, involves a constant ratio of change and, therefore, a constant ratio of change in the amount of change. If b is a positive number greater than one, the trend is upward and the amount of change is undergoing a constant percentage of increase; if b is a positive number smaller than one, the trend is downward and the amount of change shows a constant percentage of decrease.

Over long periods of time, chronological series are not likely to show either a constant amount of change or a constant ratio of change. It is much more likely that an increasing series[4] will show an increasing amount of change but a decreasing ratio of change. This is true of the data of Charts 13.10 and 13.11, which show domestic production of ice cream.

It is also possible that an increasing series may show a decline in the amount of increase. Decreasing absolute growth is not often encountered, but we shall discuss one curve of this type, the modified exponential, since it serves as an excellent introduction to the more important Gompertz and logistic curves. Before beginning a consideration of the modified exponential curve, passing mention may be made of three other curve types which may describe a decreasing amount of growth. These are:

(1) Modified polynomials, such as $Y_c = a + bX^{\frac{1}{2}}$, $Y_c = a + bX^{\frac{1}{2}} + cX$, and others. When three or more constants are present, one (or more) constants may be negative, in which case the curve may ultimately turn down.

---

[4] Series which are declining may show a decreasing amount of change. The decreasing amount of change may represent a decreasing or constant (but usually decreasing) ratio of change. To avoid possible confusion, most of the discussion concerning asymptotic growth curves will deal with increasing series.

(2) Straight line to $\log X$. The expression is $Y_c = a + b \log X$. This curve type should not be used unless there is a logical justification for considering the logarithms of time.

(3) A parabolic curve to $\log Y$, which is written $\log Y_c = aX^b$, may be fitted by least squares by writing it $\log \log Y_c = \log a + b \log X$.

Note that, when using the logarithm of X, the X origin cannot be taken at the middle of the period.

The modified exponential. This curve not only describes a trend in which the amount of growth declines by a constant percentage, but the curve also approaches an upper limit, called the *asymptote*. This is an

TABLE 13.4

Hypothetical Data for Modified Exponential Curve

(Asymptote $k = 114$)

X	Y	Partial totals	Y increment	Per cent of preceding increment
(1)	(2)	(3)	(4)	(5)
0	50		. . .	. . .
1	66	116.0000	16	. . .
2	78		12	75
3	87	165.0000	9	75
4	93.75		6.75	75
5	98.8125	192.5625	5.0625	75

important property of growth curves, since many time series seem to approach an upper limit. The equation of the modified exponential is

$$Y_c = k + ab^x,$$

where k is the asymptote.

As noted in footnote 4, we shall give our attention primarily to increasing series, but Chart 13.7 shows four shapes which this equation may assume. It must be clear that our interest centers on part 1 of Chart 13.7, since that is the only one of the four which represents an increasing series with an upper asymptote. There are occasions when one might wish to use a trend like that in part 3 of Chart 13.7. This would be true for a declining series tending to have a constant percentage of decrease in the amount of decrease. Death rates from a specific disease may behave in this fashion.

The reader may find it illuminating to substitute various values for k, a, and b in the equation for the modified exponential and to draw for himself curves like those shown in Chart 13.7. This will provide him with specific illustrations of the situations stated generally in that chart. Note that negative values of b are of no interest to us.

The first two columns of Table 13.4 show a series which has a constant percentage decrease in its amount of growth.   As can be seen in Columns 4 and 5, each first difference is 75 per cent of the preceding first difference. The increments of increase are Δ_1, Δ_2, Δ_3, Δ_4, and Δ_5, and

$$\frac{\Delta_2}{\Delta_1} = \frac{\Delta_3}{\Delta_2} = \frac{\Delta_4}{\Delta_3} = \frac{\Delta_5}{\Delta_4} = 0.75.$$

Referring to Chart 13.8, the horizontal broken line near the top of the chart is the value k that the curve of this series approaches; in this case k

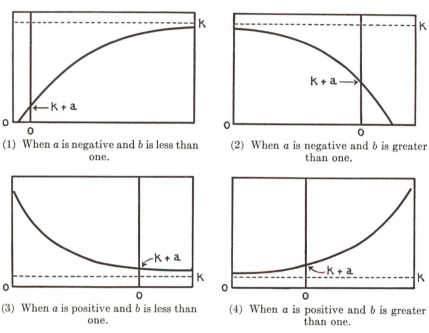

(1) When a is negative and b is less than one.

(2) When a is negative and b is greater than one.

(3) When a is positive and b is less than one.

(4) When a is positive and b is greater than one.

Chart 13.7.   Four Forms of the Modified Exponential Curve, $Y_c = k + ab^X$.

is 114.   This means that, if we should extend the trend line indefinitely, it would approach closer and closer to this value, but never quite equal it. The second constant, a, the value obtained by subtracting the asymptote k from the trend value when X is zero, in this instance is -64.   The third constant, b, is, of course, the ratio between successive increments of growth, or 0.75 for this series.   In Chart 13.8 the vertical broken line when $X = 1$ is $-64(0.75) = -48$; when $X = 2$, it is $-64(0.75)^2 = -36$; and so on for the other values of X.   Thus these vertical broken lines are described by the expression ab^X.   This is true when $X = 0$ also, since $-64(0.75)^0 = -64$.   In the diagram, ab^X is represented by the height of the shaded area.   If now, in turn, we subtract from k the value of each of the vertical broken lines, we have the trend values.   The vertical

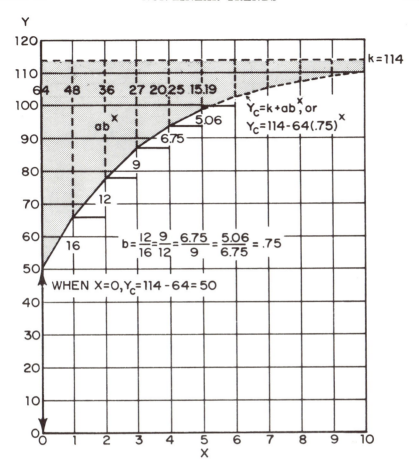

Chart 13.8. A Modified Exponential Equation Fitted to the Data of Table 13.4.

broken lines are subtracted from k because the sign of a is negative. Thus:

X	$k + ab^x$	$= Y_c$
0	$114 - 64$	$= 50$
1	$114 - 48$	$= 66$
2	$114 - 36$	$= 78$
3	$114 - 27$	$= 87$
4	$114 - 20.25$	$= 93.75$
5	$114 - 15.1875$	$= 98.8125$

Since the sign of a is negative, the increments of growth are declining. As is already obvious, for this series of data the equation is $Y_c = 114 - 64(0.75)^x$.

This curve has three constants: k, the asymptote; a, the distance between the value of Y_c when $X = 0$ and the asymptote; and b, the ratio between successive first differences. Three equations are therefore required for fitting it. These are obtained by first dividing the data into three equal sections, as in Table 13.4. Then the Y values are totaled for each section, as in Column 3. The results are:

For the first third............ $\Sigma_1 Y = 116.$
For the second third........ $\Sigma_2 Y = 165.$
For the third third.......... $\Sigma_3 Y = 192.5625.$

Let us note what 116 represents in terms of our equation. It is the sum of $50 + 66$. But 50 is $k + ab^0$ and 66 is $k + ab^1$; so

$$116 = 2k + a + ab.$$

This is Equation I. The other two are obtained in similar fashion. The three equations are:

I. $116 = 2k + a + ab.$
II. $165 = 2k + ab^2 + ab^3.$
III. $192.5625 = 2k + ab^4 + ab^5.$

In order to solve for b, we first subtract Equation I from Equation II, obtaining Equation A; and then subtract Equation II from Equation III, obtaining Equation B. Thus:

A. $49 = ab^3 + ab^2 - ab - a$
$\quad = a(b^3 + b^2 - b - 1).$
B. $27.5625 = ab^5 + ab^4 - ab^3 - ab^2$
$\quad = ab^2(b^3 + b^2 - b - 1).$

The constant b is now obtained by dividing Equation B by Equation A. We shall call the resulting equation C.

C. $\dfrac{27.5625}{49} = \dfrac{ab^2(b^3 + b^2 - b - 1)}{a(b^3 + b^2 - b - 1)}:$

$b^2 = 0.5625.$
$b = 0.75.$

The value of a may now be gotten by substituting in Equation A or B.

A. $49 = a(0.75^3 + 0.75^2 - 0.75 - 1).$

$$a = \frac{49}{-0.765625} = -64.$$

The remaining constant k may be computed by substituting the values of a and b in any of the original equations.

I. $116 = 2k - 64 - 64(0.75).$
$2k = 228.$
$k = 114.$

The values of the constants are thus found to be those which we knew to be correct. The equation was not obtained by the method of least squares, but was so fitted that the three partial totals of the trend values were the same as those of the original data. In this case, since the original data conform to the equation type perfectly, the fitted curve passes through all of the original points.

The logical procedure, which has been explained, can be developed into more convenient formulas, which are as follows:[5]

$$b^n = \frac{\Sigma_3 Y - \Sigma_2 Y}{\Sigma_2 Y - \Sigma_1 Y}.$$

$$a = (\Sigma_2 Y - \Sigma_1 Y) \frac{b - 1}{(b^n - 1)^2}.$$

$$k = \frac{1}{n}\left[\Sigma_1 Y - \left(\frac{b^n - 1}{b - 1}\right) a \right],$$

where n is the number of years in each third of the data. Solving by these formulas requires, of course, that b be obtained first, then a, and finally k.

If the expressions for a and b are substituted in the expression just given for k, we obtain

$$k = \frac{1}{n}\left[\frac{(\Sigma_1 Y)(\Sigma_3 Y) - (\Sigma_2 Y)^2}{\Sigma_1 Y + \Sigma_3 Y - 2\Sigma_2 Y} \right],$$

which enables us to obtain the asymptote without first computing a and b.

Since time series do not often behave in such a manner that a modified exponential is a logical fit or a good description of the series, no illustration is given of the fit of $Y_c = k + ab^x$ to a set of actual data. As noted earlier, the treatment of the modified exponential curve is intended as an introduction to the two other growth curves to be discussed in the following pages.

The Gompertz curve. In the form which is of primary concern to us, the Gompertz curve describes a trend in which the growth increments of the logarithms are declining by a constant percentage. Thus, the natural values of the trend would show a declining ratio of increase, but the ratio does not decrease by either a constant amount or a constant percentage. The equation for the Gompertz curve is

$$Y_c = ka^{b^x},$$

which may be put in logarithmic form

$$\log Y_c = \log k + (\log a) b^x.$$

---

[5] The derivation of these formulas is given in Appendix S, section 13.1.

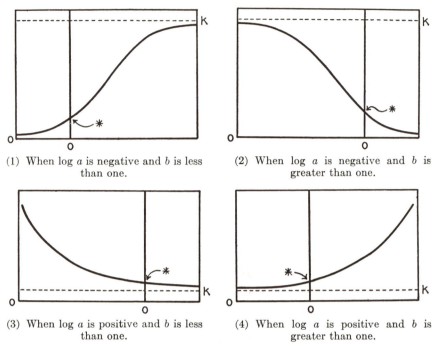

(1) When log a is negative and b is less than one.

(2) When log a is negative and b is greater than one.

(3) When log a is positive and b is less than one.

(4) When log a is positive and b is greater than one.

Chart 13.9.   Four Forms of the Gompertz Curve, $Y_c = ka^{b^x}$. The vertical values at the points marked (*) are antilog (log k + log a).

The four parts of Chart 13.9 show four shapes which the Gompertz equation may assume.   While the statistician might occasionally find use for the Gompertz curve to describe trends of the types shown[6] in parts 2 and 3 of Chart 13.9, our major interest centers in the form shown in part 1 of the chart.   This curve (and also the curve in part 2) has an upper and a lower asymptote, the lower asymptote being zero.   Only positive values of b are considered in Chart 13.9, since negative values of b do not yield useful curves.

Whatever has been said about the behavior of the modified exponential curve applies also to the logarithmic form of the Gompertz curve.   The Gompertz curves shown in Chart 13.9 would, if put in logarithmic form (or plotted on semi-logarithmic paper), look like the corresponding parts of Chart 13.7.   The fitting of the Gompertz curve is to the logarithms of the observed data and may be accomplished in a manner exactly paral-

---

[6] Deaths of railway employees, accidents in factories, specific death rates, and other declining series might be described by a Gompertz curve having a lower asymptote at the right.   Whether there is or is not an upper asymptote will depend upon the behavior of the data to which the curve is fitted.

leling the fit of the modified exponential.   The expressions are

$$b^n = \frac{\Sigma_3 \log Y - \Sigma_2 \log Y}{\Sigma_2 \log Y - \Sigma_1 \log Y}.$$

$$\log a = (\Sigma_2 \log Y - \Sigma_1 \log Y) \frac{b-1}{(b^n-1)^2}.$$

$$\log k = \frac{1}{n} \left[\Sigma_1 \log Y - \left(\frac{b^n-1}{b-1}\right) \log a \right].$$

If it is desired to obtain the value of k without first computing $\log a$ and b, use

$$\log k = \frac{1}{n} \left[\frac{(\Sigma_1 \log Y)(\Sigma_3 \log Y) - (\Sigma_2 \log Y)^2}{\Sigma_1 \log Y + \Sigma_3 \log Y - 2\Sigma_2 \log Y} \right].$$

Using this expression first enables one quickly to ascertain if the upward trend has an upper asymptote; computing k in this manner also provides a check of the value of the k obtained by the formula first given. Whether or not there is an upper asymptote for an increasing series may also be ascertained by noting if $(\Sigma_3 \log Y - \Sigma_2 \log Y)$ is greater than or less than $(\Sigma_2 \log Y - \Sigma_1 \log Y)$. If the first difference exceeds the second difference, b^n (and, therefore, b) is greater than one, and there is no upper asymptote for the increasing series; the curve of such an increasing series would resemble that shown in part 4 of Chart 13.9. If the first difference is less than the second, b is less than one, and the curve of an increasing series would look like part 1 of Chart 13.9.

The data of Table 13.5, which are shown also in Charts 13.10 and 13.11, will serve as the basis for an illustration of the fit of the Gompertz curve. The computation of the required sums of the logarithms is carried out in the fourth column of Table 13.5. Using the expressions previously given, we obtain

$$b^n = \frac{\Sigma_3 \log Y - \Sigma_2 \log Y}{\Sigma_2 \log Y - \Sigma_1 \log Y}.$$

$$b^{11} = \frac{30.851086 - 29.607045}{29.607045 - 23.595860} = \frac{1.244041}{6.011185} = 0.20695437.$$

Log b^{11} = 9.31587418 $-$ 10 = 109.31587418 $-$ 110.
Log b = 9.937806744 $-$ 10.
   b = 0.86657549.

$$\text{Log } a = (\Sigma_2 \log Y - \Sigma_1 \log Y) \frac{b-1}{(b^n-1)^2},$$

$$= 6.011185 \frac{-0.13342451}{(-0.79304563)^2} = 6.011185 \frac{-0.13342451}{0.62892137},$$

$$= (6.011185)(-0.21214816) = -1.2752618.$$

$$\text{Log } k = \frac{1}{n}\left[\Sigma_1 \log Y - \left(\frac{b^n - 1}{b - 1}\right) \log a \right],$$

$$= \frac{1}{11}\left[23.595860 - \left(\frac{-0.79304563}{-0.13342451}\right)(-1.2752618) \right],$$

$$= 2.834158.$$

Check, using

$$\text{Log } k = \frac{1}{n}\left[\frac{(\Sigma_1 \log Y)(\Sigma_3 \log Y) - (\Sigma_2 \log Y)^2}{\Sigma_1 \log Y + \Sigma_3 \log Y - 2\Sigma_2 \log Y} \right],$$

$$= \frac{1}{11}\left[\frac{(23.595860)(30.851086) - (29.607045)^2}{23.595860 + 30.851086 - 2(29.607045)} \right] = 2.834158.$$

Trend Equation:

$$\text{Log } Y_c = 2.834158 - 1.2752618(0.8665755)^X.$$
$$Y_c = 682.59(0.0530565)^{(0.8665755)^X}.$$
Origin, 1929. X units, 1 year.

The natural form of the trend equation is obtained by looking up the anti-logarithms of $\log k$ and $\log a$. Since $\log a = -1.2752618$ is a negative logarithm, it must be rewritten $\log a = 8.7247382 - 10$ before the value of $a = 0.0530565$ can be obtained from Appendix R. Note that $b = 0.8665755$, which indicates that the ratio of increase each year is declining: more specifically, that each difference between successive logarithmic trend values is about 0.87 times (or 87 per cent of) the preceding difference. Whenever $b < 1$, the value of $b - 1$ is negative, resulting in a negative value for $\log a$, if $\Sigma_2 \log Y$ exceeds $\Sigma_1 \log Y$. (See the equation for $\log a$.) If $\log a$ is negative, a is less than one.

For our data, when X is zero (the value of X for 1920), $b^X = 1.0$ and $a^{b^X} = 0.0530565$, with the result that for 1929 $Y_c = (682.6)(0.0530565) = 36.2$, the value shown for 1929 in the last column of Table 13.5. The greater the value of X, the smaller the value of b^X. As X increases, b^X approaches zero and a^{b^X} approaches 1.0, with the result that Y_c approaches k, or 683, the upper asymptote.

The procedure for computing the trend values is shown in Table 13.5. Note that $\Sigma_1 \log Y_c = \Sigma_1 \log Y$, $\Sigma_2 \log Y_c = \Sigma_2 \log Y$, and $\Sigma_3 \log Y_c = \Sigma_3 \log Y$ to at least six digits. These agreements are noted by check marks in the column headed "Log Y_c." The trend values have been plotted on Charts 13.10 and 13.11 and have been extended in both directions to indicate more clearly the shape of the fitted curve. The extension of the trend to 2000 is not intended as a forecast, although the Gompertz curve is sometimes used to assist in making predictions. The asymptote is shown on both of the charts, and the approach of the trend to the asymptote is apparent.

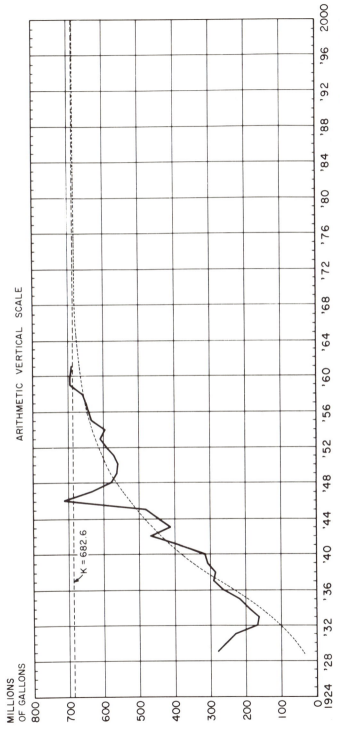

MILLIONS
OF GALLONS

ARITHMETIC VERTICAL SCALE

K = 682.6

Chart 13.10. Domestic Production of Ice Cream, 1929–1961, and Trend as Shown by a Gompertz Curve. Note that this chart has an arithmetic vertical scale. The Gompertz curve has been extended to show the general shape of the curve. Data from Table 13.5.

271

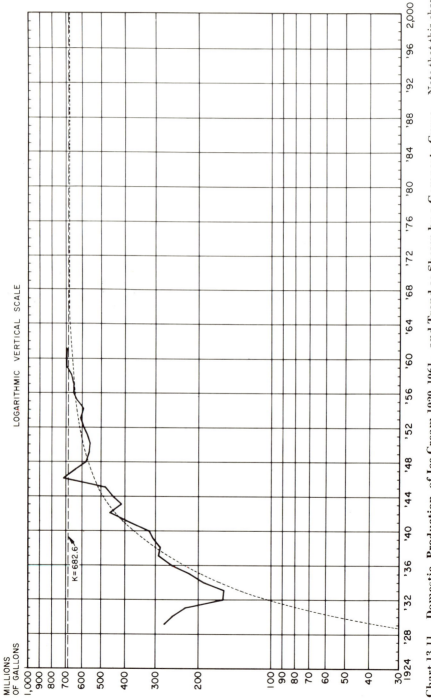

Chart 13.11.   Domestic Production of Ice Cream 1929–1961,   and Trend as Shown by a Gompertz Curve.   Note that this chart has a logarithmic vertical scale.   The Gompertz Curve has been extended to show the general shape of the curve.   Data from Table 13.5.

TABLE 13.5

Computation of Values for Fit of Gompertz Curve to United States Ice Cream Production 1929–1961

(Millions of gallons)

Year	X	Pro-duc-tion	Log Y	b^X	$(\text{Log } a)b^X$	Log Y_c $= \log k +$ $(\log a)b^X$	Y_c
						Computation of trend values	
1929	0	277.2	2.442793	1.0000000	-1.275262	1.558896	36.2
1930	1	255.4	2.407221	0.8665755	-1.105111	1.729047	53.6
1931	2	226.4	2.354876	0.7509543	-0.957663	1.876495	75.2
1932	3	168.0	2.225309	0.6507585	-0.829888	2.004270	101.0
1933	4	161.8	2.208979	0.5639324	-0.719162	2.114996	130.3
1934	5	191.6	2.282396	0.4886907	-0.623209	2.210949	162.5
1935	6	219.1	2.340642	0.4234877	-0.540058	2.294100	196.8
1936	7	258.6	2.412629	0.3669841	-0.468001	2.366157	232.4
1937	8	291.1	2.464042	0.3180196	-0.405558	2.428600	268.3
1938	9	286.4	2.456973	0.2755883	-0.351447	2.482711	303.9
1939	10	305.8	2.485437	0.2388184	-0.304556	2.529602	338.5
$\Sigma_1 \log Y$	...	...	23.595860	...	...	23.595823$\surd$	...
1940	11	318.1	2.502564	0.2069544	-0.263921	2.570237	371.7
1941	12	390.3	2.591399	0.1793417	-0.228708	2.605450	403.1
1942	13	464.2	2.666705	0.1554131	-0.198192	2.635966	432.5
1943	14	411.6	2.614475	0.1346772	-0.171749	2.662409	459.6
1944	15	444.9	2.648262	0.1167081	-0.148833	2.685325	484.5
1945	16	477.2	2.678700	0.1011365	-0.128976	2.705182	507.2
1946	17	713.8	2.853577	0.0876425	-0.111767	2.722391	527.7
1947	18	631.0	2.800029	0.0759488	-0.096855	2.737303	546.1
1948	19	576.5	2.760799	0.0658155	-0.083932	2.750226	562.6
1949	20	558.1	2.746712	0.0570341	-0.072733	2.761425	577.3
1950	21	554.4	2.743823	0.0494244	-0.063029	2.771129	590.4
$\Sigma_2 \log Y$	...	...	29.607045	...	...	29.607043$\surd$	...
1951	22	568.8	2.754960	0.0428300	-0.054619	2.779539	601.9
1952	23	592.7	2.772835	0.0371155	-0.047332	2.786826	612.1
1953	24	605.1	2.781827	0.0321634	-0.041017	2.793141	621.1
1954	25	596.8	2.775829	0.0278720	-0.035544	2.798614	628.9
1955	26	628.5	2.798305	0.0241532	-0.030802	2.803356	635.9
1956	27	641.3	2.807061	0.0209306	-0.026692	2.807466	641.9
1957	28	649.9	2.812847	0.0181380	-0.023131	2.811027	647.2
1958	29	658.0	2.818226	0.0157179	-0.020044	2.814114	651.8
1959	30	697.9	2.843793	0.0136208	-0.017370	2.816788	655.8
1960	31	697.6	2.843606	0.0118034	-0.015052	2.819106	659.3
1961	32	694.7	2.841797	0.0102286	-0.013044	2.821114	662.4
$\Sigma_3 \log Y$	...	...	30.851086	...	...	30.851091$\surd$	...

Data from *Historical Statistics of United States, Colonial Times to 1957*, p. 292; *Agricultural Statistics*, 1961, p. 400 and 1963, p. 397.

In Chart 13.10 it will be noticed that the amount of growth is small at first, then becomes larger until it reaches a point of inflection, after which it declines and finally approaches, but never reaches, zero. This general shape of the trend is common to many industries and has led to the conclusion that it describes a law of growth. According to this interpretation, this trend is a function of population growth, the curve of which typically is similar in appearance, but it is also partly due to the development of the individual industry. It is believed that the growth of an industry may be divided into four stages:

(1) Period of experimentation,
(2) Period of growth into the social fabric,
(3) Through the point where growth increases but at a diminishing rate,
(4) Period of stability.

These stages are not very specifically demarcated. It is claimed for this type of curve that it is useful in forecasting the future of an industry, since it not only is a logical curve but, on account of its tendency to flatten out, tends to be conservative in its forecasts. The horizontal dashed lines of Charts 13.10 and 13.11 would seem to indicate that the upper limit of ice cream production in the United States would be about 683 million gallons. This low figure is due to the influence of the depression years, 1930–1935.

The logistic curve. This curve, which is also known as the Pearl-Reed curve, is, in its simplest form,

$$\frac{1}{Y_c} = k + ab^x.$$

From this expression it should be clear that it is merely a modified exponential in terms of the reciprocals of the Y values; the first differences of the reciprocals of the Y_c values are declining by a constant percentage. A modified exponential could therefore be fitted, by the method of partial totals, to the reciprocals of the observed Y values, and the reciprocals of the fitted values so obtained taken as the trend values. However, this curve is more often written[7]

$$Y_c = \frac{k}{1 + 10^{a+bx}}$$

and, although the procedure is more subjective, fitted by the method of selected points. In this form, the logistic curve will always have an upper asymptote of k and a lower asymptote of zero; it looks like part 1

---

[7] Usually $e = 2.71828$ is used, instead of 10, in the denominator, giving

$$Y_c = \frac{k}{1 + e^{a+bx}}.$$

The a values and the b values in the two forms will differ, but both forms describe the same curve, and the Y_c values are slightly easier to compute from the expression using 10 in the denominator.

or part 2 of Chart 13.9. In the form $\dfrac{1}{Y_c} = k + ab^x$, the logistic could assume forms similar to all four of those shown in Chart 13.9.

To fit the equation

$$Y_c = \frac{k}{1 + 10^{a+bx}}$$

by the method of selected points requires choosing three years, x_0, x_1, and x_2, equidistant from each other: one near the beginning of the period, one in the middle, and one near the end. The three selected values through which the fitted curve will pass are the Y values associated with these three years. These Y values are designated y_0, y_1, and y_2. The origin on the X-axis is at the year designated x_0, and n is the number of years from x_0 to x_1 or from x_1 to x_2. The three constants are obtained as follows:

$$k = \frac{2y_0 y_1 y_2 - y_1^2(y_0 + y_2)}{y_0 y_2 - y_1^2}.$$

$$a = \log \frac{k - y_0}{y_0}.$$

$$b = \frac{1}{n}\left[\log \frac{y_0(k - y_1)}{y_1(k - y_0)}\right].$$

As an illustration, Table 13.6 shows the procedure for fitting a logistic curve to data of the population of Continental United States for 1820–1960. The population data are shown graphically in Chart 13.12. This period, including 15 decennial figures, was used instead of the entire period 1790–1960 in order that comparison could be made with the method of partial sums of reciprocals, mentioned previously.[8] In Table 13.6, the three selected points are

y_0, the geometric mean of the values for 1820, 1830, and 1840;

y_1, the geometric mean of the values for 1880, 1890, and 1900; and

y_2, the geometric mean of the values for 1940, 1950, and 1960.

Consequently, x_0 is at 1830, x_1 at 1890, and x_2 at 1950, as shown in the second column of Table 13.6. Averages of three decennial figures were used in order to minimize the effect of a single unusually high or low

---

[8] For 1810–1950 the method of partial sums yields $k = 185.9$ millions. The fit in Table 13.6 shows $k = 208.8$ for the method of selected points for 1820–1960. The method of selected points for 1790–1950 (using the geometric means of the first three, middle three, and last three years as those points) gives $k = 189.9$ millions. Several other methods of fitting a logistic curve are given in K. R. Nair, "The Fitting of Growth Curves," in Oscar Kempthorne, et al., editors, *Statistics and Mathematics in Biology*, The Iowa State College Press, Ames, Iowa, 1954, pp. 119–132.

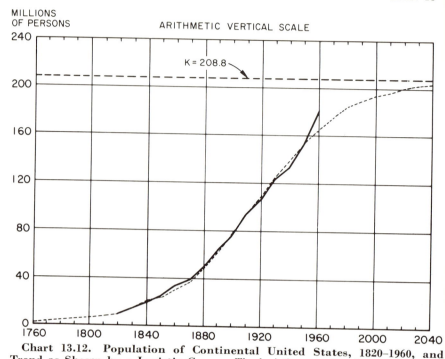

MILLIONS OF PERSONS

ARITHMETIC VERTICAL SCALE

Chart 13.12. Population of Continental United States, 1820–1960, and Trend as Shown by a Logistic Curve. The logistic curve has been extended to show the general shape of the curve. Data of Table 13.6.

TABLE 13.6

Computation of Values for Fit of Logistic Curve to Data of Population of Continental United States, 1820–1960

Year	x	X	Popula-tion in millions Y	y	Computation of trend values				
					$0.1346810X$	Log μ = 1.181505 − 0.1346810X	μ	$1 + \mu$	$Y_c = \dfrac{208.827}{1 + \mu}$
(1)	(2)	(3)	(4)	(5)	(6)	(7)	(8)	(9)	(10)
1820	...	− 1	9.6	...	−0.1346810	1.316186	20.71	21.71	9.6
1830	x_0	0	12.9	12.9(y_0)	0	1.181505	15.19	16.19	12.9✓
1840	...	1	17.1	...	0.1346810	1.046824	11.14	12.14	17.2
1850	...	2	23.2	...	0.269362	0.912143	8.169	9.169	22.8
1860	...	3	31.4	...	0.404043	0.777462	5.990	6.990	29.9
1870	...	4	39.8	...	0.538724	0.642781	4.393	5.393	38.7
1880	...	5	50.2	...	0.673405	0.508100	3.221	4.221	49.5
1890	x_1	6	62.9	62.1(y_1)	0.808086	0.373419	2.363	3.363	62.1✓
1900	...	7	76.0	...	0.942767	0.238738	1.733	2.733	76.4
1910	...	8	92.0	...	1.077448	0.104057	1.271	2.271	92.0
1920	...	9	105.7	...	1.212129	−0.030624	0.9319	1.9319	108.1
1930	...	10	122.8	...	1.346810	−0.165305	0.6834	1.6834	124.1
1940	...	11	131.7	...	1.481491	−0.299986	0.5012	1.5012	139.1
1950	x_2	12	150.7	152.7(y_2)	1.616172	−0.434667	0.3676	1.3676	152.7✓
1960	...	13	179.3	...	1.750853	−0.569348	0.2696	1.2696	164.5

Data from *Statistical Abstract of the United States, 1964*, p. 5. The y values of Column 5 are geometric means of three values centered at x_0, x_1, and x_2. The negative logarithms in Column 7 must be rewritten in their alternative forms with negative characteristic and positive mantissa (e.g., −0.030624 = 9.969376 − 10) before the values of μ can be obtained.

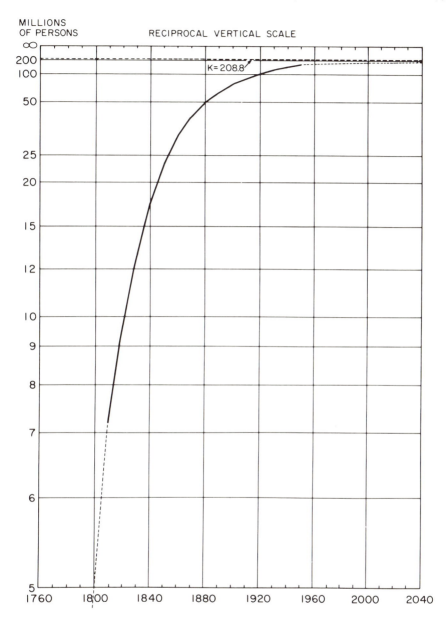

Chart 13.13. Population of Continental United States, 1820–1960, and Trend as Shown by a Logistic Curve. The logistic curve has been extended to show the general shape of the curve. Note that this chart has a reciprocal vertical scale and that, owing to the compression of the upper part of the scale, the curve of the observed data and the trend line virtually coincide. Data of Table 13.6.

value; the geometric mean was used in preference to the arithmetic mean, since the population growth is more nearly a geometric progression than an arithmetic progression. The value of n is 6, the number of years from x_0 to x_1 or from x_1 to x_2. Using the y_0, y_1, and y_2 values shown in Table 13.6, we obtain the values of k, a, and b as follows:

$$k = \frac{2y_0y_1y_2 - y_1^2(y_0 + y_2)}{y_0y_2 - y_1^2},$$

$$= \frac{2(12.9)(62.1)(152.7) - (62.1)^2(12.9 + 152.7)}{(12.9)(152.7) - (62.1)^2},$$

$$= 208.827.$$

$$a = \log \frac{k - y_0}{y_0},$$

$$= \log \frac{208.827 - 12.9}{12.9} = \log 15.188140,$$

$$= 1.181505.$$

$$b = \frac{1}{n} \log \frac{y_0(k - y_1)}{y_1(k - y_0)},$$

$$= \frac{1}{6} \left[\log \frac{12.9(208.827 - 62.1)}{62.1(208.827 - 12.9)} \right] = \frac{1}{6} \log 0.15556570,$$

$$= \frac{1}{6} (9.19191396 - 10) = \frac{1}{6} (-0.80808604),$$

$$= -0.1346810.$$

Trend equation:

$$Y_c = \frac{208.827}{1 + 10^{(1.181505 - 0.134681X)}}.$$

Origin, 1830. X units, 10 years.

The computation of the trend values for this logistic equation is shown in the last five columns of Table 13.6. The procedure consists first of writing

$$\mu = 10^{a+bX}$$

so that

$$Y_c = \frac{k}{1 + \mu}.$$

In our equation,

$$\mu = 10^{(1.181505 - 0.134681X)}$$

and
$$\log \mu = (\log 10)(1.181505 - 0.1346810X),$$
$$= 1.0(1.181505 - 0.134681X),$$
$$= 1.181505 - 0.134681X.$$

The values of μ are obtained in Columns 6, 7, and 8 of Table 13.6.   In Column 9 of this table, the values of $1 + \mu$ are shown, and the Y_c values are gotten in Column 10.   A check on the computations may be had by comparing the Y_c values for 1830, 1890, and 1950 with the values of y_0, y_1, and y_2, since the curve must pass through the three selected points.   The check marks in Column 10 of Table 13.6 indicate that agreement is present.

The trend values have been plotted in Charts 13.12 and 13.13, and the trend has been extended in both directions to show more clearly the fundamental shape of the curve.   Note that the agreement between the observed data and the trend frequently is so close that the two can hardly be distinguished.   Note, too, that Chart 13.13 uses a *reciprocal* vertical scale, and that in this chart the logistic curve is similar in appearance to the modified exponential curve.

The logistic curve was mentioned in 1838, and later discussed more fully, by P. F. Verhulst.   In 1920 it was developed independently by Raymond Pearl and Lowell J. Reed.   It is not infrequently referred to as the Pearl-Reed curve.   Pearl and Reed have used the curve to describe the growth of an albino rat and of a tadpole's tail, the number of yeast cells in a nutritive solution, the number of fruit flies in a bottle (on a limited food supply), and, most interesting of all, the number of human beings in a geographical area.   In each case, the phenomenon measured is population growth, either the number of cells in an organism or the number of individuals in a region.   The law of growth which the logistic curve describes is stated by Pearl as follows:[9]

> In a spatially limited universe the amount of increase which occurs in any particular unit of time, at any point of the single cycle of growth, is proportional to two things, viz.: (a) the absolute size already attained at the beginning of the unit interval under consideration, and (b) the amount still unused or unexpended in the given universe (or area) of actual and potential resources for the support of growth.

In the case of human populations, a new development may expand the available subsistence and allow a new cycle of growth.   For instance, mankind may pass through a hunting stage, an agricultural stage, and an industrial stage.   Each cultural epoch may then be described by a new

---

[9] Raymond Pearl, *The Biology of Population Growth*, Alfred A. Knopf, New York, 1925, p. 22.

logistic curve spliced onto the old one. Thus,

$$Y_c = k_1 + \frac{k_2}{1 + 10^{a+bX}}$$

describes a curve in which k_1 is the new lower limit and $k_1 + k_2$ the new upper limit. In this equation, k_1 is below the upper limit k_0 of the previous logistic and indicates the value at which the previous one was interrupted.

Apparently waves of immigration and human institutions do not change the fundamental shape of the curve, although they may modify the steepness of its slope somewhat. Also, the growth may not be symmetrical: the point of inflection need not be halfway between the upper and the lower asymptotes, nor need the two parts of the curve be of the same shape. A skewed logistic may be obtained by a slight modification of the previous formulae, by writing

$$Y_c = \frac{k}{1 + 10^{a+bX+cX^2}}.$$

The theory advanced by Raymond Pearl is not, however, universally accepted. Some argue that, although the logistic curve is appropriate enough for fruit flies in a bottle, its extension to human society is unwarranted. Human beings have, and exercise, the power of modifying their environment and rationally controlling their rate of reproduction.

One use to which the logistic curve is sometimes put is to forecast the size of the future population. Forecasts based merely upon the extension of a curve are of dubious value, since they assume no important changes in any of the underlying influences on a series.[10] The extended trend value of our logistic curve for 1970 is 174.4 million, which is obviously too low. A trend such as we have fitted may also be used to estimate population for earlier years, when reliable records did not exist. Thus, the population of what is now the continental United States may be estimated from our equation to have been about 3.9 million in 1790. A better estimate for 1790 might have been obtained if we had included 1800 and 1810 when determining the constants for the logistic equation.

Comparison of the Gompertz and logistic curves. The Gompertz and logistic curves are similar in that they both can be used to describe an increasing series which is increasing by a decreasing percentage of growth, or a decreasing series which is decreasing by a decreasing percentage of decline. They differ in that the Gompertz curve involves a constant ratio of successive first differences of the log Y_c values, while the logistic

---

[10] See footnote 5 in Chapter 5.

curve entails a constant ratio of successive first differences of the $\dfrac{1}{Y_c}$ values.

For the types of series to which we are interested in applying these curves, both have upper and lower asymptotes.

The first differences of the trend values of a Gompertz curve form a curve resembling a skewed frequency distribution, as shown in part A of Chart 13.14. The first differences of the trend values of a logistic curve,

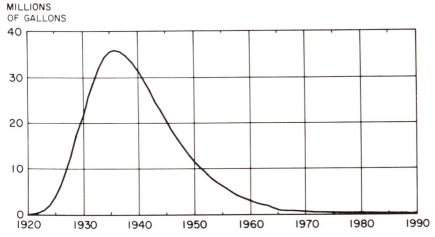

Chart 13.14A.   First Differences of the Gompertz Trend Values of Domestic Production of Ice Cream, 1920–1990.

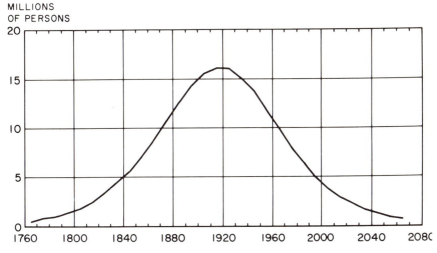

Chart 13.14B.   First Differences of the Logistic Trend Values for Population of Continental United States, 1770–2070.

of the type discussed here, form a curve resembling a normal frequency distribution (see Chapter 23), as shown in part B of Chart 13.14. Because of this characteristic of the logistic curve, observed data are sometimes plotted on arithmetic probability paper[11] (see Chart 23.9 and the accompanying discussion) to see if the trend appears to be a straight line. If so, the logistic curve may be fitted.

When plotted on semi-logarithmic paper, the Gompertz curve has the appearance of a modified exponential curve; when plotted on a grid with a reciprocal vertical scale and an arithmetic horizontal scale (alternatively, $\frac{1}{Y_c}$ and X may be plotted on arithmetic paper), the logistic curve has the appearance of a modified exponential curve.

SELECTING A TREND TYPE

This, and the preceding chapter, have not attempted an exhaustive treatment of the types of trends that may be utilized. However, a sufficient variety has been given to meet most of the needs for time series analysis. With such a large number of trend types available, how can one decide which to use? First, the trend type should be compatible with the behavior of the forces which we seek to measure. If the object is solely to obtain cyclical deviations, the trend should pass through the approximate center of each cycle. If it is desired to extend the trend for purposes of forecasting, the trend and its extension should conform to expectations dictated by logic. If, for instance, the series is such that it may logically be expected to flatten out, an asymptotic curve should be selected. When the objective is solely historical study, the future behavior of the curve is not so important.

The first step in deciding what trend type to use should always consist of plotting the observed data on arithmetic paper and then, if the trend is not linear but either (1) upward and concave upward or (2) downward and concave upward, on semi-logarithmic paper. Examination of the plotted data will frequently provide an adequate basis for deciding upon the type of trend to use. When further guidance is needed, an approximate trend may be drawn by inspection and the following tests *applied to the smoothed curve:*

1. If the first differences tend to be constant, use a straight line.
2. If the second differences tend to be constant, use a second-degree

---

[11] This involves: (1) assuming an asymptote and (2) expressing the observed data as percentages of the asymptote, before plotting. More than one asymptote may be tried.

curve.

3. If the first differences tend to decrease by a constant percentage, use a modified exponential.

4. If the approximate trend, when plotted on arithmetic paper, is a straight line, use a straight line.

5. If the approximate trend, when plotted on semi-logarithmic paper, is a straight line, use an exponential curve.

6. If the approximate trend, when plotted on semi-logarithmic paper, resembles a modified exponential, use a Gompertz curve.

7. If the approximate trend, when plotted on a grid with a reciprocal vertical scale and an arithmetic horizontal scale, resembles a modified exponential, use a logistic curve. Alternatively, $\frac{1}{Y_c}$ and X may be plotted on an arithmetic grid.

8. If the first differences resemble a skewed frequency curve, use a Gompertz curve, or a more complex logistic curve than the one described here.

9. If the first differences resemble a normal frequency curve, use a logistic curve.

10. If the first differences of the logarithms are constant, use an exponential curve.

11. If the second differences of the logarithms are constant, fit a second-degree curve to the logarithms.

12. If the first differences of the logarithms are changing by a constant percentage, use a Gompertz curve.

13. If the first differences of the reciprocals are changing by a constant percentage, use a logistic curve.

14. If the approximate trend values (or the original data), when expressed as percentages of a selected asymptote, appear linear on arithmetic probability paper, use a logistic curve.

Series are sometimes encountered which appear to have had a trend of one type during one part of the period and a different trend of the same, or a different, type during another part of the period. Changes in trend are most likely to have occurred during the 1930's.

Rarely, several trends, each having the same number of constants, appear equally suitable for a series of data. In such an event, that one is to be preferred from which the squared deviations of the Y values are a minimum. In making such a comparison, curves fitted to Y values should not be compared with those fitted to log Y values.

Occasionally, none of the previously mentioned aids will enable one to decide what trend type to use. This may be because the approximate trend was not properly selected. Or, it may be that the series does not conform to any simple mathematical description.   In a dynamic world, the forces in operation are seldom allowed to work out their full effects before other factors make themselves felt.   As a result, any trend type may be appropriate for only a relatively short period.

CHAPTER 14

Analysis of Time Series:

PERIODIC MOVEMENTS I—CONSTANT SEASONAL PATTERNS

As indicated in Chapter 11, there are many types of periodic movements, including those that repeat themselves daily, weekly, monthly, or annually. In this chapter most attention will be given to those monthly movements within a year commonly known as *seasonal* movements. The principles laid down can easily be applied to the various other types of periodic movements. It will be the plan of this discussion to start with data which lend themselves to very simple treatment, and gradually to introduce more complex methods as they are required. Consideration of seasonal movements that vary in their pattern from year to year will, however, be reserved for the following chapter. In general, all of the methods involve averaging, in some manner, the values of the different Januaries, then the values of the different Februaries, and so forth, but differ chiefly in the degree to which the data are refined before being averaged.

AN INTRODUCTORY ILLUSTRATION

Averages of unadjusted data. When the data do not contain cyclical movements or trend to any appreciable extent, it will suffice to average the data without making any previous adjustment. An illustration of such data is the number of books issued and renewed for home use at the main loan desk of the Rutgers University Library during the spring semester, 1965. The data are shown in Table 14.1, from which were excluded those weeks in which a holiday occurred, as, for example, the week of the Easter vacation. Below each column of data is given the average of that column. The averages, one for each day of the week, constitute a measure of the intraweek fluctuation in circulation of books. For convenience, however, it may be desirable to express this measure in percentage form. By dividing each of the six daily averages by the average of those six averages (which is the average per day for the entire period), and expressing each of the six daily averages as a percentage, we obtain the index shown in the last row of Table 14.1.

TABLE 14.1

Computation of Index of Intra-Week Variation, Using Averages of Unadjusted Data, of the Number of Books Issued and Renewed for Home Use at the Main Loan Desk of the Rutgers University Library, Spring Semester, 1965

Week beginning:	Monday	Tuesday	Wednesday	Thursday	Friday	Saturday	Average per day
Feb. 8	665	748	722	734	604	456	654.8
Feb. 15	701	787	686	822	649	730	729.2
Feb. 22	1,000	939	816	703	506	535	749.8
Mar. 1	642	612	792	712	277	691	621.0
Mar. 8	862	794	700	739	607	470	695.3
Mar. 15	597	819	627	703	609	510	644.2
Apr. 5	754	884	1,224	777	744	603	831.0
Apr. 12	696	765	748	703	714	578	700.7
Apr. 19	834	979	862	906	675	498	792.3
Arithmetic mean	750.1	814.1	797.4	755.4	598.3	563.4	713.1
Index............	105.2	114.2	111.8	105.9	83.9	79.0	100.0

Data from Main Loan Desk, Rutgers University Library.

Percentages of simple averages. A glance at the data of average circulation per day for the nine weeks, shown in the last column of Table 14.1, makes it clear that activity was greater in some weeks than in others. The procedure which was followed in Table 14.1 allowed the weeks of larger circulation to exert more weight on the daily averages, and thus on the index, than that exerted by the weeks of smaller circulation. It might be thought offhand that such extra weight is highly desirable, but it must be remembered that we are trying to determine a typical pattern, and it does not necessarily follow that weeks of large circulation are weeks having a typical pattern. If the figures for each day of a given week are expressed as percentages of the average for that week, as in Table 14.2, each week will be of equal importance in determining the index of intra-week variation. Furthermore, by putting the data into percentage form, we can more readily detect erratic variations from the typical weekly pattern. A study of such percentage data for each day may lead one to select some average other than the arithmetic mean. Thus, in the present instance, the percentage data of Table 14.2 have been put into arrays in Table 14.3 and in Chart 14.1. It is clear, from Chart 14.1, that a periodic movement is present. It is clear, too, that there are a few extreme values which do not fit into the general pattern. The effect of such extremes can be greatly decreased by using the median for each day; or, the extreme values can be eliminated by using the arithmetic mean of a central group of values for each day. In Table 14.3 the average of the middle 7 values for each day is shown.

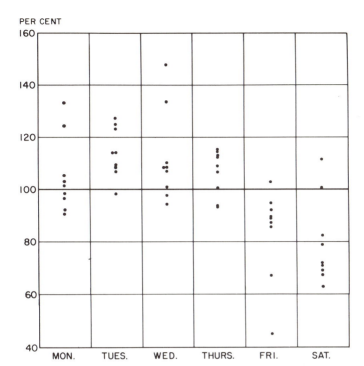

Chart 14.1. Arrays of Percentages of Daily Averages for Each Week for Number of Books Issued and Renewed for Home Use at the Main Loan Desk of the Rutgers University Library, Spring Semester, 1965. Data of Table 14.3.

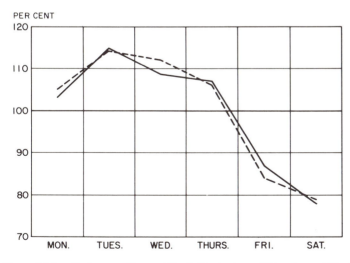

Chart 14.2. Indexes of Intra-Week Variation of Number of Books Issued and Renewed for Home Use at the Main Loan Desk of the Rutgers University Library, Spring Semester, 1965. Data from Tables 14.1 and 14.3.

TABLE 14.2

Percentages* of Daily Averages for Each Week for Number of Books Issued and Renewed for Home Use at the Main Loan Desk of the Rutgers University Library, Spring Semester, 1965

(The daily averages for each week are shown in the last column of Table 14.1.)

Week beginning:	Monday	Tuesday	Wednesday	Thursday	Friday	Saturday
Feb. 8	101.6	114.2	110.3	112.1	92.2	69.6
Feb. 15	96.1	107.9	94.1	112.7	89.0	100.1
Feb. 22	133.4	125.2	108.8	93.8	67.5	71.3
Mar. 1	103.4	98.6	127.5	114.7	44.6	111.3
Mar. 8	124.0	114.2	100.7	106.3	87.3	67.6
Mar. 15	92.7	127.1	97.3	109.1	94.5	79.2
Apr. 5	90.7	106.4	147.3	93.5	89.5	72.6
Apr. 12	99.3	109.2	106.8	100.3	101.9	82.5
Apr. 19	105.3	123.6	108.8	114.4	85.2	62.9

* Each row averages 100.0.
Based on data of Table 14.1.

TABLE 14.3

Computation of Index of Intra-Week Variation, Using Percentages of the Daily Average for Each Week, of the Number of Books Issued and Renewed for Home Use at the Main Loan Desk of the Rutgers University Library, Spring Semester, 1965

Rank	Monday	Tuesday	Wednesday	Thursday	Friday	Saturday	Average
1	133.4	127.1	147.3	114.7	101.9	111.3	...
2	124.0	125.2	127.5	114.4	94.5	100.1	...
3	105.3	123.6	110.3	112.7	92.2	82.5	...
4	103.4	114.2	108.8	112.1	89.5	79.2	...
5	101.6	114.2	108.8	109.1	89.0	72.6	...
6	99.3	109.2	106.8	106.3	87.3	71.3	...
7	96.1	107.9	100.7	100.3	85.2	69.6	...
8	92.7	106.4	97.3	93.8	67.5	67.6	...
9	90.7	98.6	94.1	93.5	44.6	62.9	...
Mean of middle seven..	103.2	114.4	108.6	107.0	86.5	77.6	99.6
Index................	103.6	114.9	109.1	107.5	86.9	78.0	100.0

Data of Table 14.2.

Since these six figures are modified means, they do not average exactly 100.0. Instead, they average 99.6 and are adjusted to average 100.0 by dividing each of them by 99.6 and multiplying by 100 to obtain the index shown in the last row of Table 14.3. The indexes of Tables 14.1 and 14.3 are shown in Chart 14.2. They do not differ greatly, because the nine weeks are not greatly different in importance.

SEASONAL INDEXES OF MONTHLY DATA

A seasonal index, showing the typical intra-year movement of a series, is ordinarily based upon monthly data, but such an index may be constructed from weekly[1] data.   While a seasonal index could be made from daily data, the index would be likely to reflect intra-month and intra-week movements as well as seasonal variations.   In this text we shall limit our attention to seasonal indexes obtained from monthly data.

Before setting out to compute a seasonal index, one should be sure that a seasonal movement is present in the series.   This may be apparent from experience with the subject matter represented by the data.   In the case of the book-circulation data of Table 14.1, the librarians knew that intra-week variations were present, so no preliminary examination of the data was necessary.   Similarly, the reader knows that seasonal variations exist in the consumption of ice cream, the use of gasoline, department store sales, and in various other series.   However, the investigator may not always know if the series in which he is interested has a seasonal, and, unless he assures himself that a seasonal movement is present, it is conceivable that he might perform the extensive calculations to be described later and learn at the very end of his work that his index figures were all approximately 100.0.

To ascertain if a seasonal is present in a series, it will usually suffice to draw a curve of the data such as the lighter line of Chart 14.3 or to make a chart like Chart 14.4.   In some instances, it may not be possible to be sure there is a seasonal movement by examining charts of the raw data and it may be necessary to proceed far enough with the analysis to make charts like Charts 14.1 and 14.6.   Occasionally charts such as Chart 15.2 must be constructed before a decision can be made.

A seasonal index based on percentages of trend.   If a series of monthly data exhibits secular trend, a seasonal index computed by either of the simple methods previously described will have an upward or downward bias, depending on the direction of the trend.   Thus, if the trend were upward and linear, each December would be higher than the preceding January by an amount equal to $\frac{11}{12}$ of the annual growth, even if there were no genuine seasonal movement present.   Because of this fact, the seasonal index, which is supposed to exhibit seasonal movements only, would slope upward; and, if there were a true seasonal movement, the December index number would be too high relative to the January index number by $\frac{11}{12}$ of the annual growth.   Of course, the trend may not be upward and linear.   It may be downward and linear, in which case the December figure would be too low.   If the trend is non-linear, its effect on a seasonal index computed as in Table 14.1 or Table 14.3 cannot be so simply stated, but the effect is present and is often pronounced.

---

[1] The procedure is described on pages 528–538 of the first edition of this text.

The first really useful procedure for computing a seasonal index was designed to overcome this difficulty and was based on per-cent-of-trend data. In this method, the first step consists of determining a trend equation for the data and obtaining the monthly trend values. Next, the original monthly data are expressed as percentages of the monthly trend values. These percentages are put into a table like Table 14.3 but having 12 columns, one for each month. The seasonal index is then obtained from twelve monthly medians or modified means just as in the last two rows of Table 14.3.

The per-cent-of-trend method ignores the disturbing effect of cyclical ups and downs. The highs and lows of cycles would appear as extreme dots in a chart like Chart 14.1 but which would have twelve arrays instead of six. This method depends upon the averaging process, that is, upon the use of the median or a modified mean, to eliminate the effect of cyclical highs and lows. At present, it is not a widely used method, but it may be applied to series having cyclical movements which are unimportant relative to the seasonal movements.

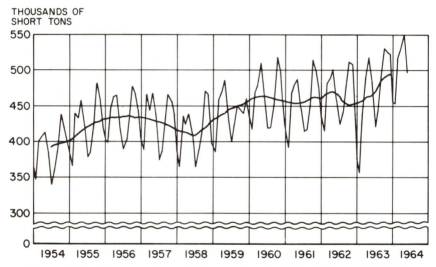

Chart 14.3. Consumption of Newsprint by United States Publishers, January 1954–December 1964, and Centered Twelve-Month Moving Average. Data of Table 14.5.

Percentages of centered 12-month moving averages. The data which we shall use to illustrate the determination of a seasonal index, which does not change from year to year, have to do with the consumption of newsprint by United States publishers. Charts 14.3 and 14.4 make it clear that a seasonal movement is present and that it is approximately the same from year to year. Chart 14.4 may be termed a "year-over-year" chart, since each year is arbitrarily placed above the preceding year; the curve for each year has been plotted to the same vertical scale, but at a different level.

The data of newsprint consumption have not been adjusted for calendar variation.   The reason for not making this adjustment is that the published data are not so adjusted.   If a seasonal index were to be made from

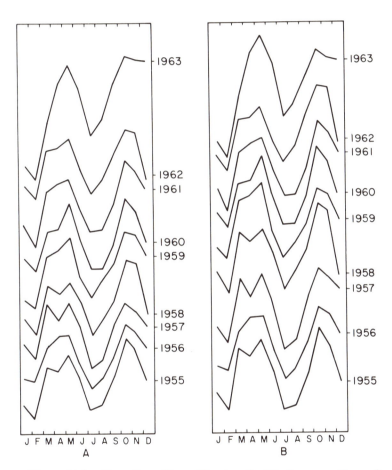

Chart 14.4.   Year-Over-Year Charts of: (A) Consumption of Newsprint and (B) Percentages of Twelve-Month Moving Average, 1954–1963.   Data of Table 14.5.   In each part of the chart, the curve for each year is placed just above the curve for the preceding year.   This is accomplished by using the same vertical scale for each of the nine curves, but raising or lowering the scale, as necessary.

the data adjusted for calendar days, then all monthly figures, *including new ones as they appear*, would have to be adjusted before they could be compared to the typical seasonal movement. Users of such data are, not infrequently, more interested in the monthly figures than in the per-day figures, the length of a month being sometimes thought of as contributing its part toward the typical seasonal variation. The procedure for computing an index of seasonal variation is the same whether the data have or have not been adjusted for calendar variation.

The percentage-of-12-month-moving-average method, which is ordinarily referred to merely as the per-cent-of-moving-average method (or just moving-average method) is in wide current use. It differs from the per-cent-of-trend method only in that the original data are expressed as percentages of the moving average instead of as percentages of trend. Computing the centered 12-month moving average involves more work than does the determination of trend values, but the resulting seasonal index is a better one. This is so because the moving average is a fairly good estimate of trend and cyclical movements combined.

A 12-month moving average is a series of averages which embraces, first, the first 12 months of a series; next, the second to thirteenth months; then the third to fourteenth months; and so on. To be more specific, let us consider the data of newsprint consumption by United States publishers, shown in Table 14.4. The first figure for the 12-month moving average is the average of the first 12 months, January 1954–December 1954. In Column 4 of the table this is seen to be 390.25. Note that, being the average of the 12-month period January–December 1954, this figure is centered between June and July 1954. The second moving-average figure, 392.00, covers the period February 1954–January 1955 and is centered between July and August 1954. Each figure in Column 4 of Table 14.4 is the arithmetic mean of the six original figures which precede it and the six original figures which follow it.

Since the figures in Column 4 of Table 14.4 fall between each pair of months, while the original data in Column 2 are for calendar months and are centered at the middle of each month, it is necessary to adjust the moving averages so that they will be in step with the original data. This process is called *centering*[2] and involves computing a two-month moving average of the 12-month moving averages. Columns 5 and 6 of Table 14.4 show how this is done. The result is a series of moving averages, properly centered and beginning with July 1954. These moving averages have been plotted in Chart 14.3.

---

[2] Some statisticians do not bother to center a 12-month moving average, but arbitrarily place the average for each 12 months opposite the seventh month, contending that the loss in accuracy is more than offset by the saving in time. If a centered 12-month moving average is computed by the method described on the following pages and illustrated in Table 14.5, and if a mask is used to obtain the moving totals (see F. E. Croxton and S. Klein, *Workbook in Applied General Statistics*, fifth edition, Prentice-Hall, Inc., Englewood Cliffs, N. J., 1967), the centered 12-month moving average can be obtained almost as quickly as can the uncentered 12-month moving average.

TABLE 14.4

Computation of Centered 12-Month Moving Average for Consumption of Newsprint by United States Publishers, January 1954–June 1964

Year and month	Consumption (thousands of short tons)	12-month moving total	12-month moving average Col. 3 ÷ 12	2-month moving total	Centered 12-month moving average Col. 5 ÷ 2
(1)	(2)	(3)	(4)	(5)	(6)
1954					
January....	363				
February...	346	...	...	...	...
March.....	400	...	...	...	...
April.......	415	...	...	...	...
May.......	422	...	...	...	...
June.......	384	...	...	...	...
July.......	339	4,683	390.25	782.25	391.1
August.....	361	4,704	392.00	785.58	392.8
September..	388	4,723	393.58	790.41	395.2
October....	437	4,762	396.83	795.08	397.5
November..	420	4,779	398.25	799.25	399.6
December..	408	4,812	401.00	805.17	402.6
		4,850	404.17		
1955					
January....	384	4,889	407.42	811.59	405.8
February...	365	4,913	409.42	816.84	408.4
March.....	439	4,950	412.50	821.92	411.0
April.......	432	4,992	416.00	828.50	414.3
May.......	455	5,034	419.50	835.50	417.8
June.......	422	5,045	420.42	839.92	420.0
July.......	378	5,063	421.92	842.34	421.0
August.....	385	5,096	424.67	846.59	423.3
September..	425	5,103	425.25	849.92	425.0
October....	479	5,133	427.75	853.00	426.5
November..	462	5,142	428.50	856.25	428.1
December..	419	5,142	428.50	857.00	428.5
1963					
January....	376	5,460	455.00	909.83	454.9
February...	356	5,458	454.83	909.75	454.9
March.....	435	5,459	454.92	910.75	455.4
April.......	490	5,470	455.83	913.16	456.6
May.......	516	5,488	457.33	916.00	458.0
June.......	483	5,504	458.67	924.09	462.0
July.......	421	5,585	465.42	937.42	468.7
August.....	443	5,664	472.00	952.00	476.0
September..	490	5,760	480.00	966.92	483.5
October....	529	5,843	486.92	977.00	488.5
November..	524	5,881	490.08	983.00	491.5
December..	522	5,915	492.92	986.92	493.5
		5,928	494.00		
1964					
January....	455	...	...	...	...
February...	452	...	...	...	...
March.....	518	...	...	...	...
April.......	528	...	...	...	...
May.......	550	...	...	...	...
June.......	496	...	...	...	...

Data from various issues of *Survey of Current Business*.

It is clear from Chart 14.3 that the centered moving-average figures do not reflect, to any appreciable degree, either the seasonal movement or irregular movements. It is not so clear, from Chart 14.3, that the moving average follows, approximately, the combined trend and cyclical pattern, since there is little cyclical movement in the series of newsprint consumption during the period under consideration. That a centered 12-month moving average does, indeed, describe the approximate trend and cyclical movements[3] may also be observed in Chart 15.1.

Before proceeding with the computation of the seasonal index for newsprint consumption, it will be well to look again at Table 14.4 and to note that the procedures indicated in that table are more laborious than necessary. We do not need to compute the moving average of Column 4. We could, instead, compute a two-month *moving total* of the figures in Column 3 and then divide each of these totals by 24 to obtain exactly the same figures as are shown in Column 6 of Table 14.4. There is, however, an even more expeditious procedure, which we shall employ. Consider the centered moving average for July 1954. This figure was obtained by totaling the value for January 1954, *twice* the value for February 1954, *twice* the value for each of the following months through December 1954, and the value for January 1955, and dividing this total by 24. Similarly, the average for August 1954 is the result of dividing by 24 the sum of: the February 1954 value, twice each of the next 11 values, and the value for February 1955. In other words, what we have actually done in computing a centered 12-month moving average is to compute a 13-month moving average with the months weighted 1, 2, 2, 2, 2, 2, 2, 2, 2, 2, 2, 2, 1.

Table 14.5 shows the computation of the weighted 13-month moving total and of the 12-month centered moving average. The procedure is as follows:

1. Using an adding machine, compute the weighted 13-month moving total for July of each year and also the last moving total, which in Table 14.5 is for December 1963. The total for each July will include values

---

[3] When a series shows pronounced cyclical movements, the centered 12-month moving average may not move high enough into the cyclical peaks or low enough into the cyclical lows. It should be clear why this is so, since, when a centered 12-month moving average is centered at a cyclical high point, the average would be influenced not only by the value for the middle month, but also by the six preceding and the six following months, all or most of which would have values lower than that of the middle month. The reverse would be true when the moving average is centered at a cyclical low point. Because of the foregoing, some statisticians smooth and alter the moving-average curve, usually by a freehand process, to obtain what is believed to be a better estimate of the combined trend and cyclical movements. The original values are then expressed as percentages of the values on this new curve.

TABLE 14.5

Short Method of Computing Centered 12-Month Moving Average and Percentages of Moving Average for Consumption of Newsprint by United States Publishers, January 1954–June 1964

Year and month	Consumption (thousands of short tons)	13-month moving total weighted 1, 2, 2, · · · , 2, 2, 1	Centered 12-month moving average Col. 3 ÷ 24	Per cent of 12-month moving average Col. 2 ÷ Col. 4
(1)	(2)	(3)	(4)	(5)
1954				
January.................	363	...	...	...
February...............	346	...	...	...
March..................	400	...	...	...
April..................	415	...	...	...
May....................	422	...	...	...
June...................	384	...	...	...
July...................	339	9,387√	391.1	86.7
August.................	361	9,427	392.8	91.9
September..............	388	9,485	395.2	98.2
October................	437	9,541	397.5	109.9
November...............	420	9,591	399.6	105.1
December...............	408	9,662	402.6	101.3
1955				
January.................	384	9,739	405.8	94.6
February...............	365	9,802	408.4	89.4
March..................	439	9,863	411.0	106.8
April..................	432	9,942	414.3	104.3
May....................	455	10,026	417.8	108.9
June...................	422	10,079	420.0	100.5
July...................	378	10,108√	421.2	89.7
August.................	385	10,159	423.3	91.0
September..............	425	10,199	425.0	100.0
October................	479	10,236	426.5	112.3
November...............	462	10,275	428.1	107.9
December...............	419	10,284	428.5	97.8
1956				
January.................	402	10,295	429.0	93.7
February...............	398	10,324	430.2	92.5
March..................	446	10,352	431.3	103.4
April..................	462	10,360	431.7	107.0
May....................	464	10,364	431.8	107.5
June...................	422	10,395	433.1	97.4
July...................	389	10,426√	434.4	89.5
August.................	403	10,421	434.2	92.8
September..............	435	10,427	434.5	100.1
October................	477	10,424	434.3	109.8
November...............	468	10,406	433.6	107.9
December...............	444	10,420	434.2	102.3
1957				
January.................	408	10,417	434.0	94.0
February...............	387	10,385	432.7	89.4
March..................	463	10,367	432.0	107.2
April..................	442	10,354	431.4	102.5
May....................	466	10,327	430.3	108.3
June...................	434	10,304	429.3	101.1
July...................	374	10,274√	428.1	87.4
August.................	386	10,230	426.3	90.5
September..............	434	10,179	424.1	102.3
October................	465	10,131	422.1	110.2
November...............	453	10,084	420.2	107.8
December...............	436	10,031	418.0	104.3

TABLE 14.5 (*Continued*)

Year and month	Consumption (thousands of short tons)	13-month moving total weighted 1, 2, 2, · · · , 2, 2, 1	Centered 12-month moving average Col. 3 ÷ 24	Per cent of 12-month moving average Col. 2 ÷ Col. 4
(1)	(2)	(3)	(4)	(5)
1958				
January.................	386	9,997	416.5	92.7
February................	365	9,990	416.3	87.7
March..................	434	9,971	415.5	104.5
April...................	423	9,955	414.8	102.0
May....................	438	9,972	415.5	105.4
June...................	409	9,942	414.3	98.7
July....................	365	9,909√	412.9	88.4
August.................	388	9,938	414.1	93.7
September..............	413	9,982	415.9	99.3
October................	470	10,050	418.8	112.2
November..............	465	10,140	422.5	110.1
December..............	394	10,206	425.3	92.6
1959				
January.................	395	10,261	427.5	92.4
February................	385	10,331	430.5	89.4
March..................	458	10,402	433.4	105.7
April...................	467	10,460	435.8	107.2
May....................	484	10,505	437.7	110.6
June...................	429	10,593	441.4	97.2
July....................	400	10,695√	445.6	89.8
August.................	423	10,763	448.5	94.3
September..............	449	10,806	450.3	99.7
October................	492	10,828	451.2	109.0
November..............	488	10,864	452.7	107.8
December..............	459	10,923	455.1	100.9
1960				
January.................	432	10,976	457.3	94.5
February................	416	10,993	458.0	90.8
March..................	470	10,995	458.1	102.6
April...................	477	11,025	459.4	103.8
May....................	510	11,059	460.8	110.7
June...................	462	11,066	461.1	100.2
July....................	420	11,054√	460.6	91.2
August.................	420	11,020	459.2	91.5
September..............	454	10,995	458.1	99.1
October................	517	10,996	458.2	112.8
November..............	497	10,974	457.3	108.7
December..............	457	10,935	455.6	100.3
1961				
January.................	422	10,913	454.7	92.8
February................	392	10,903	454.3	86.3
March..................	469	10,897	454.0	103.3
April...................	479	10,889	453.7	105.6
May....................	486	10,886	453.6	107.1
June...................	447	10,904	454.3	98.4
July....................	413	10,932√	455.5	90.7
August.................	417	10,967	457.0	91.2
September..............	451	11,002	458.4	98.4
October................	512	11,022	459.3	111.5 –
November..............	499	11,043	460.1	108.5
December..............	473	11,066	461.1	102.6
1962				
January.................	434	11,086	461.9	94.0
February................	415	11,121	463.4	89.6
March..................	481	11,174	465.6	103.3

TABLE 14.5 (*Concluded*)

Year and month	Consumption (thousands of short tons)	13-month moving total weighted 1, 2, 2, · · · , 2, 2, 1	Centered 12-month moving average Col. 3 ÷ 24	Per cent of 12-month moving average Col. 2 ÷ Col. 4
(1)	(2)	(3)	(4)	(5)
April...............	487	11,201	466.7	104.3
May................	499	11,209	467.0	106.9
June................	457	11,186	466.1	98.0
July................	423	11,096✓	462.3	91.5
August.............	442	10,979	457.5	96.6
September..........	479	10,874	453.1	105.7
October............	511	10,831	451.3	113.2
November..........	508	10,851	452.1	112.4
December..........	441	10,894	453.9	97.2
1963				
January............	376	10,918	454.9	82.7
February...........	356	10,917	454.9	78.3
March.............	435	10,929	455.4	95.5
April..............	490	10,958	456.6	107.3
May................	516	10,992	458.0	112.7
June................	483	11,089	462.0	104.5
July................	421	11,249✓	468.7	89.8
August.............	443	11,424	476.0	93.1
September..........	490	11,603	483.5	101.3
October............	529	11,724	488.5	108.3
November..........	524	11,796	491.5	106.6
December..........	522	11,843✓	493.5	105.8
1964				
January............	455	...	...	...
February...........	452	...	...	...
March.............	518	...	...	...
April..............	528	...	...	...
May................	550	...	...	...
June................	496	...	...	...

Data from source given below Table 14.4.

from the preceding January to the following January, inclusive. The total for December 1963 will include values from June 1963 through June 1964. These values are entered in Column 3 of Table 14.5 and serve as check values for the moving totals to be obtained in step 2.

2. Using an adding machine[4] which will subtract, enter the weighted moving total figure for July 1954. *Subtract* the values for January and February 1954, *add* the values for January and February 1955, and *subtotal*. This subtotal is the weighted moving total for August 1954.

---

[4] If an adding machine with a subtraction bar is not available, a calculating machine may be used. It is possible to subtract on an adding machine which has no subtraction bar by adding the complement of a number (for example, the complement of 276 would be entered as 99999724 on an eight-column adding machine). However, adding complements is not recommended for use in step 2, as the operator is likely to make numerous mistakes.

```
9,387 S
    363
    346
    384
    365
9,427 S
    346
    400
    365
    439
9,485 S
    400
    415
    439
    432
9,541 S
    415
    422
    432
    455
9,591 S
    422
    384
    455
    422
9,662 S
    384
    339
    422
    378
9,739 S
    339
    361
    378
    385
9,802 S
    361
    388
    385
    425
9,863 S
    388
    437
    425
    479
9,942 S
    437
    420
    479
    462
10,026 S
    420
    408
    462
    419
10,079 S
    408
    384
    419
    402
10,108 S
    384
    365
    402
    398
10,159 S
```

Next *subtract* the values for February and March 1954, *add* the values for February and March 1955, and *subtotal*. This second subtotal is the value for September 1954. Continue the process of subtracting two values, adding two values, and subtotaling, as shown in the accompanying reproduction of a portion of an adding-machine tape. When the subtotal is obtained for July 1955, it should agree with the figure already obtained. Agreement is indicated for all of the July figures, and for December 1963, by check marks in Column 3 of Table 14.5.

3. Compute the centered moving average by dividing each figure in Column 3 of Table 14.5 by 24. This division may be accomplished most expeditiously by placing the reciprocal of 24 (which is 0.04166667) in the keyboard of a calculating machine and multiplying it by the values shown in Column 3 of Table 14.5. The machine need not be cleared between multiplications, since it is merely necessary to increase or decrease the multiplier to obtain the next product. If a calculating machine having automatic multiplication is being used, it will probably be preferable to clear out the result of each multiplication before proceeding to the next one; 0.04166667 should be retained in the machine for all of the multiplications. The results are shown in Column 4 of Table 14.5.

The next step in computing the seasonal index consists of expressing each original value as a percentage of the corresponding centered moving average. The results of this step are shown in Column 5 of Table 14.5 and in Chart 14.5. The logic of the procedure is as follows: Time series are assumed to be composed of $T \times C \times S \times I$ (Trend $\times$ Cycle $\times$ Seasonal $\times$ Irregular). The 12-month moving average is a rough estimate of $T \times C$ because the 12-month average smoothes out seasonal movements and, for the most part, irregular movements, since the latter are largely movements of small amplitude and short duration. If now we divide the original data by the 12-month moving average, we have an estimate of the seasonal and irregular movements combined:

Chart 14.5 shows quite clearly the presence of the seasonal movement, which seems to be approximately the same from year to year. It is not exactly the same, since the spring peak is usually May, but sometimes April; also, the fall peak occurs in October, but occasionally November is almost as high.

From this point on, the procedure parallels that used for the library-circulation data expressed in percentage terms. First, however, we make Table 14.6, which puts the per-cent-of-moving-average data into a form

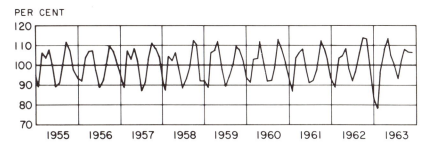

Chart 14.5. Percentages of Centered Twelve-month Moving Average for Consumption of Newsprint by United States Publishers, 1955–1963. Data of Table 14.5 or 14.6.

which facilitates the construction of the arrays, which are shown in Table 14.7. Notice that only those years for which 12 per-cent-of-moving-average figures were available are included in Tables 14.6 and 14.7.

After making a table of the monthly arrays, a chart, such as Chart 14.6, should be constructed. A chart of the monthly arrays is often useful in helping one to decide what measure of central tendency to use in averaging the months; in addition, it gives a general indication of the seasonal pattern.

There are two ways of deciding what items to eliminate. One way is to consider each array of Chart 14.6 separately and to eliminate items that appear to be unusually high or low, perhaps studying each large deviation individually and eliminating those for which a special circumstance can be discovered. If this method is followed, one array might use an average of all items; another might employ the median; a third, the central five items; a fourth, all items except the two highest; and so on. On account of the extreme subjectivity of the method, it is dangerous unless the statistician possesses a high order of knowledge and judgment. An alternative method, which is probably more frequently used, consists of computing the same type of modified mean for each month. No

TABLE 14.6

Percentages of Centered 12-Month Moving Averages for Consumption of Newsprint by United States Publishers, 1955-1963

Year	January	February	March	April	May	June	July	August	September	October	November	December
1955	94.6	89.4	106.8	104.3	108.9	100.5	89.7	91.0	100.0	112.3	107.9	97.8
1956	93.7	92.5	103.4	107.0	107.5	97.4	89.5	92.8	100.1	109.8	107.9	102.3
1957	94.0	89.4	107.2	102.5	108.3	101.1	87.4	90.5	102.3	110.2	107.8	104.3
1958	92.7	87.7	104.5	102.0	105.4	98.7	88.4	93.7	99.3	112.2	110.1	92.6
1959	92.4	89.4	105.7	107.2	110.6	97.2	89.8	94.3	99.7	109.0	107.8	100.9
1960	94.5	90.8	102.6	103.8	110.7	100.2	91.2	91.5	99.1	112.8	108.7	100.3
1961	92.8	86.3	103.3	105.6	107.1	98.4	90.7	91.2	98.4	111.5	108.5	102.6
1962	94.0	89.6	103.3	104.3	106.9	98.0	91.5	96.6	105.7	113.2	112.4	97.2
1963	82.7	78.3	95.5	107.3	112.7	104.5	89.8	93.1	101.3	108.3	106.6	105.8

Data from Table 14.5.

TABLE 14.7

Arrays of Percentages of Centered 12-Month Moving Averages and Computation of Seasonal Index for Consumption of Newsprint by United States Publishers, 1955–1963

Rank (or description of row)	January	February	March	April	May	June	July	August	September	October	November	December	Mean
1	94.6	92.5	107.2	107.3	112.7	104.5	91.5	96.6	105.7	113.2	112.4	105.8	…
2	94.5	90.8	106.8	107.2	110.7	101.1	91.2	94.3	102.3	112.8	110.1	104.3	…
3	94.0	89.6	105.7	107.0	110.6	100.5	90.7	93.7	101.3	112.3	108.7	102.6	…
4	94.0	89.4	104.5	105.6	108.9	100.2	89.8	93.1	100.1	112.2	108.5	102.3	…
5	93.7	89.4	103.4	104.3	108.3	98.7	89.8	92.8	100.0	111.5	107.9	100.9	…
6	92.8	89.4	103.3	104.3	107.5	98.4	89.7	91.5	99.7	110.2	107.9	100.3	…
7	92.7	87.7	103.3	103.8	107.1	98.0	89.5	91.2	99.3	109.8	107.8	97.8	…
8	92.4	86.3	102.6	102.5	106.9	97.4	88.4	91.0	99.1	109.0	107.8	97.2	…
9	82.7	78.3	95.5	102.0	105.4	97.2	87.4	90.5	98.4	108.3	106.6	92.6	…
10. Total of middle seven	654.1	622.6	729.6	734.7	760.0	694.3	629.1	647.6	701.8	777.8	758.7	705.4	…
11. Mean of middle seven	93.4	88.9	104.2	105.0	108.6	99.2	89.9	92.5	100.3	111.1	108.4	100.8	100.2
12. Seasonal index	93.2	88.7	104.0	104.8	108.4	99.0	89.7	92.3	100.1	110.9	108.2	100.6	100.0

* Each item of row 11 divided by 100.2 and multiplied by 100. Alternatively, each item may be multiplied by the correction factor $(1 \div 100.2)100 = 0.998004$. Data from Table 14.6.

generally applicable rule can be set up for the selection of the appropriate modified mean, but the exclusion of the one highest value and one lowest value or the two highest and the two lowest values will often be found to be satisfactory.   The number of items to exclude depends partly on the number of cycles included in a series; the larger the number of cyclical highs and lows which are reflected in the percentages of moving average (because they have not been completely smoothed out by the moving average), the more extreme items which may need to be excluded.   For

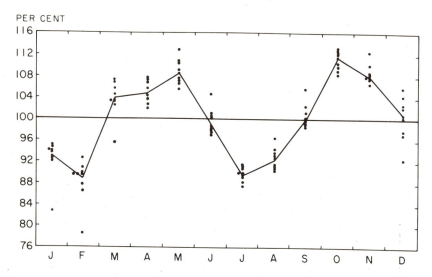

Chart 14.6.   Arrayed Percentages of Moving Average and Seasonal Index for Consumption of Newsprint by United States Publishers, 1955–1963.   Data of Table 14.7.   The highest and lowest value in each array was excluded for purposes of computing the seasonal index.

the newsprint consumption data of Table 14.7, we have used the mean of the middle seven values, with the results shown in the next-to-the-last row of the table.

The 12 modified means average 100.2.   When each modified mean is divided by 100.2 and multiplied by 100, we get the seasonal index[5] shown in the last row of Table 14.7 and in Chart 14.7.   Note that the 12 values of the seasonal index average 100.0.   This is important, since seasonal variations will later be removed from the original data by dividing the original data by the seasonal index.   If the seasonal index were to average less than 100.0, the adjusted figures would all be a little too large; if the

---

[5] A seasonal index based on the mean of the middle five items in Table 14.7 is frequently so nearly the same that the curve can hardly be distinguished from that shown in Chart 14.6.   The greatest difference in the illustration above for any one month is 0.2.

seasonal index were to average more than 100.0, the adjusted figures would all be slightly too small.

Link relatives. At one time the link-relative method was the most widely used method of obtaining a seasonal index. The computations involved are less extensive than those required by the moving-average method, but the link-relative method is less satisfactory than the moving-average method; in particular, it is not readily adaptable to the determination of changing seasonal movements, a topic treated in the following chapter.

The first step in this method consists of expressing each monthly value as a percentage of the preceding monthly value. These are the link relatives. From this point on, the procedure[6] is the same as shown in Table 14.7, except that the 12 monthly averages are generally found to contain some residual trend, which was not eliminated by computing the link relatives. Adjustment for this residual trend must be made before the seasonal index is obtained.

ADEQUACY OF THE SEASONAL INDEX

One test of a seasonal index is provided by the chart of the arrays, as shown in Chart 14.6. If the individual arrays are widely dispersed (that is, cover a wide range vertically), we can have little confidence in the seasonal index. The less the dispersion of the individual monthly arrays, the more uniform is the seasonal movement from year to year.

It is possible to ascertain (by the method described in Chapter 24) whether a given modified mean differs significantly from 100. Or, using the method of analysis of variance (discussed in Chapter 26), to ascertain whether the 12 modified means as a group differ significantly from each other. However, these procedures are of dubious value, primarily because the distributions from which the means were computed were not random distributions, and also because the means were modified means, computed after part of the data had been rejected.

A practical test of the adequacy of a seasonal index is to use it to eliminate the seasonal variation in the series, and then to observe whether any residual seasonal movements are present. We shall return to this point in Chapter 16.

---

[6] The method is more fully described on pages 486–492 of the first edition of this text. The advantages and disadvantages of the link-relative method are set forth there in more detail.

CHAPTER 15

Analysis of Time Series:

PERIODIC MOVEMENTS II—CHANGING SEASONAL PATTERNS

In Chapter 14 we considered procedures for determining seasonal indexes for series having patterns which underwent little or no change during the period with which we were concerned. Some time series have seasonal patterns which change. Changes may be progressive—which is to say that the seasonal pattern varies gradually from year to year—or they may be of a more abrupt nature, reflecting, for example, changes in the date of Easter or the shifting date of some important event, such as the New York automobile show, as was mentioned in Chapter 11.

PROGRESSIVE CHANGES IN SEASONAL PATTERN

A moving seasonal. Chart 15.1 shows monthly data of the linage of newspaper advertising for 52 cities in the United States from January 1953 to December 1964. As will be clear later, this series has a progressive change in seasonal pattern: the pattern is not the same throughout the period with which we are concerned. This is often referred to as a *moving seasonal.* From a chart such as Chart 15.1, it is not always possible to ascertain whether the seasonal pattern is fixed or moving. To make this decision, it is usually necessary to proceed part way with the seasonal analysis (through step 2 of the procedure which follows); luckily, the initial steps are the same for the determination of either a constant or a moving seasonal.

Computation of a moving seasonal index. A moving seasonal index may be obtained as follows:

1. Compute a centered 12-month moving average of the original data. Since the procedure is exactly the same as shown in Columns 2, 3, and 4 of Table 14.5 for the data of newsprint consumption, the computation of the moving average is not shown here. However, the moving average is shown graphically in Chart 15.1.

2. Express the original data as percentages of the moving average. These figures are shown in Table 15.1.

3. Plot the data of Table 15.1 on 12 charts, *one chart for each month*, as shown in the 12 parts of Chart 15.2. These 12 monthly charts may be drawn on separate sheets of graph paper or on one large sheet, as may be convenient. In any event, they should not be too small in view of the use which is to be made of them in the next two steps.

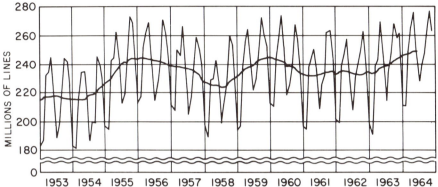

Chart 15.1. Newspaper Advertising in the United States, 1953–1964, and Twelve-Month-Centered Moving Average, July 1932–June 1964. Data from various issues of *Survey of Current Business.* Moving average computed as shown in Table 14.5.

4. Reference to Chart 15.2 shows that January, February, March, and October have slight downward trends. Several months show upward trends, for example, May, July, August, and December. The monthly trends may be linear or non-linear. Also as Chart 15.2 shows, a month may have a trend which declines and then rises, or vice versa. The fourth step consists of determining a trend for each of the 12 monthly charts. This may be done by drawing freehand trend lines, by fitting mathematical curves, or by using a moving average (for example, a five-term moving average) as a guide and smoothing the moving average freehand. However the trend lines are obtained, they should be relatively simple curves and should not slope too steeply, up or down, at the ends. It must be realized that the trends we are concerned with here are not affected by the same forces that are associated with secular trend. The monthly trends are very unlikely to continue in a given direction indefinitely, but are more likely to move to a certain level and then remain more or less stable until new factors bring about a change from that level. For purposes of illustration, the 12 trend lines in Chart 15.2 were drawn freehand. If we wish to have a seasonal index for a year later than that shown in a chart such as Chart 15.2, in order to deseasonalize the monthly data as they become available, we may use the seasonal index for the last year shown (as is done in Table 16.3) or we may extend the monthly trend lines.

5. From the monthly charts of Chart 15.2, read the trend values and

TABLE 15.1

Percentages of Centered 12-Month Moving Averages for Newspaper Advertising in the United States, 1954–1963

Year	January	February	March	April	May	June	July	August	September	October	November	December
1954	85.1	84.1	100.6	108.6	109.2	100.8	86.1	92.0	100.2	111.3	107.7	102.6
1955	86.9	85.3	105.5	105.0	111.0	103.1	89.4	91.9	102.3	113.0	110.6	99.8
1956	87.4	89.8	103.2	107.3	110.6	98.6	88.2	93.9	101.1	112.1	109.2	101.3
1957	87.9	86.8	104.8	103.3	112.3	102.0	86.7	92.5	103.9	112.4	109.3	105.5
1958	87.1	83.4	101.2	101.6	107.4	100.9	88.5	94.6	100.0	114.7	110.9	100.7
1959	83.8	84.3	100.8	108.0	111.4	99.6	92.0	97.3	102.2	112.1	107.0	103.1
1960	86.9	86.2	100.4	105.8	113.1	103.9	90.6	94.0	101.2	112.4	109.3	102.4
1961	84.3	81.4	102.1	104.7	108.0	102.3	89.6	96.6	99.6	112.0	111.9	104.0
1962	86.4	85.3	101.3	105.2	109.9	97.5	88.8	98.8	103.1	111.1	112.5	100.7
1963	84.4	81.0	101.5	102.2	113.8	102.5	89.0	97.1	102.2	110.3	105.9	106.6

Original data from various issues of *Survey of Current Business*. Moving average computed as shown in Table 14.5.

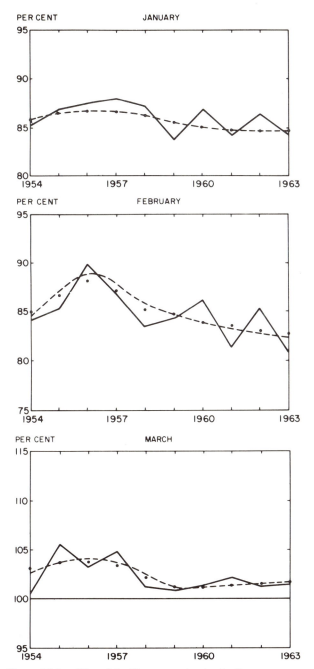

Chart 15.2.   Monthly Charts to Assist in Determination of Moving Seasonal Index for Newspaper Advertising in the United States, 1954–1963.   Data from Table 15.1.   To avoid obscuring details, these charts show no guide lines.   When used to aid in the computation of a moving seasonal index, charts such as these would have finely ruled grids.   The values in Table 15.2 are read from the smooth curves.   The values in Table 15.3 are the dots which are just above, just below, or on the smooth curves.

307

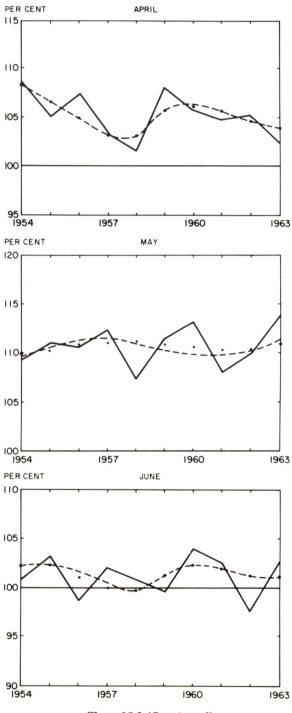

Chart 15.2 (Continued).

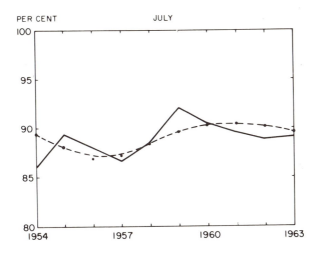

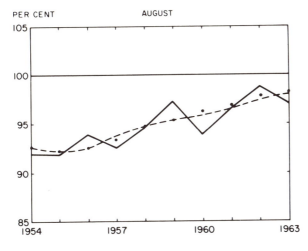

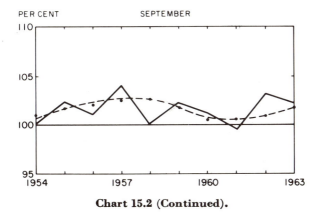

Chart 15.2 (Continued).

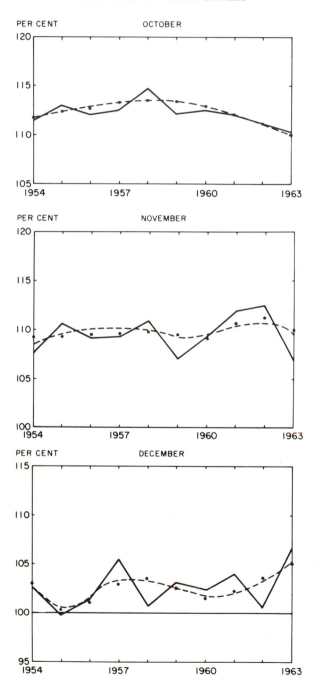

Chart 15.2 (Concluded).

enter them in a table.   These are first approximations of the moving seasonal and are shown in Table 15.2.

6. It will be noticed that the 12 values for each year, shown in Table 15.2, in only one instance total 1,200.0.   The final step consists of adjusting the first approximation figures of Table 15.2 so that each annual total will be 1,200.0, but at the same time retaining smooth, well-fitting trends for the 12 parts of Chart 15.2.   The results of this step are shown in Chart 15.2 by means of dots and in Table 15.3, which gives the moving seasonal index.   Note that the total for each year is now 1,200.0.   If the 12 monthly trend lines are linear, they may be fitted mathematically by a procedure[1] which automatically results in the annual totals each being 1,200.0.

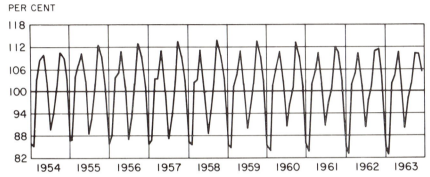

PER CENT

Chart 15.3.   Moving Seasonal Index for Newspaper Advertising in the United States, 1954–1963.   Data from Table 15.3.

The moving seasonal pattern for newspaper advertising is shown graphically in Chart 15.3.   Note how the relative importance of April and May changes over the period.   Another interesting point brought out in Chart 15.3 is the very gradual change in the amplitude of the seasonal variation over the period.

The reader may have noted that steps 4 and 6 in the determination of a moving seasonal index may involve subjective considerations.   This does not constitute a weakness in the procedure, but it does suggest that better results are more likely to be obtained by an experienced worker who is familiar with the series being studied than by one not so well equipped.   The procedure for obtaining a moving seasonal index, which has been described in the preceding paragraphs, is occasionally modified by using a 12-month moving average, not centered, but arbitrarily placed opposite the seventh (or sixth) month.

If a series that contains a moving seasonal is deseasonalized by a constant seasonal index, the adjusted data will contain not only the irregular movements actually present in the series, but additional irregularities

---

[1] See R. J. Foote and Karl A. Fox, *Seasonal Variation: Methods of Measurement and Tests of Significance*, pp. 6–7, issued by the Bureau of Agricultural Economics as *Agricultural Handbook No. 48.*

TABLE 15.2

First Approximation to Moving Seasonal Index for Newspaper Advertising in the United States, 1954–1963

Month	1954	1955	1956	1957	1958	1959	1960	1961	1962	1963
January	85.8	86.4	86.7	86.6	86.3	85.5	85.1	84.8	84.7	84.7
February	84.8	87.1	88.8	87.7	85.8	84.7	84.0	83.3	82.8	82.4
March	102.7	103.6	104.1	103.7	102.4	101.1	101.2	101.3	101.4	101.7
April	108.3	107.0	104.8	103.2	103.0	104.4	106.3	105.6	104.7	103.9
May	109.5	110.6	111.2	111.4	111.0	110.3	109.8	109.8	110.3	111.6
June	102.2	102.3	101.5	100.4	99.8	101.2	102.2	101.9	101.1	101.0
July	89.2	88.1	87.1	87.3	88.3	89.6	90.2	90.2	90.1	89.8
August	92.6	92.2	92.5	93.8	94.8	95.3	95.9	96.5	97.4	98.0
September	100.6	101.7	102.3	102.7	102.6	101.8	100.8	100.5	100.9	101.8
October	110.7	112.2	112.9	113.2	113.4	113.4	113.0	112.0	111.0	110.1
November	108.7	109.5	110.0	110.0	110.0	109.4	109.6	110.3	110.7	109.8
December	102.6	100.5	101.6	103.3	103.3	102.6	101.9	102.1	103.3	105.3
Total	1,197.7	1,201.2	1,203.5	1,203.3	1,200.7	1,199.3	1,200.0	1,198.9	1,198.4	1,200.1

Data from Chart 15.2.

TABLE 15.3

Moving Seasonal Index for Newspaper Advertising in the United States, 1954–1963

Month	1954	1955	1956	1957	1958	1959	1960	1961	1962	1963
January	85.8	86.4	86.7	86.6	86.3	85.5	85.1	84.8	84.7	84.7
February	85.0	86.7	88.1	87.1	85.2	84.7	84.0	83.5	83.0	82.8
March	103.2	103.6	103.8	103.4	102.2	101.1	101.2	101.3	101.4	101.7
April	108.3	107.0	104.8	103.2	103.0	104.4	106.1	105.6	104.7	103.9
May	109.9	110.2	110.8	111.0	111.1	110.9	110.5	110.4	110.4	110.9
June	102.2	102.3	101.0	100.0	99.8	101.2	102.2	101.9	101.1	101.0
July	89.2	88.1	87.0	87.2	88.3	89.6	90.2	90.2	90.1	89.8
August	92.6	92.2	92.5	93.3	94.8	95.3	96.2	96.9	97.8	98.2
September	100.9	101.7	102.0	102.4	102.6	101.8	100.6	100.5	100.9	101.8
October	110.7	112.2	112.8	113.2	113.4	113.4	113.0	112.0	111.0	110.1
November	109.2	109.3	109.5	109.6	109.9	109.5	109.2	110.7	111.2	110.0
December	103.0	100.3	101.0	103.0	103.4	102.6	101.7	102.2	103.7	105.1
Total	1,200.0	1,200.0	1,200.0	1,200.0	1,200.0	1,200.0	1,200.0	1,200.0	1,200.0	1,200.0

Data from Chart 15.2.

where the constant seasonal index has undercorrected or overcorrected. Unless one knows that the series with which he is working has a fixed seasonal movement, it is always wise to make the 12 monthly charts of Chart 15.2. These will reveal whether a moving seasonal is present; if the seasonal is constant, the trends will be horizontal lines.

The reader may have noted that steps 4 and 6 in the determination of a moving seasonal index may involve subjective considerations. This does not constitute a weakness in the procedure, but it does suggest that better results are more likely to be obtained by an experienced worker who is familiar with the series being studied than by one not so well equipped. The procedure for obtaining a moving seasonal index, which has been described in the preceding paragraphs, is occasionally modified by using a 12-month moving average, not centered, but arbitrarily placed opposite the seventh (or sixth) month.

If a series that contains a moving seasonal is deseasonalized by a constant seasonal index, the adjusted data will contain not only the irregular movements actually present in the series, but additional irregularities where the constant seasonal index has undercorrected or overcorrected. Unless one knows that the series with which he is working has a fixed seasonal movement, it is always wise to make the 12 monthly charts of Chart 15.2. These will reveal whether a moving seasonal is present; if the seasonal is constant, the trends will be horizontal lines.

Footnote 3 of Chapter 14 pointed out that a 12-month moving average may not move high enough into cyclical peaks or low enough into cyclical troughs. Partly to correct for this characteristic of the moving average, the Division of Research and Statistics of the Board of Governors of the Federal Reserve System has used a more complex procedure[2] than the one just illustrated.

The Federal Reserve procedure differs in two respects from the method used in this text: first, the moving average (which is not centered) is modified by a freehand curve; and second, the seasonal index first obtained is revised twice. This method requires knowledge of the field represented by the data and a high order of judgment. It requires a higher quality of work and more time than most of the mechanical methods. For one slightly erratic series, for example, it was found that determining and eliminating seasonal for data covering a 14-year period required about a half-day's work of a professional nature and two days of clerical work. However, this yielded more accurate seasonal adjustments than could be obtained by applying a mathematical process. It also yielded a knowledge of other characteristics of the underlying series that were valuable for other reasons.

---

[2] For an outline of this procedure, see the second edition of this text, pp. 350–351.

SUDDEN VARIATIONS IN SEASONAL PATTERNS

Seasonal patterns may change abruptly, rather than gradually, and then the device of a moving seasonal would be inapplicable. Such changes may involve merely the relative importance of two consecutive months, or may involve a change in the entire pattern. The most frequently encountered change of the first type is that occasioned by the varying date of Easter.

Adjustment for Easter. A number of statistical series are affected materially by changes in the date of Easter, which may range from March 22 to April 25. Retail sales and money in circulation are two of the series so affected. Department store sales, in particular, show the effects of the customary apparel purchases before Easter. A late Easter will tend to make April sales heavy relative to March, and, within limits, the later in April that Easter occurs, the greater is this tendency. On the other hand, when Easter occurs in March, March sales and possibly February sales will be increased.[3]

Sudden changes in entire seasonal pattern. It was mentioned, in Chapter 11, that one year an automobile show was held in New York not only in January, but also in November, the November show being in lieu of the show originally planned for the following January. For some years thereafter the show was held in November. The importance of the New York show stemmed from the fact that it was at these shows that most new models of automobiles were revealed to the public. Before the change, the seasonal movement of automobile sales showed a high in the spring (a few months after the show) and a low in the fall and winter. After the change, two seasonal highs each year were in evidence, one in the spring and one very late in the year.

When a sudden change in an entire seasonal pattern occurs, it is merely necessary to compute two seasonal indexes, one for the period preceding the change and one for the years following the change. The two indexes may be either constant or changing, whichever is appropriate for the series.

Short-time shifts in timing. The varying date of Easter affects materially only March and April; changing the date of the automobile show affected chiefly a few months preceding and following it. Weather conditions, however, which also vary from year to year, may result in early harvests one year and late harvests the next; and not only may the marketing of the product begin at different times in different years, but the flow of goods during the entire year may be affected, the effect being to shift the whole pattern a few months to the left or right. Likewise, consumer demand may vary in timing, depending on how early the weather changes.

---

[3] For a detailed explanation of a procedure used by the Federal Reserve System for making Easter adjustments in the department store sales series, see the second edition of this text, pp. 352–359.

Such shifting seasonal patterns present a difficult problem.   Perhaps the most practical solution is to regard the situation as a special case of a sudden change in entire pattern, to group together the years (not necessarily adjacent) which show the same timing in their seasonal turns, and to compute as many seasonal indexes as there are groups of years.   In computing such indexes, there is no reason why the calendar year must be taken as a unit.   Rather, if the subject matter has to do with agriculture, the year should be related to the crop year.   Perhaps the central month should be the seasonal high or the seasonal low.

Varying amplitude.   Some economic series retain more or less the same general seasonal pattern from year to year but have a tendency to vary either gradually or suddenly in amplitude.   This is particularly true of stocks of agricultural commodities.   For example, stocks of agricultural crops show varying seasonal amplitude from year to year depending upon the amount carried over from the preceding year, the size of the harvest, and the amount consumed.   Likewise, shipments of livestock are likely to vary in the amplitude of their seasonal swing.   Here the variation may have something to do with the advantage of immediately selling the livestock, as compared with holding them for further fattening or a price increase.   Since the relative advantages of these policies (discussed on page 130) are likely to vary in cycles, so the amplitude of the seasonal variation is likely to change in cycles, and the change in pattern might conceivably be treated as a moving seasonal.   Another case is that of increased seasonal amplitude in manufacturing, brought about by a general cyclical tendency toward hand-to-mouth buying.   It is apparent that this change also might be thought of as a moving seasonal, the progression being cyclical rather than trend-like.

It must be apparent that, when the amplitude of a seasonal movement is not changing gradually but changing suddenly, and in the main unpredictably, a moving seasonal cannot overcome the difficulty any better than it can that of short-time shifts in the entire seasonal pattern.   Any of the types of seasonal indexes hitherto described would in some years show too great amplitude and in other years too small amplitude.   The method of correcting a seasonal index for sudden changes in amplitude will not be described in detail in this volume,[4] but in general the procedure consists of determining the relationship that exists *for the 12 months of each year* between (1) the seasonal index expressed as deviations from 100 and (2) the percentage deviations of the original values from the 12-month centered moving average, the latter percentage deviations being adjusted to average zero.   The relationship between the 12 pairs of values for each year yields an *amplitude ratio* which indicates the correction to be applied (by multiplication) to the original seasonal values expressed as deviations from 100.   To each of these deviations 100 is then added.

---

[4] For a full description, with tables and charts, see the first edition of this text, pp. 518–524.

A word of caution may be in order: if a moving seasonal has been used, a change in the amplitude ratio does not necessarily indicate a change in the seasonal amplitude of the original data. A gradual increase in the seasonal amplitude, for instance, would be reflected in the moving seasonal index rather than in the amplitude ratio; but the moving seasonal would fail to register any sudden departures from the general trend in amplitude change.

FURTHER REFINEMENTS OF METHOD

Continuity of seasonal indexes. A stable seasonal index averages 100 per cent, not only for the 12-month period selected for the index, but for any consecutive 12-month period. The latter, however, is not true for any of the seasonals explained in this chapter, though in the case of a progressive or moving seasonal the discrepancy is nominal only. Particularly in the case of seasonal indexes corrected for variations in amplitude, however, the discrepancy may assume alarming proportions. The difficulty manifests itself in discontinuity of the seasonally adjusted data at the point where one year ends and the next begins. Let us assume, for instance, that the unadjusted seasonal index numbers for December 1963 and January 1964 are each 100 per cent, the amplitude adjustment to be applied, let us say, to calendar years. Now, suppose further that the amplitude ratios are 0.5 and 1.5, respectively. This makes the adjusted December 1963 index number 50 per cent and the January 1964 number 150. It is apparent that there will be an enormous drop in the seasonally adjusted data between December and January. Yet a little thought will convince one that the change in amplitude does not take place entirely in a month's time, but represents a transition of several months' duration.

Although there is no entirely satisfactory solution for this difficulty, one remedy, which is very laborious, is to compute an amplitude ratio for each consecutive 12-month period of the entire series. For instance, if the data ran from 1954 through 1964, the first 12-month period would run from January 1954 through December 1954, the second from February 1954 through January 1955, and so on. Altogether there would be 121 such 12-month periods and the same number of amplitude ratios. We could speak of these ratios collectively as a *moving amplitude ratio*. Following the analogy of a 12-month moving average, these ratios should be centered by a 2-month moving average, leaving 120 amplitude ratios, running from July 1954 through June 1964. The seasonal index numbers are then multiplied by these amplitude ratios to obtain the final seasonal index numbers.

This procedure is laborious, and it is not entirely satisfactory. Although there is no sharp break in the continuity of the series, it has the defect that not any 12 consecutive seasonal index numbers are centered on 100 per cent. A less accurate but also much less laborious procedure than the one just described is to compute an amplitude ratio for each standard year, center the ratio on the sixth or seventh month, and interpolate arithmetically from one year to the next.

Combinations of seasonal types. It is frequently true that the seasonal variation of a series may be gradually changing in pattern, shifting in its timing, or varying in amplitude, or some combination of the three. For data showing shifts in timing and changes in amplitude, the procedure for obtaining final seasonal indexes might be: (1) break data into sub-periods according to occurrence of seasonal high; (2) compute stable seasonal for each such sub-period; (3) using these seasonal indexes, compute amplitude ratios for each year (possibly using the method of interpolation described above); (4) multiply the seasonal index numbers by the appropriate amplitude ratios.

Other combinations of seasonal behavior may call for different treatment. Considerable ingenuity is frequently required to measure seasonal variation successfully. Unfortunately, there is no way of telling when we have arrived at the best solution of the problem. Complexity of procedure does not guarantee that the results obtained accurately describe the movement which we set out to measure. Particularly if the data are originally unreliable, great refinement of method is likely to be largely wasted effort.[5]

Logical basis of methods of construction. With the exception of the adjustment for Easter, referred to on page 314, the methods described in this chapter are more or less empirical in nature, depending for their validity upon the results which they produce. A method is held to be satisfactory if the deseasonalized data: (1) do not show similarity of intra-year pattern (other than cyclical) in different years; (2) are not extremely irregular in their movements; and (3) are of about the same magnitude as the original data in 12-month periods.

The Easter adjustment, on the other hand, attempts to find a functional relationship between April sales minus March sales and the date of Easter. Carrying this idea further, it might be possible to find a numerical relationship over time between length of daylight and sales of incandescent lamps; or between temperature and sales of ice; or between a combination of temperature and snowfall and sale of galoshes. Computation of seasonal indexes by such a method would carry us far into the field of correlation, which is treated in Chapters 19–22. Furthermore, it

---

[5] For advanced work, see E. J. Hannan, "The Estimation of a Changing Seasonal Pattern," *The Journal of the American Statistical Association*, Vol. 59, No. 308, December 1964, pp. 1063–1077.

would be difficult to measure the importance, let us say, of Christmas by correlating sales with some other factor.

Intermediate between these two types of methods is that which obtains a first-approximation seasonal index by an empirical method, and then seeks to smooth this index by fitting a curve to the seasonal index numbers on the theory that the seasonal movement would present a smooth pattern if the period covered were long enough to permit an exact cancelling out of all irregular movements. Freehand smoothing of the seasonal curve is practiced by a few statisticians. The fitting of a mathematical curve is not usually advocated. Not only may logical objections be raised, but there may be social factors that disturb the smoothness of contour inherent in a simple mathematical curve.

CHAPTER 16

Analysis of Time Series:

CYCLICAL MOVEMENTS—ADJUSTING TIME SERIES FOR TREND, SEASONAL, AND IRREGULAR MOVEMENTS

In Chapter 11 it was pointed out that monthly time series are typically the product of the four important movements: secular trend (T), seasonal variation (S), cyclical movements (C), and irregular fluctuations (I). Chapters 12 and 13 were devoted to consideration of types of trends, how to select the appropriate type, and methods of trend fitting. Chapters 14 and 15 gave attention to types of seasonal variation and the determination of indexes of seasonal variation. In this chapter, we shall first discuss the elimination of trend from annual time series data. Following this, both seasonal variation and trend will be eliminated from monthly data, and irregular movements will be smoothed. The final result will be a set of adjusted data showing primarily the cyclical movements of the series.

ADJUSTING ANNUAL DATA FOR TREND

It is, of course, obvious that annual data, which show but one figure for each year, cannot contain any seasonal variation. Neither can annual data show irregular movements, although it is possible for an episodic movement (such as one due to a severe strike or a conflagration) to be important enough to affect an annual total.

Table 12.2 showed the computations necessary for determining a straight-line trend for newspaper advertising for 1932–1960. The trend values resulting from use of the equation were given in the last column of Table 12.2 for 1932–1964. Chart 12.3 showed both the observed annual data and the trend. Table 16.1 repeats the observed data for 1932–1964 and the trend values for the same years. In Table 16.1 we have also computed the per-cent-of-trend values for each year. These are obtained by *dividing* each of the original figures by the corresponding trend value and multiplying by 100. The results are shown in Chart

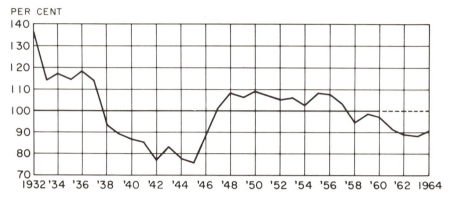

Chart 16.1. **Annual Data of Newspaper Advertising in the United States Adjusted for Trend, 1932–1964.** The 100 per cent base is shown as a broken line for 1961–1964 because the trend was fitted to the years 1932–1960 and extended to 1964. Data of Table 16.1.

TABLE 16.1

Adjustment for Trend of Newspaper Advertising in the United States, 1932–1964

(Original data and trend values in millions of lines)

Year	Original data Y	Trend values Y_c	Per cent of trend $100(Y \div Y_c)$	Year	Original data Y	Trend values Y_c	Per cent of trend $100(Y \div Y_c)$
1932	1,164.8	857.4	135.9	1949	2,302.1	2,154.0	106.9
1933	1,065.5	933.7	114.1	1950	2,440.2	2,230.3	109.4
1934	1,178.9	1,010.0	116.7	1951	2,478.3	2,306.6	107.4
1935	1,246.0	1,086.2	114.7	1952	2,505.4	2,382.8	105.1
1936	1,380.0	1,162.5	118.7	1953	2,610.5	2,459.1	106.2
1937	1,409.8	1,238.8	113.8	1954	2,581.3	2,535.4	101.8
1938	1,225.4	1,315.0	93.2	1955	2,843.5	2,611.6	108.9
1939	1,243.6	1,391.3	89.4	1956	2,911.0	2,687.9	108.3
1940	1,268.6	1,467.6	86.4	1957	2,829.1	2,764.2	102.3
1941	1,313.2	1,543.9	85.1	1958	2,685.6	2,840.4	94.6
1942	1,241.8	1,620.1	76.6	1959	2,865.3	2,916.7	98.2
1943	1,396.4	1,696.4	82.3	1960	2,888.6	2,993.0	96.5
1944	1,361.3	1,772.7	76.8	1961	2,777.0*	3,069.3	90.5
1945	1,391.6	1,848.9	75.3	1962	2,798.3*	3,145.5	89.0
1946	1,729.7	1,925.2	89.8	1963	2,858.6*	3,221.8	88.7
1947	2,008.6	2,001.5	100.4	1964	2,973.4*	3,298.1	90.2
1948	2,263.3	2,077.7	108.9				

* Not used for computing trend. Original data from various issues of *Survey of Current Business.* Trend values from Table 12.2.

16.1.   Annual data provide only very rough indicators of the fluctuations of a time series, but Chart 16.1 shows that marked fluctuations have occurred in annual newspaper advertising linage.

In Table 16.1, trend was eliminated by division, rather than by subtraction. If the trend values had been subtracted from the original figures, the result would have been deviations in abolute terms (millions of lines) rather than relative terms.   For most purposes, it is more useful to know whether the variations are large, or small, in relation to some logical base, such as the trend.   Thus, a deviation of 50 is ten times as important when judged with respect to a trend value of 200 as it is when compared with a trend value of 2,000.

ADJUSTMENT OF MONTHLY DATA

Although there are other methods of arriving at estimates of the cyclical movements of time series, some of which are mentioned at the end of this chapter, the so-called "residual method" is most commonly used. This method consists of eliminating seasonal variation and trend, thus obtaining the cyclical-irregular movements.   Symbolically,[1]

$$(T \times S \times C \times I) \div S = T \times C \times I \text{ and}$$
$$(T \times C \times I) \div T = C \times I.$$

Next, the data are usually smoothed in order to obtain the cyclical movements, which are sometimes termed the *cyclical relatives*, since they are always percentages.   It is because the cyclical-irregular or the cyclical movements remain as residuals that this procedure is referred to as the *residual* method.

Deseasonalizing.   As pointed out in Chapter 11, a seasonal index may be computed for the purpose of studying the seasonal movement itself, the objective being to avoid or minimize the consequences of the seasonal changes, to smooth out the seasonal fluctuations, or to take advantage of them.   On the other hand, we may be interested in studying a time series undisturbed by seasonal variation, and this we accomplish by adjusting the observed data for seasonal variation.

The computation of a seasonal index and its use to deseasonalize a set of monthly data may be but one step in the isolation of cyclical movements, the other steps (to be described shortly) being the adjustment for trend and the smoothing of irregular movements.   Not infrequently, however, it may be desired to study economic and business series adjusted only for seasonal variation.   Thus, businessmen, in making decisions,

---

[1] The concept of $T \times S \times C \times I$ is more generally useful than is that of $T + S + C + I$.   This is because S, C, and I tend to remain more nearly constant in magnitude relative to trend, rather than in absolute terms.   Furthermore, the movements are ordinarily more meaningful when considered relative to each other than when considered in absolute terms.   Thus, it is possible to compute a seasonal index which remains constant over a period of years, to determine a seasonal index which is changing because of alterations in the relative importance of the months, and to compare the percentage fluctuations of cyclical movements.   Occasionally series are encountered for which better results are obtained if the seasonal movement is considered constant in absolute rather than relative terms.   This is discussed on pages 323–326.

may consider not so much whether their sales are increasing (or decreasing) relative to a not-too-easily-visualized combination of trend and seasonal movements, but rather in relation to the ordinarily expected sales for the particular season of the year.   It is of interest that many deseasonalized series appear in the *Federal Reserve Bulletin,* issued by the Board of Governors of the Federal Reserve System, and in the *Survey of Current Business,* published by the Office of Business Economics of the Department of Commerce.

The elimination of seasonal variation is ordinarily accomplished by dividing the original values by the seasonal index (and multiplying the results by 100), as shown in Table 16.2 for the data of newsprint consumption.   That is: $(T \times S \times C \times I) \div S = T \times C \times I$, so that the deseasonalized data contain trend, cyclical and irregular movements.   The deseasonalized data of Table 16.2, together with the original figures of newspaper consumption, are shown in Chart 16.2, where it is apparent that the curve of the deseasonalized data is much the smoother of the two.   Because the period covered consists of but nine years, neither the original data nor the deseasonalized data show cyclical movements.   The data of newsprint consumption were chosen as an illustration in Chapter 14, not because they would or would not show cyclical movements after seasonal variations were removed, but because the series seemed to have a seasonal which, when tested by drawing the twelve monthly charts of the per-cent-of-moving-average data (like Chart 15.2), did not appear to change from year to year.   However, the curve of the deseasonalized data suggests that the seasonal index may not be very

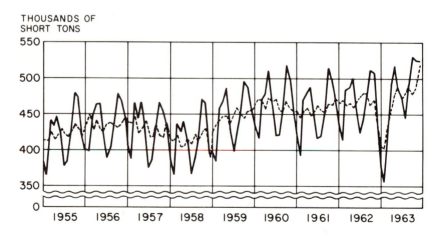

Chart 16.2.   Consumption of Newsprint by United States Publishers (Solid Line) and Deseasonalized Data (Broken Line), 1955–1963.   Data of Table 16.2.

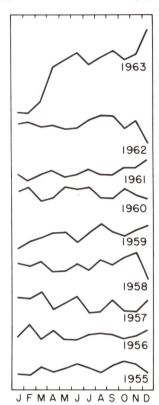

Chart 16.3. Year-Over-Year Chart of Deseasonalized Data of Consumption of Newsprint by United States Publishers, 1955–1963. Data of Table 16.2.

satisfactory because of the sharp peaks and troughs remaining.   Under these circumstances, the monthly charts should be re-examined.   The peaks and troughs shown in the deseasonalized data do not represent residual seasonal fluctuations, but rather unusually high and low original values for those months for non-seasonal reasons, as may be seen in Table 16.2.

Test of seasonal.   A practical test of a seasonal index is to see whether its use has eliminated all of the seasonal movement from the series.   A chart of the type of Chart 16.2 may be used for this purpose, but a year-over-year chart of the deseasonalized data, Chart 16.3, is better.   From this chart it may be seen that the fluctuations still present in the deseasonalized data are largely irregular movements which stand out because of the lack of cyclical fluctuations in the series.   When residual seasonal movements are present in an adjusted series, the curves of a year-over-year chart will show some similarity with each other.

Correction by subtraction of seasonal.   It occasionally happens, as in Chart 16.3 for the year 1963, that grotesque results are obtained when seasonal is eliminated by dividing by a seasonal index.   This is especially

TABLE 16.2

Elimination of Seasonal Variations from Data of Consumption of Newsprint by United States Publishers, 1955–1963

(Original and deseasonalized data in thousands of short tons)

Year and month	Original data	Seasonal index	Deseasonalized data Col. 2 ÷ Col. 3	Year and month	Original data	Seasonal index	Deseasonalized data Col. 2 ÷ Col. 3
(1)	(2)	(3)	(4)	(1)	(2)	(3)	(4)
1955				**1958**			
January.....	384	93.2	412.0	January.....	386	93.2	414.2
February....	365	88.7	411.5	February....	365	88.7	411.5
March......	439	104.0	422.1	March......	434	104.0	417.3
April.......	432	104.8	412.2	April.......	423	104.8	403.6
May........	455	108.4	419.7	May........	438	108.4	404.1
June........	422	99.0	426.3	June	409	99.0	413.1
July........	378	89.7	421.4	July........	365	89.7	406.9
August......	385	92.3	417.1	August......	388	92.3	420.4
September...	425	100.1	424.6	September ..	413	100.1	412.6
October.....	479	110.9	431.9	October.....	470	110.9	423.8
November...	462	108.2	427.0	November...	465	108.2	429.8
December...	419	100.6	416.5	December...	394	100.6	391.7
1956				**1959**			
January.....	402	93.2	431.3	January.....	395	93.2	423.8
February....	398	88.7	448.7	February....	385	88.7	434.0
March......	446	104.0	428.8	March......	458	104.0	440.4
April.......	462	104.8	440.8	April.......	467	104.8	445.6
May........	464	108.4	428.0	May........	484	108.4	446.5
June........	422	99.0	426.3	June........	429	99.0	433.3
July........	389	89.7	433.7	July........	400	89.7	445.9
August......	403	92.3	436.6	August......	423	92.3	458.3
September ..	435	100.1	434.6	September ..	449	100.1	448.6
October.....	477	100.9	430.1	October.....	492	100.9	443.6
November...	468	108.2	432.5	November...	488	108.2	451.0
December...	444	100.6	441.4	December...	459	100.6	456.3
1957				**1960**			
January.....	408	93.2	437.8	January.....	432	93.2	463.5
February....	387	88.7	436.3	February....	416	88.7	469.0
March......	463	104.0	445.2	March......	470	104.0	451.9
April.......	442	104.8	421.8	April.......	477	104.8	455.2
May........	466	108.4	429.9	May........	510	108.4	470.5
June........	434	99.0	438.4	June........	462	99.0	466.7
July........	374	89.7	416.9	July........	420	89.7	468.2
August......	386	92.3	418.2	August......	420	92.3	455.0
September ..	434	100.1	433.6	September ..	454	100.1	453.5
October.....	465	110.9	419.3	October.....	517	110.9	466.2
November...	453	108.2	418.7	November...	497	108.2	459.3
December...	436	100.6	433.4	December...	457	100.6	454.3

TABLE 16.2 (*Concluded*)

Elimination of Seasonal Variations from Data of Consumption of Newsprint by United States Publishers, 1955–1963

Year and month	Original data	Seasonal index	Deseasonalized data Col. 2 ÷ Col. 3
(1)	(2)	(3)	(4)
1961			
January..................	422	93.2	452.8
February.................	392	88.7	441.9
March...................	469	104.0	451.0
April....................	479	104.8	457.1
May.....................	486	108.4	448.3
June....................	447	99.0	451.5
July....................	413	89.7	460.4
August..................	417	92.3	451.8
September...............	451	100.1	450.5
October.................	512	110.9	461.7
November...............	499	108.2	461.2
December...............	473	100.6	470.2
1962			
January..................	434	93.2	465.7
February.................	415	88.7	467.9
March...................	481	104.0	462.5
April....................	487	104.8	464.7
May.....................	499	108.4	460.3
June....................	457	99.0	461.6
July......	423	89.7	471.6
August..................	442	92.3	478.9
September...............	479	100.1	478.5
October.................	511	110.9	460.8
November...............	508	108.2	469.5
December...............	441	100.6	438.4
1963			
January..................	376	93.2	403.4
February.................	356	88.7	401.4
March...................	435	104.0	418.3
April....................	490	104.8	467.6
May.....................	516	108.4	476.0
June....................	483	99.0	487.9
July....................	421	89.7	469.3
August..................	443	92.3	480.0
September...............	490	100.1	489.5
October.................	529	110.9	477.0
November...............	524	108.2	484.3
December...............	522	100.6	518.9

Data from Tables 14.5 and 14.7.

likely to be the case when the seasonal movement typically falls almost to zero at one or more months. Then, if in any given year the original data remain materially above zero for those months, division by the extremely low seasonal index percentage will raise the deseasonalized data to a very sharp peak. Even though a seasonal movement may not fall to or near zero, there are rare instances in which a seasonal pattern may be constant in absolute rather than relative terms. This will be apparent if the percentages of moving average tend to be large when the original data are at a low level and small when the original data are at a high level.

A simple expedient is as follows. Compute a seasonal index by whatever method seems appropriate. The index is now converted into terms of the original data by multiplying the seasonal index numbers (expressed as percentage deviations) each year by the average value of the original series for that year. Seasonal is then eliminated by subtracting, algebraically, the seasonal index from the original data.

It may be desirable to compute the index number, in the first instance, in such a way as to obtain a seasonal index in absolute rather than relative terms. This will be so if the seasonal movements each year seem to be similar in absolute magnitude rather than in percentage deviations. Inspection of a chart of the original data may indicate whether this is true. If the evidence indicates that an index of absolute deviations should be computed, it is necessary only to adapt one of the methods with which the reader is already familiar. For instance, if the moving-average method is used, the moving average is subtracted from, instead of divided into, the original data; and the index from that point is constructed as usual, the final index being adjusted to total zero by the addition or subtraction of a correction factor. Incidentally, it might be noted that any of the devices explained in Chapter 14 may be based on the subtraction method of computing seasonal. The link-relative method (described in Chapter 14) can also be adapted very easily as follows: (1) obtain link differences by subtracting the preceding month from each month; (2) average these link differences, month by month; (3) let the first-month link difference be zero, and chain the links by successive addition; (4) correct chain differences for (upward) trend by successive subtraction of a correction factor; (5) adjust chain differences to total zero by addition or subtraction of a constant correction factor.

Adjustment for seasonal and trend. To serve as an illustration for most of the balance of this section, we shall use the data of newspaper advertising linage, for which the trend was ascertained in Chapter 12 and for part of which a moving seasonal index was computed in Chapter 15. The usual procedure consists, first, of removing the seasonal fluctuations, giving

$$(T \times S \times C \times I) \div S = T \times C \times I$$

and, next, eliminating trend to give

$$(T \times C \times I) \div T = C \times I.$$

We shall use the data of newspaper advertising linage from January 1932 to December 1964. The original, unadjusted data are shown in Chart 16.4. The removal of seasonal variation is accomplished exactly as described for the data of consumption of newsprint, by dividing the original data by the seasonal index. This procedure is indicated in Table 16.3. For newspaper advertising, the seasonal indexes used were: (1) a moving seasonal index for 1932–1963, and (2) the 1963 values repeated for 1964. The use of the 1963 seasonal index for 1964 follows the usual practice when it is not possible (because of unavailability of subsequent data) to extend the moving seasonal index. The determination of the 1954–1963 portion of the moving seasonal index was described in the preceding chapter, the index appearing in Table 15.3. The seasonal indexes were shown graphically in Chart 11.9. The deseasonalized data of newspaper advertising are shown in Column 4 of Table 16.3 and in Chart 16.4.

The next step consists of eliminating trend, the procedure being the same as that shown in Table 16.1, except that we are now dealing with monthly data and must put the trend equation into monthly terms. Note that while our present illustration concerns the years 1932–1964, the trend equation was fitted to the period 1932–1960 and was extended through 1964. On page 244, the trend, in monthly terms, was found to be

$$Y_c = 160.6982 + 0.5297X.$$
Origin, July 1946. X units, 1 month.

The trend values shown in Column 5 of Table 16.3 were obtained from this equation. Now, the deseasonalized values in Column 4 of Table 16.3 are each divided by the corresponding trend value $[(T \times C \times I) \div T = C \times I]$ to produce the cyclical-irregular values in Column 6 of the table. These cyclical-irregular values are shown in Chart 16.5. It is important to note that the values shown in Column 6 of Table 16.3 are percentages, not millions of lines. When seasonal movements are eliminated by dividing by a seasonal index (which is a series of percentages), the deseasonalized data are always in the same units as were the original data. Trend, however, is in terms of the original units, so that when the trend of a series is eliminated by dividing, the resulting figures are percentages.

In Table 16.3 the cyclical-irregular movements were obtained by eliminating, first, seasonal variation and then trend. In symbols, the procedure was

$(T \times S \times C \times I) \div S = T \times C \times I$, the deseasonalized data, and

$(T \times C \times I) \div T = C \times I$, the cyclical-irregular movements.

TABLE 16.3

Adjustment of Data of United States Newspaper Advertising for Seasonal Variation and for Trend, 1933–1964

(Original data, deseasonalized data, and trend values in millions of lines.)

Year and month	Original data $T \times S \times C \times I$	Seasonal index	Deseasonalized data $T \times C \times I$ Col. (2) ÷ Col. (3) × 100	Trend values T	Cyclical-irregular percentages $C \times I$ Col. (4) ÷ Col. (5)
(1)	(2)	(3)	(4)	(5)	(6)
1933					
January..........	78.0	87.1	89.6	74.8	119.8
February.........	72.5	83.5	86.8	75.4	115.1
March........,....	76.4	106.5	71.7	75.9	94.5
April............	91.1	108.8	83.7	76.4	109.6
May.............	94.6	111.2	85.1	76.9	110.7
June............	93.2	103.3	90.2	77.5	116.4
July............	78.3	86.5	90.5	78.0	116.0
August..........	86.3	88.7	97.3	78.5	123.9
September.......	92.6	98.9	93.6	79.1	118.3
October.........	106.0	112.0	94.6	79.6	118.8
November.......	99.8	108.5	92.0	80.1	114.9
December.......	96.7	105.0	92.1	80.7	114.1
1934					
January..........	82.5	86.2	95.7	81.2	117.9
February.........	80.8	84.0	96.2	81.7	117.7
March...........	103.6	106.5	97.3	82.2	118.4
April............	107.5	108.7	98.9	82.8	119.4
May.............	112.1	112.2	99.9	83.3	119.9
June............	103.6	102.2	101.4	83.8	121.0
July............	83.2	85.4	97.4	84.4	115.4
August..........	87.7	87.3	100.5	84.9	118.4
September.......	96.4	99.3	97.1	85.4	113.7
October.........	108.8	112.1	97.1	86.0	112.9
November.......	107.0	108.7	98.4	86.5	113.8
December........	105.7	107.4	98.4	87.0	113.1
1963					
January..........	197.7	84.7	233.4	265.6	87.9
February.........	190.3	82.8	229.8	266.2	86.3
March...........	238.7	101.7	234.7	266.7	88.0
April............	241.1	103.9	232.1	267.2	86.9
May.............	268.7	110.9	242.3	267.8	90.5
June............	243.1	101.0	240.7	268.3	89.7
July............	212.5	89.8	236.6	268.8	88.0
August..........	233.1	98.2	237.4	269.4	88.1
September.......	246.7	101.8	242.3	270.0	89.7
October.........	267.7	110.1	243.1	270.4	89.9
November.......	258.4	110.0	234.9	270.9	86.7
December.......	260.6	105.1	248.0	271.5	91.3
1964					
January..........	210.6	84.7	248.6	272.0	91.4
February.........	210.4	82.8	254.1	272.5	93.2
March...........	248.0	101.7	243.9	273.1	89.3
April............	265.1	103.9	255.1	273.6	93.2
May.............	275.9	110.9	248.8	274.1	90.8
June............	247.0	101.0	244.6	274.7	89.0
July............	226.5	89.8	252.2	275.2	91.6
August..........	238.0	98.2	242.4	275.7	87.9
September.......	248.2	101.8	243.8	276.2	88.3
October.........	265.0	110.1	240.7	276.8	87.0
November.......	276.4	110.0	251.3	277.3	90.6
December.......	262.3	105.1	249.6	277.8	89.8

Newspaper advertising linage from various issues of *Survey of Current Business*.

Seasonal index: changing for 1933–1953 from worksheets not shown, changing for 1954–1963 from Table 15.3, 1964 same as 1963. Trend values from the equation given on page 327.

If it were desirable to do so, we could, of course, eliminate first trend and then seasonal variation, thus:

$(T \times S \times C \times I) \div T = S \times C \times I$, the data adjusted for trend, and $(S \times C \times I) \div S = C \times I$, the cyclical-irregular movements.

Another possibility consists of multiplying together the trend and seasonal values (the seasonal percentages being used as decimal ratios) and eliminating both of those movements at the same time. In symbols, this is

$(T \times S \times C \times I) \div (T \times S) = C \times I$, the cyclical-irregular movements.

Table 16.4 illustrates these three possible procedures for newspaper advertising linage for 1963. Note that the final results by the three methods, which are shown in Column 6 of each part of Table 16.4, either agree exactly or occasionally differ by 0.1 because of rounding.

Of the three procedures for adjusting for seasonal variation and trend, the one first described is most frequently used, since it is often desired to study a series adjusted for seasonal variation as well as to observe the cyclical-irregular movements. Since one rarely is interested in adjusting a monthly series for trend alone, the second procedure is not often used. If the sole purpose of the analysis is to obtain the cyclical-irregular movements (either as a final objective or as a step toward getting the cyclical movements), the third method shown in Table 16.4 will be slightly less time-consuming than either of the others, since most types of calculating machines can more quickly perform the series of multiplications which replaces one of the two series of divisions present in the other methods.

However the cyclical-irregular movements are obtained, those values are often referred to as percentages of "normal." The term "normal" is frequently used in economics, business, psychology, statistics, and in other fields, and it is not always used with the same meaning. In this instance, "normal" refers to the combined trend and seasonal movements of a series, the thought being that from a long-run point of view it is normal for an industry to increase (or decrease) in some steady fashion, and that from a short-run viewpoint it is normal for seasonal variation to be present. Taken together, both movements are "normal."

Smoothing irregular movements. The interplay of a multitude of forces, other than those already eliminated, is largely responsible for the irregular movements which are usually to be seen in the curve of a series adjusted for seasonal variation and trend. The irregular fluctuations in newspaper advertising linage are apparent in Chart 16.5. Occasionally, irregular fluctuations may occur because the seasonal index which was used was not as good as might be desired. Earlier consider-

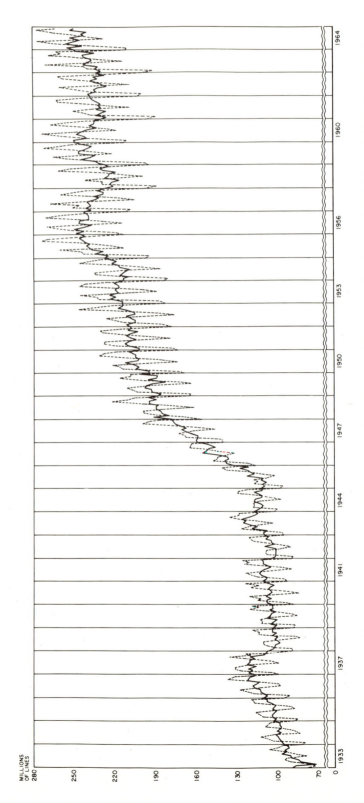

Chart 16.4. Newspaper Advertising in the United States (Broken Line) and Deseasonalized Data (Solid Line), 1933–1934. Data from Table 16.3 and from worksheets (not shown) for the years omitted from that table.

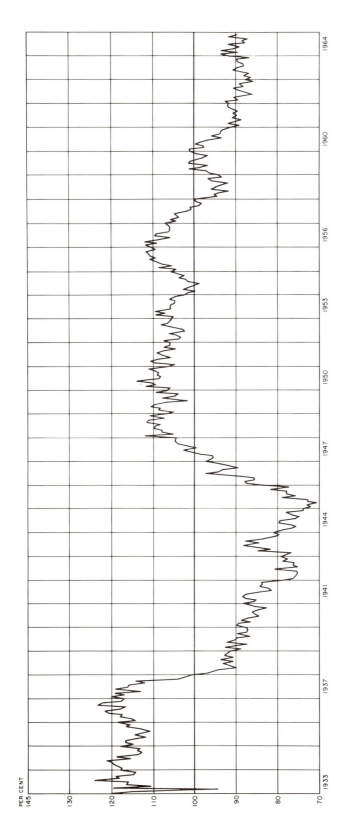

PER CENT

Chart 16.5. Newspaper Advertising in the United States Adjusted for Seasonal Movements and for Trend, 1933–1964. Data from Table 16.3 and from worksheets (not shown) for the years omitted from that table; see also the source note for Table 16.3.

TABLE 16.4

Three Methods of Obtaining Cyclical-Irregular Movements of United States Newspaper Advertising for 1963

I. Adjustment for seasonal variation and then for trend.

Month	Original data $T \times S \times C \times I$	Seasonal index S	Deseasonalized data $T \times C \times I$ [Col. (2) ÷ Col. (3)] × 100	Trend values T	Cyclical-irregular percentages $C \times I$ Col. (4) ÷ Col. (5)
(1)	(2)	(3)	(4)	(5)	(6)
January......	197.7	84.7	233.4	265.6	87.9
February.....	190.3	82.8	229.8	266.2	86.3
March........	238.7	101.7	234.7	266.7	88.0
April.........	241.1	103.9	232.1	267.2	86.9
May..........	268.7	110.9	242.3	267.8	90.5
June.........	243.1	101.0	240.7	268.3	89.7
July.........	212.5	89.8	236.6	268.8	88.0
August.......	233.1	98.2	237.4	269.4	88.1
September.....	246.7	101.8	242.3	270.0	89.7
October......	267.7	110.1	243.1	270.4	89.9
November.....	258.4	110.0	234.9	270.9	86.7
December.....	260.6	105.1	248.0	271.5	91.3

II. Adjustment for trend and then for seasonal variation.

Month	Original data $T \times S \times C \times I$	Trend values T	Per cent of trend $S \times C \times I$ Col. (2) ÷ Col. (3)	Seasonal index S	Cyclical-irregular percentages $C \times I$ Col. (4) ÷ Col. (5)
(1)	(2)	(3)	(4)	(5)	(6)
January........	197.7	265.6	74.4	84.7	87.9
February.......	190.3	266.2	71.5	82.8	86.3
March..........	238.7	266.7	89.5	101.7	88.0
April...........	241.1	267.2	90.2	103.9	86.8
May............	268.7	267.8	100.3	110.9	90.5
June...........	243.1	268.3	90.6	101.0	89.7
July...........	212.5	268.8	79.1	89.8	88.0
August.........	233.1	269.4	86.5	98.2	88.1
September......	246.7	270.0	91.4	101.8	89.8
October........	267.7	270.4	99.0	110.1	89.9
November......	258.4	270.9	95.4	110.0	86.7
December......	260.6	271.5	96.0	105.1	91.3

III. Adjustment for combined trend and seasonal movements.

Month	Original data $T \times S \times C \times I$	Trend values T	Seasonal index S	"Normal" values $T \times S$ Col. (3) × Col. (4)	Cyclical-irregular percentages $C \times I$ Col. (2) ÷ Col. (5)
(1)	(2)	(3)	(4)	(5)	(6)
January........	197.7	265.6	84.7	224.8	87.9
February.......	190.3	266.2	82.8	220.4	86.3
March.........	238.7	266.7	101.7	271.2	88.0
April..........	241.1	267.2	103.9	277.6	86.8
May...........	268.7	267.8	110.9	297.0	90.5
June..........	243.1	268.3	101.0	271.0	89.7
July..........	212.5	268.8	89.8	241.4	88.0
August........	233.1	269.4	98.2	264.6	88.1
September......	246.7	270.0	101.8	274.9	89.8
October........	267.7	270.4	110.1	297.7	89.9
November......	258.4	270.9	110.0	298.0	86.7
December......	260.6	271.5	105.1	285.3	91.3

Data from sources given below Table 16.3.

ation of the seasonal index for newspaper advertising linage has indicated that it was satisfactory.

Irregular fluctuations cannot be completely eliminated from a series without the accompanying danger of over-smoothing. However, the

TABLE 16.5

Computation of Cyclical Movements for Data of United States Newspaper Advertising, 1933–1964

Year and month	Cyclical irregular percentages $C \times I$	Three-month moving total weighted 1, 2, 1 of Col. (2)	Cyclical percentages C Col. (3) ÷ 4	Year and month	Cyclical irregular percentages $C \times I$	Three-month moving total weighted 1, 2, 1 of Col. (2)	Cyclical percentages C Col. (3) ÷ 4
(1)	(2)	(3)	(4)	(1)	(2)	(3)	(4)
1933				**1963**			
January.....	119.8	474.6	118.7	January.....	87.9	347.7	86.9
February....	115.1	444.5	111.1	February....	86.3	348.5	87.1
March......	94.5	413.7	103.4	March......	88.0	349.2	87.3
April........	109.6	424.4	106.1	April........	86.9	352.3	88.1
May........	110.7	447.4	111.9	May........	90.5	357.6	89.4
June........	116.4	459.5	114.9	June........	89.7	357.9	89.5
July........	116.0	472.3	118.1	July........	88.0	353.8	88.5
August......	123.9	482.1	120.5	August......	88.1	353.9	88.5
September ..	118.3	479.3	119.8	September ..	89.7	357.4	89.4
October.....	118.8	470.8	117.7	October.....	89.9	356.2	89.1
November...	114.9	462.7	115.7	November...	86.7	354.6	88.7
December...	114.1	461.0	115.3	December...	91.3	360.7	90.2
1934				**1964**			
January.....	117.9	467.6	116.9	January.....	91.4	367.3	91.8
February....	117.7	471.7	117.9	February....	93.2	367.1	91.8
March......	118.4	473.9	118.5	March......	89.3	365.0	91.3
April........	119.4	477.1	119.3	April........	93.2	366.5	91.6
May........	119.9	480.2	120.1	May........	90.8	363.8	91.0
June........	121.0	477.3	119.3	June........	89.0	360.4	90.1
July........	115.4	470.2	117.6	July........	91.6	360.1	90.0
August......	118.4	465.9	116.5	August......	87.9	355.7	88.9
September ..	113.7	458.7	114.7	September ..	88.3	351.5	87.9
October.....	112.9	453.3	113.3	October.....	87.0	352.9	88.2
November...	113.8	453.6	113.4	November...	90.6	358.0	89.5
December...	113.1	457.9	114.5	December...	89.8	...	...

Cyclical-irregular percentages from Table 16.3.

irregular movements can be smoothed, so as to bring the cyclical movements into clearer relief, by the use of a short-term moving average. From an examination of Chart 16.5 it appears that most of the irregular movements are of one month's duration, although occasionally, as in the first half of 1934, they appear to last longer than one month. To smooth out these movements, we could use a two-month moving average, except that the values of such an average should be plotted between each pair of months. If we were to average three months, the average would appropriately fall opposite the center month, but we would encounter another serious predicament: if the first and third months were high and the second month low, the resulting average would be high; if the first and third months were low and the second month high, the average

would be low.   A three-month average would therefore sometimes introduce reverse fluctuations into the series.   Both of the foregoing difficulties may be overcome by using a three-month moving average weighted
1, 2, 1, which is, of course, a centered two-month moving average.   Table
16.5 indicates how this average is obtained: first a three-month moving
total weighted 1, 2, 1 is gotten for the cyclical-irregular values, and then
the moving-total values are each divided by 4 to arrive at the moving
average.   The moving totals should be obtained by use of an adding
machine, each total being obtained separately and not by use of successive
subtotals as was done when we computed a 13-month weighted moving
total in Table 14.5.   The moving averages should be gotten from the
moving totals by multiplying by 0.25, rather than by dividing by 4, since
most calculating machines will produce the results faster when a constant
multiplier is used.   Note that the figures in the second column of Table
16.5 are the same as those in Column 6 of Table 16.3.   In actual practice,
Columns 3 and 4 of Table 16.5 would be included as additional columns
of Table 16.3.   Two separate tables are shown here because of the difficulty of showing so large a table on the printed page of this text.   Note
that there will be no three-month moving-average figure for the first
month and the last month of a series.

The result of smoothing the cyclical-irregular values by the use of a
three-month moving average weighted 1, 2, 1 is shown in Chart 16.6.
It is clear that this curve is much smoother than the curve of Chart 16.5,
although there are a few spots where the moving average was of too short
duration to smooth out the irregular fluctuations completely.   Irregular
movements are not often entirely eliminated from a series.   Their complete elimination may call for freehand smoothing or use of a moving
average of longer duration than three months.   In any event, the smoothing process must not hide the turning points of the cyclical movements.
Since a four-month moving average would have the same shortcomings
as a two-month moving average, the practicable moving average, next
longer in duration than the one used in Table 16.5, would be a (weighted)
five-month moving average.   Five-month moving-average values are
set opposite the third month of each set of five months.   The months are
often weighted 1, 2, 4, 2, 1, which gives greatest weight to the center
month and least weight to the end months.   Since this weight pattern
totals 10, the moving averages may be computed from the moving totals
without use of a calculating machine.

The irregular movements.   The irregular movements themselves may
be obtained by dividing the cyclical-irregular values, shown in Column 2
of Table 16.5, by the cyclical values, which are in Column 4 of the same
table.   The computation of the irregular movements is not shown, but
Chart 16.7 shows these, month by month, and Chart 16.8 give a frequency distribution of the irregular variations.   If the irregular move-

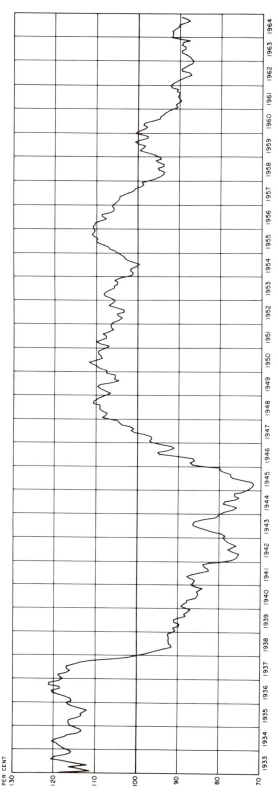

Chart 16.6. Cyclical Movements of Newspaper Advertising in the United States, 1933–1964. Data from Table 16.5 and from worksheets (not shown) for the years omitted from that table.

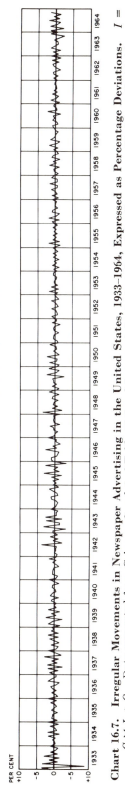

Chart 16.7. Irregular Movements in Newspaper Advertising in the United States, 1933–1964, Expressed as Percentage Deviations. $I = C \times I \div C$. Data computed from Columns 2 and 4 of Table 16.5 and from worksheets (not shown) for the years omitted from that table.

ments were of a random character, they might be expected to form a normal curve. Although the curve of Chart 16.8 is nearly symmetrical ($\beta_1 = 0.1169$), it is leptokurtic, having $\beta_2 = 3.41$. If the deviation of -8.6, not shown in Chart 16.8, is included in the computations, both skewness and leptokurtosis are increased greatly, for $\beta_1 = 0.6226$ and $\beta_2 = 10.83$. This is the sort of frequency distribution to be expected for the irregular movements of a time series, since, in addition to minor fluctuations, there are ordinarily others that are episodic in nature and the effects of which may continue (or cumulate) over several months. The data of newspaper advertising are rather "well behaved" in this respect, the deviations continuing on the same side of the zero line[2] of Chart 16.8 for five months at a time only once, for four months at a time only two times, and for three months at a time fourteen times.

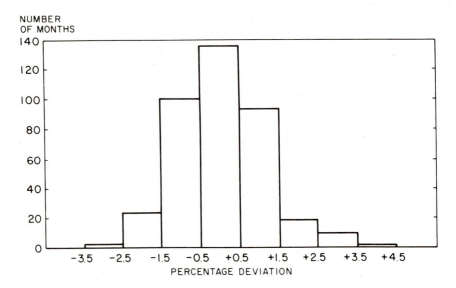

NUMBER OF MONTHS

PERCENTAGE DEVIATION

Chapter 16.8. Frequency Distribution of Irregular Movements in Newspaper Advertising in the United States, 1932–1964. The irregular movements are $I = C \times I \div C$ and are expressed as percentage deviations. Data computed from columns 2 and 4 of Table 16.5 and from worksheets (not shown) for the years omitted from that table.

Comparing cyclical movements. One reason for wishing to isolate cyclical movements in a time series is the desire to compare them with the cyclical movements in one or more other series. Occasionally it may be thought that one series more or less consistently precedes another at its

---

[2] This is not easy to see from the chart. The counts were made from the data upon which the chart is based.

cyclical turning points.[3]   However, when two series differ in regard to
the amplitude of their fluctuations expressed in absolute terms, some
difficulty is experienced in comparing the timing of those fluctuations.
The more marked the difference in amplitudes, the more important it is
to make some sort of an adjustment for that difference.

As an illustration we shall use the Index of Durable Manufactures and
the Index of Nondurable Manufactures for January 1959–December
1964, both of which are issued by the Board of Governors of the Federal
Reserve System.   Chart 16.9 shows these two series, adjusted for trend
and seasonal movements, with irregular fluctuations smoothed, and
expressed as cyclical deviations.   Cyclical deviations give the same curve
as cyclical percentages; the values are merely expressed differently, for
example, 102.5 is +2.5, 101.2 is +1.2, 100 is 0, 98.3 is −1.7, 96.4 is −3.6,
and so forth.   Although the two series in Chart 16.9 are not markedly
different in regard to their cyclical fluctuations, it is clear that the Index
of Durable Manufactures shows greater amplitude than does the Index of
Nondurable Manufactures.

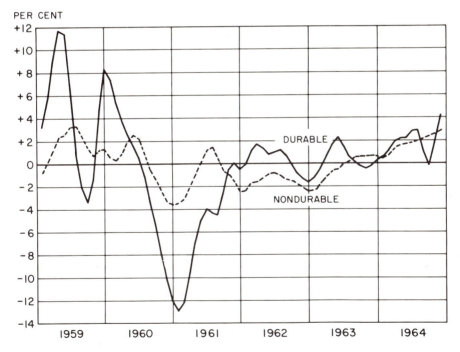

**Chart 16.9.   Cyclical Deviations of Federal Reserve Index of Production
of Durable Manufacturers and of Index of Nondurable Manufactures,
1959–1964.**   For sources of data, see note to Table 16.6.

---

[3] Lead-lag relationships are discussed in Chapter 22.

One possible method of comparing the amplitude of the cyclical movements more easily consists of using different vertical scales for the two series.   While this is a simple solution, it is not easy to decide just what relationship the two vertical scales should bear to each other; for example, if the maximum fluctuations were to be made to cover the same vertical distances, the series of greater amplitude might be compressed too much in some portions.   A more satisfactory procedure consists of expressing each series in terms of its own standard deviation and employing but one vertical scale.

Table 16.6 indicates the procedure for computing the value of s for the

TABLE 16.6

Computation of s for Cyclical Deviations of Federal Reserve Index of Production of Nondurable Manufactures and Cyclical Deviations in Terms of s, 1959–1964

(The original index figures had 1957 = 100 through October 1961 and 1957–1959 = 100 after that date.)

Year and month (1)	Cyclical deviations* y (2)	Squares of Col. (2) y^2 (3)	Cyclical deviations in terms of s Col. (2) ÷ s (4)
1959			
January.............	...	...	...
February............	−0.7	0.49	−0.04
March...............	+0.1	0.01	+0.01
April...............	+1.4	1.96	+0.08
May.................	+2.3	5.29	+0.13
June................	+2.6	6.76	+0.15
July................	+3.2	10.24	+0.18
August..............	+3.3	10.89	+0.19
September...........	+2.5	6.25	+0.14
October.............	+1.3	1.69	+0.07
November............	+0.7	0.49	+0.04
December............	+1.1	1.21	+0.06
1964			
January.............	+0.6	0.36	+0.03
February............	+0.5	0.25	+0.03
March...............	+0.8	0.64	+0.05
April...............	+1.3	1.69	+0.07
May.................	+1.6	2.56	+0.09
June................	+1.7	2.89	+0.10
July................	+1.8	3.24	+0.10
August..............	+2.0	4.00	+0.11
September...........	+2.2	4.84	+0.12
October.............	+2.5	6.25	+0.14
November............	+2.6	6.76	+0.15
December............	+2.9	8.41	+0.16
Total..............	+1.6	223.56	...

* Cyclical deviations may be expected to total very nearly zero if the trend was fitted by least squares to data covering the same period as the data under consideration.

Deseasonalized data from various issues of *Federal Reserve Bulletin*.   Trend and irregular movements removed by the writers.

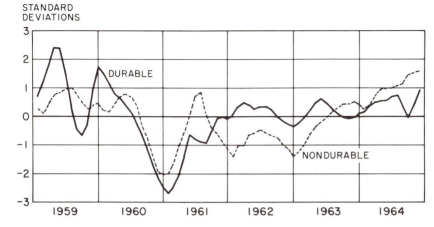

STANDARD
DEVIATIONS

Chart 16.10.   Cyclical Deviations, in Units of Their Standard Deviations, of Index of Production of Durable Manufactures and Index of Production of Nondurable Manufactures, 1959–1964.   For sources of data, see note to Table 16.6.

Index of Nondurable Manufactures.   The formula used for obtaining s is the one employed for ungrouped data in Chapter 10.   As shown below Table 16.6, $s = 1.774$ for the Index of Nondurable Manufactures. Similar computations give $s = 4.785$ for the Index of Durable Manufactures.   The last column of Table 16.6 shows the cyclical deviations for the Index of Nondurable Manufactures expressed in terms of $s = 1.774$. Similar computations were made for the Index of Durable Manufactures. Both series are shown in Chart 16.10, where it is clear that in this instance the amplitude of the fluctuations of the two series is now vastly dissimilar. Although the cyclical fluctuations of time series cannot be expected to be distributed normally,[4] it is interesting to note that the values for both series are within ± 3 standard deviations.   This will not always be true; values of ± 4, or even more, are occasionally found.

A chart such as Chart 16.10 is sometimes referred to as a *cycle chart*, since its object is to facilitate the comparison of cyclical movements.   The vertical scale of such a chart, when seen in a nontechnical publication, may be labeled "cycle values" with no specific mention of the fact that the values are in terms of s.   The omission is ordinarily an intentional one, since readers of the newspaper or magazine might not understand the meaning of s.

A more striking illustration of two series with fluctuations of different amplitude, but dealing with annual data, is given in Charts 22.4 and 22.7, which show data of number of employees in transportation and public

---

[4] The normal curve is discussed in Chapter 23.   The characteristic of s which is referred to here was mentioned on pages 195–197.

utilities and in contract construction, first as deviations from trend and then as deviations from trend in terms of s.

OTHER METHODS OF ESTIMATING CYCLICAL MOVEMENTS

Although the residual method of isolating cyclical movements involves extensive computation, it is the most widely used procedure. Brief mention will be made of three other methods.

Direct analysis. One possibility consists of expressing each month as a percentage of the corresponding month of the preceding year. This operation results in roughly eliminating seasonal variation and secular trend. However, some residual trend will remain, since the percentages will tend to be above 100 if the trend is upward, but below 100 if the trend is downward. Even if the residual trend is eliminated, the resulting "cycles" are somewhat different from the sort of fluctuations previously discussed; the percentages represent cyclical changes rather than the cyclical level. Thus, a year (or other) period may be high, not because it was at a high level, but because the preceding year was especially low. This method has the advantage of paralleling the business man's often expressed comparison of a given month with the same month a year ago.

A variation of the direct method expresses each month as a percentage of the average for the corresponding month for several previous years. The number of years to consider depends upon the length of the cycles in the series, the average length of the cycles often being used. This involves a decision concerning the length of the individual cycles, before the cyclical movements have been obtained. Furthermore, it is rare that cycles in economic series are uniform in duration (or amplitude), so that rather serious distortion of the data may still result.

Harmonic analysis. When the cyclical movements of a series are of about the same duration and amplitude, a sine-cosine or similar type of curve, having regular undulatory movements, may be fitted. Such a curve may be fitted to the cyclical-irregular data or to the data after the irregular movements have been smoothed. Since series having cyclical movements of fairly regular periodicity and amplitude are rare in the social sciences and in business, we shall not discuss the fitting of a harmonic series in this volume.[5]

Reference-cycle analysis. When several time series are being studied, it would, of course, be possible to compare the cyclical movements of each series with the cyclical movements of every other series under consideration. A procedure, involving "reference dates," has been designed by the National Bureau of Economic Research as a device which

---

[5] The procedure for fitting a sine-cosine curve was described in the first edition of this text, pp. 554–560.

allows one not only to compare each series with a standard set of dates and to observe the behavior of individual series during expansion and contraction of general business, but also to compare the results for the various individual series. The following description is oversimplified, but it should give the reader a general idea of the method.

The first step is the selection of the reference dates, which are the dates of the peaks and troughs of business cycles. To avoid any possible misunderstanding, it may be well to point out that "business cycles" means the cyclical fluctuations in *general* business activity, not the cycles in any one field or area. The reference dates, which are applied to all individual series, were chosen after examination of a large number of economic time series and after study of "the contemporary reports of observers of the business scene."

The next step consists of processing the data of the individual series in order to obtain a cyclical pattern for each series for the period between each two successive reference troughs. Each period is the same for all series, enabling one to compare the results for the various series. The processing of each series proceeds as follows:

(1) The data are adjusted for seasonal variation.

(2) The seasonally adjusted data are divided into "reference-cycle segments," these segments corresponding to the intervals between adjacent reference troughs.

(3) For each segment, the monthly values are expressed as percentages of the average of all the values in the segment. These are "reference-cycle relatives." Note that, as a result of this step, all series, no matter what the original unit, are in percentage form. Note also that this step eliminates inter-cycle trend, since the average of the relatives for each cycle is 100; but it does not eliminate intra-cycle trend. The inclusion of intra-cycle trend is regarded as desirable, since it "helps to reveal and to explain what happens during business cycles."

(4) Each reference-cycle segment is now broken into nine stages, to correspond to the same nine stages in the business cycle, and the reference-cycle relatives are averaged for each of the nine stages. The nine stages are identified as:

    I. The three months centered on the initial trough.
    II. The first third of the expansion period.
    III. The second third of the expansion period.
    IV. The last third of the expansion period.
    V. The three months centered on the peak.
    VI. The first third of the contraction period.
    VII. The second third of the contraction period.
    VIII. The last third of the contraction period.
    IX. The three months centered on the terminal trough.

The nine stage averages for each reference-cycle segment serve to reduce the erratic movements in a series and give a reference-cycle pattern for the particular series under consideration.

The National Bureau of Economic Research also makes use of specific-cycle analysis. This differs from the procedure already described in that the turning points, the stages, and the pattern are determined from each individual series, itself. We shall not give any further attention to specific-cycle analysis in this text, except to point out that charts may be prepared for a particular series, showing both specific cycles and reference cycles in order that the two may be compared. The cycles may also be compared by other means, including the computation of "leads" and "lags" and an "index of conformity."

CHAPTER 17

Fundamentals in Index Number Construction

MEANING AND USES OF INDEX NUMBERS

Index numbers are devices for measuring differences in the magnitude of a group of related variables. These differences may have to do with the price of commodities, the physical quantity of goods produced, marketed, or consumed, or such concepts as "intelligence," "beauty," or "efficiency." The comparisons may be between periods of time; between places; between like categories, such as persons, schools, or objects. Thus, we may have index numbers comparing the cost of living at different times or in different countries or localities, the physical volume of production in different years, or the efficiency of different school systems. A few uses to which index numbers are put are described below.

(1) Perhaps the best-known type of index is that of the change in price level over a period of time. Such indexes have been in use longer and currently are the most numerous. One use of price index numbers, with which the reader is already familiar, is that of *deflating* a value series in order to convert it into physical terms. Referring back to Table 11.1, we find that weekly wages were reduced to weekly real wages by dividing by the Consumer Price Index. Similarly, we might wish to convert a time series representing value of construction contracts awarded to a physical basis by deflating with an index of construction costs.

Price movements may be studied in order to discover their cause, or their effect on the economic community. In order to study such economic relationships, it is customary to compare changes in the price level with changes in other series, such as gold, bank reserves, bank deposits, bank debits, and the physical volume of production. Studies of this nature may involve, not only the average change in price relatives, but also: (a) dispersion of price relatives; (b) shape of frequency distributions of price relatives; (c) alterations in the relative positions of such percentages (displacement of prices); (d) changes in price with changes in quantity offered for sale; (e) changes in volume of purchases or production with changes in price (elasticity of demand or supply); (f) frequency with which different prices change; (g) magnitude of price changes with changes in demand.

Changes in the price level may be measured in order to control them. Thus, the increase in official price of gold in 1933–1934 was in part an attempt to raise the general price level. If index numbers showed the price level to be higher after the price of gold was raised, this result might be taken as an indication that the gold policy was effective.

Occasionally, governmental influence is exercised not to raise, lower, or stabilize the price level, but to raise one group of prices relative to another. Thus, the United States Government has considered various devices, and tried some, to raise agricultural prices to an official "parity" with industrial prices. A *parity index* is described in Chapter 18.

In increasing numbers since World War II, collective-bargaining agreements have been made which provide automatic wage adjustments resulting from changes in consumer price index numbers. A few business contracts also have been effected to make similar adjustments, based upon wholesale price indexes. Such adjustments are generally referred to as "escalator (or escalation) clauses." These agreements or contracts ordinarily contain two sections: one specifies the index to be used, usually one made by the United States Bureau of Labor Statistics; the other defines the base amount which is to be multiplied by the percentage changes in the index. In most wage contracts having escalator clauses, provision is made that any downward adjustment shall not be below the original base amount. The Bureau of Labor Statistics has estimated that there are over 3,500,000 workers who are covered by contracts containing escalator clauses tied to the Consumer Price Index issued by that Bureau. Illustrations of average price comparisons between different regions are not common. It is very difficult to make such comparisons, since the relative importance of goods produced and/or consumed in the different places varies so widely. One interesting illustration of such an index is the "cost of living of United Nations Personnel" for 45 cities throughout the world. In this index, New York City = 100. However, the index relates to United Nations personnel only and does not relate to the cost of living of the general population.

(2) Several organizations compile indexes comparing physical changes over a period of time. These relate to the physical volume of trade, industrial production, factory production, sales, stocks of goods, imports and exports, and so forth. We have already used such indexes in our analysis of time series. They are extremely useful for the historical study of secular trends, seasonal variations, and business cycles, and are indispensable for persons who wish to keep abreast of current business conditions.

(3) Forecasting indexes are compiled by most forecasting organiza-

tions.   Although many of the indexes seem sound in theory, and in practice when applied to periods before they were actually used, unfortunately most of them do not work when put to current use.   Some statistical aspects of forecasting are discussed in Chapter 22.

(4) Other varieties of indexes are diverse in nature and few in number. As an illustration of one type, an index of "crime potential" was constructed in 1966 by Ohio State University criminologists, led by Dr. Walter C. Reckless, who used a simple 24 question test.[1]

PROBLEMS IN THE CONSTRUCTION OF INDEX NUMBERS

Among the problems which the statistician encounters in index-number construction are:

(1) Definition of the purpose for which the index is being compiled.
(2) Selection of series for inclusion in index.
(3) Selection of sources of data.
(4) Collection of data.
(5) Selection of base.
(6) Method of combining data.
(7) System of weighting.

Before gathering data and making calculations, it is important to know what we are trying to measure, and also how we intend to use our measures.   An index number properly designed for the purpose in hand is a most useful and powerful tool; if not properly compiled and constructed, it can be a dangerous one.   If we wish to know changes in the cost of constructing private dwellings, we should not gather prices of heavy structural steel.   Similarly, if we wish to measure the changes in family clothing costs, we should not gather prices of cotton by the bale.   To measure the course of retail trade, we should use a sample of department store sales, and not data from jobbers and wholesalers.

When attempting to measure the well-being of the consumer, by converting his money income into "real" income—that is, by deflating (see Table 11.1)—it obviously would be a mistake to use a wholesale price series as a deflator.   Also, if we wish to measure the output of goods available to the consumer, we would not use an index of industrial production, but rather attempt to compile an index from various consumer goods industries.

Not all of the seven problems listed above are of equal importance, nor are they always independent of one another.   Thus, a simple system of weighting would require a different, and usually larger, list of commodities

---

[1] United Press "An Index on Crime Potential," *Pacific Stars and Stripes*, April 8, 1966, p. 10.

for a price index than would a method that employs a separate weighting system for each subgroup of an index. Likewise, as will be explained later, the weighting system to use depends in part upon the method of combining the data. It is convenient to include both the method and the system of weighting in one formula, and to discuss both points in the same section. Likewise, problems 2 and 3, noted above, should be considered together. A more complete understanding of these points may result if the behavior of price relatives is considered first.

AN ILLUSTRATION OF THE BEHAVIOR OF PRICE RELATIVES

The United States Bureau of Labor Statistics at the present time compiles an index of wholesale prices consisting of approximately 2,200 separate commodities or series. This index is described in the following chapter. The Bureau also publishes wholesale price indexes for a number of groups and subgroups and price relatives for individual commodities.

The indexes for all commodities combined and for the three major subgroups are shown in Chart 17.1. To facilitate comparison, the four

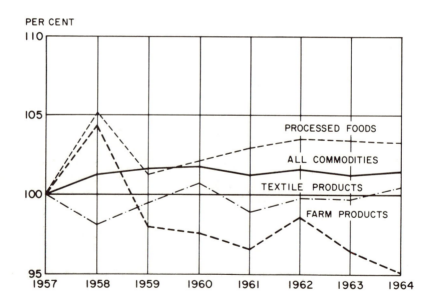

Chart 17.1. United States Bureau of Labor Statistics Index Number of Wholesale Prices of All Commodities, Farm Products, Processed Foods, and Commodities Other Than Farm Products and Processed Foods, 1947–1953. The figures have been converted from 1947–1949 = 100 to 1947 = 100 in order that the behavior of the four series may be compared more readily. Data from U. S. Department of Commerce, Office of Business Economics, *Business Statistics*, 1953, p. 27, and *Survey of Current Business*, February 1954, outside back cover page.

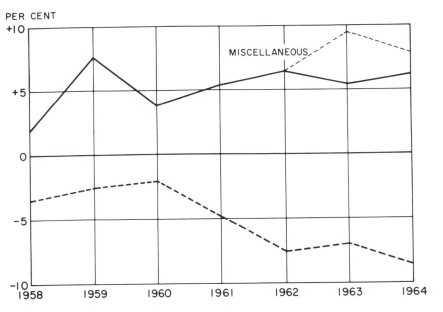

PER CENT

Chart 17.2. Maximum Deviations from the United States Bureau of Labor Statistics Wholesale Price Index Number for "All Commodities Other than Farm Products and Processed Foods." Shown by the 13 Subgroups Comprising that Index, 1958–1964. Deviations represent the difference between the most divergent sub-groups and the "Other Commodities" index number for each year; for example, in 1962 the figures were 107.4 − 100.8 = +6.6 and 93.3 − 100.8 = −7.5. The light broken line follows the deviations shown for 1962 and 1963 for Miscellaneous Products which departed markedly from the next highest sub-group (shown by solid line) for those years. Data from *Statistical Abstract of the United States*, 1964, pp. 352–353, and *Survey of Current Business*, June 1965, p. S-8.

indexes are shown with 1957 = 100 instead of in relation to the published base, 1957–1959 = 100. This is accomplished by dividing each index by its value for 1957. One other major subgroup, "all commodities other than farm products and processed foods," is analyzed in Chart 17.2, which shows the range of the most divergent of the 13 subgroups of this major group.

In Chart 17.2, the deviations from the group index are plotted to show the range, in any one year, for that subgroup which registered the largest number of percentage points above the group index and for that subgroup falling furthest below the group index. In 1963 and 1964 the price index for miscellaneous products rose so far above the other subgroups that it is shown by means of a light broken line; the points on the solid curve for 1963 and 1964 represent the next-to-the-highest subgroup.

Of special interest in Chart 17.2 is the fact that the further we go from the base period, the greater the tendency for subgroup prices to diverge from the group index. However, should the group index turn down and approach 100, it is quite likely that the subgroup indexes will draw closer together again.

Another point often stated, but not borne out by the data covering the limited period here studied, is that when the price trend is upward, the distribution of the price relatives of the component series of an index is also positively skewed. Many persons are of the opinion that this is an inherent characteristic of frequency distributions of price relatives, since prices can increase indefinitely, but can decline only to zero.[2] On the other hand, it may be suggested that prices and price relatives are dominated more by the laws of economics than by those of mathematics. The limits of price advances or price declines are certainly influenced by the willingness of persons to buy and to sell at different prices. However, the direction of price change probably has some effect upon the direction of the skewness of the components of an index.

DATA FOR INDEX NUMBERS

Although the method of combining the variables is of considerable importance in constructing index numbers, it is insignificant when compared with the problem of selecting the data that are the raw materials of the index. Too much emphasis cannot be put upon this point. The data must be accurate and homogeneous, and the sample representative. A sample cannot be expected to be representative unless an adequate number of items is included. To state the idea in other language: a sufficiently large sample of relevant items must be selected to obtain reliable index numbers.

As noted before, the commodities to be chosen for a price index, and the type of quotation to be selected, depend on what is being measured. A wholesale price index requires wholesale prices. An index of prices paid by consumers necessitates not only retail prices of food, but rents,

---

[2] This is not literally true, as can be seen from the following examples: (1) United States Treasury bills, usually 90-day paper, are ordinarily sold to banks and other investors at a discount—that is, they are sold for less than face value and redeemed three months later at face value. The difference measures the yield to the investor, or the price to the Treasury. One year the Treasury sold 12 series of bills for more than face value, in effect paying a negative price. The bill buyers, getting a negative yield, paid a slight premium for the privilege of holding the bills. (2) In another year a metal goods manufacturer in New York City was able to sell magnesium shavings and other magnesium scrap to dealers. Later in the same year, he was unable to dispose of it by sale and had to have it carted away. Thus, the positive price which he had received for the scrap early in the year became a negative, or below-zero, price later in the year.

gas and electric rates, clothing prices, transportation, medical care, and so forth, applying to the class of persons for whom the cost of living is to be ascertained. An index of the changing cost of constructing frame houses in Atlanta, Georgia, should include those materials and items of labor that are used in frame houses built in Atlanta. The prices should be the Atlanta prices of those materials and the wages should be the wages in Atlanta of the kind of labor used. These examples indicate one reason why it is important to bear in mind at all times the purpose for which the index is being compiled. The purpose of the index and just what it seeks to measure will also influence the selection of the base, the weights used, and the formula employed.

When selecting the sources of data for index numbers, we may rely on regularly published quotations or obtain periodic special reports from the merchants, producers, exporters, or others who possess the basic information needed. Under either circumstance, we must make sure that the data pertain strictly to the thing being measured. Thus, if retail food price changes are being measured, quotations should be from supermarkets, chain stores, independent stores, and any other important outlets. These different sources should not be mixed indiscriminately, but should be appropriately weighted when combined. Neither should first-of-the-month quotations, middle-of-the-month quotations, and end-of-the-month quotations ordinarily be combined in one index.

The discussion immediately following is in part an application of principles discussed in earlier chapters of this book, especially Chapter 2. The great importance of the proper choice of data for index numbers justifies a bringing together of these principles, even though some duplication is involved.

Accuracy. Some statistical data that appear in precise printed form cannot be depended upon. If the person or company reporting the data uses the data for operational or tax purposes, they are likely to be accurate; but if the data are merely statistical reports furnished to an outside agency, they may be compiled originally by careless and indifferent clerks whose sole interest is in filling the form with ink marks as quickly as possible. It therefore behooves the statistician to ascertain how the data are collected, and to select his source with discrimination.

Comparability. Standard grades of the same commodity are, of course, comparable between different dates; however, a 1914 automobile cannot be compared with a present-day automobile. Nor could the price of a "standard" automobile be computed for different years, since in not more than one year could such a standard automobile ordinarily be found. In the case of highly manufactured goods, which are further developed over the years, the upward bias of price quotations is greatest; but it is present, also, in the case even of some agricultural commodities, since their production, also, involves more processing in later than in earlier years. It is likely, therefore, that most price index numbers have an upward bias.

A similar problem arises when one article passes out of wide use and its place is taken by a different commodity serving somewhat the same purpose. For instance, the stagecoach of 100 years ago has been superseded by the streamlined air-conditioned train, the pressurized plane, and the de luxe bus. If we should find that the fare from Washington, D. C., to Philadelphia were the same in the two periods, we should not conclude that the cost of the same service had remained the same, because the service, too, has changed. Less time is required to make the trip and it is now made in much greater comfort.

Representativeness. Since index numbers are usually obtained from samples, we must try to obtain a sample that behaves like the population from which it is drawn. Probably the most satisfactory way of accomplishing this is to divide the original data into groups and subgroups and to draw a representative sample from each of these. Stratification into groups and subgroups is employed because the various groups and subgroups of commodities, affected by different economic factors, may be expected to display patterns of behavior which are distinctive to each group and also different from other groups and from the over-all index. For example, if an index of wholesale prices is being made, we should expect price (or quantity) movements of foods to be different from those of building materials. One reason for this is that the demand for food products is inelastic, while that for building materials (which are durable goods, the purchase of which can be postponed) is elastic. Furthermore, the supply of foods, over short periods of time, is dependent to a considerable extent on the weather, while the supply of building materials is subject to conscious control of the fabricators.

In choosing the commodities from a group, it is desirable to pick ones which tend to conform most closely to the central tendency of the group, if that central tendency can be determined. Having selected commodities that are reasonably representative of the group from which they were picked, it is desirable to ascertain whether proportionate representation has been obtained for each group. If, upon the basis of dollar value, the sample for one group (or groups) constitutes too small or too large a proportion of the entire group, commodities may be added to or dropped from the group sample. When such an adjustment is not feasible (for example, if the group were "structural steel" and the sample constituted 100 per cent of the group), an alternative consists of applying appropriate weights.

A further test of the representativeness of the sample can sometimes be employed: Do the value changes of the sample coincide with those of the population? This test should be applied not only to the whole sample, but to the various groups and subgroups into which it is divided.[3]

Adequacy. In Chapter 24 it will be shown that the reliability of the arithmetic mean of a random sample is directly related to the square root of the *number* of items included. Furthermore, in a finite population, the larger the *proportion* of items included in the sample (see Appendix S, section 24.2), the more reliable is the mean of the sample. The absolute number of items to use cannot be stated in precise and fixed terms. As just noted, commodities (items) are ordinarily selected from the various component groups, so that the sample is a stratified one rather than a random one. Furthermore, in selecting the items from the groups, the more important items are ordinarily chosen first, after which as many suitable items are included as resources will permit. Thus, the items are not taken at random within each stratum. As a result of these two situations, ordinary reliability formulas are not applicable.

For the index-number illustrations used in the remainder of this chapter, five citrus fruits have been selected: Florida grapefruit, California lemons, and three categories of oranges. The prices for all five fruits are the auction prices per box on the principal markets. The use of these figures involves some artificality, because the total production was used, including not only "production having value," but also fruit consumed on the farm, donated to charity, or unharvested or not utilized on account of economic conditions, as well as fruit used for juice, concentrates, and so on. For this reason, the various indexes computed in the following pages of this chapter must be considered merely as illustrations of the behavior of the various formulas and weighting schemes which are discussed.

The season for each fruit begins with the bloom of one year and ends with the completion of the harvest the following year. As explained below Table 17.7, "1959" indicates the crop year 1958–1959, and similarly for other years. The fruits used for the calculations which follow, their seasons, and the weight per box are:

Fruit	Season	Net contents per box
Grapefruit, Florida	Sept. 1 to July 31	80 pounds
Lemons, California	Nov. 1 to Oct. 31	76 pounds
Oranges, Florida	Oct. 1 to July 31	90 pounds
Oranges, California, both varieties	Oct. 1 to Dec. 31 of following year	75 pounds

---

[3] This test is similar to Irving Fisher's "total value criterion," which states that the price index multiplied by the quantity index should equal the ratio of change of the total value of the population.

SELECTION OF BASE

Regardless of the formula employed for weighting and combining the data, it is customary (although not necessary) to select some period of time as 100 per cent with which to compare the other index numbers. A month is ordinarily too short a period to use as base period, since any one month is likely to be unusual on account of accidental or seasonal influences. A year is sometimes used. However, it is often true that no one year is sufficiently "normal" to be a good basis of comparison. Business and prices are always advancing or receding with the business cycle. Though not so specific, an average of several years is usually a better base. The period 1910 through 1914 has sometimes been used as a price base, particularly for agricultural products. In the past four decades, the statistical agencies of the United States Government have successively shifted to several other bases: for example, 1926, 1935–1939, 1947–1949, 1957–1959, and special-purpose ones, such as September 1, 1939 and June 1950. A useful solution is to employ the period of years that is used by some of the other indexes with which the one being constructed is likely to be employed.

Although a particular base may be satisfactory for a number of years, that base becomes less meaningful as time passes, and it eventually becomes desirable to shift to a more recent period. Among the reasons are: (1) the dispersion of price relatives may become so great that no average is reliable; (2) because of permanent currency depreciation, growth of population, technological developments, and other reasons, new and higher levels may have been attained by income, prices, production, and consumption; (3) the pattern of consumption may change to such an extent that no aggregate of commodities can be found which includes the major expenditures common to both periods; (4) the quality of many commodities, nominally the same, changes progressively with time. An indirect basis of comparison may be had by utilizing a chain index system, which involves, essentially, the comparison of each year (or sub-period thereof) with the preceding year. This method, which is not completely satisfactory, is explained in the following chapter.

AGGREGATIVE PRICE INDEX NUMBERS

There are two methods of constructing index numbers: (1) by computing aggregate values; (2) by averaging relatives. By the first method, as will be explained in this section, the prices or quantities are made comparable, are automatically weighted by being reduced to dollar values, and then are combined into aggregate values. In the following section the method of averaging relatives will be explained. There it will be shown that the two methods are, under certain conditions, merely alternative methods of obtaining the same result. The aggregative method obtains the result directly, and produces a result that has a simple and clear meaning; the method employing relatives is more roundabout, and its meaning is more technical. Nevertheless, there are situations in which the aggregative method is not applicable, and recourse must then be had to the averaging of relatives.

Simple aggregates. Table 17.1 illustrates the construction of a simple aggregative price index. The prices of each commodity in any given year are merely added together to give the index number for that year. It is then frequently convenient to designate some year as a base, which is set equal to 100. In this illustration all of the index numbers are expressed in the final row as a percentage of the 1959 number, found by dividing each one of the numbers by the value in the base period ($32.85) and multiplying by 100.

It must be apparent that the influence which a commodity exerts on a simple aggregative index depends on the price per unit of quotation. In this instance, the predominant item varies from year to year; in none of the years, however, is grapefruit predominant. The weighting of an aggregative index by one commercial unit of each commodity represented is illogical in that it neglects to consider the actual importance of the different commodities; it is haphazard in that the relative influence of the different commodities is determined by factors quite irrelevant to the purpose of the price index. The problem would in no sense be solved if all commodities were reduced to a price per pound, for some commodities, such as diamonds, are very costly per pound and yet are not very important in our economic life, while coal, which is of tremendous importance, is relatively cheap per pound. Furthermore, some goods, such as electric power or human labor, cannot be reduced to a pound basis. Still another solution is to take as the unit of quotation the amount that can be purchased for one dollar in the base year. But this is scarcely more logical, since it would be very unusual if the same amount of money were spent on each commodity in every year.

Before consideration of the construction of weighted aggregative index numbers, it may be helpful to state symbolically the method we have just used. The formula is

$$P = \frac{\Sigma p_n}{\Sigma p_o},$$

where P means price index; p refers to the price of an individual commodity, the subscript o refers to the base period, from which price changes are measured, and the subscript n refers to the given period which is being compared with the base. Now if the formula for a particular year (say 1964, with 1959 being the base) is to be stated, it could be written

$$P_{59,64} = \frac{\Sigma p_{64}}{\Sigma p_{59}}.$$

Weighted aggregates. In order to allow each commodity to have a reasonable influence on the index, it is advisable to use a deliberately weighted rather than a simple aggregate of prices, which, as we have seen, involves concealed weighting. To construct a weighted aggregative index, a list of definite quantities of specified commodities is taken, and calculations are made to determine what this aggregate of goods is worth each year at current prices. Obviously the process is merely that of multiplying each unit price by the number of units and summing the resulting values for each period. The procedure, using the quantities produced in 1959 as multipliers, is illustrated in Table 17.2. The reader, having followed the reasoning to this point, will realize now that *aggregative index numbers of price measure the changing value of a fixed aggregate of goods*. Since the total cost or value changes while the components of the aggregate do not, these changes must be due to price changes. It appears

TABLE 17.1

Construction of Simple Aggregative Index Numbers of Citrus Fruit Prices 1959–1964*

(Prices are per box.)

Fruit	1959	1960	1961	1962	1963	1964
Grapefruit, Florida...................	$4.41	$ 4.32	$ 4.49	$ 5.88	$ 6.09	$ 5.94
Lemons, California..................	7.10	7.22	7.18	8.56	7.28	8.38
Oranges, California, navel.............	7.66	9.24	10.26	9.22	7.72	7.20
Oranges, California, Valencia.........	8.36	7.48	7.94	7.62	9.34	6.68
Oranges, Florida....................	5.32	6.48	5.09	7.73	7.78	6.18
Aggregate.......................	$32.85	$34.74	$34.96	$39.01	$38.21	$34.38
Index number (per cent of 1959).....	100.0	105.8	106.4	118.8	116.3	104.7

* The crop year 1958–1959 is designated 1959, and similarly for other years, since most harvesting and consequently the marketing occurs in the later year.

Data from U. S. Department of Agriculture, *Agricultural Statistics, 1964*, p. 171, and *1965*, p. 172, and from correspondence with U. S. Department of Agriculture.

TABLE 17.2

Construction of Aggregative Index Numbers of Citrus Fruit Prices, 1959–1964, Weighted by Production in 1959*

(Quantities in thousands of boxes; values in thousands of dollars.)

Fruit	1959 production	Value of 1959 quantity at price of specified year					
		1959	1960	1961	1962	1963	1964
Grapefruit, Florida...........	30,500	134,505	131,760	136,945	179,340	185,745	181,170
Lemons, California...........	17,100	121,410	123,462	122,778	146,376	124,488	143,298
Oranges, California, navel.....	13,500	103,410	124,740	138,510	124,470	104,220	97,200
Oranges, California, Valencia..	17,300	144,628	129,404	137,362	131,826	161,582	115,564
Oranges, Florida.............	91,500	486,780	592,920	465,735	707,295	711,870	565,470
Aggregate value...........	...	990,733	1,102,286	1,001,330	1,289,307	1,287,905	1,102,720
Index number (per cent of 1959).................	...	100.0	111.3	101.1	130.1	130.0	111.3

* See note to Table 17.1 concerning crop years.

Based on price data in Table 17.1 and production data from various issues of *Agricultural Statistics* and U. S. Department of Agriculture, Crop Reporting Board, *Annual Crop Summary*, December 1965, p. 97.

that this type of index number measures the very thing sought if we wish to determine changes in the cost of living, that is, the cost of a fixed "market basket" of goods and services. The general formula for the aggregative price index is

$$P = \frac{\Sigma p_n q}{\Sigma p_o q}.$$

The symbols are those used earlier, but a new one has been added: q refers to the quantity of the commodity produced, marketed, or consumed (that is, the quantity weight, or multiplier). Since the index numbers constructed in Table 17.2 were weighted by base-year quantities, we may write the formula more specifically

$$P = \frac{\Sigma p_n q_o}{\Sigma p_o q_o}.$$

Comparing Tables 17.1 and 17.2, it will be seen that, in the simple aggregative index, the importance of particular items varied from year to year because their prices varied from year to year; but, when base-year quantity weights were introduced, Florida oranges became most important.

Selection of weights. Although in the preceding illustration 1959 quantities were used as weights, this simple procedure is but one of several possible systems. It would have been just as easy to have taken, say, 1964 quantities as weights. If the quantity of each commodity marketed changed from year to year in the same proportion, it would make no difference to what period the weights referred, for the results would be identical. In fact, however, the relative importance of the different commodities is constantly changing, and this is due in part to the change in the relative prices of the different commodities, which in turn result from changes in supply and demand. Therein lies a great source of difficulty for which there is no completely satisfactory solution. The answer depends in part on what the analyst thinks a price index is supposed to do.

One view is that such an index number measures the changing cost of a constant aggregate of goods. Another view concerns itself not with the goods level of analysis, but with the satisfactions level; an index number, according to this view, should measure the changing cost of goods yielding the same utility or satisfaction at two periods, or two places. Thus, suppose we compare the cost of living of two groups of similar persons at two periods (or places), these groups having at the two periods (or places) the same tastes and capacity for enjoyment, as well as an income that will purchase, and does purchase, the same amount of satisfaction. The commodities, of course, will be different, but if the expenditures were $6,000 the first year and $6,600 the second year, we may conclude that the cost of living has gone up 10 per cent. It goes without saying that no one has accurately made a measurement of this kind. Although it seems feasible to measure only the varying value of a fixed aggregate of goods, yet the analyst should select a list of goods that will avoid the certainty of bias in a known direction with respect to the cost of obtaining equal satisfactions at different times. The following suggestions have been made for solving this knotty problem.

1. *Use base-period quantities as weights.* This is the method we have used for illustrative purposes in Table 17.2. However, even if there has been no change in the tastes or environment of purchasers between the two periods, purchases of those commodities that have increased relatively in price will decline relatively, and purchases of commodities that have decreased relatively in price will increase relatively. It is entirely possible that this type of index might record an increase in the price level, whereas by increasing the relative amounts purchased of commodities that decline in price, the same amount of satisfaction might actually be bought by a given individual at a lower total cost. This type of index, then, has in a sense an upward bias. It might be said that this index marks an upper limit to the price change. This method is sometimes known as *Laspeyres' method,* and, as previously stated, can be defined symbolically,

$$P = \frac{\Sigma p_n q_o}{\Sigma p_o q_o}.$$

2. *Use given-period quantities.* That is, use the weights that pertain to the year which is to be compared with the base period. This method involves the selection of a new set of weights each year, or even more often. But frequently it is impossible to obtain current quantity weights, and, even if they are available, the labor of computation is approximately doubled. Furthermore, although each period is thereby directly comparable with the base year, the comparison of the different years among themselves is not valid, for the reason that the aggregate of goods differs each year.

If we think of 1966 as being the base period for an index of consumers' prices, the base-year weighting system answers the question: If it cost me $500 a month to live in 1966, how much would it cost me this year to live the way I did that year? The given-year weighting system answers a different question: If I could have supported my *present* scale of living in 1966 with $500 per month, how much must I spend this year? A theoretical objection to asking such a question is that undue weight is given to the commodities that have declined in price. It is the relative decline in price that may be responsible for their increased purchase, and, although it is price change which we are trying to measure, yet our weighting is partly determined by relative price changes. Thus this method may be said to have a downward bias, and marks the lower limit of price change. It is sometimes known as *Paasche's method* and has the following formula:

$$P = \frac{\Sigma p_n q_n}{\Sigma p_o q_n}.$$

3. *Use the average (or total) quantities of base and given years.* This is a compromise solution, although it is one which has no general bias in any known direction. But again, as in method 2, we have shifting weights and a resulting lack of comparability among the different years. The method was proposed independently by the English economists Marshall and Edgeworth, and the formula

$$P = \frac{\Sigma p_n (q_o + q_n)}{\Sigma p_o (q_o + q_n)}$$

is sometimes called the *Marshall-Edgeworth formula.*

4. *Average together the quantities for all the years which the index numbers include.* Though perhaps an excellent solution for a historical study, this plan is impracticable if the index is to be kept up to date, since it means current revision of weights and continuous recomputation of the complete set of index numbers.

5. *Average together the quantities of several years which are thought to be typical.* This again is a compromise solution, but it is practical and is very frequently adopted. The list of quantities used will, however, eventually become obsolete. When that is the case, a new index can be constructed and spliced to the old one. Methods for so doing will be considered in the following chapter. The construction of an index number of 1964 citrus fruit prices, using as weights the average quantities for 1959, 1960, and 1961, is illustrated in Table 17.3. The index number varies only 1.2 percentage points from that employing base-year weights. The formula for this particular index number may be written

$$P = \frac{\Sigma p_{64} q_{59-61}}{\Sigma p_{59} q_{59-61}}.$$

Of course, the results are the same whether average-quantity or total-quantity weights are used.

6. *Determine the highest common factor.* The weights are the quantities of each commodity common to each year, either to the base and the given year, or to all the years under comparison. In the latter case, this would mean that, for any commodity, the smallest amount marketed in any of the years under comparison would be taken. Usually, then, the quan-

tities of the different commodities taken would not each be for the same year. This ingenious device has been suggested by J. M. Keynes to avoid the sort of bias inherent in methods 1 and 2, already described. Its virtue is its modesty: the device avoids trying that which cannot be done perfectly. However, if the values of quantities that are common to the different periods are small compared with total expenditures, or if they constitute in different periods a varying proportion of the total, or if the satisfaction derived from this aggregate of goods varies, the method is no more accurate and, quite likely, is less accurate than method 5.

TABLE 17.3

Construction of 1964 Aggregative Index Number of Citrus Fruit Prices, Weighted by Production* in 1959, 1960, and 1961

(Production in thousands of boxes, values in thousands of dollars.)

Fruit	Production			Total production 1959–1961	Average production 1959–1961	Price per box		Value of 1959–1961 average production at price in	
	1959	1960	1961			1959	1964	1959	1964
Grapefruit, Florida...........	30,500	31,600	35,000	97,100	32,370	4.41	5.94	142,752	192,278
Lemons, California...........	17,100	13,600	15,200	45,900	15,300	7.10	8.38	108,630	128,214
Oranges, California, navel......	13,500	9,000	7,600	30,100	10,030	7.66	7.20	76,830	72,216
Oranges, California, Valencia...	17,300	16,000	13,100	46,400	15,470	8.36	6.68	129,329	103,340
Oranges, Florida..............	91,500	86,700	113,400	291,600	97,200	5.32	6.18	517,104	600,696
Aggregate value............	...	...	...	...	...	...	...	974,645	1,096,744
Index number (per cent of 1959)...................	...	...	...	...	...	...	...	100.0	112.53

* The index number is the same whether the weights used are total or average production for the three years. See note to Table 17.1 concerning crop years.
Data from sources given below Table 17.1 and Table 17.2.

7. *Make two index numbers, each with a different set of weights, and average the two together, usually geometrically.* The two systems of weighting chosen are ordinarily base- and given-year weights. The formula then becomes

$$P = \sqrt{\frac{\Sigma p_n q_o}{\Sigma p_o q_o} \times \frac{\Sigma p_n q_n}{\Sigma p_o q_n}}.$$

It is frequently called Fisher's "ideal" index number, because it conforms to certain tests of consistent behavior which Irving Fisher considered appropriate.[4] On the other hand, it is difficult to say precisely just what such an index number does measure.

A general criticism of any weighting system which involves the use of a

---

[4] See Irving Fisher, *The Making of Index Numbers*, Houghton Mifflin Company, Boston, 1927, p. 220.

different set of weights for each index number is that, although each index number may validly be compared with that of the base year, logically the index numbers of no other two years (such as 1963 and 1964) can be compared with each other. This criticism applies to given-year weights, to the average of base- and given-year weights, to the highest-common-factor method when the quantities selected are common only to the two years being compared, and to the "ideal" index number. It does not apply to base-year weights, average weights of all years, typical weights, or the highest-common-factor method when the quantities common to all years are used.

Although the theory of weight selection is interesting and involves logical analysis of a high order, it is easy to overestimate its practical importance. Consider the following results obtained from the citrus fruit data:

System of weighting	1964 index number
Simple aggregative	104.7
1959 quantity weights (base-year weights)	111.3
1959–1961 average quantity weights	112.5
1964 quantity weights (given-year weights)	111.2
"Ideal" index number	111.2

In this case there is a very great difference between the simple and the weighted index numbers, but little difference between the systems of weighting. The different weight systems substantially agree because the importance of the weights relative to each other was about the same in the four systems. If, however, both the prices and quantities had varied greatly in their relative magnitude, the different weightings might have given markedly different results. If all prices moved in the same direction and changed at the same ratio, it would make no difference what system of weighting were chosen. But if it so happens that commodities which are changing *greatly* in relative importance during the period are also undergoing price changes materially different from the average, then the matter of weighting becomes important. It is usually of slight importance whether exact weights are used, or only approximate weights. Thus, Table 17.4 is exactly like Table 17.3 except that the quantity weights are rounded to one digit, but the results vary by only 1.17. The explanation is that the rounding did not appreciably change the relative importance of the weights. For all practical purposes, sufficiently accurate results will usually be obtained if exact weights are given to the few more important commodities, and rounded weights to the numerous unimportant commodities.[5]

Although only approximate accuracy is necessary in choosing weights,

---

[5] Irving Fisher recommends that the quantities be rounded to 1, 10, 100 or 1,000.

accuracy in price quotations is, in practice, of much greater importance. This, of course, results from the fact that some prices are apt to show marked changes from year to year, while others change little. This is the same as saying that the ratio of the prices to each other changes from year to year.

Over a number of years, various changes take place: commodities shift considerably in their relative importance; old commodities disappear from use and are succeeded by new commodities; models, styles, or grades of a commodity become obsolete and cease to be manufactured, with new

TABLE 17.4

Construction of 1964 Aggregative Index Number of Citrus Fruit Prices, Weighted by Average Production* in 1959, 1960, and 1961 Rounded to One Digit

(Production in thousands of boxes; values in thousands of dollars.)

Fruit	Average production 1959–1961 rounded	Price per box		Value of 1959–1961 average production at price in	
		1959	1964	1959	1964
Grapefruit, Florida...............	30,000	$4.41	$5.94	132,300	178,200
Lemons, California...............	20,000	7.10	8.38	142,000	167,600
Oranges, California, navel..........	10,000	7.66	7.20	76,600	72,000
Oranges, California, Valencia.......	20,000	8.36	6.68	167,200	133,600
Oranges, Florida.................	100,000	5.32	6.18	532,000	618,000
Aggregate value...............	...	...	...	1,050,100	1,169,400
Index number (per cent of 1959)..	...	...	...	100.0	111.36

* See note to Table 17.1 concerning crop years.
Data from sources given below Tables 17.1 and 17.2.

models, styles, or grades taking their place; marketing centers shift, so that a price quotation at the new center must replace that at the old; f.o.b. price quotations may give way to delivered prices, or vice versa. Under any of these circumstances it may be desirable to express each index number, not as a percentage of the original base, but as a percentage of the preceding period. Such an index might employ any of the formulas given above, utilizing weights pertaining to either or both of the years or months being compared. Frequently these separate percentages are chained back to the original base by a process of successive multiplication. Such an index, known as a *chain* index, will be further described in the following chapter. When substituting one commodity for another, or when changing weights, overlapping data are needed for only a single period, as a direct comparison is made only between the prices (or quantities) of the current period and those of the preceding period.

AVERAGES OF PRICE RELATIVES

Two basic steps are involved in constructing indexes by averaging price relatives.

1. *Convert the actual prices for each series to percentages of the base period.* These percentages are called price relatives, since they are expressed, not in dollars and cents, but as percentages relative to the price in the base period. The upper part of Table 17.5 shows the price relatives for the

TABLE 17.5

Construction of Index Numbers of Citrus Fruit Prices, 1959–1964,* by Use of Simple Arithmetic Mean of Price Relatives

Fruit	1959	1960	1961	1962	1963	1964
Grapefruit, Florida.............	100.0	98.0	101.8	133.3	138.1	134.7
Lemons, California.............	100.0	101.7	101.1	120.6	102.5	118.0
Oranges, California, navel........	100.0	120.6	133.9	120.4	100.8	94.0
Oranges, California, Valencia....	100.0	89.5	95.0	91.1	111.7	79.9
Oranges, Florida..............	100.0	121.8	95.7	145.3	146.2	116.2
Total......................	500.0	531.6	527.5	610.7	599.3	542.8
Average (per cent of 1959)....	100.0	106.3	105.5	122.1	119.9	108.6

* See note to Table 17.1 concerning crop years.
Based on data in Table 17.1

TABLE 17.6

Construction of Index Numbers of Citrus Fruit Prices, 1959–1964,* by Use of Arithmetic Means of Price Relatives Weighted by Base-Year (1959) Values

(Values in thousands of dollars.)

Fruit	1959 value	Price relative of specified year multiplied by 1959 value					
		1959	1960	1961	1962	1963	1964
Grapefruit, Florida..........	134,505	134,505	131,815	136,926	179,295	185,751	181,178
Lemons, California..........	121,410	121,410	123,474	122,746	146,420	124,445	143,264
Oranges, California, navel....	103,410	103,410	124,712	138,466	124,506	104,237	97,205
Oranges, California, Valencia.	144,628	144,628	129,442	137,397	131,756	161,549	115,558
Oranges, Florida...........	486,780	486,780	592,898	465,848	707,291	711,672	565,638
Total.................	...	990,733	1,102,341	1,001,383	1,289,268	1,287,654	1,102,843
Index number (per cent of 1959)...	...	100.0	111.3	101.1	130.1	130.0	111.3

* See note to Table 17.1 concerning crop years.
Based on price relatives in Table 17.5 and 1959 value data in Table 17.2.

five citrus fruits from 1959 through 1964. Each of these series of relatives was computed by dividing the price in the given year by the price in the base year.

2. *Average the price relatives for each year separately,* thus obtaining a series of index numbers. In the lower part of Table 17.5 a simple arithmetic mean of the relatives has been used. The shortcoming of this method is that each relative (irrespective of the importance of the commodity which it represents) influences the index number for a given year according to its percentage of increase or decrease over the base

period.   Chart 17.3 shows the index and the five series of price relatives. From this chart it may be seen that in 1961 and 1963 two relatives declined, while three increased, but the index fell because the two relatives which declined more than offset the three which increased.   The two relatives which declined might have represented minor components of the index; the result would have been the same.   It may be worthwhile to point out that the simple arithmetic mean of price relatives is equivalent to a weighted aggregative index, where the weights are the amount of each commodity purchasable by $1.00 (or any specified amount) in the base year.   This is the same as weighting by the reciprocals of base-year prices.

It is, of course, possible to use averages other than the arithmetic mean, for example, the geometric mean, the median, or the harmonic mean, and some attention will be given to this topic later.   More important, however, is the application of weights to the relatives.   These weights should be *value* weights, in contrast to the *quantity* weights used with the aggregative method.   The reason for this will be apparent shortly.   Table 17.6 shows the computation of an index of citrus fruit prices with the relatives of Table 17.5 weighted by the value of each fruit in the base year, 1959.   As is apparent from the table, the procedure consists of: (1) multiplying the relatives by their weights, (2) summing these products year by year, and (3) dividing these totals for each year by the sum of the weights.   The results are the same as those obtained for the aggregative

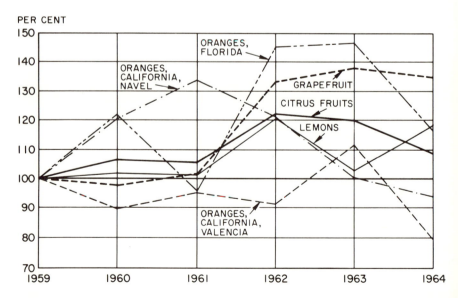

Chart 17.3.   Simple Arithmetic Average Index Number of Citrus Fruit Prices and Price Relatives of Each of the Five Fruits, 1959–1964.   1959 = 100. Data from Table 17.5.

index with base-year-quantity weights (Table 17.2) even though the numbers were rounded. That this should be so can be demonstrated simply. Let us first take a single commodity, Florida oranges, and show that (A) the base-year (1959) value weight applied to the given-year (1964) relative produces the same result as (B) the base-year (1959) quantity times the given-year (1964) price. That is:

(A)...The price relative for 1964 is $6.18 ÷ $5.32
          = 1.1617, or 116.17 per cent;
      the base-year value times the 1964 price
          relative is.......... $486,780,000 × 1.1617 = $565,492,326.
(B)...The base-year quantity times the given-
      year price is........... 91,500,000 × $6.18 = $565,470,000.

(Table 17.6 shows $565,638,000 for Florida oranges for 1964 because the 1964 relative was taken as 116.2.)

This relationship is true, not only for each individual commodity, but for groups of commodities[6] as well. In symbols:

$$\frac{\Sigma \dfrac{p_n}{p_o} p_o q_o}{\Sigma p_o q_o} = \frac{\Sigma p_n q_o}{\Sigma p_o q_o}.$$

---

[6] More generally, the following relationships may be stated with regard to price index numbers:

(1) An arithmetic average of relatives weighted by base-year values ($p_o q_o$) is the equivalent of an aggregative index weighted with base-year quantities.

(2) Similarly, an arithmetic average of relatives weighted by the product of base-year prices and given-year quantities ($p_o q_n$) is the equivalent of an aggregative index weighted with given-year quantities.

(3) A harmonic average of relatives weighted by given-year values ($p_n q_n$) is the equivalent of an aggregative index weighted with given-year quantities. Thus,

$$1 \div \frac{\Sigma \left(\dfrac{1}{p_n \div p_o} p_n q_n\right)}{\Sigma p_n q_n} = 1 \div \frac{\Sigma \left(\dfrac{p_o}{p_n} p_n q_n\right)}{\Sigma p_n q_n},$$

$$= \frac{\Sigma p_n q_n}{\Sigma \left(\dfrac{p_o}{p_n} p_n q_n\right)} = \frac{\Sigma p_n q_n}{\Sigma p_o q_n}.$$

(4) Similarly, it may be shown that a harmonic average of relatives weighted by the product of base-year quantities and given-year prices ($p_n q_o$) is the equivalent of an aggregative index weighted with base-year quantities.

These generalizations may be stated in the form of guides to the construction of index numbers, when the index numbers are to be constructed from relatives:

(a) If it is desired to use the arithmetic average of relatives, the value weights should be the products of the base prices and whatever quantities are desired.

(b) If it is desired to use an average of relatives employing value weights that are the product of given-year prices and quantities of some period, the harmonic average should be used.

Under no circumstances should the arithmetic average of relatives be used with values involving given-year prices, since this gives extra weight to a commodity merely because it has gone up in price. Such a procedure results in an upward bias.

Evidently the method of weighted average of relatives with base-year-value weights is usually a roundabout method of doing what may more easily be accomplished by direct means using aggregates with base-year-quantity weights. Furthermore, the meaning of an aggregative index seems clearer to most persons than does an average of relatives. Why, then, should not the aggregative method always be used? One reason is that the price relatives themselves are occasionally worth studying, not only because an individual series may hold special significance for the reader, but because a study of groups of relatives may assist in selecting a sample or determining what group indexes to make. In connection with frequency distributions, it was observed that an average never gives a complete picture of any situation. Other measures may be worth making. Another reason is that the series to be combined can sometimes be obtained only in the form of relatives, or, they may have meaning only as relatives because, as in the case of quantity indexes, a series may consist of several subseries expressed in different physical units. The use of relatives is more common in the construction of quantity indexes (to be discussed later) than in the making of price indexes, since the components of quantity indexes are themselves often indexes or relatives.

Commodity weights versus group weights. The same practical advice may be offered concerning value weights that was given concerning quantity weights—only approximate accuracy is necessary. Nevertheless, the following consideration becomes important when only a limited number of commodities is chosen: Should the value weight selected for any given commodity be the value of *that commodity* entering the market, or should it refer to the whole *group* of commodities which the commodity represents? The answer to this question is that, unless it is practicable to increase the number of items in some groups (and perhaps decrease the number in others) sufficiently to obtain proportionate value representation for the different groups, it is decidedly better to adjust the weights of the different items so as to obtain such group representation. Most satisfactory results will be obtained if we select as large a number of commodities from each group as feasible, and at the same time give additional weight to those elements that are under-represented.

Another method of accomplishing the same result is to select as many commodities as convenient for each group, to compute separate group indexes, and then to combine the group indexes into a general index, using the appropriate weights. Since the group indexes are relatives, their combination presents no new problem. It might further be noticed that weighting of commodities may in a sense be regarded as a substitute for selecting the number of commodities from the different groups in proportion to the value of those groups.

Types of averages. *The geometric mean.* Sometimes it is argued that the geometric mean should be used for averaging price relatives.

Let us consider a simple case using only two commodities and involving the measurement of price level between two countries. Using Country A as the base, we get the following results, showing that, according to the arithmetic mean, the price level in Country B is 25 per cent higher than in Country A.

Commodity	Country A		Country B	
	Unit price	Price relative (per cent)	Unit price	Price relative (per cent)
Wheat (bushel)...	$0.80	100	$1.60	200
Cotton (pound)...	.12	100	.06	50
Arithmetic mean	...	100	...	125
Geometric mean	...	100	...	100

Now let us see what happens if Country B is taken as the base and the price level in Country A is expressed relative to that of Country B.

Commodity	Country A		Country B	
	Unit price	Price relative (per cent)	Unit price	Price relative (per cent)
Wheat (bushel)...	$0.80	50	$1.60	100
Cotton (pound)...	.12	200	.06	100
Arithmetic mean	...	125	...	100
Geometric mean	...	100	...	100

From these calculations, the arithmetic mean indicates that the price level in Country A is 25 per cent higher than in Country B.

The results of the computations in the two tables appear to be inconsistent. However, they are inconsistent, not because of a shortcoming of the arithmetic mean, but because of hidden weights which are not the same in the two situations. When Country A was the base, it was assumed that the amounts of wheat and cotton purchased in Country A would be the number of units of wheat ($1\frac{1}{4}$ bushels) and the number of units of cotton ($8\frac{1}{3}$ pounds) purchased by $1.00 (or other specified amount of money), and *that the same weights would hold for Country B*. That is, for Country A:

$1\frac{1}{4}$ bushels of wheat @ $0.80 = $1.00; relative = 100;
$8\frac{1}{3}$ pounds of cotton @ .12 = 1.00; relative = 100;

and for Country B:

$1\frac{1}{4}$ bushels of wheat @ $1.60 = $2.00; relative = 200;
$8\frac{1}{3}$ pounds of cotton @ .06 = .50; relative = 50.

On this basis, the price level in Country B is 25 per cent higher than in Country A.

When Country B was the base, it was assumed that the amounts of wheat and cotton purchased in Country B would be the number of units of wheat ($\frac{5}{8}$ bushels) and the number of units of cotton ($16\frac{2}{3}$ pounds) purchased by $1.00 (or other specified amount of money), and *that the same weights would hold for Country A*.

This gives, for Country B:

$\frac{5}{8}$ bushels of wheat   @ $1.60 = $1.00; relative = 100;
$16\frac{2}{3}$ pounds of cotton @   .06 = $1.00; relative = 100;

and for Country A:

$\frac{5}{8}$ bushels of wheat   @ $0.80 = $0.50; relative = 50;
$16\frac{2}{3}$ pounds of cotton @   .12 = 2.00; relative = 200.

Use of this set of weights indicates that the price level in Country A is 25 per cent higher than in Country B.

Now, the geometric mean is sometimes advocated because it gives consistent results in situations such as those shown in the two tables above. The results are consistent because, with either country as the base, the index number for the other country is 100, as may be seen in the tables. But the geometric mean yields consistent results only because of the assumption inherent in it. This is that the value of the two commodities purchased be in the same ratio in the two countries. This means that more wheat would be bought in Country A than in Country B, and that more cotton would be bought in Country B than in A.

In the foregoing paragraphs, no weights had been specified for the index numbers which were made. We have already seen that relatives should be weighted by properly selected values, and for the illustrations just given those weights should be determined upon the basis of the actual value of the commodities sold in the two countries.

Another argument for the geometric mean is based upon the assertion that frequency distributions of price relatives tend to form a normal distribution when plotted on paper having a logarithmic X scale. Such a frequency distribution, but not of price relatives, is shown in Charts 23.13 and 23.14. The reasoning runs as follows: the doubling of a price represents as important a divergence (and is as likely to occur) as a decline to one-half of its former level; it is as likely to increase to $\frac{3}{2}$ of the base period as to fall to $\frac{2}{3}$ of the base period; it is as likely to rise to infinity as it is to fall to zero. The resulting frequency distribution therefore tends to be normal geometrically, and the geometric mean, which coincides with the mode of such a distribution, is the appropriate average. This argument is logical but is based upon premises that are not fully established. We are not sure that a price is as likely to double as to drop one-half, or as likely to increase 50 per cent as to drop one-third; and, unless balancing of this sort takes place, we do not have an appropriate basis for using the geometric mean.

It should not be thought that the geometric mean must never be used; it merely is to be doubted that it has any inherent general superiority over the arithmetic mean. It is the belief of the authors that the average to use is determined in large part by the use for which the index numbers are intended. If, as is very often the case, we wish to compare the amount of money required at two different times or in two different places to purchase the same commodities (or perhaps the same amount of satisfaction by like individuals, with tastes and environment held constant), the weighted arithmetic mean should be used. This is because, as has been shown, such an index number may also be regarded as a weighted aggregative index number. On the other hand, if the primary object is the study of price relatives, including their average behavior, the geometric mean may be useful.

The mode, the median, and the harmonic mean. Use of the mode is virtually never advocated, the primary reason being that ordinarily no clearly defined mode would be present in a group of price relatives. The median is seldom used, but it might be appropriate if doubt exists concerning the accuracy or representative character of some of the data. Of course, the presence of such a doubt may actually mean that the basic data were not properly gathered. Use of the harmonic mean has been suggested (see Chapter 18) if it is desired to use the reciprocal of a price index as an index of the purchasing power of money.

Comparison of the four types of price indexes. Before beginning the consideration of quantity indexes, it may be well to pause a moment

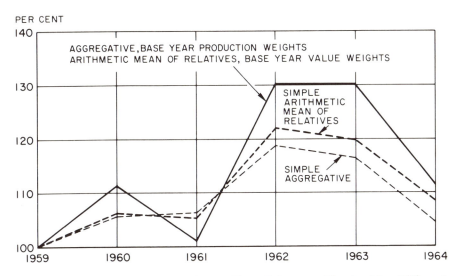

Chart 17.4. Index Numbers of Citrus Fruit Prices, as Obtained by Different Methods, 1959–1964. Data from Tables 17.1, 17.2, 17.5, and 17.6.

and to compare the results of the four types of price indexes which have been discussed. Chart 17.4 shows these four indexes, but it has three curves rather than four, because two of the indexes coincide. As we already know, the two that are alike are the aggregative with base-year-quantity weights and the arithmetic average of relatives weighted by base-year values. Note the general agreement of all three curves, although there are some important differences in magnitude (for example, in 1962 and 1963) and one in direction. The simple aggregative and the simple arithmetic average of relatives, both of which have logical shortcomings, both failed to go high enough in four years and in the case of the simple aggregative moved in the wrong direction in 1961.

QUANTITY INDEX NUMBERS

Aggregative type. An aggregative index number of quantity (physical volume) is the counterpart of the corresponding price index. Thus, the construction of a simple aggregative quantity index would involve the formula

$$Q = \frac{\Sigma q_n}{\Sigma q_o},$$

and Table 17.7 shows the computation of such a quantity index for citrus fruits. Ordinarily, an index computed in this way is obviously illogical, since it involves adding quantities expressed in different units, such as tons, thousands of board feet, kilowatt hours, and so on. For the citrus fruit, it would have been possible to express all production in terms of pounds, but even this would not yield a satisfactory index, since the relative importance of each fruit in the economy would have been ignored.

Using base-year prices as weights, the formula becomes

$$Q = \frac{\Sigma q_n p_o}{\Sigma q_o p_o}.$$

The construction of this weighted aggregative quantity index, with 1959 = 100, is shown in Table 17.8.

Just as the aggregative index number of price measures the changing value of a fixed aggregate of goods at varying prices, so the aggregative index number of physical volume measures the changing value of a varying aggregate of goods at fixed prices. The price index answers the question: If we buy the same assortment of goods each year, but at *different prices*, how much will we spend each year? The physical volume index answers the question: If we buy *varying quantities* of specified goods each year, but at the same price, how much will we spend each year? While in the former case the difference in amount spent was due to price change, in the latter case the difference must, of course, be attributed to changes in quantities bought and sold, since prices were held constant. Thus an index, computed by use of the formula last given, tells us the comparative quantities (produced, sold, consumed, and so forth) for each of the periods covered.

Various methods of weighting are available for the construction of quantity index numbers, and in general the same considerations apply that were discussed in connection with price index numbers. In obtaining price weights which are averages of two or more years, the average prices should be weighted-average prices, obtained by dividing the total value sold in these years by the total number of units in those same years. Thus, if average quantities of base and given years are used, we have the rather formidable-looking formula

TABLE 17.7

Construction of Simple Aggregative Index Numbers of Citrus Fruit Production, 1959–1964*

(Quantities in thousands of boxes.)

Fruit	1959	1960	1961	1962	1963	1964
Grapefruit, Florida............	30,500	31,600	35,000	30,000	26,800	31,900
Lemons, California............	17,100	13,600	15,200	12,400	15,800	13,500
Oranges, California, navel........	13,500	9,000	7,600	12,600	15,500	15,600
Oranges, California, Valencia....	17,300	16,000	13,100	16,200	15,500	16,000
Oranges, Florida..............	91,500	86,700	113,400	74,500	58,300	86,200
Aggregate...................	169,900	156,900	184,300	145,700	131,900	163,200
Index number (per cent of 1959)	100.0	92.3	108.5	85.8	77.6	96.1

* See note to Table 17.1 concerning crop years.
Data from sources given below Table 17.2.

TABLE 17.8

Construction of Aggregative Index Numbers of Citrus Fruit Production, 1959–1964, Weighted by Prices in 1959*

(Values in thousands of dollars.)

Fruit	1959 price per box	Value of amount produced in specified year at 1959 price					
		1959	1960	1961	1962	1963	1964
Grapefruit, Florida..............	$4.41	134,505	139,356	154,350	132,300	118,188	140,679
Lemons, California................	7.10	121,410	96,560	107,920	88,040	112,180	95,850
Oranges, California, navel..........	7.66	103,410	68,940	58,216	96,516	118,730	119,496
Oranges, California, Valencia........	8.36	144,628	133,760	109,516	135,432	129,580	133,760
Oranges, Florida.................	5.32	486,780	461,244	603,288	396,340	310,156	458,584
Aggregate value................	...	990,733	899,860	1,033,290	848,628	788,834	948,369
Index number (per cent of 1959)...	...	100.0	90.8	104.3	85.7	79.6	95.7

* See note to Table 17.1 concerning crop years.
Based on quantity data of Table 17.7 and 1959 price data in Table 17.1.

$$Q = \frac{\Sigma q_n \left(\dfrac{p_o q_o + p_n q_n}{q_o + q_n} \right)}{\Sigma q_o \left(\dfrac{p_o q_o + p_n q_n}{q_o + q_n} \right)}.$$

Likewise, if the common-factor method is used, the price weight should be derived from the largest value that is common to all the years in question.

Averages of relatives. This method of constructing quantity index numbers is strictly analogous to the method applied to the measuring of price changes. The procedure is illustrated by Tables 17.9 and 17.10.

As was found to be true with price index numbers, the use of base-year value weights produces the same result as the aggregative method employing base-year-quantity weights, except for differences due to rounding.

Because of ease of computation and simplicity of meaning, the aggregative method is to be preferred to the average-of-relatives method whenever it is applicable. As noted before, there are circumstances when the

TABLE 17.9

Construction of Index Numbers of Citrus Fruit Production, 1959–1964,*
by Use of Simple Arithmetic Mean of Quantity Relatives

Fruit	1959	1960	1961	1962	1963	1964
Grapefruit, Florida.............	100.0	103.6	114.8	98.4	87.9	104.6
Lemons, California.............	100.0	79.5	88.9	72.5	92.4	78.9
Oranges, California, navel........	100.0	66.7	56.3	93.3	114.8	115.6
Oranges, California, Valencia....	100.0	92.5	75.7	93.6	89.6	92.5
Oranges, Florida..............	100.0	94.8	123.9	81.4	63.7	94.2
Total......................	500.0	437.1	459.6	439.2	448.4	485.8
Average (per cent of 1959).....	100.0	87.4	91.9	87.8	89.7	97.2

* See note to Table 17.1 concerning crop years.
Based on data in Table 17.7.

TABLE 17.10

Construction of Index Numbers of Citrus Fruit Production, 1959–1964,*
by Use of Arithmetic Means of Quantity Relatives Weighted
by Base-Year (1959) Values

(Values in thousands of dollars.)

Fruit	1959 value	Quantity relative of specified year multiplied by 1959 value					
		1959	1960	1961	1962	1963	1964
Grapefruit, Florida.................	134,505	134,505	139,347	154,412	132,353	118,230	140,692
Lemons, California..................	121,410	121,410	96,521	107,933	88,022	112,183	95,792
Oranges, California, navel...........	103,410	103,410	68,974	58,220	96,482	118,715	119,542
Oranges, California, Valencia........	144,628	144,628	133,781	109,483	135,372	129,587	133,781
Oranges, Florida....................	486,780	486,780	461,467	603,120	396,239	310,079	458,547
Total.........................	...	990,733	900,090	1,033,168	848,468	788,794	948,354
Index number (per cent of 1959)....	...	100.0	90.9	104.3	85.6	79.6	95.7

* See note to Table 17.1 concerning crop years.
Based on quantity relatives in Table 17.9 and 1959 value data in Table 17.8.

aggregative method cannot be used. Not previously mentioned is the situation that obtains when the relatives which are to be averaged are percentages, not of a fixed base but of a changing normal. Here, of course, the average-of-relatives method is necessary. In other words, the aggregative method cannot be used if an index of business cycles is to be constructed, since the data to be averaged are percentages of trend and seasonal.

Usually the weights selected for an average of quantity relatives are in proportion to the values in exchange of the different series. Occasionally, some consideration is given also to the relative amplitude of the different series, if they are cyclical relatives. If an index is constructed, not for the purpose of *measuring* changes but for the purpose of *forecasting* changes, the basis of selecting will be, not the economic importance of the different series represented, but their importance for purposes of forecasting.

Chapter 18 will describe methods of constructing a number of important indexes and will discuss certain points of technique and theory not covered in this chapter.

CHAPTER 18

Index Number Theory and Practice

The object of this chapter is twofold. First, the theory of index numbers and certain refinements of technique will be further discussed. Second, a description of a number of indexes will be given. The indexes were selected partly on account of their wide usefulness, and partly on account of the interesting technique which they employ. In general it will be found that in actual practice the procedures outlined in Chapter 17 will not be followed exactly, but that in each case there will be circumstances which justify special modifications of method.

INDEX NUMBER CONCEPTS

Mathematical tests. One school of thought on index numbers believes that there may be such a thing as a perfect index number formula, and that such a formula can be recognized by its ability to meet certain mathematical tests of consistency. Whether or not those tests are logically valid is an open question. Not only can an index be considered "ideal" if it meets those tests, according to this theory, but other indexes that do not meet them can be graded according to how closely they approximate them in actual practice.

The tests are derived by the logic of analogy. Anything that is true of an individual commodity should also be true of a group of commodities considered as a whole. If a box of oranges was worth 125 per cent as much in 1967 as it was in 1965, then the 1965 price was 80 per cent of the 1967 price. Reasoning by analogy, if an index number for 1967 was 125 with respect to a 1965 base, then the index number for 1965 should be 80 with respect to a 1967 base. In other words, an index number should work backward as well as forward.

Again, suppose that a commodity increases from 40 cents to 60 cents and that the sales increase from 2 units to 4 units. The price is 150 per cent of the base year, the quantity sales are 200 per cent, while the value is $1.50 \times 2.00 = 3.00$ times the base year, or 300 per cent of the base year. This is verified by noting that $\dfrac{0.60 \times 4}{0.40 \times 2} = 3$. Once more reasoning from analogy, it may be argued that a price index times a quantity index computed from the same data should equal the relative value of the transactions in the given year with respect to the base year. In other words, if

$$\frac{p_n}{p_o} \times \frac{q_n}{q_o} = \frac{p_n q_n}{p_o q_o},$$

then it should be true that

$$P \times Q = \frac{\Sigma p_n q_n}{\Sigma p_o q_o}.$$

As indicated in the preceding paragraph, there are two tests which are considered especially important by the "mathematical test" school. These may be called: (1) the *time* reversal test; (2) the *factor* reversal test.

The time reversal test may be stated more precisely as follows: If the time subscripts of a price (or quantity) index number formula be interchanged, the resulting price (or quantity) formula should be the reciprocal of the original formula. If we take the formula

$$\frac{\Sigma p_n q_o}{\Sigma p_o q_o}$$

and interchange the time subscripts, the resulting formula is

$$\frac{\Sigma p_o q_n}{\Sigma p_n q_n}.$$

But

$$\frac{\Sigma p_n q_o}{\Sigma p_o q_o} \times \frac{\Sigma p_o q_n}{\Sigma p_n q_n} \neq 1;$$

hence the test is not met. On the other hand, the formula

$$\sqrt{\frac{\Sigma p_n q_o}{\Sigma p_o q_o} \times \frac{\Sigma p_n q_n}{\Sigma p_o q_n}}$$

becomes

$$\sqrt{\frac{\Sigma p_o q_n}{\Sigma p_n q_n} \times \frac{\Sigma p_o q_o}{\Sigma p_n q_o}},$$

the product of the two expressions is unity, and Irving Fisher's "ideal" index meets the time reversal test.

The factor reversal test may be stated in this way: If the p and q factors in a price (or quantity) index formula be interchanged, so that a quantity (or price) index formula is obtained, the product of the two indexes should give the true value ratio

$$\frac{\Sigma p_n q_n}{\Sigma p_o q_o}.$$

Again taking the formula

$$\frac{\Sigma p_n q_o}{\Sigma p_o q_o},$$

we transform it into

$$\frac{\Sigma q_n p_o}{\Sigma q_o p_o}.$$

This is a quantity index, but since

$$\frac{\Sigma p_n q_o}{\Sigma p_o q_o} \times \frac{\Sigma q_n p_o}{\Sigma q_o p_o} \neq \frac{\Sigma p_n q_n}{\Sigma p_o q_o},$$

the test is not met.   However, we find that

$$\sqrt{\frac{\Sigma p_n q_o}{\Sigma p_o q_o} \times \frac{\Sigma p_n q_n}{\Sigma p_o q_n}}$$

transforms into

$$\sqrt{\frac{\Sigma q_n p_o}{\Sigma q_o p_o} \times \frac{\Sigma q_n p_n}{\Sigma q_o p_n}}.$$

The product of these two "ideal" indexes is

$$\frac{\Sigma p_n q_n}{\Sigma p_o q_o},$$

and the test is met.

Fisher's "ideal" index number is so called because it is one of an extremely limited number of indexes that meet both of these tests.

Relationship of formula to use.   The concept of an "ideal" index is attacked by index number students belonging to a different school of thought on the ground that the analyst cannot say exactly what the "ideal" index measures; he can only assert vaguely that it measures a change in the price level, or use some similar expression.   In one approach, the logical procedure is to ask a specific question, and then to devise a formula which will answer that specific question.   For instance, the formula $\frac{\Sigma p_n q_o}{\Sigma p_o q_o}$ applied to retail prices compares the cost in the present year with the cost in the base year of supporting the physical scale of living which obtained in the base year.   While this is a specific question, it may not be the most useful question to ask.   Just what is an appropriate question to ask is an important problem facing the person conducting the investigation.   In Chapter 17 Keynes was interpreted as believing it appropriate that, for measuring changes in the value of money, one should first seek an index number that would measure the changing cost of aggregates of goods yielding the same utility to similar groups of persons at two periods.   Now the formula $\dfrac{\Sigma p_n q_o}{\Sigma p_o q_o}$ assumes that, if their tastes

do not change, people will continue to buy the same amounts of goods no matter how great the price rise or fall, while actually there is a shift from those items which are becoming more expensive to those which are becoming cheaper.   This formula, then, would have an upward "bias," since the cost of obtaining the same quantity of goods would be higher than the cost of obtaining the same quantity of utility.   The formula $\dfrac{\Sigma p_n q_n}{\Sigma p_o q_n}$, on the other hand, compares the cost of supporting one's present

physical scale of living with its cost in the base year.   This formula, from the same point of view, has a downward "bias," since no sensible person would have bought the same goods in the base year as he does now (even granting the same tastes and environment), because the relative prices of goods would have been different.   The cost of obtaining the present year's bill of goods in the base year would have been greater than the cost of obtaining the current year's economic satisfactions.

Fisher's "ideal" index formula is the geometric mean of two index numbers biased (or inappropriate) in opposite directions; and many persons hold that the average of two wrong answers does not necessarily give one right answer, even though the two errors are in opposite directions and even though the formula is internally consistent.   On the other hand, it is doubtful that Keynes' common-factor method will in actual practice answer Keynes' question any better than (if as well as) the "ideal" index number.   Changes in relative prices with consequent changes in relative quantities purchased may reduce the value of the common factor to a small proportion of the total goods bought.   Nevertheless, it is still another attempt to arrive at a logical decision as to exactly what one is trying to measure.

For purposes of measuring changes in the value of money (purchasing power of the dollar), it is customary to use the reciprocal of a price index.   In another approach, however, it is argued that this is illogical. Just as a price index averages together price changes of specific commodities, so a purchasing power index should average together changes in the purchasing power of the dollar for specific commodities.   If the price of corn is \$.50 per bushel, the purchasing power of the dollar for corn is 2 bushels.   Designating units of purchasing power per dollar by the symbol u, this school suggests the purchasing power index number formula:

$$\text{Purchasing power} = \frac{\Sigma\left(\dfrac{u_n}{u_o}\,p_o q_o\right)}{\Sigma p_o q_o}.$$

But since $u = \dfrac{1}{p}$, we may write

$$\text{Purchasing power} = \frac{\Sigma \left(\dfrac{p_o}{p_n}\, p_o q_o \right)}{\Sigma p_o q_o}.$$

This expression is the reciprocal of the harmonic mean of price relatives weighted by base-year values, since the latter is

$$1 \div \frac{\Sigma \left(\dfrac{1}{p_n \div p_o}\, p_o q_o \right)}{\Sigma p_o q_o} = 1 \div \frac{\Sigma \left(\dfrac{p_o}{p_n}\, p_o q_o \right)}{\Sigma p_o q_o} = \frac{\Sigma p_o q_o}{\Sigma \left(\dfrac{p_o}{p_n}\, p_o q_o \right)}.$$

The formula above is still in effect (though not in concept) the reciprocal of a price index, though not the usual index based on the arithmetic mean. Presumably it would be possible to alter somewhat the weighting system without doing violence to the concept.

If we accept the idea that the purpose of an index number determines its formula, we need not, necessarily, abandon the "ideal" formula. It would be possible to maintain that, although the formula is not a perfect solution to every index number problem, nevertheless there are purposes for which it is especially suited, as for instance the analysis of value changes into constituent price changes and quantity changes. However, it seemingly would have to be abandoned as a theoretically sound index if we take the position that every index number must answer a specific question couched in layman's English.

THE CHAIN INDEX

In its simplest form, the chain index is one in which the figures for each year (or subperiod thereof) are first expressed as percentages of the preceding year. These percentages are then chained together by successive multiplication to form a chain index. Table 18.1 shows the computation of a weighted aggregative chain index of citrus fruit prices. As noted above the table, the prices are weighted by production in the first year of each pair of years. These products are summed for each year and each sum is expressed as a percentage of the sum for the preceding year, as shown in the next-to-the-last column of the table. The results of the "chaining" procedure are shown in the last column of the table. They are obtained as follows: (1) the 1960 percentage, 111.3, is the 1960 chain index number; (2) since the 1961 percentage figure is 0.2 per cent greater than 1960, the 1961 chain index number is $1.113 \times 1.002 = 1.115$, or 111.5 per cent; (3) the 1962 percentage figure is 1.348 of the 1961 figure,

TABLE 18.1

*Construction of Weighted Aggregative Chain Index of Citrus Fruit Prices,** *
1959–1964

(For each pair of years, the weights are the productions in the first year.   Values in thousands of dollars.)

| Year | Price × production in first year of each pair of years | | | | | Sum of products | Per cent of preceding year of each pair | Chain index |
	Grape-fruit	Lemons, California	Oranges, California, navel	Oranges, California, Valencia	Oranges, Florida			
1959	134,505	121,410	103,410	144,628	486,780	990,733	100.0	100.0
1960	131,760	123,462	124,740	129,404	592,920	1,102,286	111.3	111.3
1960	136,512	98,192	68,940	133,760	461,244	898,648	100.0	...
1961	141,884	97,648	92,340	127,040	441,303	900,215	100.2	111.5
1961	157,150	109,136	77,976	104,014	577,206	1,025,482	100.0	...
1962	205,800	130,112	70,072	99,822	876,582	1,382,388	134.8	150.3
1962	176,400	106,144	116,172	123,444	575,885	1,098,045	100.0	...
1963	182,700	90,272	97,272	151,308	579,610	1,101,162	100.3	150.8
1963	163,212	115,024	119,660	144,770	453,574	996,240	100.0	...
1964	159,192	132,404	111,600	103,540	360,294	867,030	87.0	131.2

* See note to Table 17.1 concerning crop years.
Based on price data in Table 17.1 and production data in Table 17.7.

so the chain index number for 1962 is 1.115 × 1.348 = 1.503, or 150.3 per cent; and so on for the other years.

The advantages of a chain index are: (1) commodities may readily be dropped, if they are no longer relevant; (2) new commodities may be introduced; and (3) weights may be changed.   Thus, account may readily be taken of basic changes in production, distribution, and consumption habits, of quality changes, of any hiatus in some of the data, and of other similar changes that cannot readily be handled in a fixed-base index number.   The principle of the chain index is employed in several instances later in this chapter.

The disadvantage of the chain index is that, while the percentage-of-previous-year figures give accurate comparisons of year-to-year changes, the long-range comparisons of the chained percentages are not strictly valid.   However, when the index-number user wishes to make year-to-year comparisons, as is so often done by the business man, the percentages of the preceding year provide a flexible and useful tool.

SUBSTITUTING NEW COMMODITIES AND CHANGING WEIGHTS

Sometimes it is necessary or desirable to drop a commodity from an index, to add a new commodity, to substitute one commodity for another, or to change the weight of a commodity.   Substituting one commodity

TABLE 18.2

Construction of Weighted Aggregative Index of Citrus Fruit Prices, Showing Substitution of California Valencia Oranges for California Navel Oranges with No Change in Weights,* 1959, 1962, 1963, and 1964

Fruit	1959			1962			1963		1964	
	Quantity weights (millions of boxes) q_{59}	Price (dollars per box) p_{59}	Product (millions of dollars) $p_{59}q_{59}$	Price (dollars per box) p_{62}	Product, old series (millions of dollars) $p_{62}q_{59}$	Product, new series (millions of dollars) $p_{62}q_{59}$	Price (dollars per box) p_{63}	Product, new series (millions of dollars) $p_{63}q_{59}$	Price (dollars per box) p_{64}	Product, new series (millions of dollars) $p_{64}q_{59}$
Grapefruit, Florida	30.5	4.41	134.505	5.88	179.340	179.340	6.09	185.745	5.94	181.170
Lemons, California	17.1	7.10	121.410	8.56	146.376	146.376	7.28	124.488	8.38	143.298
Oranges, California, navel	13.5	7.66	103.410	9.22	124.470	…	…	…	…	…
Oranges, California, Valencia	…	…	…	7.62	…	102.870#	9.34	126.090#	6.68	90.180#
Total	…	…	359.325	…	450.186	428.586	…	436.323	…	414.648
Index number, old series	…	…	100.00	…	125.29	125.29	…	…	…	…
Index number, new series	…	…	…	…	…	125.29	…	127.55	…	121.22

* See note to Table 17.1 concerning crop years. Prices are season average price per box at principal auction markets.

California Valencia orange price × California navel orange quantity in 1959.

Data from various issues of *Agricultural Statistics*, from correspondence with U. S. Department of Agriculture, and from *Annual Crop Summary*, December 1965, p. 97.

for another will ordinarily involve also a change of weight. These adjustments involve an application of the chain index. As an illustration of substitution, we shall construct an index of citrus fruit prices for the years 1959 (the base year), 1962, 1963, and 1964. For the purposes of our illustration, we shall substitute California Valencia oranges for California navel oranges in 1962.

Table 18.2 shows the computation of a weighted aggregative index for 1959 and 1962 using base-year-quantity weights, and it may be seen that the 1962 index number is 125.29 for the "old series" using California navel oranges, California lemons, and Florida grapefruit. The substitution of California Valencia for California navel oranges is made, in 1962, by multiplying the Valencia orange price by the navel weight, giving the product shown in the table: 102.870 million dollars. The total of the products for the 1962 "new series" is 428.586 million dollars, and this total is set equal to the already determined 1962 index number, 125.29. The 1963 and 1964 products for California Valencia oranges are determined as was the figure for 1962, and sums of products are gotten for 1963 and 1964. The index numbers for 1963 and 1964 are then obtained by these relationships:

For 1963—

$$\frac{428.586}{125.29} = \frac{436.323}{\text{index number for 1963}};$$

$$\text{Index number for 1963} = 127.55.$$

For 1964—

$$\frac{428.586}{125.29} = \frac{414.648}{\text{index number for 1964}};$$

$$\text{Index number for 1964} = 121.22.$$

The procedure used in Table 18.2 underweights California Valencia oranges because its unit price in 1962 was less than California navel oranges.[1] The weight given to Valencia oranges was also too low in

---

[1] When it is reasonable to continue to use the base-year weight for a substitute commodity, an adjustment for the different unit prices of the old and new commodity may be made by computing:

1962 because only 12.6 million boxes of navel oranges and 16.2 million boxes of Valencia oranges were produced.   There is no exaggeration due to quantities employed in 1963, when the production of both approximated 15.5 million boxes.   In 1964, there was only a slight underweighting of Valencia oranges because the production of Valencia and navel oranges was 16.0 and 15.6 million boxes respectively.   Obviously the weights should have been revised when Valencia oranges were substituted for navel oranges.

Such a revision of weights is made in Table 18.3.   Here the 1962 index number for the "old series" is again 125.29.   The "new series" of weighted aggregates for 1962 uses 1926 quantity weights, and the sum of the products for the "new series" for 1962 is 405.988 million dollars, which is set equal to an index number of 125.29.   The index numbers for 1963 and 1964 are then obtained, as before, from the relationship:

For 1963—

$$\frac{405.988}{125.29} = \frac{424.280}{\text{index number for 1963}};$$

$$\text{Index number for 1963} = 130.93.$$

For 1964—

$$\frac{405.988}{125.29} = \frac{390.328}{\text{index number for 1964}};$$

$$\text{Index number for 1964} = 120.46.$$

Dropping a commodity without adding a new one or adding a new commodity which is not a substitute for an old one would, of course, involve a change of weights.   The procedure would be similar to that of Table 18.3.   Changing weights without adding or dropping a commodity could also be handled in similar fashion.

$$\text{New Weight} = \frac{\text{Old Unit Price}}{\text{New Unit Price}} \times \text{Old Weight}.$$

The procedure is then similar to that given in Table 18.3.   See the first edition of this text, pp. 623–626.

TABLE 18.3

Construction of Weighted Aggregative Index of Citrus Fruit Prices, Showing Substitution of California Valencia Oranges for California Navel Oranges and Shift from Base-Year Weights to 1962 Weights,* 1959, 1962, 1963, 1964

Fruit	1959 quantity weights (millions of boxes) q_{59}	1959		1962		1962 quantity weights (millions of boxes) q_{62}	1962		1963		1964	
		Price (dollars per box) p_{59}	Product (millions of dollars) $p_{59}q_{59}$	Price (dollars per box) p_{62}	Product (millions of dollars) $p_{62}q_{59}$		Price (dollars per box) p_{62}	Product, new series (millions of dollars) $p_{62}q_{62}$	Price (dollars per box) p_{63}	Product, new series (millions of dollars) $p_{63}q_{62}$	Price (dollars per box) p_{64}	Product, new series (millions of dollars) $p_{64}q_{62}$
Grapefruit, Florida.........	30.5	4.41	134.505	5.88	179.340	30.0	5.88	176.400	6.09	182.700	5.94	178.200
Lemons, California.........	17.1	7.10	121.410	8.56	146.376	12.4	8.56	106.144	7.28	90.272	8.38	103.912
Oranges, California, navel...	13.5	7.66	103.410	9.22	124.470	...	...	...	...	...	...	...
Oranges, California, Valencia......	...	...	...	...	...	16.2	7.62	123.444	9.34	151.308	6.68	108.216
Total........			359.325		450.186			405.988		424.280		390.328
Index number, old series..			100.0		125.29							
Index number, new series..								125.29		130.93		120.46

* See note to Table 17.1 concerning crop years. Prices are season average prices per box at principal auction markets.
Data from sources given below Table 18.2.

DESCRIPTIONS OF INDEXES

The remainder of this chapter will be devoted to brief descriptions of a number of indexes designed to measure price changes, changes in physical volume, general and specific business movements, and other changes and differences. No index is explained in full detail, and the reader should bear in mind that a two- or three-page description of an index can do little more than mention some of the more important features of that index.

PRICE INDEXES

The Consumer Price Index. This index,[2] compiled by the United States Department of Labor on a 1957–1959 base, is entitled, "Consumer Price Index for Urban Wage Earners and Clerical Workers." It is generally referred to as "The Consumer Price Index" and, as its name indicates, is a statistical measure of retail price change. It is not, strictly speaking, a cost-of-living-index, since it does not measure changes in kinds and amounts of goods and services which people buy or the total amount they spend for living. Neither does it measure differences in living costs between different places.

The retail prices which make up the index are divided into eight major groups: food, housing, apparel, transportation, medical care, personal care, reading and recreation, and other goods and services. Food and housing are further divided into subgroups. The approximately 400 commodities and services which are included were selected as being representative of the price trends of subgroups of related items and include the cost of such diverse commodities and services as rice, pork chops, canned salmon, potatoes, men's topcoats, men's work gloves, women's wool suits, rent, mortgage interest, electricity, sheets, tablecloths, automobiles, gasoline, office visits to (and home visits by) physicians, eyeglasses, and haircuts. The 400 commodities are representative of the "market basket" of goods and services comprising the pattern of living of city workers' families (of 2 or more persons) and single persons. They were selected as the result of an "expenditures survey" of 4,300 families and 500 single persons among wage earners and clerical workers in 50 urban areas.

Price data of the 400 commodities and services are collected from 50 urban areas, selected so as to be representative of those city characteristics which affect the way in which families spend their money. Thus, such factors as size, climate, population density, and income level are taken into consideration. Within each city, price quotations are gotten from those sources from which families of wage and salary workers obtain goods and services. For items purchased from stores, for example,

---

[2] This description is based on U. S. Bureau of Labor Statistics, *The Consumer Price Index: A Short Description of the Index as Revised, 1964.*

quotations are obtained from representative chain stores, independent stores, department stores, and specialty stores. For each item, the prices reported by the various sources are averaged, with appropriate weights, to ascertain average price changes for the city.

Index numbers are prepared monthly for the United States and for each of five large cities, and quarterly for the other cities. Price changes within each city are averaged and combined by a procedure which is essentially a weighted aggregative, the weights being the proportionate expenditure in the "market basket" for the subgroup (which each item represents) in the survey of families and single persons referred to above. When the price changes for the various cities are combined to obtain figures for the United States, each city is given a weight "proportionate to the wage-earner and clerical-worker population it represents in the index." City weights are adjusted as new Census population figures become available. As noted in the preceding chapter, this index is frequently used as the basis of reference for escalator clauses in wage agreements.

United States Bureau of Labor Statistics Index of Wholesale Commodity Prices. This index, on a 1957–1959 base, is kept up to date on an annual, monthly, weekly, and, for spot prices, daily basis. It measures the general rate and direction of the composite price movements in primary markets and the specific rates and directions of price movements for individual commodities and groups of commodities. The majority of the quotations used in the index are producers' prices rather than wholesalers' prices. The index is designed to measure price changes between periods of time, not changes occasioned by shifts in quality, quantity, terms of sale, and so on.

The index includes approximately 2,200 commodities ranging from raw material to finished products, which are "intended to account, directly or indirectly, for all sales of all products (including both imports and exports) at the primary market level in the United States." The "primary market level" refers to the first important commercial transaction for each commodity.

The commodities included in the index are classified into 15 major groups and 93 subgroups. Each subgroup is further divided into product classes, which are groups of commodities "produced by one or more related industries, and which are also characterized by similarity of price movement, raw materials, or production process." The major groups are:

1. Farm Products
2. Processed Foods
3. Textile Products and Apparel
4. Hides, Skins, and Leather Products

5. Fuels and Related Products and Power
6. Chemicals and Allied Products
7. Rubber and Products
8. Lumber and Wood Products
9. Pulp, Paper, and Allied Products
10. Metals and Metal Products
11. Machinery and Motive Products
12. Furniture and Other Household Durables
13. Nonmetallic Mineral Products
14. Tobacco Products and Bottled Beverages
15. Miscellaneous Products

Groups 3 through 15 are also combined into a still larger category, "all commodities other than farm products and processed foods"—that is to say, industrial products. As a result, the three divisions, (1) farm products, (2) processed foods, and (3) all commodities other than farm products and processed foods, are available.

The 2,200 commodities do not constitute a random sample. They are generally the most important ones in each field or, in some cases, though not important in terms of sales volume, "appear to offer good representation of price movements because of certain industry or trade characteristics." The selection of commodities was based upon "knowledge of each industry and its important products" and ordinarily was preceded by "consultation with leading trade associations and manufacturers in each field."

The index is basically a weighted aggregative with 1958 quantities being frequently, but not always, used as the weights. To cope with the necessity of making allowances for changing specifications of individual commodities, the Bureau computes commodity indexes "by chaining together the month-to-month price relatives and weighting these by the value of sales, rather than the absolute prices weighted by physical quantities." This procedure also facilitates substitution of one commodity for another and alteration of the system of weights.

Indexes of Prices Paid by and Received by Farmers; Parity Ratio. To facilitate attempts to raise agricultural prices to an official "parity" with industrial prices, the Agricultural Marketing Service computes two indexes with the legally specified base 1910–1914. One is called the "Index of Prices Paid by Farmers" and is termed the *Parity Index* when interest on farm mortgage debt, taxes on farm real estate, and cash wages paid to hired hands are included. The other index is referred to as the "Index of Prices Received by Farmers." The ratio of the index of prices received to the Parity Index, for any given period, is the "parity ratio."

The index of prices paid by farmers includes about 350 items. Index numbers are published monthly for 18 subgroups.   Six of these subgroups are combined to form an index of expenditures for family living; nine of them are brought together to make an index of expenditures for producing farm products.   These two major group indexes are merged with interest paid, taxes, and wage rates to form the Index of Prices Paid by Farmers. When combining the prices of individual commodities, quantity weights are used.   In most cases, the weights were derived from a survey of expenditures, by dividing the expenditure for each commodity by the average price of that commodity in specific years, such as 1937–1941, 1953–1957, and others.   When subgroup and group component indexes are combined, they are usually weighted by the amounts spent by farmers during those same years.   The index does not measure price changes alone, since it is affected by changes in quality of the commodities commonly stocked by merchants and changes in quality of goods bought by farmers as they adjust to higher or lower income levels.

The index of prices received is based upon approximately 60 commodities which make up about 95 per cent of total cash receipts from marketings of all farm commodities, including both crop and livestock but not timber and forest products and certain other minor categories. The prices used to make the index are those for "all grades and qualities of the important agricultural commodities at the point of first sale, which generally is the local market."   The index is essentially a weighted aggregative.   United States average prices for individual commodities are combined into subgroup indexes, the weights being the quantities sold by farmers during specific years as noted above.   When subgroup indexes are combined to form group and all-commodity indexes, the weights are "the percentage which cash receipts from marketing for the particular commodity subgroups bear to the total for the same period." Like the index of prices paid, this index does not measure price changes alone, since it involves average prices for all grades and qualities of the various commodities.

The "parity ratio" mentioned at the outset undertakes to measure the extent to which prices received by farmers are higher or lower in relation to the prices they pay than they were in the base period, 1910–1914. This parity ratio was first provided for in the Agricultural Adjustment Act of 1933, which undertook to "re-establish prices to the farmer at a level that will give agricultural commodities a purchasing power with respect to the articles that farmers buy equivalent to the purchasing power of agricultural commodities of the base period," which was set at 1910–1914.

Common stock prices. The New York Stock Exchange Common Stock Index[3] includes the prices of all of the more than 1,250 common stocks

[3] The information in this section was taken from the pamphlet *Measure of the Market*, issued by the New York Stock Exchange, and from the Exchange's Research Department, which kindly checked the description given here.

listed on the Exchange.   Using modern computing equipment, the index is calculated up to the second during each trading day and appears on the Exchange's ticker each hour and half hour.   It was first released July 14, 1966.   Each stock price is weighted by the number of listed shares of that stock.   This aggregative index uses the close of the market on December 31, 1965 as the base, at which time it was set at 50.00.   This is approximately the then-current average price per share, in dollars, of all listed common stocks.

The index is conveniently referred to as the NYSE Common Stock Index.   It has been computed, on a daily close basis, back to May 28, 1964.   This was the last date on which the weekly index of the Securities and Exchange Commission appeared.   To provide historical continuity the NYSE Common Stock Index has been linked to the SEC weekly index of common stock prices to make the NYSE Common Stock Index available on a weekly basis from January 7, 1939 to May 28, 1964.

Daily adjustments are made for changes in capitalization, new listings, and delistings.   Adjustments are also made for rights to purchase shares of a company (after the issue goes ex-rights), rights to subscribe to other issues of the same or a subsidiary company, and for mergers or acquisitions involving listed companies.   These adjustments are accomplished by appropriate increases or decreases of the base (December 31, 1965) market value, the objective being to retain the level of the index at the value it had before the list change.   As an illustration consider that rights financing had added $2 billion to the market value of all listed common stocks, that the base value had been $600 billion, and that the market value, before the rights financing, had been $660 billion.   Preceding the rights financing the index was

$$(\$660 \text{ billion} \div \$600 \text{ billion}) \times 50.00 = 55.00.$$

After the rights financing the market value was $662 billion.   The adjusted base market value becomes

$$\frac{\$662 \text{ billion}}{\$660 \text{ billion}} \times \$600 \text{ billion} = \$601.82 \text{ billion}$$

and the current index is

$$\frac{\$662 \text{ billion}}{\$601.82 \text{ billion}} \times 50.00 = 55.00,$$

the same value as before the rights financing.   Changes in prices due to stock splits, reverse splits, and stock dividends are compensated for by simply changing the number of shares of the issues affected according to the split or dividend ratios.

In addition to the Common Stock Index, the Exchange issues, hourly, a Finance Index, a Transportation Index, a Utility Index, and an Industrial Index.   As of July 14, 1966, the Finance Index was composed of

75 issues, the Transportation Index included 76 issues, the Utility Index was made up of 136 issues, and the Industrial Index embraced almost 1,000 issues. The number of issues in each index changes, but not substantially, from time to time. In the Finance Index are issues of closed-end investment companies, savings and loan holding companies, real estate holding and investment companies, and others in commercial and installment finance, banking, insurance, and related fields. The Transportation Index consists of issues representing railroads, airlines, shipping, motor transport, and other operating, leasing, and holding companies in the transportation field. Constituting the Utility Index are issues of operating, holding, and transmission companies in gas, electric power, and communications. The Industrial Index is composed of NYSE-listed stocks not included in the three preceding indexes. These issues represent a wide variety of industrial corporations in many fields of manufacturing, merchandising, and service. The four indexes have been computed, on a daily close basis, back from July 14, 1966 to December 31, 1965, at which time each was set at 50.00.

INDEXES OF PHYSICAL VOLUME AND OF BUSINESS ACTIVITY

Federal Reserve Index of Industrial Production. This index, which is issued monthly by the Board of Governors of the Federal Reserve System, uses 1957–1959 as the base period and measures changes in the physical volume of output in manufacturing and mining. Individual series are combined to form indexes for products and industries and for groups of industries in conformity with the Standard Industrial Classification Manual developed by the Bureau of the Budget. The over-all index, Industrial Production, is divided among Manufactures, Mining, and Utilities. These three are divided into subgroups with Manufactures having two major subgroups: Durable Manufactures and Non-durable Manufactures.

The industries covered by the Index of Industrial Production account for over one-third of the national income. Among the important areas of the economy which are not covered are: construction, transportation, trade, services, and agriculture.

The index is intended to measure physical output, but a great many industries do not, or cannot, provide physical output data. As a result, the Board must sometimes use related series which tend to fluctuate more or less closely with output. Among these are man-hours, shipments, and materials consumed. In some instances, the monthly series can be corrected after annual data of physical output become available. The basic figures are expressed in terms of output per working day.

The method of combining the data for the individual series involves: (1) converting each series into percentages of the average monthly output in the base period, 1957–1959; (2) multiplying each series of relatives by a base-year weight factor expressed as a percentage of the weight assigned to all the series; and (3) adding the products resulting from step (2). The weights used are based on value added in 1957–1959, value added being the difference between the value of products and the cost of materials or supplies consumed.   In some instances, data of value added are not available but must be estimated.   Index numbers for the major industry groups and for the larger categories (durable and nondurable manufactures, manufactures, minerals, and utilities) are given on a seasonally adjusted basis as well as unadjusted.

Other indexes of physical volume and of business activity. Numerous organizations compile and publish indexes of "industrial activity," "economic activity," and "business activity."   Among them are the American Telephone and Telegraph Company, the New York Times, the Bureau of Business Research of the University of Pittsburgh, and the Bureau of Economic Research of Rutgers—The State University.[4]

INDEXES OF QUALITATIVE CHANGES OR DIFFERENCES

As an illustration of the flexibility of use of index numbers in connection with qualitative matters we may cite one researcher who used them to compare the counties of Oklahoma with respect to housing according to certain criteria at a certain time.   These indexes, did not, therefore, involve changes from one period to the next but rather geographical differences.

Sixteen housing measures for each of the 77 counties of Oklahoma were used to construct four different indexes of rural-farm housing.   Each index yielded an index number for each county.   In one of these the counties were merely ranked with respect to each of the 16 measures; then the ranks were added and divided by 16.   In the second index, each county received a relative for each of the 16 series, the relative being based on the ratio between (1) the county value in a series to (2) the corresponding figure for the state.   The third index employed standard scores (see pages 200–201) while the fourth used factor analysis.[5]   The researcher, who was primarily interested in comparing these four methods, concluded that they produced equally satisfactory indexes of housing.

Non-chronological index numbers, which undertake to measure geographical differences or differences between categories, are not often encountered, and relatively few are in current use.   Attempts have been

---

[4] See, for example, G. Bry, C. Boschan, and R. Kilgore, *A Monthly Index of Manufacturing Production in New Jersey*, Bureau of Economic Research, Rutgers—The State University, 1963, 133 pages.   For a description of the series and the seasonal and trend adjustments employed by widely varying organizations, see the second edition of this text, pp. 444–446.

[5] Factor analysis is beyond the scope of this text.

made to use index numbers to measure the adequacy of state care of mental patients, with comparisons being undertaken both between states and between two different years; to compare the religious work of dioceses;[6] to rate the agricultural value of soils;[7] and to compare state systems with each other.

At the beginning of Chapter 17 it was noted that index numbers may be employed to make chronological, geographical, or categorical comparisons in various areas of human activity. Since the vast majority of indexes have to do with price variations and many others deal with fluctuations of production, the illustrations in the preceding paragraphs were mentioned in order to call attention to some of the diverse fields in which index-number technique has been used. The reader may readily sense its applicability to other sociological or educational data, to psychology, to medicine, and to other fields far removed from the monetary and physical-volume concepts of economics and business.

---

[6] See J. E. Ross, *An Index Number for American Dioceses*, The Shield Press, Racine, Wisconsin, and the National Catholic Welfare Conference, Washington, D. C., undated pamphlet.

[7] See R. Earl Storie, *An Index for Rating the Agricultural Value of Soils*, Bulletin 556 of the California Agricultural Experiment Station, Berkeley, California.

CHAPTER 19

Correlation I: Two-variable Linear Correlation

One of the chief objectives of science is to estimate values of one factor by reference to the values of an associated factor. "The scientific method . . . consists in the careful and laborious classification of facts, in the comparison of their relationship and sequences, and finally in the discovery by the aid of disciplined imagination of a brief statement or *formula*, which in a few words resumes a wide range of facts. Such a formula . . . is termed a scientific law."[1] When the relationship is of a quantitative nature, the appropriate statistical tool for discovering and measuring the relationship and expressing it in a brief formula is known as *correlation*.

A SIMPLE EXPLANATION

It may surprise some of us to know that there is a very close relationship between temperature and the frequency with which crickets chirp. If, for instance, we should count the number of chirps made by a cricket in 15 seconds and add it to 37, we could closely approximate the Fahrenheit temperature at that time. Or, if we should multiply the degrees Fahrenheit by 3.78 and subtract 137 from the result, we could estimate the number of chirps to be expected from a cricket in one minute. This relationship would be found remarkably accurate, unless the temperature was below 45°. When the weather is colder than 45°, crickets do not chirp. Likewise, it might not be accurate appreciably beyond 75°, since observations have not been made beyond that temperature, and we do not know, therefore, if the relationship holds for higher temperatures.

The relationship between these two variables—temperature and cricket chirps—is displayed in Chart 19.1, known as a *scatter diagram*. Each dot represents an observation of one cricket. Thus, observation A represents a cricket which, at a temperature of 59.0°, chirped 85 times per minute. The reader should notice that temperature is plotted along the X-axis, while chirps per minute are plotted along the Y-axis. This is done

---

[1] Karl Pearson, *The Grammar of Science*, Adam and Charles Black, London, 1900, p. 77.

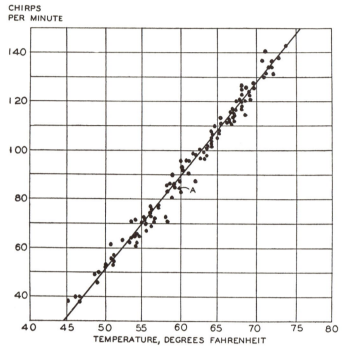

CHIRPS
PER MINUTE

TEMPERATURE, DEGREES FAHRENHEIT

Chart 19.1. Temperature and Chirps per Minute of 115 Crickets. Data provided by Mr. Bert. E. Holmes.

because the number of chirps per minute appears to be a direct result of the temperature. In this case it is also true that we wish to estimate the number of chirps to be expected at a given temperature; temperature is therefore the independent variable, and chirps per minute the dependent variable. Even though it were temperature we wished to estimate, it would nevertheless be best to show the causal factor on the X-axis. When the causal relationship is not clear, or when neither factor can be said to be the cause of the other, then the variable to be estimated should be plotted on the Y-axis.

Judging from Chart 19.1, we see that the relationship between the two variables is linear, for the straight line appears to be as good a fit as a more complicated curve. The equation of this line[2] is

$$Y_c = -137.22 + 3.777X.$$

From this equation, estimates of chirps can be made for any desired temperature within the limits of the observations shown on the chart. Thus, if we wish to estimate the number of chirps when the temperature is 59.0° (observation A), we find the number by substituting 59.0 for X in the equations. Thus

---

[2] This equation was fitted by the authors to data furnished by Bert E. Holmes.

$$Y_c = -137.22 + (3.777)(59.0) = 86 \text{ chirps.}$$

The estimate could be read, although less accurately, directly from the estimating line plotted on the chart. Although the estimate (86) does not agree perfectly with the actual observation of 85 chirps, the discrepancy is not large.

We cannot fail to be impressed with the adequacy of the generalization expressed in the equation $Y_c = -137.22 + 3.777X$. Since most of the dots are very close to the line, it appears that frequency of chirps has been adequately explained by reference to temperature. The slight variations from the estimating line are unexplained and may be due to differences between individual crickets, differences associated with the time of day or year in which the observations were made, humidity, and inaccuracies of observation of temperature or number of chirps. Also,

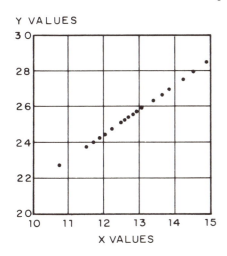

Chart 19.2. A Scatter Diagram Illustrating Perfect Linear Correlation. The correlation would also be perfect if the line on which the dots lie had a negative, instead of a positive, slope. From F. E. Croxton, *Elementary Statistics with Applications in Medicine and the Biological Sciences*, Dover Publications, Inc., New York, 1959, p. 112.

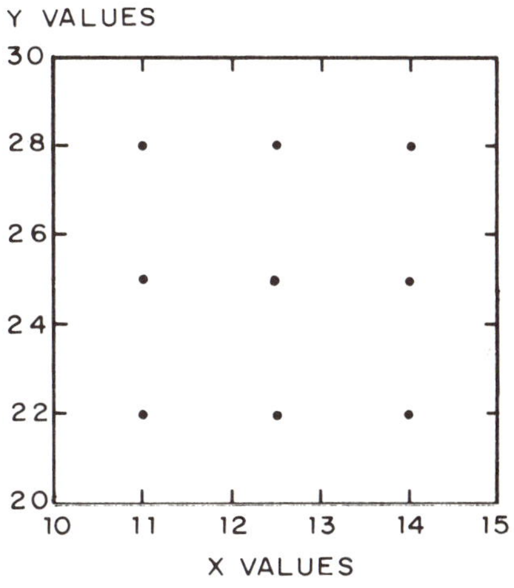

Chart 19.3. A Scatter Diagram Illustrating No Correlation. Various other arrangements of dots are possible which will also show no correlation. From same source as Chart 19.2.

the temperature at the spot where the cricket is chirping may be different from that where the observer is standing. This might be the case if the cricket were under a stone. An examination of other causes of variation, in addition to temperature, involves consideration of three or more variables, a procedure for which will be considered in Chapter 21 under the heading of "Multiple Correlation."

The closeness of the relationship may be expressed in general terms by stating that the *coefficient of correlation, r, is* +0.9919. Since ±1.0 is perfect correlation (see Chart 19.2) and 0 is no correlation (see Chart 19.3), it should be obvious that one almost never finds a higher coefficient than +0.9919. The plus sign indicates that the correlation is positive— that is, that the chirps increase as the temperature increases. Had chirps decreased with increasing temperature, the correlation would have been negative, or inverse; the sign of r would have been negative, as would the sign of b in the estimating equation; and the estimating line would have sloped downward to the right.

An illustration of rather low correlation (−0.11) is given by Chart 19.4. In this case, brain weight was estimated by cranial capacity, and legislative ability by a rather complicated system of scoring. But even if we assume that all measurements are accurate, the evidence certainly does not suggest that legislators should be selected solely from head measurements. Perhaps there are additional factors which account for legislative ability; for example, intelligence, education, initiative, honesty, social awareness, and other traits are doubtless important.

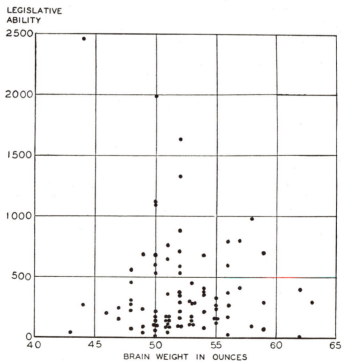

Chart 19.4. Estimates of Brain Weight and Legislative Ability of 89 Members of Congress. Data from "Brain Weight and Legislative Ability in Congress," by Arthur MacDonald, *Congressional Record*, April 12, 1932.

CORRELATION THEORY

Correlation may be thought of as involving three types of measurements, which may conveniently be made in the following order:

(1) An *estimating*, or *regression*,[3] *equation* which describes the functional relationship between the two variables. As the name indicates, one object of such an equation is to make estimates of one variable from another.

(2) A measure of the divergence of the actual values of the dependent variable from their estimated or computed values. This measure is analogous to a standard deviation and gives an idea, in *absolute* terms, of the *dependability of estimates*. It is called the *standard error of estimate* ($s_{Y.X}$).

(3) A measure of the *degree* of relationship, or *correlation* (r), between the variables, independent of the units or terms in which they were originally expressed. The square of this measure (r^2) enables us to state the *relative* amount of variation in the dependent variable which has been explained by the estimating equation.

The estimating equation. Foresters sometimes find it convenient to estimate the height growth of trees from their growth in diameter, since this procedure is quicker than direct measurements of the growth in height. The scatter diagram, Chart 19.5, shows the breast-high diameter growth and the growth in height of 20 trees, together with the estimating line which describes the nature of the relationship between the two variables. This straight line has been so fitted that the sum of the squares of the Y deviations from it is less than those from any other straight line. A curve fitted in this manner is usually considered by statisticians to be the best with which to estimate values of one variable when values of the other variable are known. The fitting of such a line is similar to the fitting of a trend, and requires the use of the following normal equations:

$$\text{I.}\quad \Sigma Y = Na + b\Sigma X.$$
$$\text{II.}\quad \Sigma XY = a\Sigma X + b\Sigma X^2.$$

It will be remembered that the normal equations were discussed in Chapter 12.

Table 19.1 shows the computations that are necessary to determine the values which must be substituted. The substitution yields:

$$\text{I.}\quad 173 = 20a + 90.7b.$$
$$\text{II.}\quad 856.0 = 90.7a + 453.93b.$$

---

[3] The term "regression" entered statistical literature as a result of the use of correlation by Galton to study biological regression (that is, the tendency to revert to a common type or average). Since correlation analysis is applied to many types of problems, the term "estimating" seems more appropriate.

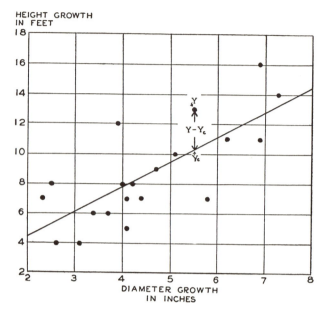

Chart 19.5. Breast-High Diameter Growth and Height Growth of 20 Forest Trees. Data of Table 19.1.

Multiplication of all the items in Equation I by 4.535 permits us to cancel out a by subtracting Equation I from Equation II. Thus

$$
\begin{array}{rll}
\text{II.} & 856.0 &= 90.7a + 453.93b. \\
(\text{I} \times 4.535). & 784.555 &= 90.7a + 411.3245b. \\
\hline
& 71.445 &= 42.6055b. \\
& b &= 1.676896.
\end{array}
$$

We may now substitute the value of b in Equation I in order to find the value of a.

$$
\begin{array}{rl}
\text{I.} & 173 = 20a + 152.094467. \\
& a = 1.045277.
\end{array}
$$

The values for a and b are checked by substituting in Equation II. While this does not prove that no errors in computation have been made, yet if the correct numbers were substituted in the two normal equations, either no errors, or counterbalancing errors, have been made. Since $a = 1.045$ and $b = 1.677$, the equation of the line which enables us to estimate the growth in height of trees in this particular forest when their growth in diameter is known may be stated as

$$
Y_c = 1.045 + 1.677X.
$$

TABLE 19.1

Determination of Values Used in Computing Estimating Equation for Growth in Diameter and Height of 20 Forest Trees

Rank in diameter growth (smallest to largest)	Diameter growth at breast height in inches X	Height growth in feet Y	XY	X^2	Y^2
1	2.3	7	16.1	5.29	49
2	2.5	8	20.0	6.25	64
3	2.6	4	10.4	6.76	16
4	3.1	4	12.4	9.61	16
5	3.4	6	20.4	11.56	36
6	3.7	6	22.2	13.69	36
7	3.9	12	46.8	15.21	144
8	4.0	8	32.0	16.00	64
9	4.1	5	20.5	16.81	25
10	4.1	7	28.7	16.81	49
11	4.2	8	33.6	17.64	64
12	4.4	7	30.8	19.36	49
13	4.7	9	42.3	22.09	81
14	5.1	10	51.0	26.01	100
15	5.5	13	71.5	30.25	169
16	5.8	7	40.6	33.64	49
17	6.2	11	68.2	38.44	121
18	6.9	11	75.9	47.61	121
19	6.9	16	110.4	47.61	256
20	7.3	14	102.2	53.29	196
Total	90.7	173	856.0	453.93	1,705

Data from Donald Bruce and F. X. Schumacher, *Forest Mensuration*, First Edition, McGraw-Hill Book Company, New York, 1935, p. 124. Courtesy of Publisher and Authors.

Suppose now we wish to estimate the height growth of a tree which grew 5.5 inches in diameter. Substituting in the equation, we have

$$Y_c = 1.045 + (1.677)(5.5),$$
$$= 10.268 \text{ feet.}$$

Dependability of estimates. However, we should not expect all trees which grew 5.5 inches in diameter to have grown exactly 10.268 feet in height, for the dots of the scatter diagram do not all lie on the fitted line. Rather, 10.268 should be thought of as an estimate of the average height growth of all trees of the diameter growth indicated. We should expect variations from this value the same as from the arithmetic mean of a frequency distribution. It is therefore pertinent to inquire what proportion of trees may be expected to fall within any range of error in which we may be interested, assuming, of course, that we have a representative sample.

To do this, it is necessary to compute the standard deviation of the Y values, not from their mean, but from the line of estimation. On Chart 19.6, the vertical distance from the line of estimate to any Y value represents the difference between the observed Y value and the estimated Y value. The estimated Y values, Y_c, are obtained by solving the estimating equation for each measurement of diameter growth, or X value. The deviation $Y - Y_c$ represents the error that would have been made in one particular instance. To obtain a summary measure of those deviations, they may be squared, summed, divided by N, and the square root

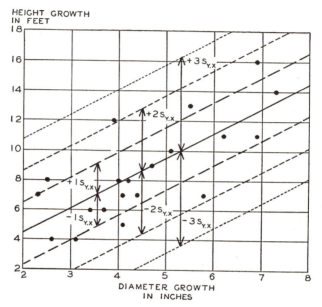

Chart 19.6. Estimating Equation and Zones of ±1, ±2, and ±3 Standard Errors of Estimate, for Diameter Growth and Height Growth of 20 Forest Trees. Data of Table 19.2.

extracted. This is the *standard error of estimate*,[4] the symbol for which is $s_{Y.x}$. Its formula may be written

$$s_{Y.x} = \sqrt{\frac{\Sigma(Y - Y_c)^2}{N}}.$$

In this illustration

$$s_{Y.x} = \sqrt{\frac{88.75}{20}} = \sqrt{4.438} = 2.107 \text{ feet.}$$

Calculations are shown in Table 19.2, Columns 7 and 10. Ordinarily the more expeditious method of calculation, which is explained on page 405.

---

[4] Although this measure is called the "standard error of estimate," it is not a standard error in the sense used in Chapters 24 and 25. $s_{Y.x}$ is the *standard deviation* of the Y values around the estimating equation $Y_c = a + bX$.

TABLE 19.2

Computation of Total Variation, Explained Variation, and Unexplained Variation, for Height Growth of 20 Forest Trees as Estimated by Their Diameter Growth

Rank in diameter growth (smallest to largest) (1)	Diameter growth at breast height in inches X (2)	Height growth in feet Y (3)	Y_c (4)	Deviations			Squared deviations		
				$y = Y - \bar{Y}$ (5)	$y_c = Y_c - \bar{Y}$ (6)	$y_s = Y - Y_c$ (7)	$y^2 = (Y - \bar{Y})^2$ (8)	$y_c^2 = (Y_c - \bar{Y})^2$ (9)	$y_s^2 = (Y - Y_c)^2$ (10)
1	2.3	7	4.902	-1.65	-3.748	2.098	2.7225	14.0475	4.4016
2	2.5	8	5.238	-0.65	-3.412	2.762	0.4225	11.6417	7.6286
3	2.6	4	5.405	-4.65	-3.245	-1.405	21.6225	10.5300	1.9740
4	3.1	4	6.244	-4.65	-2.406	-2.244	21.6225	5.7888	5.0355
5	3.4	6	6.747	-2.65	-1.903	-0.747	7.0225	3.6214	0.5580
6	3.7	6	7.250	-2.65	-1.400	-1.250	7.0225	1.9600	1.5625
7	3.9	12	7.585	3.35	-1.065	4.415	11.2225	1.1342	19.4922
8	4.0	8	7.753	-0.65	-0.897	0.247	0.4225	0.8046	0.0610
9	4.1	5	7.921	-3.65	-0.729	-2.921	13.3225	0.5314	8.5322
10	4.1	7	7.921	-1.65	-0.729	-0.921	2.7225	0.5314	0.8482
11	4.2	8	8.088	-0.65	-0.562	-0.088	0.4225	0.3147	0.0077
12	4.4	7	8.424	-1.65	-0.226	-1.424	2.7225	0.0511	2.0278
13	4.7	9	8.927	0.35	0.277	0.073	0.1225	0.0767	0.0053
14	5.1	10	9.598	1.35	0.948	0.402	1.8225	0.8987	0.1616
15	5.5	13	10.268	4.35	1.618	2.732	18.9225	2.6179	7.4638
16	5.8	7	10.772	-1.65	2.122	-3.772	2.7225	4.5029	14.2280
17	6.2	11	11.442	2.35	2.792	-0.442	5.5225	7.7953	0.1954
18	6.9	11	12.616	2.35	3.966	-1.616	5.5225	15.7292	2.6115
19	6.9	16	12.616	7.35	3.966	3.384	54.0225	15.7292	11.4515
20	7.3	14	13.287	5.35	4.637	0.713	28.625	21.5018	0.5084
Total....	90.7	173	173.004	0	0.004	-0.004	208.5500	119.8085	88.7548

would be used.   The above method is used solely to explain the meaning of the measure.

This measure may be interpreted in a manner strictly analogous to that of the standard deviation of a frequency distribution.   It yields an estimate of the range above and below the line of estimation within which 68.27 per cent of the items may be expected to fall if the scatter is normal. In practice we frequently think of this measure as the range within which about $\frac{2}{3}$ of the values will be found.   For the case in hand ($s_{Y.x} = 2.107$), we may expect to find about $\frac{2}{3}$ of the items of Chart 19.6 within the narrow band $\pm s_{Y.x}$ shown in the diagram; about 95 per cent (ideally 95.45) within the wider band that includes $\pm 2s_{Y.x}$; and practically all within $\pm 3s_{Y.x}$ (theoretically, with a large number of items, 99.73 per cent of the cases).   A count of the dots shows that within $\pm s_{Y.x}$ of the line of estimate, 13 of the 20 items (65 per cent) are found; within $\pm 2s_{Y.x}$ of the line, 19 of the items (95 per cent) appear; and within $\pm 3s_{Y.x}$ are included all 20 of the items.   The slight discrepancies may have been due to the fact that the sample was small and the scatter not normally distributed around the estimating equation.

Although the standard error of estimate is a measure of the dispersion of *all of the* Y *values* around the estimating equation, and is therefore a general or over-all measure of dispersion, it is nevertheless often used to indicate the dependability of specific estimates.   It was calculated that trees with growth in diameter of 5.5 inches should average 10.268 feet in height growth.   We may now amplify the statement by saying that, if our sample is representative, about $\frac{2}{3}$ of such trees should vary in height growth between 8.16 feet and 12.38 feet (10.268 $\pm$ 2.107); or, considering a slightly wider range, about 95 out of 100 should lie between 6.05 feet and 14.48 feet.   The proportion lying within any other range could readily be computed also by referring to Appendix E.

These statements concerning range of error have to do, not with certainty, but only with expectation.   We have used only 20 items, and, even though the sample may have been carefully chosen, another sample of 20 would not give us precisely the same results as those obtained above. It might be that we could reduce uncertainty further, not only by increasing the size of our sample, but also by comparing variations in height growth with some other factor in addition to diameter growth—for example, age, since as trees grow older their rate of growth may change. Also, the character and quantity of plant food in the soil and the degree of crowding of the trees might be considered.   Even if several factors in addition to diameter growth were considered (this is multiple correlation, discussed in Chapter 21), there would still be some unexplained variations, and therefore still some uncertainty.

The correlation coefficient and explained variation.   Another measure closely related to the estimating equation and to the standard error of estimate, is the coefficient of correlation r.   The estimating equation $Y_c = a + bX$ is a statement of the way in which the dependent variable changes with variations in the independent variable. $s_{Y.x}$ is an indication of the amount of dispersion in the dependent variable which we have failed to account for by our line of estimation, but it is stated in terms of the original data—in the case of the diameter-growth and height-growth data, in feet. When stating the degree of relationship between two variables, it is convenient to be able to employ concise numerical terms which are independent of the units of the original data and to express the degree of relationship between two series even if we do not know either the equation of the line of estimation or $s_{Y.x}$. To be sure, something is lost by so compressing the information, since it does not enable us to make an estimate of the value of one variable from the other, or to tell, in absolute magnitude, the degree of accuracy of any estimate we may make. But something is gained, too, since one coefficient can be compared with any other, regardless of the subject matter of the different correlations. As has been stated, the coefficient of correlation is a number varying from $+1$, through zero, to -1. The sign indicates whether the slope of the line of relationship is positive or negative, while the magnitude of the coefficient indicates the degree of association. When there is absolutely no relationship between the variables, r is 0.

A clear understanding of the meaning of the coefficient of correlation is given by the following approach. One measure of variability, called *variation* or *total variation*, is the sum of the squares of the deviations of the Y values from their mean, $\Sigma(Y - \bar{Y})^2$. This total variation can be broken up into two parts: (1) that which has been explained by our line of relationship, and (2) that which we have failed to explain. The *total variation* in height growth of the trees of our distribution, as indicated by the calculations in Column 8 of Table 19.2, is 208.55. The amount of variation which we have explained by our line of relationship is the sum of the squares of the deviations of the estimated Y values from their own mean (which is also the mean of the original Y values, as may be seen by dividing the totals of Columns 3 and 4 of Table 19.2 by N),[5] that is, $\Sigma(Y_c - \bar{Y})^2$. The *explained variation* is shown in Column 9 of Table 19.2 to be 119.81. The *unexplained variation* is the sum of the squares of the deviations of the Y values from their estimated values, $\Sigma(Y - Y_c)^2$. The unexplained variation is shown in Column 10 of Table 19.2 to be 88.75.

Let us summarize our findings:

Variation	Symbol and formula	Amount of variation*	Per cent of total variation
Unexplained...............	$\Sigma y_s^2 = \Sigma(Y - Y_c)^2$	88.75	42.6
Explained...............	$\Sigma y_c^2 = \Sigma(Y_c - \bar{Y})^2$	119.81	57.4
Total...	$\Sigma y^2 = \Sigma(Y - \bar{Y})^2$	208.55	100.0

* Because of rounding in Table 19.2, the two components slightly exceed the total. Later it will be seen that $\Sigma y_s^2 = 88.74$.

[5] See Appendix S, section 19.1, Equation 2.

It will be seen that we have explained 57.4 per cent of the variation in the dependent variable. Expressed as a ratio to one, 0.574, this is the *coefficient of determination*, r^2. The *coefficient of correlation*, r, is the square root of the coefficient of determination and has a value of $+0.758$ (the sign being the same as that of b), and may be thought of as the square root of the proportion of the total variation in the dependent variable that has been explained by use of the estimating equation. r will, of course, always be larger than r^2, unless $r^2 = 0$ or 1.0, when $r = r^2$. One outstanding advantage of the foregoing method of explaining the coefficient of determination and the coefficient of correlation is that the concept will also serve to explain non-linear and multiple coefficients, which are discussed in Chapters 20 and 21.

It may be helpful to some readers to be able to visualize the information of Table 19.2. Chart 19.7 shows, for the data of height and diameter growth:

A. The deviations of the actual Y values from their mean.

Chart 19.7. Total Deviations, Explained Deviations, and Unexplained Deviations for Height Growth of 20 Forest Trees as Explained by Their Diameter Growth. Data of Table 19.2.

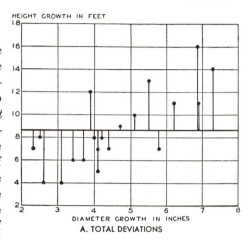

A. TOTAL DEVIATIONS

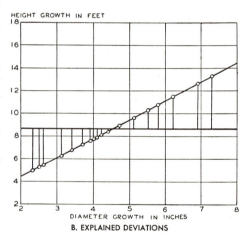

B. EXPLAINED DEVIATIONS

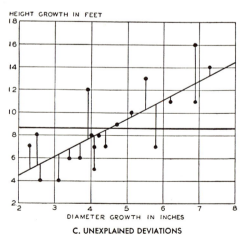

C. UNEXPLAINED DEVIATIONS

The deviations of the computed Y values from their mean. (Note again that $\overline{Y}_c = \overline{Y}$.)

C. The deviations of the actual Y values from the computed Y values.

The proportion of variation which has been explained was 0.574. The proportion which we failed to explain was 0.426. This is k^2, the coefficient of nondetermination.[6] Note that under all conditions $r^2 + k^2 = 1.0$. Note also that the maximum possible value for r^2 is 1.0 (when r is also 1.0); this would occur if all of the dots of the scatter diagram were on the line of estimation, as in Chart 19.2. If no variation were explained, r^2 (and r) would be zero, since the estimating equation would coincide with $\overline{Y}$.

As can be seen from Table 19.2, or from the summary of findings, total variation equals explained variation plus unexplained variation:[7]

$$\Sigma y^2 = \Sigma y_c^2 + \Sigma y_s^2;$$
$$208.55 = 119.81 + 88.75.$$

The equation may also be written

$$\Sigma y_c^2 = \Sigma y^2 - \Sigma y_s^2.$$

As computed in the preceding paragraphs,

$$r^2 = \frac{\Sigma y_c^2}{\Sigma y^2},$$

but we can also write[8]

$$r^2 = \frac{\Sigma y^2 - \Sigma y_s^2}{\Sigma y^2} = 1 - \frac{\Sigma y_s^2}{\Sigma y^2},$$

$$= 1 - \frac{88.75}{208.55} = 1 - 0.426 = 0.574,$$

which is the same value obtained before.

It was mentioned parenthetically, on page 462, that the sign of r is the same as the sign of b in the estimating equation. The sign of r can also be determined from inspection of the scatter diagram, unless the correla-

---

[6] While $r^2 + k^2 = 1.0$, $r + k > \pm 1.0$ unless $r = \pm 1.0$ or 0. k is called the coefficient of alienation.

[7] For algebraic proof, see Appendix S, section 19.1, Equation 7.

[8] Taking the square root gives the correlation coefficient:

$$r = \sqrt{1 - \frac{\Sigma y_s^2}{\Sigma y^2}} = \sqrt{1 - \frac{\Sigma y_s^2 \div N}{\Sigma y^2 \div N}} = \sqrt{1 - \frac{s_{Y.X}^2}{s_Y^2}}.$$

Reference will be made to this last expression later in the chapter.

tion is very low. The methods previously described for determining the value of r^2 or r were presented to explain the *meaning*[9] of the coefficients. They are too laborious to employ for day-to-day computations. Other formulas, more useful for purposes of calculation, will be given further on in this chapter.

The product-moment formula. The coefficient of correlation may be approached from a number of different points of view. As noted before, the explanation already given is particularly englightening, since essentially the same idea can be applied to curvilinear and to multiple correlation. But the following explanation is also simple and, for certain purposes, extremely useful.

In the estimating equation, b tells us the normal amount by which the dependent variable changes with a change of one unit in the independent variable. It is the slope or $\dfrac{y}{x}$ ratio of any point on the estimating equation, when y and x are defined as deviations from the mean of the series, so that the estimating equation becomes $y_c = bx$, and b is obtained by finding[10] the value of $\dfrac{\Sigma xy}{\Sigma x^2}$. Although this constant b is essential for purposes of estimation, still it cannot tell us the *degree* of relationship between the variables, since they are not directly comparable with each other. The X series and the Y series do not have the same dispersion, and they may even be in different physical units. However, comparability between the terms of the ratio $\dfrac{y}{x}$ can be obtained by dividing the numerator by s_Y and the denominator by s_X or by dividing the entire

---

[9] The correlation coefficient may also be explained in this manner: If the two variables X and Y are thought of as being composed of elements equally likely to be present in any item (some of which are common to X and Y, but some of which occur in the one and not the other), then the coefficient of determination of the entire population is the product of the two proportions of common elements, and the coefficient of correlation is their geometric mean. Let us take 5 disks (elements) marked on one side as follows (the other side being blank):

If we should throw all 5 disks into the air, when they fall, any number of X's from 0 to 4 might appear, and also from 0 to 3 Y's. Whenever an X appears, the chances that a Y will also appear on the same disk are 2 out of 4; likewise, whenever a Y appears, the chances are 2 out of 3 that an X will appear on the same disk. If we should throw these disks into the air a number of times, counting the X's and Y's each time, there would be correlation between the number of X's that appear from throw to throw and the number of Y's. The most likely value of r^2 is $\frac{2}{4} \times \frac{2}{3} = 0.333$, while the most likely value of r is $\sqrt{\frac{2}{4} \times \frac{2}{3}} = +0.58$. The larger the number of throws, the greater will be the tendency for r to approach this value. For a demonstration of this, see

[10] See Appendix S, section 19.2.

expression by $\dfrac{s_Y}{s_X}$. Thus, b is transformed into r as follows:[11]

$$r = \frac{\Sigma xy}{\Sigma x^2} \div \frac{s_Y}{s_X} = \frac{\Sigma xy}{\Sigma x^2} \cdot \frac{s_X}{s_Y} = \frac{(\Sigma xy)(s_X)}{N s_X^2 s_Y} = \frac{\Sigma xy}{N s_X s_Y} = \frac{\Sigma xy}{\sqrt{\Sigma x^2 \Sigma y^2}}.$$

In either of the last two forms, the ratio is known as the *product-moment* form of the coefficient of correlation. Thus it may be seen that r is merely the slope of the estimating equation when both numerator and denominator are in standard deviation units.

Now, since

$$r = b \div \frac{s_Y}{s_X},$$

$$b = r \frac{s_Y}{s_X},$$

and

$$y_c = r \frac{s_Y}{s_X} x.$$

Use of the estimating equation in this form will be made later in the chapter.[12]

---

[11] Another way of getting the same result is to think of r as a special case of b; namely, when the original data have been made comparable by expressing them in units of their own standard deviations. Thus,

$$\frac{\Sigma xy}{\Sigma x^2} \text{ becomes } \frac{\Sigma \left(\dfrac{x}{s_X}\right)\left(\dfrac{y}{s_Y}\right)}{\Sigma \left(\dfrac{x}{s_X}\right)^2} = \frac{\Sigma xy}{s_X s_Y} \cdot \frac{s_X^2}{\Sigma x^2} = \frac{\Sigma xy}{s_X s_Y} \cdot \frac{s_X^2}{N s_X^2} = \frac{\Sigma xy}{N s_X s_Y}.$$

The formula is often stated as $r = \dfrac{1}{N} \Sigma \left(\dfrac{x}{s_X} \cdot \dfrac{y}{s_Y}\right)$. The reason for the adjective *product-moment* becomes clear when it is realized that the word *moment* refers to the average of some power of the deviations from a mean. Thus, r is the first moment of the product of the variables when each has been previously stated in terms of its own standard deviation. For proof that

$$\frac{\Sigma y_c^2}{\Sigma y^2} = \frac{(\Sigma xy)^2}{\Sigma x^2 \Sigma y^2},$$

see Appendix S, section 19.3.

[12] No previous mention has been made of the estimating equation $X_c = a' + b'Y$, which minimizes the squared horizontal deviations. For this equation, the normal equations are:

I. $\Sigma X = Na' + b'\Sigma Y,$

II. $\Sigma XY = a'\Sigma Y + b'\Sigma Y^2.$

In the form $x_c = b'y$, $b' = \dfrac{\Sigma xy}{\Sigma y^2}$ and $x_c = r \dfrac{s_X}{s_Y} y.$

In the portions of this text dealing with linear correlation, we shall give exclusive attention to problems involving the estimating equation $Y_c = a + bX$. There are situations in which the estimating equation $X_c = a' + b'Y$ is appropriate and still other situations calling for estimating equations differing from either of these.

PRACTICAL METHODS OF COMPUTATION

The previous illustration involved a limited number of paired items in order to illustrate the theory of correlation as concisely as possible. In most practical problems, however, we have a large number of pairs of items. In practice, therefore, it is advisable to modify the foregoing methods slightly in order to save time.

As a preliminary step in a correlation problem, a scatter diagram should always be drawn. If only an approximate idea of the degree of relationship is required, inspection of the scatter plot yields satisfactory results. After a little experience in correlating, the statistician may be able to make surprisingly close estimates of r, by inspection, from the scatter diagram, and these may be good enough to help him to detect gross mistakes in computations of r. The scatter diagram may frequently be used for exploratory purposes and may occasionally yield sufficient information to eliminate the need for determining the coefficient of correlation.

We have already seen that

$$b = \frac{\Sigma xy}{\Sigma x^2}.$$

Since the first normal equation is

$$\Sigma Y = Na + b\Sigma X,$$
$$\frac{\Sigma Y}{N} = a + b\frac{\Sigma X}{N}, \text{ and}$$
$$a = \overline{Y} - b\overline{X}.$$

From these expressions, a and b may be obtained without solving the two normal equations simultaneously. We must, however, compute:[13]

$$\overline{X} = \frac{90.7}{20} = 4.535. \quad \overline{Y} = \frac{173}{20} = 8.65.$$
$$\Sigma xy = \Sigma XY - \overline{X}\Sigma Y,$$
$$= 856.0 - (4.535)(173) = 71.445.$$
$$\Sigma x^2 = \Sigma X^2 - \overline{X}\Sigma X,$$
$$= 453.93 - (4.535)(90.7) = 42.6055.$$
$$\Sigma y^2 = \Sigma Y^2 - \overline{Y}\Sigma Y,$$
$$= 1,705 - (8.65)(173) = 208.55.$$

The last summation will be needed later.

Then we obtain

$$b = \frac{\Sigma xy}{\Sigma x^2} = \frac{71.445}{42.6055} = 1.676896;$$
$$a = \overline{Y} - b\overline{X} = 8.65 - (1.676896)(4.535),$$
$$= 1.045277,$$

---

[13] For proof of the expressions for the summations, see footnote 3 in Chapter 21.

giving the estimating equation

$$Y_c = 1.045 + 1.677X.$$

Next we compute ΣY_c^2 by use of the expression[14]

$$\Sigma Y_s^2 = a\Sigma Y + b\Sigma XY,$$
$$= (1.045277)(173) + (1.676896)(856.0),$$
$$= 1,616.26,$$

and Σy_s^2 from

$$\Sigma y_s^2 = \Sigma Y^2 - \Sigma Y_c^2,$$
$$= 1,705 - 1,616.26 = 88.74.$$

We may compute either

$$\Sigma y_c^2 = a\Sigma Y + b\Sigma XY - \bar{Y}\Sigma Y,$$
$$= (1.045277)(173) + (1.676896)(856.0) - (8.65)(173),$$
$$= 119.81,$$

or

$$\Sigma y_c^2 = b\Sigma xy,$$
$$= (1.676896)(71.445) = 119.81,$$

and obtain Σy_s^2 from the alternative expression

$$\Sigma y_s^2 = \Sigma y^2 - \Sigma y_c^2,$$
$$= 208.55 - 119.81 = 88.74.$$

A convenient formula for obtaining $s_{Y.X}^2$ is

$$s_{Y.X}^2 = \frac{\Sigma y_s^2}{N} = \frac{88.74}{20} = 4.437,$$

and

$$s_{Y.X} = 2.106 \text{ feet.}$$

The coefficient of correlation is then obtained by the usual expression

$$r^2 = \frac{\Sigma y_c^2}{\Sigma y^2} = \frac{119.81}{208.55} = 0.574,$$

and

$$r = +0.758.$$

If preferred, r may be obtained by use of one of the expressions given in footnote 8.

---

[14] Proof that $\Sigma Y_c^2 = a\Sigma y + b\Sigma XY$ is given in Appendix S, section 19.1, Equation 3. Proof that $\Sigma y_s^2 = \Sigma Y^2 - \Sigma Y_c^2$ is given in the same section, Equation 5. For proof that $\Sigma y_c^2 = b\Sigma xy$, see Equation 6. For proof that $\Sigma y_s^2 = \Sigma y^2 - \Sigma y_c^2$, see Equation 7.

If all that is wanted is the value of r, it is most expeditious to make use of a formula which does not call for the value of a or b. It has previously been noted that

$$r = \frac{\Sigma xy}{N s_X s_Y}.$$

By substituting $X - \bar{X}$ for x and $Y - \bar{Y}$ for y and simplifying, this becomes[15]

$$r = \frac{N\Sigma XY - (\Sigma X)(\Sigma Y)}{\sqrt{[N\Sigma X^2 - (\Sigma X)^2][N\Sigma Y^2 - (\Sigma Y)^2]}}.$$

Entering the necessary values from Table 19.1 gives:

$$r = \frac{(20)(856.0) - (90.7)(173)}{\sqrt{[(20)(453.93) - (90.7)^2][(20)(1,705) - (173)^2]}},$$
$$= +0.758.$$

Note that this expression automatically supplies the sign for r.

SOME CAUTIONS

Correlation and causation. The coefficient of correlation must be thought of, not as something that proves causation, but only as a measure of co-variation. Any one of the following situations may, in fact, obtain:

1. *A variation in either variable may be caused (directly or indirectly) by a variation in the other.* The variable that is supposed to be the cause of variations in the other is usually taken as the independent variable and plotted along the X-axis. Thus, because dividends on stocks are thought to affect stock prices, rather than vice versa, a "dividends" series would be made the independent variable. It is a logical process which determines the statistician's belief that there is causal relationship between the two variables, and his belief as to which is cause and which is effect. It must be evident, then, that the coefficient of correlation in itself does not say that X causes Y, any more than it says that Y causes X.

2. *Co-variation of the two variables may be due to a common cause or causes affecting each variable in the same way, or in opposite ways.* If it should be found that there is correlation between automobile accidents

---

[15] For derivation of this expression, see Appendix S, section 19.4. Having obtained r by the expression above, it is possible to get the estimating equation and $s_{Y.X}$ from the formulas used with correlation of grouped data:

$$Y_c - \bar{Y} = r\frac{s_Y}{s_X}(X - \bar{X})$$

and

$$s_{Y.X} = s_Y \sqrt{1 - r^2}.$$

per 1,000 persons and per capita federal income tax payments, it should not hastily be concluded that it takes an automobile accident to jar a person into paying his income tax; nor is it necessarily true that making large tax payments incapacitates a person for driving carefully.   It is quite possible, however, that in states where the average income is high, the per capita income tax will be large, a large proportion of the people will own automobiles, and accidents will be numerous.

3. *The causal relationship between the two variables may be a result of interdependent relationships.*   Thus, a high price for a commodity stimulates its production; but increased production may increase or decrease the cost of a commodity, depending upon the period of time under observation and whether it is an increasing- or decreasing-cost industry, and through the change in cost the price will be affected.

4. *The correlation may be due to chance.*   Even though there may be no relationship whatever between the variables in the universe from which the sample is drawn, it may be that enough of the paired variables that are selected may vary together, just by chance, to give a fair degree of correlation.   Thus it might be found that, in a given group of male students, there was positive correlation between the size of their shoes and the amount of money in their pockets.   Yet it is hard to develop a theory as to why this should be so, and the chances are that another sample would yield quite different results.   In Chapter 26 brief attention will be given to measurement of the reliability of r.

Heterogeneity.[16]   In observational data, heterogeneity in a frequency distribution may often be spotted by bi-modality or the presence of a few items which are too far out of line with the other items to be considered a matter of chance.   On the scatter diagram, such heterogeneity may show up as a tendency for the dots to cluster into two or more groups, or for one or more dots to be far removed from the others on the chart.   Where heterogeneity is observed, it is better to classify the data on some rational basis and correlate each group separately.   Individual items clearly governed by a different set of causes should be eliminated before correlating.   If these common-sense steps are not taken, one may obtain a misleading impression, not only as to the degree of correlation, but sometimes even as to its sign.

Chart 19.8A is an illustrative scatter diagram showing low correlation. In Chart 19.8B, the two component groups are shown by means of different symbols, and it is seen that two fairly high correlations are present. It is also possible that two different groups, each having little or no

---

[16] In the following paragraphs the material dealing with heterogeneity is based on a discussion of the same topic in F. E. Croxton, *Elementary Statistics with Applications in Medicine and the Biological Sciences*, Dover Publications, Inc., New York, 1959, Chap. 6.   Charts 19.8, 19.9, and 19.10 are also from the book.

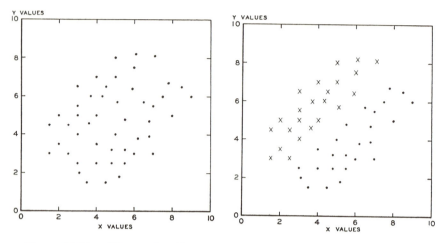

Chart 19.8A. Illustrative Scatter Diagram Showing Low Correlation: Two Dissimilar Groups Not Identified. From F. E. Croxton, *Elementary Statistics with Applications in Medicine and the Biological Sciences*, Dover Publications, Inc., New York, 1959, p. 128.

Chart 19.8B. Same Scatter Diagram as in Chart 19.8A, but Indicating Fairly High Correlation for Each of Two Dissimilar Groups, Shown by Crosses and Dots. From the same source as Chart 19.8A.

correlation, could be so located on a scatter plot that, if they were combined, moderate positive (or negative) correlation would appear to be present.

Another sort of heterogeneity is shown in Chart 19.9. There are nine clustered dots in Chart 19.9 which show low correlation, $r = +0.32$, and one dot far removed from the others. For all ten dots, $r = +0.79$. The presence of a single, almost certainly non-homogeneous (or, at least, non-comparable) observation such as this may result in an even higher correlation coefficient when little or no correlation exists for the other observations. It is altogether possible that Chart 19.9 illustrates also the sort of heterogeneity mentioned in the preceding paragraph; the upper four dots of the cluster of nine may represent a category different from that represented by the lower five dots. In any event, the investigator should look into that possibility.

It should be fairly obvious that the reverse of the situation shown in Chart 19.9 might also occur. That is to say, a cluster of dots might show high correlation, but one extreme dot might be so located that its inclusion with the others would result in low correlation. Chart 19.10 shows a situation in which a low correlation is made even lower through the inclusion of an extreme pair of values. r is decreased from $+0.348$ to $+0.290$.

Errors of measurement. Since errors in the measurement of the two variables are ordinarily not correlated, such errors reduce the size of r below its true value. Such *attenuation* can be corrected if the magnitude of the errors is known.

Use of averages. If the data to be correlated are first grouped into a number of size groups according to the independent variable, if $\overline{X}$ and $\overline{Y}$ are computed for each group, and if these means are correlated, the

correlation among the means will be higher than among the individual items taken as a whole (unless $r = 1.0$ for the ungrouped data). This is so because there is now no dispersion of the actual values around the various column means. Likewise, if the grouping and averaging is done for a number of rows of the dependent variable, the correlation will be increased. If the

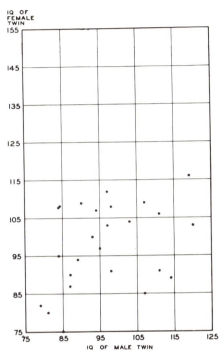

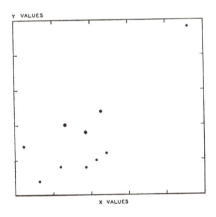

Chart 19.9. Scatter Diagram Illustrating a Type of Heterogeneity. The correlation is increased because of the presence of an atypical item in the upper right corner. This chart is drawn from actual data, the source and nature of which are withheld. Chart from page 129 of the source given below Chart 19.8A.

Chart 19.10. Scatter Diagram Illustrating a Type of Heterogeneity. The correlation is decreased because of the presence of a possibly atypical item at the top of the chart. The data represent the I.Q.'s of 26 fraternal twins of unlike sex and are from A. H. Wingfield, *Twins and Orphans*, J. M. Dent and Sons, Ltd., London and Toronto, pp. 121–123. Chart from page 111 of the reference given below Chart 19.8A.

increased. If the data are grouped according to both variables, so that data are grouped according to both variables, so that there is a number of cells, and if $\overline{X}$ and $\overline{Y}$ are computed for each cell and these paired cell means (rather than their mid-values) correlated, the correlation will be increased. The increase will be unimportant provided there is a large number of cells. As an illustration, the correlation of state averages will ordinarily be higher than that of the county values.

reveals that a curved line could more appropriately be fitted to the data than a straight line, r is a misleading measure, understating the closeness of the relationship. A curved line should be fitted, and a coefficient of non-linear correlation should be computed, following the procedure explained in Chapter 20. So doing will yield a higher coefficient and one which reflects more accurately the closeness of the relationship. Sometimes it may be better to transform one or both of the variables into logarithms, reciprocals, or some other function before correlating.

Elimination of relevant data. For instance, if retail sales and payrolls are correlated for cities ranging from 100,000 to 500,000 population, the correlation will usually not be so high as if cities from 10,000 to 5,000,000 are included. This is so because retail sales and payrolls are both positively correlated with population; and, when the range of values along both axes is extended, Σy_c^2 is increased without a corresponding increase in Σy_s^2. For data of this type, one must remember to guard against heterogeneity of the type illustrated in Chart 19.10. Consider also a different situation: if placement scores were correlated with monthly earnings for workers having two to five years' experience, the correlation might be higher than if all employees of this type were included, since earnings generally vary directly with experience, while placement scores are not necessarily correlated positively with experience.

CORRELATION OF GROUPED DATA

When the number of pairs of items to be correlated is large, time is saved if the data are grouped before calculations are undertaken. First the data are tallied,[17] as in Table 19.3, which shows the relationship between per cent rural farm and per cent with incomes under $3,000 for all counties in Iowa. This table resembles a scatter diagram except that each point, instead of being plotted exactly, is merely entered in the appropriate cell. Thus, a county with 5 per cent rural farm, and with 10 per cent with incomes under $3,000, would be tallied in the extreme lower left corner.

Table 19.4 is a correlation table. The figures in the center of each cell are taken from Table 19.3. The f_Y values are obtained by adding the numbers horizontally; the f_X values, by adding vertically. These two sets of figures will be recognized as frequency distributions of the dependent and independent variables, respectively. The total frequencies, or counties N, for each distribution are, of course, the same: 99. The three other columns and rows in the table are identical with those to which we are accustomed for computing the mean and standard deviation from a frequency distribution, except that here we have two frequency distributions, one of the X values (running horizontally) and another of the Y

---

[17] Sorting, instead of tallying, may be easier and less subject to error. This is particularly true if the data are on cards or if punch-card equipment is available.

values (running vertically). For ease in computation, deviations are measured in terms of class intervals from assumed means, that of X being chosen as 5.5 per cent and that of Y as 5.0 per cent.

TABLE 19.3

Tabulation of Per Cent Rural Farm and Per Cent With Incomes Under

$3,000 for Counties in Iowa, 1960

Per cent with incomes under $3,000 (Y)

Y	2.5-7.9	8.0-13.4	13.5-18.9	19.0-24.4	24.5-29.9	30.0-35.4	35.5-40.9	41.0-46.4	46.5-51.9	52.0-57.4
55.0-59.9									/ (1)	(1)
50.0-54.9						/ (1)			/ (1)	(1)
45.0-49.9				/ (1)				/ (1)	// (2)	/ (1) (2)
40.0-44.9								//// (4)	/// (3)	// (2)
35.0-39.9				/// (3)	//// (4)	//// (4)	THL (5)	THL / (6)	/ (1)	(1)
30.0-34.9					THL (5)	THL // (7)	THL THL (12)	/ (1)	/ (1)	(1)
25.0-29.9			/ (1)	//// (4)	THL /// (8)	/ (1)	/ (1)	/ (1)		
20.0-24.9	/ (1)	/// (3)	/ (1)	/ (1)						
15.0-19.9		//// (4)	//// (4)							
10.0-14.9	//// (4)									

Per cent rural farm (X)

Data from U. S. Bureau of the Census, *U. S. Census of Population: 1960*, Vol. I, *Characteristics of the Population*, Part 17, *Iowa*, pp. 17-166–17-168.

Since xy values are required for r, these also are computed for each cell and totaled. This is done by multiplying the X deviation by the Y deviation (shown in the upper part of each cell), and finally multiplying this product by the appropriate frequency. The results are shown in boldface type in the lower part of each cell. It will be noticed that the first and third quadrants are positive, while those in the second and fourth are, of course, negative. The algebraic total of these products is shown in the lower right-hand corner of the table. There is no subscript for f in the expression $\Sigma fd'_X d'_Y$, since each cell frequency is common to an X class and to a Y class.

When correlating grouped data, it is most expeditious to compute r first, after which the estimating equation and the standard error of estimate may be obtained.[18]

To obtain r directly from ungrouped data, the following formula was used:

$$r = \frac{N\Sigma XY - (\Sigma X)(\Sigma Y)}{\sqrt{[N\Sigma X^2 - (\Sigma X)^2][N\Sigma Y^2 - (\Sigma Y)^2]}}.$$

---

[18] It is, of course, possible to set up the two normal equations and obtain the estimating equation first. For the method of doing this, see the first edition of this text, p. 675 and pp. 856–857.

For grouped data, X is replaced by d'_X and Y by d'_Y, the symbol f is introduced, and the expression becomes

$$r = \frac{N\Sigma fd'_X d'_Y - (\Sigma f_X d'_X)(\Sigma f_Y d'_Y)}{\sqrt{[N\Sigma f_X(d'_X)^2 - (\Sigma f_X d'_X)^2][N\Sigma f_Y(d'_Y)^2 - (\Sigma f_Y d'_Y)^2]}}.$$

TABLE 19.4

Correlation Table of Per Cent Rural Farm (X) and Per Cent With Incomes Under \$3,000 (Y) for Counties in Iowa, 1960

Class limits / Y	X Mid-value	2.5–7.9 (5.2)	8.0–13.4 (10.7)	13.5–18.9 (16.2)	19.0–24.4 (21.7)	24.5–29.9 (27.2)	30.0–35.4 (32.7)	35.5–40.9 (38.2)	41.0–46.4 (43.7)	46.5–51.9 (49.2)	52.0–57.4 (54.7)	f_Y	d'_Y	$f_Y d'_Y$	$f_Y(d'_Y)^2$
55.0–59.9	57.45										+15 / 1 / 15	1	5	5	25
50.0–54.9	52.45							0 / 1 / 0	+8 / 1 / 8			2	4	8	32
45.0–49.9	47.45					−6 / 1 / −6			+3 / 1 / 3	+6 / 2 / 12	+9 / 1 / 9	5	3	15	45
40.0–44.9	42.45								+2 / 4 / 8	+4 / 3 / 12	+6 / 2 / 12	9	2	18	36
35.0–39.9	37.45					−2 / 3 / −6	−1 / 4 / −4	0 / 4 / 0	+1 / 5 / 5	+2 / 6 / 12	+3 / 1 / 3	23	1	23	23
30.0–34.9	32.45						0 / 5 / 0	0 / 7 / 0	0 / 12 / 0	0 / 1 / 0	0 / 1 / 0	26	0	0	0
25.0–29.9	27.45				+3 / 1 / 3	+2 / 4 / 8	+1 / 8 / 8	0 / 1 / 0	−1 / 1 / −1			15	−1	−15	15
20.0–24.9	22.45			+10 / 1 / 10	+8 / 3 / 24	+6 / 1 / 6	+4 / 1 / 4					6	−2	−12	24
15.0–19.9	17.45		+15 / 4 / 60	+12 / 4 / 48								8	−3	−24	72
10.0–14.9	12.45	+24 / 4 / 96										4	−4	−16	64
f_x		4	5	7	2	9	17	13	23	13	6	$N=99$	…	$\Sigma f_Y d'_Y=$ 2	$\Sigma f_Y(d'_Y)^2=$ 336
d'_x		−6	−5	−4	−3	−2	−1	0	1	2	3	…	…		
$f_x d'_x$		−24	−25	−28	−6	−18	−17	0	23	26	18	$\Sigma f_x d'_x = -51$		$\Sigma fd'_x d'_Y =$ 349	
$f_x(d'_x)^2$		144	125	112	18	36	17	0	23	52	54	$\Sigma f_x(d'_x)^2 = 581$			

Data from Table 19.3.

Substituting in this formula, we have

$$r = \frac{(99)(349) - (-51)(2)}{\sqrt{[(99)(581) - (-51)^2][(99)(336) - (2)^2]}},$$

$$= \frac{34{,}653}{\sqrt{(54{,}918)(33{,}260)}},$$

$$= +0.8108.$$

The following measures are readily computed from values shown in Table 19.4 by methods already familiar to the reader:

$$\overline{X} = 35.367 \qquad \overline{Y} = 32.551$$
$$s_X = 13.0191 \qquad s_Y = 9.2105$$

To obtain the estimating equation, we use

$$Y_c - \overline{Y} = r \frac{s_Y}{s_X} (X - \overline{X}).$$

Substituting in this equation, we have

$$Y_c - 32.551 = 0.8108 \frac{9.2105}{13.0191} (X - 35.367), \text{ or}$$

$$Y_c = 12.264 + 0.5736X.$$

Now since, as shown in footnote 8,

$$r^2 = 1 - \frac{s_{Y \cdot X}^2}{s_Y^2},$$

$$s_{Y \cdot X}^2 = s_Y^2(1 - r^2), \text{ and}$$

$$s_{Y \cdot X} = s_Y \sqrt{1 - r^2}.$$

Substituting gives:

$$s_{Y \cdot X} = 9.2105 \sqrt{1 - (0.8108)^2},$$
$$= 5.388.$$

Effect of grouping. The values obtained from the grouped data are not exactly the same as would have been obtained had the computations been based upon ungrouped data. Although the difference is ordinarily slight if there are at least 12 groups in each direction, the coefficient of correlation computed from the grouped data tends to be too small. It will be recalled that one formula for the correlation coefficient is

$$r = \frac{\Sigma xy}{N s_X s_Y}.$$

The errors from grouping tend to offset each other in the numerator, provided the X and Y distributions are approximately symmetrical. However, the standard deviations in the denominator tend to be too large, and Sheppard's correction should be used if the conditions under which this correction is appropriate are met.

If the 169 items are correlated, ungrouped $r = +0.8317$ which is, of course, higher than the value of $r = +0.8108$ for the grouped data of Table 19.4. If Sheppard's correction is applied (by subtracting $\dfrac{N^2}{12}$ from each expression enclosed in brackets in the formula for r for grouped data), r is found to be $+0.8271$. Actually, the validity of the use of Sheppard's correction for these data is open to doubt, since both series are of limited range.

CORRELATION OF RANKED DATA

Sometimes statistical series are composed of items the exact magnitude of which cannot be ascertained but which are ranked according to size or some other criterion. Thus, in Column 2 of Table 19.5, we have listed 10 basketball teams in order of their United Press rankings, as of February 14, 1966. In Column 3 we have listed the same teams in order of their Associated Press rankings. We wish to determine the extent of agreement between the two sets of authorities.

Since the coefficient of correlation previously explained is not designed to deal with ranked data, we shall use *Spearman's rank correlation coefficient*, the formula for which is

$$r_{\text{rank}} = 1 - \frac{6\Sigma D^2}{N(N^2 - 1)},$$

in which D refers to the difference in rank between paired items in the two series. In Table 19.5, it will be seen that the sum of the positive differences equals the sum of the negative differences, and thereby provides a check on the accuracy of the subtractions. Substituting the values in the formula, we have

$$r_{\text{rank}} = 1 - \frac{6(18)}{10(100 - 1)} = +0.9.$$

The formula gives the sign of the correlation coefficient, positive in this case. Whenever there is a tie in rank, the two or more positions should be split among the different items. Thus, had Duke and Texas Western tied for second and third in U.P. rankings, each would have been ranked

TABLE 19.5

Computation of Values for Correlation of Ranked Data: Basketball Team Rankings by Two News Services, February 14, 1966

Team	Ranking		Difference in Rank, D Col. (2) − Col. (3)		D^2
	U.P.I.	A.P.	+	−	
(1)	(2)	(3)	(4)	(5)	(6)
Kentucky.....................	1	1	...	...	...
Duke.........................	2	2	...	...	...
Texas Western................	3	3	...	...	...
Providence...................	4	6	...	2	4
Loyola (Chicago)..............	5	4	1	...	1
St. Joseph's (Penna.)..........	6	8	...	2	4
Kansas.......................	7	7	...	...	...
Vanderbilt....................	8	5	3	...	9
Nebraska.....................	9	9	...	...	...
Michigan.....................	10	10	...	...	...
Total.....................	...	...	4	4	18

Data from *The Record*, Hackensack, N. J., February 15, 1966, p. 33.

2.5; while if Duke, Texas Western, and Providence had tied for second, third, and fourth, each would have received a rank of 3.[19]

Two paired series of values are sometimes converted into ranks and r_{rank} computed to provide a quick estimate of r for the paired values. For instance, one might rank American League outfielders according to their batting averages and according to their fielding records and correlate these two sets of ranks. While r_{rank} may be computed more quickly than r, some time must always be spent in ranking the data. Also, it is well to remember that, if one wants only a rough estimate of the degree of correlation present, it may be had from a scatter diagram of the original values.

The reason the rank method is not so accurate as the ordinary method is that all of the information concerning the data is not utilized. Thus, the first differences of the values of the items in a series arranged in order of magnitude are almost never constant; usually these differences become smaller toward the middle of the array. If such first differences were constant, then r and r_{rank} would give identical results.[20] If the values, however, are distributed normally, there may be applied to r_{rank} a correction which will give the same result that would be obtained by comput-

---

[19] For a discussion, see W. L. Taylor, "Correcting the Average Rank Correlation Coefficient for Ties in Rankings," *Journal of the American Statistical Association*, Vol. 59, No. 307, September 1964, pp. 872–880.

[20] For proof, see Appendix S, section 19.5.

ing r directly. These corrections always serve to increase the correlation; however, they are very small, in no case increasing the correlation by so much as 0.02. Furthermore, the correction is not always appropriate. In the present illustration, we have only the upper tails of (possibly) normal distributions; if plotted, the data might appear as reverse-J distributions.

CORRELATION OF DATA IN 2 × 2 TABLES

Data are often encountered which fall into a dichotomous classification on each axis. Sometimes a correlation coefficient may be desired[21] for such a "2 × 2" table.

Table 19.6 shows data of the academic rank and academic output of 36 teachers in a department of a state university. Is there correlation between academic rank and academic output, as shown by the data of Table 19.6?

One method of obtaining a correlation coefficient for a 2 × 2 table consists of applying the product-moment formula. If we designate the values in a 2 × 2 table thus:

a_1	b_1	$a_1 + b_1$
a_2	b_2	$a_2 + b_2$
$a_1 + a_2$	$b_1 + b_2$	N

it may be shown[22] that the product-moment formula becomes

$$r = \frac{a_1 b_2 - a_2 b_1}{\sqrt{(a_1 + b_1)(a_2 + b_2)(a_1 + a_2)(b_1 + b_2)}}.$$

For Table 19.6 we obtain

$$r = \frac{(10)(13) - (5)(8)}{\sqrt{(18)(18)(15)(21)}} = \frac{130 - 40}{\sqrt{102{,}060}} = \frac{90}{319.5} = +0.282.$$

This expression will not yield a meaningful sign for r unless the two dichotomies are arranged as in Table 19.6, or unless *both* dichotomies are reversed; reversing only one changes the sign.

---

[21] Table 25.6 is a 2 × 2 table for which a correlation coefficient was not desired. However, the chi-square analysis discussed in Chapter 25 could be applied to the data of Table 19.6.

[22] The formula given above results from a simplification of the numerator of the expression developed in G. U. Yule and M. G. Kendall, *An Introduction to the Theory of Statistics*, twelfth edition, rev., Charles Griffin and Co., London, 1940, pp. 252–253. The development assumes that only two values are possible for each variable. This is true of both variables in Table 25.6. In Table 19.6 it is true of academic rank, since the two categories may be thought of as "full professor" and "not full professor." It is not true of academic output. For an extended treatment of 2 × 2 tables, see M. G. Kendall and A. Stuart, *The Advanced Theory of Statistics*, Vol. 2, *Inference and Relationship*, Charles Griffin and Co., London, 1961, Chap. 23, *et seq.*

TABLE 19.6

Academic Rank and Academic Output of 36 Teachers in a Department of a State University

Academic rank	Academic output		Total
	High	Low	
High..............	10	8	18
Low..............	5	13	18
Total............	15	21	36

Academic rank was "high" for full professors, "low" for all other grades. Academic output was measured by a system of points for each of a number of activities, such as books written, articles written, papers read, and so forth.

Another method of correlating data in a 2 × 2 table involves computing the *coefficient of mean square contingency, C*. This is computed from the expression[23]

$$C = \sqrt{\frac{(a_1b_2 - b_1a_2)^2}{[(a_1 + b_1)(a_2 + b_2)(a_1 + a_2)(b_1 + b_2)] + (a_1b_2 - b_1a_2)^2}},$$

which gives, for our illustration,

$$C = \sqrt{\frac{[(10)(13) - (5)(8)]^2}{[(18)(18)(15)(21)] + [(10)(13) - (5)(8)]^2}},$$

$$= \sqrt{\frac{8,100}{102,060 + 8,100}} = \sqrt{0.073529} = 0.271.$$

The computations do not automatically provide a sign for C, but a sign may often be supplied from examination of the data. In this case, it would be positive.

One advantage of the coefficient of mean square contingency is that its use is not limited to 2 × 2 tables. It may be used for larger tables, the formula for C being that given in footnote 23.

A disadvantage of C is the fact that C does not have a maximum value of 1.0. Its maximum value is less than 1.0; for example, it is 0.707 for a 2 × 2 table, 0.816 for a 3 × 3 table, and 0.949 for a 10 × 10 table. For

---

[23] This is a modification of the usual expression

$$C = \sqrt{\frac{\chi^2}{N + \chi^2}},$$

which makes it unnecessary to compute χ^2 for 2 × 2 tables. Chi-square is discussed in Chapter 25. For tables larger than 2 × 2, the usual expression would be used.

a table having the same number of columns as it has rows, the maximum value of C may be had from:

$$\sqrt{\frac{\text{number of columns (or rows)} - 1}{\text{number of columns (or rows)}}}.$$

Corrections may be made for this shortcoming of C, but they are not wholly satisfactory.

Various other methods of correlating data in 2×2 tables are available.[24] Among these are: tetrachoric correlation, the method of unlike signs, the cosine π method, and the method of concurrent deviations.

---

[24] See, for example, Kendall and Stuart, *op. cit.*, Chap. 26; and the first edition of this text, pp. 688–689.

CHAPTER 20

Correlation II: Two-variable Non-linear Correlation

The preceding chapter considered the simplest type of relationship between two variables: a constant amount of increase in the dependent variable associated with a unit increase in the independent variable. Not always, however, is the linear hypothesis satisfactory. The data of diameter growth and height growth of the trees, shown in Chart 19.5, were adequately described by a linear estimating equation. The relationship between the diameter and the volume of trees is not linear, as may be seen in Chart 20.1, which presents the data of Table 20.1. As noted in the table, the volume figures represent one-tenth of the number of board feet of lumber in a tree. The 20 pairs of values are for ponderosa pine trees selected at random from a Tree Measurement Book from the Coconino National Forest in Arizona.

POLYNOMIALS

Second-degree curve. To describe the relationship between diameter and volume, we shall first employ an estimating equation of the type

$$Y_c = a + bX + cX^2$$

and compare our results with those obtained when using a straight line. After considering an estimating equation of the type

$$Y_c = a + bX + cX^2 + dX^3,$$

for a different set of illustrative data, we shall return to the data of diameter and volume of ponderosa pine trees and examine several possible transformations of those data.

For a second-degree curve, three normal equations are required. They are:

$$\text{I.} \quad \Sigma Y = Na + b\Sigma X + c\Sigma X^2;$$
$$\text{II.} \quad \Sigma XY = a\Sigma X + b\Sigma X^2 + c\Sigma X^3;$$
$$\text{III.} \quad \Sigma X^2 Y = a\Sigma X^2 + b\Sigma X^3 + c\Sigma X^4.$$

419

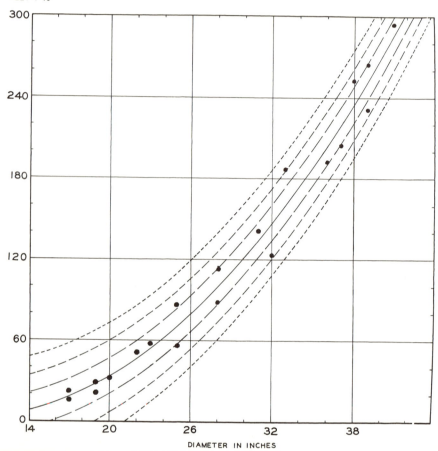

Chart 20.1. **Diameter and Volume of Twenty Ponderosa Pine Trees and Second-Degree Estimating Equation, with Zones of ±1, ±2, and ±3 Standard Errors of Estimate.** Data of Table 20.1. Estimating equation shown by solid line.

Substituting the values obtained in Table 20.1, we have

$$
\begin{aligned}
\text{I.} && 2{,}460 &= 20a + 569b + 17{,}437c; \\
\text{II.} && 83{,}777 &= 569a + 17{,}437b + 567{,}749c; \\
\text{III.} && 2{,}949{,}733 &= 17{,}437a + 567{,}749b + 19{,}361{,}917c.
\end{aligned}
$$

In order to get the values of a, b, and c, it is necessary to solve these three equations simultaneously. In describing one procedure for solving three simultaneous equations, we shall first state each step in general

TABLE 20.1

Computation of Values Used for Determining Measures of Relationship Based on Straight-Line and on Second-Degree Curve for Diameter and Volume of Twenty Ponderosa Pine Trees

Diameter at breast height (inches) X	Volume* (board feet ÷ 10) Y	XY	X^2Y	X^2	X^3	X^4	Y^2
36	192	6,912	248,832	1,296	46,656	1,679,616	36,864
28	113	3,164	88,592	784	21,952	614,656	12,769
28	88	2,464	68,992	784	21,952	614,656	7,744
41	294	12,054	494,214	1,681	68,921	2,825,761	86,436
19	28	532	10,108	361	6,859	130,321	784
32	123	3,936	125,952	1,024	32,768	1,048,576	15,129
22	51	1,122	24,684	484	10,648	234,256	2,601
38	252	9,576	363,888	1,444	54,872	2,085,136	63,504
25	56	1,400	35,000	625	15,625	390,625	3,136
17	16	272	4,624	289	4,913	83,521	256
31	141	4,371	135,501	961	29,791	923,521	19,881
20	32	640	12,800	400	8,000	160,000	1,024
25	86	2,150	53,750	625	15,625	390,625	7,396
19	21	399	7,581	361	6,859	130,321	441
39	231	9,009	351,351	1,521	59,319	2,313,441	53,361
33	187	6,171	203,643	1,089	35,937	1,185,921	34,969
17	22	374	6,358	289	4,913	83,521	484
37	205	7,585	280,645	1,369	50,653	1,874,161	42,025
23	57	1,311	30,153	529	12,167	279,841	3,249
39	265	10,335	403,065	1,521	59,319	2,313,441	70,225
569	2,460	83,777	2,949,733	17,437	567,749	19,361,917	462,278

* Volume was ascertained by means of the "Scribner decimal C" rule, which is described in D. Bruce and F. X. Schumacher, *Forest Mensuration*, McGraw-Hill Book Company, New York, pp. 159–163.

Data supplied by courtesy of the Forest Service of the United States Department of Agriculture. The figures are a random sample from a Tree Measurement Book from the Coconino National Forest in Arizona.

terms and then indicate the specific operation for this problem. The steps are:

1. Multiply normal equation I by such a number that the coefficient of one unknown will become the same as the coefficient of the same unknown in normal equation II. For our data, normal equation I is multiplied by $\Sigma X \div N = 28.45$ to yield

   (I × 28.45). $69,987 = 569a + 16,188.05b + 496,082.65c.$

2. Subtract modified equation *I* from *II*, or vice versa, to yield Equation A, which will contain two unknowns. For the present problem, Equation A will contain only b and c.

$$\begin{aligned}
\text{II.} \quad 83{,}777 &= 569a + 17{,}437b && + 567{,}749c. \\
\text{(I} \times 28.45\text{).} \quad 69{,}987 &= 569a + 16{,}188.05b + 496{,}082.65c. \\
\text{A.} \quad 13{,}790 &= && 1{,}248.95b + 71{,}666.35c.
\end{aligned}$$

3. Multiply normal equation II by such a number that the coefficient of the unknown which is not in Equation A will be the same in II as in normal equation III. In our problem, we multiply normal equation II by $\Sigma X^2 \div \Sigma X = 30.644991$, obtaining

(II $\times$ 30.644991).

$$2{,}567{,}345.411 = 17{,}437a + 534{,}356.708b + 17{,}398{,}662.995c.$$

4. Subtract modified equation II from III, or vice versa, to get Equation B, which will contain the same two unknowns as Equation A. For our data, we have:

$$\text{III.} \quad 2{,}949{,}733 \qquad = 17{,}437a + 567{,}749b \qquad + 19{,}361{,}917c$$

(II $\times$ 30.644991).

$$\begin{aligned}
2{,}567{,}345.411 &= 17{,}437a + 534{,}356.708b + 17{,}398{,}662.995c \\
\text{B.} \quad 382{,}387.589 &= \phantom{17{,}437a +} \; 33{,}392.292b + 1{,}963{,}254.005c
\end{aligned}$$

5. Solve Equations A and B simultaneously (the procedure was described on pages 236–237) to obtain the values of the two constants in those equations. Doing this for the data of diameter and volume of the trees gives:

$$b = -5.620315;$$
$$c = +0.2903663.$$

6. Substitute, in any one of the normal equations, the values computed in Step 5 in order to find the value of the unknown which was not in Equations A and B. Using I, we have

$$2{,}460 = 20a + (569)(-5.620315) + (17{,}437)(0.2903663).$$
$$20a = 594.842;$$
$$a = 29.7421.$$

7. As a check, substitute the values obtained in Steps 5 and 6 in a normal equation not used in Step 6. Employing Equation II gives

$$83{,}777 = (569)(29.7421) - (17{,}437)(-5.620315) + (567{,}749)(0.2903663),$$
$$= 83{,}776.9987.$$

The second-degree equation for estimating tree volume from diameter is

$$Y_c = 29.7 - 5.62X + 0.2904X^2.$$

This equation is shown on Chart 20.1 by a solid line. In view of the appearance of the scatter diagram and the estimating equation, the reader may be surprised that b has a negative sign. The reason is that Chart 20.1 shows only part of the curve. If the chart were to be redrawn with a horizontal scale beginning at zero, the estimating equation would be seen to be roughly U-shaped.

For a tree having a diameter of 30 inches, the estimated volume would be

$$Y_c = 29.7 - (5.62)(30) + (0.2904)(30)^2,$$
$$= 122.1 \text{ tens of board feet.}$$

Total variation is computed by means of the same expression that was used for linear correlation,

$$\Sigma y^2 = \Sigma Y^2 - \bar{Y}\Sigma Y,$$
$$= 462{,}278 - (123)(2{,}460) = 159{,}698.$$

Since we have the values of a, b, and c, we can ascertain the explained variation, which is[1]

$$\Sigma y_{cY.XX^2}^2 = a\Sigma Y + b\Sigma XY + c\Sigma X^2 Y - \bar{Y}\Sigma Y,$$
$$= (29.7421)(2{,}460) + (-5.620315)(83.777)$$
$$\qquad\qquad + (0.2903663)(2{,}949{,}733) - (123)(2{,}460),$$
$$= 156{,}235.5.$$

We may now obtain $\Sigma y_{sY.XX^2}^2$ in the same manner as for linear correlation:

$$\Sigma y_{sY.XX^2}^2 = \Sigma y^2 - \Sigma y_{cY.XX^2}^2,$$
$$= 159{,}698 - 156{,}235.5 = 3{,}462.5.$$

The standard error of estimate is

$$s_{Y.XX^2} = \sqrt{\frac{\Sigma y_{sY.XX^2}^2}{N}},$$
$$= \sqrt{\frac{3{,}462.5}{20}} = 13.2 \text{ tens of board feet.}$$

The zones of ± 1, 2, and $3s_{Y.XX^2}$, around the estimating equation, are shown in Chart 20.1 by broken lines. Estimates of volume, such as that made for a tree having a diameter of 30 inches, may be written ± 13.2.

The coefficient of determination is, as before, the ratio of explained

---

[1] $Y.XX^2$ is a rather awkward subscript, but it indicates quite clearly that we are dealing with measures computed in relation to an estimating equation employing the first and second powers of the independent variable.

variation to total variation

$$r_{Y.XX^2}^2 = \frac{\Sigma y_{cY.XX^2}^2}{\Sigma y^2},$$

$$= \frac{156,235.5}{159,698} = 0.978.$$

The coefficient of correlation is the square root of this figure,

$$r_{Y.XX^2} = 0.989,$$

but it has no sign. The reason for the lack of a sign is that, when an estimating equation is curvilinear, the relationship between the two variables may be positive in one portion of the equation but negative in another portion.

Comparison of results with those obtained from the use of a straight line. From the appearance of Chart 20.1, it is quite clear that the relationship between the diameter and volume of the ponderosa pine trees is non-linear, and we shall see, in Chapter 26, that the correlation resulting from the use of the second-degree curve is significantly higher than that based upon a straight line. For the present, we are interested only in comparing the results just obtained with those for a straight-line relationship. Using N and the appropriate summations from Table 20.1, the solution of the normal equations

$$\text{I.} \quad \Sigma Y = Na + b\Sigma X \text{ and}$$
$$\text{II.} \quad \Sigma XY = a\Sigma X + b\Sigma X^2$$

gives

$$a = -191.124274 \text{ and}$$
$$b = 11.041275.$$

The straight-line estimating equation is

$$Y_c = -191.1 + 11.04X.$$

This equation is shown, by means of a solid line, on Chart 20.2, and it is clear that a straight line is not a satisfactory description of the relationship.

Explained variation, from the straight line, is

$$\Sigma y_c^2 = a\Sigma Y + b\Sigma XY - \bar{Y}\Sigma Y,$$
$$= (-191.124274)(2,460) + (11.041275)(83,777) - (123)(2,460),$$
$$= 152,259.2.$$

Total variation is

$$\Sigma y^2 = \Sigma Y^2 - \bar{Y}\Sigma Y,$$
$$= 462,278 - (123)(2,460) = 159,698,$$

VOLUME, BOARD
FEET ÷ 10

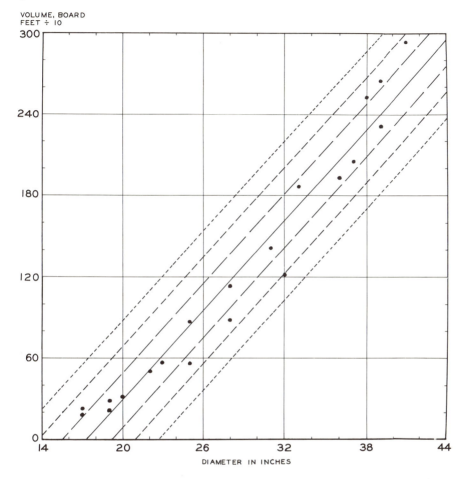

Chart 20.2.   Diameter and Volume of Twenty Ponderosa Pine Trees and Straight-line Estimating Equation, With Zones of ±1, ±2, and ±3 Standard Errors of Estimate. Data of Table 20.1.   Estimating equation shown by solid line.

the same as for the second-degree curve, and

$$\Sigma y_s^2 = \Sigma y^2 - \Sigma y_c^2,$$
$$= 159{,}698 - 152{,}259.2 = 7{,}438.8.$$

The standard error of estimate is

$$s_{Y.X} = \sqrt{\frac{\Sigma y_s^2}{N}}$$

$$= \sqrt{\frac{7{,}438.8}{20}} = 19.3 \text{ tens of board feet.}$$

a decidedly larger value than was obtained when the second-degree curve was used. The zones of ± 1, 2, and $3s_Y$ are shown on Chart 20.2 by broken lines.

As was to be expected, the linear coefficients of determination and correlation are smaller[2] than those based upon the second-degree curve. They are:

$$r^2 = \frac{\Sigma y_c^2}{\Sigma y^2} = \frac{152,259.2}{159,698} = 0.953, \text{ and}$$

$$r = +0.976.$$

Third-degree curve. As an illustration of the third-degree curve, and, incidentally, also of the law of diminishing returns, we shall use data derived from experiments with nitrogen fertilizer and tobacco yield at Tifton, Georgia. One thousand pounds of fertilizer per acre were applied to five different plots. Of the active ingredients, phosphoric acid and potash were held constant at 8 per cent and 5 per cent, respectively; and the nitrogen was made to vary as follows: none, 2 per cent, 3 per cent, 4 per cent, 5 per cent. Presumably the experiment was so conducted that differences in yield were not attributable to differences in soil fertility, drainage, and so forth, between plots. The experiment was repeated in three different years. Of the total variation, what proportion can be explained by the varying amount of nitrogen used? While it is possible that the experiment was not perfectly designed, the data indicate almost perfect correlation when the relationship is assumed to be of the type

$$Y_c = a + bX + cX^2 + dX^3.$$

This can be roughly verified by inspection of the scatter diagram, Chart

---

[2] It is possible to set up a measure

$$r^2_{YX^2.X} = \frac{\Sigma y^2_{cY.XX^2} - \Sigma y_c^2}{\Sigma y^2 - \Sigma y_c^2},$$

which expresses (1) the increase in explained variation, attributable to the use of X^2, as a ratio of (2) the amount of variation unexplained by using X alone. Dividing the numerator and denominator of the above expression by Σy^2 allows us to write

$$r^2_{YX^2.X} = \frac{r^2_{Y.XX^2} - r^2}{1 - r^2}.$$

This measure is strictly analogous to the coefficient of partial determination, discussed in the next chapter. It will be referred to again in Chapter 26 when we undertake to ascertain whether the non-linear coefficient of determination is significantly larger than the linear coefficient.

20.3.   The heavy horizontal lines are the average yields for each of the percentages of nitrogen which are given.   These means are not necessary for the solution of the problem, but are useful in discovering the type of curve to fit.

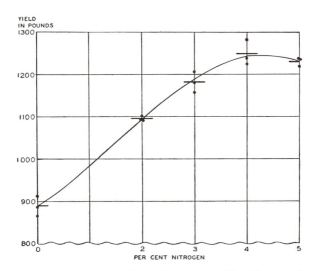

Chart 20.3.   Per Cent Nitrogen in Fertilizer and Yield Per Acre of Tobacco, at Tifton, Georgia. Data of Table 20.2.   The horizontal lines show the average yield per acre for each percentage of nitrogen, while the curve represents values computed from the third-degree equation.

Solution of normal equations.   Since four constants must be found, four normal equations of the following type must be used:[3]

$$\text{I.} \quad \Sigma Y = Na + b\Sigma X + c\Sigma X^2 + d\Sigma X^3;$$
$$\text{II.} \quad \Sigma XY = a\Sigma X + b\Sigma X^2 + c\Sigma X^3 + d\Sigma X^4;$$
$$\text{III.} \quad \Sigma X^2 Y = a\Sigma X^2 + b\Sigma X^3 + c\Sigma X^4 + d\Sigma X^5;$$
$$\text{IV.} \quad \Sigma X^3 Y = a\Sigma X^3 + b\Sigma X^4 + c\Sigma X^5 + d\Sigma X^6.$$

---

[3] Had three observations been taken for 1 per cent nitrogen, the origin could conveniently have been taken at the mean of the X values (2.5).   Then the sum of the odd powers of X would have been zero, and would have disappeared from the normal equations.   We should then have had two pairs of normal equations to solve simultaneously:

I. $\Sigma Y = Na + c\Sigma X^2$;

III. $\Sigma X^2 Y = a\Sigma X^2 + c\Sigma X^4$.

II. $\Sigma XY = b\Sigma X^2 + d\Sigma X^4$;

IV. $\Sigma X^3 Y = b\Sigma X^4 + d\Sigma X^6$.

The values required are computed in Table 20.2, and their substitutions result in the following normal equations:

I. $16,934 = 15a + 42b + 162c + 672d;$

II. $50,630 = 42a + 162b + 672c + 2,934d;$

III. $197,198 = 162a + 672b + 2,934c + 13,272d;$

IV. $822,884 = 672a + 2,934b + 13,272c + 61,542d.$

Following our previous procedure, we may solve together Equations I and II; II and III; III and IV, in each case eliminating a.   This gives three equations:

A. $48,222 = 666b + 3,276c + 15,786d;$

B. $80,256 = 1,980b + 14,364c + 82,116d;$

C. $790,152 = 23,724b + 178,416c + 1,051,020d.$

We may now solve together A and B and then B and C, eliminating b. The equations are thus reduced to two:

D. $- 42,029,064 = 3,079,944c + 23,432,976d;$

E. $-339,492,384 = 12,492,144c + 132,899,616d.$

Solving Equations D and E simultaneously, we find that

$$d = -4.4648847$$

and

$$c = 20.323899.$$

By substituting these values in Equation A, B, or C, we find that

$$b = 78.263630.$$

Substituting the values found for b, c, and d in Equation I, II, III, or IV, we find

$$a = 890.32389.$$

It is advisable to check the values of d, c, b, and a at each step, since any error made in the early stages will vitiate all subsequent computations. One method of checking is to calculate each of the constants twice, by substituting in two different equations.   Possibly even better is to substitute all of the constants known at any time in one of the remaining equations.   For instance, if the value of a has been found by substituting values of b, c, and d in Equation I, a final check may be made by substituting a, b, c, and d in Equation IV.   Thus,

$822,884 = 672(890.32389) + 2,934(78.263630) + 13,272(20.323899)$
$$+ 61,542(-4.4648847)$$

$= 598,297.65 + 229,625.49 + 269,738.79 - 274,777.93$

$= 822,884.00.$

TABLE 20.2

Computation of Values Required to Obtain Measures of Relationship Between Per Cent Nitrogen in Fertilizer and Yield per Acre of Tobacco, Tifton, Georgia

(Fertilizer is 1,000 pounds per acre; P_2O_5 and K_2O are 8 per cent and 5 per cent, respectively. The yields on all plots were unusually high in year 2; consequently, they were reduced by a factor which reduced their average to the average of year 1 and year 3.)

Plot number and year	Per cent nitrogen X	Yield in pounds Y	XY	X^2Y	X^3Y	X^2	X^3	X^4	X^5	X^6	Y^2
Plot A:											
Year 1	0	867	0	0	0	0	0	0	0	0	751,689
Year 2	0	889	0	0	0	0	0	0	0	0	790,321
Year 3	0	914	0	0	0	0	0	0	0	0	835,396
Plot B:											
Year 1	2	1,094	2,188	4,376	8,752	4	8	16	32	64	1,196,836
Year 2	2	1,101	2,202	4,404	8,808	4	8	16	32	64	1,212,201
Year 3	2	1,092	2,184	4,368	8,736	4	8	16	32	64	1,192,464
Plot C:											
Year 1	3	1,206	3,618	10,854	32,562	9	27	81	243	729	1,454,436
Year 2	3	1,180	3,540	10,620	31,860	9	27	81	243	729	1,392,400
Year 3	3	1,157	3,471	10,413	31,239	9	27	81	243	729	1,338,649
Plot D:											
Year 1	4	1,281	5,124	20,496	81,984	16	64	256	1,024	4,096	1,640,961
Year 2	4	1,238	4,952	19,808	79,232	16	64	256	1,024	4,096	1,532,644
Year 3	4	1,224	4,896	19,584	78,336	16	64	256	1,024	4,096	1,498,176
Plot E:											
Year 1	5	1,235	6,175	30,875	154,375	25	125	625	3,125	15,625	1,525,225
Year 2	5	1,237	6,185	30,925	154,625	25	125	625	3,125	15,625	1,530,169
Year 3	5	1,219	6,095	30,475	152,375	25	125	625	3,125	15,625	1,485,961
	42	16,934	50,630	197,198	822,884	162	672	2,934	13,272	61,542	19,377,528

$$\bar{Y} = \frac{16,934}{15} = 1,128.933 \text{ pounds.}$$

Data from W. J. Spillman, *Use of the Exponential Yield Curve in Fertilizer Experiments*, United States Department of Agriculture, Technical Bulletin No.

Actually the five columns containing powers of X are not necessary. The quickest way to obtain these column totals is to look up the sums of the required powers of the first five natural numbers, subtract 1 (since $X = 1$ is missing), and multiply by 3 (since there are three years)

The estimating equation, then is

$$Y_c = 890.32 + 78.264X + 20.324X^2 - 4.4649X^3.$$

Using this equation, the Y_c values may be computed as follows:

X	$a + bX$	cX^2	dX^3	Y_c (pounds)
0	890.32	0	0	890.3
1	968.58	20.32	$-$ 4.46	984.4
2	1,046.85	81.30	$-$ 35.72	1,092.4
3	1,125.11	182.92	-120.56	1,187.5
4	1,203.37	325.18	-285.76	1,242.8
5	1,281.64	508.10	-558.12	1,231.6

If we omit the Y_c value for $X = 1$ (since there is no observation for $X = 1$), sum the other Y_c values, and multiply the result by 3 (since there were three observations for each X value) we obtain 16,933.8 pounds, which is in agreement with the ΣY value of Table 20.2.

As can be seen from Chart 20.3, there is a point of inflection at about $1\frac{1}{2}$ per cent nitrogen, and the curve reaches a maximum of nearly 1,250 pounds shortly after the nitrogen reaches 4 per cent. These are, respectively, the points of diminishing marginal returns and diminishing total returns. How to locate these points more exactly is explained in Appendix S, section 20.1.

Correlation coefficient and standard error of estimate. To compute $r_{Y.XX^2X^3}$ and $s_{Y.XX^2X^3}$, we need $\Sigma y^2_{cY.XX^2X^3}$, Σy^2, and $\Sigma y^2_{sY.XX^2X^3}$. These are:

$$\Sigma y^2_{cY.XX^2X^3} = a\Sigma Y + b\Sigma XY + c\Sigma X^2Y + d\Sigma X^3Y - \bar{Y}\Sigma Y,$$

$$= (890.32389)(16,934) + (78.263630)(50,630)$$
$$+ (20.323899)(197,198) + (-4.4648847)(822,884)$$
$$- (1,128.93333)(16,934),$$
$$= 255,624.$$

$$\Sigma y^2 = \Sigma Y^2 - \bar{Y}\Sigma Y,$$
$$= 19,377,528 - (1,128.93333)(16,934),$$
$$= 260,171.$$

$$\Sigma y^2_{sY.XX^2X^3} = \Sigma y^2 - \Sigma y^2_{cY.XX^2X^3},$$
$$= 260,171 - 255,624 = 4,547.$$

From these we obtain

$$r^2_{Y.XX^2X^3} = \frac{\Sigma y^2_{cY.XX^2X^3}}{\Sigma y^2},$$

$$= \frac{255,624}{260,171} = 0.983.$$

$$r_{Y.XX^2X^3} = 0.991.$$

$$s_{Y.XX^2X^3} = \sqrt{\frac{\Sigma y^2_{sY.XX^2X^3}}{N}},$$

$$= \sqrt{\frac{4,547}{15}} = 17.4 \text{ pounds.}$$

Doolittle method. It must be confessed that, when there are as many as four equations to solve simultaneously, the above procedure is somewhat laborious. Furthermore, no check can be applied until the value of d is obtained. Even that does not check the accuracy of any work except the solution of the two equations (D and E) necessary to obtain c and d. All of the preceding work could have been honeycombed with errors and still the solution of these two equations would check. It is not until all of the constants are obtained that we have any real check on the accuracy of the solution of the four normal equations. If the final check fails, all of the work must be repeated.

Fortunately there is available for solving equations of this type simultaneously a systematic method that provides frequent checks on accuracy and is less laborious than the above procedure when there are four or more equations. It is known as the Doolittle method, having been developed by M. H. Doolittle. Like many labor-saving devices in statistics, the method at first seems very confusing. To a certain extent there is a substitution of complexity of procedure for repetitive drudgery.[4] In a multiple correlation problem (see Chapter 21), when there are four or more independent variables, it is especially advisable to use the Doolittle method for the solution of the simultaneous equations.

USE OF TRANSFORMATIONS

Instead of using a second-degree curve, or a curve of higher order, as an estimating equation, we may convert the readings for one or both variables into a different form. The most frequently used transformations involve logarithms, reciprocals, roots or powers, and logarithms of logarithms. Frequently, a transformation will show a linear relationship between the two converted series. We shall consider the use of logarithms, roots, and reciprocals for the data of diameter and volume of ponderosa pine trees which were used earlier in this chapter. First we shall examine the transformations graphically. Correlation analysis of the data will then be made for the transformations that appear most appropriate. The other transformations will be dealt with in symbolic terms only.

Preliminary examination. Based upon our experience with the semi-logarithmic chart in Chapter 5, it seems reasonable to think that the scatter diagram of Chart 20.1 might straighten out if we were to use a

---

[4] For a detailed illustration of this method, see the second edition of this text, pp. 498–503.

grid with a logarithmic vertical scale. In this event, we would use an estimating equation of the type[5]

$$(\log Y)_c = \log a + X \log b.$$

Such a scatter diagram is shown in Chart 20.4, and it is clear that the relationship between log Y and X is not linear.

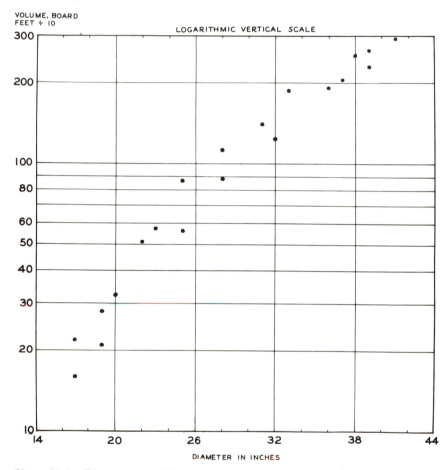

VOLUME, BOARD
FEET ÷ 10

LOGARITHMIC VERTICAL SCALE

DIAMETER IN INCHES

Chart 20.4. Diameter and Volume of Twenty Ponderosa Pine Trees Plotted on a Semi-Logarithmic Grid. Data of Table 20.3.

---

[5] The symbol $(\log Y)_c$ is used, rather than $\log Y_c$, to make clear that we are dealing with "the computed value of log Y," not "the logarithm of the computed value of Y." For parallel reasons, use is made in the following paragraphs of $(\sqrt{Y})_c$ rather than $\sqrt{Y_c}$ and $\left(\dfrac{1}{Y}\right)_c$ rather than $\dfrac{1}{Y_c}$.

In Chart 20.5, the same data have been plotted on a grid having both vertical and horizontal logarithmic scales. This transformation calls for the use of an estimating equation of the type

$$(\log Y)_c = \log a + b \log X.$$

The scatter diagram of Chart 20.5 indicates that the relationship between $\log Y$ and $\log X$ is virtually linear.[6]

Another transformation is possibly more logical than either of the two already tried. Since the volume of a cylinder is directly related to its

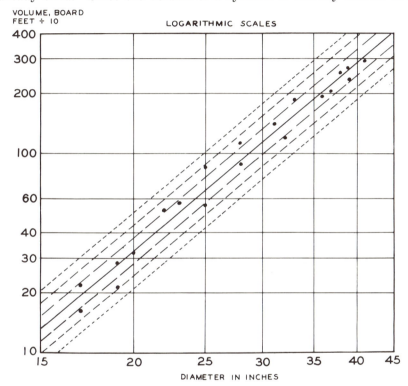

VOLUME, BOARD FEET ÷ 10

LOGARITHMIC SCALES

DIAMETER IN INCHES

Chart 20.5. Diameter and Volume of Twenty Ponderosa Pine Trees and Estimating Equation of Type (Log $Y)_c$ = log a + b log X, With Zones of ±1, ±2, and ±3 Standard Errors of Estimate, Shown on a Logarithmic Grid. Data of Table 20.3. Estimating equation shown by solid line.

---

[6] Occasionally an estimating equation of the type

$$Y_c = a + b \log X$$

is appropriate. For an illustration, see F. E. Croxton, *Elementary Statistics With Applications in Medicine and the Biological Sciences*, Dover Publications, Inc., New York, 1959, pp. 152–157.

length and to the square of the radius (or diameter) of its circular cross section, it would seem reasonable to try a transformation involving $\sqrt{Y}$ and X.   Of course, a tree is not a cylinder,[7] but Chart 20.6 shows a scatter diagram which appears to be more nearly linear than the preceding one. For this relationship, the estimating equation would be of the type[8]

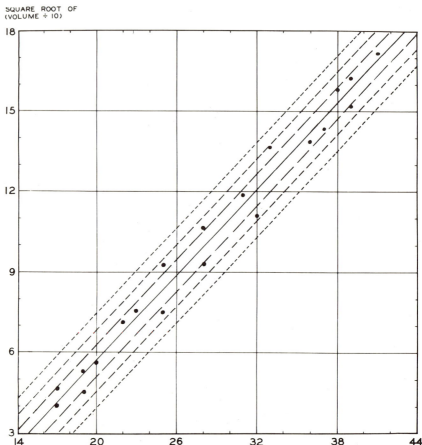

SQUARE ROOT OF
(VOLUME ÷ 10)

DIAMETER IN INCHES

Chart 20.6.   Diameter and Square Root of Volume of Twenty Ponderosa Pine Trees and Estimating Equation of Type $(\sqrt{\overline{Y}})_c = a + bX$, with Zones of ±1, ±2, and ±3 Standard Errors of Estimate, Shown on an Arithmetic Grid.   Data of Table 20.4.   Estimating equation shown by solid line.   A square root vertical scale could have been used for this chart.   A grid using a square root vertical scale and an arithmetic horizontal scale was not used here since paper ruled in this manner is not readily available to the reader.   The equally spaced vertical scale values could be 0, 1, 4, 9, 16, 25, and so on.

---

[7] See page 234 of the second edition of the reference mentioned below Table 20.1.

[8] See note 5.

$$(\sqrt{Y})_c = a + bX.$$

Although it is not reasonable to expect that $\frac{1}{Y}$ and X will produce a linear scatter diagram for these data, Chart 20.7 has, nevertheless, been prepared.   It is clear that this relationship is not suitable for these data, although it is sometimes useful for other series.   The estimating equation would be of the type[9]

$$\left(\frac{1}{Y}\right)_c = a + bX.$$

The reader may have noticed that the grids used for Charts 20.4 and 20.5 were so designed that the actual X values and Y values were plotted. Charts 20.6 and 20.7 did not employ special grids, but used arithmetic scales, and the $\sqrt{Y}$ and $\frac{1}{Y}$ values were plotted against the X values. Special grids could have been used for Charts 20.6 and 20.7; they were not used because they are not readily available to the reader.

We shall now proceed to compute the various correlation measures for the log Y, log X relationship and for the $\sqrt{Y}$, X relationship.   The log Y, X relationship and the $\frac{1}{Y}$, X relationship will be considered in terms of symbols only.   Because each of the four equation types which are involved calls for but two unknowns in the estimating equation, all procedures will parallel those for linear correlation of ungrouped data as described in Chapter 19.   The formulas will be the same as those previously used, except that, (1) log Y, $\sqrt{Y}$, or $\frac{1}{Y}$ will be substituted for Y, and (2) log X will be substituted for X when we use the log Y, log X relationship.

Since the four transformations which will be considered involve the logarithms, square roots, or reciprocals of the Y values, two points should be borne in mind: (1) the least-squares fit does not minimize the sum of the squares of the $Y - Y_c$ values; it minimizes the sum of the squares of the deviations of the *transformed observed* Y *values* from the *computed transformed* Y *values;* and (2) when stating the amount of dispersion of the actual Y values from the estimating equation, the standard error of estimate must be added to and subtracted from the computed Y values when both are in terms of transformed units; after the addition and subtraction, the results may be re-converted to units of the original Y series.

The log Y, log X relationship.   Chart 20.5 indicated that the

---

[9] See note 5.

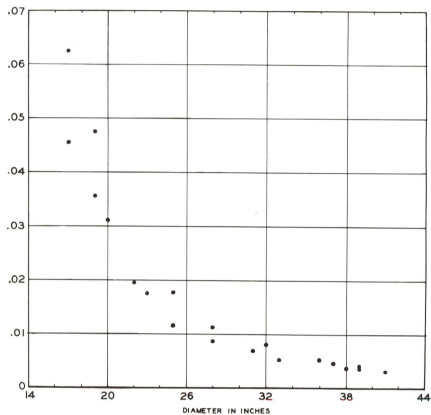

RECIPROCAL OF
(VOLUME ÷ 10)

DIAMETER IN INCHES

Chart 20.7. Diameter and Reciprocal of Volume of Twenty Ponderosa Pine Trees, Shown on an Arithmetic Grid. Data from Table 20.1, which does not show the reciprocals of the Y values.

relationship between diameter and volume was nearly linear when both series were expressed in terms of logarithms. The estimating equation is of the type

$$(\log Y)_c = \log a + b \log X,$$

and the constants $\log a$ and b are obtained by solving simultaneously the normal equations

I. $\qquad \Sigma \log Y = N \log a + b \, \Sigma \log X;$

II. $\Sigma(\log X \cdot \log Y) = \log a \, \Sigma \log X + b \, \Sigma(\log X)^2.$

Substituting, in these equations, the values from Table 20.3 (logarithms are in Appendix R) gives

I. $38.727389 = 20 \log a + 28.728012b;$

II. $56.619891 = 28.728012 \log a + 41.581145b.$

Simultaneous solution yields

$$\log a = -2.569125 \text{ and }$$
$$b = 3.136656.$$

The estimating equation may now be written

$$(\log Y)_c = -2.569125 + 3.136656 \log X.$$

Since the estimating equation which we are using is the linear form of

$$Y_c = aX^b,$$

the estimating equation, in terms of the original data, is

$$Y_c = 0.002697 X^{3.136656}.$$

(Note that $\log a = -2.569125 = 7.430875 - 10$, and its antilog is 0.002697.) The estimating equation is shown on Chart 20.5, which has

TABLE 20.3

Computation of Values Used for Determining Measures of Relationship Between Logarithm of Diameter and Logarithm of Volume of Twenty Ponderosa Pine Trees

(Logarithms are obtained from Appendix R.)

Diameter at breast height (inches) X	Volume* (board feet ÷ 10) Y	$\log X$	$\log Y$	$\log X \cdot \log Y$	$(\log X)^2$	$(\log Y)^2$
36	192	1.556303	2.283301	3.553508	2.422079	5.213463
28	113	1.447158	2.053078	2.971128	2.094266	4.215129
28	88	1.447158	1.944483	2.813974	2.094266	3.781014
41	294	1.612784	2.468347	3.980911	2.601072	6.092737
19	28	1.278754	1.447158	1.850559	1.635212	2.094266
32	123	1.505150	2.089905	3.145621	2.265477	4.367703
22	51	1.342423	1.707570	2.292281	1.802100	2.915795
38	252	1.579784	2.401401	3.793695	2.495717	5.766727
25	56	1.397940	1.748188	2.443862	1.954236	3.056161
17	16	1.230449	1.204120	1.481608	1.514005	1.449905
31	141	1.491362	2.149219	3.205264	2.224161	4.619142
20	32	1.301030	1.505150	1.958245	1.692679	2.265477
25	86	1.397940	1.934498	2.704312	1.954236	3.742283
19	21	1.278754	1.322219	1.690793	1.635212	1.748263
39	231	1.591065	2.363612	3.760660	2.531488	5.586662
33	187	1.518514	2.271842	3.449824	2.305885	5.161266
17	22	1.230449	1.342423	1.651783	1.514005	1.802100
37	205	1.568202	2.311754	3.625297	2.459258	5.344207
23	57	1.361728	1.755875	2.391024	1.854303	3.083097
39	265	1.591065	2.423246	3.855542	2.531488	5.872121
569	2,460	28.728012	38.727389	56.619891	41.581145	78.177518

* See note to Table 20.1.
For source of data, see Table 20.1.

logarithmic scales, and on Chart 20.8, which has arithmetic scales. Total variation is[10]

$$\Sigma(\log y)^2 = \Sigma(\log Y)^2 - (\overline{\log Y})\Sigma \log Y,$$

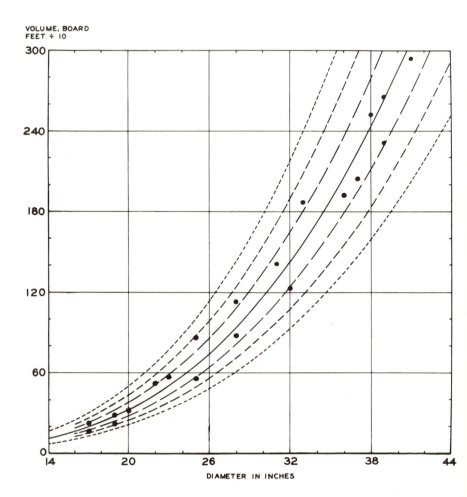

VOLUME, BOARD
FEET ÷ 10

DIAMETER IN INCHES

Chart 20.8. Diameter and Volume of Twenty Ponderosa Pine Trees and Estimating Equation of Type $(\text{Log } Y)_c = \log a + b \log X$ with Zones of ± 1, ± 2, and ± 3 Standard Errors of Estimate, Shown on an Arithmetic Grid. Data of Table 20.3. Estimating equation shown by solid line.

---

[10] Note that $\Sigma(\log y)^2 = \Sigma[\log Y - (\overline{\log Y})]^2 = \Sigma\left(\log Y - \dfrac{\Sigma \log Y}{N}\right)^2$. It is *not* $\Sigma[\log (Y - \overline{Y})]^2$. Similarly, $\Sigma(\log y)_c^2 = \Sigma[(\log Y)_c - (\overline{\log Y})]^2$ and $\Sigma(\log y)_s^2 = \Sigma[\log Y - (\log Y)_c]^2$.

where $\overline{\log Y} = \dfrac{\Sigma \log Y}{N} = \dfrac{38.727389}{20} = 1.93636945.$ The numerical value for total variation is

$$\Sigma(\log y)^2 = 78.177518 - (1.93636945)(38.727389),$$
$$= 3.186985.$$

Explained variation is[11]

$$\Sigma(\log y)_c^2 = \log a \ \Sigma \log Y + b \ \Sigma(\log X \cdot \log Y) - (\overline{\log Y})\Sigma \log Y,$$
$$= (-2.569125)(38.727389) + (3.136656)(56.619891)$$
$$- (1.93636945)(38.727389),$$
$$= 3.111085.$$

Unexplained variation may now be obtained by subtraction:

$$\Sigma(\log y)_s^2 = \Sigma(\log y)^2 - \Sigma(\log y)_c^2,$$
$$= 3.186985 - 3.111085 = 0.075900.$$

The coefficients of determination and correlation are

$$r_{\log Y.\log X}^2 = \frac{\Sigma(\log y)_c^2}{\Sigma(\log y)^2} = \frac{3.111085}{3.186985} = 0.976 \text{ and}$$

$$r_{\log Y.\log X} = +0.988.$$

We may show a sign for the correlation coefficient, because the relationship between $\log Y$ and $\log X$ is linear.

Since only two constants are involved in the estimating equation, we may compute the coefficient of correlation by using the modified product-moment formula. It will be recalled that this expression allows us to obtain the correlation coefficient without first ascertaining the constants in the estimating equation. For $\log Y$ and $\log X$,

$$r_{\log Y.\log X}$$
$$= \frac{N\Sigma(\log X \cdot \log Y) - (\Sigma \log X)(\Sigma \log Y)}{\sqrt{[N\Sigma(\log X)^2 - (\Sigma \log X)^2][N\Sigma(\log Y)^2 - (\Sigma \log Y)^2]}},$$
$$= \frac{20(56.619891) - (28.728012)(38.727389)}{\sqrt{[20(41.581145) - (28.728012)^2][20(78.177518) - (38.727389)^2]}},$$
$$= +0.988.$$

The standard error of estimate is

$$s_{\log Y.\log X} = \sqrt{\frac{\Sigma(\log y)_s^2}{N}} = \sqrt{\frac{0.075900}{20}} = 0.061604.$$

[11] If we were computing $\Sigma(\log y)_c^2$ and $\Sigma(\log y)_s^2$ from both $(\log Y)_c = \log a + b \log X$ and $(\log Y)_c = \log a + X \log b$, we would probably wish to distinguish, by means of symbols or otherwise, between the two methods of obtaining explained variation and unexplained variation.

The zones of ± 1, 2, and 3 standard errors of estimate are shown on Charts 20.5 and 20.8. Note that, on Chart 20.8, the zones of scatter depart more and more from the estimating equation as the value of X increases. On Chart 20.5, the zones are always equidistant because the scales are logarithmic.

It may be well to illustrate the computation of one Y_c value and to show how the standard error of estimate is employed. To ascertain the value of $(\log Y)_c$ when $X = 30$ (for which $\log X = 1.477121$), we write

$$(\log Y)_c = -2.569125 + (3.136656)(1.477121),$$
$$= 2.064095.$$

The antilog of this is 115.9, so that $Y_c = 115.9$ tens of board feet. To obtain the limits of $\pm$ one standard error of estimate, we write

$$\text{antilog } [(\log Y)_c \pm s_{\log Y \cdot \log x}] = \text{antilog } (2.064095 \pm 0.061604),$$
$$= \text{antilog } 2.002491 \text{ and } 2.125699,$$
$$= 100.6 \text{ and } 133.6 \text{ tens of board feet.}$$

For the limits of $\pm$ two standard errors of estimate, we compute

$$\text{antilog } [(\log Y)_c \pm 2s_{\log Y \cdot \log x}] = \text{antilog } (2.064095 \pm 0.123208),$$
$$= 87.3 \text{ and } 153.9 \text{ tens of board feet.}$$

For the limits of $\pm$ three standard errors of estimate:

$$\text{antilog } [(\log Y)_c \pm 3s_{\log Y \cdot \log x}] = \text{antilog } (2.064095 \pm 0.184812),$$
$$= 75.7 \text{ and } 177.4 \text{ tens of board feet.}$$

In a similar manner, limits may be obtained for estimates of volume based upon other values of X. It must be remembered, of course, that the $(\log Y)_c$ value and the $s_{\log Y \cdot \log x}$ value must be combined before antilogs are looked up in the table. Alternatively, the standard error of estimate may be applied to the Y_c values in the form of a ratio. For example,

$$\text{antilog } s_{\log Y \cdot \log x} = \text{antilog } 0.061604 = 1.1524 \text{ and}$$
$$\text{antilog } -s_{\log Y \cdot \log x} = \text{antilog } -0.061604 = \text{antilog } 9.938396 - 10,$$
$$= 0.8678.$$

Any Y_c values computed from our estimating equation may now be multiplied by these ratios to obtain the limits of $\pm$ one standard error of estimate. For the case where $X = 30$ and $Y_c = 115.9$, we get

$$115.9 \times 1.1524 = 133.6 \text{ and}$$
$$115.9 \times 0.8678 = 100.6 \text{ tens of board feet,}$$

the same values that were obtained before.   For limits of $\pm$ two or three standard errors of estimate, the procedure is the same, except that the initial step involves multiplying $s_{\log Y . \log X}$ by 2 or 3, or the ratios just obtained may be squared and cubed.

The $\sqrt{Y}$, X relationship.   Because the scatter diagram of Chart 20.6 appears to be more nearly linear than does that of Chart 20.5, we should expect to obtain a higher coefficient of determination or correlation for the $\sqrt{Y}$, X relationship than for the log Y, log X relationship.   However, the coefficients which we are about to compute cannot be much

TABLE 20.4

Computation of Values Used for Determining Measures of Relationship Between Diameter and Square Root of Volume of Twenty Ponderosa Pine Trees

(Square roots may be obtained from Appendix Q.)

Diameter at breast height (inches) X	Volume* (board feet ÷ 10) Y	$\sqrt{Y}$	$X\sqrt{Y}$	X^2
36	192	13.86	498.96	1,296
28	113	10.63	297.64	784
28	88	9.38	262.64	784
41	294	17.15	703.15	1,681
19	28	5.29	100.51	361
32	123	11.09	354.88	1,024
22	51	7.14	157.08	484
38	252	15.87	603.06	1,444
25	56	7.48	187.00	625
17	16	4.00	68.00	289
31	141	11.87	367.97	961
20	32	5.66	113.20	400
25	86	9.27	231.75	625
19	21	4.58	87.02	361
39	231	15.20	592.80	1,521
33	187	13.67	451.11	1,089
17	22	4.69	79.73	289
37	205	14.32	529.84	1,369
23	57	7.55	173.65	529
39	265	16.28	634.92	1,521
569	2,460	204.98	6,494.91	17,437

* See note to Table 20.1.
For source of data, see Table 20.1.

higher than those just obtained, since we found $r^2_{\log Y . \log X} = 0.976$ and $r_{\log Y . \log X} = +0.988$.

The estimating equation is of the type

$$(\sqrt{Y})_c = a + bX$$

and the normal equations are

$$\text{I.} \quad \Sigma \sqrt{Y} = Na + b\Sigma X;$$
$$\text{II.} \quad \Sigma X \sqrt{Y} = a\Sigma X + b\Sigma X^2.$$

Substituting values from Table 20.4 (squares and square roots are given in Appendix Q), we have

$$\text{I.} \quad 204.98 = 20a + 569b; \text{ and}$$
$$\text{II.} \quad 6{,}494.91 = 569a + 17{,}437b;$$

which, when solved simultaneously, give

$$a = -4.8587836 \text{ and}$$
$$b = 0.5310293.$$

The estimating equation, then, is

$$(\sqrt{Y})_c = -4.86 + 0.531X,$$

which is shown on Chart 20.6, where $\sqrt{Y}$ values and X values are plotted, and on Chart 20.9, on which the Y and X values appear.

Total variation is computed from[12]

$$\Sigma(\sqrt{y})^2 = \Sigma(\sqrt{Y})^2 - \overline{\sqrt{Y}}\,\Sigma\sqrt{Y} = \Sigma Y - \overline{\sqrt{Y}}\,\Sigma\sqrt{Y},$$

where $\overline{\sqrt{Y}} = \dfrac{\Sigma\sqrt{Y}}{N} = \dfrac{204.98}{20} = 10.249.$ Total variation is

$$\Sigma(\sqrt{y})^2 = 2{,}460 - (10.249)(204.98) = 359.1600.$$

Explained variation is

$$\Sigma(\sqrt{y})_c^2 = a\Sigma\sqrt{Y} + b\Sigma X\sqrt{Y} - \overline{\sqrt{Y}}\,\Sigma\sqrt{Y},$$
$$= (-4.8587836)(204.98) + (0.5310293)(6{,}494.91)$$
$$- (10.249)(204.98),$$
$$= 352.1940.$$

Unexplained variation is

$$\Sigma(\sqrt{y})_s^2 = \Sigma(\sqrt{y})^2 - \Sigma(\sqrt{y})_c^2,$$
$$= 359.1600 - 352.1940 = 6.9660.$$

---

[12] Note that $\Sigma(\sqrt{y})^2 = \Sigma(\sqrt{Y} - \overline{\sqrt{Y}})^2 = \Sigma\left(\sqrt{Y} - \dfrac{\Sigma\sqrt{Y}}{N}\right)^2.$ It is *not* $\Sigma(\sqrt{Y - \overline{Y}})^2.$ Similarly, $\Sigma(\sqrt{y})_c^2 = \Sigma[(\sqrt{Y})_c - \overline{\sqrt{Y}}]^2$ and $\Sigma(\sqrt{y})_s^2 = \Sigma[\sqrt{Y} - (\sqrt{Y})_c]^2.$

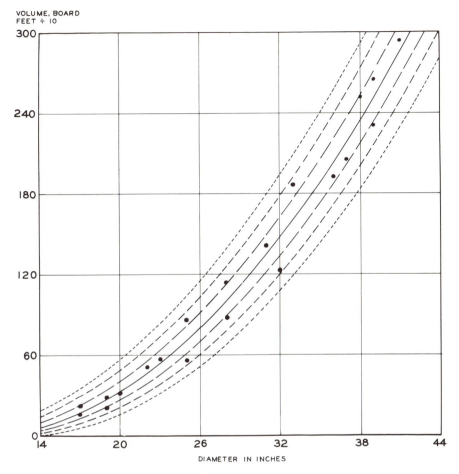

Chart 20.9. Diameter and Volume of Twenty Ponderosa Pine Trees and Estimating Equation of Type $(\sqrt{Y})_c = a + bX$, With Zones of ± 1, ± 2, and ± 3 Standard Errors of Estimate, Shown on an Arithmetic Grid. Data of Table 20.4. Estimating equation shown by solid line.

The coefficient of determination is obtained from

$$r^2_{\sqrt{Y} \cdot X} = \frac{\Sigma(\sqrt{y})_c^2}{\Sigma(\sqrt{y})^2},$$

$$= \frac{352.1940}{359.1600} = 0.981.$$

This value is slightly larger than that obtained from use of the second-degree equation $(r^2_{Y \cdot XX^2} = 0.978)$ and also larger than when the logarithmic estimating equation $(r^2_{\log Y \cdot \log X} = 0.976)$ was employed. The coefficient of correlation is the square root of the coefficient of determination,

$$r_{\sqrt{Y} \cdot X} = +0.990;$$

or, if a and b have not been computed, it may be ascertained from

$$r_{\sqrt{Y} \cdot X} = \frac{N\Sigma X \sqrt{Y} - (\Sigma X)(\Sigma \sqrt{Y})}{\sqrt{[N\Sigma X^2 - (\Sigma X)^2][N\Sigma Y - (\Sigma \sqrt{Y})^2]}},$$

$$= \frac{20(6,494.91) - (569)(204.98)}{\sqrt{[20(17,437) - (569)^2][20(2,460) - (204.98)^2]}},$$

$$= +0.990.$$

The standard error of estimate is

$$s_{\sqrt{Y} \cdot X} = \sqrt{\frac{\Sigma(\sqrt{y})_s^2}{N}} = \sqrt{\frac{6.9660}{20}} = 0.590.$$

The zones of ± 1, 2, and 3 standard errors of estimate appear on Charts 20.6 and 20.9. As in the case of the logarithmic relationship, the zones become wider, in absolute terms, as X increases. This may be seen in Chart 20.9. On Chart 20.6 the zones are equidistant because $\sqrt{Y}$ values were plotted.

When $X = 30$, the value of Y_c is obtained as follows:

$$(\sqrt{Y})_c = -4.86 + (0.531)(30) = 11.07.$$

Since $(\sqrt{Y})_c = 11.07$, $Y_c = (11.07)^2 = 122.5$ tens of board feet. To get the limits of $\pm$ one standard error of estimate, we compute

$$[(\sqrt{Y})_c \pm s_{\sqrt{Y} \cdot X}]^2 = (11.07 \pm 0.59)^2 = 109.8 \text{ and } 136.0 \text{ tens of board feet.}$$

The limits of $\pm$ two standard errors of estimate are computed from

$$[(\sqrt{Y})_c \pm 2s_{\sqrt{Y} \cdot X}]^2 = [11.07 \pm 2(0.59)]^2$$
$$= 97.8 \text{ and } 150.1 \text{ tens of board feet.}$$

For the limits of $\pm$ three standard errors of estimate,

$$[(\sqrt{Y})_c \pm 3s_{\sqrt{Y} \cdot X}]^2 = [11.07 \pm 3(0.59)]^2$$
$$= 86.5 \text{ and } 164.9 \text{ tens of board feet.}$$

In a similar manner, limits may be computed for other estimates of volume. It is important to remember that the $(\sqrt{Y})_c$ and the $s_{\sqrt{Y} \cdot X}$ values must be combined before the squares are obtained.

Comparison of the three non-linear relationships for diameter and volume of trees. Although it is clear that any one of the three non-linear estimating equations is preferable to the linear equation for describing the correlation between the diameter and volume of ponderosa pine trees, it is not at all obvious which one of the three non-linear equations is superior, since all of them give coefficients of determination which differ only in the third decimal place. All round to 0.98. It is rather unusual to find that several equation types give coefficients so nearly alike that there is little room for choice between them. However, it must be remembered that, in one sense, the coefficients are not strictly comparable. The second-degree curve explained 97.8 per cent $(r^2_{Y.XX^2} = 0.978)$ of the variation in the Y values. The logarithmic estimating equation explained 97.6 per cent $(r^2_{\log Y.\log X} = 0.976)$ of the variation in the *logarithms* of the Y values. The estimating equation using $\sqrt{Y}$ and X explained 98.1 per cent $(r^2_{\sqrt{Y}.X} = 0.981)$ of the variation in the *square roots* of the Y values.

The three standard errors of estimate cannot be compared with each other, since they are in different units. For the second-degree curve, the standard error of estimate is always 13.2 board feet $\div$ 10. When the logarithmic estimating equation is used, the standard error of estimate is always 15.2 per cent of the estimate in a positive direction or 13.2 per cent of the estimate in a negative direction. As pointed out in Chapter 19, the standard error of estimate is an over-all measure of the dispersion of actual values from estimated values, which is nevertheless applied to specific estimates. Table 20.5 shows estimates of volume of Ponderosa pine trees made by each of the three non-linear methods and the amount of error represented by one standard error of estimate in each direction, when $X = 18, 30,$ and 40. Estimates made by the second-degree curve and by the $\sqrt{Y}$, X relationship are not much different; all three equations give about the same estimate of volume when $X = 18$. In absolute terms, the error is constant whether X is large or small, when the second-degree equation is used; for either of the other two equation types, the error becomes greater as X increases. For small values of X, the logarithmic relationship shows the smallest errors; while for large values of X, the second-degree curve shows the smallest errors. The $\sqrt{Y}$, X relationship is generally intermediate between these two.

One criterion that has been suggested for comparing the suitability of different equation types consists of computing a Y_c value for each observed value of X and calculating $\sqrt{\dfrac{\Sigma(Y - Y_c)^2}{N}}$. This is $s_{Y.XX^2}$ for the second-degree equation, and, since the least-squares fit minimized $\Sigma(Y - Y_c)^2$, the value of $s_{Y.XX^2} = 13.2$ would be expected to be smallest. It is somewhat surprising that the $\sqrt{Y}$, X relationship, which involved a least-squares fit to the $\sqrt{Y}$ values, also gives 13.2 as the standard deviation of the Y values around the Y_c values. For the logarithmic relationship, which involved a least-squares fit to the log Y values, the standard deviation of the Y values around the Y_c values is 14.9. In each instance, the unit is tens of board feet.

Another criterion consists of undertaking to ascertain the estimating equation around which the Y values are most nearly normally distributed. Since N is only 20, this hardly seems appropriate for this example.

TABLE 20.5

Estimates of Volume of Ponderosa Pine Trees and Zones of $\pm$ One Standard Error of Estimate for Three Equation Types When $X = 18$, 30, and 40 Inches

(The values in the body of the table are board feet $\div$ 10.)

Estimating equation	$X = 18$ inches			$X = 30$ inches			$X = 40$ inches		
	Negative error	Y_c	Positive error	Negative error	Y_c	Positive error	Negative error	Y_c	Positive error
Second-degree..	13.2	22.5	13.2	13.2	122.1	13.2	13.2	268.9	13.2
Logarithmic....	3.0	23.3	3.6	15.3	115.9	17.7	37.8	285.8	43.5
$\sqrt{Y}, X$........	5.2	22.1	5.9	12.7	122.5	13.5	19.0	268.3	19.7

As indicated at the outset, there is little basis for choice among the three non-linear equation types. Perhaps the information presented in the preceding paragraphs, together with the logical implication of the $\sqrt{Y}, X$ relationship, mentioned on pages 433–434, may cause one to be inclined to choose it. When several procedures are of about equal merit, it is not inappropriate to choose the simplest one or the one which is easiest to compute. On this basis, too, we might select the $\sqrt{Y}, X$ relationship.

The log Y, X relationship. When correlating logarithms of Y values with X values, the estimating equation is of the type

$$(\log Y)_c = \log a + X \log b.$$

The normal equations are

$$\text{I.} \quad \Sigma \log Y = N \log a + \log b \ \Sigma X;$$
$$\text{II.} \quad \Sigma(X \cdot \log Y) = \log a \ \Sigma X + \log b \ \Sigma X^2.$$

Total variation is[13]

$$\Sigma(\log y)^2 = \Sigma(\log Y)^2 - (\overline{\log Y})\Sigma \log Y;$$

explained variation is[14]

$$\Sigma(\log y)_c^2 = \log a \ \Sigma \log Y + \log b \ \Sigma(X \cdot \log Y) - (\overline{\log Y})\Sigma \log Y; \text{ and}$$

---

[13] See note 10.
[14] See note 11.

unexplained variation is

$$\Sigma(\log y)_s^2 = \Sigma(\log y)^2 - \Sigma(\log y)_c^2.$$

The coefficient of determination may be obtained from

$$r_{\log Y.X}^2 = \frac{\Sigma(\log y)_c^2}{\Sigma(\log y)^2}.$$

The coefficient of correlation is, of course, the square root of the coefficient of determination. If $\log a$ and $\log b$ are not needed, $r_{\log Y.X}$ may be computed from

$$r_{\log Y.X} = \frac{N\Sigma(X \cdot \log Y) - (\Sigma X)(\Sigma \log Y)}{\sqrt{[N\Sigma X^2 - (\Sigma X)^2][N\Sigma(\log Y)^2 - (\Sigma \log Y)^2]}}.$$

The standard error of estimate is

$$s_{\log Y.X} = \sqrt{\frac{\Sigma(\log y)_s^2}{N}}.$$

The $\dfrac{1}{Y}$, X relationship. For this relationship, the estimating equation is of the type

$$\left(\frac{1}{Y}\right)_c = a + bX.$$

The normal equations are

$$\text{I.} \qquad \Sigma\frac{1}{Y} = Na + b\Sigma X;$$

$$\text{II. } \Sigma\left(X \cdot \frac{1}{Y}\right) = a\Sigma X + b\Sigma X^2.$$

Total variation is[15]

$$\Sigma\left(\frac{1}{y}\right)^2 = \Sigma\left(\frac{1}{Y}\right)^2 - \left(\frac{\overline{1}}{Y}\right)\Sigma\frac{1}{Y},$$

---

[15] Note that $\Sigma\left(\dfrac{1}{y}\right)^2 = \Sigma\left[\dfrac{1}{Y} - \left(\dfrac{\overline{1}}{Y}\right)\right]^2 = \Sigma\left(\dfrac{1}{Y} - \dfrac{\Sigma\dfrac{1}{Y}}{N}\right)^2$. It is *not* $\Sigma[1 \div (Y - \overline{Y})]^2$. Similarly, $\Sigma\left(\dfrac{1}{y}\right)_c^2 = \Sigma\left[\left(\dfrac{1}{Y}\right)_c - \left(\dfrac{\overline{1}}{Y}\right)\right]^2$ and $\Sigma\left(\dfrac{1}{y}\right)_s^2 = \Sigma\left[\dfrac{1}{Y} - \left(\dfrac{1}{Y}\right)_c\right]^2$.

where $\left(\dfrac{\overline{1}}{Y}\right) = \dfrac{\Sigma \dfrac{1}{Y}}{N}.$

Explained variation is

$$\Sigma \left(\frac{1}{y}\right)_c^2 = a\Sigma \frac{1}{Y} + b\Sigma X \frac{1}{Y} - \left(\frac{\overline{1}}{Y}\right) \Sigma \frac{1}{Y},$$

and unexplained variation is

$$\Sigma \left(\frac{1}{y}\right)_s^2 = \Sigma \left(\frac{1}{y}\right)^2 - \Sigma \left(\frac{1}{y}\right)_c^2.$$

The coefficient of determination may be computed from

$$r_{\frac{1}{Y}.X}^2 = \frac{\Sigma \left(\dfrac{1}{y}\right)_c^2}{\Sigma \left(\dfrac{1}{y}\right)^2},$$

and the square root is $r_{\frac{1}{Y}.X}$. Alternatively, the correlation coefficient may be had from

$$r_{\frac{1}{Y}.X} = \frac{N\Sigma X \dfrac{1}{Y} - (\Sigma X)\left(\Sigma \dfrac{1}{Y}\right)}{\sqrt{[N\Sigma X^2 - (\Sigma X)^2]\left[N\Sigma \left(\dfrac{1}{Y}\right)^2 - \left(\Sigma \dfrac{1}{Y}\right)^2\right]}},$$

which does not call for the values of a and b. The standard error of estimate is

$$s_{\frac{1}{Y}.X} = \sqrt{\frac{\Sigma \left(\dfrac{1}{y}\right)_s^2}{N}}.$$

THE CORRELATION RATIO, η

When data are arranged in a correlation table as in Table 20.6 and when a non-linear relationship is present, it is sometimes of interest to know the value of the correlation coefficient which would result if the arithmetic means of the columns were used instead of an estimating equation. Chart 20.10 shows, by the use of horizontal lines, the column means of Table 20.6. It also shows, for purposes of comparison, a second-degree curve fitted to the data. The measure of correlation, based upon the means of the columns, is $\eta_{Y.X}$, the correlation ratio. It is similar to the correlation coefficients that we have already discussed in that it is the square root of the proportion of the total variation in the Y series that

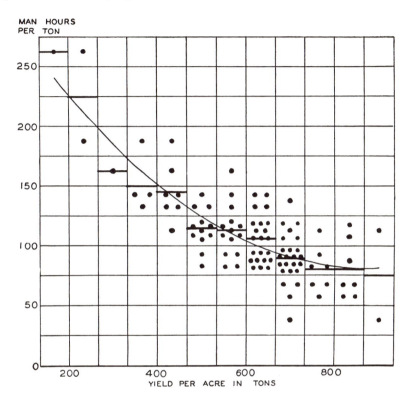

Chart 20.10. Yield per Acre and Man-Hours Per Ton Required to Harvest Broom Corn in East-Central Illinois. Horizontal lines indicate average man-hours per ton for each yield, while curve represents computed values from equation $Y_c = 325.6794 - 0.5658420X +0.0003275019X^2$. This equation was computed on pp. 721–725 of the first edition of this text. Data from source given below Table 20.6.

has been explained by the variation of the column means.[16] That is

$$\eta_{Y.X} = \sqrt{\frac{\text{variation explained by column means}}{\text{total variation of the } Y \text{ series}}},$$

---

[16] There is also a correlation ratio, $\eta_{X.Y}$, which is the square root of the proportion of the total variation in the X series that has been explained by the variation of the row means.

or, in symbols,[17]

$$\eta_{Y.x}^2 = \frac{\sum_1^k [N_c(\bar{Y}_c - \bar{Y})^2]}{\sum(Y - \bar{Y})^2} = \frac{\sum_1^k \left[\frac{\left(\sum_1^{N_c} Y\right)^2}{N_c} \right] - \bar{Y}\sum Y}{\sum Y^2 - \bar{Y}\sum Y},$$

$$= \frac{\sum_1^k \left[\frac{\left(\sum_1^{N_c} Y\right)^2}{N_c} \right] - \frac{(\sum Y)^2}{N}}{\sum Y^2 - \frac{(\sum Y)^2}{N}},$$

where $\bar{Y}_c$ is the arithmetic mean of a column,

N_c is the number of items in a column,

$\sum\limits_1^{N_c}$ indicates a summation over the N_c items in a column, and

$\sum\limits_1^{k}$ indicates a summation over the k columns.

Since the data of a correlation table are in terms of class intervals, this expression must be rewritten as for a frequency distribution or as for a correlation coefficient computed from a correlation table. The expression becomes

$$\eta_{Y.x}^2 = \frac{\sum_1^k \left[\frac{\left(\sum_1^{N_c} f_Y d_Y'\right)^2}{N_c} \right] - \frac{(\sum f_Y d_Y')^2}{N}}{\sum f_Y(d_Y')^2 - \frac{(\sum f_Y d_Y')^2}{N}}.$$

Substituting the values from Table 20.6 gives

$$\eta_{Y.x}^2 = \frac{150.60065 - \frac{(16)^2}{103}}{220 - \frac{(16)^2}{103}} = \frac{148.115}{217.515},$$

$$= 0.681,$$

indicating that 68 per cent of the variation in man hours (the Y variable) has been explained by the use of the column means. The correlation

---

[17] Proof of the equality of the first and last of the three expressions follows that shown in Appendix S, section 26.1.

TABLE 20.6

Computations Required to Obtain Correlation Ratio Between Yield Per Acre of Broom Corn and Man-Hours Per Ton Required for Harvesting in East-Central Illinois

(Yield per acre in tons, X)

Cost in hours (Y)

Class	Mid-value	d'y	133.34–199.99 (166.67)		200.00–266.66 (233.33)		266.67–333.33 (300.00)		333.34–399.99 (366.67)		400.00–466.66 (433.33)		466.67–533.33 (500.00)		533.34–599.99 (566.67)		600.00–666.66 (633.33)		666.67–733.33 (700.00)		733.34–799.99 (766.67)		800.00–866.66 (833.33)		866.67–933.33 (900.00)		Entire distribution		
			f	fyd'y	f	fyd'y	f	fyd'y	f	fyd'y	f	fyd'y	f	fyd'y	f	fyd'y	f	fyd'y	f	fyd'y	f	fyd'y	f	fyd'y	f	fyd'y	fy	fyd'y	fy(d'y)²
250.00–274.99	262.50	6	1	6	1	6																						2	12	72
225.00–249.99	237.50	5																												
200.00–224.99	212.50	4																												
175.00–199.99	187.50	3			1	3			1	3	1	3															3	9	27
150.00–174.99	162.50	2					1	2			1	2			1	2											3	6	12
125.00–149.99	137.50	1							3	3	4	4	3	3	2	2	4	4	1	1							17	17	17
100.00–124.99	112.50	0									1	0	7	0	7	0	8	0	5	0	1	0	2	0	1	0	32	0	0
75.00–99.99	87.50	−1											2	−2	4	−4	10	−10	14	−14	3	−3	1	−1			34	−34	34
50.00–74.99	62.50	−2																	3	−6	3	−6	4	−8			10	−20	40
25.00–49.99	37.50	−3																	1	−3					1	−3	2	−6	18
Description of row:																													
1. Total			1	6	2	9	1	2	4	6	7	9	12	1	14	0	22	−6	24	−22	7	−9	7	−9	2	−3	103	−16	
2. $\dfrac{\Sigma f y d'y}{N_e}$			6.0000000		4.5000000		2.0000000		1.5000000		1.2857142		.0833333		.0000000		−.2727273		−.9166667		−1.2857142		−1.2857142		−1.5000000				
3. $\dfrac{(\Sigma f y d'y)^2}{N_e}$			36.00000		40.50000		4.00000		9.00000		11.57143		.08333		.00000		1.63636		20.16667		11.57143		11.57143		4.50000				150.60085

Data adapted from a chart on page 27 of *An Economic Study of Broom Corn Production*, by R. S. Washburn and J. H. Martin, U. S. Department of Agriculture, Technical Bulletin No. 349.

ratio is the square root of this value, so

$$\eta_{Y.X} = \sqrt{0.681} = 0.825.$$

The correlation ratio has no sign, since the relationship is not necessarily positive, or negative, for all values of the two series with which one may be dealing. Furthermore, the horizontal axis may represent qualitative categories rather than numerical values.

The correlation ratio is of interest primarily because of its relationship to the curvilinear correlation coefficient. The correlation ratio is always equal to or larger than the correlation coefficient obtained by use of a curve fitted to the grouped data, provided the number of constants in the equation is equal to or smaller than the number of columns used in computing $\eta_{Y.X}$. Both $\eta_{Y.X}$ and the curvilinear correlation coefficient become larger as the number of columns or the number of constants in the equation is increased.

There are several limitations to the usefulness of the correlation ratio. First, the data must be grouped—not necessarily on both axes, but the independent variable must be grouped. Second, if the number of groups for the independent variable is increased, the value of the correlation ratio increases, becoming 1.0 if the groups become so numerous that there is only one observation in each group. Third, there is no estimating equation, and therefore no satisfactory way of making estimates of the dependent variable.

CHAPTER 21

Correlation III: Multiple and Partial Correlation

PRELIMINARY EXPLANATION

Simple correlation. Before plunging into the discussion of multiple and partial correlation, it will be useful to review briefly the elementary principles of two-variable linear correlation, since the more refined measures involve simply an extension of the procedures already discussed. First, an estimating equation of the type

$$Y_c = a + bX$$

was computed by the method of least squares. This permitted us to make estimates of the value of the dependent variable from values of the independent variable. Next, it was demonstrated that the total variation of the dependent variable was the sum of: (1) the explained variation and (2) the variation which we had failed to explain by our hypothesis; that is, that

$$\Sigma y^2 = \Sigma y_c^2 + \Sigma y_s^2.$$

It should be remembered that we computed Σy^2 by the formula

$$\Sigma y^2 = \Sigma Y^2 - \bar{Y}\Sigma Y;$$

and that Σy_c^2 was computed from the expression

$$\Sigma y_c^2 = \Sigma Y_c^2 - \bar{Y}\Sigma Y,$$

in which

$$\Sigma Y_c^2 = a\Sigma Y + b\Sigma XY$$

or, more simply,

$$\Sigma y_c^2 = b\Sigma xy.$$

453

The standard error of estimate $s_{Y \cdot x}$, which is $\sqrt{\dfrac{\Sigma y_s^2}{N}}$, enabled us to judge the range of error of our estimates of the dependent variable. Σy_s^2 was obtained by subtracting the explained variation from the total variation; that is,

$$\Sigma y_s^2 = \Sigma y^2 - \Sigma y_c^2.$$

Finally, a measure was computed that permitted us to state the proportion of total variation which had been explained by variations in the computed values of the dependent variable. This ratio,

$$r^2 = \frac{\Sigma y_c^2}{\Sigma y^2},$$

was known as the *coefficient of determination*, and its square root was called the *coefficient of correlation*.

Multiple correlation. Exactly the same principles are involved in multiple correlation as in simple correlation, but the procedure is more laborious, since there is more than one independent variable. Also, it is necessary to use slightly different symbols. The illustration in this chapter will deal with the relationship between median income by regions, and per cent professional, technical and kindred workers, median school years completed, and per cent migrant in those same regions. Median income is the dependent variable, and the other three are independent variables.

To simplify computations so that they can be shown in full in this chapter, the United States has been divided into 19 regions of approximately equal population and more or less homogeneous characteristics. With the exception of New York State, which has been divided into New York City and upstate New York, the boundaries of these regions follow state boundaries. The composition of the different regions can be observed by reference to Table 21.1. Selection of homogeneous areas of equal population serves to make the statistical results more meaningful in that each region is given proper weight in the calculations. On the other hand, use of only 19 observations with an equation of 4 constants does make the degrees of freedom (see the section in Chapter 26 dealing with the significance of multiple-correlation coefficients) rather small. The results obtained must therefore be regarded as primarily of illustrative importance.

It simplifies the notations somewhat if, instead of using different letters, each of the variables is designated by the letter X, differentiating between the variables by means of subscripts. This is particularly true if the number of variables is large. We shall therefore designate our variables in this manner:

Dependent Variable:
    Median Income.. X_1
Independent Variables:
    Per cent professional, technical and kindred workers........... X_2
    Median school years completed............................ X_3
    Per cent migrant.. X_4

TABLE 21.1

Nineteen Relatively Homogeneous Regions in the United States of Approximately Equal Population in 1960

Region number	Population in millions	States included
1	8.0	Maine, New Hampshire, Vermont, Massachusetts, Rhode Island
2	8.6	Connecticut, New Jersey
3	7.8	New York City
4	9.0	New York, excluding New York City
5	11.3	Pennsylvania
6	9.7	Ohio
7	12.5	Indiana, Michigan
8	10.1	Illinois
9	7.4	Wisconsin, Minnesota
10	7.1	Iowa, Missouri
11	6.7	North Dakota, South Dakota, Nebraska, Kansas, Colorado
12	12.8	Delaware, Maryland, District of Columbia, Virginia, North Carolina
13	11.3	South Carolina, Georgia, Florida
14	8.5	West Virginia, Kentucky, Tennessee
15	8.7	Alabama, Mississippi, Louisiana
16	6.4	Arizona, New Mexico, Arkansas, Oklahoma
17	7.5	Montana, Idaho, Wyoming, Washington, Oregon, Utah, Nevada
18	15.7	California
19	9.6	Texas

In the pages that follow, we shall start with variables 1, 2, and 3, and, after explaining the basic concepts and computations, variable 4 will be introduced. The first step in the correlation procedure is to obtain an equation which includes both of the independent variables as a means of estimating median income. The estimate is labeled $X_{c1.23}$, since it is an estimate of variable X_1 computed from variables X_2 and X_3. Since there are two independent variables, there will be two b's. The equation type will be

$$X_{c1.23} = a_{1.23} + b_{12.3}X_2 + b_{13.2}X_3.$$

A word concerning the meaning of the b's and their subscripts is necessary. These *net coefficients of estimation* indicate the effect on X_1 of a change in the accompanying independent variable when allowance has been made[1] for the other independent variable. Thus, $b_{12.3}$ is an estimate of the variation in median income associated with a variation in per cent professional, etc. workers, independent of variation in median school years completed. The social scientist is accustomed to saying "other things being equal." The other thing which is held equal in this instance is median schooling in the different regions. As between regions that have the same median schooling but differ with respect to per cent professional, etc. workers, each variation of one per cent in professional, etc. workers between regions will normally be accompanied by a variation of $b_{12.3}$ in median income. The other b coefficient in the estimating equation is interpreted analogously, the figure to the right of the decimal point in the subscript indicating the factor that is held constant. Of course, really to know the effect on incomes of per cent professional, etc. workers alone, we should hold constant *all* other factors, not just median school years completed. As we introduce more and more variables, this desirable situation is more and more closely approximated. The constant $a_{1.23}$ is the hypothetical value for median income when the other factors considered have a value of zero. The estimate of median income for any region is the sum of the net amounts associated with each independent variable plus the value for a.

We might observe at this point that the natural scientist can often design his experiment so as to control a number of the variables, such, for instance, as temperature, humidity, or air pressure. The biologist and the agricultural experimenter can control their variables to a considerable extent. On the other hand, economics and sociology, and most of the social sciences, generally have to use the observational rather than the experimental method. Since workers in these fields usually have only very limited control, if any, over the material they must use, they must attempt to hold some of the variables constant statistically (rather than experimentally) by means of the techniques explained in this chapter.[2]

---

[1] Technically, allowance is made for a variable by subtracting its effect on the other variables. Thus, if

$$x_{s1.2} = x_1 - x_{c1.2};$$
$$x_{s3.2} = x_3 - x_{c3.2};$$
$$x_{s1.3} = x_1 - x_{c1.3};$$
$$x_{s2.3} = x_2 - x_{c2.3};$$

then $b_{12.3}$ is the slope of $x_{s1.3}$ on $x_{s2.3}$, and $b_{13.2}$ is the slope of $x_{s1.2}$ on $x_{s3.2}$. Specifically:

$$b_{12} = \frac{\Sigma x_1 x_2}{\Sigma x_2^2}, \text{ but } b_{12.3} = \frac{\Sigma x_{s1.3} x_{s2.3}}{\Sigma x_{s2.3}^2};$$

$$b_{13} = \frac{\Sigma x_1 x_3}{\Sigma x_3^2}, \text{ but } b_{13.2} = \frac{\Sigma x_{s1.2} x_{s3.2}}{\Sigma x_{s3.2}^2}.$$

[2] Another method, usually not practical, is to select from the observed data observations that have a constant value with respect to all independent variables except the one being studied.

As in previous instances, the total variation of the dependent series is the sum of two quantities: (1) the variation in the estimated values of that series from their mean, and (2) the variation of the actual values from the estimated values, that is,

$$\Sigma x_1^2 = \Sigma x_{c1.23}^2 + \Sigma x_{s1.23}^2.$$

The procedure for computing measures of relationship is essentially the same as with simple correlation. The standard error of estimate is

$$s_{1.23} = \sqrt{\frac{\Sigma x_{s1.23}^2}{N}},$$

and the *coefficient of multiple determination is*

$$R_{1.23}^2 = \frac{\Sigma x_{c1.23}^2}{\Sigma x_1^2}.$$

$R_{1.23}^2$ states the proportion of total variation that is present in the variations of the computed, or $X_{c1.23}$, values, and which has been explained by reference to the independent variables. The coefficient of multiple correlation $R_{1\ 23}$ is the square root of the coefficient of multiple determination. R has no sign, since the association may be positive with one but negative with the other independent variable. It is interesting to note at this point that, as additional associated independent variables are brought into a problem, $R_{1.23...m}$ approaches 1.0 and $s_{1.23...m}$ approaches zero. If we were able to include all pertinent independent variables, $R_{1.23...m}$ would be 1.0, and we could make perfect estimates of X_1.

Partial correlation. We have seen that the use of variable X_2 resulted in a certain amount of explained variation, indicated by $\Sigma x_{c1.2}^2$, but some of the variation in the dependent variable was not explained; this was $\Sigma x_{s1.2}^2$. Introducing variable X_3, in addition to X_2, gave explained variation indicated by $\Sigma x_{c1.23}^2$, which must exceed $\Sigma x_{c1.2}^2$ if variable X_3 is germane to the problem. In any event, $\Sigma x_{c1.23}^2$ cannot be smaller than $\Sigma x_{c1.2}^2$.

Now, the amount of variation unexplained by X_2 was $\Sigma x_{s1.2}^2$, but X_3 explained an additional amount of variation, indicated by $\Sigma x_{c1.23}^2 - \Sigma x_{c1.2}^2$. If we write

$$\frac{\Sigma x_{c1.23}^2 - \Sigma x_{c1.2}^2}{\Sigma x_{s1.2}^2},$$

we have $r_{13.2}^2$, the coefficient of partial determination. To put the above expression in words and to state it more generally, we may say that the coefficient of partial determination is the ratio of: (1) *the increase in the variation of the computed values of the dependent variable resulting from the introduction of another independent variable to* (2) *the variation that had not been explained before the introduction of the new variable.*

Since

$$\Sigma x_{s1.2}^2 = \Sigma x_1^2 - \Sigma x_{c1.2}^2,$$

the expression for $r_{13.2}^2$ may be written in either of the two following ways:

$$r_{13.2}^2 = \frac{\Sigma x_{c1.23}^2 - \Sigma x_{c1.2}^2}{\Sigma x_{s1.2}^2} \text{ or } \frac{\Sigma x_{c1.23}^2 - \Sigma x_{c1.2}^2}{\Sigma x_1^2 - \Sigma x_{c1.2}^2}.$$

If the numerator and denominator of the expression last given are divided by Σx_1^2, we have

$$r_{13.2}^2 = \frac{R_{1.23}^2 - r_{12}^2}{1 - r_{12}^2}.$$

In this form the coefficient of partial determination may be regarded as the ratio of: (1) the increase in the *proportion* of variation of the computed values of the dependent variable resulting from the introduction of another independent variable to (2) the *proportion* of the variation that had not been explained before the introduction of the new variable.

The square root of $r_{13.2}^2$, $r_{13.2}$, is the coefficient of partial correlation and takes the sign of $b_{13.2}$ in the estimating equation. The subscript 13.2 for the coefficient of partial correlation indicates, for our problem, that the correlation is between median income, X_1, and median school years, X_3, when per cent professional, technical and kindred workers, X_2, has been held constant at a value of $\overline{X}_2$. If we could pick out regions that are exactly alike with respect to occupation, the simple correlation between median income and median school years for those regions would tend to be the same as the above coefficient of partial correlation. One purpose of partial (or net) correlation coefficients is to indicate the relative importance of the different independent variables in a problem in explaining variations in the dependent variable.

COMPUTATION PROCEDURE

Computation of sums. Since this chapter will require a considerable number of measures of relationship among the four variables, it will be convenient to compute at one time all of the values that are needed in the different formulas. The original data for the four series, together with their sums and arithmetic means, are shown in Table 21.2. The individual squares and products and the sums of the squares and products

TABLE 21.2

Medium Income, Per Cent Professional, Technical, and Kindred
Workers, Median School Years Completed, and Per Cent
Migrant for 19 Regions of the United States, 1960

Region	Median income (1,000's of dollars) X_1	Per cent professional, technical and kindred workers X_2	Median school years completed X_3	Per cent migrant X_4
1	5.9	11.7	11.3	12.9
2	6.8	12.5	10.7	15.8
3	6.1	11.1	10.1	11.2
4*	6.7	13.7	11.2	15.9
5	5.7	10.7	10.2	10.0
6	6.2	10.9	10.9	14.0
7	6.1	10.9	10.8	14.4
8	6.6	10.7	10.5	12.8
9	5.8	10.7	10.6	15.4
10	5.1	9.8	10.3	18.0
11	5.2	11.3	11.4	22.9
12	5.1	11.0	9.8	19.4
13	4.3	9.2	9.8	24.2
14	4.1	9.3	8.8	13.7
15	3.8	9.2	8.9	15.4
16	4.5	11.1	10.3	24.0
17	5.9	12.0	12.0	23.7
18	6.7	13.7	12.1	24.5
19	4.9	10.8	10.4	20.7
Total	105.5	210.3	200.1	328.9
Mean	5.552632	11.068421	10.531579	17.310526

* Data for New York, excluding New York City, were computed from the relationship:

$$N_\text{upstate} \, \text{Med}_\text{upstate} = N_\text{state} \, \text{Med}_\text{state} - N_\text{city} \, \text{Med}_\text{city}.$$

Median income, per cent professional, technical and kindred workers, median school years completed, and per cent migrant were weighted by the population of each state to arrive at a weighted arithmetic mean for each region.

Data from U. S. Bureau of the Census, *U. S. Census of Population: 1960*, Vol. I, *Characteristics of the Population*, Part I, *United States Summary*, pp. I-248, I-249, I-277.

TABLE 21.3

Computation of Squares, Products, and Sums for Measures of Relationship Between Median Income and Three Independent Variables, for 19 Regions of the United States, 1960

Region	X_1^2	X_1X_2	X_1X_3	X_1X_4	X_2^2	X_2X_3	X_2X_4	X_3^2	X_3X_4	X_4^2
1	34.81	69.03	66.67	76.11	136.89	132.21	150.93	127.69	145.77	166.41
2	46.24	85.00	72.76	107.44	156.25	133.75	197.50	114.29	169.06	249.64
3	37.21	67.71	61.61	68.32	123.21	112.11	124.32	102.01	113.12	125.44
4	44.89	91.79	75.04	106.53	187.69	153.44	217.83	125.44	178.08	252.81
5	32.49	60.99	58.14	59.00	114.49	109.14	107.00	104.04	102.00	100.00
6	38.44	67.58	67.58	86.80	118.81	118.81	152.60	118.81	152.60	196.00
7	37.21	66.49	65.88	87.84	118.81	117.72	156.96	116.64	155.52	207.36
8	43.56	70.62	69.30	84.48	114.49	112.35	136.96	110.25	134.40	163.84
9	33.64	62.06	61.48	89.32	114.49	113.42	164.78	112.36	163.24	237.16
10	26.01	49.98	52.53	91.80	96.04	100.94	176.40	106.09	185.40	324.00
11	27.04	58.76	59.28	119.08	127.69	128.82	258.77	129.96	261.06	524.41
12	26.01	56.10	49.98	98.94	121.00	107.80	213.40	96.04	190.12	376.36
13	18.49	39.56	42.14	104.06	84.64	90.16	222.64	96.04	237.16	585.64
14	16.81	38.13	36.08	56.17	86.49	81.84	127.41	77.44	120.56	187.69
15	14.44	34.96	33.82	58.52	84.64	81.88	141.68	79.21	137.06	237.16
16	20.25	49.95	46.35	108.00	123.21	114.33	266.40	106.09	247.20	576.00
17	34.81	70.80	70.80	139.83	144.00	144.00	284.40	144.00	284.40	561.69
18	44.89	91.79	81.07	164.15	187.69	165.77	335.65	146.41	296.45	600.25
19	24.01	52.92	50.96	101.43	116.64	112.32	223.56	108.16	215.28	428.49
Total	601.25	1,184.22	1,121.47	1,805.82	2,357.17	2,230.81	3,659.19	2,121.17	3,488.48	6,100.35

Based on data in Table 21.2.

are shown in Table 21.3.   From these we obtain the sums of the squared deviations and the sums of the products of deviations.   For example,[3]

$$\Sigma x_1^2 = \Sigma X_1^2 - \overline{X}_1 \Sigma X_1.$$
$$\Sigma x_2^2 = \Sigma X_2^2 - \overline{X}_2 \Sigma X_2.$$

$$\Sigma x_1 x_2 = \Sigma X_1 X_2 - \overline{X}_1 \Sigma X_2 \text{ or } \Sigma X_1 X_2 - \overline{X}_2 \Sigma X_1.$$
$$\Sigma x_1 x_3 = \Sigma X_1 X_3 - \overline{X}_1 \Sigma X_3 \text{ or } \Sigma X_1 X_3 - \overline{X}_3 \Sigma X_1.$$

Using these, and similar formulas for the other sums, gives:[4]

$$\Sigma x_1^2 = 601.25 - (5.552632)(105.5) = 15.447.$$
$$\Sigma x_2^2 = 2{,}357.17 - (11.068421)(210.3) = 29.481.$$
$$\Sigma x_3^2 = 2{,}121.17 - (10.531579)(200.1) = 13.801.$$
$$\Sigma x_4^2 = 6{,}100.35 - (17.310526)(328.9) = 406.918.$$

$$\Sigma x_1 x_2 = 1{,}184.22 - (5.552632)(210.3) = 16.502.$$
$$\Sigma x_1 x_3 = 1{,}121.47 - (5.552632)(200.1) = 10.388.$$
$$\Sigma x_1 x_4 = 1{,}805.82 - (5.552632)(328.9) = -20.441.$$

$$\Sigma x_2 x_3 = 2{,}230.81 - (11.068421)(200.1) = 16.019.$$
$$\Sigma x_2 x_4 = 3{,}659.19 - (11.068421)(328.9) = 18.786.$$

$$\Sigma x_3 x_4 = 3{,}488.48 - (10.531579)(328.9) = 24.644.$$

Gross measures of relationship.   Simple correlation is in reality gross correlation, since it measures the relationship between two variables, without any adjustment by correlation technique for the effects of other

---

[3] The derivation of these equations is fairly obvious.

$$\Sigma x_1^2 = \Sigma (X_1 - \overline{X}_1)^2,$$
$$= \Sigma (X_1^2 - 2\overline{X}_1 X_1 + \overline{X}_1^2),$$
$$= \Sigma X_1^2 - 2\overline{X}_1 \Sigma X_1 + N\overline{X}_1^2,$$
$$= \Sigma X_1^2 - 2\overline{X}_1 \Sigma X_1 + \overline{X}_1 \Sigma X_1,$$
$$= \Sigma X_1^2 - \overline{X}_1 \Sigma X_1.$$
$$\Sigma x_1 x_2 = \Sigma [(X_1 - \overline{X}_1)(X_2 - \overline{X}_2)],$$
$$= \Sigma (X_1 X_2 - \overline{X}_1 X_2 - \overline{X}_2 X_1 + \overline{X}_1 \overline{X}_2),$$
$$= \Sigma X_1 X_2 - \overline{X}_1 \Sigma X_2 - \overline{X}_2 \Sigma X_1 + N \overline{X}_1 \overline{X}_2,$$
$$= \Sigma X_1 X_2 - \overline{X}_1 \Sigma X_2 - \frac{\Sigma X_1 \Sigma X_2}{N} + \frac{\Sigma X_1 \Sigma X_2}{N},$$
$$= \Sigma X_1 X_2 - \overline{X}_1 \Sigma X_2.$$

---

[4] In Table 21.2 the observations have two or three significant digits.   Therefore, the products in Table 21.3 are usually recorded to four or five digits.   The various measures in this chapter computed from these values cannot contain more than two or three significant digits.   More have been recorded, however, in order to afford internal checks on computations and to contribute to the accuracy of final results based on intermediate computations.

variables. Using the symbols developed in the introductory section, we compute the following measures if we wish to correlate median income X_1 with per cent professional, technical and kindred workers X_2 alone:

Estimating equation:

$$X_{c1.2} = a_{1.2} + b_{12}X_2 \qquad \text{or} \qquad x_{c1.2} = b_{12}x_2.$$

Normal equations:

$$\text{I.} \quad \Sigma X_1 = N a_{1.2} + b_{12}\Sigma X_2 \qquad \text{or} \qquad \overline{X}_1 = a_{1.2} + b_{12}\overline{X}_2.$$

$$a_{1.2} = \overline{X}_1 - b_{12}\overline{X}_2.$$

$$\text{II.} \quad \Sigma X_1 X_2 = a_{1.2}\Sigma X_2 + b_{12}\Sigma X_2^2 \qquad \text{or} \qquad \Sigma x_1 x_2 = b_{12}\Sigma x_2^2.$$

$$b_{12} = \frac{\Sigma x_1 x_2}{\Sigma x_2^2}.$$

Total variation:

$$\Sigma x_1^2 = \Sigma X_1^2 - \overline{X}_1\Sigma X_1.$$

Sum of squares of computed values and explained variation:

$$\Sigma X_{c1.2}^2 = a_{1.2}\Sigma X_1 + b_{12}\Sigma X_1 X_2. \qquad \Sigma x_{c1.2}^2 = b_{12}\Sigma x_1 x_2.$$

$$\text{(Sum of explained squares)} \qquad \text{(Explained variation)}$$

Unexplained variation:

$$\Sigma x_{s1.2}^2 = \Sigma X_1^2 - \Sigma X_{c1.2}^2 \qquad \text{or} \qquad \Sigma x_1^2 - \Sigma x_{c1.2}^2.$$

Standard error of estimate,

$$s_{1.2} = \sqrt{\frac{\Sigma x_{s1.2}^2}{N}},$$

$$= \sqrt{\frac{\Sigma X_1^2 - \Sigma X_{c1.2}^2}{N}} \qquad \text{or} \qquad \sqrt{\frac{\Sigma x_1^2 - \Sigma x_{c1.2}^2}{N}}.$$

Coefficient of correlation:

$$r_{12} = \sqrt{\frac{\Sigma X_{c1.2}^2 - \overline{X}_1\Sigma X_1}{\Sigma X_1^2 - \overline{X}_1\Sigma X_1}} \qquad \text{or} \qquad \sqrt{\frac{\Sigma x_{c1.2}^2}{\Sigma x_1^2}}.$$

The reader may already have noticed that we have merely set down the various equations and formulas used in simple correlation, but with slightly different symbols.

Results of computations based on these expressions are given below, In order to avoid needless labor, the formulas shown on the right above. using deviations from means, are used.

Constants for estimating equation:

$$b_{12} = \frac{16.502}{29.481} = +0.55975.$$

$$a_{1.2} = 5.5526 - (0.55975)(11.068421) = -0.6429.$$

Estimating equation:

$$X_{c1.2} = -0.6429 + 0.55975X_2.$$
$$x_{c1.2} = +0.55975x_2.$$

Total variation:

$$\Sigma x_1^2 = 601.25 - (5.552632)(105.5) = 15.447.$$

Explained variation:

$$\Sigma x_{c1.2}^2 = (0.55975)(16.502) = 9.237.$$

Unexplained variation:

$$\Sigma x_{s1.2}^2 = 15.447 - 9.237 = 6.210.$$

Standard error of estimate:

$$s_{1.2}^2 = \frac{6.210}{19} = 0.3268.$$

$$s_{1.2} = 0.571.$$

Coefficient of correlation:

$$r_{12}^2 = \frac{9.237}{15.447} = 0.59798.$$

$$r_{12} = 0.7733.$$

Following the same procedure for variable 3, we obtain:

$$b_{13} = +0.75270;$$
$$a_{1.3} = -2.3745;$$
$$\Sigma x_{c1.3}^2 = 7.819;$$
$$\Sigma x_{s1.3}^2 = 7.628;$$
$$s_{1.3} = 0.634;$$
$$r_{13}^2 = 0.50618;$$
$$r_{13} = +0.7115.$$

Chart 21.1 shows scatter diagrams of the simple relationship between median income and each of the independent variables being considered.

The correlation coefficients for these three relationships and the coefficients of correlation between the three independent variables are:

$$r_{12} = +0.7733. \qquad r_{23} = +0.7942.$$
$$r_{13} = +0.7115. \qquad r_{24} = +0.1715.$$
$$r_{14} = -0.2578. \qquad r_{34} = +0.3289.$$

It is interesting to note, at this point, that per cent professional, technical and kindred workers, X_2, showed the highest gross correlation with median income, and that per cent migrant, X_4,

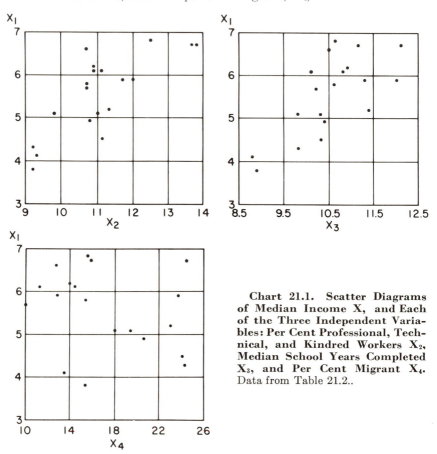

Chart 21.1. Scatter Diagrams of Median Income X, and Each of the Three Independent Variables: Per Cent Professional, Technical, and Kindred Workers X_2, Median School Years Completed X_3, and Per Cent Migrant X_4. Data from Table 21.2..

showed the lowest. Later we shall see whether the independent variables retain the same rank in importance when the effect of the other variables is removed.

Two independent variables: multiple correlation. Naturally, we can expect to estimate median income more accurately if we take two independent variables into consideration, rather than only one. Hence, let us make estimates from both per cent professional, etc. workers and median school years. The estimating-equation type is

$$X_{c1.23} = a_{1.23} + b_{12.3}X_2 + b_{13.2}X_3,$$

or, in terms of deviations,

$$x_{c1.23} = b_{12.3}x_2 + b_{13.2}x_3.$$

The 1.23 subscripts after X_c and a tell us that we are estimating values of X_1 (median income) from variables X_2 (per cent professional, etc. workers) and X_3 (median school years). The first b indicates the normal change in median income associated with a unit change in per cent professional, etc. workers for regions that have the same median school years composition; the second b tells us the normal change in median income associated with a unit change in median school years for regions of the same per cent professional, etc. workers.

The normal equations required are:

I. $\Sigma X_1 = Na_{1.23} + b_{12.3}\Sigma X_2 + b_{13.2}\Sigma X_3;$

II. $\Sigma X_1 X_2 = a_{1.23}\Sigma X_2 + b_{12.3}\Sigma X_2^2 + b_{13.2}\Sigma X_2 X_3;$

III. $\Sigma X_1 X_3 = a_{1.23}\Sigma X_3 + b_{12.3}\Sigma X_2 X_3 + b_{13.2}\Sigma X_3^2.$

Considerable labor may be saved if the normal equations are put in terms of deviations from the means. In this case, the first equation disappears, since Σx_1, Σx_2, and Σx_3 are each zero. The remaining two equations are:

II. $\Sigma x_1 x_2 = b_{12.3}\Sigma x_2^2 + b_{13.2}\Sigma x_2 x_3;$

III. $\Sigma x_1 x_3 = b_{12.3}\Sigma x_2 x_3 + b_{13.2}\Sigma x_3^2.$

Making the required substitutions, we have:

II. $16.502 = 29.481 b_{12.3} + 16.019 b_{13.2};$

III. $10.388 = 16.019 b_{12.3} + 13.801 b_{13.2}.$

Solving these simultaneous equations gives:

$$b_{12.3} = +0.40820;$$
$$b_{13.2} = +0.27889.$$

To get $a_{1.23}$, we use Equation I, dividing it by N, obtaining:

$\overline{X}_1 = a_{1.23} + b_{12.3}\overline{X}_2 + b_{13.2}\overline{X}_3.$

$a_{1.23} = \overline{X}_1 - b_{12.3}\overline{X}_2 - b_{13.2}\overline{X}_3,$

    $= 5.552632 - (0.40820)(11.068421) - (0.27889)(10.531579),$

    $= -1.9026.$

The estimating equation, then, is

$$X_{c1.23} = -1.903 + 0.408X_2 + 0.279X_3.$$

The explained variation is[5]

$$\Sigma x_{c1.23}^2 = b_{12.3}\Sigma x_1 x_2 + b_{13.2}\Sigma x_1 x_3,$$
$$= (0.40820)(16.502) + (0.27889)(10.388)$$
$$= 9.633.$$

The other measures of relationship are now computed in a manner precisely similar to that employed when there was only one independent variable.

$$\Sigma x_{s1.23}^2 = \Sigma x_1^2 - \Sigma x_{c1.23}^2,$$
$$= 15.447 - 9.633 = 5.814.$$
$$s_{1.23}^2 = \frac{\Sigma x_{s1.23}^2}{N} = \frac{5.814}{19} = 0.3060;$$
$$s_{1.23} = 0.553.$$
$$R_{1.23}^2 = \frac{\Sigma x_{c1.23}^2}{\Sigma x_1^2} = \frac{9.633}{15.447} = 0.6236;$$
$$R_{1.23} = 0.7897.$$

Since the coefficient of multiple determination, $R_{1.23}^2$, is 0.6236, we have explained 62 per cent of the variation present in X_1. Notice that $R_{1.23}^2$ is greater than either r_{12}^2 or r_{13}^2; the value of r_{12}^2 was found to be 0.59798, while r_{13}^2 was 0.50618.

The standard error of estimate, $s_{1.23}$, was ascertained to be 0.553, which is smaller than either $s_{1.2} = 0.571$ or $s_{1.3} = 0.634$. Estimates made of X_1 using the two independent variables X_2 and X_3 will be more satisfactory than estimates made by use of either X_2 or X_3 alone. More specifically, the standard deviation of the X_1 values around the estimating equation

$$X_{c1.23} = a_{1.23} + b_{12.3}X_2 + b_{13.2}X_3$$

is less than the standard deviation of the X_1 values around

$$X_{c1.2} = a_{1.2} + b_{12}X_2$$

or around

$$X_{c1.3} = a_{1.3} + b_{13}X_3.$$

Two independent variables: partial correlation. When only one independent variable (per cent professional, etc. workers) was considered, the explained variation was $\Sigma x_{c1.2}^2 = 9.237$. When two independent variables (per cent professional, etc. workers and median school years) were used, the explained variation was increased to $\Sigma x_{c1.23}^2 = 9.633$. Therefore, the increase in the variation explained by median school years is

---

[5] Also, $\Sigma x_{c1.23}^2 = \Sigma X_{c1.23}^2 - \bar{X}_1 \Sigma X_1$, where $\Sigma X_{c1.23}^2 = a_{1.23}\Sigma X_1 + b_{12.3}\Sigma X_1 X_2 + b_{13.2}\Sigma X_1 X_3$.

$$\Sigma x_{c1.23}^2 - \Sigma x_{c1.2}^2 = 9.633 - 9.237 = 0.396.$$

After taking per cent professional, etc. workers alone into consideration, the variation remaining to be explained was

$$\Sigma x_{s1.2}^2 = \Sigma x_1^2 - \Sigma x_{c1.2}^2,$$
$$= 15.447 - 9.237 = 6.210.$$

The proportion of the variation previously unexplained, then, which was explained by including median school years also, is the ratio

$$\frac{0.39616}{6.210} = 0.06379.$$

As noted before, this ratio is known as the *coefficient of partial determination*, the square root of which is the *coefficient of partial correlation*. That is,

$$r_{13.2}^2 = \frac{\Sigma x_{c1.23}^2 - \Sigma x_{c1.2}^2}{\Sigma x_1^2 - \Sigma x_{c1.2}^2} = \frac{\Sigma x_{c1.23}^2 - \Sigma x_{c1.2}^2}{\Sigma x_{s1.2}^2}$$
$$= \frac{9.633 - 9.237}{6.210} = 0.06379;$$
$$r_{13.2} = +0.2525.$$

The sign of this coefficient of partial correlation is the same as the sign of $b_{13.2}$ in the estimating equation. This coefficient is a measure of the closeness of relationship between median income and median school years when per cent professional, etc. workers has been held constant statistically; it is the simple correlation coefficient which would be expected for regions of the same per cent professional, etc. workers. As previously stated, if the numerator and denominator of the above expression for $r_{13.2}^2$ are both divided by Σx_1^2, we obtain a formula showing the relationship between the partial determination coefficient and two gross determination coefficients. Thus,

$$r_{13.2}^2 = \frac{R_{1.23}^2 - r_{12}^2}{1 - r_{12}^2},$$
$$= \frac{0.62363 - 0.59798}{1 - 0.59798} = 0.06379;$$
$$r_{13.2} = +0.2525.$$

Note that each of the values recorded in this formula is that in the preceding formula divided by 15.447 (in fact, this is the procedure we have already employed to obtain $R_{1.23}^2$ and r_{12}^2). This formula may then be used as a check[6] on the final division needed to compute $R_{1.23}^2$ and r_{12}^2.

---

[6] Note, however, that there is a tendency for the numerator and denominator to lose a significant digit because of the division by Σx_1^2.

Also, it may be used when r_{12}^2 is computed by some procedure other than $r_{12}^2 = \dfrac{\Sigma x_{c1.2}^2}{\Sigma x_1^2}$, or when the coefficients of determination, or coefficients of correlation, but not the original data, are given.

As a companion measure to $r_{13.2}$, we should obtain the partial coefficient $r_{12.3}$, which measures the relationship between median income and per cent professional, etc. workers when median school years has been held constant. This is done by finding the increase in the variation of the computed values by using per cent professional, etc. workers and median school years in our estimating equation rather than using median school years alone. Thus:

$$
\begin{aligned}
r_{12.3}^2 &= \frac{\Sigma x_{c1.23}^2 - \Sigma x_{c1.3}^2}{\Sigma x_{s1.3}^2} = \frac{9.633 - 7.819}{7.628}, \\
&= \frac{R_{1.23}^2 - r_{13}^2}{1 - r_{13}^2} = \frac{0.62363 - 0.50619}{0.49381}, \\
&= 0.23782; \\
r_{12.3} &= +0.4877.
\end{aligned}
$$

Partial coefficients, such as $r_{13.2}$ and $r_{12.3}$, are often referred to as *first-order* coefficients, since one variable has been held constant. Simple coefficients are called *zero-order* coefficients, since no variables were held constant. Later in the chapter, we shall consider $r_{12.34}$, $r_{13.24}$, and $r_{14.23}$, which are *second-order* coefficients. Stated generally, the order designation indicates the number of variables that have been held constant statistically.

The gross correlation between median income and per cent professional, technical and kindred workers, r_{12}, it will be recalled, was $+0.7733$. Removing the effect of variations in median school years from both variables has decreased the relationship materially, since $r_{12.3} = +0.4877$. Similarly, r_{13}, the gross correlation between median income and median school years, was $+0.7115$. Removing the effect of variations in per cent professional, etc. workers resulted in $r_{13.2} = +0.2525$, again a decided decrease. Both decreases cited are due to the very high correlation, $+0.7942$, between per cent professional, etc. workers and median school years completed. Removing the effect of first one and then the other negatively influenced the partial correlation coefficients.

Relationship between $R_{1.23}$ and the measures of gross and partial correlation. The reader may be surprised to note that $R_{1.23}$ is but 0.7897 while r_{12} is $+0.7733$ and r_{13} is $+0.7115$. It is not a characteristic of these measures that the multiple coefficient is the sum of the two gross coefficients. The relationship is more complex than that.[7] It may be said, however, that for given values of r_{12} and r_{13} having the same sign, the less the duplication in the independent variables (that is the lower their positive or the higher their negative correlation) the higher will be the multiple correlation. In the present instance, most interestingly, $r_{23} = 0.7942$ and therefore reflects a great deal of duplication in these two variables. Hence, the addition of either median school years or per cent professional, technical and kindred workers does not materially improve the correlation over that obtained from the use of either independent variable alone. Quite the contrary, in fact it lowers it.[8]

Neither is the multiple coefficient of correlation the sum of the two partial coefficients. However, there is an additive relationship (derived from the expressions just given for $r_{12.3}^2$ and $r_{13.2}^3$) which may be written in either of two forms:

$$
\begin{aligned}
R_{1.23}^2 &= r_{12}^2 + r_{13.2}^2(1 - r_{12}^2), \\
&= 0.5980 + (0.0638)(1 - 0.5980) = 0.6236, \text{ or} \\
R_{1.23}^2 &= r_{13}^2 + r_{12.3}^2(1 - r_{13}^2), \\
&= 0.5062 + (0.2378)(1 - 0.5062) = 0.6236.
\end{aligned}
$$

It is interesting to note the thought behind these equations. The first one, for example, involves the sum of: (1) the proportion of variation explained by using one independent variable and (2) the product of (a) the proportion of variation unexplained by that independent variable, $1 - r_{12}^2$, and (b) the proportion of (a) explained as a result of using the other independent variable in addition to the first one, $r_{13.2}^2$.

Three independent variables: multiple correlation. In the preceding paragraphs, we considered the two independent variables, per cent professional, technical and kindred workers, X_2, and median school years completed, X_3. If we add a third independent variable, per cent migrant, X_4, we use an estimating equation of the type

---

[7] The relationship is as follows:

$$
R_{1.23}^2 = \frac{r_{12}^2 + r_{13}^2 - 2r_{12}r_{13}r_{23}}{1 - r_{23}^2}.
$$

In this case,

$$
R_{1.23}^2 = \frac{0.5980 + 0.5062 - 2(0.7733)(0.7115)(0.7942)}{1 - 0.6307} = 0.6326;
$$

$$
R_{1.23} = 0.7897.
$$

---

[8] For a more conventional situation, one in which the addition of still another independent variable improves the correlation over that obtained from the use of either independent variable alone, see the second edition of this text, pp. 545–546.

$$X_{c1.234} = a_{1.234} + b_{12.34}X_2 + b_{13.24}X_3 + b_{14.23}X_4.$$

To obtain the four constants, four normal equations are required if we use X-values. They are

I. $\Sigma X_1 = Na_{1.234} + b_{12.34}\Sigma X_2 + b_{13.24}\Sigma X_3 + b_{14.23}\Sigma X_4;$

II. $\Sigma X_1 X_2 = a_{1.234}\Sigma X_2 + b_{12.34}\Sigma X_2^2 + b_{13.24}\Sigma X_2 X_3 + b_{14.23}\Sigma X_2 X_4;$

III. $\Sigma X_1 X_3 = a_{1.234}\Sigma X_3 + b_{12.34}\Sigma X_2 X_3 + b_{13.24}\Sigma X_3^2 + b_{14.23}\Sigma X_3 X_4;$

IV. $\Sigma X_1 X_4 = a_{1.234}\Sigma X_4 + b_{12.34}\Sigma X_2 X_4 + b_{13.24}\Sigma X_3 X_4 + b_{14.23}\Sigma X_4^2.$

However, by using x-values, we eliminate normal equation I, as before, giving

II. $\Sigma x_1 x_2 = b_{12.34}\Sigma x_2^2 + b_{13.24}\Sigma x_2 x_3 + b_{14.23}\Sigma x_2 x_4;$

III. $\Sigma x_1 x_3 = b_{12.34}\Sigma x_2 x_3 + b_{13.24}\Sigma x_3^2 + b_{14.23}\Sigma x_3 x_4;$

IV. $\Sigma x_1 x_4 = b_{12.34}\Sigma x_2 x_4 + b_{13.24}\Sigma x_3 x_4 + b_{14.23}\Sigma x_4^2.$

Substituting in normal equations II, III, and IV the sums of squared deviations and the sums of products of deviations, obtained earlier, we have

II. $16.502 = 29.481 b_{12.34} + 16.019 b_{13.24} + 18.786 b_{14.23};$

III. $10.388 = 16.019 b_{12.34} + 13.801 b_{13.24} + 24.644 b_{14.23};$

IV. $-20.441 = 18.786 b_{12.34} + 24.644 b_{13.24} + 406.918 b_{14.23}.$

Since the procedure for solving three simultaneous equations was given on pages 420–422, it will not be repeated here. The solution yields

$$b_{12.34} = +0.31911;$$
$$b_{13.24} = +0.55874;$$
$$b_{14.23} = -0.09880.$$

If we write normal equation I in the form

$$a_{1.234} = \overline{X}_1 - b_{12.34}\overline{X}_2 - b_{13.24}\overline{X}_3 - b_{14.23}\overline{X}_4,$$

we can substitute the values of the arithmetic means from Table 21.1 and the b-values just given, obtaining

$$a_{1.234} = 5.552632 - (0.31911)(11.068421) - (0.55874)(10.531579)$$
$$- (0.09880)(17.310526).$$
$$= -2.1535.$$

The estimating equation, then, is

$$X_{c1.234} = -2.1535 + 0.31911 X_2 + 0.55874 X_3 - 0.09880 X_4.$$

Explained variation is

$$\Sigma x_{c1.234}^2 = b_{12.34}\Sigma x_1 x_2 + b_{13.24}\Sigma x_1 x_3 + b_{14.23}\Sigma x_1 x_4,$$
$$= (0.31911)(16.502) + (0.55874)(10.388)$$
$$+ (-0.09880)(-20.441),$$
$$= 13.0897,$$

and unexplained variation is

$$\Sigma x^2_{s1.234} = \Sigma x^2_1 - \Sigma x^2_{c1.234},$$
$$= 15.447 - 13.0897 = 2.3573.$$

We can now compute the standard error of estimate, which is

$$s_{1.234} = \sqrt{\frac{\Sigma x^2_{s1.234}}{N}} = \sqrt{\frac{2.3573}{19}} = 0.352.$$

The coefficient of multiple determination and the coefficient of multiple correlation are

$$R^2_{1.234} = \frac{\Sigma x^2_{c1.234}}{\Sigma x^2_1} = \frac{13.0897}{15.447} = 0.8474;$$

$$R_{1.234} = 0.9205.$$

Before proceeding to compute partial coefficients, it is desirable to see what improvement in our relationship has resulted from using variable X_4. It will be recalled that $R^2_{1.23}$ was 0.6236, indicating that we had explained 62 per cent of the variation in X_1 by referring to X_2 and X_3. We have just found $R^2_{1.234}$ to be 0.8474. Now, by use of the three independent variables, we have explained 85 per cent of the variation in the dependent variable.[9] Not only does $R^2_{1.234}$ exceed $R^2_{1.23}$, but it is also larger than either $R^2_{1.24}$ or $R^2_{1.34}$. Neither of these last two coefficients has been previously computed. They are

$$R^2_{1.24} = 0.7551 \text{ and } R^2_{1.34} = 0.7774.$$

It had been noted previously (page 466) that $R^2_{1.23}$ was larger than either r^2_{12} or r^2_{13}. The reader can verify (1) that $R^2_{1.24}$ exceeds either r^2_{12} or r^2_{14}, and (2) that $R^2_{1.34}$ is larger than either r^2_{13} or r^2_{14}.

As the value of R^2 or R increases with the addition of appropriate independent variables, the value of the standard error of estimate decreases. We previously found $s_{1.23}$ to be 0.553; now we see that $s_{1.234} = 0.352$. The values of $s_{1.24}$ and $s_{1.34}$ (neither of which was computed before) are each larger than $s_{1.234}$; they are

$$s_{1.24} = 0.446 \text{ and } s_{1.34} = 0.425.$$

It is clear that estimates of suicide rates made from the use of all three of the independent variables will be more satisfactory than estimates made by using any two of them. Stated more exactly, the standard deviation of the X_1 values around the estimating equation

---

[9] It must be remembered that adding another independent variable causes the loss of an additional degree of freedom. Thus, it may occasionally happen that the value of R^2 may be increased, but the increase may not be significant. Testing the significance of partial and multiple coefficients of determination is discussed toward the end of Chapter 26.

$$X_{c1.234} = a_{1.234} + b_{12.34}X_2 + b_{13.24}X_3 + b_{14.23}X_4$$

is smaller than the standard deviation of the X_1 values around

$$X_{c1.23} = a_{1.23} + b_{12.3}X_2 + b_{13.2}X_3,$$

or around

$$X_{c1.24} = a_{1.24} + b_{12.4}X_2 + b_{14.2}X_4,$$

or around

$$X_{c1.34} = a_{1.34} + b_{13.4}X_3 + b_{14.3}X_4.$$

Three independent variables: partial correlation. Paralleling the procedure previously used,

$$
\begin{aligned}
r_{14.23}^2 &= \frac{\Sigma x_{c1.234}^2 - \Sigma x_{c1.23}^2}{\Sigma x_1^2 - \Sigma x_{c1.23}^2}, \\
&= \frac{13.090 - 9.633}{15.447 - 9.633} = 0.59454; \\
r_{14.23} &= -0.7711.
\end{aligned}
$$

Since $r_{14.23}^2 = 0.5945$, the use of independent variable X_4 enabled us to explain 59 per cent of the variation which X_2 and X_3 had failed to explain. The sign of $r_{14.23}$ is negative, to agree with the sign of $b_{14.23}$, and this coefficient measures the relationship between median income X_1 and per cent migrant X_4, when X_2 and X_3 have been held constant statistically. At a later point we shall obtain the values of $r_{13.24}$ and $r_{12.34}$, which are, respectively, measures of the correlation between variables X_1 and X_3 with X_2 and X_4 held constant and between variables X_1 and X_2 with X_3 and X_4 held constant.

The value of $r_{14.23}^2$ may also be obtained from the expression

$$
\begin{aligned}
r_{14.23}^2 &= \frac{R_{1.234}^2 - R_{1.23}^2}{1 - R_{1.23}^2}, \\
&= \frac{0.84740 - 0.62363}{1 - 0.62363} = 0.59454; \\
r_{14.23} &= -0.7711.
\end{aligned}
$$

Four or more independent variables. When there are four or more variables, it is advisable to use the Doolittle method (or some other systematic procedure) for the solution of the simultaneous equations.[10]

Multiple-partial coefficients. Just as the coefficient of partial determination measures: (1) the increase in the amount of variation of the computed values of the dependent variable resulting from the introduction of another independent variable relative to (2) the variation

---

[10] The normal equations (and other generalized expressions derived from them) are given on pp. 549–551 and the Doolittle method is described on pp. 498–503 of the second edition of this text.

which had not been explained before the introduction of the new variable, so the multiple-partial coefficient of determination measures the relative increase resulting from the introduction of two or more new independent variables.

ANOTHER APPROACH TO MULTIPLE AND PARTIAL CORRELATION COEFFICIENTS

Sometimes one is presented with the results of a study which show only the zero-order correlation coefficients for a number of variables. If multiple and partial coefficients are wanted, it is possible to obtain them from the zero-order coefficients. The formulas which we shall use for the partial coefficients will also serve to indicate why partial correlation coefficients sometimes become larger and sometimes smaller as more variables are held constant. In the preceding discussion we considered, first, multiple correlation coefficients and then partial coefficients. For the present treatment, it will be advantageous to consider partial coefficients first, since the multiple coefficients for four or more variables are most conveniently obtained by using certain of the partial coefficients.

First-order partial correlation coefficients. Any first-order coefficient may be determined from the values of three zero-order coefficients. For example,

$$r_{13.2} = \frac{r_{13} - r_{12}r_{23}}{\sqrt{1 - r_{12}^2}\sqrt{1 - r_{23}^2}}.$$

Since we shall compute eight of these first-order coefficients, and the reader may wish to ascertain the values of others, there are listed below all of the zero-order r, r^2, $1 - r^2$, and $\sqrt{1 - r^2}$ values. We shall use some of the $1 - r^2$ values for computing multiple coefficients.

$$
\begin{aligned}
r_{12} &= +0.7733; & r_{12}^2 &= 0.5980; \\
r_{13} &= +0.7115; & r_{13}^2 &= 0.5062; \\
r_{14} &= -0.2578; & r_{14}^2 &= 0.0665; \\
r_{23} &= +0.7942; & r_{23}^2 &= 0.6307; \\
r_{24} &= +0.1715; & r_{24}^2 &= 0.0294; \\
r_{34} &= +0.3289. & r_{34}^2 &= 0.1081.
\end{aligned}
$$

$$
\begin{aligned}
1 - r_{12}^2 &= 0.4020; & \sqrt{1 - r_{12}^2} &= 0.6340; \\
1 - r_{13}^2 &= 0.4938; & \sqrt{1 - r_{13}^2} &= 0.7027; \\
1 - r_{14}^2 &= 0.9335; & \sqrt{1 - r_{14}^2} &= 0.9662; \\
1 - r_{23}^2 &= 0.3693; & \sqrt{1 - r_{23}^2} &= 0.6077; \\
1 - r_{24}^2 &= 0.9706; & \sqrt{1 - r_{24}^2} &= 0.9852; \\
1 - r_{34}^2 &= 0.8919. & \sqrt{1 - r_{34}^2} &= 0.9444.
\end{aligned}
$$

When four variables are involved in a correlation problem, there are twelve possible first-order coefficients.[11] For our purposes, we shall compute only eight of these: the six having X_1 as the dependent variable and two others, $r_{24.3}$ and $r_{34.2}$, which will be used to obtain second-order partial coefficients. If our objective were merely to obtain the three second-order coefficients, shown in the next section, we would not need the last two of the six first-order coefficients having X_1 as the dependent variable.

$$r_{13.2} = \frac{r_{13} - r_{12}r_{23}}{\sqrt{1 - r_{12}^2}\sqrt{1 - r_{23}^2}} = \frac{0.7115 - (0.7733)(0.7942)}{(0.6340)(0.6077)} = +0.2526.$$

$$r_{14.2} = \frac{r_{14} - r_{12}r_{24}}{\sqrt{1 - r_{12}^2}\sqrt{1 - r_{24}^2}} = \frac{-0.2578 - (0.7733)(0.1715)}{(0.6340)(0.9852)} = -0.6251.$$

$$r_{14.3} = \frac{r_{14} - r_{13}r_{34}}{\sqrt{1 - r_{13}^2}\sqrt{1 - r_{34}^2}} = \frac{-0.2578 - (0.7115)(0.3289)}{(0.7027)(0.9444)} = -0.7411.$$

$$r_{12.3} = \frac{r_{12} - r_{13}r_{23}}{\sqrt{1 - r_{13}^2}\sqrt{1 - r_{23}^2}} = \frac{0.7733 - (0.7115)(0.7942)}{(0.7027)(0.6077)} = +0.4876.$$

$$r_{13.4} = \frac{r_{13} - r_{14}r_{34}}{\sqrt{1 - r_{14}^2}\sqrt{1 - r_{34}^2}} = \frac{0.7115 - (-0.2578)(0.3289)}{(0.9662)(0.9444)} = +0.8727.$$

$$r_{12.4} = \frac{r_{12} - r_{14}r_{24}}{\sqrt{1 - r_{14}^2}\sqrt{1 - r_{24}^2}} = \frac{0.7733 - (-0.2578)(0.1715)}{(0.9662)(0.9852)} = +0.8588.$$

$$r_{24.3} = \frac{r_{24} - r_{23}r_{34}}{\sqrt{1 - r_{23}^2}\sqrt{1 - r_{34}^2}} = \frac{0.1715 - (0.7942)(0.3289)}{(0.6077)(0.9444)} = -0.1563.$$

$$r_{34.2} = \frac{r_{34} - r_{23}r_{24}}{\sqrt{1 - r_{23}^2}\sqrt{1 - r_{24}^2}} = \frac{0.3289 - (0.7942)(0.1715)}{(0.6077)(0.9852)} = +0.3219.$$

We can now see why first-order coefficients are sometimes larger and sometimes smaller than zero-order coefficients. Consider three of the first-order coefficients: (1) $r_{13.2}$ is smaller than r_{13}. Notice that r_{12} and r_{23} have like signs, both being positive and that the value of the numerator of the expression for $r_{13.2}$ is much smaller than r_{13}. The fact that the denominator is less than 1.0 serves to increase the result. (2) $r_{14.2}$ is larger than r_{14}, both being negative. The product of r_{12} and r_{24} does not exceed r_{14}. Since r_{12} and r_{24} have like signs, and since r_{14} is negative, the value of the numerator of the expression for $r_{14.2}$ is larger than r_{14}. The denominator is less than 1.0. Therefore, it was not large enough to change the result sufficiently to make it equal or less than the value of r_{14}. (3)

---

[11] Proof that these formulas are the equivalent of those we have been using is given in Appendix S, section 21.1. The labor of computation can be materially shortened if values of $\sqrt{1 - r^2}$ are looked up in J. R. Miner, *Tables of $\sqrt{1 - r^2}$ and $1 - r^2$ for Use in Partial Correlation and Trigonometry*, Johns Hopkins Press, Baltimore, or Truman Lee Kelley, *The Kelley Statistical Tables*, revised edition, The Macmillan Company, New York, 1948.

$r_{34.2}$ is only slightly smaller (that is it shows a lower degree of correlation) than r_{34}. Since the product of r_{23} and r_{24} does not exceed r_{34}, since r_{23} and r_{24} have like signs, positive, and since r_{34} is positive, the value of the numerator in the expression for $r_{34.2}$ is a smaller positive value than r_{34}. The denominator, though smaller than 1.0, was not small enough to increase the result to a point where it would equal or exceed r_{34}.

Second-order partial correlation coefficients. Second-order coefficients may be obtained from first-order coefficients. We shall compute only those second-order coefficients having X_1 as the dependent variable. They are:

$$r_{14.23} = \frac{r_{14.2} - r_{13.2}r_{34.2}}{\sqrt{1 - r_{13.2}^2}\sqrt{1 - r_{34.2}^2}} = \frac{(-0.6251) - (0.2526)(0.3219)}{\sqrt{1 - (0.2526)^2}\sqrt{1 - (0.3219)^2}}$$
$$= -0.7711.$$

$$r_{13.24} = \frac{r_{13.2} - r_{14.2}r_{34.2}}{\sqrt{1 - r_{14.2}^2}\sqrt{1 - r_{34.2}^2}} = \frac{(0.2526) - (-0.6251)(0.3219)}{\sqrt{1 - (-0.6251)^2}\sqrt{1 - (0.3219)^2}}$$
$$= +0.6141.$$

$$r_{12.34} = \frac{r_{12.3} - r_{14.3}r_{24.3}}{\sqrt{1 - r_{14.3}^2}\sqrt{1 - r_{24.3}^2}} = \frac{0.4876 - (-0.7411)(-0.1563)}{\sqrt{1 - (-0.7411)^2}\sqrt{1 - (-0.1563)^2}}$$
$$= +0.5606.$$

Alternative formulas, giving the same results, are available for all three of the second-order coefficients. They are:

$$r_{14.23} = \frac{r_{14.3} - r_{12.3}r_{24.3}}{\sqrt{1 - r_{12.3}^2}\sqrt{1 - r_{24.3}^2}};$$

$$r_{13.24} = \frac{r_{13.4} - r_{12.4}r_{23.4}}{\sqrt{1 - r_{12.4}^2}\sqrt{1 - r_{23.4}^2}};$$

$$r_{12.34} = \frac{r_{12.4} - r_{13.4}r_{23.4}}{\sqrt{1 - r_{13.4}^2}\sqrt{1 - r_{23.4}^2}}.$$

Notice that $r_{13.24}$ is larger than $r_{13.2}$. On the other hand, $r_{13.24}$ is smaller than $r_{13.4}$. Similar comparisons may be made between the other second-order coefficients and the appropriate first-order coefficients.

In general form[12] for m variables

---

[12] Other forms may also be written. However, this is the most logical form, since partial coefficients are being built up from those of lower order, using in turn variables X_2, X_3, X_4, . . . , X_m. It would be possible to drop from the subscript of the first r in the numerator, not $(m - 1)$, as was done here, but any subscript other than 1 or m. For example, if 3 were dropped, the three coefficients would have as subscripts: $_{1m.24\cdots(m-1)}$; $_{13.24\cdots(m-1)}$; and $_{m3.24\cdots(m-1)}$.

$$r_{1m.23\cdots(m-1)} = \frac{r_{1m.23\cdots(m-2)} - r_{1(m-1).23\cdots(m-2)}r_{m(m-1).23\cdots(m-2)}}{\sqrt{1 - r^2_{1(m-1).23\cdots(m-2)}}\sqrt{1 - r^2_{m(m-1).23\cdots(m-2)}}}.$$

It is interesting to pause at this point and inspect some of the results of our computations. Below are shown the zero-order, first-order, and second-order coefficients involving X_1 as the dependent variable:

$$r_{12} = +0.7733 \qquad r_{12.3} = +0.4876 \qquad r_{12.34} = +0.5606$$
$$r_{12.4} = +0.8588$$
$$r_{13} = +0.7115 \qquad r_{13.2} = +0.2526 \qquad r_{13.24} = +0.6141$$
$$r_{13.4} = +0.8727$$
$$r_{14} = -0.2578 \qquad r_{14.2} = -0.6251 \qquad r_{14.23} = -0.7711$$
$$r_{14.3} = -0.7411$$

When no allowance had been made for the effect of other variables, X_2 (per cent professional, etc. workers) ranked first and X_4 (per cent migrant) ranked last. When adjustment was made for X_4, median school years X_3 was ahead of per cent professional, etc. workers X_2; when adjustment was made for X_3, per cent migrant X_4 was ahead of per cent professional, etc. workers X_2; when adjustment was made for X_2, per cent migrant X_4 ranked above median school years X_3. Finally, when two independent variables were held constant, per cent migrant X_4 was first and per cent professional, etc. workers X_2 was last.

Multiple coefficients. It has already been pointed out in footnote 7 that three-variable multiple coefficients may be obtained from the zero-order coefficients. Thus:

$$R^2_{1.23} = \frac{r^2_{12} + r^2_{13} - 2r_{12}r_{13}r_{23}}{1 - r^2_{23}},$$
$$= \frac{0.5980 + 0.5062 - 2(0.7733)(0.7115)(0.7942)}{0.3693},$$
$$= 0.6236.$$
$$R_{1.23} = 0.7897.$$

$$R^2_{1.24} = \frac{r^2_{12} + r^2_{14} - 2r_{12}r_{14}r_{24}}{1 - r^2_{24}},$$
$$= \frac{0.5980 + 0.0665 - 2(0.7733)(-0.2578)(0.1715)}{1 - 0.0294},$$
$$= 0.7551.$$
$$R_{1.24} = 0.8689.$$

$$R^2_{1.34} = \frac{r^2_{13} + r^2_{14} - 2r_{13}r_{14}r_{34}}{1 - r^2_{34}},$$

$$= \frac{0.5062 + 0.0665 - 2(0.7115)(-0.2578)(0.3289)}{1 - 0.1081},$$

$$= 0.7774.$$

$$R_{1.34} = 0.8817.$$

Using formulas similar to those given on page 469

$R^2_{1.23} = r^2_{12} + r^2_{13.2}(1 - r^2_{12}) = 0.5980 + (0.0638)(0.4020) = 0.6236.$
$R_{1.23} = 0.7897.$
$R^2_{1.24} = r^2_{12} + r^2_{14.2}(1 - r^2_{12}) = 0.5980 + (0.3908)(0.4020) = 0.7551.$
$R_{1.24} = 0.8689.$
$R^2_{1.34} = r^2_{13} + r^2_{14.3}(1 - r^2_{13}) = 0.5062 + (0.5492)(0.4938) = 0.7774.$
$R_{1.34} = 0.8817.$
$R^2_{1.234} = r^2_{12} + r^2_{13.2}(1 - r^2_{12}) + r^2_{14.23}(1 - R^2_{1.23}),$
$\qquad = 0.5980 + (0.0638)(0.4020) + (0.5946)(0.3764)$
$\qquad = 0.8474.$
$R_{1.234} = 0.9205.$

Rearranging the formula for $r^2_{13.2}$ given on page 467, we may also write

$$1 - R^2_{1.23} = (1 - r^2_{12})(1 - r^2_{13.2}).$$
$$R^2_{1.23} = 1 - [(1 - r^2_{12})(1 - r^2_{13.2})].$$

This expression may be put into a general form for m variables by writing

$$R^2_{1.234\cdots m} = 1 - [(1 - r^2_{12})(1 - r^2_{13.2})(1 - r^2_{14.23}) \cdots (1 - r^2_{1m.23\cdots(m-1)})].$$

A variation of this expression is

$$R^2_{1.234\cdots m} = 1 - [(1 - R^2_{1.234\cdots(m-1)})(1 - r^2_{1m.23\cdots(m-1)})].$$

Coefficients of estimation and standard errors of estimate.
When only the values of the zero-order coefficients are known it is not feasible to undertake to ascertain the various b-values and the standard error of estimate. However, if s_1, or Σx^2_1 and N, are known, we can obtain the standard error of estimate from

$$s_{1.234\cdots m} = s_1 \sqrt{1 - R^2_{1.234\cdots m}}.$$

Not having solved the m normal equations (see footnote 10), the coefficients of estimation may be obtained from

$$b_{1m.23\cdots(m-1)} = r_{1m.23\cdots(m-1)} \frac{s_{1.234\cdots m}}{s_{m.123\cdots(m-1)}}.$$

Other measures of the individual importance of the independent variables. We have already considered the coefficients of partial determination or correlation as measures of the individual importance of the three independent variables. Two other measures of the individual importance of the independent variables are occasionally used. These are: (1) beta coefficients, and (2) coefficients of separate determination. The beta coefficients should not be confused with β_1 and β_2 used to describe a frequency distribution. The two sets of measures are entirely different in nature.[13]

MULTIPLE CURVILINEAR CORRELATION

As in the case of relationships between two variables, the relationship between a dependent variable and one or more independent variables is sometimes non-linear. When this is true, we may use a polynomial or we may transform one or more variables into logarithms, reciprocals, roots, or powers, or convert in some other manner.

Polynomials. If the relationship between X_1 and X_2 appears to be non-linear, while that between X_1 and X_3 is linear, the equation type

$$X_{c1.22'3} = a_{1.22'3} + b_{12.2'3}X_2 + b_{12'.23}X_2^2 + b_{13.22'}X_3$$

might be used. This equation would, presumably, result in a greater amount of explained variation than would use of

$$X_{c1.23} = a_{1.23} + b_{12.3}X_2 + b_{13.2}X_3.$$

The increase in the amount of explained variation may be tested for significance by using the methods described for partial coefficients of determination in Chapter 26. A polynomial was used for a non-linear multiple correlation analysis on pages 779–784 of the first edition of this text.

Transformations. Using logarithms, reciprocals, roots, powers, or some other function of the values of one (or more) of the series may result in reducing a non-linear relationship to linear form. For example, an estimating equation might be of one of the following types:

$$X_{c1.23} = a_{1.23} + b_{12.3} \log X_2 + b_{13.2}X_3;$$

$$X_{c1.23} = a_{1.23} + b_{12.3}X_2 + b_{13.2} \sqrt{X_3};$$

$$X_{c1.23} = a_{1.23} + b_{12.3}\frac{1}{X_2} + b_{13.2}X_3;$$

$$\log X_{c1.23} = a_{1.23} + b_{12.3}X_2 + b_{13.2}X_3.$$

---

[13] For a discussion and illustration of the uses of beta coefficients and coefficients of separate determination, see the second edition of this text, pp. 557–559.

Various combinations are also possible. When using a transformation, one should, if possible, formulate a hypothesis concerning the nature of the relationship between the variables, as was done in the case of the

$$(\sqrt{Y})_c = a + bX$$

transformation employed for the data of ponderosa pine trees in Chapter 20.

Graphic Method. Statisticians in the United States Department of Agriculture have developed an extremely flexible technique by which curves of net relationship and a coefficient of multiple correlation may be obtained through successive approximations by means of charts and use of mathematics no more advanced than simple arithmetic. While this method has distinct limitations, it is useful as an exploratory tool in determining the appropriate type of equation to fit by mathematical methods.

Although the graphic method is extremely flexible, it is also highly subjective. Rarely would two statisticians obtain curves exactly alike from the same data. Consequently, good results can be obtained only by persons of experience and good judgment. This is in contrast to the mathematical procedure based on the method of least squares, in which case (barring mistakes) only one possible result can be had for a given equation type. A practical difficulty is also inherent in the graphic method when a large number of variables is employed. The graphic approach is not explained in this edition of this text, but the interested reader is referred to pages 784–789 of the first edition.

CHAPTER 22

Correlation IV: Correlation of Time Series

The problem of correlating the cyclical fluctuations of two, or more, time series is basically the same as that of correlating non-chronological series. However, when correlating time series, we must take cognizance of the fact that trend is usually present in annual data and that both trend and seasonal variation, as well as irregular fluctuations, may be found in monthly data.

ANNUAL DATA

Table 22.1 shows data of the average annual number of employees in transportation and public utilities and in contract construction in the United States for each year, 1952 through 1963. From the numerical data, little can be grasped concerning the behavior of the two series; but when the two series are shown graphically in Charts 22.1 and 22.2, it is apparent that: (1) the trend of employment in transportation and public utilities is downward, (2) the trend of employment in contract construction is upward, and (3) the *fluctuations* of the two series are positively correlated.

Correlation of data unadjusted for trend. When correlating two time series, we are interested in knowing whether the fluctuations of the series move in the same direction or in opposite directions, and whether the association is high or low. If our concern is with the trends of the two series, rather than with their fluctuations, we would not correlate the two trends, since they would of necessity show perfect linear or non-linear correlation. Trends are compared either graphically or by examining the trend equations. When time series data, unadjusted for trend, are correlated, the resulting coefficient reflects both the relationship existing between the fluctuations and that between the two trends. The data of employment in transportation and public utilities and in contract construction are shown as a scatter diagram in Chart 22.3 and the value of the correlation coefficient is found, in Table 22.1, to be -0.373. This

TABLE 22.1

Correlation of Employment in Transportation and Public Utilities and in Contract Construction, in the United States, 1952–1963

(Thousands of employees.)

Year	Transportation and public utilities X	Contract construction Y	XY	X²	Y²
1952	4,248	2,634	11,189,232	18,045,504	6,937,956
1953	4,290	2,623	11,252,670	18,404,100	6,880,129
1954	4,084	2,612	10,667,408	16,679,056	6,822,544
1955	4,141	2,802	11,603,082	17,147,881	7,851,204
1956	4,244	2,999	12,727,756	18,011,536	8,994,001
1957	4,241	2,923	12,396,443	17,986,081	8,543,929
1958	3,976	2,778	11,045,328	15,808,576	7,717,284
1959	4,011	2,960	11,872,560	16,088,121	8,761,600
1960	4,004	2,885	11,551,540	16,032,016	8,323,225
1961	3,903	2,816	10,990,848	15,233,409	7,929,856
1962	3,903	2,909	11,353,827	15,233,409	8,462,281
1963	3,913	3,029	11,852,477	15,311,569	9,174,841
Total	48,958	33,970	138,503,171	199,981,258	96,398,850

Data from *Statistical Abstract of the United States, 1964*, p. 220.

$$r = \frac{N\Sigma XY - (\Sigma X)(\Sigma Y)}{\sqrt{[N\Sigma X^2 - (\Sigma X)^2][N\Sigma Y^2 - (\Sigma Y)^2]}},$$

$$= \frac{12(138,503,171) - (48,958)(33,970)}{\sqrt{[12(199,981,258) - (48,958)^2][12(96,398,850) - (33,970)^2]}},$$

$$= -0.373.$$

coefficient seems low in view of the agreement of the fluctuations of the two series shown in Charts 22.1 and 22.2. The difficulty lies in the fact that the two trends are in opposite directions. The effect of trend may be eliminated by correlating percentages of trend instead of correlating the raw data. Alternatively, we may compute the partial correlation coefficient $r_{12.3}$, where the two series are X_1 and X_2 and where time is X_3. Sometimes the effect of trend is decreased by correlating either (1) the amounts of change from each year to the next for the two series or (2) the percentages of change from each year to the next for the two series. We shall examine each of these procedures in turn.

Correlation of percentages of trend. Obviously, the first step consists of determining an appropriate trend for each of the series. For our illustration, linear trends will suffice, and Table 22.2 shows the computation of the trend equation, the trend values, and the percentages of trend for number of employees in transportation and public utilities. Similar computations are shown for number of employees in contract construction in Table 22.3. The two sets of per-cent-of-trend data have

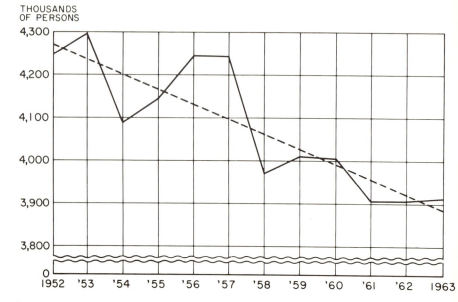

Chart 22.1. Number of Employees in Transportation and Public Utilities in the United States, and Straight-Line Trend, 1952–1963.   Data from Table 22.2.

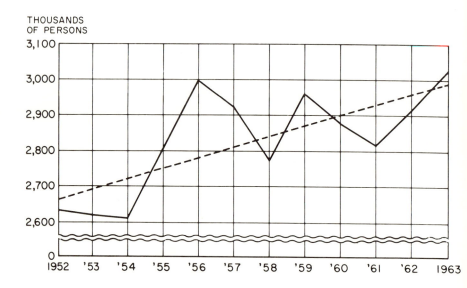

Chart 22.2.   Number of Employees in Contract Construction in the United States, and Straight-Line Trend, 1952–1963.   Data from Table 22.3.

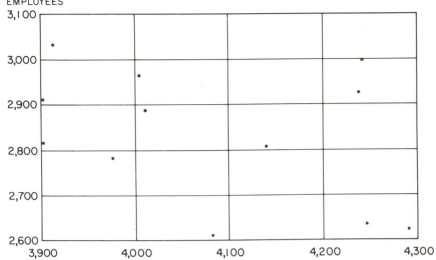

CONTRACT CONSTRUCTION
EMPLOYEES

TRANSPORTATION AND PUBLIC UTILITIES EMPLOYEES

Chart 22.3. Scatter Diagram of Number of Employees in Transportation and Public Utilities and in Contract Construction, 1952–1963. Data of Table 22.1.

TABLE 22.2

Determination of Trend and Computation of Per-Cent-of-Trend Values for Employment in Transportation and Public Utilities, 1952–1963

Year	X	Employees (thousands) Y	XY	Trend values Y_c	Per cent of trend $[Y \div Y_c]$
1952	−11	4,248	−46,728	4,273.7	99.40
1953	− 9	4,290	−38,610	4,238.5	101.22
1954	− 7	4,084	−28,588	4,203.2	97.16
1955	− 5	4,141	−20,705	4,168.0	99.35
1956	− 3	4,244	−12,732	4,132.7	102.69
1957	− 1	4,241	− 4,241	4,097.4	103.50
1958	1	3,976	3,976	4,062.2	97.88
1959	3	4,011	12,033	4,026.9	99.61
1960	5	4,004	20,020	3,991.7	100.31
1961	7	3,903	27,321	3,956.4	98.65
1962	9	3,903	35,127	3,921.1	99.54
1963	11	3,913	43,043	3.885.9	100.70
Total	0	48,958	−10,084	. . .	. . .

Data from source given below Table 22.1.

$$N = 12. \quad \Sigma X^2 = 2(286) = 572.$$
$$a = \frac{\Sigma Y}{N} = \frac{48,958}{12} = 4,079.8.$$
$$b = \frac{\Sigma XY}{\Sigma X^2} = \frac{-10,084}{572} = -17.63.$$
$$Y_c = 4,079.8 - 17.63X.$$
Origin, between 1957 and 1958.
X units, $\frac{1}{2}$ year.

483

TABLE 22.3

Determination of Trend and Computation of Per-Cent-of-Trend
Values for Employment in Contract Construction, 1952–1963

Year	X	Employees (thousands) Y	XY	Trend values Y_c	Per cent of trend $[Y \div Y_c]$
1952	−11	2,634	−28,974	2,667.4	98.75
1953	− 9	2,623	−23,607	2,697.1	97.25
1954	− 7	2,612	−18,284	2,726.8	95.79
1955	− 5	2,802	−14,010	2,756.5	101.65
1956	− 3	2,999	− 8,997	2,786.3	107.63
1957	− 1	2,923	− 2,923	2,816.0	103.80
1958	1	2,778	2,778	2,845.7	97.62
1959	3	2,960	8,880	2,875.4	102.94
1960	5	2,885	14,425	2,905.1	99.31
1961	7	2,816	19,712	2,934.8	95.95
1962	9	2,909	26,181	2,964.5	98.13
1963	11	3,029	33,319	2,994.3	101.16
Total	0	33,970	8,500	...	...

Data from source given below Table 22.1.

$$N = 12. \quad \Sigma X^2 = 2(286) = 572.$$

$$a = \frac{\Sigma Y}{N} = \frac{33,970}{12} = 2,830.8.$$

$$b = \frac{\Sigma XY}{\Sigma X^2} = \frac{8,500}{572} = 14.86.$$

$$Y_c = 2,830.8 + 14.86X.$$

Origin, between 1957 and 1958.
X units, $\frac{1}{2}$ year.

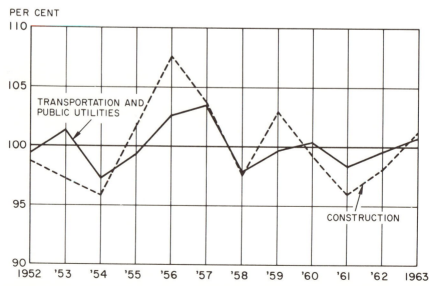

Chart 22.4. Percentages of Trend of Number of Employees in Transportation and Public Utilities and in Contract Construction, 1952–1963. Data of Tables 22.2 and 22.3.

been plotted in Chart 22.4, where it may be seen that when one series is above (or below) its trend line, the other series is usually also above (or below) its trend line.   Chart 22.4 gives us an adequate picture of the closeness of the relationship; however, that purpose is served better by Chart 22.5, which is a scatter diagram of the two series of percentages of trend.   From this scatter plot it is clear that fairly high positive correlation is present between the percentages of trend for the two series, and the value of r is found, in Table 22.4, to be $+0.739$.

Chart 22.5.   **Scatter Diagram of Percentages of Trend on Number of Employees in Transportation and Public Utilities and in Contract Construction, 1952–1963.**   Data of Table 22.4.

The situation pictured in the foregoing tables and charts is but one of four possibilities.[1]   They are:

1. The fluctuations of two time series may be positively correlated, but the trends may be in opposite directions.   Correlating the data without adjusting for trend, instead of correlating percentages of trend, will result in lowering the positive correlation coefficient or may even change it to a negative coefficient, if the trends are marked in relation to the

[1] Throughout the discussion in this chapter, we consider only linear trends and linear correlation.   When dealing with non-linear trends and/or non-linear correlation of fluctuations, the results of failing to eliminate trend cannot be so simply stated as when only linear relationships are involved.   However, if a trend is non-linear, it is just as important that its effect be eliminated as if the trend were linear.

fluctuations as in our data. In the illustration, $r = +0.739$ for the per-cent-of-trend data, while $r = -0.373$ for the unadjusted employment data.

2. The fluctuations of two time series may be positively correlated, and the trends may be in the same direction. Correlating the data

TABLE 22.4

Correlation of Percentages of Trend of Employment in Transportation and Public Utilities and in Contract Construction, 1952–1963

Year	Transportation and public utilities X	Construction Y	XY	X^2	Y^2
1952	99.40	98.75	9,815.7500	9,880.3600	9,751.5625
1953	101.22	97.25	9,843.6450	10,245.4884	9,457.5625
1954	97.16	95.79	9,306.9564	9,440.0656	9,175.7241
1955	99.35	101.65	10,098.9275	9,870.4225	10,332.7225
1956	102.69	107.63	11,052.5247	10,545.2361	11,584.2169
1957	103.50	103.80	10,743.3000	10,712.2500	10,774.4400
1958	97.88	97.62	9,555.0456	9,580.4944	9,529.6644
1959	99.61	102.94	10,253.8543	9,922.1521	10,596.6436
1960	100.31	99.31	9,961.7861	10,062.0961	9,862.4761
1961	98.65	95.95	9,465.4675	9,731.8225	9,206.4025
1962	99.54	98.13	9,767.8602	9,908.2116	9,629.4969
1963	100.70	101.16	10,186.8120	10,140.4900	10,233.3456
Total	1,200.01	1,199.98	120,051.9284	120,039.0893	120,134.2576

Data from Tables 22.2 and 22.3.

$$r = \frac{N\Sigma XY - (\Sigma X)(\Sigma Y)}{\sqrt{[N\Sigma X^2 - (\Sigma X)^2][N\Sigma Y^2 - (\Sigma Y)^2]}},$$

$$= \frac{12(120{,}051.9284) - (1{,}200.01)(1{,}199.98)}{\sqrt{[12(120{,}039.0893) - (1{,}200.01)^2][12(120{,}134.2576) - (1{,}199.98)^2]}},$$

$$= +0.739.$$

without adjusting for trend, instead of correlating percentages of trend, will result in increasing the positive correlation coefficient. (If the percentages of trend showed $r = +1.0$, ignoring the trends and correlating the unadjusted data could not result in a higher value for r.) Although the data cover an extremely short period, the production of pig iron and the production of steel ingots and steel for castings for 1958–1964 will serve to illustrate the principle involved. Table 22.5 shows the data, the behavior of which may be seen in Chart 22.6. Chart 22.6 also shows the trends of the two series, both of which are upward. It is apparent from the chart that the fluctuations of the two series about their trends have a high positive correlation. Correlating, first, the unadjusted data, we find in Table 22.5 that $r = +0.995$. When the two series are each put in terms of percentages of trend, the values are those shown in Table 22.6. This table shows, also, that correlating the per-cent-of-trend data yields

$r = +0.965$. The per-cent-of-trend figures are so closely related that ignoring the trends could not increase the coefficient very much.

TABLE 22.5

Correlation of Production of Pig Iron and Production of Steel Ingots and Steel for Castings, 1958–1964

(Millions of short tons.)

Year	Pig iron X	Steel ingots and steel for castings Y	XY	X^2	Y^2
1958	57.2	85.3	4,879.16	3,271.84	7,276.09
1959	60.2	93.4	5,622.68	3,624.04	8,723.56
1960	66.5	99.3	6,603.45	4,422.25	9,860.49
1961	64.6	98.0	6,330.80	4,173.16	9,604.00
1962	65.6	98.3	6,448.48	4,303.36	9,662.89
1963	71.8	109.3	7,847.74	5,155.24	11,946.49
1964	85.6	126.9	10,862.64	7,327.36	16,103.61
Total	471.5	710.5	48,594.95	32,277.25	73,177.13

Data from various issues of *Statistical Abstract of the United States* and from *Survey of Current Business*, February 1965, p. S-32.

$$r = \frac{N\Sigma XY - (\Sigma X)(\Sigma Y)}{\sqrt{[N\Sigma X^2 - (\Sigma X)^2][N\Sigma Y^2 - (\Sigma Y)^2]}},$$

$$= \frac{7(48,594.95) - (471.5)(710.5)}{\sqrt{[7(32,277.25) - (471.5)^2][7(73,177.13) - (710.5)^2]}},$$

$$= +0.995.$$

3. The fluctuations of two time series may be negatively correlated, but the trends may be in the same direction. Correlating the data without adjusting for trend, instead of correlating percentages of trend, will result in lowering the negative correlation coefficient or may even change it to a positive coefficient if the trends are pronounced in relation to the fluctuations.

4. The fluctuations of two time series may be negatively correlated and the trends may be in opposite directions. Correlating the data without adjusting for trend, instead of correlating percentages of trend, will result in increasing the negative correlation coefficient. (If the percentages of trend showed $r = -1.0$, ignoring the trends and correlating the unadjusted data could not result in a higher value for r.)

If two time series are to be correlated, and if both series have horizontal trends, it is, of course, not necessary to express the data as percentages of trend. However, if one of the two series has an upward or downward trend, a suitable correlation of the fluctuations of the two series will not be obtained unless trend is eliminated from the series showing trend.

It occasionally happens that annual data for one series are regularly known, or made available, before the corresponding yearly figure for

TABLE 22.6

Correlation of Percentages of Trend of Production of Pig Iron and Production of Steel Ingots and Steel for Castings, 1958–1964

Year	Pig iron X	Steel ingots and steel for castings Y	XY	X²	Y²
1958	102.4	100.6	10,301.44	10,485.76	10,120.36
1959	100.9	103.3	10,422.97	10,180.81	10,670.89
1960	104.7	103.5	10,836.45	10,962.09	10,712.25
1961	95.9	96.6	9,263.94	9,196.81	9,331.56
1962	92.1	91.8	8,454.78	8,482.41	8,427.24
1963	95.7	97.1	9,292.47	9,158.49	9,428.41
1964	108.5	107.7	11,652.90	11,772.25	11,534.76
Total	700.2	700.3	70,224.95	70,238.62	70,225.47

The per-cent-of trend figures were obtained from the production data of Table 22.5, using the trends shown in Chart 22.6.

$$r = \frac{N\Sigma XY - (\Sigma X)(\Sigma Y)}{\sqrt{[N\Sigma X^2 - (\Sigma X)^2][N\Sigma Y^2 - (\Sigma Y)^2]}},$$

$$= \frac{7(70,224.95) - (700.2)(700.3)}{\sqrt{[7(70,238.62) - (700.2)^2][7(70,225.47) - (700.3)^2]}},$$

$$= +0.965.$$

another, closely correlated series. In such a situation, if the correlation is high, a useful estimate may be made for the series which is not so promptly available. The procedure consists of: (1) expressing the figure which is first available as a percentage of the extended trend for that series, (2) estimating a per-cent-of-trend figure for the other series by use of an estimating equation obtained from a table like Table 22.4, and (3) converting this estimated per-cent-of-trend figure into the units in which the series is expressed (tons, dollars, index numbers, and so on) by taking the estimated per cent of trend of the extended trend value for that series. We shall not give a numerical illustration of the foregoing, since most series are available on a monthly basis, and, when data are already known for eleven months of a year, an estimate of the annual total for that series based only on the annual total for another series can be of little use. It should be clear that the procedure assumes a continuation of the relationship existing between the two sets of fluctuations, and also a continuation of the two trend lines.

Correlation of fluctuations when data have been divided by s. In Chapter 16 it was pointed out that time series having different amplitudes of fluctuation are easier to compare graphically if each set of adjusted data is

MILLIONS OF
SHORT TONS

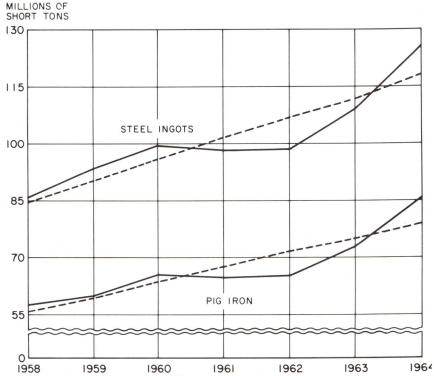

Chart 22.6. **Production of Pig Iron and Production of Steel Ingots and Steel for Castings, with Straight-line Trends, 1958–1964.** Data of production from Table 22.5. The trends were computed from these figures.

divided by its standard deviation. When two series[2] of deviations have been expressed in terms of their respective standard deviations, the product-moment formula for the correlation coefficient becomes

$$r = \frac{\Sigma xy}{N s_X s_Y} = \frac{1}{N} \Sigma \left(\frac{x}{s_x} \cdot \frac{y}{s_y} \right).$$

Thus we obtain r by merely (1) multiplying the paired values, (2) adding, and (3) dividing by N. (Note that $s_X = s_x$ and $s_Y = s_y$, since adding, or subtracting, a constant does not alter the value of s for a series of values.) The data of employment in transportation and public utilities and in contract construction provide a good illustration, since it is apparent in Chart 22.4 that the fluctuations in construction employment are more pronounced, in terms of percentages of trend, than the fluctuations

---

[2] The series may be chronological or non-chronological. For example, two sets of paired grades expressed as deviations from their means and in terms of their standard deviations (sometimes called *standard scores*) may be correlated as shown in Table 22.7.

TABLE 22.7

Correlation of Percentage Deviations From Trend Expressed in Terms of
s for Employment in Transportation and Public Utilities and
in Contract Construction, 1952–1963

Year	Transportation and public utilities			Contract construction			$\dfrac{x}{s_x} \times \dfrac{y}{s_y}$
	x	x^2	$\dfrac{x}{s_x}$	y	y^2	$\dfrac{y}{s_y}$	
1952	−0.60	0.3600	−0.341	−1.25	1.5625	−0.368	+0.125488
1953	+1.22	1.4884	+0.694	−2.75	7.5625	−0.810	−0.562140
1954	−2.84	8.0656	−1.615	−4.21	17.7241	−1.240	+2.002600
1955	−0.65	0.4225	−0.370	+1.65	2.7225	+0.486	−0.179820
1956	+2.69	7.2361	+1.530	+7.63	58.2169	+2.248	+3.439440
1957	+3.50	12.2500	+1.991	+3.80	14.4400	+1.120	+2.229920
1958	−2.12	4.4944	−1.206	−2.38	5.6644	−0.701	+0.845406
1959	−0.39	0.1521	−0.222	+2.94	8.6436	+0.866	−0.192252
1960	+0.31	0.0961	+0.176	−0.69	0.4761	−0.203	−0.035728
1961	−1.35	1.8225	−0.768	−4.05	16.4025	−1.193	+0.916224
1962	−0.46	0.2116	−0.262	−1.87	3.4669	−0.551	+0.144362
1963	+0.70	0.4900	+0.398	+1.16	1.3456	+0.342	+0.136116
Total	...	37.0893	...	...	138.2576	...	+8.869616

The x and y values are the values in the last columns of Table 22.2 and Table 22.3 expressed as deviations from 100.00. The sum of the percentage deviations from a trend line is ordinarily not exactly zero. However, if the trend has been fitted by least squares to data covering the same period as the data under consideration, the discrepancy may be expected to be so slight that it may be ignored. Including the correction factors $\left(\dfrac{\Sigma x}{N}\right)^2$ and $\left(\dfrac{\Sigma y}{N}\right)^2$ below does not alter the figures in the third decimal place for s_x and s_y.

$$s_x = \sqrt{\frac{\Sigma x^2}{N}} = \sqrt{\frac{37.0893}{12}} = 1.758.$$

$$s_y = \sqrt{\frac{\Sigma y^2}{N}} = \sqrt{\frac{138.2576}{12}} = 3.394.$$

$$r = \frac{1}{N} \Sigma \left(\frac{x}{s_x} \cdot \frac{y}{s_y}\right) = \frac{1}{12} (+8.869616) = +0.739.$$

in the other series. In fact, for all of the 12 years shown in Chart 22.4, the construction employment per-cent-of-trend values are farther removed from the 100 line than are the values for transportation and public utility employment. In Table 22.7 the two series are expressed as percentage deviations from trend, and the necessary computations are made for the determination of the standard deviations. Below the table it is seen that s_x, the standard deviation for transportation and public utilities employment, is 1.758, and that s_y, the standard deviation for contract construction employment, is 3.394. Table 22.7 also shows the $\dfrac{x}{s_x}$ and $\dfrac{y}{s_y}$ values. These two sets of values are shown, as time series, in Chart 22.7. What has been accomplished by dividing each series by its standard deviation may be seen by comparing Charts 22.7 and 22.4. If a scatter plot were to be drawn of the $\frac{x}{s_x}$ and $\frac{y}{s_y}$ values, it would be *exactly the same as Chart 22.5*, except that the scales would differ. Table 22.7 shows the computation of r for the $\frac{x}{s_x}$ and $\frac{y}{s_y}$ values, and it is found to be $+0.739$, identical with the value obtained in Table 22.4.

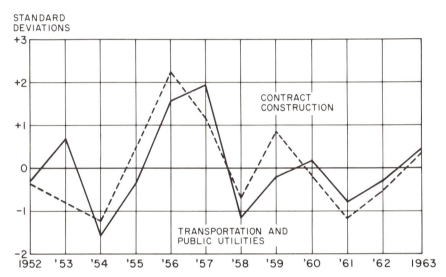

STANDARD DEVIATIONS

Chart 22.7.   Employment in Transportation and Public Utilities and in Contract Construction, Expressed as Percentage Deviations from Trend and in Terms of Their Standard Deviations, 1952–1963.   Data from Table 22.7.

Correlation of unadjusted data with time as a third variable. Another procedure for correlating the fluctuations of two time series consists of determining the partial correlation existing between the two series when time is held constant.   The partial correlation coefficient which is computed is $r_{12.3}$, where X_1 and X_2 are the two time series and X_3 represents the years, which, for convenience, are taken with the origin in the middle of the period.   Table 22.8 shows the sums necessary for determining r_{12}, r_{13}, and r_{23} and, from these, $r_{12.3}$.   Note that all of the totals shown in Table 22.8 could have been obtained from Tables 22.1, 22.2, and 22.3.   From the computations shown below Table 22.8, we find $r_{12.3} = +0.737$.

If it were desired to express the relationship existing between the three variables by means of a multiple estimating equation, such as was used in Chapter 21, and if number of employees in transportation and public utilities were the dependent[3] variable X_1, we would use the equation type

$$X_{c1.23} = a_{1.23} + b_{12.3}X_2 + b_{13.2}X_3,$$

where, as in Table 22.8, X_2 refers to employees in contract construction and X_3 is time, with the origin for X_3 between 1957 and 1958 and the X_3 units one year. If such an equation is used to estimate an annual figure for one series from a more promptly available figure for another series, it assumes the continuation of the straight-line trends for both series and a continuation of the same relationship between the fluctuations of the two series.

It is of more than passing interest that the partial and multiple correlation analysis set forth in Table 22.8 is exactly the same as if we were to correlate the *amounts of deviation from the trends* in Tables 22.2 and 22.3. To demonstrate this, Table 22.9 has been made, which shows the absolute deviations from trend for employment in transportation and public utilities and in contract construction. Below Table 22.9 it is seen that, when the absolute deviations from trend are correlated, $r = +0.737$, the same value obtained for $r_{12.3}$ in Table 22.8.

Since the multiple and partial correlation procedure produces the same results as correlating absolute differences from trend, the former procedure is subject to the same disadvantage as the latter. This disadvantage was noted on pages 319–321, where it was pointed out that *relative* deviations from trend are usually more meaningful than *absolute* deviations from trend. Sometimes the value of r obtained for the absolute deviations from trend is slightly larger than that for the percentages of trend, but this should not be construed as an argument in favor of using absolute deviations from trend. One or a few large absolute deviations would have a marked effect on the value of r, as noted in Chapter 19 (see Charts 19.9 and 19.10 and accompanying discussion).

Correlation of amounts of change or percentages of change. Occasionally, the relationship between the fluctuations of two time series may be studied by computing the amount of change from each year to the following year for both series and then correlating the paired amounts of change, which will have positive and negative values. This procedure is not recommended since: (1) using amounts of change results in the loss of one pair of values and (2) if the trend is non-linear, the first differences of values fluctuating around that trend will still contain a trend element.

---

[3] If contract construction employment were the dependent variable, the equation would be

$$X_{c2.13} = a_{2.13} + b_{21.3}X_1 + b_{23.1}X_3,$$

or the identification of variables X_1 and X_2 could be interchanged and the equation given above could be used.

TABLE 22.8

Computations for Partial and Multiple Correlation of Employment in Transportation and Public Utilities, X_1, Employment in Contract Construction, X_2, and Time, X_3, 1952–1963

(Employment figures in thousands.)

Year	Transportation and public utilities employees X_1	Contract construction employees X_2	Time X_3	X_1X_2	X_1X_3	X_2X_3	X_1^2	X_2^2
1952	4,248	2,634	−11	11,189,232	−46,728	−28,974	18,045,504	6,937,956
1953	4,290	2,623	−9	11,252,670	−38,610	−23,607	18,404,100	6,880,129
1954	4,084	2,612	−7	10,667,408	−28,588	−18,284	16,679,056	6,822,544
1955	4,141	2,802	−5	11,603,082	−20,705	−14,010	17,147,881	7,851,204
1956	4,244	2,999	−3	12,727,756	−12,732	−8,997	18,011,536	8,994,001
1957	4,241	2,923	−1	12,396,443	−4,241	−2,923	17,986,081	8,543,929
1958	3,976	2,778	1	11,045,328	3,976	2,778	15,808,576	7,717,284
1959	4,011	2,960	3	11,872,560	12,033	8,880	16,088,121	8,761,600
1960	4,004	2,885	5	11,551,540	20,020	14,425	16,032,016	8,323,225
1961	3,903	2,816	7	10,990,848	27,321	19,712	15,233,409	7,929,856
1962	3,903	2,909	9	11,353,827	35,127	26,181	15,233,409	8,462,281
1963	3,913	3,029	11	11,852,477	43,043	33,319	15,311,569	9,174,841
Total	48,958	33,970	0	138,503,171	−10,084	8,500	199,981,258	96,398,850

Data from source given below Table 22.1.

$$\Sigma X_3^2 = 2(286) = 572.$$

$$r_{12} = \frac{N\Sigma X_1X_2 - (\Sigma X_1)(\Sigma X_2)}{\sqrt{[N\Sigma X_1^2 - (\Sigma X_1)^2][N\Sigma X_2^2 - (\Sigma X_2)^2]}}$$

$$= \frac{12(133,503,171) - (48,958)(33,970)}{\sqrt{[12(199,981,258) - (48,958)^2][12(96,398,850) - (33,970)^2]}}$$

$$= -0.372824.$$

$$r_{13} = \frac{N\Sigma X_1X_3 - (\Sigma X_1)(\Sigma X_3)}{\sqrt{[N\Sigma X_1^2 - (\Sigma X_1)^2][N\Sigma X_3^2 - (\Sigma X_3)^2]}}$$

$$= \frac{12(-10,084) - (48,958)(0)}{\sqrt{[12(199,981,258) - (48,958)^2][12(572) - (0)^2]}}$$

$$= -0.859264.$$

$$r_{23} = \frac{N\Sigma X_2X_3 - (\Sigma X_2)(\Sigma X_3)}{\sqrt{[N\Sigma X_2^2 - (\Sigma X_2)^2][N\Sigma X_3^2 - (\Sigma X_3)^2]}}$$

$$= \frac{12(8,500) - (33,970)(0)}{\sqrt{[12(96,398,850) - (33,970)^2][12(572) - (0)^2]}}$$

$$= +0.732452.$$

$$r_{12.3} = \frac{r_{12} - r_{13}r_{23}}{\sqrt{1 - r_{13}^2}\sqrt{1 - r_{23}^2}} = \frac{-0.372824 - (-0.859264)(0.732452)}{\sqrt{1 - (-0.859264)^2}\sqrt{1 - (0.732452)^2}}$$

$$= +0.737.$$

This trend element could even be in the opposite direction to the original trend.

Alternatively, percentages of change may be computed for each of the two series and the paired percentages may be correlated. Here again, we would have one fewer pair of values than the number of years involved.

Also, the percentages of trend would still contain an element of trend if the trend for a series were not an exponential curve (page 257).

Note that in both of these procedures different functions of the basic data than those previously discussed would be correlated.

TABLE 22.9

Correlation of Absolute Deviations From Trend of Employment in Transportation and Public Utilities and in Contract Construction, 1952–1963

(Thousands.)

Year	Transportation and public utilities X	Contract construction Y	XY	X^2	Y^2
1952	− 25.7	− 33.4	+ 858.38	660.49	1,115.56
1953	+ 51.5	− 74.1	− 3,816.15	2,652.25	5,490.81
1954	−119.2	−114.8	+13,684.16	14,208.64	13,179.04
1955	− 27.0	+ 45.5	− 1,228.50	729.00	2,070.25
1956	+111.3	+212.7	+23,673.51	12,387.69	45,241.29
1957	+143.6	+107.0	+15,365.20	20,620.96	11,449.00
1958	− 86.2	− 67.7	+ 5,835.74	7,430.44	4,583.29
1959	− 15.9	+ 84.6	− 1,345.14	252.81	7,157.16
1960	+ 12.3	− 20.1	− 247.23	151.29	404.01
1961	− 53.4	−118.8	+ 6,343.92	2,851.56	14,113.44
1962	− 18.1	− 55.5	+ 1,004.55	327.61	3,080.25
1963	+ 27.1	+ 34.7	+ 940.37	734.41	1,204.09
Total	+ 0.3	+ 0.1	+61,068.81	63,007.15	109,088.19

The deviations were obtained from the employment and trend data of Tables 22.2 and 22.3.

$$r = \frac{N\Sigma XY - (\Sigma X)(\Sigma Y)}{\sqrt{[N\Sigma X^2 - (\Sigma X)^2][N\Sigma Y^2 - (\Sigma Y)^2]}},$$

$$= \frac{12(61,068.81) - (0.3)(0.1)}{\sqrt{[12(63,007.15) - (0.3)^2][12(109,088.19) - (0.1)^2]}},$$

$$= +0.737.$$

Problems in correlating time series. It must be evident that the value of the correlation coefficient is affected by the type of trend fitted to the data, and by the period to which it is fitted. If a period of 10 years is being correlated, it would not be logical to use for one series a section of a trend fitted over a 100-year period and for the other a trend fitted to data extending over 10 years only. The former trend would, in all likelihood, fail to pass through the approximate center of each cycle, and might not even touch some of the cycles. Consequently, the correlation coefficient might understate or overstate the degree of relationship between the cycles of the two series. It must also be apparent that the use of an inflexible trend for one series and a flexible trend for the other would produce similar results. If we wish to correlate cyclical movements, it seems best therefore to use a trend that goes approximately through the center of each cycle. It may be that no simple mathematical curve will be satisfactory and that a relatively subjective method may have to be resorted to, at least as a first approximation.

Another problem to consider is whether the Pearsonian method of correlation, based on the second moments, is appropriate for correlating time series. The fluctuations of a time series are not usually distributed normally around the trend line. There are sometimes a few extreme deviations, which, when squared, largely determine the value of r. With this problem in mind, some authorities suggest the use of the rank method when the extreme deviations are particularly large. Another solution is the use of a formula based on first moments, rather than second.[4] In view of the fact that interest frequently centers in whether two series are moving in the same general direction (positive or negative) at the same time, without regard to the magnitude either of their level or of their change, it may be that a method applicable to 2 × 2 tables (see pages 416–418) would be appropriate.

A further difficulty in correlating time series is that we have no logical basis for estimating the reliability of the coefficient of correlation. The chief objection to the use of any reliability test for r for time series is that the different observations are not randomly distributed—each observation in a time series is related to values in that series for preceding and subsequent points of time. Furthermore, we cannot ordinarily generalize concerning the exact nature of this interrelationship. Perhaps this difficulty will become more obvious when we ask how many independent observations are contained in the cyclical relatives used in Table 22.7. Although there are 12 years, there are not 12 independent observations. There are approximately three complete cycles (measuring from trough to trough). Are there, then, only three independent observations? There are more than three, since each observation in a cycle is not completely dependent on the preceding values. If we now had monthly data, would we have 144 independent observations for the 12 years? Of course not. But how many we would have, it is impossible to say. What has just been said may be clearer when the reader understands the concept of "degrees of freedom." This is discussed in Chapter 24 and again, with particular reference to correlation, in Chapter 26.

---

[4] Another formula of interest is

$$C_2 = \frac{\Sigma s (2N - \Sigma|s|)}{N^2},$$

where s refers to the smaller of each pair of items when each series is expressed as deviations from the mean in terms of average deviations $\left(\dfrac{x}{AD_x} \text{ and } \dfrac{y}{AD_y}\right)$. When summing algebraically, s is positive if the signs of the paired deviations are alike, and negative if they are unlike.

All of the preceding illustrations have dealt with chronological series expressed in physical terms. None were in monetary units. When a series is in terms of dollars, it should ordinarily be adjusted for price changes by dividing by an appropriate price index. Such a situation is encountered when we examine the relationship existing between the price and production of an agricultural crop such as oats, hay, wheat, or citrus fruits. The correlation present may be between price and production for the same years or between price for each year and production for the following year.

The foregoing discussion has dealt only with correlation of two time series, although it was mentioned at the outset that we might correlate two or more time series. If one is undertaking to explain, statistically, the annual fluctuations in the price of pork, he would undoubtedly bring into his analysis not only the production of pork, but the price and production of corn, and probably the price and production of beef and other meats. A problem of this type is more complicated than those which we have considered here, since multiple correlation of several variables is involved. However, the procedures are exactly those set forth for multiple and partial correlation in Chapter 21. Whatever the number of variables being considered, appropriate adjustment must be made for the trend of each series.

MONTHLY DATA

When correlating monthly time series, it is necessary, not only to adjust for trend, but to deseasonalize the data as well. If the data were not deseasonalized, we would be, to a large extent, merely correlating the seasonal fluctuations instead of the cyclical movements. In addition, it is also usually desirable to smooth the adjusted data by means of a short-term moving average (as explained in Chapter 16) in order to remove the irregularities due to accidental movements.

Synchronous relationships. Sometimes one is interested in correlating two monthly time series in order to ascertain whether the two move together. Thus, such a correlation might be made if two organizations issue indexes purporting to measure the same aspect of economic activity. Or, a research bureau may be interested in knowing whether an index of business conditions, computed upon the basis of a few component series, agrees closely enough in its depicting of cyclical movements with a more comprehensive index which is also more expensive to construct. Again, one may be interested in comparing time series (for example, department store sales) for two, or more, of the twelve Federal Reserve districts.

Lag and lead. Frequently one is interested in finding a monthly time series which *moves ahead* of a second series and which may therefore be used to forecast the second series. The relationship which one hopes

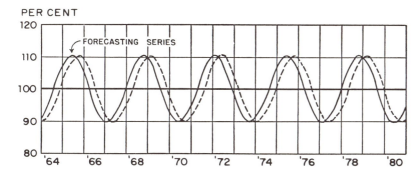

PER CENT

Chart 22.8.   Two Illustrative Series Showing One Series Regularly
Preceding the Other.

to find is something like the ideal one illustrated in Chart 22.8, although
the cycles would almost never have the regularity shown in this chart.
In Chart 22.8, the forecasting index is seen to move, regularly, ahead of
the series to be forecasted.   When such a situation obtains, the earlier
moving series (that is, the forecasting index) is said to "lead" the other
series.   Also, the later-moving series is said to "lag" the earlier-moving
series.   One will very rarely find a lag-lead relationship as uniform as that
depicted in Chart 22.8.   In fact, since 1941, lagging relationships between
economic time series have not been at all clear-cut, owing first to World
War II and then to the Korean War and to defense production.

Chart 22.9 shows the Federal Reserve Index of Production of Durable
Manufactures and the Federal Reserve Index of Nondurable Manufactures for the period February 1959–December 1964.   These indexes
were adjusted for seasonal movements by the Federal Reserve Board.
The writers removed trend and smoothed the irregular movements by
means of a three-month moving average weighted 1, 2, 1.   The actual
situation depicted in Chart 22.9 is much different from the illustrative
one shown in Chart 22.8, where one series regularly preceded the other.
Examination of Chart 22.9 reveals several interesting points: the low
points in the Index of Nondurable Manufactures appear to coincide with
similar low points in the Index of Durable Manufactures in 1961 and
1963; the high points in the Index of Durable Manufactures in 1959,
1960 and 1961 seem to precede by some months a high in the other index.

In general, the Index of Durable Manufactures seems to precede the
other index.   We shall compute several correlation coefficients to ascertain when the closest agreement is present.   First, correlating the two
series synchronously, we find $r = +0.600$.   Next, pairing the values
with the Index of Nondurable Manufactures leading the index of Durable
Manufactures by one month, we obtain $r = +0.519$.   Here, the pairing
starts out with February 1959 for the Index of Nondurable Manufactures
paired with March 1959 for the Index of Durable Manufactures and

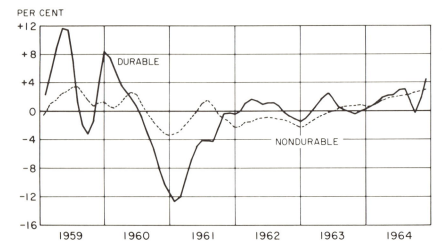

Chart 22.9.   Cyclical Movements of Federal Reserve Index of Production of Durable Manufactures and of Index of Production of Nondurable Manufactures, 1959–1964.   Data from Table 22.10 and from worksheets (not shown) for the years omitted from that table.   Both indexes were adjusted for trend and for seasonal and irregular movements, and were expressed as percentage deviations.

finishes with November 1964 for the leading series paired with December 1964 for the lagging series.   Since the lag between the two series is none too clear in Chart 22.9, we try a pairing with the Index of Durable Manufactures leading by one month, for which the computations are indicated in Table 22.10.   This yields $r = +0.628$ which is higher than the value first obtained so we will pursue the illustration further in this direction.

Trying now two months lead for the Index of Durable Manufactures, we obtain $r = +0.608$ which is lower than the coefficient for a one month lead of that index.   Next we compute the correlation coefficient with the Index of Durable Manufactures leading by three months and get $r = +0.555$ which is smaller than the value just obtained for two months lead.   Little is to be gained by computing additional values of r for the purposes of this illustration, so we will summarize the results as follows:

Leading series	*Value of r*
Index of Nondurable Manufactures leads by:	
One month	+0.519
Two months	+0.416
Three months	+0.328
Synchronous	+0.600
Index of Durable Manufactures leads by:	
One month	+0.628
Two months	+0.608
Three months	+0.555

The highest correlation coefficient was found when the Index of Durable

Manufactures led by one month. However, that index would not serve as a very satisfactory forecasting series for the Index of Nondurable Manufactures, because the value of r does not indicate close enough agreement.

It is not always necessary for one time series to lead another one in order for it to be useful as an indicator of the behavior of the second series. The Bureau of Business and Economic Research of the University of Maryland reports[5] that Baltimore bank debits are correlated $+0.9998$

TABLE 22.10

Determination of Correlation Between Federal Reserve Index of Durable Manufactures and Index of Nondurable Manufactures, February 1959–December 1964, With the Index of Durable Manufactures Leading by One Month

(Both indexes have as the base 1957 = 100 up to Oct. 1961 and 1957–1959 = 100 after that date. Both indexes are adjusted for seasonal, trend, and irregular movements, and are expressed as percentage deviations.)

Year and month	Index of Durable Manufactures X	Indication of pairing	Index of Nondurable Manufactures Y	XY	X^2	Y^2
1959: Feb.	+ 3.2		−0.7	. . .	10.24	. . .
Mar.	+ 5.7		+0.1	+ 0.32	32.49	0.01
Apr.	+ 9.0		+1.4	+ 7.98	81.00	1.96
May	+11.7		+2.3	+ 20.70	136.89	5.29
June	+11.4		+2.6	+ 30.42	129.96	6.76
July	+ 6.7		+3.2	+ 36.48	44.89	10.24
Aug.	+ 1.0		+3.3	+ 22.11	1.00	10.89
Sept.	− 2.1		+2.5	+ 2.50	4.41	6.25
Oct.	− 3.4		+1.3	− 2.73	11.56	1.69
Nov.	− 1.4		+0.7	− 2.38	1.96	0.49
Dec.	+ 4.5		+1.1	− 1.54	20.25	1.21
1964: July	+ 2.8		+1.8	+ 3.96	7.84	3.24
Aug.	+ 2.9		+2.0	+ 5.60	8.41	4.00
Sept.	+ 1.2		+2.2	+ 6.38	1.44	4.84
Oct.	− 0.2		+2.5	+ 3.00	0.04	6.25
Nov.	+ 1.8		+2.6	− 0.52	3.24	6.76
Dec.	+ 4.2		+2.9	+ 5.22	. . .	8.41
Total	− 2.9		2.3	+376.04	1,607.97	223.07

Deseasonalized data from various issues of *Federal Reserve Bulletin.*

$$r = \frac{N\Sigma XY - (\Sigma X)(\Sigma Y)}{\sqrt{[N\Sigma X^2 - (\Sigma X)^2][N\Sigma Y^2 - (\Sigma Y)^2]}},$$

$$= \frac{70(376.04) - (-2.9)(2.3)}{\sqrt{[70(1,607.97) - (-2.9)^2][70(223.07) - (2.3)^2]}} = +0.628.$$

---

[5] University of Maryland, Bureau of Business and Economic Research, *Studies in Business and Economics*, Vol. 6, No. 3, "Maryland Economic Indices," p. 10.

with Maryland bank debits, and that Maryland bank debits are correlated +0.9853 with bank debits in the United States. The Bureau
notes that "turns in direction of the Baltimore series may be expected
to indicate turns in the State and the Nation." The usefulness of this
relationship lies in the fact that data for Baltimore would be available
more promptly than are data for Maryland or for the United States.

Procedure for use of lead and lag as an aid in forecasting. If
it is desired to make use of a lead-lag relationship to assist in forecasting
the cyclical movements of a series (the lagging series), the procedure
may be as follows:

1. Plot the lagging series on a large sheet of semi-transparent cross-
section paper. The exploratory work in this and the following three
steps may be done with data adjusted for seasonal. Trend (unless it is
very marked) and irregular movements need not be removed, although it
is better if they have been eliminated.

2. Consider what series may logically be expected to precede the lagging series, and plot each of these series on a separate sheet of semi-
transparent graph paper. The horizontal scales used in Steps 1 and 2
must be the same. The vertical scales may be adjusted so that the
fluctuations of the series which are to be compared are roughly the same.

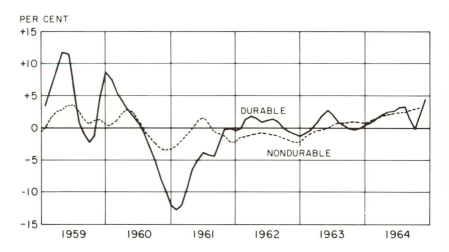

**Chart 22.10. Cyclical Movements of Federal Reserve Index of Produc-
tion of Durable Manufactures and of Index of Production of Nondurable
Manufactures, 1959–1964, with Index of Nondurable Manufactures Moved
One Month to the Left.** Data from Table 22.10 and from worksheets (not
shown) for the years omitted from that table. Both series were adjusted for trend
and for seasonal and irregular movements, and were expressed as percentage
deviations.

3. Place the chart of one of the presumably leading series on top of the chart for the lagging series (or vice versa), place both above a source of light, and move the chart of the lagging series to the left until the closest agreement between the cyclical movements of the two series is obtained. Chart 22.10 shows how this might appear. If closer agreement is obtained by moving the leading series to the left, then it doesn't lead— it lags!

4. Repeat Step 3 for any other series which might move ahead of the series for which forecasts are desired.

5. When a series has been found that appears regularly to precede the lagging series, adjust both series for trend and irregular movements and compute the value of r for the best visual estimate of the lead shown by the graphs of these adjusted series.

6. Compute the values of r for longer and shorter leads than that used in Step 5 in order to arrive at the highest value of r. This was two months in the preceding illustration.

7. If the value of r is high enough to warrant doing so, an estimating equation of the type

$$Y_c = a + bX,$$

or possibly a non-linear equation, may be computed. Here, Y_c is the estimated cyclical value for the lagging series and X is the observed cyclical value of the leading series. If the probing in Steps 3 and 4 should reveal more than one leading series, a forecasting equation such as those for multiple correlation (Chapter 21) would be used.

One investment advisory service[6] has used multiple correlation, with one independent variable leading by a year, to obtain a rating for stocks. In this analysis, the dependent variable is the average annual price of a stock, while the independent variables are: annual dividends per share, annual earnings per share, the average monthly price of the stock for the preceding year, a measure of market "climate" or sentiment, and time. Market climate itself is obtained by a process of multiple correlation and represents the difference, over a long period of time, between a composite stock price average and estimates of that average based on earnings, dividends, and time.

The slowness with which most economic and business data are reported and the scarcity of time series on a basis shorter than a month are factors that impair the usefulness of correlation as a forecasting device. It is quite possible that weekly, daily, or hourly data might bring to light relationships which are known and utilized only by a few "insiders." The theorist argues that all economic processes are interrelated. It does not seem logical that the cause-and-effect relationships which supposedly surround us on every side must always take a month or more for their

---

[6] The Value Line Investment Survey.

development.   There must be many that work out in a few days, a few hours, or nearly instantaneously.   If the market hears that a new industrial use has suddenly been announced for copper, it does not wait weeks or even hours to show its reaction in a price change.   As data are made available upon a weekly, daily, or more frequent basis, it is conceivable that very useful lag-lead relationships may be obtained.

Some cautions.   It may have been noticed that the heading of the preceding section referred to the use of lead and lag *as an aid* in forecasting.   A leading correlation that has been observed for a number of years in the past will not be applicable to future months unless the relationship between the series continues as before.   If underlying economic (or other) conditions change, the relationship may be altered.   Forecasting by this, or any other, device should be attempted only in connection with a thorough knowledge of the series under consideration and of the conditions affecting those and allied series.

The use of lead-lag correlations in forecasting is also subject to other objections or shortcomings.   Among these are:

1. As pointed out in Chapter 19, the value of r may be unduly influenced by one or a few extreme values.   Some statisticians even argue that one's visual impression of the amount of lead is preferable.

2. The lag may be different at recession from what it is at revival.

3. Interest often centers mainly on turning points, while r gives equal importance to leads and lags at all phases of the cycle.   It may be profitable to be able to foretell merely when to expect a change in direction, even though the amount of change cannot be forecast.

4. It is a laborious process to compute r for a large number of lead-lag hypotheses.

5. In addition to criticisms of the coefficient of correlation as a measure of relationship for time series, one may also criticize the nature of the variations correlated, arguing that a person can more accurately predict the future with respect to the present than he can with respect to some normal, which is often difficult to estimate correctly.

In Chapter 26, attention will be given to the reliability of correlation coefficients computed from random samples.   Since the coefficients obtained from lead-lag relationships are not for random samples, the procedures in Chapter 26 are not applicable to the correlation coefficients for leading and lagging series.

CHAPTER 23

Describing a Frequency Distribution
by a Fitted Curve

A frequency distribution usually represents a sample drawn from a much larger population or universe. Even though a sample is composed of but a few hundred or a few score items, it may be reasonably representative of the larger universe from which it was drawn. Since it is virtually never possible to measure all of the individuals or items comprising a universe, we must form our notion of the larger group from a study of a sample. We may therefore fit any one of a number of types of curves to a frequency distribution in order to attempt to describe what appears to be the general form of the curve for the entire population.

The purpose in fitting a curve to a frequency distribution may be any one of the following:

(1) We may wish to ascertain whether a given curve describes the general shape of the distribution. For example, we may wish to demonstrate that the chance errors involved when making repeated measurements of the same object or phenomenon may be described by a normal curve. Chart 23.1 is a normal curve and Chart 23.2 shows such a curve fitted to a series of repeated measurements.

(2) Somewhat similar to the foregoing is the fitting of a curve to values obtained from repeated samples taken from the same population. An illustration of this is included as Exercises 27 and 28 in the fifth edition of the *Workbook*[1] designed to accompany this text. In those exercises, a normal curve is fitted to a frequency distribution of arithmetic means computed from random samples. While sample arithmetic means tend to form a normal curve around the arithmetic mean of the population, other statistical values may form other types of curves. Further consideration will be given to the behavior of values computed from samples in Chapters 24, 25, and 26.

---

[1] Frederick E. Croxton and Sidney Klein, *Workbook in Applied General Statistics*, fifth edition, Prentice-Hall, Inc., Englewood Cliffs, N. J., 1967.

(3) It may be desired to generalize concerning the proportions of items which should be expected to fall above, below, or between certain values. For example, we may take the case of fitting a curve to a frequency distribution of the length of life of incandescent lamp bulbs; from such a procedure we are enabled to infer what proportion might, in general, be expected to burn 1,500 hours or more (or more or less than any specified

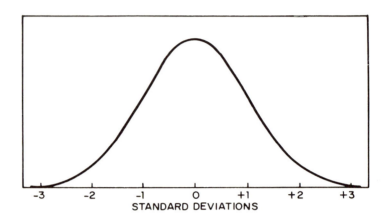

STANDARD DEVIATIONS

Chart 23.1.   The Normal Curve.

number of hours).   Similarly, in the case of the data shown in Charts 23.5 and 23.6, we may determine the number of items which in general would be expected to occur above, below, or between any two X values. In like fashion, the life insurance actuary may fit a curve to, or graduate data having to do with, deaths classified by age and thus determine the expected number of individuals dying during each year of life or surviving given ages.

(4) Sometimes it is possible to determine, from a curve fitted to a given distribution, the probable distribution of values in a closely associated series.   For example, a normal curve fitted to the measurements of the circumferences of men's necks enables us to ascertain the probable number of collars of each size which would be needed.   This has been done in Chart 23.8 and Table 23.5.

This chapter will not attempt a comprehensive treatment of the topic of fitting frequency curves.   We shall consider only the symmetrical curve known as the *normal curve*, and then, briefly, binomials and two of the simpler skewed curves.

THE NORMAL CURVE

Development of the normal curve.   The concept of the normal curve (pictured in Chart 23.1) appears to have been originally developed by Abraham De Moivre and explained in 1733 in a mathematical treatise.[2] Gauss later used the curve to describe the theory of accidental errors of measurements involved in the calculation of orbits of heavenly bodies. Because of Gauss' work, this curve is sometimes referred to as the *Gaussian curve.*

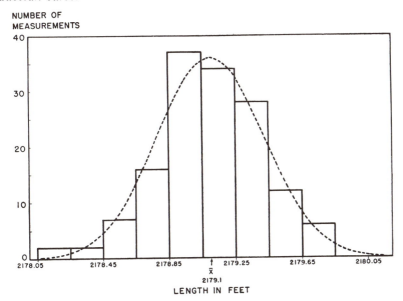

NUMBER OF
MEASUREMENTS

LENGTH IN FEET

Chart 23.2. Normal Curve Fitted to 144 Measurements of the Length of a Line. Measurements from L. D. Weld, *Theory of Errors and Least Squares,* The Macmillan Company, New York, p. 147.

Chart 23.2 shows a column diagram of 144 measurements of a line and a normal curve of error fitted to these measurements. Concerning the normal curve, it will be observed: (1) that small errors are more frequent than large ones, (2) that very large errors are unlikely to occur, and (3) that positive and negative errors of the same numerical magnitude are equally likely to occur. Because the normal curve has been used extensively to describe errors of measurement, it is sometimes referred to as the "normal curve of error." However, this term is misleading, since errors of measurement, even though unbiased, do not always follow the normal curve.

Explanation of the formula. Chart 23.3 pictures an apparatus which will help us to understand the formula for the normal curve. The device consists of a number of troughs, open at one end and placed as

[2] *Approximatio ad Summam Terminorum Binomii* $(a + b)^n$ *in Seriem expansi*, Nov. 12, 1733, being a second supplement to *Miscellanea Analytica*, 1730. See Karl Pearson, *Historical Note on the Origin of the Normal Curve of Errors*, Biometrika, Vol. 16 (1924), pp. 402–404; also, Helen M. Walker, *Studies in the History of Statistical Method*, pp. 13–17, 22–23, Williams and Wilkins, Baltimore, 1929.

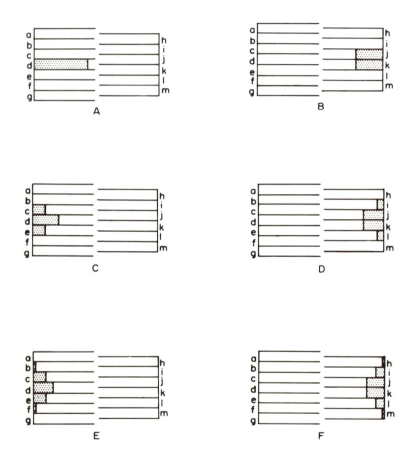

Chart 23.3.   **Apparatus to Illustrate the Expansion of the Binomial**
$(\frac{1}{2} + \frac{1}{2})$.

shown in section A of Chart 23.3. Trough d is filled with sand or some similar granular substance. If the apparatus is tipped so that the left-

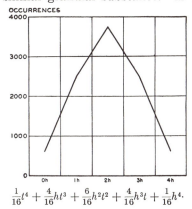

$$\frac{1}{16}t^4 + \frac{4}{16}ht^3 + \frac{6}{16}h^2t^2 + \frac{4}{16}h^3t + \frac{1}{16}h^4.$$

Chart 23.4A. Expected Results of 10,000 Tosses of Four Coins.

hand side rises (section B of Chart 23.3), the sand in trough d will flow $\frac{1}{2}$ into trough j and $\frac{1}{2}$ into trough k. This represents the binomial $(\frac{1}{2} + \frac{1}{2})$. If the right-hand side of the machine is then raised (section C of Chart 23.3), the sand from j will flow $\frac{1}{2}$ into c and $\frac{1}{2}$ into d, while the sand from k will flow $\frac{1}{2}$ into d and $\frac{1}{2}$ into e. Of the total amount of sand, we now have $\frac{1}{4}$ in c, $\frac{1}{2}$ in d, and $\frac{1}{4}$ in e, representing the expansion of the binomial $(\frac{1}{2} + \frac{1}{2})^2$. Again tipping the device, as in section D of Chart 23.3, $\frac{1}{2}$ of the sand from c flows into i, and $\frac{1}{2}$ into j; $\frac{1}{2}$ of the sand from d flows into j, and $\frac{1}{2}$ into k; and $\frac{1}{2}$ of the

sand from e flows into k, and $\frac{1}{2}$ into l. The result is that $\frac{1}{8}$ of all the sand is in i, $\frac{3}{8}$ is in j, $\frac{3}{8}$ is in k, and $\frac{1}{8}$ is in l, representing the expansion of the binomial $(\frac{1}{2} + \frac{1}{2})^3$. Tipping the apparatus as in section E of Chart 23.3 causes the sand to flow $\frac{1}{16}$ into b, $\frac{4}{16}$ into c, $\frac{6}{16}$ into d, $\frac{4}{16}$ into e, and $\frac{1}{16}$ into f, representing the expansion of $(\frac{1}{2} + \frac{1}{2})^4$. Once more tipping the machine (section F of Chart 23.3) results in putting $\frac{1}{32}$ of the sand into h, $\frac{5}{32}$ into i, $\frac{10}{32}$ into j, $\frac{10}{32}$ into k, $\frac{5}{32}$ into l, and $\frac{1}{32}$ into m, which is the expansion of $(\frac{1}{2} + \frac{1}{2})^5$.

The device would become clumsy if we attempted to carry the expansion of the binomial much farther. We may obtain similar results by tossing coins—a procedure which eliminates the necessity of constructing any apparatus. It is assumed that we are tossing perfect

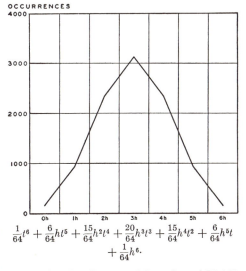

$$\frac{1}{64}t^6 + \frac{6}{64}ht^5 + \frac{15}{64}h^2t^4 + \frac{20}{64}h^3t^3 + \frac{15}{64}h^4t^2 + \frac{6}{64}h^5t$$
$$+ \frac{1}{64}h^6.$$

Chart 23.4B. Expected Results of 10,000 Tosses of Six Coins.

coins which are evenly balanced and which will not stand on edge. With such a coin, the chances of throwing a tail or a head are identical and may be expressed by $\frac{1}{2}t + \frac{1}{2}h$.

If two coins are tossed simultaneously, we may obtain either no heads (two tails), a tail and a head, or two heads. In order for no heads to appear, both coins must fall tails up. To obtain one head, one coin may show a tail and the other a head, or the first coin may show a head, the other a tail. Two heads may appear only if both coins show heads. Since one head may occur in two ways, while no heads may occur in but one way, it follows that there is twice as great a probability of throwing one head as of throwing no heads. Similarly, there is twice as great a chance of throwing one head as there is of throwing two heads. We may express the probabilities arising from tossing two coins by

$$(\tfrac{1}{2}t + \tfrac{1}{2}h)^2,$$

in which the exponent 2 indicates the number of coins being tossed. Expanding this binomial gives

$$\tfrac{1}{4}t^2 + \tfrac{1}{2}th + \tfrac{1}{4}h^2.$$

Therefore, if two perfect coins are thrown 1,200 times, we could expect to obtain t^2 (no heads) 300 times, th (one head) 600 times, and h^2 (two heads) 300 times.

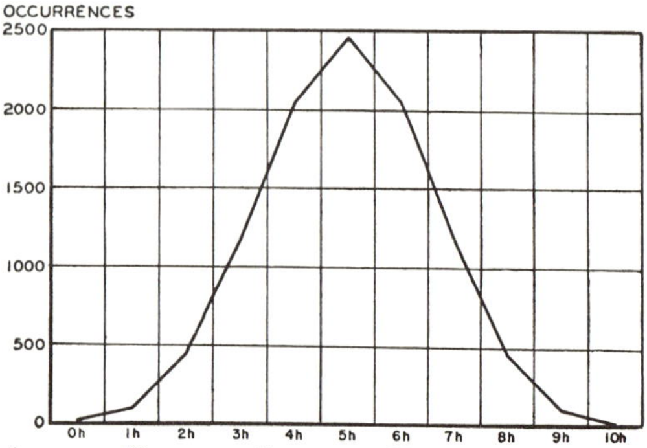

OCCURRENCES

$$\frac{1}{1024}t^{10} + \frac{10}{1024}ht^9 + \frac{45}{1024}h^2t^8 + \frac{120}{1024}h^3t^7 + \frac{210}{1024}h^4t^6$$
$$+ \frac{252}{1024}h^5t^5 + \frac{210}{1024}h^6t^4 + \frac{120}{1024}h^7t^3 + \frac{45}{1024}h^8t^2 + \frac{10}{1024}h^9t$$
$$+ \frac{1}{1024}h^{10}.$$

Chart 23.4C. Expected Results of 10,000 Tosses of Ten Coins. The probability of each combination is indicated by the binomial expansion shown under each part of Chart 23.4.

If three coins are tossed, we have the expression

$$(\tfrac{1}{2}t + \tfrac{1}{2}h)^3 = \tfrac{1}{8}t^3 + \tfrac{3}{8}t^2h + \tfrac{3}{8}th^2 + \tfrac{1}{8}h^3,$$

indicating that, if 1,200 throws were made, there should be no heads 150 times, one head 450 times, two heads 450 times, and three heads 150 times.

The results to be expected from tossing 4 coins are shown in section A of Chart 23.4, while the results to be expected from tossing 6 and 10 coins are shown, respectively, in parts B and C. All of these curves are symmetrical, and, as the number of coins tossed becomes greater, the curve becomes smoother. When ten coins are tossed, there are eleven points to be plotted (see part C); but if 100 coins were tossed, there would be 101 points to plot and the curve would appear virtually the same as that of Chart 23.1. As N approaches infinity, $(\tfrac{1}{2}t + \tfrac{1}{2}h)^N$ approaches as a limit[3]

---

[3] Another limit of the binomial is the Poisson distribution, which the binomial approaches if one of the fractions is very small and N approaches infinity. Fitting the Poisson distribution is described in F. E. Croxton, *Elementary Statistics with Applications in Medicine and the Biological Sciences*, Dover Publications, Inc., New York, 1959, pp. 41–49.

$$Y_c = \frac{1}{\sigma \sqrt{2\pi}} e^{\frac{-x^2}{2\sigma^2}},$$

which is the expression for the normal curve.   The symbols are as follows:

Y_c = the computed height of an ordinate at distance x from the arithmetic mean;

σ = the standard deviation of the population;

π = the constant, 3.14159; $\sqrt{2\pi}$ = 2.5066;

e = the constant, 2.71828, the base of the Naperian system of logarithms; and

x = a selected deviation from the arithmetic mean.

Substituting the two constants mentioned above, we may write

$$Y_c = \frac{1}{2.5066\sigma} 2.71828^{\frac{-x^2}{2\sigma^2}}.$$

FITTING THE NORMAL CURVE

In Chart 23.2 a normal curve was shown fitted to a series of measurements of a line.   It will be observed that those figures were repeated measurements of the same thing.   In Chart 23.5 we have a different type of data, representing measurements of a number of individuals from a homogeneous population.   The chance errors involved in repeated measurements of the same thing not infrequently follow a normal curve. However, the measurements of a number of differential individuals in respect to some characteristic may or may not follow such a curve.   A distribution of the heights of a homogeneous group of adult individuals, for example, could be expected to be essentially normal, but a distribution of the weights of the same individuals would be noticeably skewed to the right.   While the basal diameter of the egg-capsules of the snails in Chart 23.5 may be described by the fitted normal curve, it is quite likely that the weights of these same eggs would show definite skewness.

The fitted curve in Chart 23.5 indicates the shape of the distribution we should expect if our sample were much larger, or if we had measured the entire population.   It implies that, if a larger group were studied, we should find a few instances with basal diameters both smaller and larger than those found in the sample.

Fitting the normal curve to data of physical ability.   Table 23.1 shows a distribution of the distances which 303 high school freshman girls were able to throw a baseball.   These data are akin to those from which Chart 23.5 was drawn in that they are measurements for a number of different individuals.   It may be observed that very few of the girls threw the baseball less than 45 feet and very few threw it 115 feet or farther.   The column diagram of Chart 23.6 shows the data of Table 23.1.

NUMBER OF
EGG-CAPSULES

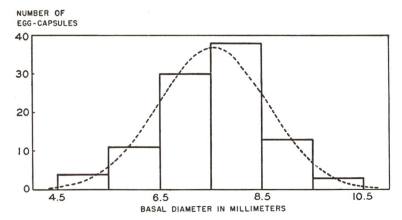

Chart 23.5. Normal Curve Fitted to Basal Diameters of 99 Egg-Capsules of a Marine Snail, *Sipho curtus.* Data of basal diameters from Gunnar Thorson, *Studies on the Egg-Capsules and Development of Arctic Marine Prosobranchs*, p. 7, Meddelelser om Grønland-udgione af-Kommissionen for Videnskabelige Endersøgelser i Grønland.

TABLE 23.1

Baseball Throws for Distance by 303 First-Year High School Girls

Distance in feet	Number of girls
15 but under 25	1
25 but under 35	2
35 but under 45	7
45 but under 55	25
55 but under 65	33
65 but under 75	53
75 but under 85	64
85 but under 95	44
95 but under 105	31
105 but under 115	27
115 but under 125	11
125 but under 135	4
135 but under 145	1
Total..........	303

Data from Leonora W. Stewart and Helen West, The Froebel School, Gary, Indiana. Measurements were made in 1935.

To fit a normal curve to an observed frequency distribution, we rewrite the equation

$$Y_c = \frac{Ni}{2.5066s} \, 2.71828^{\frac{-x^2}{2s^2}},$$

where N is the number of observations in the sample,

i is the class interval of the sample distribution, and
s is the standard deviation of the sample.

We could use $\hat{\sigma} = \sqrt{\dfrac{\Sigma x^2}{N-1}}$, an estimate of σ, which is discussed in the following chapter, instead of s when fitting a normal curve to a set of observed data. However, we ordinarily prefer s, since it measures the dispersion of a sample of the observed size, rather than being an estimate of the dispersion in the population. Furthermore, for a frequency distribution having a large enough N to warrant the fit of a normal curve, the difference between s and $\hat{\sigma}$ is so slight as to have little or no effect on the fit. For the data of Table 23.1, for example, $s = 20.95$ feet and $\hat{\sigma} = 20.98$ feet.

The complete fitting process consists of two steps; first, the determination of the values of a number of ordinates in order to ascertain the exact outline of the fitted curve, and, second, the computation of the proportionate areas for the portions of the curve that are important to us.

Ordinates. Referring again to the formula for the normal curve,

$$Y_c = \frac{Ni}{2.5066s}\, 2.71828^{\frac{-x^2}{2s^2}},$$

it appears that we need the values of N, $\overline{X}$, and s in order to fit a normal curve to a distribution. Computing by procedures described in preceding chapters, we find $\overline{X} = 80.63$ feet and $s = 20.95$ feet. As there were 303 girls, $N = 303$.

We shall first compute the ordinate to be erected at the mean. This is designated as Y_0 and is the maximum ordinate of the fitted curve. Since $x = 0$ at the mean, we have

$$Y_0 = \frac{303 \times 10}{2.5066 \times 20.95}\, 2.71828^{\frac{-0^2}{2(20.95)^2}}.$$

In the expression above, the exponent of 2.71828 is zero. Since a number raised to the zero power is one, $2.71828^{\frac{-0^2}{2(20.95)^2}} = 1$. It is apparent, then, that the expression $e^{\frac{-x^2}{2s^2}}$ is always equal to 1 for the ordinate erected at the mean and

$$Y_0 = \frac{Ni}{2.5066s}.$$

Therefore,

$$Y_c = \frac{Ni}{2.5066s}\, e^{\frac{-x^2}{2s^2}} = Y_0\, 2.71828^{\frac{-x^2}{2s^2}}.$$

For the problem in hand,

$$Y_0 = \frac{303 \times 10}{2.5066 \times 20.95} = 57.7.$$

We now wish to erect enough additional ordinates on either side of Y_0 to enable us to sketch a reasonably smooth curve. If we select successive distances of 4.19 feet from the mean, we shall erect ordinates at steps of $\frac{1}{5}s$ from the mean. The first pair of ordinates (since the curve is symmetrical) are to be erected at $x = \pm 4.19$ feet from the mean ($X = 84.82$ and 76.44 feet), using the expression

$$Y_c = 57.7 \times 2.71828^{\frac{-(4.19)^2}{2(20.95)^2}}.$$

In order to determine the value Y_c, it is not necessary to compute $2.71828^{\frac{-(4.19)^2}{2(20.95)^2}}$ but merely to refer to Appendix D. Looking up the appropriate value of $\frac{x}{s}$, which in this case is $\frac{4.19}{20.95} = 0.20$, we find that

$$2.71828^{\frac{-(4.19)^2}{2(20.95)^2}} = 0.98020$$

and

$$Y_c = 57.7 \times 0.98020 = 56.6.$$

For the next pair of ordinates, $x = \pm 8.38$ feet ($X = 89.01$ feet and 72.25 feet) and

$$Y_c = 57.7 \times 2.71828^{\frac{-(8.38)^2}{2(20.95)^2}}.$$

Here the ratio of $\frac{x}{s}$ is 0.40 and, referring to Appendix D, we have

$$Y_c = 57.7 \times 0.92312 = 53.3.$$

The process of determining the heights of the ordinates can be handled most expeditiously by use of a table similar to Table 23.2. The ordinates in the upper and lower parts of the table are identical, since the fitted curve is symmetrical.

The fitted curve is shown in Chart 23.6. It follows the general shape of the sample, but smooths out the irregularities and indicates what might be expected if the performance of a very large number of comparable girls could be recorded. What we have done so far gives merely the shape of the fitted curve and a visual impression of the suitability of the fit, which appears good in this instance.

Areas. We have not yet undertaken to say what proportion of high school freshman girls may be expected to throw a baseball: (1) any specified number of feet or more, (2) any specified number of feet or less, or (3) a distance equal to or greater than one specified value but equal to

TABLE 23.2

Determination of Ordinates of Normal Curve Fitted to Data of Baseball Throws for Distance by First-Year High School Girls

($\overline{X} = 80.63$ feet; $s = 20.95$ feet, $Y_0 = 57.7$)

X (in feet, where ordinates are to be erected)	x (in feet, deviation of X from $\overline{X}$)	$\dfrac{x}{s}$	Proportionate height of ordinate $2.71828^{\frac{-x^2}{2s^2}}$ (Appendix D)	Height of ordinate [Col. 4 $\times$ Y_0]
(1)	(2)	(3)	(4)	(5)
13.59	-67.04	3.20	0.00598	0.3
17.78	-62.85	3.00	0.01111	0.6
21.97	-58.66	2.80	0.01984	1.1
26.16	-54.47	2.60	0.03405	2.0
30.35	-50.28	2.40	0.05614	3.2
34.54	-46.09	2.20	0.08892	5.1
38.73	-41.90	2.00	0.13534	7.8
42.92	-37.71	1.80	0.19790	11.4
47.11	-33.52	1.60	0.27804	16.0
51.30	-29.33	1.40	0.37531	21.7
55.49	-25.14	1.20	0.48675	28.1
59.68	-20.95	1.00	0.60653	35.0
63.87	-16.76	0.80	0.72615	41.9
68.06	-12.57	0.60	0.83527	48.2
72.25	$-\ 8.38$	0.40	0.92312	53.3
76.44	$-\ 4.19$	0.20	0.98020	56.6
80.63	0	0	1.00000	57.7
84.82	$+\ 4.19$	0.20	0.98020	56.6
89.01	$+\ 8.38$	0.40	0.92312	53.3
93.20	$+12.57$	0.60	0.83527	48.2
97.39	$+16.76$	0.80	0.72615	41.9
101.58	$+20.95$	1.00	0.60653	35.0
105.77	$+25.14$	1.20	0.48675	28.1
109.96	$+29.33$	1.40	0.37531	21.7
114.15	$+33.52$	1.60	0.27804	16.0
118.34	$+37.71$	1.80	0.19790	11.4
122.53	$+41.90$	2.00	0.13534	7.8
126.72	$+46.09$	2.20	0.08892	5.1
130.91	$+50.28$	2.40	0.05614	3.2
135.10	$+54.47$	2.60	0.03405	2.0
139.29	$+58.66$	2.80	0.01984	1.1
143.48	$+62.85$	3.00	0.01111	0.6
147.67	$+67.04$	3.20	0.00598	0.3

or less than another larger value. Neither have we attempted to say what proportion of girls may be expected to fall into each of the various classes of the frequency distribution. Expected frequencies are ascertained by integrating the fitted curve. However, the procedure is greatly simplified, and no knowledge of integration is needed, if we make use of a table of the areas under the normal curve such as Appendix E. This appendix gives the proportionate area under the curve which is between an ordinate at $\overline{X}$ and an ordinate at specified $\dfrac{x}{s}$ distances in

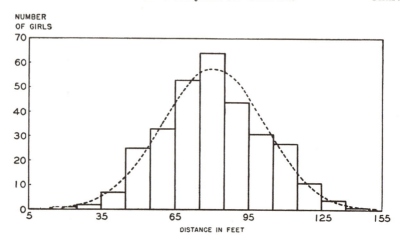

NUMBER
OF GIRLS

Chart 23.6. Normal Curve Fitted to Data of Baseball Throws for Distance by First-Year High School Girls. Data from Tables 23.1 and 23.2.

either direction (not both directions) from $\bar{X}$. This statement is illustrated by the small chart shown with Appendix E. The largest proportionate area shown in Appendix E is 0.50, since the area under the entire curve is 1.0.

To ascertain the proportion of girls that may be expected to throw a baseball 100 feet or more, we first determine the proportion that may be expected between the values of $\bar{X} = 80.63$ feet and $X = 100$ feet and then subtract this proportion from 0.50. At $X = 100$ feet, $x = 100 - 80.63 = 19.37$ feet, and, since $s = 20.95$,

$$\frac{x}{s} = \frac{19.37}{20.95} = 0.92.$$

Referring to Appendix E, it appears that 0.3212 of the area is between the two values, and therefore $0.50 - 0.3212 = 0.1788$, or about 18 per cent, of the area is at or beyond $X = 100$ feet.

If we wish to know what proportion of girls may be expected to throw a baseball 50 feet or less, the procedure parallels that just given. The reader should work this out for himself. The answer is 7.2 per cent.

We can avoid the subtractions involved in the two preceding paragraphs if we refer to Appendix G, which shows areas in one tail of the normal curve. This appendix and Appendix H, which gives areas in two tails of the normal curve, will be particularly useful in connection with part of the subject matter of Chapter 24.

To determine the proportion of girls who may be expected to throw a baseball between 87 and 100 feet, we compute the area under the curve from $\bar{X} = 80.63$ feet to $X = 87$ feet, and the area from $\bar{X} = 80.63$ feet to 100 feet, and then take the difference between these two figures. The

TABLE 23.3

Determination of Expected Frequencies in Each Class for Baseball Throws for Distance by First-Year High School Girls

($\bar{X} = 80.63$ feet; $s = 20.95$ feet)

Distance in feet (1)	Limits of classes		x deviation from mean to limit (4)	$\dfrac{x}{s}$ (5)	Proportion of area between mean and limit (Appendix E) (6)	Proportion of area in each class (7)	Expected frequencies in each class $N = 303^*$ (8)
	Lower limits (2)	Upper limits (3)					
Under 5	...		...	...	0.5000	0.0001	0.2
5 but under 15	5		75.63	3.61	0.4999	0.0008	0.9
15 but under 25	15		65.63	3.13	0.4991	0.0030	3.2
25 but under 35	25		55.63	2.66	0.4961	0.0107	9.1
35 but under 45	35		45.63	2.18	0.4854	0.0300	20.2
45 but under 55	45		35.63	1.70	0.4554	0.0666	35.0
55 but under 65	55		25.63	1.22	0.3888	0.1154	50.6
65 but under 75	65		15.63	0.75	0.2734	0.1670	
75 but under 85 {	75	85	5.63	0.27	0.1064	0.1896	57.4
		95	4.37	0.21	0.0832		
85 but under 95		95	14.37	0.69	0.2549	0.1717	52.0
95 but under 105		105	24.37	1.16	0.3770	0.1221	37.0
105 but under 115		115	34.37	1.64	0.4495	0.0725	22.0
115 but under 125		125	44.37	2.12	0.4830	0.0335	10.2
125 but under 135		135	54.37	2.60	0.4953	0.0123	3.7
135 but under 145		145	64.37	3.07	0.4989	0.0036	1.1
145 but under 155		155	74.37	3.55	0.4998	0.0009	0.3
155 and over		...	...	...	0.5000	0.0002	0.1
Total..........	...	...	...	...	...	1.0000	303.0

* One decimal is usually shown in this column in order that the total of the expected frequencies will agree, to within 0.1 or 0.2, with the total of the observed frequencies. This is of importance in making the χ^2 test of Table 25.10.

first proportionate area is obtained by using

$$x = 6.37 \text{ feet and}$$

$$\frac{x}{s} = \frac{6.37}{20.95} = 0.30.$$

Appendix E shows that 0.1179 of the area is between $\overline{X} = 80.63$ feet and $X = 87$ feet. We already know that 0.3212 of the area is between $\overline{X} = 80.63$ feet and $X = 100$ feet, so the proportionate area between 87 feet and 100 feet is

$$0.3212 - 0.1179 = 0.2033, \text{ or about 20 per cent.}$$

Referring to Table 23.3, the expected frequencies in each class of the frequency distribution are obtained as follows:

1. In Column (1) of the table, enter the classes of the original distribution, allowing for one or two additional classes at each end, since the fitted curve should usually have a greater range than the sample. Theoretically the fitted curve is of unlimited range in both directions. Allow two spaces for the class in which the mean falls.

2. In Column (2), write the lower limits of each class below the mean in value and the lower limit of the class which contains the mean.

3. In Column (3), write the upper limit of each class above the mean in value and the upper limit of the class which includes the mean.

4. We shall ascertain first the proportionate area between the mean

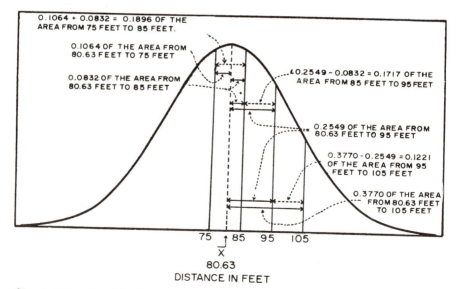

Chart 23.7. **Graphic Representation of the Procedure in Columns (6) and (7) of Table 23.3.**

(80.63 feet) and the upper limit (85 feet) of the class in which the mean falls. The deviation of the upper limit from the mean is 4.37 feet; this value is entered in Column (4). Since $s = 20.95$ feet,

$$\frac{x}{s} = \frac{4.37}{20.95} = 0.21.$$

This value is entered in Column (5). Now, looking up 0.21 in Appendix E, we find that 0.0832 of the area is between the mean and 85 feet. This value is entered in Column (6). The procedure is shown graphically in Chart 23.7.

5. The next step consists of determining the proportionate area between the mean and the upper limit of the first class above the mean. This limit is 95 feet; $x = 14.37$ feet and

$$\frac{x}{s} = \frac{14.37}{20.95} = 0.69.$$

Looking up 0.69 in Appendix E shows that 0.2549 of the area would be expected to be between the mean and 95 feet. This value is entered in Column (6). If 0.2549 of the area is found between 80.63 and 95 feet, while 0.0832 of the area occurs between 80.63 and 85 feet, there would be $0.2549 - 0.0832 = 0.1717$ of the area between 85 and 95 feet. The result of this subtraction is entered in Column (7); this procedure is also indicated graphically in Chart 23.7.

6. The procedure in Step 5 is repeated for each class above the mean in value. The proportionate areas from the mean to the upper limit of each class are ascertained, and then the proportions from the mean to the upper limit of the preceding class are subtracted, as shown in the table.

7. The proportionate areas between the mean and the lower limits shown in Column (2) of the table are next determined. Since these areas are also cumulative, successive subtraction is again necessary.

8. We now have entered in Column (7) the proportionate areas for each class except the class containing the mean. We have determined, in Column (6), that 0.0832 of the area is between the mean and 85 feet, and that there is 0.1064 of the area between the mean and 75 feet. Adding these two figures gives 0.1896, the proportion of the area in this class [see Column (7) and Chart 23.7].

9. The total of Column (7) should be 1.0000, as there is 0.5000 of the area from the mean to either extreme of the distribution. In order to see the agreement between the observed and the expected frequencies, we include Column (8), which is obtained by multiplying 303 by the proportionate area of each class.

A comparison of the expected frequencies, shown in Column (8) of Table 23.3, with the observed frequencies of Table 23.1 reveals a general agreement of the figures, the difference being greatest for the class "85

NUMBER OF
STUDENTS

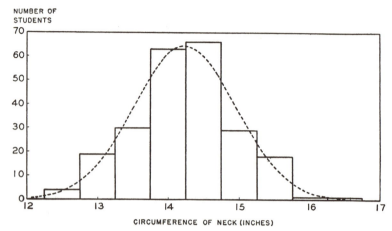

CIRCUMFERENCE OF NECK (INCHES)

Chart 23.8. Normal Curve Fitted to Neck Circumference of 231 Male College Students. Based on data of Table 23.4.

but under 95 feet." A test of the "goodness of fit" of the normal curve will be described in Chapter 25.

The normal curve and collar sizes. To illustrate another use of the normal curve, let us assume that a maker of collars is considering the production of a collar styled especially for college men. Since college men represent a selected group, it would be desirable to adjust the manufacturing schedule to their particular requirements. Extensive data on the circumference of the necks of college men are not available, but Table 23.4 shows the neck measurements of 231 male college students. To fit a normal curve, we need $\overline{X} = 14.232$ inches and $s = 0.719$ inches. The column diagram of the observed data and the fitted curve are shown in Chart 23.8.

Our problem, in this instance, is not to determine the expected propor-

TABLE 23.4

Neck Circumference of 231 Male College Students

Mid-values (in inches)	Number of students
12.5	4
13.0	19
13.5	30
14.0	63
14.5	66
15.0	29
15.5	18
16.0	1
16.5	1
Total	231

Source of data confidential.

TABLE 23.5

Determination of Expected Distribution of Collar Sizes for Male College Students

($\bar{X}$ = 14.232 inches; s = 0.719 inches)

| Collar size | Corresponding neck circumference | Limits of classes | | x from mean to limit | $\dfrac{x}{s}$ | Proportion of area between mean and limit (Appendix E) | Proportion of area in each class | Expected frequencies N = 1,000 |
| | | Lower limits | Upper limits | | | | | |
(1)	(2)	(3)	(4)	(5)	(6)	(7)	(8)	(9)
...	Smaller than 11.5	...		...	...	0.5000	0.0001	0.1
12½	11.5 but under 12.0	11.5		2.732	3.80	0.4999	0.0009	0.9
13	12.0 but under 12.5	12.0		2.232	3.10	0.4990	0.0070	7.0
13½	12.5 but under 13.0	12.5		1.732	2.41	0.4920	0.0356	35.6
14	13.0 but under 13.5	13.0		1.232	1.71	0.4564	0.1103	110.3
14½	13.5 but under 14.0	13.5		0.732	1.02	0.3461	0.2206	220.6
15	14.0 but under 14.5	14.0	14.5	0.232 0.268	0.32 0.37	0.1255 0.1443	0.2698	269.8
15½	14.5 but under 15.0		15.0	0.768	1.07	0.3577	0.2134	213.4
16	15.0 but under 15.5		15.5	1.268	1.76	0.4608	0.1031	103.1
16½	15.5 but under 16.0		16.0	1.768	2.46	0.4931	0.0323	32.3
17	16.0 but under 16.5		16.5	2.268	3.15	0.4992	0.0061	6.1
17½	16.5 but under 17.0		17.0	2.768	3.85	0.4999	0.0007	0.7
...	17.0 or larger		...	...	...	0.5000	0.0001	0.1
Total	...	...	...	...	...		1.0000	1,000.0

tion of college men having necks "12.75 but under 13.25" inches in circumference, "13.25 but under 13.75" inches in circumference, and so forth, but rather to determine the number of collars of each size (by half sizes) which should be made. Experience shows that, on the average, collars are worn about $\frac{3}{4}$ of an inch larger than the circumference of the neck. This means that collars size 14 would be worn by men whose necks averaged 13.25 inches, and, since we are dealing with half sizes, the necks would range from 13 to 13.5 inches in circumference. The first column of Table 23.5 lists the collar sizes, while the second column shows the corresponding neck circumferences. It is for these classes that we need to ascertain the theoretical frequencies. This is done in the remainder of the columns, and the expected frequencies ($N = 1,000$) are shown in Column (9). If our basic data are representative, there would be about 270 customers in a thousand calling for size 15 collars, 221 asking for size $14\frac{1}{2}$, 213 requesting size $15\frac{1}{2}$, and so on. It is interesting to observe that we might expect only 8 out of a thousand of this group to ask for size 13 or smaller and but 7 out of a thousand to require 17 or larger.

Suitability of the normal curve. As previously pointed out, the normal curve is only one of a number of kinds of curves which may be

TABLE 23.6

Cumulative Distribution of Baseball Throws for Distance by 303 First-Year High School Girls

Distance in feet	Number of girls	Per cent of total
Less than 25	1	0.33
Less than 35	3	0.99
Less than 45	10	3.30
Less than 55	35	11.55
Less than 65	68	22.44
Less than 75	121	39.93
Less than 85	185	61.06
Less than 95	229	75.58
Less than 105	260	85 81
Less than 115	287	94.72
Less than 125	298	98.35
Less than 135	302	99.67
Less than 145	303	100.00

Cumulative data of Table 23.1.

fitted to a frequency distribution. It should in no sense be thought of as a form having general applicability to all distributions. Since this is true, what guides are there which will tell us when to fit a normal curve, or, when fitted, if it is suitable?

1. The plotted curve or column diagram of the sample distribution serves as a very crude guide. If there is marked skewness present, it will be apparent, as will also any irregularities.

2. The sample data may be cumulated and put into percentage form, as in Table 23.6; these cumulative percentages may then be plotted on arithmetic probability paper,[4] as in Chart 23.9.   If the resulting curve is approximately a straight line, we may proceed with assurance to fit a normal curve.

3. The values of β_1 and β_2 may be computed as described in Chapter 10, and, by methods which are set forth in Chapter 26, we may ascertain whether β_1 differs significantly from zero and whether β_2 differs significantly from 3.0.   For the throws of a baseball by high school freshman girls, $\beta_1 = 0.0104$ and $\beta_2 = 2.7724$.   Neither of these values differs significantly from the value for a normal curve.

4. After the curve has been fitted and the expected frequencies have been determined for the various classes, a test of "goodness of fit" may be made.   This test is described in Chapter 25, and indicates that the fit of the normal curve to the data of baseball throws by girls is satisfactory.

BINOMIALS

It was previously shown that the expansion of a symmetrical binomial $(\frac{1}{2} + \frac{1}{2})^N$ can be approximated experimentally by tossing coins.   An *asymmetrical* binomial may be expanded experimentally in a similar fashion.

Experimental construction of skewed binomials.   Let us consider, first, a single die, four sides of which are colored black.   If we toss this die, it is apparent that the probability (π) of having a white side come up is 1 out of 3, or $\frac{1}{3}$, while the probability $(\tau = 1 - \pi)$ of obtaining a black side is 2 out of 3, or $\frac{2}{3}$. Using A (which has no numerical value) to indicate the occurrence of a white side and B (which also has no numerical value) to indicate the non-occurrence of a white side, that is, the occurrence of a black side, we may express the situation as

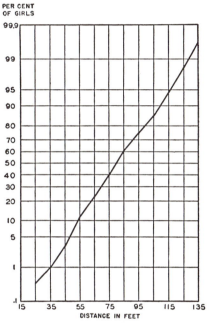

Chart 23.9.   Cumulative Distribution of Baseball Throws for Distance by 303 First-Year High School Girls, Shown on Arithmetic Probability Paper.   Based on data of Table 23.6.

---

[4] The vertical scale is so designed that the ogive of a normal curve will appear as a straight line.

$$\tau B + \pi A \text{ or } \tfrac{2}{3}B + \tfrac{1}{3}A,$$

which indicates that, if the die (assumed to be perfectly balanced) is tossed 1,500 times, we should expect a black side to appear 1,000 times and a white side 500 times.

If, now, we toss two dice (each having four black sides), there may appear either no white faces (2 black faces), one white face (a white face and a black face), or two white faces. The expression is

$$(\tfrac{2}{3}B + \tfrac{1}{3}A)^2 = \tfrac{4}{9}B^2 + \tfrac{4}{9}BA + \tfrac{1}{9}A^2.$$

Therefore, if 1,800 throws are made, we should expect to obtain no white faces 800 times, one white face 800 times, and two white faces 200 times.

OCCURRENCES IN THOUSANDS

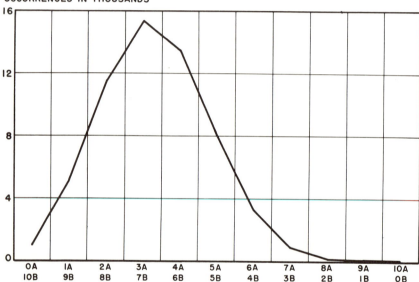

Chart 23.10. Expected Results of 59,049 Throws of 10 Dice, Each Having Four Black Sides and Two White Sides. The expected occurrences are given by $\left(\tfrac{2}{3}B + \tfrac{1}{3}A\right)^{10}$

$$= \tfrac{1,024}{59,049}B^{10} + \tfrac{5,120}{59,049}AB^{9} + \tfrac{11,520}{59,049}A^{2}B^{8} + \tfrac{15,360}{59,049}A^{3}B^{7} + \tfrac{13,440}{59,049}A^{4}B^{6} + \tfrac{8,064}{59,049}A^{5}B^{5}$$
$$+ \tfrac{3,360}{59,049}A^{6}B^{4} + \tfrac{960}{59,049}A^{7}B^{3} + \tfrac{180}{59,049}A^{8}B^{2} + \tfrac{20}{59,049}A^{9}B + \tfrac{1}{59,049}A^{10}.$$

If three such dice are thrown, the expression is

$$(\tfrac{2}{3}B + \tfrac{1}{3}A)^3 = \tfrac{8}{27}B^3 + \tfrac{12}{27}B^2A + \tfrac{6}{27}BA^2 + \tfrac{1}{27}A^3.$$

It will be observed that the binomial is beginning to show its skewed nature. This will be more clearly seen if we consider throwing ten dice, each with four black sides. The expression is $(\frac{2}{3}B + \frac{1}{3}A)^{10}$, which is shown graphically in Chart 23.10. The curve is definitely skewed as a result of the fact that τ and π are unequal.

If τ is a larger fraction and π is smaller, the skewness will be even greater. Let us consider as an illustration a four-sided pyramidal die with one white side and three black sides. It will be necessary to consider the "down" side as the one obtained at a throw. For throwing one die, the expression is $\frac{3}{4}B + \frac{1}{4}A$.

A Four-Sided Die, Each Side of Which Is an Equilateral Triangle.

If 10 of these four-sided dice are thrown, their behavior is indicated by $(\frac{3}{4}B + \frac{1}{4}A)^{10}$. The expansion of this binomial is shown in Chart 23.11, which is noticeably more skewed than the curve of Chart 23.10.

Fitting a binomial. It is apparent from the expression for a binomial that it is a device most useful for fitting to discrete data. In order to fit a binomial to a series of observed data, the following three

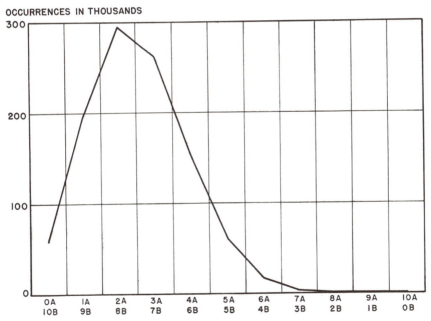

OCCURRENCES IN THOUSANDS

Chart 23.11. **Expected Results of 1,048,576 Throws of 10 Four-Sided Dice, Each Having Three Black Sides and One White Side.** The expected occurrences are given by $\left(\frac{3}{4}B + \frac{1}{4}A\right)^{10} = \frac{59,049}{1,048,576}B^{10} + \frac{196,830}{1,048,576}AB^9 + \frac{295,245}{1,048,576}A^2B^8$

$+ \frac{262,440}{1,048,576}A^3B^7 + \frac{153,090}{1,048,576}A^4B^6 + \frac{61,236}{1,048,576}A^5B^5 + \frac{17,010}{1,048,576}A^6B^4 + \frac{3,240}{1,048,576}A^7B^3$

$+ \frac{405}{1,048,576}A^8B^2 + \frac{30}{1,048,576}A^9B + \frac{1}{1,048,576}A^{10}.$

steps are necessary: (1) Determine the proper value of π, which also gives us τ, since $\tau = 1 - \pi$. The size of π determines the degree of skewness of the curve. If $\pi = 0.50$, then $\tau = 0.50$ and the curve is symmetrical. The farther removed π is from 0.50, in either direction, the greater the skewness. If $\pi < 0.50$, the curve is positively skewed; if $\pi > 0.50$, it is negatively skewed. When population values (π and τ) are not known, or when a reasonable assumption concerning them cannot be made, we have no alternative but to employ proportions determined from the sample. These we call p and q. (2) Expand the binomial $(\tau + \pi)^N$ or $(q + p)^N$, where N = the number of categories minus one, since there are

TABLE 23.7

Number of Male Pigs Born In Litters of Five

Number of males	Number of litters having specified number of males
0	2
1	20
2	41
3	35
4	14
5	4
Total	116

Data from A. S. Parkes, "Studies on the Sex-Ratio and Related Phenomena. The Frequencies of Sex Combinations in Pig Litters," *Biometrika*, Vol. 15, pp. 373–381. Parkes fits a binomial to the same series using $p = 0.4876$, as determined for litters of 4 to 12 pigs. His expected frequencies are identical with ours.

$N + 1$ terms in the expanded binomial. N is also the number of items in a sample. (3) Multiply each of the fractions of the expanded binomial by k, the number of samples.

Table 23.7 shows a distribution of the number of male pigs occurring in litters of five pigs. The data are for 116 such litters; so $N = 5$ and $k = 116$. Altogether there are $5 \times 116 = 580$ pigs of both sexes and $(0 \times 2) + (1 \times 20) + (2 \times 41) + (3 \times 35) + (4 \times 14) + (5 \times 4) = 283$ male pigs. The proportion of male pigs, p, is therefore

$$\frac{283}{580} = 0.4879$$

and $q = 0.5121$.

As pointed out above, the fitting is accomplished by expanding $k(q + p)^N$. Substituting 5 for N, but retaining the other symbols, we have

TABLE 23.8

Binomial $k(q + p)^N$ Fitted to Distribution of Number of Male Pigs Born in Litters of Five

$(k = 116; q = 0.5121; p = 0.4879; N = 5)$

Number of males (power of p) (1)	Expression* (2)	Log k (3)	Log C (4)	Log of indicated power of q (5)	Log of indicated power of p (6)	Σ of logs $[(3) + (4) + (5) + (6)]$ (7)	Expected frequencies $k = 116$ [antilog of (7)] (8)
0	$k \cdot C_0 \cdot q^5 \cdot p^0 = (116)\ (1)(0.5121)^5(0.4879)^0$	2.064458	...	48.546775 − 50	...	0.611233	4.1
1	$k \cdot C_1 \cdot q^4 \cdot p^1 = (116)\ (5)(0.5121)^4(0.4879)^1$	2.064458	0.698970	38.837420 − 40	9.688331 − 10	1.289179	19.5
2	$k \cdot C_2 \cdot q^3 \cdot p^2 = (116)(10)(0.5121)^3(0.4879)^2$	2.064458	1.000000	29.128065 − 30	19.376662 − 20	1.569185	37.1
3	$k \cdot C_3 \cdot q^2 \cdot p^3 = (116)(10)(0.5121)^2(0.4879)^3$	2.064458	1.000000	19.418710 − 20	29.064993 − 30	1.548161	35.3
4	$k \cdot C_4 \cdot q^1 \cdot p^4 = (116)\ (5)(0.5121)^1(0.4879)^4$	2.064458	0.698970	9.709355 − 10	38.753324 − 40	1.226107	16.8
5	$k \cdot C_5 \cdot q^0 \cdot p^5 = (116)\ (1)(0.5121)^0(0.4879)^5$	2.064458	...	...	48.441655 − 50	0.506113	3.2
Total	....						116.0

* C_0, C_1, etc., are the binomial coefficients, the multipliers for each term of the binomial expansion.

$$C_0 = 1, C_1 = N, C_2 = \frac{N(N-1)}{1 \cdot 2}, C_3 = \frac{N(N-1)(N-2)}{1 \cdot 2 \cdot 3}, \text{ etc.}$$

$$k(q + p)^5 = k(q^5 + 5q^4p + 10q^3p^2 + 10q^2p^3 + 5qp^4 + p^5),$$

where the exponent of p indicates the number of males born in a litter of 5.

The numerical expression to use in fitting the binomial is $(0.5121 + 0.4879)^5$, and, since $k = 116$, we should expand $116(0.5121 + 0.4879)^5$. This becomes

$$116[(0.5121)^5 + 5(0.5121)^4(0.4879) + 10(0.5121)^3(0.4879)^2$$
$$+ 10(0.5121)^2(0.4879)^3 + 5(0.5121)(0.4879)^4 + (0.4879)^5].$$

The computations are most conveniently carried out by means of logarithms, as shown in Table 23.8. Although the powers could be obtained and the multiplications could be performed for this problem by the use of a calculating machine, the use of logarithms is essential when a binomial is raised to an appreciably higher power.

Chart 23.12 shows the observed and the expected frequencies. The observed data have been presented by means of separated bars to suggest the discrete nature of the series. A test of "goodness of fit," similar to that described in Chapter 25, indicates good agreement between the observed and expected frequencies.

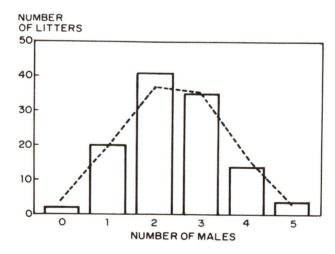

Chart 23.12. **Binomial Fitted to Distribution of Number of Male Pigs Born in Litters of Five.** Data from Tables 23.7 and 23.8.

It should not be assumed that all discrete series may be fitted by the method just explained. Some data are better described by other distributions, as, for example, the Poisson, the fitting of which is described elsewhere by one of the writers.[5]

---

[5] See the reference in note 3.

SKEWED CURVES

The binomials just discussed are suitable for fitting to discrete data, but are not accurate enough to use with continuous data. A fitted binomial consists of a series of ordinates erected at specific points on the X-axis (see Chart 23.12). If this procedure were applied to a distribution of continuous data (or to discrete data where the X units are small in relation to the class interval), we should be erecting an ordinate at the mid-value of each class, instead of determining the area under a smooth curve. Obviously, the greater the number of classes, the less would be the difference between these two procedures.

There are a great many types of skewed curves which may be fitted to frequency distributions. It is the purpose of this volume, not to enter into an extended consideration of this topic, but merely to sketch briefly the procedure involved in fitting two of the simpler types.[6]

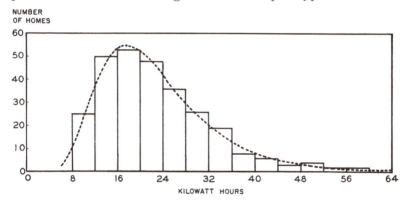

NUMBER
OF HOMES

KILOWATT HOURS

Chart 23.13. Logarithmic Normal Curve Fitted to Kilowatt Hours of Electricity Used per Month in 282 Medium-Class Homes in an Eastern City. Based on data of Table 23.9.

The logarithmic normal curve. Some distributions which are skewed to the right become symmetrical when plotted in terms of the logarithms of their X values or, alternately, when plotted on graph paper having a logarithmic X-scale. The column diagram of Chart 23.13 shows the monthly use of electricity by 282 medium-class homes in an eastern city, drawn from the data of Table 23.9. It is apparent that the series is decidedly skewed in a positive direction. In Chart 23.14 these data have been re-plotted but against a logarithmic X-scale. When the curve is extended to the horizontal axis at $X = 6$ kilowatt hours (the class just below the first one shown in the table), the approximate symmetrical nature of the series in terms of logarithmic X values is apparent. A further indication of this is shown in Chart 23.15, which presents the

---

[6] For a more detailed discussion, see: W. P. Elderton, *Frequency Curves and Correlation*, fourth edition, Cambridge University Press, London, 1953.

NUMBER
OF HOMES

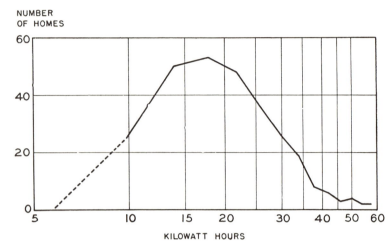

Chart 23.14.   Kilowatt Hours of Electricity Used Per Month in 282
Medium-Class Homes in an Eastern City.   Logarithmic X-scale.   Data
of Table 23.9.   Frequencies are plotted at logarithmic mid-values of classes.

TABLE 23.9

Kilowatt Hours of Electricity
Used Per Month in Med-
ium-Class Homes in
an Eastern City

Kilowatt hours (mid-values)	Number of homes
10	25
14	50
18	53
22	48
26	36
30	26
34	19
38	8
42	6
46	3
50	4
54	2
58	2
Total	282

Data from Electrical Testing Laboratories, New York City.   Name of city
withheld by request.

cumulative percentage frequencies plotted on logarithmic probability
paper.

Fitting a logarithmic normal curve.   The procedure for fitting a
logarithmic normal curve is essentially the same process as that of fitting
a normal curve, except that we use the arithmetic mean $\bar{X}_{\log}$ and the

PER CENT
OF HOMES

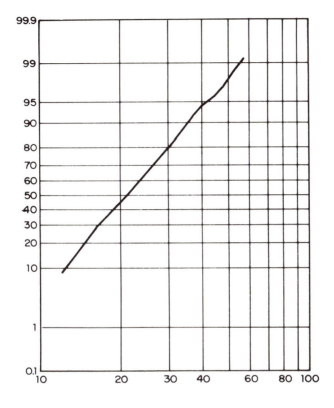

KILOWATT HOURS

Chart 23.15. Kilowatt Hours of Electricity Used per Month in 282 Medium-Class Homes in an Eastern City. Shown on logarithmic probability paper. Based on data of Table 23.9.

standard deviation $s_{\log}$ of the logarithms of the X values. The values of $\bar{X}_{\log}$ and $s_{\log}$ may be computed by making use of the mid-values of the logarithms of the class limits. Ideally the classes should be so chosen that the class intervals are equal in a logarithmic sense, thus making the logarithmic mid-values equidistant from each other. Usually we deal with ready-formed frequency distributions of arithmetically equal class intervals, and with such distributions the direct computation of $\bar{X}_{\log}$ and $s_{\log}$ is laborious. The inconvenience of computing these logarithmic values has been eliminated by use of formulas based upon the quartiles, data which are readily computed. Furthermore, there are certain advantages to the procedure. Unless the data are very regular, this method avoids the disturbing effects of irregular extreme items. The expressions are given below.

$$\bar{X}_{\log} = \frac{\log Q_1 + \log Q_3 + 1.2554 \log Q_2}{3.2554},$$

This is the weighted average of the three quartiles, the weights being proportional to the heights of normal-curve ordinates erected at these values.

$$s_{\log} = 0.7413(\log Q_3 - \log Q_1).$$

This expression grows out of the fact that in a normal curve 50 per cent of the items are included within $\pm Q$ of the median (or mean), and also that 50 per cent of the items are included within $\pm 0.674s$ of the mean. It is therefore obvious that

$$s = \frac{1}{0.6745} Q = 1.4825Q.$$

Since

$$\frac{Q_3 - Q_1}{2} = Q,$$

it follows that

$$Q_3 - Q_1 = 2Q, \text{ and } s = 0.7413(Q_3 - Q_1).$$

For the data of electric consumption, $Q_1 = 15,6400$ kwh., Q_2 (the median) $= 21.0833$ kwh., and $Q_3 = 27.9444$ kwh.

$$\bar{X}_{\log} = \frac{\log 15.6400 + \log 27.9444 + 1.2554 \log 21.0833}{3.2554},$$

$$= \frac{1.194237 + 1.446295 + 1.2554(1.323939)}{3.2554},$$

$$= \frac{4.302605}{3.2554} = 1.321682.$$

$$s_{\log} = 0.7413(\log 27.9444 - \log 15.6400),$$
$$= 0.7413(1.446295 - 1.194237),$$
$$= 0.7413(0.252058),$$
$$= 0.186851.$$

Using these two values, the expected frequencies in each class may be determined in a manner strictly parallel to that previously described for the normal curve. As before, Appendix E is used and the procedure is set forth in Table 23.10.

TABLE 23.10

Determination of Expected Frequencies for Logarithmic Normal Curve Fitted to Data of Kilowatt Hours of Electricity Used per Month in 282 Medium-Class Homes in an Eastern City

$$(\bar{X}_{log} = 1.321682; \; s_{log} = 0.186851)$$

Kilowatt hours consumed	Logarithm of limits of classes		$\dfrac{x_{log}}{(\log \text{ of limit} - \bar{X}_{log})}$	$\dfrac{x_{log}}{s_{log}}$	Cumulative proportionate frequencies (Appendix E)	Proportionate frequencies	Expected frequencies $N = 282$
	Lower limits	Upper limits					
(1)	(2)	(3)	(4)	(5)	(6)	(7)	(8)
Below 4	...			...	0.5000	0.0001	...
4 but less than 8	0.602060		0.719622	3.85	0.4999	0.0124	3.5
8 but less than 12	0.903090		0.418592	2.24	0.4875	0.0843	23.8
12 but less than 16	1.079181		0.242501	1.30	0.4032	0.1675	47.2
16 but less than 20	1.204120		0.117562	0.63	0.2357	0.1919	54.1
20 but less than 24	1.301030		0.020652	0.11	0.0438	0.1655	46.7
		1.380211	0.058529	0.31	0.1217	0.1269	35.8
24 but less than 28		1.447158	0.125476	0.67	0.2486	0.0879	24.8
28 but less than 32		1.505150	0.183468	0.98	0.3365	0.0597	16.8
32 but less than 36		1.556303	0.234621	1.26	0.3962	0.0370	10.4
36 but less than 40		1.602060	0.280378	1.50	0.4332	0.0241	6.8
40 but less than 44		1.643453	0.321771	1.72	0.4573	0.0153	4.3
44 but less than 48		1.681241	0.359559	1.92	0.4726	0.0100	2.8
48 but less than 52		1.716003	0.394321	2.11	0.4826	0.0061	1.7
52 but less than 56		1.748188	0.426506	2.28	0.4887	0.0040	1.1
56 but less than 60		1.778151	0.456469	2.44	0.4927	0.0025	0.7
60 but less than 64		1.806180	0.484498	2.59	0.4952	0.0016	0.5
64 but less than 68		1.832509	0.510827	2.73	0.4968	0.0032	0.9
68 or more					0.5000		
Total	...	...	...	...	...	1.0000	281.9

The ordinates are computed from the expression[7]

$$Y_c = \frac{0.4343Ni}{2.5066Xs_{\log}} \, 2.71828^{\frac{-x_{\log}^2}{2s_{\log}^2}},$$

which may be simplified for purposes of computation to

$$Y_c = \frac{0.17326Ni}{Xs_{\log}} \, 2.71828^{\frac{-x_{\log}^2}{2s_{\log}^2}}.$$

X is the arithmetic value of the point on the X-axis at which the ordinate is to be erected. The values of $2.71828^{\frac{-x_{\log}^2}{2s_{\log}^2}}$ are obtained from Appendix D and the $\dfrac{x_{\log}}{s_{\log}}$ values are given by

$$\frac{x_{\log}}{s_{\log}} = \frac{\log X - \overline{X}_{\log}}{s_{\log}}.$$

The procedure for determining the ordinates parallels that for the normal curve which was shown in Table 23.2. The fitted curve is shown in Chart 23.13 and the correspondence between that curve and the column diagram is apparent.

Davies suggests a logarithmic coefficient of skewness

$$\mathrm{Sk}_{\log} = \frac{\log Q_1 + \log Q_3 - 2 \log Q_2}{\log Q_3 - \log Q_1}$$

and points out that a series which yields a coefficient of less than 0.15 (or perhaps even 0.20) may tentatively be considered as logarithmically normal. If, however, a skewed distribution is not inherently logarithmic, it may sometimes be adjusted by shifting the X values until the desired skewness is obtained; after fitting, the X values are again shifted. This correction c is obtained by

---

[7] It will be recalled that the expression for the normal curve is

$$Y_c = \frac{Ni}{2.5066s} \, 2.71828^{\frac{-x^2}{2s^2}}.$$

For fitting the logarithmic normal curve, the expression cannot be used in this form, since s is in terms of logarithms ($s_{\log}$), while the class intervals i are equal arithmetically. We therefore multiply i by the adjustment factor $\dfrac{\log_{10} e}{X}$ or $\dfrac{0.4343}{X}$, to compensate for the fact that the intervals are not geometrically equal. We thus have

$$Y_c = \frac{0.4343}{X} \cdot \frac{Ni}{2.5066s_{\log}} \, 2.71828^{\frac{-x_{\log}^2}{2s_{\log}^2}}.$$

$$c = \frac{Q_2^2 - Q_1 Q_3}{Q_1 + Q_3 - 2Q_2}.$$

This value is added to the class limits and to the quartiles, after which $\overline{X}_{\log}$ and $s_{\log}$ are computed. The fitting proceeds as in Table 23.10, but the shifted class limits are used. After the expected frequencies have been ascertained, the class limits are shifted back to their original values. It is obvious that this device extends the usefulness of the logarithmic normal curve.

Fitting a normal curve with adjustment for skewness. The formulas previously given for the normal curve enabled us to fit a symmetrical curve from a knowledge of $\overline{X}$, s, and N. We have just considered one method of fitting a skewed curve. Another procedure that is useful for certain skewed distributions consists of using also a measure of skewness $\alpha_3 = \sqrt{\beta_1}$ and thereby making a correction to the fit of a normal curve. This is sometimes referred to as a second approximation curve. The equation[8] is

$$Y_c = \frac{Ni}{2.5066s} 2.71828^{\frac{-x^2}{2s^2}} - \left\{ \frac{Ni}{2.5066s} 2.71828^{\frac{-x^2}{2s^2}} \left[\frac{\alpha_3}{2} \left(\frac{x}{s} - \frac{x^3}{3s^3} \right) \right] \right\}.$$

TABLE 23.11

Computation of $\overline{X}$, s, and α_3 for Depth of Sapwood

Depth in inches (mid-values)	f	d'	fd'	$f(d')^2$	$f(d')^3$
1.0	2	−7	− 14	98	− 686
1.3	29	−6	−174	1,044	− 6,264
1.6	62	−5	−310	1,550	− 7,750
1.9	106	−4	−424	1,696	− 6,784
2.2	153	−3	−459	1,377	− 4,131
2.5	186	−2	−372	744	− 1,488
2.8	193	−1	−193	193	− 193
3.1	188	0	0	0	0
3.4	151	1	151	151	151
3.7	123	2	246	492	984
4.0	82	3	246	738	2,214
4.3	48	4	192	768	3,072
4.6	27	5	135	675	3,375
4.9	14	6	84	504	3,024
5.2	5	7	35	245	1,715
5.5	1	8	8	64	512
Total	1,370	...	−849	10,339	− 12,249

Data from W. A. Shewhart, *Economic Control of Quality of Manufactured Product*, p. 77, D. Van Nostrand Co., Princeton, N. J., 1931. Courtesy of D. Van Nostrand Co., Inc.

$$\nu_1 = \frac{\Sigma f d'}{N} = -0.619708.$$

$$\nu_2 = \frac{\Sigma f(d')^2}{N} = 7.546715.$$

---

[8] The expression includes the first two terms of the Gram-Charlier series. For a further discussion, see W. A. Shewhart, *op. cit.* pp. 84–94.

$$\nu_3 = \frac{\Sigma f(d')^3}{N} = -8.940876.$$

$$\overline{X} = \overline{X}_d + \frac{\Sigma fd'}{N} i = 3.1 - [(0.619708)(0.3)],$$

$$= 2.9141 \text{ inches.}$$

Since Sheppard's correction is not applied, we have

$$\pi_2 = \nu_2 - \nu_1^2 = 7.162677.$$
$$\pi_3 = \nu_3 - 3\nu_1\nu_2 + 2\nu_1^3 = 4.613422.$$
$$s = i \sqrt{\pi_2} = 0.8029 \text{ inches.}$$
$$\alpha_3 = \sqrt{\beta_1} = \sqrt{\frac{\pi_3^2}{\pi_2^3}}, \text{ or } \frac{\pi_3}{\sqrt{\pi_2^3}} = +0.2407.$$

The expression preceding the minus sign is that for the normal curve, while the expression in braces represents the modification for skewness. In order to determine the expected frequencies, the above equation must be integrated. This is accomplished via tables. To use them, we write

$$\int_0^x f(x)dx = F_1\left(\frac{x}{s}\right) - \alpha_3 F_2\left(\frac{x}{s}\right),$$

where $F_1\left(\dfrac{x}{s}\right)$ represents the areas of the normal curve (given in Appendix E) and $\alpha_3 F_2\left(\dfrac{x}{s}\right)$ represents the modification for skewness. Values of $F_2\left(\dfrac{x}{s}\right)$ are obtained from Appendix F and are then multiplied by α_3.

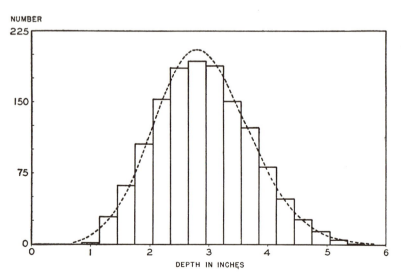

Chart 23.16. Second Approximation Curve Fitted to Depth of Sapwood. Based on data of Table 23.11.

TABLE 23.12

Determination of Expected Frequencies for Data of Depth of Sapwood by Means of a Second Approximation Curve

($\bar{X}$ = 2.9141 inches; s = 0.8029 inches; α_3 = +0.2407)

Depth in inches (mid-values)	Limits of classes		x	$\dfrac{x}{s}$	$F_1\left(\dfrac{x}{s}\right)$	$F_2\left(\dfrac{x}{s}\right)$	$\alpha_3 F_2\left(\dfrac{x}{s}\right)$	$F_1\left(\dfrac{x}{s}\right) - \alpha_3 F_2\left(\dfrac{x}{s}\right)$ [Col. 6 − Col. 8]	Expected proportionate frequencies	Expected frequencies N = 1,370
	Lower limits	Upper limits								
(1)	(2)	(3)	(4)	(5)	(6)	(7)	(8)	(9)	(10)	(11)
.4	0.25		2.6641	3.318	0.4995	−0.0692	−0.0167	0.5162	0.0002	..
.7	0.55		2.3641	2.944	0.4984	−0.0732	−0.0176	0.5160	0.0018	2
1.0	0.85		2.0641	2.571	0.4949	−0.0802	−0.0193	0.5142	0.0067	9
1.3	1.15		1.7641	2.197	0.4860	−0.0893	−0.0215	0.5075	0.0185	25
1.6	1.45		1.4641	1.824	0.4659	−0.0958	−0.0231	0.4890	0.0403	55
1.9	1.75		1.1641	1.450	0.4265	−0.0921	−0.0222	0.4487	0.0723	99
2.2	2.05		0.8641	1.076	0.3590	−0.0724	−0.0174	0.3764	0.1077	148
2.5	2.35		0.5641	0.703	0.2590	−0.0402	−0.0097	0.2687	0.1373	188
2.8 {	2.65		0.2641	0.329	0.1289	−0.0103	−0.0025	0.1314	} 0.1493	} 205
		2.95	0.0359	0.045	0.0179	0.0002		0.0179		
3.1		3.25	0.3359	0.418	0.1621	0.0162	0.0039	0.1582	0.1403	192
3.4		3.55	0.6359	0.792	0.2858	0.0484	0.0116	0.2742	0.1160	159
3.7		3.85	0.9359	1.166	0.3782	0.0787	0.0189	0.3593	0.0851	117
4.0		4.15	1.2359	1.539	0.4381	0.0943	0.0227	0.4154	0.0561	77
4.3		4.45	1.5359	1.913	0.4721	0.0949	0.0228	0.4493	0.0339	46
4.6		4.75	1.8359	2.287	0.4889	0.0871	0.0210	0.4679	0.0186	25
4.9		5.05	2.1359	2.660	0.4961	0.0782	0.0188	0.4773	0.0094	13
5.2		5.35	2.4359	3.034	0.4988	0.0720	0.0173	0.4815	0.0042	6
5.5		5.65	2.7359	3.408	0.4997	0.0686	0.0165	0.4832	0.0017	2
5.8		5.95	3.0359	3.781	0.4999	0.0672	0.0162	0.4837	0.0005	1
6.1		6.25	3.3359	4.155*	0.5000	0.0667*	0.0161	0.4839	0.0002	..
6.4		6.55	3.6359	4.528*	0.5000	0.0666*	0.0160	0.4840	0.0001	..

* For values of $F_2\left(\dfrac{x}{s}\right)$ beyond the range given in Appendix F, use the expression

$$F_2\left(\frac{x}{s}\right) = \frac{1}{15.036}\left\{1 - \left[1 - \left(\frac{x}{s}\right)^2\right] 2.71828^{-\frac{x^2}{2s^2}}\right\}.$$

The values of $2.71828^{-\frac{x^2}{2s^2}}$ may be conveniently read from the table of ordinates of the normal curve (Appendix D), or from a more extensive table in Karl Pearson, *Tables for Statisticians and Biometricians*, pp. 2–8, Cambridge University Press, London, 1914.

The values for z shown in the latter table yield $2.71828^{-\frac{x^2}{2s^2}}$ when multiplied by 2.5066.

To illustrate this method, we use the data of Table 23.11, which are shown graphically in Chart 23.16. The fitting procedure[9] for a second approximation curve is shown in Table 23.12. The values of N, $\overline{X}$, s, and α_3 having been obtained (Table 23.11), the steps are as follows:

1. Make entries in Columns (1) to (6) inclusive, as was done in fitting a normal curve.

2. Refer to Appendix F and enter in Column (7) the $F_2\left(\dfrac{x}{s}\right)$ values associated with each $\dfrac{x}{s}$ value of Column (5). Negative signs are entered in this column for the percentages associated with class limits of Column (2).

3. In Column (8), multiply each value of Column (7) by α_3. Signs are shown.

4. To produce Column (9), the values in Column (8) are subtracted algebraically from the values in Column (6).

5. The cumulative proportionate frequencies of Column (9) are decumulated in Column (10), as was done for the normal curve. The result is a series of figures showing expected frequencies on the basis of the second approximation for $N = 1.0000$. One of the shortcomings of this curve is that it may occasionally produce negative frequencies at one end, or, if we do not extend the fit far enough to produce these negative frequencies, the total may slightly exceed 1.0000. In this instance Column (10) totals 1.0002.

6. In Column (11) the expected frequencies are prorated among the classes so that the total equals N for the sample.

---

[9] Sheppard's correction has not been applied in the computation of the second moment, partly because high contact is not present at the left in Chart 23.16. Furthermore, Shewhart points out (*op. cit.*, p. 78) that the corrected standard deviation (0.798211) differs more from the standard deviation of the ungrouped data (0.802555) than does the uncorrected standard deviation (0.802895). When high contact is not present at both ends of a distribution, overcorrection of a moment is not unusual. It arises because the corrections allow for non-existent classes at the extremes.

CHAPTER 24

Statistical Significance I: Arithmetic Means

In this and the two following chapters, we shall be interested in the behavior of statistical measures computed from samples. This is an important topic, since the statistical worker will nearly always be dealing with data which constitute a sample rather than a population. Usually, it is not possible to consider all of the items in a population. For example, it would be utterly impracticable to attempt to obtain data of the heights of all the adult males in the United States. If data of this sort were needed, a much smaller expenditure of time and money would be involved if a suitable sample were to be studied. Furthermore, the study of a properly representative sample can be expected to give satisfactory results, the reliability of which may be stated exactly. However, in this book we can consider only random samples.[1]

HOW SAMPLE ARITHMETIC MEANS ARE DISTRIBUTED

Data of the mileage run by each of many thousands of automobile tires of the same size, quality, and make, used on similar vehicles under comparable road conditions, show an arithmetic mean ($\overline{X}_{\wp}$) of 15,200 miles and a standard deviation (σ) of 1,248 miles. If we select a random sample of 25 tires, we would expect the arithmetic mean of the random sample to be in the general neighborhood of 15,200 miles. A second random sample of 25 items would not yield exactly the same arithmetic mean as the first, but it, too, should be in the general neighborhood of 15,200. Our first concern is with the behavior of arithmetic means of random samples. Since we shall be dealing with only random samples, and since we shall not be considering geometric, harmonic, or other means, we shall simply say *sample mean* to refer to the arithmetic mean of a random sample.

The arithmetic mean of sample means. If a number of random

---

[1] A *random* sample was defined on page 23.

samples, each of 25 tires, were to be taken from the tire population just mentioned, some of the sample means would exceed 15,200 miles and some would fall below 15,200 miles.   One, or a very few, might happen to be exactly 15,200 miles.   The arithmetic mean of sample means would tend to equal $\overline{X}_\wp$.

Consider a more specific illustration: Walter A. Shewhart[2] constructed a population of 998 items, having positive and negative values ranging from -3.0 to 3.0, and with $\overline{X}_\wp = 0$.   It is not important at this point that the population was as nearly normal as it was possible to make it. From this population Shewhart drew 1,000 samples ($k = 1,000$) of 4 items ($N = 4$) each.   The arithmetic mean of the 1,000 sample means was 0.014.   If a larger number of sample means had been taken, it is reasonable to believe that the arithmetic mean of the sample means would have been more nearly zero, since it may be shown that, if all possible samples (K) of size N are drawn from a population, the arithmetic mean of the sample means will equal the population mean.[3]   That is,

$$\frac{\overline{X}_1 + \overline{X}_2 + \overline{X}_3 + \cdots + \overline{X}_K}{K} = \overline{X}_\wp.$$

Skewness of sample means.   If sample means are from a population which has no skewness, the distribution of sample means will not be skewed.   If the population is skewed, the distribution of sample means will show *less* skewness, the skewness being inversely related to the size of the sample, according to the relationship

$$\beta_{1_{\overline{x}}} = \frac{\beta_{1_\wp}}{N}.$$

Shewhart's population of 998 items had $\beta_{1_\wp} = 0$.   The distribution of the 1,000 sample means, together with the population, is shown in Chart 24.1.   It may be seen that the distribution of the sample means is nearly symmetrical.   Shewhart does not compute the value of $\beta_{1_{\overline{x}}}$ for the 1,000 sample means, but for the frequency distribution in class intervals of 0.25, shown in Chart 24.1, $\beta_{1_{\overline{x}}}$ has been found to be 0.0027.

Chart 24.2 shows the distribution of the arithmetic means of 100 samples of 10 items each and the distribution of the skewed population from which the samples were drawn.   For the population, $\beta_{1_\wp} = 0.096$. If all possible samples of $N = 10$ had been drawn, the skewness of the sample means would have been

---

[2] Walter A. Shewhart, *op. cit.*, pp. 167, 442–445, and 454–463.

[3] See Appendix S, section 24.1.

$$\beta_{1_{\bar{x}}} = \frac{\beta_{1_\wp}}{N} = \frac{0.096}{10} = 0.0096.$$

For the 100 samples, $\beta_{1_{\bar{x}}} = 0.0031$. It is clear that the skewness of the sample means is much less than the skewness in the population.

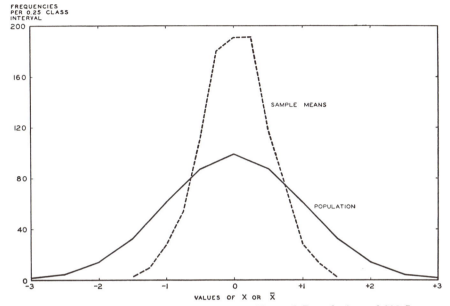

Chart 24.1. Distribution of Shewhart's Normal Population of 998 Items and of 1,000 Sample Means for Samples Having $N = 4$. The class intervals were 0.50 for the population and 0.25 for the sample means. Based on data from W. A. Shewhart, *Economic Control of Quality of Manufactured Product*, D. Van Nostrand Co., Princeton, N. J., 1931, pp. 167, 442–445, and 454–463.

Shewhart[4] has drawn samples from a population which is much more skewed than that shown in Chart 24.2. His right-triangular universe and the distribution of 1,000 sample means ($N = 4$) are shown in Chart 24.3. The skewness of the right-triangular universe is indicated by $\beta_{1_\wp} = 0.320$.

For samples of 4, we would expect the skewness to be about

$$\beta_{1_{\bar{x}}} = \frac{\beta_{1_\wp}}{N} = \frac{0.320}{4} = 0.080.$$

For the distribution of the 1,000 sample means, the skewness has been computed to be 0.062. While this value of $\beta_{1_{\bar{x}}}$ is larger than those just

---

[4] The population data are from page 183 of the reference given in footnote 2. The data of sample means were obtained by correspondence from Dr. Walter A. Shewhart. All skewness and kurtosis values (except those for the normal population) were computed by the writers.

obtained for the other two sets of samples, it must be remembered, first, that the skewness is much less than that of the population and, second, that populations as skewed as this are not often encountered.

Kurtosis of sample means. The kurtosis of a distribution of sample means may be expected to be closer to 3.0 (the value for a normal distribution) than the kurtosis of the population from which the samples were taken. The relationship is

$$\beta_{2_{\bar{x}}} - 3 = \frac{\beta_{2_{p}} - 3}{N}, \text{ or}$$

$$\beta_{2_{\bar{x}}} = \frac{\beta_{2_{p}} - 3}{N} + 3.$$

For Shewhart's normal population, the value of $\beta_{2_{p}}$ was 3.0, and the distribution of sample means (Chart 24.1) would be expected to have $\beta_{2_{\bar{x}}} = 3.0$. For Shewhart's 1,000 sample means, $\beta_{2_{\bar{x}}}$ was 2.98.

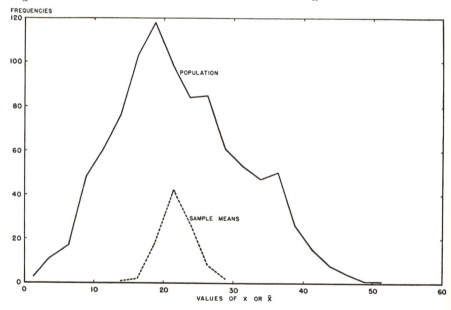

Chart 24.2. Distribution of Skewed Population of 972 Items and of 100 Sample Means for Samples Having $N = 10$. The population consisted of the weekly earnings of 972 wage earners. Class intervals were $2.50 for both series.

Shewhart also constructed a rectangular population,[5] shown in Chart 24.4A, which is extremely platykurtic, having $\beta_{2_{p}} = 1.80$. From this population he obtained 1,000 sample means ($N = 4$), the distribution of which is also given in Chart 24.4A. This curve looks as if it might be nearly mesokurtic. The kurtosis of these sample means would be

---

[5] See footnote 4.

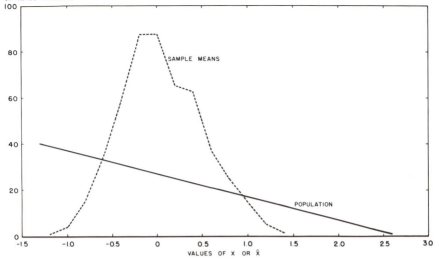

Chart 24.3. Distribution of Shewhart's Right-Triangular Population of 820 Items and of 1,000 Sample Means for Samples Having $N = 4$. The class intervals were 0.1 for the population and 0.2 for the sample means. For source of data, see footnote 4.

expected to be

$$\beta_{2\bar{x}} = \frac{\beta_{2_\wp} - 3}{4} + 3 = \frac{1.80 - 3}{4} + 3,$$

$$= 2.70.$$

For the 1,000 sample means, $\beta_{2\bar{x}} = 2.99$.

Shewhart did not consider a leptokurtic population, but Alfred J. Kana designed such a population of 1,000 items, which is shown in Chart 24.4B. From this population, Kana obtained 400 sample means ($N = 5$), the distribution of which also appears in Chart 24.4B. The kurtosis of the population was $\beta_{2_\wp} = 7.927$. Selecting samples of five items each could be expected to yield

$$\beta_{2\bar{x}} = \frac{\beta_{2_\wp} - 3}{N} + 3 = \frac{7.927 - 3}{5} + 3 = 3.985.$$

Only 400 samples were drawn, but for this group of samples it was found that $\beta_{2\bar{x}} = 4.190$, a value much nearer to 3.0 than the value of $\beta_{2_\wp}$.

Sample means and the normal curve. From what has been said, it is clear that the distribution of sample means is normal when those means have been computed from random samples from a normal population. If a population is skewed, the skewness present in sample means drawn from that population will be much less, the skewness being inversely related to the size of the sample as indicated by

$$\beta_{1\bar{x}} = \frac{\beta_{1_\wp}}{N}.$$

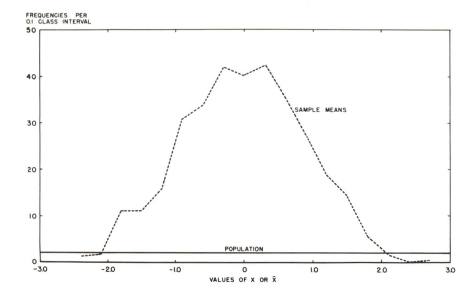

Chart 24.4A. Distribution of Shewhart's Rectangular (Platykurtic) Population of 122 Items and of 1,000 Sample Means for Samples Having $N = 4$. The class intervals were 0.1 for the population and 0.3 for the sample means. For source of data, see footnote 4.

If a population is leptokurtic or platykurtic, the distribution of sample means drawn from that population will be more nearly mesokurtic, as shown by

$$\beta_{2\bar{x}} = \frac{\beta_{2\varphi} - 3}{N} + 3.$$

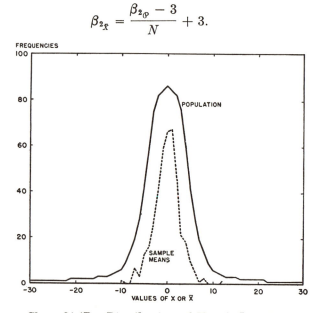

Chart 24.4B. Distribution of Kana's Leptokurtic Population of 1,000 Items and of 400 Sample Means for Samples Having $N = 5$. The class intervals were 1.0 for both series. The kurtosis values, given in the text, were computed from ungrouped data for both series. Data from Alfred J. Kana.

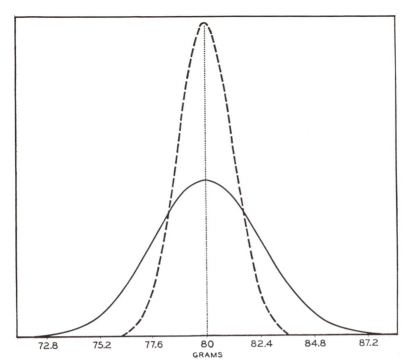

Chart 24.5. Distribution of Sample Arithmetic Means for $N = 25$, When $\overline{X}_\mathcal{P} = 80$ Grams and $\sigma = 12$ Grams (Solid Curve) and When $\overline{X}_\mathcal{P} = 80$ Grams and $\sigma = 6$ Grams (Broken Curve).

As a consequence of these two relationships, statisticians consider sample means to be distributed normally unless there is reason to believe that the population from which they were taken departs markedly from normal.

Dispersion of sample means. A glance at any of the four preceding charts will reveal that the dispersion of sample means is much less than the dispersion of the population from which those sample means came. The relationship is[6]

$$\sigma_{\bar{x}} = \frac{\sigma}{\sqrt{N}}.$$

For the population data of Chart 24.1, we have $\sigma = 1.0070$ and $N = 4$. Consequently,

$$\sigma_{\bar{x}} = \frac{1.0070}{\sqrt{4}} = 0.5035.$$

For the 1,000 sample means, the standard deviation may be computed using the expression

$$\sqrt{\frac{(\overline{X}_1 - \overline{X}_\mathcal{P})^2 + (\overline{X}_2 - \overline{X}_\mathcal{P})^2 + \cdots + (\overline{X}_{1,000} - \overline{X}_\mathcal{P})^2}{1,000}}.$$

The value of the standard deviation for the frequency distribution of sample means, shown in Chart 24.1, is 0.503, which agrees very closely

---

[6] See Appendix S, section 24.2. Note that, as shown in the proof, the expression used above is not valid unless the population is large in relation to N.

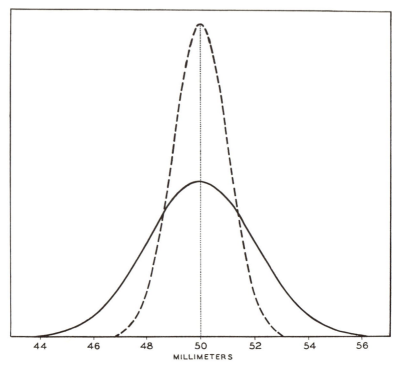

MILLIMETERS

Chart 24.6. **Distribution of Sample Arithmetic Means for $\overline{X}_\wp = 50$ mm and $\sigma = 8$ mm, When $N = 16$ (Solid Curve) and When $N = 64$ (Broken Curve).**

with the value of 0.5035 that would have been obtained if we could have considered all possible samples of $N = 4$.

From the expression

$$\sigma_{\bar{x}} = \frac{\sigma}{\sqrt{N}}.$$

it is obvious that (1) the greater the dispersion of the population, the greater the dispersion of sample means taken from that population; and (2) the larger the size of the samples, the smaller the dispersion of sample means. These points are illustrated in Chart 24.5, which shows the distributions of sample means for two different values of σ when N is unchanged, and in Chart 24.6, which shows the distributions of sample means for two sample sizes from the same population.

SIGNIFICANCE OF THE DIFFERENCE BETWEEN $\overline{X}$ AND $\overline{X}_\wp$ WHEN $\overline{X}_\wp$ AND σ ARE KNOWN

A difference between $\overline{X}$ and $\overline{X}_\wp$ that is not significant. Consider the tire-mileage data referred to previously for which $\overline{X}_\wp = 15,200$ miles and $\sigma = 1,248$ miles. If random samples of 100 tires are to be drawn, we would expect the sample means to have

$$\sigma_{\bar{x}} = \frac{\sigma}{\sqrt{N}} = \frac{1,248}{\sqrt{100}} = 124.8 \text{ miles.}$$

Consequently, the sample means would be distributed as shown in Chart 24.7. In this chart, particular attention has been called to the deviations of $\pm 1.96\sigma_{\bar{x}}$ and $\pm 2.58\sigma_{\bar{x}}$. As may be seen from the chart, $\pm 1.96\sigma_{\bar{x}}$ cuts off 5 per cent of the area of the curve in the two tails, while $\pm 2.58\sigma_{\bar{x}}$ cuts off 1 per cent of the area of the curve in the two tails. These percentages may be obtained from the table of areas of the normal curve (Appendix E) which we used in the preceding chapter or, more readily, from Appendix H, which shows areas in two tails of the normal curve. The two deviations shown in Chart 24.7 are those which denote, for the normal curve, the 0.05 level and the 0.01 level. Significance tests make frequent use of the 0.05 and 0.01 levels, although other levels—for example, 0.001, 0.005, 0.02, and 0.025—are also employed.

One sample of 100 items, allegedly a random sample and supposedly drawn from the population mentioned in the preceding paragraph, was found to have $\bar{X} = 15,269$ miles. We are interested in knowing whether it is reasonable to believe that this sample mean is the arithmetic mean of a random sample from the population having $\bar{X}_\wp = 15,200$ miles and $\sigma = 1,248$ miles. The difference between $\bar{X}$ and $\bar{X}_\wp$ is 69 miles. In order to be able to refer to the normal curve, we express this difference in terms of $\sigma_{\bar{x}}$, which has already been ascertained to be 124.8 miles.

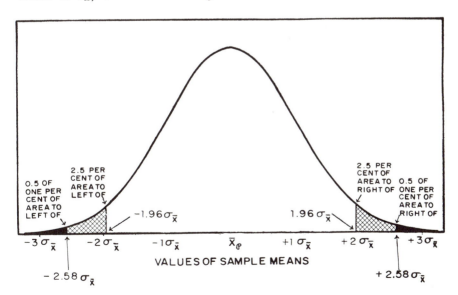

Chart 24.7. Expected Distribution of Sample Arithmetic Means, From a Normal Population, Showing the 0.05 and 0.01 Levels.

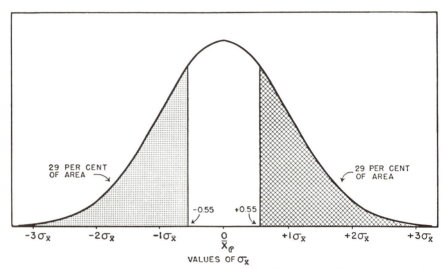

29 PER CENT OF AREA

29 PER CENT OF AREA

-0.55   +0.55

$-3\sigma_{\bar{x}}$ $-2\sigma_{\bar{x}}$ $-1\sigma_{\bar{x}}$ 0 $+1\sigma_{\bar{x}}$ $+2\sigma_{\bar{x}}$ $+3\sigma_{\bar{x}}$

$\bar{X}_\varphi$

VALUES OF $\sigma_{\bar{x}}$

Chart 24.8. Expected Distribution of Sample Means and Chances of Obtaining Sample Means Differing From $\bar{X}_\varphi$ by $\pm 0.55\sigma_{\bar{x}}$ or More.

Therefore,

$$\frac{x}{\sigma} = \frac{\bar{X} - \bar{X}_\varphi}{\sigma_{\bar{x}}} = \frac{15,269 - 15,200}{124.8} = \frac{69}{124.8} = 0.55.$$

Referring to Chart 24.8, we may see the area under the normal curve (the cross-hatched portion) which is cut off by a deviation of $+0.55\sigma_{\bar{x}}$. From Appendix G, which shows areas in one tail of the normal curve, this cross-hatched tail is found to include 29 per cent of the area under the curve. Since we know that sample means both exceed and fall below $\bar{X}_\varphi$, we consider also the tail of the normal curve cut off by $-0.55\sigma_{\bar{x}}$, which is the stippled portion in Chart 24.8. This tail, too, includes 29 per cent of the area under the curve, and the two tails combined contain 58 per cent ($P = 0.58$) of the area under the curve. From this we conclude that, since a difference of $\pm 0.55\sigma_{\bar{x}}$ may occur so frequently through the operations of random sampling, there is no adequate basis for thinking that the sample mean was not the mean of a random sample from the population under consideration.

The foregoing involved setting up the hypothesis that the sample mean was the mean of a random sample from the population having $\bar{X}_\varphi = 15,200$ miles and $\sigma = 1,248$ miles. This hypothesis is referred to as a "null hypothesis," since it is a hypothesis of no difference between $\bar{X}$ and $\bar{X}_\varphi$. The next step consisted of testing the hypothesis by computing a significance ratio $\frac{x}{\sigma}$ and determining the probability of obtaining a deviation equal to or greater than that observed, as a result of random sampling. Our test casts much doubt (if P is small) or little doubt (if P is large) on the hypothesis. Since P was found to be 0.55, our hypothesis was not impugned.

Note that we did not "prove" the hypothesis. Statistically, a hypothesis can never be "proven" or "disproven." By means of repeated experiments which always yield consistent differences, or lack of them, an investigator might eventually consider a hypothesis false or valid. Statistical tests, however, can merely cast much or little doubt upon a hypothesis, thus discrediting or failing to discredit the hypothesis.

A difference between $\overline{X}$ and $\overline{X}_{\varphi}$ that is significant. Consider another sample of 100 tires having $\overline{X} = 14{,}738$ miles. To test the hypothesis that this mean is the mean of a random sample from the population having $\overline{X}_{\varphi} = 15{,}200$ miles and $\sigma = 1{,}248$ miles, we compute

$$\frac{x}{\sigma} = \frac{\overline{X} - \overline{X}_{\varphi}}{\sigma_{\bar{x}}} = \frac{14{,}738 - 15{,}200}{124.8} = \frac{462}{124.8} = 3.70.$$

Referring to Appendix H, which shows areas in two tails of the normal curve, we find that $P = 0.000216$. This is pictured in Chart 24.9. Since a difference such as that observed could be expected to occur so infrequently as a result of random sampling, the null hypothesis is not tenable. The sample mean may have been the mean of a non-random sample from the population under consideration, it may have been the mean of a random sample from a different population, or it may have been the mean of a non-random sample from a different population. In any event, we feel justified in declaring that it is not (that is, it is extremely unlikely to be) the mean of a random sample from the population having $\overline{X}_{\varphi} = 15{,}200$ miles and $\sigma = 1{,}248$ miles.

The two tests which we have made were both two-tail (or two-sided) tests, since we considered either plus or minus differences as tending to discredit the null hypothesis. Sometimes, as we shall see in later portions of this text, a positive divergence will tend to discredit a hypothesis, while a negative difference will not; in such a case, we should consider only the area in the right tail of the appropriate curve. When a negative difference tends to discredit a hypothesis, but a positive difference does not, we take cognizance of the area in the left tail of the curve.[7]

The value of P and significance. We have just considered two differences, one of which was declared "significant" and one "not-significant." These examples were purposely selected to illustrate conclusions that would be obvious once P had been determined. How small should be the value of P in order for a difference to be declared significant? This is not an easy question to answer, since the answer depends largely

---

[7] There are also situations in which we may wish to make a two-tail test with unequal areas in the two tails. For a more advanced discussion of hypotheses testing, see Kendall and Stuart, *op. cit.*, Chaps. 22 and 23.

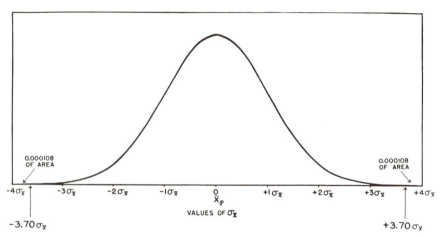

0.000108
OF AREA

0.000108
OF AREA

-4σ_x̄   -3σ_x̄   -2σ_x̄   -1σ_x̄   0 X̄_φ   +1σ_x̄   +2σ_x̄   +3σ_x̄   +4σ_x̄

VALUES OF σ_x̄

-3.70σ_x̄   +3.70σ_x̄

Chart 24.9. Expected Distribution of Sample Means and Chances of Obtaining Sample Means Differing from $\overline{X}_\varphi$ by $\pm 3.70\sigma_{\overline{X}}$ or More.

upon the nature of the phenomenon being considered and the consequences of being wrong.

For the sample having $\overline{X} = 14{,}738$ miles, we found P to be 0.000216 and considered the null hypothesis to be discredited. Actually, it is possible that the hypothesis was true and our conclusion wrong, since random samples would show a deviation equal to or greater than $3.70\sigma_{\bar{x}}$ exactly 216 times in a million.

Type I errors. When a null hypothesis is actually true, and when the difference under consideration is declared not significant (that is, the hypothesis is not impugned), the conclusion is correct. When a null hypothesis is actually true, but when the difference involved is declared significant (that is, the hypothesis is discredited), we say that a "Type I error" has been made. If we use $P = 0.05$ as our criterion of significance, declaring significant all differences having $P \leqq 0.05$, we shall make exactly 1 out of 20 Type I errors in the long run; if we use $P = 0.01$ as our criterion of significance, declaring significant all differences having $P \leqq 0.01$, we will make 1 out of 100 Type I errors in the long run. It must be clear that, the lower the value of P which is used as a criterion, the fewer Type I errors that will be made. Unfortunately, decreasing the proportion of Type I errors serves to increase the sort of error described in the next paragraph.

Type II errors. When a null hypothesis is actually false and when the difference under consideration is declared significant, the conclusion is correct. When a null hypothesis is actually false, but when the difference being examined is declared not significant, we say that a "Type II error" has been made. If we use $P = 0.05$ as the criterion, we cannot say how frequently Type II errors will occur, since we cannot know how false the hypothesis may be.   The sample (or samples) may be a non-random one from the population involved, or the sample may be a random or non-random one from a population other than the one involved.   In this situation, we can merely say that, if we use $P = 0.05$ as a criterion, we should expect to make fewer Type II errors than if $P = 0.01$ is employed.[8]

Choice of criterion.   For practical purposes, the probability which is to serve as the criterion of significance should be chosen in the light of the type of error which should be avoided.   If Type I errors should be as few as possible, P should be very small.   If Type II errors should be few, P should be larger.   Consider the following examples:

An agricultural experiment station has developed a new hay crop which is believed to be superior to existing crops, such as alfalfa, lespedeza, clover, and the like.   In order for a farmer to raise the new crop, he must invest heavily in special machinery for sowing the seed and for harvesting. If, in the comparison of the new crop with the present crops, a Type I error were made, farmers who planted the new crop would incur heavy expenses but would find the new hay to be no better than that formerly fed to their stock.   As a result, the farmers would have experienced heavy losses.   If a Type II error were made, the new crop, though better, would not be introduced and, while farmers would have failed to gain the advantages that would have resulted, they would have incurred no actual loss.

---

[8] We may, however, state the probability of Type II errors if we set up an alternative hypothesis.   The left curve in the accompanying diagram represents a test (using 0.05 in the right tail as the criterion) of the hypothesis that $\bar{X}$ is the mean of a random sample from a population having $\bar{X}_\wp$ as its mean, only positive values of $\bar{X} - \bar{X}_\wp$ serving to discredit the hypothesis.

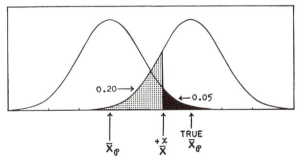

Any value of $\bar{X}$ falling between $-\infty$ and $+x$ would cause us to accept the hypothesis. If the *true value* of $\bar{X}_\wp$ is that shown at the center of the right curve, then the probability of a Type II error is represented by the shaded area, which is about 0.20.   Other alternative hypotheses may also be set up.   Note that if the *true* $\bar{X}_\wp$ is farther to the right, the probability of Type II errors is decreased; if the *true* $\bar{X}_\wp$ is farther to the left, the probability of Type II errors is increased.   From the chart it is also clear that, if the black area (representing the probability of Type I errors if $\bar{X}_\wp$ at the left is the *true* mean) is decreased, the probability of Type II errors (if the *true* $\bar{X}_\wp$ is as noted on the chart) is increased; if the black area is increased, the shaded area is decreased.

In such a situation as this, P should be very small, say 0.01 or 0.001, to warrant one in declaring the observed difference to be significant.

One year, the United States Food and Drug Administration acted against a chemical manufacturing concern, alleging that digitalis sold by the firm was half-strength. The difficulty said to be involved was that persons using this digitalis and becoming accustomed to it might experience serious consequences if they shifted to a full-strength digitalis. In the case of a drug such as this, it is important that the day-to-day production be kept in conformance with the standard (population). As tests are made of each batch, it is essential that no batch should be appreciably stronger or weaker than the population. If, in testing a batch, a Type I error were made (that is, if the batch is said to differ significantly from the population when it actually does not), the result would be that the batch would be discarded or reprocessed. On the other hand, if a Type II error were made, we would be stating that the batch did not differ significantly from the population when a real difference was actually present, and serious harm, even death, might result to persons using the drug. In such a situation it is clearly more important to avoid Type II errors than Type I errors, and P should therefore be fairly large, say 0.10 or, preferably, larger.

There will be frequent occasions when one cannot say whether Type I or Type II errors are more serious. If one is testing the difference of the mean IQ's of male cooks and of male dishwashers,[9] such a situation arises. Here the investigator might be satisfied to use $P = 0.05$ as a criterion.

From the foregoing it should be clear that the same value of P should not be used as a criterion for all tests. The appropriate level will depend on the circumstances. One should never state that a result is significant or not significant without also giving the value of P, which may ordinarily be read with sufficient accuracy from existing tables, interpolation being rarely called for. Alternatively, one may say: "significant at the 0.01 (or other) level." Sometimes an investigator will say: "Significant at the 0.05 (or other) level but not significant at the 0.02 (or other) level." Stating the value of P allows the reader to draw his own conclusion concerning significance.

Another important consideration is the desirability of deciding, in advance of attacking a problem, the criterion of significance that will be used. This avoids the possibility that the P value which is obtained may influence one in setting his criterion. This is particularly likely to happen if one "hopes" for a significant or non-significant difference.

Probability and everyday occurrences. The reader may feel that the conclusions regarding significance and based upon probabilities involve a new basis of thinking which he has not encountered before.

---

[9] Differences between two samples means are disussed on pages 560–565.

This may be true, in that we are using some of the most elementary ideas of mathematical probability.[10] However, basing decisions upon probability of some sort has been an everyday occurrence throughout everyone's life. The student studying for an examination considers the parts of the course about which the instructor is likely to ask questions and the portions not likely to be covered in the examination. This crude subjective sort of probability serves as a guide to him as he reviews. The baseball coach must consider the chances (or "play the percentages," as the radio commentators say) before he orders a squeeze play or before he puts in a right-handed batting pinch hitter, batting at 0.240, to replace a left-handed batting regular, batting at 0.290, to face a left-handed pitcher. Before one approaches his boss for a raise, he usually considers whether today, tomorrow, or some other day will likely be most propitious. On a much larger scale, unions are not likely to demand wage increases during the slackest months of the year or during a depression. Similarly, utilities are not apt to ask for rate increases when business is in the doldrums.

Size of sample. Occasionally one may wish to know the sample size which will give a specified degree of assurance that sample means will fall within designated limits. For the data of tire mileage, where $\overline{X}_{\wp} = $ 15,200 miles and $\sigma = 1,248$ miles, what sample size would result in sample means varying within ± 200 miles for 98 out of 100 samples? The answer is obtained by substituting in the expression

$$\frac{x}{\sigma} = \frac{\overline{X} - \overline{X}_{\wp}}{\sigma_{\bar{x}}}$$

the known and designated values and the value of $\dfrac{x}{\sigma}$ (from Appendix H or the last row of Appendix I) which cuts off two tails which include two per cent of the area of the normal curve. Since the $\dfrac{x}{\sigma}$ value is 2.326, we have

$$2.326 = \frac{200}{\dfrac{1,248}{\sqrt{N}}}.$$

$$200\sqrt{N} = (2.326)(1,248) = 2,902.8.$$

$$\sqrt{N} = 14.5.$$

$$N = 210.$$

SIGNIFICANCE OF THE DIFFERENCE BETWEEN $\overline{X}$ AND $\overline{X}_{\wp}$ WHEN σ IS NOT KNOWN

The preceding discussion has dealt only with the procedure which is

---

[10] See, for example, Mood and Graybill, *op. cit.*, pp. 6–52.

applicable when $\bar{X}_p$ and σ are known. It is very unusual for population values to be available. This will be obvious if we enumerate the most important conditions under which population values may be known. They are:

(1) A complete census may have been taken. Thus, from the most recent United States census $\bar{X}$ and σ could be computed for ages of all persons enumerated. (Note that the rounding tendency, mentioned on pages 20–21, would affect the accuracy of these, or any other, age figures not based on correctly reported dates of birth.)

(2) Population values may be known as the result of extensive experience. This is the type of situation illustrated by the tire-mileage data.

(3) Much like the preceding is the setting up of a "control population" to serve as a standard in quality control. Here, many units are manufactured under carefully controlled conditions, and the statistical values computed from these units are treated as population data. Day-to-day production figures are then compared with the population data.

(4) Population values may be known or assumed upon the basis of hypothesis or theory. Cases are encountered most frequently when dealing with proportions rather than means. In a test to ascertain

TABLE 24.1

Breaking Strength of 10 Specimens of 0.104-Inch Diameter Hard-drawn Copper Wire

Specimen	Breaking strength in pounds X	X^2
1	578	334,084
2	572	327,184
3	570	324,900
4	568	322,624
5	572	327,184
6	570	324,900
7	570	324,900
8	572	327,184
9	596	355,216
10	584	341,056
Total	5,752	3,309,232

Data from American Society for Testing Materials, *Supplements to 1933 A.S.T.M. Manual on Presentation of Data*, "Supplement A—Presenting Plus and Minus Limits of Uncertainty of an Observed Average," p. 1, reprinted from Proceedings of the American Society for Testing Materials, Vol. 35, Part 1, Philadelphia.

$$\bar{X} = \frac{5752}{10} = 575.2 \text{ pounds.}$$

$$\hat{\sigma} = \sqrt{\frac{3,309,232}{9} - \frac{(5752)^2}{10 \cdot 9}},$$

$$= \sqrt{75.73} = 8.70 \text{ pounds.}$$

whether tea drinkers could differentiate between tea sweetened with sugar and with saccharine, the population proportions might be assumed to be 0.50 for each sweetening agent. In a preference test for four brands of coffee, the population proportions would be taken as 0.25 for each brand.

A difference between $\overline{X}$ and $\overline{X}_\wp$ that is not significant. Tests have been made of the breaking strength of ten pieces of hard-drawn copper wire, as shown in Table 24.1. The arithmetic mean of the ten values is 575.2 pounds. With 0.01 as our criterion, let us test the hypothesis that $\overline{X} = 575.2$ pounds is the mean of a random sample from a population having $\overline{X}_\wp = 577.0$ pounds. Now we do not know σ, and, since we lack σ, we must make an estimate of σ from the data of the sample. This estimate is obtained from the expression[11]

$$\hat{\sigma} = \sqrt{\frac{\Sigma x^2}{N-1}},$$

$$= \sqrt{\frac{\Sigma X^2}{N-1} - \frac{(\Sigma X)^2}{N(N-1)}} \text{ for ungrouped data,}$$

$$= i\sqrt{\frac{\Sigma f(d')^2}{N-1} - \frac{(\Sigma fd')^2}{N(N-1)}} \text{ for grouped data.}$$

$\hat{\sigma}^2$ is called an "unbiased" estimate of σ^2, since[12]

$$\frac{\hat{\sigma}_1^2 + \hat{\sigma}_2^2 + \cdots + \hat{\sigma}_K^2}{K} = \sigma^2.$$

s^2 is not an unbiased estimate of σ^2, since

$$\frac{s_1^2 + s_2^2 + \cdots + s_K^2}{K} < \sigma^2.$$

Now that we have $\hat{\sigma}$, we are in a position to make an estimate of $\sigma_{\overline{X}}$.

---

[11] The basic expression for $\hat{\sigma}$ is developed in Appendix S, section 24.3. The forms for ungrouped and for grouped data are obtained from this basic expression by the same procedure as that given in Appendix S, section 10.2.

[12] See Appendix S, section 24.3.

This is[13]

$$\hat{\sigma}_{\bar{x}} = \frac{\hat{\sigma}}{\sqrt{N}}.$$

For the data of breaking strength of copper wire, the computation of $\hat{\sigma}$ is shown below Table 24.1, and

$$\hat{\sigma}_{\bar{x}} = \frac{8.70}{\sqrt{10}} = 2.75 \text{ pounds.}$$

We may now compute the significance ratio

$$\frac{\bar{X} - \bar{X}_{\wp}}{\hat{\sigma}_{\bar{x}}}.$$

This significance ratio differs from those previously used because the denominator is an estimate of $\sigma_{\bar{x}}$. Because of this substitution, we are no longer in a position to refer to the normal curve, but must make use of the t distribution, which, though symmetrical, is more widely dispersed than is the normal curve. This may be seen in Chart 24.10. The spread of the t distribution depends upon the number of "degrees of freedom" (n) present, the dispersion being greatest for $n = 1$ and decreasing as n increases. As n approaches infinity, the t distribution approaches the normal distribution as a limit. This tendency is apparent from a look at Chart 24.10. For significance tests involving a single sample mean, such as the one under consideration, $n = N - 1$ because we used the deviations of N values about their own mean in order to compute $\hat{\sigma}$. In other words, we employed, not N, but $N - 1$ independent deviations.

For the data of breaking strength of copper wire,

$$t = \frac{\bar{X} - \bar{X}_{\wp}}{\hat{\sigma}_{\bar{x}}} = \frac{575.2 - 577.0}{2.75} = \frac{1.8}{2.75} = 0.65.$$

The value of P is ascertained by referring to Appendix I for $n = N - 1 = 10 - 1 = 9$ and $t = 0.65$. This appendix table is somewhat different from the preceding table of the normal curve. Both tables show areas in two tails of the respective distributions, but Appendix H shows values

---

[13] If s is known for a sample, it may be converted into $\hat{\sigma}$ by use of

$$\hat{\sigma} = \sqrt{\frac{N}{N-1}}\, s.$$

However, such a conversion is not necessary, since we can write

$$\hat{\sigma}_{\bar{x}} = \frac{s}{\sqrt{N-1}}.$$

It must be clear that, as N increases, the numerical difference between s and $\hat{\sigma}$ becomes of negligible importance. Nevertheless, it is incorrect to use s as an estimate of σ.

of P for selected values of $\dfrac{x}{\sigma}$, while Appendix I shows values of t for specified values of n and P.   From Appendix I it is seen that $0.50 < P < 0.60$, and we conclude that there is no significant difference between $\bar{X}$ and $\bar{X}_\varphi$. Chart 24.11, which shows a t distribution for 9 degrees of freedom, illustrates what has been done.

A difference between $\bar{X}$ and $\bar{X}_\varphi$ that is significant.   Norman C. Wiley[14] gives data of tests of strength of three-inch manila rope, showing, for one sample, $N = 16$, $\bar{X} = 9{,}959$ pounds, and $s = 248$ pounds.   Using the 0.01 level as a criterion, we shall test the hypothesis that $\bar{X} = 9{,}959$ pounds is the mean of a random sample from a population having $\bar{X}_\varphi = 10{,}148$ pounds.   In order to obtain $\hat{\sigma}_{\bar{x}}$, we make use of the expression given in footnote 13,

$$\hat{\sigma}_{\bar{x}} = \frac{s}{\sqrt{N-1}} = \frac{248}{\sqrt{15}} = \frac{248}{3.873} = 64.03.$$

Then we compute

$$t = \frac{\bar{X} - \bar{X}_\varphi}{\hat{\sigma}_{\bar{x}}} = \frac{9{,}959 - 10{,}148}{64.03}$$

$$= \frac{189}{64.03} = 2.95.$$

From the t table of Appendix I, it appears that P is almost exactly 0.01, and we reject the hypothesis.   The foregoing is shown graphically in Chart 24.12.   Note that, if we had used the normal table of Appendix H, the probability would have been misleadingly small, about 0.003!   The difference in the two probabilities would have been much less if the sample had been larger.   As may be seen in Chart 24.10 and in Appendix I, the t distribution seems to begin to approximate the normal distribution at about $n = 20$.   Some statisticians customarily refer to the normal table when $n \geqq 30$, but this seems to have been due to the fact that, for some time, the available t tables gave no values of t between $n = 30$ and $n = \infty$.   Appendix I lists t values for $n = 30, 40, 60, 120$, and ∞.   It is best to use the t table in all cases where $\hat{\sigma}$ has been used as an estimate of σ.

Confidence limits of $\bar{X}_\varphi$.   In the illustration just given, it was concluded that the sample mean was not the mean of a random sample from a population having $\bar{X}_\varphi = 10{,}148$ pounds.   From a knowledge of the sample alone, what can be said about the limits within which $\bar{X}_\varphi$ may be expected to occur?   We want two values for $\bar{X}_\varphi$, which we shall call $\bar{X}_{\varphi_1}$ and $\bar{X}_{\varphi_2}$ and which will be, respectively, smaller than and larger than

---

[14] The sample data are from *Statistical Methods as an Aid in Revising Specifications*, by N. C. Wiley, a preprint of a paper delivered at the forty-first annual meeting of the American Society for Testing Materials.

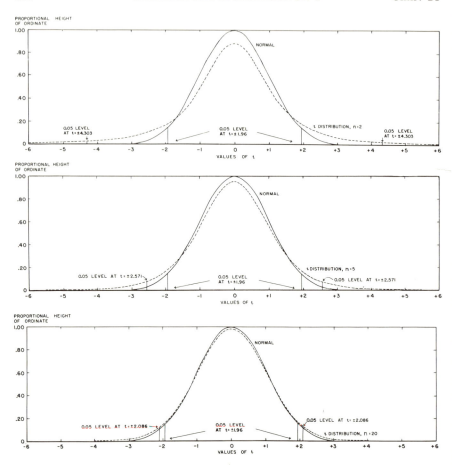

Chart 24.10. Comparison of the t Distribution for $n = 2$, $n = 5$, and $n = 20$ with the Normal Distribution. The values of t, shown above, are $\frac{z}{\sigma}$ values for the normal curve. The ordinates of the t distribution are obtained from the expression

$$Y_c = \sqrt{\frac{2}{n}} \frac{\left(\dfrac{n-1}{2}\right)!}{\left(\dfrac{n-2}{2}\right)!} \frac{1}{\left(1 + \dfrac{t^2}{n}\right)^{\frac{n+1}{2}}}.$$

This gives a maximum ordinate which approaches 1.0 as n approaches infinity, and thus is comparable to the expression

$$Y_c = e^{\frac{-x^2}{2\sigma^2}}$$

for the normal curve. The computation of $\dfrac{\left(\dfrac{n-1}{2}\right)!}{\left(\dfrac{n-2}{2}\right)!}$ may be clarified by an illustra-

tion. If $n = 11$, the numerator is 5!, while the denominator is 4.5 . The value of 4.5! is given by $4.5 \times 3.5 \times 2.5 \times 1.5 \times 0.5 \times \sqrt{\pi}$.

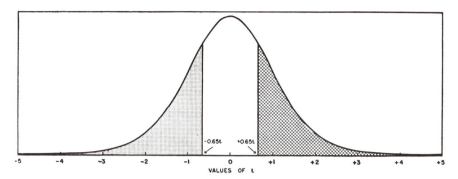

Chart 24.11. The *t* Distribution for *n* = 9, Showing Probability of Obtaining *t* = ±0.65 or More. Between 0.50 and 0.60 of the area under the curve is in the two tails.

$\overline{X}$. These are the "confidence limits" of $\overline{X}_{\wp}$. The first step consists of deciding how often we are willing to be wrong in our statement of confidence limits. Suppose that we can allow ourselves to be wrong not more than 5 times in 100. In that case, we want the 95 per cent confidence limits. These limits are obtained by determining:

(1) the value of $\overline{X}_{\wp_1}$, so located that $\overline{X}$ cuts off the *upper* $2\frac{1}{2}$ per cent tail of the distribution of sample means around $\overline{X}_{\wp_1}$, and

(2) the value of $\overline{X}_{\wp_2}$, so located that $\overline{X}$ cuts off the *lower* $2\frac{1}{2}$ per cent tail of the distribution of sample means around $\overline{X}_{\wp_2}$.

Both of these values may be had from the following expression, in which we substitute the already computed values of $\overline{X}$ and $\hat{\sigma}_{\overline{x}}$ and the *t* value for the appropriate confidence limits:

$$\overline{X} = \overline{X}_{\wp} \pm t\hat{\sigma}_{\overline{x}}.$$

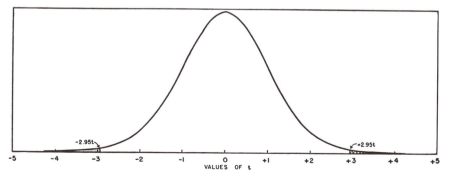

Chart 24.12. The *t* Distribution for *n* = 15, Showing Probability of Obtaining *t* = ±2.95 or More. Almost exactly 0.01 of the area under the curve is in the two tails.

Since we want the 95 per cent confidence limits, and since $n = 15$, the value of t (from Appendix I) is 2.131. We have, then

$$9,959 = \overline{X}_\varphi \pm (2.131)(64.03).$$
$$\overline{X}_\varphi = 9,959 \pm 136.4,$$
$$= 9,822.6 \text{ and } 10,095.4 \text{ pounds.}$$

The foregoing procedure is illustrated in Chart 24.13.

We are not *sure* that the population mean falls within the limits just given, but we are 95 per cent confident that it does so. In other words, if many determinations of 95 per cent confidence limits are made, we can expect those limits to include the population value 95 times out of 100 and to exclude the population value 5 times in 100. Roger P. Doyle computed the 95 per cent confidence limits of $\overline{X}_\varphi$ for each of Shewhart's 1,000 samples from a normal population. Using $\overline{X}, \hat{\sigma},$ and $n = 3$ for each sample, he ascertained 1,000 pairs of confidence limits and noted, for each pair, whether they did or did not include $\overline{X}_\varphi = 0$. His confidence limits were right in 951 instances, wrong in 49.

While the preceding illustration obtained 95 per cent confidence limits, any desired limits may be computed, by merely substituting the appropriate t value, together with the values of $\overline{X}$ and $\hat{\sigma}_{\bar{x}}$ obtained from the sample. Limits such as 99.9, 99.8, 99, 98, 96, 95, and 90 are often used. Confidence limits representing less than 90 per cent confidence are not often wanted, since they do not express a very high degree of confidence.

The determination of confidence limits for proportions, sample variances (s^2 or $\hat{\sigma}^2$), and correlation coefficients will be discussed in the two following chapters. For these measures, as well as for arithmetic means, the statistical worker should carefully consider the maximum and minimum *possible* values for the measure in question. Occasionally, the very nature of the variable sets limits, beyond which values cannot occur, and which should take precedence over computed confidence limits.

The expression for determining the confidence limits of $\overline{X}_\varphi$ was written

$$\overline{X} = \overline{X}_\varphi \pm t\hat{\sigma}_{\bar{x}},$$

rather than

$$\overline{X}_\varphi = \overline{X} \pm t\hat{\sigma}_{\bar{x}},$$

which would have given the same results. The purpose of doing this was to stress the fact that sample means are distributed around $\overline{X}_\varphi$. Chart 24.13 also attempts to make this clear. There is no such thing as a distribution of population means around $\overline{X}$.

The illustrations given on the preceding 7 pages all involved $\hat{\sigma}_{\bar{x}}$ and the t distribution. It may be well to stress the point that variations in the value of t occur because of sampling variations of $\hat{\sigma}$ as well as because

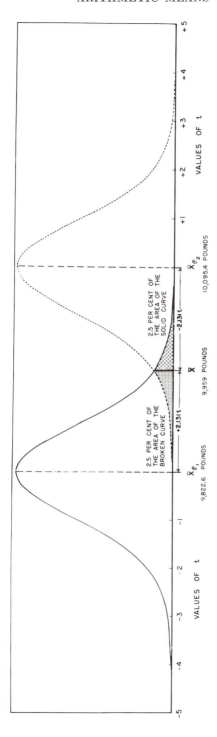

Chart 24.13.   The 95 Per Cent Confidence Limits for $\bar{X}_\varphi$ for Strength of Three-Inch Manila Rope, $n = 15$.

of sampling variations of $\bar{X}$. A large value of t (and therefore a small P value) may result from the fact that $\bar{X}$ differs greatly from $\bar{X}_\varphi$, or because $\hat{\sigma}$ is smaller than σ, or both. A small value of t (and therefore a large P value) may occur because $\bar{X}$ closely approximates $\bar{X}_\varphi$, or because $\hat{\sigma}$ exceeds σ, or both. When σ is known, the only sampling variations present are those of $\bar{X}$.

SIGNIFICANCE OF THE DIFFERENCE BETWEEN TWO SAMPLE MEANS

Independent samples. From archaeological excavations conducted at a certain site, 16 lower first molars were recovered.[15] We do not have the measurements of each of the 16 teeth, but we know that $\bar{X}_1 = 13.57$ millimeters and $s_1 = 0.72$ millimeters. From a nearby site, 9 lower first molars were taken with $\bar{X}_2 = 13.06$ and $s_2 = 0.62$ millimeters. Using $P = 0.05$ as a criterion, is there a significant difference in the mean length of these two groups of lower first molars? To make this test, we set up the null hypothesis that the two sample means are from the same population in regard to $\bar{X}_\varphi$, and we test this hypothesis by determining the probability of t, where t is the ratio of $\bar{X}_1 - \bar{X}_2$ to an estimate of the standard error of the difference between the two sample means.

As shown in Appendix S, section 24.4, the standard error of the difference between two sample means $\sigma_{\bar{X}_1-\bar{X}_2}$ is given by

$$\sigma_{\bar{X}_1-\bar{X}_2} = \sqrt{\sigma_{\bar{X}_1}^2 + \sigma_{\bar{X}_2}^2},$$

provided that the two samples are independent. Non-independent samples are considered later in this chapter. The expression just given may be written[16]

$$\sigma_{\bar{X}_1-\bar{X}_2} = \sqrt{\frac{\sigma^2}{N_1} + \frac{\sigma^2}{N_2}} = \sigma\sqrt{\frac{1}{N_1} + \frac{1}{N_2}}.$$

We cannot make use of this formula for our problem, since we do not know the value of σ. (If we knew σ, we would almost certainly know $\bar{X}_\varphi$ as well, since σ is computed around $\bar{X}_\varphi$. If we knew $\bar{X}_\varphi$, it would be more meaningful to compare $\bar{X}_1$ and $\bar{X}_2$ with $\bar{X}_\varphi$ than to compare the two sample means with each other.) Consequently, we make an estimate of

---

[15] Based upon illustrative figures used in a lecture by Professor Egon Pearson at Columbia University.

[16] The assumption is made that the two samples are from the same population in regard to variance, σ^2. This assumption is not unreasonable for our problem, since an F test, described in Chapter 26, reveals that there is not a significant difference between $\hat{\sigma}_1^2$ and $\hat{\sigma}_2^2$. When two samples are believed to be from populations of unequal variance, and when $N_1 = N_2$, or when $N_1 \approx N_2$ and both are large, an approximate test may be made by using

$$\hat{\sigma}_{\bar{X}_1-\bar{X}_2} = \sqrt{\frac{\hat{\sigma}_1^2}{N_1} + \frac{\hat{\sigma}_2^2}{N_2}}.$$

the value of σ, from the information given by the two samples. This estimate[17] is

$$\hat{\sigma}_{1+2} = \sqrt{\frac{\Sigma x_1^2 + \Sigma x_2^2}{N_1 - 1 + N_2 - 1}}.$$

When the individual observations are available for each sample, as is usually the case, we may compute

$$\Sigma x^2 = \Sigma X^2 - \frac{(\Sigma X)^2}{N} \qquad \text{for ungrouped data, or}$$

$$\Sigma x^2 = i^2 \left[\Sigma f(d')^2 - \frac{(\Sigma f d')^2}{N} \right] \qquad \text{for grouped data.}$$

For the problem at hand, we do not have the individual observations, but we do have s_1 and s_2. Since

$$s_1 = \sqrt{\frac{\Sigma x_1^2}{N_1}} \qquad \text{and} \qquad s_2 = \sqrt{\frac{\Sigma x_2^2}{N_2}},$$

$$\Sigma x_1^2 = N_1 s_1^2 \qquad \text{and} \qquad \Sigma x_2^2 = N_2 s_2^2.$$

We therefore compute

$$\Sigma x_1^2 = 16(0.72)^2 = 8.29;$$
$$\Sigma x_2^2 = 9(0.62)^2 = 3.46.$$

The estimated value of σ is then obtained.

$$\hat{\sigma}_{1+2} = \sqrt{\frac{8.29 + 3.46}{16 - 1 + 9 - 1}} = 0.715.$$

The estimated standard error of the difference between the two means may now be computed:

$$\hat{\sigma}_{\bar{X}_1 - \bar{X}_2} = \hat{\sigma}_{1+2} \sqrt{\frac{1}{N_1} + \frac{1}{N_2}},$$

$$= 0.715 \sqrt{\tfrac{1}{16} + \tfrac{1}{9}} = 0.298.$$

---

[17] $\hat{\sigma}_{1+2}^2$ is a weighted average of the two $\hat{\sigma}^2$ values for the separate samples. See Appendix S, section 24.5. Section 24.6 shows that when $N_1 = N_2$,

$$\hat{\sigma}_{1+2} \sqrt{\frac{1}{N_1} + \frac{1}{N_2}} = \sqrt{\frac{\hat{\sigma}_1^2}{N_1} + \frac{\hat{\sigma}_2^2}{N_2}}.$$

When more than two samples are involved, the estimate of σ^2 is given by

$$\frac{\Sigma x_1^2 + \Sigma x_2^2 + \Sigma x_3^2 + \cdots}{N_1 - 1 + N_2 - 1 + N_3 - 1 + \cdots}.$$

We shall make use of this expression in connection with the discussion of analysis of variance in Chapter 26.

Finally we may obtain the desired significance ratio,

$$t = \frac{\bar{X}_1 - \bar{X}_2}{\hat{\sigma}_{\bar{X}_1-\bar{X}_2}} = \frac{13.57 - 13.06}{0.298} = \frac{0.51}{0.298} = 1.71.$$

From the first set of data, we have $n_1 = N_1 - 1 = 16 - 1 = 15$ degrees of freedom; from the second set, $n_2 = N_2 - 1 = 9 - 1 = 8$. Therefore, $n = n_1 + n_2 = 23$. Note that one degree of freedom was lost when Σx_1^2 was computed about $\bar{X}_1$ and another degree was lost when Σx_2^2 was computed about $\bar{X}_2$. From the t table of Appendix I, we find $P \approx 0.10$, and we consider the difference between $\bar{X}_1$ and $\bar{X}_2$ not significant. Chart 24.14 illustrates the foregoing.

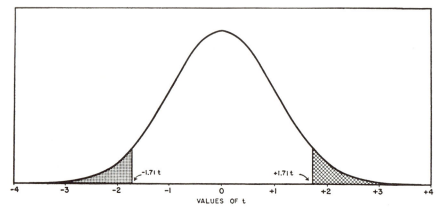

Chart 24.14. The t Distribution for $n = 23$, Showing Probability of Obtaining $t = \pm 1.71$ or More. Approximately 0.10 of the area under the curve is in the two tails.

Confidence limits of $\bar{X}_{\wp_1} - \bar{X}_{\wp_2}$. Occasionally, when it has been concluded that a significant difference exists between $\bar{X}_1$ and $\bar{X}_2$, it may be desirable to have a statement of the confidence limits of $\bar{X}_{\wp_1} - \bar{X}_{\wp_2}$. This is obtained by solving the expression[18]

$$\bar{X}_1 - \bar{X}_2 = (\bar{X}_{\wp_1} - \bar{X}_{\wp_2}) \pm t\hat{\sigma}_{\bar{X}_1-\bar{X}_2}$$

for $\bar{X}_{\wp_1} - \bar{X}_{\wp_2}$. As in the determination of confidence limits for $\bar{X}_{\wp}$, the value of t is read from Appendix I and depends upon (1) the level of confidence to be used and (2) the degrees of freedom, which are $n = N_1 - 1 + N_2 - 1$.

To illustrate the use of the expression given above, consider the yield point of structural steel (for ships) obtained from two sources. For source 1: $N_1 = 10$, $\bar{X}_1 = 45{,}948$ pounds per square inch, and $s_1 = 2{,}910$ pounds per square inch. For source 2: $N_2 = 19$, $\bar{X}_2 = 39{,}820$ pounds per square inch, and $s_2 = 2{,}510$ pounds per square inch.[19] Employing the

---

[18] As in testing the significance of the difference between $\bar{X}_1$ and $\bar{X}_2$, it is assumed that the two samples are from the same population in regard to σ^2.

[19] The data are from the source given in footnote 14.

same expressions just used for the data of lower first molars, it is found that $\hat{\sigma}_{\bar{X}_1-\bar{X}_2} = 1{,}074.9$ and

$$t = \frac{\bar{X}_1 - \bar{X}_2}{\hat{\sigma}_{\bar{X}_1-\bar{X}_2}} = \frac{45{,}948 - 39{,}820}{1{,}074.9},$$

$$= \frac{6{,}128}{1{,}074.9} = 5.7.$$

This value of t for $n = n_1 + n_2 = 9 + 18 = 27$ is far beyond the 0.001 level, so the difference between the means is significant.

To obtain the 98 per cent confidence limits of $\bar{X}_{\varphi_1} - \bar{X}_{\varphi_2}$, we use $t = 2.473$ and substitute the known values in

$$\bar{X}_1 - \bar{X}_2 = (\bar{X}_{\varphi_1} - \bar{X}_{\varphi_2}) \pm t\hat{\sigma}_{\bar{X}_1-\bar{X}_2}.$$

This gives

$$45{,}948 - 39{,}820 = (\bar{X}_{\varphi_1} - \bar{X}_{\varphi_2}) \pm (2.473)(1{,}074.9).$$
$$\bar{X}_{\varphi_1} - \bar{X}_{\varphi_2} = 6{,}128 \pm 2{,}658,$$
$$= 3{,}470 \text{ and } 8{,}786 \text{ pounds per square inch.}$$

Non-independent samples. When inherent pairing exists between the pairs of items in two samples, it usually follows that the two samples are not independent. We are not concerned if the first, and succeeding, pairs of values in the two samples just happen to be paired because they were selected in the order listed; we are concerned if, for example, the paired readings are values of IQ's of brothers and sisters or of twins, or if the values are mileages of tires on original treads and after recapping. By far the greatest majority of problems which will be encountered will deal with independent samples. However, it is extremely important that non-independent samples be recognized as such; they must not be treated as independent samples.

The data of Table 24.2 show the percentage of solids in the shaded and exposed halves of 25 grapefruit. Here, it is obvious that the two sets of data are not independent; they are inherently paired. The shaded side of grapefruit Number 1 had 8.59 per cent solids while the exposed side of the same grapefruit had 8.49 per cent solids. These two figures are inherently paired with each other, because they refer to the same individual fruit. The same is true of the figures for the other 24 grapefruit.

In order to test the significance of the difference between the means for shaded and exposed halves, we obtain the difference D between each pair of values, determine the value of $\bar{X}_D$, and ascertain whether $\bar{X}_D$ differs significantly from 0. The null hypothesis is that $\bar{X}_D$ is the mean of a random sample from a population of differences having a mean of zero.

TABLE 24.2

Percentage of Solids in the Shaded and Exposed Halves of 25 Grapefruit

Fruit	Shaded X_1	Exposed X_2	$D = X_1 - X_2$	D^2
1	8.59	8.49	0.10	0.0100
2	8.59	8.59		
3	8.09	7.84	0.25	0.0625
4	8.54	7.89	0.65	0.4225
5	8.09	8.19	−0.10	0.0100
6	8.49	7.84	0.65	0.4225
7	7.89	7.89		
8	8.59	7.89	0.70	0.4900
9	8.54	7.79	0.75	0.5625
10	7.99	7.84	0.15	0.0225
11	7.89	7.79	0.10	0.0100
12	8.09	7.84	0.25	0.0625
13	7.89	7.89		
14	8.54	8.07	0.47	0.2209
15	7.84	7.97	−0.13	0.0169
16	7.49	7.57	−0.08	0.0064
17	7.89	7.92	−0.03	0.0009
18	7.79	7.97	−0.18	0.0324
19	7.84	8.17	−0.33	0.1089
20	8.89	8.67	0.22	0.0484
21	8.54	8.07	0.47	0.2209
22	8.04	7.97	0.07	0.0049
23	8.59	8.62	−0.03	0.0009
24	8.19	7.92	0.27	0.0729
25	8.59	7.97	0.62	0.3844
Total	205.50	200.66	4.84	3.1938

Data from Paul L. Harding, Plant Physiologist, Division of Fruit and Vegetable Crops and Diseases, Bureau of Plant Industry, Soils and Agricultural Engineering, Agricultural Research Administration, United States Department of Agriculture.

$$\bar{X}_D = \frac{\Sigma D}{N} = \frac{4.84}{25} = 0.194 \text{ per cent.}$$

$$\hat{\sigma}_D = \sqrt{\frac{\Sigma D^2}{N-1} - \frac{(\Sigma D)^2}{N(N-1)}} = \sqrt{\frac{3.1938}{24} - \frac{(4.84)^2}{25(24)}},$$

$$= \sqrt{0.133075 - 0.039043} = \sqrt{0.094032},$$

$$= 0.307 \text{ per cent.}$$

$$\hat{\sigma}_{\bar{X}_D} = \frac{\hat{\sigma}_D}{\sqrt{N}} = \frac{0.307}{\sqrt{25}} = 0.061 \text{ per cent.}$$

Below Table 24.2 the computations are shown which give

$$\bar{X}_D = 0.194 \text{ per cent,}$$
$$\hat{\sigma}_D = 0.307 \text{ per cent, and}$$
$$\hat{\sigma}_{\bar{X}_D} = 0.061 \text{ per cent.}$$

We then determine the value of t,

$$t = \frac{\overline{X}_D - 0}{\hat{\sigma}_{\overline{x}_D}} = \frac{0.194 - 0}{0.061} = 3.18.$$

Since there are 24 independent D values, $n = 24$, and reference to Appendix I shows that P is between 0.01 and 0.001.

It is very important that the lack of independence between the two samples be recognized in such a problem as this. Had we followed the usual procedure, which assumes the samples to be independent, computing $\overline{X}_1 = 8.22$ per cent, $\overline{X}_2 = 8.03$ per cent, and $\hat{\sigma}_{\overline{x}_1 - \overline{x}_2} = 0.092$ per cent, we would have obtained

$$t = \frac{8.22 - 8.03}{0.092} = \frac{0.19}{0.092} = 2.07,$$

which, for $n = 48$, has $0.025 < P < 0.05$. This probability differs greatly from that found first. In fact, if one were using the 0.02 or 0.01 level as a criterion of significance, the method assuming independence of the two samples would have led him erroneously to conclude "not significant."

The possible consequences of employing the method which assumes independence of the two samples when they are not, in fact, independent may be clarified by writing $\hat{\sigma}_{\overline{x}_D}$ in its alternative form,[20]

$$\hat{\sigma}_{\overline{x}_1 - \overline{x}_2} = \sqrt{\hat{\sigma}_{\overline{x}_1}^2 + \hat{\sigma}_{\overline{x}_2}^2 - 2r\hat{\sigma}_{\overline{x}_1}\hat{\sigma}_{\overline{x}_2}},$$

when r is the correlation between the two samples. If the shorter form,

$$\hat{\sigma}_{\overline{x}_1 - \overline{x}_2} = \sqrt{\hat{\sigma}_{\overline{x}_1}^2 + \hat{\sigma}_{\overline{x}_2}^2},$$

which assumes independence, is used, the value of $\hat{\sigma}_{\overline{x}_1 - \overline{x}_2}$ will be too large when there is positive correlation between the two sets of data and too small when negative correlation is present. Ignoring the lack of independence may cause us to fail to declare a significant difference when r is positive and to erroneously declare a difference to be significant when r is negative. In most problems involving inherent pairing, the correlation will be positive, but occasional cases occur in which the correlation is negative. In any event, when inherent pairing occurs, correlation between the two series is also almost certain to be present. The chance correlation that may appear between two series having $N_1 = N_2$ and known to be independent is of no concern to us.

CONCLUSION

This chapter has made no attempt to contrast "large-number methods"

---

[20] The two forms are exact equivalents, but the expression involving r requires much more computation. For the grapefruit data, using $r = +0.577$, $\hat{\sigma}_{\overline{x}_1 - \overline{x}_2} = 0.061$, which agrees with the value for $\hat{\sigma}_{\overline{x}_D}$.

and "small-number methods." The reason is that when σ is known, the normal curve is appropriate for samples of any size, large or small. When σ is not known, and when $\hat{\sigma}$ is employed in its place, the t distribution (a "small-number method") is always the proper distribution to use. As n increases, the t distribution approaches the normal curve, so that for large samples the normal distribution is sometimes applied. However, even when n is large, the normal curve is an approximation. Sometimes, when a sample is large, s rather than $\hat{\sigma}$ is used as an estimate of σ. The numerical difference between s and $\hat{\sigma}$ is slight for large samples, but the use of s as an estimate of σ should be avoided.

Since the methods discussed in this chapter are just as applicable to small samples as to large samples, the question may arise: why bother to use large samples? The answer is that, when one makes use of large samples, a smaller observed difference $\bar{X} - \bar{X}_{(p}$ or $\bar{X}_1 - \bar{X}_2$ is necessary to obtain significance at a specified probability level. This is true, (1) because $\hat{\sigma}_{\bar{x}}$ (or $\sigma_{\bar{x}}$) and $\hat{\sigma}_{\bar{x}_1 - \bar{x}_2}$ tend to decrease with an increase in sample size, while $\bar{X} - \bar{X}_{(p}$ and $\bar{X}_1 - \bar{X}_2$ do not have a corresponding tendency to decrease, since they may either increase or decrease; also, (2) because the t value required for the specified probability level decreases as n increases. Occasionally, as a result of using small samples, one may come to the conclusion that an observed difference is not significant, when, if large samples had been used, the difference (which itself would probably change) might have been significant.

The tests discussed in this chapter undertook to ascertain whether statistical differences were or were not present. It is worth while to note that generic differences, as opposed to statistical differences, may exist, and that, when a generic difference is present, a statistical difference may or may not also be present. A generic difference is an actual difference in kind and may, for example, refer to males and females, railroad ties of different kinds of wood or preserved by different processes, or roofing nails made of copper or galvanized steel. The tests of yield points of structural steel, referred to earlier in this chapter, are an illustration of a case where a generic difference and a statistical difference were both present; the steel from Source 1 was lighter-weight material than was the steel from Source 2. If tests were to be made of the reaction times of a group of rabbits and a group of guinea pigs, it is quite possible that a statistically significant difference in reaction times might not be present although the two groups are generically different.

CHAPTER 25

Statistical Significance II: Proportions and the Chi-Square Test

In this chapter we shall consider significance tests for dealing with proportions from random samples; we shall also give attention to certain aspects of the chi-square test. The reason for combining these two topics in one chapter lies in the fact that the χ^2 test and the approximate tests for proportions represent alternative methods of arriving at identical conclusions. This will be clarified in the second part of the chapter.

PART 1: PROPORTIONS

The following discussion of proportions obtained from random samples will deal, first, with the significance of the difference between a sample proportion (p) and the proportion in the population (π) when the proportion in the population is known; second, with the confidence limits of π when only p and N are known; and, finally, with the significance of the difference between the proportions of two random samples (p_1 and p_2).

Significance of the Difference Between p and π

The exact test, $\pi = 0.50$. In a large assortment of marbles, half are black and half are white. The marbles do not differ from each other in any respect except color. Considering a black marble as an "occurrence" and a white marble as a "non-occurrence" (that is, non-occurrence of black), and using π to indicate the proportion[1] of non-occurrences in the population and τ the proportion of occurrences, we have $\pi = 0.50$ and $\tau = 0.50$. Suppose that a sample of 10 marbles is presented, which has 9 black marbles. We have then: number of occurrences, $a = 9$; number

---

[1] When the number of occurrences (α) and the number of non-occurrences (β) in a population are known, $\pi = \dfrac{\alpha}{\alpha + \beta}$ and $\tau = \dfrac{\beta}{\alpha + \beta}$. From these it is clear that $\pi + \tau = 1.0$ and $\tau = 1 - \pi$.

of non-occurrences, $b = 1$; proportion of occurrences, $p = 0.90$; proportion of non-occurrences, $q = 0.10$.   Note that

$$p = \frac{a}{a+b} = \frac{a}{N}; \quad q = \frac{b}{a+b} = \frac{b}{N};$$

$$p + q = 1.0.$$

Using $P = 0.05$ as a criterion, let us test the hypothesis that the sample is a random one from the population having $\pi = 0.50$.

Samples of $N = 10$ can have $a = 0, 1, 2, \cdots , 10$ and $\pi = 0, 0.1, 0.2, \cdots , 1.0$, according to the expression

$$(\tau B + \pi A)^{10},$$

where A and B, which have no numerical value, are used to indicate, respectively, an occurrence and a non-occurrence.   Since $\pi = 0.50$ and $\tau = 0.50$,

$$
\begin{aligned}
(\tau B + \pi A)^{10} &= (0.50B + 0.50A)^{10}, \\
&= (0.50B)^{10} + 10(0.50B)^{9}(0.50A) \\
&\quad + 45(0.50B)^{8}(0.50A)^{2} + 120(0.50B)^{7}(0.50A)^{3} \\
&\quad + 210(0.50B)^{6}(0.50A)^{4} + 252(0.50B)^{5}(0.50A)^{5} \\
&\quad + 210(0.50B)^{4}(0.50A)^{6} + 120(0.50B)^{3}(0.50A)^{7} \\
&\quad + 45(0.50B)^{2}(0.50A)^{8} + 10(0.50B)(0.50A)^{9} \\
&\quad + (0.50A)^{10}.
\end{aligned}
$$

Performing the indicated computations and placing the results in columnar form gives:

Number of occurrences of black balls a	Proportion of occurrences of black balls p	Probability
0	0	0.0010
1	0.1	0.0098
2	0.2	0.0439
3	0.3	0.1172
4	0.4	0.2051
5	0.5	0.2461
6	0.6	0.2051
7	0.7	0.1172
8	0.8	0.0439
9	0.9	0.0098
10	1.0	0.0010
		1.0000

From the foregoing, it appears that the probability of obtaining random samples having 9 or 10 black marbles is $0.0098 + 0.0010 = 0.0108$.   This is represented by the two bars at the extreme right in Chart 25.1.   Since we have no reason to believe that the samples would always contain a *larger* proportion of black marbles than did the population, we consider likewise the probability of one or no black balls, which is also 0.0108 and which is represented by the two bars at the extreme left in Chart 25.1.

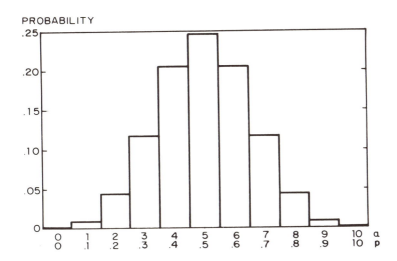

Chart 25.1. Probability of Occurrence of Values of a and p in Samples of 10 When $\pi = 0.50$. Obtained from the expansion of $(0.50B + 0.50A)^{10} = 0.0010B^{10} + 0.0098B^9A + 0.0439B^8A^2 + 0.1172B^7A^3 + 0.2051B^6A^4 + 0.2461B^5A^5 + 0.2051B^4A^6 + 0.1172 B^3A^7 + 0.0439B^2A^8 + 0.0098BA^9 + 0.0010A^{10}$.

The probability of 9 or more and 1 or fewer black marbles is therefore 0.0216. Using the criterion of 0.05, we reject the hypothesis that the sample was a random one from the population having $\pi = 0.50$. Remember that, on the basis of this criterion, we would make Type I errors in 5 per cent of our conclusions.

If we had been using 0.01 as our criterion, we would not have rejected our hypothesis. Had we been employing 0.01 as our criterion and had we been concerned with samples having ten (or no) black balls, the probability would have been 0.0020 and we would have rejected the hypothesis.

An approximate test, $\pi = 0.50$. It has already been pointed out (pages 505–509) that the normal curve is the limit of the binomial as the exponent of the binomial approaches infinity. For practical purposes, the normal curve is often considered to be a reasonably good description of the binomial

$$(0.50B + 0.50A)^N,$$

when $N \geqq 20$. Chart 25.2 shows a normal curve fitted to $(0.50B +$

$0.50A)^{20}$. As we shall see later, the apparently good description of the binomial by the normal curve is no guarantee that the procedure involving the use of the normal curve will lead us to the same conclusion as the binomial.

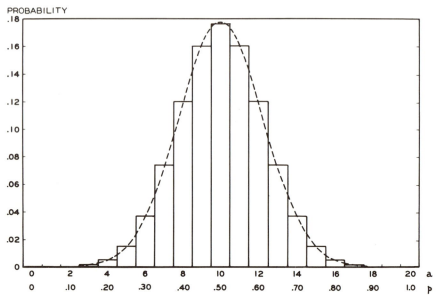

PROBABILITY

Chart 25.2.   Normal Curve Fitted to $(0.50B + 0.50A)^{20}$.

If the normal curve can be substituted for the binomial, we may compute the standard deviation of a sample percentage σ_p, ascertain the value of

$$\frac{x}{\sigma} = \frac{p - \pi}{\sigma_p},$$

and proceed as in Chapter 24 for testing $\overline{X} - \overline{X}_\wp$ when σ is known. If we had a large number of sample proportions $(p_1, p_2, p_3, \cdots, p_k)$, all from random samples from the same population, we could compute the standard deviation of those proportions from

$$\sqrt{\frac{(p_1 - \pi)^2 + (p_2 - \pi)^2 + \cdots + (p_k - \pi)^2}{k}}.$$

It is very unusual to have a large number of such p values, but it can be shown[2] that, when π is known, the standard error of p from random samples is

$$\sigma_p = \sqrt{\frac{\pi\tau}{N}}.$$

---

[2] See Appendix S, section 25.1.

Alternative forms which are sometimes useful are

$$\sigma_p = \sqrt{\frac{\pi(1 - \pi)}{N}} = \sqrt{\frac{\pi - \pi^2}{N}}.$$

Let's see whether the approximate test will lead to the same conclusion as did the exact test for the marbles, where $\pi = 0.50$, $a = 9$, $p = 0.90$, and $N = 10$. We first compute

$$\sigma_p = \sqrt{\frac{(0.50)(0.50)}{10}} = 0.158;$$

and then

$$\frac{x}{\sigma} = \frac{p - \pi}{\sigma_p} = \frac{0.90 - 0.50}{0.158} = \frac{0.40}{0.158} = 2.53.$$

From Appendix H, which shows areas in two tails of a normal curve, we find that $P = 0.0114$. Although this value for P is smaller than the value of 0.0216, obtained by use of the binomial, our conclusion is the same: if 0.05 is our criterion, the hypothesis is rejected. *Note, however, that if 0.02 had been used as the criterion, the exact method would tell us to accept the hypothesis while the approximate procedure indicates that the hypothesis should be rejected.*

A useful alternative form of the approximate test involves testing the significance of the difference between a and πN (the number of occurrences in the sample if the proportion of occurrences in the sample were the same as in the population) by use of

$$\frac{x}{\sigma} = \frac{a - \pi N}{\sigma_a}$$

where[3] $\sigma_a = \sqrt{N\pi\tau}$. For our problem,

$$\sigma_a = \sqrt{10(0.50)(0.50)} = 1.58,$$

and

$$\frac{x}{\sigma} = \frac{a - \pi N}{\sigma_a} = \frac{9 - (0.50)10}{1.58} = 2.53.$$

This is, of course, the same $\dfrac{x}{\sigma}$ value as was obtained when p and π were compared. The conclusion, too, is the same. The hypothesis is rejected.

The fact that the approximate test guided us to the same conclusion as did the exact test, even though the probability given by the normal curve was incorrect, leads to an interesting question: When $\pi = 0.50$, under what conditions may the normal curve be substituted for the binomial and the same conclusion be arrived at concerning a hypothesis? The answer depends on: (1) the size of the sample and (2) the criterion of

---

[3] See Appendix S, section 25.1 for a development of the expression for σ_a.

significance which is being used.   Since the probability resulting from use of the normal curve is *always too small*,[4] when $\pi = 0.50$, the use of the $p - \pi$ (or $a - \pi N$) test will never cause us to accept a hypothesis which the binomial would tell us to reject.   Occasionally the $p - \pi$, or $a - \pi N$, test will indicate the rejection of a hypothesis which the use of the binomial would show should be accepted.   Consider the situation when $\pi = 0.50$, $N = 60$, $a = 38$ ($p = 0.64$), and the criterion is $P = 0.05$. Using the binomial, it is found that the probability[5] of obtaining $a \leqq 22$ or $a \geqq 38$ is 0.052, and the hypothesis (that the sample is a random one from a population having $\pi = 0.50$) is accepted.   Using the normal curve, the probability[6] is found to be 0.039 and would indicate that the hypothesis should be rejected!

Yates' correction.   This correction was designed to be applied to the normal curve in order to increase the probability obtained from the use of the normal curve, so that the probability would be more nearly in agreement with the probability obtained by use of the binomial.   If Yates' correction is applied to the illustrative data just mentioned, the probability[7] is increased from 0.039 to 0.053 and the conclusion is the same as if the binomial had been used.   Note, however, that the use of Yates' correction has *over-corrected*, that is, the probability is greater than that obtained by the binomial.   This is important, since the use of the normal curve with Yates' correction will sometimes result in the accepting of a hypothesis which the binomial (and the use of the uncorrected normal curve!) would indicate should be rejected.   For example: $\pi = 0.50$, $N = 25$, $a = 4$ ($p = 0.16$), and the criterion is $P = 0.001$.   Using the binomial, the probability of obtaining $a \leqq 4$ or $a \geqq 21$ is found to be 0.000 91.   From the normal approximation, a value of $P = 0.000\ 7$ is obtained.   Applying Yates' correction, this value of P is increased to 0.001 37.   In this case, the uncorrected normal approximation agrees with the binomial, indicating that the hypothesis should be rejected.

---

[4] This will be seen to be the case for the various illustrations given in this text.   An explanation is given in the reference mentioned in footnote 7.

[5] The probability may be obtained from a table in H. G. Romig, *50–100 Binomial Tables*, John Wiley and Sons, New York, 1953.

[6] The computations are:

$$\frac{x}{\sigma} = \frac{a - \pi N}{\sigma_a} = \frac{38 - 30}{\sqrt{60(0.50)(0.50)}} = 2.066.$$

Referring to Appendix H, the value of P is seen to be 0.039.

[7] Yates' correction is not explained in this text, since (for reasons which will later be clear) its use is not advocated.   An explanation of Yates' correction is given in F. E. Croxton, *Elementary Statistics with Applications in Medicine and the Biological Sciences*, Dover Publications, Inc., New York, 1959, pp. 255–257.

For the type of problem under consideration, Yates' correction involves computing $\frac{|a - \pi N| - \frac{1}{2}}{\sigma_a}$, where $|\quad|$ means "take the absolute value," and looking up the result-

Applying Yates' correction increases the probability to such an extent that the hypothesis would be accepted!

A table for the exact test, when $\pi = 0.50$. Extensive computations of the sort just made, and referring to the 0.05, 0.02, 0.01, and 0.001 levels, show that, while the use of the normal curve will ordinarily result in the same conclusion being arrived at as if the binomial had been used, this is not by any means always the case. In addition, the use of Yates' correction will sometimes result in over-correcting to such an extent that the conclusion to accept the hypothesis will differ from the conclusion based on the binomial.

One possible solution may have occurred to the reader. That is, to make the $a - \pi N$ test both with and without Yates' correction. When the two procedures lead to the same conclusion, that conclusion will be the same as if the binomial had been used. This is true because, as we already know, the $a - \pi N$ test without correction results in a smaller P value than does the binomial, while the $a - \pi N$ test with Yates' correction yields a larger P value than does the binomial. The difficulty with this solution is that contradictory conclusions do occasionally occur.[8] Whenever the two procedures result in different conclusions, resort must be had to the binomial.

The best solution is to make use of the binomial whenever possible. Following procedures described before, it is not difficult to expand binomials up to about $N = 20$ or 30; but beyond that, the work becomes extensive. Books are now available from which one may read the values of the terms of binomials[9] for (1) $N = 2$ to $N = 49$ by steps of 1, and (2)

---

ing figure in Appendix H. For the illustration above,

$$\frac{|a - \pi N| - \frac{1}{2}}{\sigma_a} = \frac{|38 - 30| - \frac{1}{2}}{\sqrt{60(0.50)(0.50)}} = 1.936.$$

From Appendix H, $P = 0.053$.

[8] Another illustration: when using $P = 0.05$ as the criterion and with $\pi = 0.50$, $N = 100$, and $a = 40$.

[9] These are: (1) National Bureau of Standards, *Tables of the Binomial Probability Distribution*, Washington, 1949, and (2) H. G. Romig, *50–100 Binomial Tables*, John Wiley and Sons, New York, 1953. The symbols used in these references differ from those used in this text. The equivalences are:

This text	Reference (1)	Reference (2)
a	r	x
N	n	n
π	p	p

The reader is urged to remember that, when reversing cumulations of probabilities such as are given in these references, by taking one minus the cumulative probability, he must: (1) *decrease* the tabled a value by one when the original cumulation is of the "or more" type, as in the Bureau of Standards volume, and (2) *increase* the tabled a value by one when the original cumulation is of the "or less" type, as in the Romig book.

TABLE 25.1

Values of a at Selected Lower and Upper Probability Points for Specified Values of N
$\pi = 0.50$

Notes for the use of this table: (1) each a value shown for a lower probability point, together with all a values smaller than the one shown, has the indicated probability or less; (2) each a value shown for an upper probability point, together with all a values larger than the one shown, has the indicated probability or less.

N	$P \leq 0.05$ Lower 0.025 point	$P \leq 0.05$ Upper 0.025 point	$P \leq 0.02$ Lower 0.01 point	$P \leq 0.02$ Upper 0.01 point	$P \leq 0.01$ Lower 0.005 point	$P \leq 0.01$ Upper 0.005 point	$P \leq 0.001$ Lower 0.0005 point	$P \leq 0.001$ Upper 0.0005 point
5	...	...	...	...	...	...	...	...
6	0	6	...	...	...	...	...	...
7	0	7	0	7	...	...	...	...
8	0	8	0	8	0	8	...	...
9	1	8	0	9	0	9	...	...
10	1	9	0	10	0	10	...	...
11	1	10	1	10	0	11	0	11
12	2	10	1	11	1	11	0	12
13	2	11	1	12	1	12	0	13
14	2	12	2	12	1	13	0	14
15	3	12	2	13	2	13	1	14
16	3	13	2	14	2	14	1	15
17	4	13	3	14	2	15	1	16
18	4	14	3	15	3	15	1	17
19	4	15	4	15	3	16	2	17
20	5	15	4	16	3	17	2	18
21	5	16	4	17	4	17	2	19
22	5	17	5	17	4	18	3	19
23	6	17	5	18	4	19	3	20
24	6	18	5	19	5	19	3	21
25	7	18	6	19	5	20	4	21
26	7	19	6	20	6	20	4	22
27	7	20	7	20	6	21	4	23
28	8	20	7	21	6	22	5	23
29	8	21	7	22	7	22	5	24
30	9	21	8	22	7	23	5	25
31	9	22	8	23	7	24	6	25
32	9	23	8	24	8	24	6	26
33	10	23	9	24	8	25	6	27
34	10	24	9	25	9	25	7	27
35	11	24	10	25	9	26	7	28
36	11	25	10	26	9	27	7	29
37	12	25	10	27	10	27	8	29
38	12	26	11	27	10	28	8	30
39	12	27	11	28	11	28	8	31
40	13	27	12	28	11	29	9	31
41	13	28	12	29	11	30	9	32
42	14	28	13	29	12	30	10	32
43	14	29	13	30	12	31	10	33
44	15	29	13	31	13	31	10	34
45	15	30	14	31	13	32	11	34
46	15	31	14	32	13	33	11	35
47	16	31	15	32	14	33	11	36
48	16	32	15	33	14	34	12	36
49	17	32	15	34	15	34	12	37
50	17	33	16	34	15	35	13	37
55	19	36	18	37	17	38	14	41
60	21	39	20	40	19	41	16	44
65	24	41	22	43	21	44	18	47
70	26	44	24	46	23	47	20	50
75	28	47	26	49	25	50	22	53
80	30	50	29	51	28	52	24	56
85	32	53	31	54	30	55	26	59
90	35	55	33	57	32	58	29	61
95	37	58	35	60	34	61	31	64
100	39	61	37	63	36	64	33	67

for $N = 50$ to $N = 100$ by steps of 5. Values of π other than 0.50 are given, but at this point of our discussion we are interested only in $\pi = 0.50$. From these tables, Table 25.1 has been constructed, showing the value of a at various probability points and for selected values of N. With a table such as this available, one has no need to use the normal curve, with or without Yates' correction, in order to avoid the labor of expanding a binomial. Neither is it necessary to expand a binomial, since Table 25.1 gives the results of such expansions.

For samples having $N > 100$, the normal approximation will have to be used until some organization with extensive computing facilities can provide us with extended tables of binomials.

The exact test, $\pi \neq 0.50$. A cigarette company published the results of a "test" in which their product and those of three competitors were judged by eight physicians specializing in the treatment of the nose and the throat. Four of the 8 doctors indicated a preference for the company's cigarette, which we shall call brand No. 1; two preferred No. 2; none preferred No. 3; and 2 preferred No. 4. If there were no difference between the four brands, each would have an equal chance of being selected, so that the probability of brand No. 1 being preferred would be 0.25. $\pi = 0.25$. Now, we wish to evaluate, in the expression

$$(0.75B + 0.25A)^8,$$

the terms which include A^4, A^5, A^6, A^7, and A^8. As before, A indicates an occurrence—in this instance, a preference for brand No. 1, and B indicates a non-occurrence.

Table 25.2 shows the probability of each of the nine terms of the binomial. Adding the probabilities for the last five of the terms gives 0.1138, which is the probability of obtaining four or more favorable statements for brand No. 1 if the four brands are really alike. It is clear that brand No. 1 did not receive significantly more than one-fourth of the doctors' votes. If the size of the sample had been larger, there might have been a significant difference in favor of brand No. 1. However, there is no reason to believe that if N were larger, p would still be 0.50.

Note that in the foregoing we considered only the last five terms of the binomial, the terms for which $p - \pi \geq +0.25$. We ignored the first term, which is the only one for which $p - \pi \geq -0.25$. The reason for making such a one-tail test is that we were interested in knowing whether the preferences for brand No. 1 significantly *exceeded* $\pi = 0.25$.

An approximate test, $\pi \neq 0.50$. While at an Arabian horse ranch, the writer was told: "All 30 of the mares had colts this season. This is unusual, as only 70 to 80 per cent ordinarily have colts in a single season." Now $N = 30$, $a = 30$, $p = 1.0$, and, considering π to be 0.75, we are in a

TABLE 25.2

Probability of Each Term in the Expression $(0.75B + 0.25A)^8$

a Number of occurrences (number preferring brand #1)	p Proportion of occurrences (proportion preferring brand #1)	Expression	Prob- ability
0	0	$(0.75B)^8$	0.1001
1	0.125	$8(0.75B)^7(0.25A)$	0.2670
2	0.250	$28(0.75B)^6(0.25A)^2$	0.3115
3	0.375	$56(0.75B)^5(0.25A)^3$	0.2076
4	0.500	$70(0.75B)^4(0.25A)^4$	0.0865
5	0.625	$56(0.75B)^3(0.25A)^5$	0.0231
6	0.750	$28(0.75B)^2(0.25A)^6$	0.0038
7	0.875	$8(0.75B)(0.25A)^7$	0.0004
8	1.000	$(0.25A)^8$	0.0000
Total	. . .	. . .	1.0000

position to state just how unusual an occurrence this was. We merely need to evaluate the term which includes A^{30} in the expression

$$(0.25B + 0.75A)^{30},$$

where, as before, A is an occurrence (birth of a colt) and B a non-occurrence. That term has a probability of 0.000 18, or about 2 in 10,000, and is a very surprising occurrence, indeed. The ranch owner did not assign a reason for the surprising fecundity, but one would be justified in rejecting the hypothesis that the observed p of 1.0 was based on a random sample from the population represented by his past experience. Note that, again, we have made a one-tail test, since we wished to know whether $p = 1.0$ significantly *exceeded* $\pi = 0.75$.

Let us see whether the normal curve can be used as a substitute for the skewed binomial. Since $N = 30$, the sample is fairly large. However, π is 0.75 rather than 0.50, as was the case when the normal curve was used before. We compute

$$\sigma_p = \sqrt{\frac{\pi\tau}{N}} = \sqrt{\frac{(0.75)(0.25)}{30}} = 0.079$$

and

$$\frac{x}{\sigma} = \frac{p - \pi}{\sigma_p} = \frac{1.00 - 0.75}{0.079} = 3.16.$$

From Appendix G we find that a value of $\dfrac{x}{\sigma} = 3.16$ cuts off less than 0.000 97 but more than 0.000 69 of the area of a normal curve, in one tail. This approximate procedure yields a probability which is much larger than the exact procedure, but our conclusion concerning p is the same. This prompts us to raise a question which is similar to one raised earlier: When $\pi \neq 0.50$, under what conditions may the normal curve be sub-

TABLE 25.3

Values of a at Selected Lower and Upper Probability Points for Specified Values of N
$\pi = 0.20$

Notes for the use of this table: (1) each a value shown for a lower probability point, together with all a values smaller than the one shown, has the indicated probability or less, (2) each a value shown for an upper probability point, together with all a values larger than the one shown, has the indicated probability or less, (3) this table may be used when $\pi = 0.80$ by reading $N - a$ for a and reversing the lower and upper points.

N	$P \leq 0.05$		$P \leq 0.02$		$P \leq 0.01$		$P \leq 0.001$	
	Lower 0.025 point	Upper 0.025 point	Lower 0.01 point	Upper 0.01 point	Lower 0.005 point	Upper 0.005 point	Lower 0.0005 point	Upper 0.0005 point
3	. . .	3	. . .	3	. . .	. . .	. . .	. . .
4	. . .	4	. . .	4	. . .	4	. . .	. . .
5	. . .	4	. . .	4	. . .	5	. . .	5
6	. . .	4	. . .	5	. . .	5	. . .	6
7	. . .	5	. . .	5	. . .	5	. . .	6
8	. . .	5	. . .	6	. . .	6	. . .	7
9	. . .	5	. . .	6	. . .	6	. . .	7
10	. . .	6	. . .	6	. . .	7	. . .	8
11	. . .	6	. . .	7	. . .	7	. . .	8
12	. . .	6	. . .	7	. . .	7	. . .	9
13	. . .	7	. . .	7	. . .	8	. . .	9
14	. . .	7	. . .	8	. . .	8	. . .	9
15	. . .	7	. . .	8	. . .	8	. . .	10
16	. . .	8	. . .	8	. . .	9	. . .	10
17	0	8	. . .	9	. . .	9	. . .	10
18	0	8	. . .	9	. . .	9	. . .	11
19	0	8	. . .	9	. . .	10	. . .	11
20	0	9	. . .	9	. . .	10	. . .	12
21	0	9	0	10	. . .	10	. . .	12
22	0	9	0	10	. . .	11	. . .	12
23	0	10	0	10	. . .	11	. . .	13
24	0	10	0	11	0	11	. . .	13
25	0	10	0	11	0	12	. . .	13
26	1	10	0	11	0	12	. . .	14
27	1	11	0	12	0	12	. . .	14
28	1	11	0	12	0	12	. . .	14
29	1	11	0	12	0	13	. . .	15
30	1	12	0	12	0	13	. . .	15
31	1	12	1	13	0	13	. . .	15
32	1	12	1	13	0	14	. . .	16
33	1	12	1	13	0	14	. . .	16
34	2	13	1	14	1	14	. . .	16
35	2	13	1	14	1	15	0	17
36	2	13	1	14	1	15	0	17
37	2	13	1	14	1	15	0	17
38	2	14	1	15	1	15	0	17
39	2	14	2	15	1	16	0	18
40	2	14	2	15	1	16	0	18
41	3	14	2	16	1	16	0	18
42	3	15	2	16	1	17	0	19
43	3	15	2	16	2	17	0	19
44	3	15	2	16	2	17	0	19
45	3	15	2	17	2	17	0	20
46	3	16	2	17	2	18	1	20
47	3	16	3	17	2	18	1	20
48	4	16	3	17	2	18	1	21
49	4	17	3	18	2	18	1	21
50	4	17	3	18	2	19	1	21
55	5	18	4	19	3	20	1	23
60	5	19	4	21	4	21	2	24
65	6	21	5	22	4	23	3	25
70	7	22	6	23	5	24	3	27
75	8	23	6	24	6	25	4	28
80	8	24	7	26	6	27	4	30
85	9	25	8	27	7	28	5	31
90	10	27	9	28	8	29	6	32
95	11	28	9	29	9	31	6	34
100	11	29	10	31	9	32	7	35

stituted for the binomial and the same conclusion be arrived at concerning the hypothesis? The problem is now more complex, since the answer depends on: (1) the value of π, (2) the size of the sample, and (3) the criterion of significance which is used. For our purposes it will be sufficient to note, first, that when $\pi \neq 0.50$, the normal curve is a less satisfactory approximation to the binomial than when $\pi = 0.50$, for any given N. In fact, when $\pi \neq 0.50$, use of the normal curve will sometimes yield a probability that is too small and sometimes one that is too large. Second, Yates' correction can be of no assistance, since it is not designed for situations in which $\pi \neq 0.50$.

Tables for the exact test when $\pi \neq 0.50$. For situations in which $\pi \neq 0.50$, we need a series of tables, similar to Table 25.1, each table having to do with a different π value. Such an undertaking is too ambitious for an elementary text, and, in any event, the values of the terms of skewed binomials may be obtained from the two references cited in footnote 9. For purposes of illustration, Table 25.3 has been prepared, dealing with the probability points for samples of various sizes when $\pi = 0.20$ or $\pi = 0.80$.

Confidence Limits of π

Sometimes the value of p is known, but π is not known, and it is important to state the limits within which π may be expected to occur. As was noted when discussing the confidence limits of $\overline{X}$, we must first decide what confidence limits we want. Of course, the size of the sample from which p was computed must also be known. We shall proceed by considering first an approximate method and then an exact method.

An approximate method. After nearly 23 years of use, the Chicago, Milwaukee, St. Paul & Pacific Railway found that 22 out of 50 red oak ties, which had been preserved by means of creosote applied by the "full cell" process, were still in good condition. For this sample, $N = 50$, $a = 22$, and $p = 0.44$. What are the 95 per cent confidence limits of π? To obtain these two values, we employ the expression which has been used before

$$\frac{x}{\sigma} = \frac{p - \pi}{\sigma_p},$$

but write it

$$\frac{x}{\sigma} = \frac{p - \pi}{\sqrt{\dfrac{\pi - \pi^2}{N}}}.$$

We know p and N. From Appendix H or the last row of Appendix I, we obtain the $\dfrac{x}{\sigma}$ value (1.96) associated with the 95 per cent confidence limits.

The three known values are substituted in the equation just given, and it is solved[10] for π, giving:

$$1.96 = \frac{0.44 - \pi}{\sqrt{\dfrac{\pi - \pi^2}{50}}};$$

$$3.8416 = \frac{0.1936 - 0.88\pi + \pi^2}{\dfrac{\pi - \pi^2}{50}};$$

$$\frac{3.8416\pi - 3.8416\pi^2}{50} = 0.1936 - 0.88\pi + \pi^2;$$

$$0.076832\pi - 0.076832\pi^2 = 0.1936 - 0.88\pi + \pi^2;$$

$$0.1936 - 0.956832\pi + 1.076832\pi^2 = 0,$$

$$\pi = \frac{0.671125}{2.153664} \text{ and } \frac{1.242539}{2.153664}, \text{ so that}$$

$$\pi_1 = 0.312 \text{ and } \pi_2 = 0.577.$$

What we did was to determine: (1) $\pi_1 = 0.312$, which is so located that $p = 0.44$ cuts off the upper $2\frac{1}{2}$ per cent tail of a normal curve around π_1 with $\sigma_p = \sqrt{\dfrac{\pi_1 \tau_1}{N}} = \sqrt{\dfrac{(0.312)(0.688)}{50}} = 0.066$, and (2) $\pi_2 = 0.577$, which is so located that $p = 0.44$ cuts off the lower $2\frac{1}{2}$ per cent tail of a normal curve around π_2 with $\sigma_p = \sqrt{\dfrac{\pi_2 \tau_2}{N}} = \sqrt{\dfrac{(0.577)(0.423)}{50}} = 0.071$. Chart 25.3 illustrates what has been done.

The method just described gives satisfactory results when N is large and when p is not too far removed from 0.50. Its shortcoming will be apparent when we apply it to the following example.

Standard-strength digitalis was injected into each of 20 frogs. As a result, 17 of them had rapid systolic standstills (they died). Other frogs were injected with half-strength digitalis and with digitalis alleged to be

---

[10] The quadratic $0.1936 - 0.956832\pi + 1.076832\pi$ is solved by computing

$$\pi = \frac{-(-0.956832) \pm \sqrt{(0.956832)^2 - 4(0.1936)(1.076832)}}{2(1.076832)}.$$

If the first equation were to be written

$$1.96 = \frac{a - \pi N}{\sqrt{N(\pi - \pi^2)}},$$

we would, initially, have only integers on the right.

half-strength, but the results of those tests are of no concern to us in connection with this example. For the group of frogs given full-strength digitalis, $N = 20$ and $p = 0.85$. What are the 90 per cent confidence limits of π? Proceeding as before, we first obtain the $\dfrac{x}{\sigma}$ value of 1.645

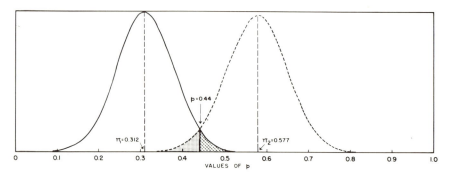

Chart 25.3. 95 Per Cent Confidence Limits of π, when $p = 0.44$ and $N = 50$, Determined by Use of σ_p and Normal Curves. The cross-hatched area is 2.5 per cent of the left curve; the stippled area is 2 5 per cent of the right curve.

from the last row of Appendix I, and then write

$$1.645 = \frac{0.85 - \pi}{\sqrt{\dfrac{\pi - \pi^2}{20}}},$$

which, when solved, yields

$$\pi_1 = 0.678 \text{ and } \pi_2 = 0.938.$$

These results seem all right until we look at Chart 25.4, which shows what we have done. Now, it is immediately apparent that the use of normal curves cannot be justified, particularly for determining π_2. The normal curve at the right indicates that values of $p > 1.0$ would occur, which is, of course, impossible.

The exact method. An exact determination of the confidence limits of π for the full-strength digitalis data requires a much more laborious procedure. Considering first the determination of π_1, we must ascertain the value of π which, when inserted in the expression

$$(\tau B = \pi A)^{20},$$

will result in $a = 17$ ($p = 0.85$) cutting off the *upper* 5 per cent tail of the binomial. This requires successive approximations, and we shall first try $\pi = 0.65$. From Table 25.4, it may be seen that, in the binomial $(0.35B + 0.65A)^{20}$, the probability of obtaining $a \geq 17$ is 0.0444. Since

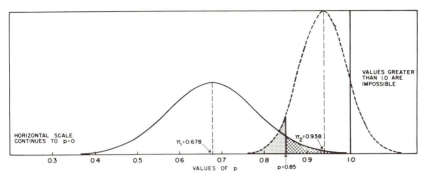

Chart 25.4. Unsatisfactory Approximation of the 90 Per Cent Confidence Limits of π when $p = 0.85$ and $N = 20$, Determined by Use of σ_p and Normal Curves. The cross-hatched area is 5 per cent of the left curve; the stippled area is 5 per cent of the right curve.

this probability is less than 0.05, we must try a slightly larger value of π. In the same table, it appears that, when $\pi = 0.66$, the probability of obtaining $a \geq 17$ is 0.0535. If two decimals are sufficient for π_1, we

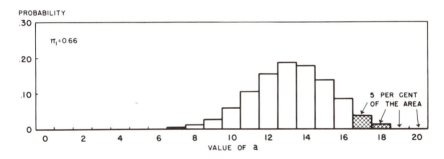

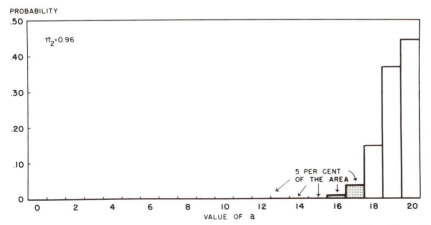

Chart 25.5. 90 Per Cent Confidence Limits of π when $N = 20$ and $a = 17$ ($p = 0.85$), Determined by Use of the Expression $(\pi B + \pi A)^N$. Data from Tables 25.4 and 25.5.

would conclude that the lower 90 per cent confidence limit of π is 0.66, as shown in the upper part of Chart 25.5. In the event that three decimals are wanted for π_1, we would note that the next value to be tried for π_1 should be larger than 0.655. A value of 0.657 was tried, with the results shown in the sixth and seventh columns of Table 25.4; for $a \geqq 17$, the probability is seen to be 0.0506. Trying, next, $\pi = 0.656$, it is seen from the table that the probability of $a \geqq 17$ is 0.0497. The value of π_1 lies between 0.656 and 0.657, but closer to 0.656 than to 0.657.

In order to obtain π_2, the upper 90 per cent confidence limit, we need to determine the value of π which, when inserted in the expression

$$(\tau B + \pi A)^{20},$$

will result in $a = 17$ ($p = 0.85$) cutting off the *lower* 5 per cent tail of the binomial. Since π_2 was 0.938 by the approximate method, we shall first try $\pi = 0.94$. From Table 25.5, it is seen that $a \leqq 17$ includes 0.1150 of the binomial, and we next try $\pi = 0.95$. This value for π_2 results in a

TABLE 25.4

Probabilities* and Cumulative Probabilities of Values of a in the Expression $(\tau B + \pi A)^{20}$, when $\pi = 0.65, 0.66, 0.657,$ and 0.656

(The probability of $a \geqq 17$ is shown in boldface type.)

(a)	$\pi = 0.65$ Probability	$\pi = 0.65$ Cumulative probability	$\pi = 0.66$ Probability	$\pi = 0.66$ Cumulative probability	$\pi = 0.657$ Probability	$\pi = 0.657$ Cumulative probability	$\pi = 0.656$ Probability	$\pi = 0.656$ Cumulative probability
(1)	(2)	(3)	(4)	(5)	(6)	(7)	(8)	(9)
0	0.0000	1.0000	0.0000	1.0000				
1	0.0000	>0.9999	0.0000	>0.9999				
2	0.0000	>0.9999	0.0000	>0.9999				
3	0.0000	>0.9999	0.0000	>0.9999				
4	0.0000	>0.9999	0.0000	>0.9999				
5	0.0003	>0.9999	0.0002	>0.9999				
6	0.0012	0.9997	0.0009	0.9998	Probabilities for $a = 0$ to $a = 16$			
7	0.0045	0.9985	0.0034	0.9989	are not needed for this problem.			
8	0.0136	0.9940	0.0108	0.9955				
9	0.0336	0.9804	0.0280	0.9846				
10	0.0686	0.9468	0.0598	0.9566				
11	0.1158	0.8782	0.1056	0.8968				
12	0.1614	0.7624	0.1537	0.7913				
13	0.1844	0.6010	0.1836	0.6376				
14	0.1712	0.4166	0.1782	0.4540				
15	0.1272	0.2454	0.1384	0.2758				
16	0.0738	0.1182	0.0839	0.1374				
17	0.0323	**0.0444**	0.0383	**0.0535**	0.0364	**0.0506**	0.0358	**0.0497**
18	0.0100	0.0121	0.0124	0.0152	0.0116	0.0142	0.0114	0.0139
19	0.0020	0.0021	0.0025	0.0028	0.0023	0.0026	0.0023	0.0025
20	0.0002	0.0002	0.0002	0.0002	0.0002	0.0002	0.0002	0.0002

* The non-cumulative probabilities may be computed as in Table 23.8. When π consists of not more than two decimals, probabilities and cumulative probabilities may be obtained from National Bureau of Standards, *Tables of the Binomial Probability Distribution*, Washington, 1949. The cumulative figures shown above were obtained from the non-cumulative figures before the non-cumulative figures were rounded.

TABLE 25.5

Probabilities* and Cumulative Probabilities of Values of a in the Expression
$(\tau B + \pi A)^{20}$, when $\pi = 0.94$, 0.95, and 0.96

(The probability of $a \leqq 17$ is shown in boldface type.)

a	$\pi = 0.94$ Probability	$\pi = 0.94$ Cumulative probability	$\pi = 0.95$ Probability	$\pi = 0.95$ Cumulative probability	$\pi = 0.96$ Probability	$\pi = 0.96$ Cumulative probability
(1)	(2)	(3)	(4)	(5)	(6)	(7)
0	0.0000	0.0000	0.0000	0.0000	0.0000	0.0000
1	0.0000	0.0000	0.0000	0.0000	0.0000	0.0000
.						
.		All omitted probabilities are zero, to four decimals.				
.						
12	0.0000	0.0000	0.0000	0.0000	0.0000	0.0000
13	0.0001	0.0001	0.0000	0.0000	0.0000	0.0000
14	0.0008	0.0009	0.0003	0.0003	0.0001	0.0001
15	0.0048	0.0056	0.0022	0.0026	0.0009	0.0010
16	0.0233	0.0290	0.0133	0.0159	0.0065	0.0074
17	0.0860	**0.1150**	0.0596	**0.0755**	0.0365	**0.0439**
18	0.2246	0.3395	0.1887	0.2642	0.1458	0.1897
19	0.3703	0.7099	0.3774	0.6415	0.3683	0.5580
20	0.2901	1.0000	0.3585	1.0000	0.4420	1.0000

* See footnote to Table 25.4.

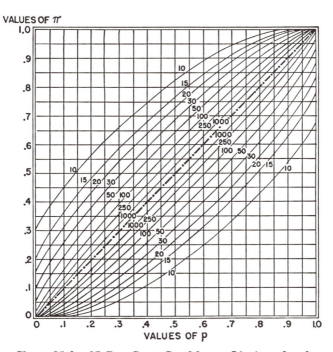

VALUES OF π

VALUES OF P

Chart 25.6. 95 Per Cent Confidence Limits of π for
Values of p from Samples of Various Sizes from 10 to
1,000. See note following title of Chart 25.7.

probability of 0.0755 (see Table 25.5) for $a \leq 17$, so we proceed to try $\pi = 0.96$, which, as shown in Table 25.5, gives a probability of 0.0439 for $a \leq 17$. We conclude that $\pi_2 = 0.96$, and this is illustrated in the lower part of Chart 25.5. Values of π intermediate between 0.95 and 0.96 could be tried, but we shall terminate the illustration at this point. The 90 per cent confidence limits (to two decimals) are $\pi_1 = 0.66$ and $\pi_2 = 0.96$.

The exact method of determining the confidence limits of π necessitates two sets of trials for each different problem. Note that, in order to make a useful estimate of the values of π_1 and π_2 which should be tried first, the approximate solution using σ_p should ordinarily precede the exact solution. If binomial tables, such as those mentioned in footnote 9, are available, the approximate solution may be omitted.

To avoid the arduous labor of expanding a number of binomials, diagrams have been prepared by Clopper and Pearson which enable one

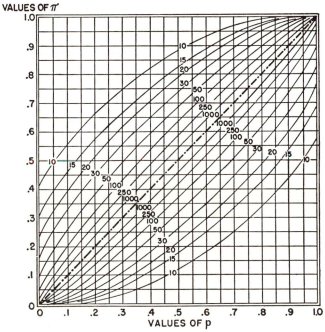

VALUES OF π

VALUES OF p

Chart 25.7. 99 Per Cent Confidence Limits of π for Values of p From Samples of Various Sizes From 10 to 1,000. Reproduced, by permission, from C. J. Clopper and E. S. Pearson, "The Use of Confidence or Fiducial Limits, "*Biometrika*, Vol. 26, p. 410. By correspondence Pearson advises that the π values "are not completely accurate as the levels at certain points were obtained by interpolation and not by direct calculation."

to read the lower and upper 0.95 and 0.99 confidence limits of π. These are shown in Charts 25.6 and 25.7.

Significance of the Difference Between p_1 and p_2

An approximate method. Reference was made earlier to 50 red oak ties which had been preserved by means of creosote applied by the "full cell" process. After 23 years of service, 22, or 44 per cent, of these ties were still in service. When these ties were laid, another group of 50 red oak ties, creosote-impregnated by the "Rueping" process, were also put into use. Of this second group, 18 ties, or 36 per cent, were still in service after the passage of 23 years. Now we have two samples: one, on which the "full cell" process was used, had $N_1 = 50$, $a_1 = 22$, and $p_1 = 0.44$; the other, on which the "Rueping" process was employed, had $N_2 = 50$, $a_2 = 18$, and $p_2 = 0.36$. We wish to know whether there is a significant difference, at the 0.05 level, between these two proportions.

The procedure is essentially the same as that used for two sample means; we shall compare the difference to the standard error of the difference. The standard error of the difference between two percentages is

$$\sigma_{p_1-p_2} = \sqrt{\sigma_{p_1}^2 + \sigma_{p_2}^2},$$

$$= \sqrt{\frac{\pi\tau}{N_1} + \frac{\pi\tau}{N_2}}.$$

Now, we do not know π, and, if we did know π, we would almost certainly wish to test p_1 against π and p_2 against π rather than to examine the significance of $p_1 - p_2$. Since we do not know π, we make an estimate, $\bar{p}$, based on the information in both samples. Thus,

$$\bar{p} = \frac{a_1 + a_2}{N_1 + N_2},$$

$$= \frac{22 + 18}{50 + 50} = 0.40.$$

Now we are in a position to compute

$$\hat{\sigma}_{p_1-p_2} = \sqrt{\frac{\bar{p}\bar{q}}{N_1} + \frac{\bar{p}\bar{q}}{N_2}},$$

$$= \sqrt{\frac{(0.40)(0.60)}{50} + \frac{(0.40)(0.60)}{50}},$$

$$= 0.098, \text{ and}$$

$$\frac{x}{\sigma} = \frac{p_1 - p_2}{\hat{\sigma}_{p_1-p_2}} = \frac{0.44 - 0.36}{0.098} = \frac{0.08}{0.098} = 0.82.$$

Referring to Appendix H, it appears that $P = 0.41$, and we conclude that the difference between p_1 and p_2 is not significant.

Exact method. When the two samples from which p_1 and p_2 are obtained are small, the approximate method just described should be abandoned in favor of the exact method. Later in this chapter it will be shown that a chi-square test for a "2 × 2" table is identical with the $p_1 - p_2$ test given above. At that point the exact test will be described.

PART 2: THE CHI-SQUARE TEST

As we shall use it, in the present discussion, the χ^2 test consists of summing a series of ratios, each ratio having been obtained by: (1) taking the difference between an observed frequency (f) and an associated population or computed frequency (f_c), (2) squaring this difference, and (3) dividing the squared difference by f_c. Thus,

$$\chi^2 = \Sigma \frac{(f - f_c)^2}{f_c}.$$

In Chapter 26 we shall make use of a slightly different aspect of chi-square when we compare $\hat{\sigma}^2$ and σ^2.

The 1 × 2 Table

Approximate method. To demonstrate the identity of the χ^2 test and the $p - \pi$ (or $a - \pi N$) test, we shall use the example employed earlier in this chapter which involved a sample of 10 marbles, 9 of which were black. Using 0.05 as our criterion, we tested the hypothesis that the sample was a random one from a population having $\pi = 0.50$ by use of σ_p and also by use of σ_a. If we make the same test by means of χ^2, we compute:

Color of marble	Observed number of marbles f	Computed number if 1:1 ratio exists f_c	$f - f_c$	$(f - f_c)^2$	$\frac{(f - f_c)^2}{f_c}$
Black......	9	5	+4	16	3.2
White......	1	5	−4	16	3.2
Total.....	10	10	0	...	6.4

This is a 1 × 2 table, since the observed frequencies occupy 1 column and 2 rows. It is the simplest type of a one-column table. From the above table, the value of χ^2 is seen to be 6.4, and we may determine the probability of such a value of χ^2 (or greater) by referring to the table of Appendix J for the appropriate number of degrees of freedom. For our problem, $n = 1$. This is so because a figure may be freely entered in one of the two boxes in the f-column. However, once this figure has been put down, the second figure is thereupon determined, since the total is 10. From Appendix J, when $n = 1$ and $\chi^2 = 6.4$, the value of P is seen to be slightly larger than 0.01, causing us to reject the hypothesis on the basis of this approximate test. If a more detailed table of χ^2 values[11] were available, we would find $P = 0.0114$, exactly the same as for the test involving σ_p (or σ_a). As a matter of fact, the $p - \pi$ test (or the $a - \pi N$ test) and the χ^2 test must produce the same final P value. Note that the $\frac{x}{\sigma}$ value obtained for the $p - \pi$ (or $a - \pi N$) test is the square root of the χ^2 value. This can be seen in broader perspective if we look at the last row of the t-table (Appendix I), which gives $\frac{x}{\sigma}$ values for the normal distribution, and the first row of the χ^2 table (Appendix J), which gives χ^2 values when $n = 1$. For any given P value, the χ^2 value will be seen always to be the square of the normal value.

The values of χ^2 shown in the first row of Appendix J are obtained from the distribution of χ^2 for one degree of freedom, which is pictured in Chart 25.8.

The χ^2 test tells us the probability of getting a disagreement between observed and computed frequencies *equal to or greater than that observed, in either direction.* For the marbles, the P value of a little more than 0.01 represented the probability of 9 or 10 black marbles and of 9 or 10 white marbles. This is true even though only one tail of the chi-square distribution (see Appendix J) is involved, because the $f - f_c$ values were squared.

Exact method. Chi-square is an approximate test for the same reason that the $p - \pi$ (or $a - \pi N$) test was an approximate test; a continuous distribution of sample values was assumed to exist, when actually only the eleven terms of the binomial $(0.50B + 0.50A)^{10}$ can occur. The exact procedure was set forth on pages 567–569 and it will not be repeated here. The approximate method, using χ^2, may be employed in place of the exact method, and the same conclusion arrived at, under exactly the same conditions that the $p - \pi$ (or $a - \pi N$) test may be used. These conditions were discussed for $\pi = 0.50$ on pages 571–573 and for $\pi \neq 0.50$ on pages 576–578.[12]

---

[11] We can also obtain this probability by looking up χ, not χ^2, in the normal-curve table of Appendix H.

[12] For an interesting development see William C. Boyd, "A Nomogram for Chi-Square," *Journal of the American Statistical Association,* Vol. 60, No. 309, March 1965, pp. 344-346.

HEIGHT OF ORDINATE

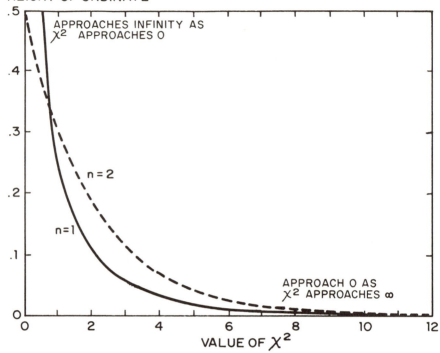

APPROACHES INFINITY AS
χ^2 APPROACHES 0

n = 2

n=1

APPROACH 0 AS
χ^2 APPROACHES ∞

VALUE OF χ^2

HEIGHT OF ORDINATE

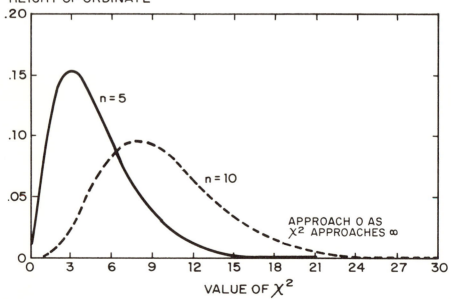

n = 5

n = 10

APPROACH 0 AS
χ^2 APPROACHES ∞

VALUE OF χ^2

Chart 25.8.   The χ^2 Distribution for $n = 1$, $n = 2$, $n = 5$, and $n = 10$.   For descriptive legend see opposite page.

Confidence limits of π. As a matter of possible interest, it may be noted that χ^2 may be used to determine the confidence limits of π. The expression is

$$\chi^2 = \frac{\left(a - \dfrac{\pi}{1-\pi} b\right)^2}{\dfrac{\pi}{1-\pi} N},$$

and it is the exact equivalent of the approximate method given earlier.

The 2 × 2 Table

Approximate method. As will shortly be made clear, the χ^2 test for a 2 × 2 table leads to the same probability, and therefore the same conclusion concerning a hypothesis, as does the $p_1 - p_2$ test described earlier. To clarify this point, we shall use the same illustration that was used for the $p_1 - p_2$ test. The data are now set up as in Table 25.6, which we call a 2 × 2 table because it has two columns and two rows of observed data. Two-column tables with more than two rows will be considered later.

There are no population frequencies in Table 25.6, but we obtain computed frequencies by noting that, if the ties treated by the two processes

TABLE 25.6

Railroad Ties in Use at End of 23-Year Test Period by Method Used to Apply Creosote Preservative

Process by which creosote was applied	In use at end of test period		Total
	Yes	No	
Full cell..........	22	28	50
Rueping.	18	32	50
Total............	40	60	100

Data from *Proceedings of the American Wood Preservers Association*, 1935, pp. 133–134.

showed no difference in regard to the number in use at the end of the test period, we would expect the first box (Row 1, Column 1) to contain $\frac{40}{100}$

Chart 25.8. The χ^2 Distribution for $n = 1$, $n = 2$, $n = 5$, and $n = 10$. Note that different scales are used for the two parts of the chart. The ordinates were computed from the expression

$$Y_c = \frac{e^{\frac{-\chi^2}{2}} (\chi^2)^{\frac{n-2}{2}}}{2^{\frac{n}{2}} \left(\dfrac{n-2}{2}\right)!},$$

which is not difficult to solve if logarithms are used. The mode of the χ^2 distribution is at $\chi^2 = n - 2$, except when $n = 1$, and then the mode is at zero, as may be seen above; the mean is at $\chi^2 = n$. As shown in the lower part of the chart, the skewness of the distribution decreases as the number of degrees of freedom increases.

of the 50 ties treated by the full cell process, and the second box (Row 1, Column 2) would be expected to have $\frac{60}{100}$ of the 50 ties treated by the same process. In like fashion, the third box (Row 2, Column 1) would have $\frac{40}{100}$ of the 50 ties treated by the Rueping process and the fourth box (Row 2, Column 2) would have $\frac{60}{100}$ of the ties treated by this process. These f_c values have been computed in Columns (2) and (3) of Table 25.7. In Columns (4), (5), (6), and (7) of that table, the computation of χ^2 is carried out and $\chi^2 = 0.67$. A 2 × 2 table, with marginal totals set, has $n = 1$, as will be explained in the next paragraph. Referring to Appendix J for $n = 1$ and $\chi^2 = 0.67$ gives $0.30 < P < 0.50$. A more detailed table of χ^2 would show $P = 0.41$, the same as for the $p_1 - p_2$ test. Note, again, that the $\frac{x}{\sigma}$ value for the $p_1 - p_2$ test, which was 0.82 (or 0.816 to three decimals), is the square root of the χ^2 value of 0.67.

TABLE 25.7

Computation of χ^2 for the Data of Table 25.6

Cell	Determination of computed frequencies		f	$f - f_c$	$(f - f_c)^2$	$\dfrac{(f - f_c)^2}{f_c}$
	Product of row and column totals	f_c Col. (2) ÷ 100				
(1)	(2)	(3)	(4)	(5)	(6)	(7)
Row 1, column 1.	50 × 40 = 2,000	20	22	+2	4	0.20
Row 1, column 2.	50 × 60 = 3,000	30	28	−2	4	0.133
Row 2, column 1.	50 × 40 = 2,000	20	18	−2	4	0.20
Row 2, column 2.	50 × 60 = 3,000	30	32	+2	4	0.133
Total.........	...	100	100	0	...	0.67

When the f_c entries are not integers, they should be carried to one decimal in order that Σf_c will not differ from Σf by as much as 1. Actually, only one of the f_c figures in Column (3) must be computed. The others may be obtained by subtraction from the row and column totals of Table 25.6.

That $n = 1$ for a 2 × 2 table with marginal totals set may be clarified by considering this small table:

		100
		150
130	120	250

which has the marginal totals given, but has no entries in the boxes. If a figure is entered in any one box, it should be clear that the figures for the other 3 boxes are thereupon determined. If 20 is written in the first box, then the figure for the second box must be 80, for the third box 110, and for the fourth box 40. Inasmuch as we were free to enter a figure in only one box, there is but one degree of freedom. For tables larger than 2 × 2, the same method will tell one the number of degrees of freedom if the marginal totals are set. It is more expeditious, however, merely to compute

$$n = (R - 1)(C - 1),$$

where R is the number of rows and C is the number of columns. The following relationship may be of interest:

Degrees of freedom lost because of marginal totals[13] ......$(R - 1) + (C - 1) + 1$
Degrees of freedom remaining, n........................ $(R - 1)(C - 1)$
    Total (number of boxes)............................ RC

The computation form shown in Table 25.7 is not required when χ^2 is computed for a 2×2 table. It was given here in order to clarify the procedure involved. The value of χ^2 for a 2×2 table may be obtained more expeditiously by use of the expression,

$$\chi^2 = \frac{(a_1 b_2 - b_1 a_2)^2 N}{N_1 N_2 N_a N_b},$$

where the symbols refer to box and total frequencies as shown below:

a_1	b_1	N_1
a_2	b_2	N_2
N_a	N_b	N

For the data of Table 25.6,

$$\chi^2 = \frac{[(22)(32) - (28)(18)]^2 100}{(50)(50)(40)(60)},$$

$$= \frac{(704 - 504)^2 100}{(2500)(2400)},$$

$$= \frac{4,000,000}{6,000,000} = 0.67.$$

This, of course, is the same value as obtained in Table 25.7.

Exact procedure. When N is small, the probability given by the χ^2 test is too small, with the result that the χ^2 test might lead to a hypothesis being discredited, whereas the exact procedure might cause one not to discredit a hypothesis.

Consider the following data dealing with two forms of treatment applied to 16 laboratory animals which had previously been inoculated with a virus. The figures for the two treatments appear so divergent

---

[13] A degree of freedom is not lost because of every marginal total. If any one vertical and any one horizontal total (including the grand total) are deleted, they may be restored from the information given by the remaining totals.

Treatment	Result		Total
	Recovered	Died	
#1...............	7	3	10
#2...............	0	6	6
Total............	7	9	16

that it may seem to the reader to be a waste of time to apply a statistical test. Nevertheless, using 0.01 as our criterion, let us see whether there is a significant difference between the two treatments. Our hypothesis is that the two groups, of 10 and 6 animals, are from the same population in respect to the proportions recovered or died. Using first the chi-square test, we get

$$\chi^2 = \frac{(a_1b_2 - b_1a_2)^2 N}{N_1 N_2 N_a N_b},$$

$$= \frac{[(7)(6) - (0)(3)]^2 16}{(10)(6)(7)(9)} = 7.47.$$

Referring to Appendix J for $n = 1$, we find $P = 0.01$ and, upon the basis of this approximate test, would conclude that our hypothesis was discredited. However, the probability is actually larger than indicated by the χ^2 test or than by the $p_1 - p_2$ test, which we already know is the same as the χ^2 test for this type of problem.

The probability of any arrangement of frequencies in the boxes of a 2×2 table, with marginal totals set, may be obtained from

$$\frac{N_1! N_2! N_a! N_b!}{N! a_1! b_1! a_2! b_2!}.$$

Solving this expression for the data resulting from the two treatments gives

$$\frac{10! 6! 7! 9!}{16! 7! 3! 0! 6!} = 0.0105.$$

This is the probability of the particular divergence which was observed. If any greater differences between the two samples (treatments) are possible, their probabilities must be added to this. (It will be remembered the χ^2 test and the $p_1 - p_2$ test give us the probability of a difference *equal to or greater than* that which was observed.) The first column of Table 25.8 shows all the possible combinations that will produce the marginal totals of our problem. There are seven in all. From the second column it may be seen that none of the combinations shows a difference greater than and in the same direction as that which was observed. However, Combination VII shows a greater difference in the opposite direction. We therefore ascertain its probability, also, which is 0.0009. Adding the two probabilities for Combinations I and VII gives

0.0114 and leads us to a different conclusion[14] from the one reached before: the hypothesis is not discredited.

TABLE 25.8

Values of p_1, p_2, and $p_1 - p_2$ and the Probability of Each of the Seven Combinations Yielding the Marginal Totals Shown Below

Combination				Proportion of row total in first column and difference		Probability of the combination from $\dfrac{N_1!N_2!N_a!N_b!}{N!a_1!b_1!a_2!b_2!}$
I	7	3	10	$p_1 =$	0.7	
	0	6	6	$p_2 =$	0	0.0105
	7	9	16	$p_1 - p_2 =$	+0.7	
II	6	4	10	$p_1 =$	0.6	
	1	5	6	$p_2 =$	0.17	0.1101
	7	9	16	$p_1 - p_2 =$	+0.43	
III	5	5	10	$p_1 =$	0.5	
	2	4	6	$p_2 =$	0.33	0.3304
	7	9	16	$p_1 - p_2 =$	+0.17	
IV	4	6	10	$p_1 =$	0.40	
	3	3	6	$p_2 =$	0.50	0.3671
	7	9	16	$p_1 - p_2 =$	−0.10	
V	3	7	10	$p_1 =$	0.30	
	4	2	6	$p_2 =$	0.67	0.1573
	7	9	16	$p_1 - p_2 =$	−0.37	
VI	2	8	10	$p_1 =$	0.20	
	5	1	6	$p_2 =$	0.83	0.0236
	7	9	16	$p_1 - p_2 =$	−0.63	
VII	1	9	10	$p_1 =$	0.10	
	6	0	6	$p_2 =$	1.0	0.0009
	7	9	16	$p_1 - p_2 =$	−0.9	
Total.........				...		1.0000

---

[14] Drawing conclusions concerning 2 × 2 tables with small frequencies may be facilitated by use of a table, prepared by D. J. Finney and R. Latscha, which shows values of a_2 significant at selected probability values when a_1, N_1, and N_2 are fixed. Provision is made for consideration of 2 × 2 tables ranging from $N_1 + N_2 = 6$ to $N_1 + N_2 = 30$. See E. S. Pearson and H. O. Hartley, *Biometrika Tables for Statisticians*, Cambridge University Press, London, 1954, pp. 65–72 and 188–193. The table originally appeared in two parts in *Biometrika*, Vol. 35, parts 1 and 2, and Vol. 40, parts 1 and 2.

As a matter of possible interest, Table 25.8 shows the probability of each of the seven combinations. Note that the seven probabilities add to 1.0000. Because of rounding, the seven figures shown in Table 25.8 total 0.9999.

If we had merely been interested in knowing whether treatment No. 1 showed a larger proportion recovering than did treatment No. 2, we would have halved the probability arrived at by the χ^2 test. This is "less than 0.005" and involves the assumption that the distribution of possible values is symmetrical, which is not the case. The correct probability is 0.0105, the probability shown in Table 25.8 for combination I.

In a practical situation, what should one do if, handling data such as those for the two treatments, he is confronted by the conclusion which was just arrived at? Further experimentation is certainly in order; possibly larger samples may result in the appearance of a significant difference, or, alternatively, may still fail to discredit the hypothesis.

Yates' correction. This correction, previously mentioned in connection with the $a - \pi N$ test, may also be applied to the χ^2 test for a 2×2 table,[15] when skewness is not present. The purpose is the same as before: to modify the approximate test so that the probability resulting from it will be in closer agreement with the exact test. Here too, Yates' correction tends to over-correct.[16] For the data of the two treatments, the use of Yates' correction leads to a probability slightly larger than 0.025, which greatly exceeds that obtained by the exact method. As stated before, the tendency to over-correct would sometimes lead us to the conclusion that a difference was not significant, whereas the exact procedure would indicate the presence of a significant difference.

$1 \times R$ Tables, Larger Than 1×2

A 1×3 table. Freshness has been an advertised feature of various brands of coffee for many years. It occurred to one concern to attempt to find out whether freshness really made any difference in the taste of coffee. To that end, a fairly comprehensive investigation was undertaken. One aspect involved 52 tasters, each of whom was given 6 cups of coffee—2 made from fresh coffee, 2 made from coffee 3 weeks old, and 2 made from coffee 5 weeks old. The tasters were asked to match the duplicate cups. Now it is possible to make 15 different matchings of the

---

[15] The correction involves computing χ^2 from the expression

$$\Sigma \frac{\{|f - f_c| - \frac{1}{2}\}^2}{f_c}.$$

For purposes of computation, a simpler form is available. It is not given here because the use of Yates' correction is not recommended.

[16] See also "Yates' Correction and the Statisticians," by Franz Adler, in *Journal of the American Statistical Association*, December 1951, pp. 490–501.

six cups.   Of these 15, only one involves a correct matching of all three
pairs.   There are six ways of having one pair correctly matched and
eight ways of having no pairs correctly matched.   It is not possible to
match two pairs correctly.   If no difference existed in the taste of fresh,
moderately stale, and stale coffee, we would expect the correct matchings
of three, one, and no pairs to be in the ratio 1:6:8.   Table 25.9 shows the
observed data and the frequencies computed on the basis of these proportions.   From these two sets of figures, χ^2 is found to be 46.08.   Since
the total is set and there are three categories of sample data,[17] $n = 2$.
(The distribution of χ^2 for two degrees of freedom is shown in Chart 25.8.)
From Appendix J it may be seen that P is much less than 0.001, and it is
clear that the matchings differ significantly from a chance distribution.
Apparently it is possible to differentiate between fresh and stale coffee.
A point worth noting, however, is that the data were so presented by the
company that it was not possible to determine, when only a single pair
was matched, how frequently the matching consisted of the two fresh
cups, or the two cups made from 3-weeks-old coffee, or the two cups made
from 5-weeks-old coffee!   Furthermore, the tasters did not identify the
matched cups as "fresh," "moderately stale," and "stale."

Other 1 × R tables.   For tables having one column and more than
three rows of observed data, the procedure would be similar to that shown
for a 1 × 3 table in Table 25.9.   The degrees of freedom would be $R - 1$,

TABLE 25.9

*Computation of χ^2 for Matching of Pairs of Cups of Coffee Made
From Fresh, Three-Weeks-Old, and Five-Weeks-Old Coffee*

Number of pairs correctly matched	f	f_c 1:6:8	$f - f_c$	$(f - f_c)^2$	$\dfrac{(f - f_c)^2}{f_c}$
Three............	15	3.5	+11.5	132.25	37.79
One..............	24	20.8	+ 3.2	10.24	0.49
None.............	13	27.7	−14.7	216.09	7.80
Total..........	52	52.0	0	. . .	46.08

unless the f and f_c values had been made to agree in regard to more characteristics than just the total.   Tables having one row and C columns are
rarely encountered, because they are apt to be of unwieldy proportions.
Such a table could be recast into a 1 × R table.

Test of "goodness of fit" as a special case of a 1 × R table.   In
Chapter 23, a normal curve was fitted to data of baseball throws for
distance by first-year high school girls.   Columns (2) and (3) of Table
25.10 show the observed data and the computed frequencies.   From
these two sets of figures, χ^2 is found to be 6.65.   Now the observed and
the fitted data have been forced to agree with each other in regard to $\overline{X}$,

---

[17] Note that the expression $(R - 1)(C - 1)$ is not applicable to a 1 × R table.

s, and N. Therefore, three degrees of freedom were lost. Since the observed data are in 13 categories, we have $n = 13 - 3 = 10$. The distribution of χ^2 for $n = 10$ is shown in Chart 25.8. From Appendix J it is seen that P is more than 0.75 but less than 0.80, and we conclude that the agreement between the observed and computed frequencies is satisfactory; we have no reason to doubt the hypothesis that the sample was a random one from a normal population.

TABLE 25.10

Chi-Square Test of Goodness of Fit for Normal Curve Fitted to Baseball Throws for Distance by First-Year High School Girls

Distance in feet (1)	f observed frequency (2)	f_c expected frequency (3)	$f - f_c$ (4)	$(f - f_c)^2$ (5)	$\dfrac{(f - f_c)^2}{f_c}$ (6)
Under 25	1	1.1	-0.1	0.01	0.01
25 but under 35	2	3.2	-1.2	1.44	0.45
35 but under 45	7	9.1	-2.1	4.41	0.48
45 but under 55	25	20.2	4.8	23.04	1.14
55 but under 65	33	35.0	-2.0	4.00	0.11
65 but under 75	53	50.6	2.4	5.76	0.11
75 but under 85	64	57.4	6.6	43.56	0.76
85 but under 95	44	52.0	-8.0	64.00	1.23
95 but under 105	31	37.0	-6.0	36.00	0.97
105 but under 115	27	22.0	5.0	25.00	1.14
115 but under 125	11	10.2	0.8	0.64	0.06
125 but under 135	4	3.7	0.3	0.09	0.02
135 or more	1	1.5	-0.5	0.25	0.17
Total............	303	303.0	0	. . .	6.65

Data from Tables 23.1 and 23.3.

To avoid the marked effect upon χ^2 of small absolute differences between f and f_c, which may occur in the end classes, it is not unusual to group several frequencies at one or both ends when making a test of "goodness of fit." Because the distribution of f values around f_c does not properly correspond to the expected distribution when f_c is small, it has been recommended that no class should have fewer than 5 or 10 computed frequencies. However, it has been shown that, if the 0.05 criterion is being used, the end frequencies need not be this large. See W. G. Cochran, "The χ^2 Correction for Continuity," *Iowa State College Journal of Science*, Vol. XVI, No. 4, pp. 421–436.

2 × 3 and Larger Tables

2 × R tables. For tables having two columns and R rows of observed data, it is not necessary to use a worksheet such as that in Table 25.7. Using the symbols to have the meanings indicated in the following table,

a_1	b_1	N_1
a_2	b_2	N_2
a_3	b_3	N_3
.	.	.
.	.	.
.	.	.
N_a	N_b	N

the value of χ^2 may be computed from the expression

$$\chi^2 = \frac{N^2}{N_a N_b} \left\{ \left(\frac{a_1^2}{N_1} + \frac{a_2^2}{N_2} + \cdots \right) - \frac{N_a^2}{N} \right\}.$$

From information provided by selective service registrants examined for military service, sample data were obtained of the number of left-handed and right-handed registrants who were examined in the six army areas. The proportions of left-handed varied from 7.8 per cent in Area IV to 9.2 per cent in Area II. Applying a χ^2 test to the data of Table 25.11 enables us to ascertain whether the proportions of left- and right-

TABLE 25.11

Number of Left-Handed and Right-Handed Registrants in a Sample* of Those Examined in Each of the Six Army Areas

Army area	Left-handed	Right-handed	Total
I	161	1,636	1,797
II	223	2,195	2,418
III	193	2,130	2,323
IV	137	1,626	1,763
V	230	2,317	2,547
VI	120	1,191	1,311
Total	1,064	11,095	12,159

* The sample consisted of the records received by the Department of the Army on June 19, June 28, and June 30, 1952.

Data from "Prevalence of Left-Handedness Among Selective Service Registrants," by B. D. Karpinos and H. A. Grossman, *Human Biology*, Vol. 25, No. 1, pp. 36–49.

handed differed significantly in the various army areas. From this table we compute

$$\chi^2 = \frac{(12,159)^2}{(1,064)(11,095)} \left\{ \frac{(161)^2}{1,797} + \frac{(223)^2}{2,418} + \frac{(193)^2}{2,323} + \frac{(137)^2}{1,763} + \frac{(230)^2}{2,547} \right.$$
$$\left. + \frac{(120)^2}{1,311} - \frac{(1,064)^2}{12,159} \right\}$$

$$= 3.98.$$

In order to ascertain the number of degrees of freedom, we compute $n = (R - 1)(C - 1) = (5)(1) = 5$. The distribution of χ^2 for $n = 5$ is shown in Chart 25.8. From Appendix J we find that P is between 0.50 and 0.70, and we conclude that the proportions of left-handed and right-handed from the six areas are not significantly different.

For tables having C columns and two rows, the expression just used for χ^2 may also be used, with appropriate changes of symbols. Alternatively, the table may be rearranged into two columns.

Tables having three or more columns and three or more rows, with marginal totals set, are most expeditiously handled by means of a computation form such as Table 25.7. The degrees of freedom are $(R - 1)(C - 1)$.

When making chi-square tests, a very large probability may occasionally appear. Some writers have pointed out that a probability of 0.99 is just as unusual as 0.01, and that, if we were to consider 0.01 as discrediting a hypothesis, then 0.99 just as clearly discredits a hypothesis as does a probability of 0.01. It is true that an occurrence having a probability of 0.99 is just as surprising as an occurrence having a probability of 0.01, but it does not follow that a probability of 0.99 discredits the hypothesis. The startling agreement between sample and population or between two samples should lead us to look, more carefully than usual, for possibly "rigged" data, for arithmetic mistakes, for previous smoothing of the data if "goodness of fit" is involved, or for a carelessly designed experiment.

As a matter of fact, either extremely large or surprisingly small values of P should cause us to re-examine the situation. Consider the following incident which was mentioned on page 11: When fluorescent lighting was first introduced, some persons believed that radiation from the lights would sterilize people. Hoping to allay their fears, a railroad, which had already installed the lights, subjected one group of rats to incandescent light and a second group to fluorescent light. The first group had the usual number of offspring, the second group had none. This seemed, indeed, to reinforce the fears of those who thought that the fluorescent lights might sterilize. The result seemed so surprising that one executive asked that the second group of rats be carefully checked. Upon examination, they were found to be all of the same sex.

CHAPTER 26

Statistical Significance III: Variances, Analysis of Variance, Measures of Skewness and Kurtosis, and Correlation Coefficients

In this, the last chapter of the book, we shall give attention to variances computed from samples, the variance of several means (analysis of variance), values of β_1 and β_2 obtained from samples, and correlation coefficients.

VARIANCES

Our consideration of sample variances, $\hat{\sigma}^2$, will parallel the treatment of arithmetic means and proportions in that we shall first consider the difference between $\hat{\sigma}^2$ and σ^2; next we shall obtain confidence limits of σ^2; and then we shall compare two sample variances. In addition, we shall give attention to one way of comparing several sample variances.

Variances of random samples from a normal population are distributed neither normally nor symmetrically. Their distribution follows a skewed curve (skewed to the right), the exact shape of which depends upon σ^2 and N. Since tables giving values of $\hat{\sigma}^2$ for several values of P would have to have both σ^2 and N as arguments, and would therefore be very extensive, it is fortunate that $(N - 1)\hat{\sigma}^2 \div \sigma^2$ follows the chi-square distribution for $N - 1$ degrees of freedom. Thus, we write

$$\chi^2 = \frac{(N - 1)\hat{\sigma}^2}{\sigma^2}.$$

In the event that s^2 is given, rather than $\hat{\sigma}^2$, we may obtain $\hat{\sigma}^2$ from the expression

$$\hat{\sigma}^2 = \frac{N}{N - 1} s^2.$$

Alternatively, we may apply the χ^2 test in the form

$$\chi^2 = \frac{Ns^2}{\sigma^2},$$

with $n = N - 1$ for χ^2.

Significance of the difference between $\hat{\sigma}^2$ and σ^2. Below Table 24.1 it may be seen that the value of $\hat{\sigma}^2$ for 10 pieces of hard-drawn copper wire was 75.73. In this case, as in most others, we do not know the value of σ^2, but, for purposes of illustration, we shall assume that $\sigma^2 = 46.42$ and test the hypothesis that $\hat{\sigma}^2 = 75.73$ is the variance of a random sample from a population having $\sigma^2 = 46.42$. We shall use 0.05 as our criterion. Computing χ^2, we find

$$\chi^2 = \frac{(N-1)\hat{\sigma}^2}{\sigma^2} = \frac{n\hat{\sigma}^2}{\sigma^2} = \frac{(9)(75.73)}{46.42} = 14.683$$

for $n = N - 1 = 9$. From the χ^2 Table of Appendix J, it is seen that, if $\sigma^2 = 46.42$, the probability of obtaining $\hat{\sigma}^2 = 75.73$ or larger, for samples of 10, is almost exactly 0.10. Our hypothesis is not discredited. Note that, in this application, χ^2 has provided us with a one-tail test, since the probability which was obtained refers to values of $\hat{\sigma}^2$ equal to or larger than that observed.

If we are interested in considering values of $\hat{\sigma}^2$ which are less than σ^2, more than one avenue of approach is open to us. We may ascertain the probability of a value of $\hat{\sigma}^2$ showing the same absolute difference, but in the opposite direction. That is, $\hat{\sigma}^2 = 17.11$. Alternatively, we may determine the value of $\hat{\sigma}^2$ which cuts off the lower 10 per cent tail of the distribution of χ^2 for $n = 9$. Considering these two, in turn, we find that, when $\hat{\sigma}^2 = 17.11$,

$$\chi^2 = \frac{(9)(17.11)}{46.42} = 3.317,$$

and the probability is about 0.05 that values of $\hat{\sigma}^2$ equal to or smaller than 17.11 would occur. The value of $\hat{\sigma}^2$ which cuts off the lower 10 per cent tail of the distribution of χ^2 is obtained by using the χ^2 value for $P = 0.90$ when $n = 9$ in Appendix J. This is 4.168, and we write

$$4.168 = \frac{9\hat{\sigma}^2}{46.42}, \qquad \text{therefore } \hat{\sigma}^2 = 21.50.$$

The fact that the χ^2 test involves the ratio of $\hat{\sigma}^2$ to σ^2 may have already suggested to the reader that, when $n = 9$ and when $\chi^2 = 14.684$ (the value of χ^2 at the upper 0.10 point), the resulting probability of 0.10 may refer to any pair of values for $\hat{\sigma}^2$ and σ^2 giving the ratio $14.684 \div 9 = 1.632$. Whenever $\dfrac{\hat{\sigma}^2}{\sigma^2} = 1.632$, the value of $\hat{\sigma}^2$ will be at the upper 0.10 point. In symbols,[1]

$$\frac{\chi^2}{n} = \frac{\hat{\sigma}^2}{\sigma^2},$$

and from this relationship the table of Appendix K was prepared. This table enables one to compute sampling limits of $\hat{\sigma}^2$ merely by dividing $\hat{\sigma}^2$ by σ^2, thus making it unnecessary to compute χ^2. For the preceding illustration, where $\hat{\sigma}^2 = 17.11$ and $\sigma^2 = 46.42$, the ratio is 0.3686. Looking up this ratio in Appendix K for $n = 9$ gives a probability (lower point) of about 0.05, the same as obtained before.

Confidence limits of σ^2. We may also employ χ^2 to obtain the confidence limits of σ^2. For the data of hard-drawn copper wire, $\hat{\sigma}^2 = 75.73$ and $N = 10$. What are the 90 per cent confidence limits of σ^2? To answer this question, we use two chi-square values from Appendix J for $n = 9$: one at the upper 0.05 point and one at the lower 0.05 point (the 0.95 point in Appendix J). These χ^2 values are 16.919 and 3.325, and we solve $\chi^2 = \dfrac{n\hat{\sigma}^2}{\sigma^2}$ for σ^2:

$$16.919 = \frac{(9)(75.73)}{\sigma_1^2},$$
$$16.919\sigma_1^2 = 681.57,$$
$$\sigma_1^2 = 40.28,$$

and

$$3.325 = \frac{(9)(75.73)}{\sigma_2^2},$$
$$3.325\sigma_2^2 = 681.57,$$
$$\sigma_2^2 = 205.0.$$

The 90 per cent confidence limits of σ^2 are 40.28 and 205.0. As before, if we compute many such 90 per cent limits from random samples from a normal population,[1] our statements will include the population value 90 per cent of the time and fail to include it 10 per cent of the time.

---

[1] The ratio $\dfrac{\hat{\sigma}^2}{\sigma^2} = \dfrac{\chi^2}{n}$ is a special case of F (see page 720) when $n_2 = \infty$.

Rodger P. Doyle computed the 90 per cent confidence limits[2] of σ^2 for each of Shewhart's 1,000 samples from a normal population. His limits included σ^2 in 904 instances but did not do so for 96 of the samples.

We may recast the χ^2 expression

$$\chi^2 = \frac{n\hat{\sigma}^2}{\sigma^2}$$

to read

$$\frac{\sigma^2}{\hat{\sigma}^2} = \frac{n}{\chi^2}$$

to enable us to make a table from which to obtain the confidence limits of σ^2. Such a table is given as Appendix L. Using it to get the 90 per cent confidence limits of σ^2, when $n = 9$, which were just obtained by use of χ^2, we would compute

$$\sigma_1^2 = 0.5319\hat{\sigma}^2 = (0.5319)(75.73) = 40.28,$$

and

$$\sigma_2^2 = 2.707\hat{\sigma}^2 = (2.707)(75.73) = 205.0.$$

Significance of the difference between two sample variances. In Chapter 24 we considered the significance of the difference between the mean lengths of two sets of lower first molars which had $N_1 = 16$, $s_1 = 0.72$, $N_2 = 9$, and $s_2 = 0.62$. We previously found that there was not a significant difference between $\bar{X}_1$ and $\bar{X}_2$. Using the 0.05 level as our criterion, let us now test the hypotheses that the two samples were from the same population in respect to σ^2.

When $\hat{\sigma}_1^2$ and $\hat{\sigma}_2^2$ are independent estimates of σ^2 from the same normal population, their ratio $\dfrac{\hat{\sigma}_1^2}{\hat{\sigma}_2^2}$ is distributed according to the F distribution with $n_1 = N_1 - 1$ and $n_2 = N_2 - 1$ degrees of freedom. If $\hat{\sigma}_1^2 = \hat{\sigma}_2^2$, the value of F is 1.0. Values of F vary from 0 to 0.999 $\cdots$ when $\hat{\sigma}_1^2 < \hat{\sigma}_2^2$ and from 1.000 $\cdots$ 1 to ∞ when $\hat{\sigma}_1^2 > \hat{\sigma}_2^2$. The F distribution is "reverse—J" shaped when $n_1 = 1$ or $n_1 = 2$ and skewed to the right when $n_1 \geqq 3$. Several F distributions are shown in Chart 26.1.

For the data of lower first molars we found, in Chapter 24, $\Sigma x_1^2 = 8.29$ and $\Sigma x_2^2 = 3.46$. Consequently,

$$\hat{\sigma}_1^2 = \frac{\Sigma x_1^2}{N_1 - 1} = \frac{8.29}{16 - 1} = 0.553,$$

$$\hat{\sigma}_2^2 = \frac{\Sigma x_2^2}{N_2 - 1} = \frac{3.46}{9 - 1} = 0.432,$$

[2] From unpublished material.

HEIGHT OF ORDINATE

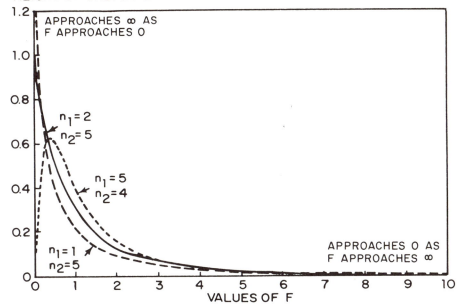

Chart 26.1. Distribution of F for $n_1 = 1$, $n_2 = 5$; $n_1 = 2$, $n_2 = 5$; and $n_1 = 5$, $n_2 = 4$. Horizontal and vertical scales extend to ∞. The ordinates of the F distribution are obtained from the expression

$$Y_c = \frac{F^{\frac{n_1-2}{2}}}{(n_1F + n_2)^{\frac{n_1+n_2}{2}}} \cdot \frac{\left(\dfrac{n_1 + n_2 - 2}{2}\right)! \, (n_1)^{\frac{n_1}{2}} (n_2)^{\frac{n_2}{2}}}{\left(\dfrac{n_1 - 2}{2}\right)! \left(\dfrac{n_2 - 2}{2}\right)!}.$$

and

$$F = \frac{0.553}{0.432} = 1.28,$$

with $n_1 = 15$ and $n_2 = 8$. Values of F for selected values of n_1 and n_2 and for probabilities of 0.10, 0.05, 0.025, 0.01, and 0.001 *in the right tail of the distribution* are given in Appendix M. Referring to that appendix, we find that $n_1 = 15$ is not given, but $n_1 = 12$ and $n_1 = 24$ are given, and so is $n_2 = 8$. It is not necessary to interpolate for $n_1 = 15$, since the probability of $F \geqq 1.28$ exceeds 0.10 whether we consider $n_1 = 12$ and $n_2 = 8$ or $n_1 = 24$ and $n_2 = 8$. The observed value of $\hat{\sigma}_1^2$ does not significantly exceed the observed value of $\hat{\sigma}_2^2$. But what about differences in the reverse direction?

If $\hat{\sigma}_1^2$ had been 0.432 with $N_1 = 16$ and $\hat{\sigma}_2^2$ had been 0.553 with $N_2 = 9$, then we would have

$$F = \frac{\hat{\sigma}_1^2}{\hat{\sigma}_2^2} = \frac{0.432}{0.553} = 0.781,$$

with $n_1 = 15$ and $n_2 = 8$. Now, the table of Appendix M does not include any F values smaller than 1.0. When a value of F is less than one, we can obtain the probability[3] of that F value or less by computing $\frac{1}{F}$, which will exceed 1.0, and reverse the degrees of freedom. That is, we would look up

$$F = \frac{1}{0.781} = 1.28$$

with $n_1 = 8$ and $n_2 = 15$. Doing this, we find that the probability of $F \geq 1.28$ when $n_1 = 8$ and $n_2 = 15$ is more than 0.10; therefore, the probability is also more than 0.10 for a value of $F \leq 0.781$ with $n_1 = 15$ and $n_2 = 8$.

Comparison of several values of $\hat{\sigma}^2$. Sometimes it is important to know whether uniformity exists between several values of $\hat{\sigma}^2$. A pencil manufacturing concern made tests of the strength of the lead of their own pencils and of pencils manufactured by five of their competitors. The tests included five pencils of each hardness, 1, 2, 2.5, 3, and 4, from each of the six companies. Each individual pencil was tested four times.

For five Number 2 pencils, made by a company which we shall call "Company D," the tests[4] showed $\hat{\sigma}_1^2 = 0.01316$, $\hat{\sigma}_2^2 = 0.05667$, $\hat{\sigma}_3^2 = 0.02787$, $\hat{\sigma}_4^2 = 0.01930$, $\hat{\sigma}_5^2 = 0.01529$. $N_1 = N_2 = N_3 = N_4 = N_5 = 4$. One way to compare these variances would be to compute F for $\hat{\sigma}_1^2$ and $\hat{\sigma}_2^2$, for $\hat{\sigma}_1^2$ and $\hat{\sigma}_3^2$, and so on. Another procedure involves comparing all of the $\hat{\sigma}^2$ values at once by means of the measure L, sometimes referred to as a criterion of likelihood.

$$L = \frac{\sqrt[k]{\hat{\sigma}_1^2 \times \hat{\sigma}_2^2 \times \cdots \times \hat{\sigma}_k^2}}{\frac{1}{k}(\hat{\sigma}_1^2 + \hat{\sigma}_2^2 + \cdots + \hat{\sigma}_k^2)},$$

if $N_1 = N_2 = \cdots = N_k$. If the samples include varying numbers of items,

$$L = \frac{\sqrt[n]{(\hat{\sigma}_1^2)^{n_1} \times (\hat{\sigma}_2^2)^{n_2} \times \cdots \times (\hat{\sigma}_k^2)^{n_k}}}{\frac{1}{n}(n_1\hat{\sigma}_1^2 + n_2\hat{\sigma}_2^2 + \cdots + n_k\hat{\sigma}_k^2)},$$

---

[3] An abbreviated table, prepared by the authors of this volume and showing both upper and lower points, may be found in F. E. Croxton, *Elementary Statistics with Applications in Medicine and the Biological Sciences*, Dover Publications, Inc., New York, 1959, pp. 334–335.

[4] The test data are shown in Table 26.3.

where $n = n_1 + n_2 + \cdots + n_k$. The numerator is the geometric mean of the $\hat{\sigma}^2$'s while the denominator is the arithmetic mean of the $\hat{\sigma}^2$'s. We already know (Chapter 9) that the geometric mean of a series of values, which are not all the same, is smaller than the arithmetic mean of those values. Also, the more divergent the values, the greater the difference between G and $\overline{X}$. Now, if $\hat{\sigma}_1^2 = \hat{\sigma}_2^2 = \cdots = \hat{\sigma}_k^2$, a condition of maximum uniformity obtains, and the value of L is 1.0. If there is any difference between the $\hat{\sigma}^2$'s, the value of L will be less than 1.0, approaching 0 as its lower limit. $L = 0$ represents a condition of maximum non-uniformity and is a theoretical limit which would not be approached in actual practice.

Computing L for the five Number 2 pencils made by Company D gives

$$L = \frac{\sqrt[5]{0.01316 \times 0.05667 \times 0.02787 \times 0.01930 \times 0.01529}}{\frac{1}{5}(0.01316 + 0.05667 + 0.02787 + 0.01930 + 0.01529)},$$

$$= \frac{0.02278}{0.02646} = 0.86.$$

It would appear, since 0.86 is not far removed from 1.0, that uniformity exists among the five values of $\hat{\sigma}^2$. However, we want to know whether $L = 0.86$ differs significantly from 1.0. The hypothesis to be tested is that the five variances were from random samples from the same population in regard to σ^2. The distribution of L, for samples drawn from a normal population, is J-shaped, as shown by the small chart above Appendix N. This appendix gives values of L at the 0.05 and 0.01 points for various values of N_i and k, where N_i refers to the number of items in any one of the samples of equal size. For our problem, $N_i = 4$ and $k = 5$, and, from Appendix N, it is seen that $L = 0.491$ is at the 0.05 point while $L = 0.370$ is at the 0.01 point. It is clear that the observed value of $L = 0.86$ does not differ significantly from 1.0; the hypothesis is not discredited.

Values of L were computed for the variances of Number 2 pencils made by each of the other five companies. In one instance, $L = 0.30$ with $N_i = 4$ and $k = 5$ as before. This value for L is beyond the 0.01 point and would be considered significantly different from 1.0.

ANALYSIS OF VARIANCE

In Chapter 24 we considered the significance of the difference between two means. The discussion of analysis of variance, which follows, deals with two or more means. In its simplest aspect, analysis of variance will have to do with two independent estimates of σ^2 which will be compared with each other by means of F.

One criterion of classification. In Table 26.1, data are shown of the length of eggs of the European cuckoo found in the nests of three other species of birds. The European cuckoo makes a practice of permitting other birds to hatch its eggs and rear its offspring. We are interested in knowing whether the mean lengths of cuckoo eggs found in the nests of the hedge-sparrow, the robin, and the wren are significantly different from each other. We shall not compare the first mean with the second, the first with the third, and the second with the third. We shall consider the three means as a group, comparing the estimated variance of those three means (one estimate of the variance in the population) with the estimated variance within the three columns (a second estimate of the variance in the population).

The data of Table 26.1 are classified according to one criterion: the species of bird in which the cuckoo's eggs were found. For such a table, there are three sources of variation.

1. *Variation between column means.* The variation between column means is obtained by taking the differences between each column mean $(\overline{X}_1, \overline{X}_2, \overline{X}_3, \cdots)$ and the "grand mean" $(\overline{X}$, the arithmetic mean of all the values), squaring each difference, multiplying each squared difference by the number of items in the appropriate column $(N_1, N_2, N_3, \cdots)$, and summing. Symbolically, this is

$$N_1(\overline{X}_1 - \overline{X})^2 + N_2(\overline{X}_2 - \overline{X})^2 + N_3(\overline{X}_3 - \overline{X})^2 + \cdots .$$

Using $\overline{X}_c$ to indicate a column mean, N_c the number of items in a column, and k_c the number of columns, variation between column means may be written

$$\sum_{1}^{k_c} [N_c(\overline{X}_c - \overline{X})^2],$$

where $\sum_{1}^{k_c}$ indicates that a summation over the k_c columns is to be made.

The expression just given calls for the computation of k_c column means and the grand mean. This is not necessary, as it is shown in Appendix S, section 26.1, that[5]

$$\sum_{1}^{k_c}[N_c(\overline{X}_c - \overline{X})^2] = \sum_{1}^{k_c}\left[\frac{\left(\sum_{1}^{N_c} X\right)^2}{N_c}\right] - \frac{(\Sigma X)^2}{N},$$

---

[5] If $N_1 = N_2 = N_3 = \cdots$, the expression

$$\sum_{1}^{k_c}\left[\frac{\left(\sum_{1}^{N_c} X\right)^2}{N_c}\right]$$

may be written

$$\frac{\sum_{1}^{k_c}\left(\sum_{1}^{N_c} X\right)^2}{N_c}.$$

TABLE 26.1

Computation of Values Required for Analysis of Variance of Data of Length of Cuckoo's Eggs Found in the Nests of Three Species of Birds

Hedge-sparrow		Robin		Wren	
X_1	X_1^2	X_2	X_2^2	X_3	X_3^2
22.0	484.00	21.8	475.24	19.8	392.04
23.9	571.21	23.0	529.00	22.1	488.41
20.9	436.81	23.3	542.89	21.5	462.25
23.8	566.44	22.4	501.76	20.9	436.81
25.0	625.00	22.4	501.76	22.0	484.00
24.0	576.00	23.0	529.00	21.0	441.00
21.7	470.89	23.0	529.00	22.3	497.29
23.8	566.44	23.0	529.00	21.0	441.00
22.8	519.84	23.9	571.21	20.3	412.09
23.1	533.61	22.3	497.29	20.9	436.81
23.1	533.61	22.0	484.00	22.0	484.00
23.5	552.25	22.6	510.76	20.0	400.00
23.0	529.00	22.0	484.00	20.8	432.64
23.0	529.00	22.1	488.41	21.2	449.44
...	...	21.1	445.21	21.0	441.00
...	...	23.0	529.00	...	...
323.6	7,494.10	360.9	8,147.53	316.8	6,698.78

Data from Oswald H. Latter, "The Egg of Cuculus Canorus," *Biometrika*, Vol. 1, p. 173.

$$N = 45$$
$$\Sigma X = 323.6 + 360.9 + 316.8 = 1,001.3.$$
$$(\Sigma X)^2 = (1,001.3)^2 = 1,002,601.69.$$
$$\Sigma X^2 = 7,494.10 + 8,147.53 + 6,698.78 = 22,340.41.$$

$$\sum_{1}^{k_c} \left[\frac{\left(\overset{N_c}{\underset{1}{\Sigma}} X \right)^2}{N_c} \right] = \frac{(323.6)^2}{14} + \frac{(360.9)^2}{16} + \frac{(316.8)^2}{15} = 22,311.1495.$$

where $\overset{N_c}{\underset{1}{\Sigma}}$ refers to a summation of the N_c items in a column and $N = N_1 + N_2 + N_3$. From the computations shown below Table 26.1,

$$\sum_{1}^{k_c} \left[\frac{\left(\overset{N_c}{\underset{1}{\Sigma}} X \right)^2}{N_c} \right] - \frac{(\Sigma X)^2}{N} = 22,311.15 - \frac{1,002,601.69}{45},$$
$$= 22,311.15 - 22,280.04,$$
$$= 31.11.$$

2. *Variation within columns.* Variations within columns is the variation of the values in the columns from the column means. It is obtained

by taking the difference between each item in a column and the column mean, squaring the differences, summing the squared differences for the column, performing the same operations for the other columns, and summing the sums for the columns. Symbolically, variation within columns is

$$\sum_{1}^{k_c} \left[\sum_{1}^{N_c} (X - \overline{X}_c)^2 \right].$$

This expression involves the computation of k_c column means and the determination of N differences. These operations are unnecessary, since Appendix S, section 26.2 shows that

$$\sum_{1}^{k_c} \left[\sum_{1}^{N_c} (X - \overline{X}_c)^2 \right] = \sum X^2 - \sum_{1}^{k_c} \left[\frac{\left(\sum_{1}^{N_c} X \right)^2}{N_c} \right];$$

and, again referring to the computations below Table 26.1, we find

$$\sum X^2 - \sum_{1}^{k_c} \left[\frac{\left(\sum_{1}^{N_c} X \right)^2}{N_c} \right] = 22{,}340.41 - 22{,}311.15,$$

$$= 29.26.$$

3. *Total variation.* Total variation is the sum of the squared deviations of all the values from the grand mean. It is the same as Ns^2, where s is the standard deviation, which was explained in Chapter 10. Symbolically, total variation is

$$\sum_{1}^{N} (X - \overline{X})^2.$$

It is not necessary to obtain the N deviations called for by this expression, since, by a procedure similar to that shown in Appendix S, section 10.2, it may be shown that

$$\sum_{1}^{N} (X - \overline{X})^2 = \sum X^2 - \frac{(\sum X)^2}{N}.$$

For the cuckoo-egg data,

$$\sum X^2 - \frac{(\sum X)^2}{N} = 22{,}340.41 - \frac{1{,}002{,}601.69}{45},$$

$$= 22{,}340.41 - 22{,}280.04 = 60.37.$$

Notice that the sum of the first two values which we obtained equals the third value. That is: variation between column means + variation within columns = total variation.   This is true for all problems such as this, since

$$\left\{\sum_1^{k_c}\left[\frac{\left(\sum_1^{N_c}X\right)^2}{N_c}\right] - \frac{(\sum X)^2}{N}\right\} + \left\{\sum X^2 - \sum_1^{k_c}\left[\frac{\left(\sum_1^{N_c}X\right)^2}{N_c}\right]\right\} = \sum X^2 - \frac{(\sum X)^2}{N}.$$

As will be seen later, no use will be made of the numerical value for total variation.   Nevertheless, it is well to compute it as a check on the other values.

Estimated variances.   It is our objective to compare the estimated variance between column means with the estimated variance within columns in order to ascertain whether the column means differ more than might be accounted for by chance.   The estimated variance within columns is our yardstick of chance variance, since the variation of the items in the columns is not affected by differences between $\overline{X}_1$, $\overline{X}_2$, $\overline{X}_3$, $\cdots$.   Estimated variance is obtained from variation by dividing variation by the appropriate number of degrees of freedom.   For our problem, estimated variance between column means has $n = 2$, since the deviations of the three column means were taken from $\overline{X}$.   For estimated variance within columns, $n = N_1 - 1 + N_2 - 1 + N_3 - 1 = 14 - 1 + 16 - 1 + 15 - 1 = 42$, since the deviations in each column were taken from the column mean.

The computation of the estimated variances is indicated in Table 26.2, and from these we get

$$F = \frac{15.56}{0.6967} = 22.3,$$

with $n_1 = 2$ and $n_2 = 42$.   The F table of Appendix M does not contain a row for $n_2 = 42$, but it is, nevertheless, clear that the probability of getting $F \geq 22.3$ is much less than 0.001, and we conclude that there is a real difference between the mean lengths of the eggs found in the nests of the three species of birds.   It is of interest that later non-statistical investigations revealed that European cuckoos exhibit what is known as *host specificity*,[6] which means that "different tribes, or gentes, exist within the species, even in the same area, each adherent to a different host species and each specialized in at least one respect for that one species."

The hypothesis which we tested was that the estimated variance between column means and the estimated variance within columns were from the same population with respect to σ^2.   The hypothesis was discredited.   If a sample is drawn from a normal homogeneous population,

---

[6] See "Social Parasites Among Birds," by Alden H. Miller, *The Scientific Monthly*, Vol. LXII, p. 243.

TABLE 26.2

Summary of Computations for Analysis of Variance of Data of Length of Cuckoo's Eggs

Source of variation	Amount of variation	Degrees of freedom	Estimated variance
Between column means.............	31.11	2	15.56
Within columns...................	29.26	42	0.6967
Total.........................	60.37	44	...

we could expect the two estimated variances just mentioned and $\hat{\sigma}^2$ (an estimate based on total variation) to be equally good estimates of σ^2. But if heterogeneity is present, as it was in our illustration, the estimated variance between column means and $\hat{\sigma}^2$ are both affected by that heterogeneity. Estimated variance within columns is not affected, and therefore provided our measure of chance variance.

The F test for the data of length of cuckoo's eggs involved a situation in which $n_1 = 2$ and $n_2 = 42$. If we had had two columns of observed data in Table 26.1, instead of three columns, n_1 would have been 1 and our problem would have been that of testing the significance of the difference between $\overline{X}_1$ and $\overline{X}_2$, which was considered in Chapter 24. In fact, whenever an estimated variance has $n_1 = 1$ in an F test, the t test is an alternative which yields the same probability. This will be clear if we look at Appendices I and M. From these it may be seen that, for any given probability, the value for t^2 is the same as the value for F when n for t equals n_2 for F and when n_1 for F is 1. An instance in which the t-test could be used in place of F occurs in the test of the estimated variance between column means shown in Table 26.6.

Two criteria of classification, one entry in each box. The data of Table 26.1 had but one criteria of classification, the type of nest in which the cuckoo's eggs were found. In Table 26.3 there are two criteria of classification: (1) the different pencils, of which there were five, and (2) the location on the pencil where the test was made, of which there were four for each pencil. Each pencil was sharpened and tested, then sharpened again and tested, and so on. It is conceivable that changes in location may be associated with a progressive increase or decrease of strength of the lead.

Table 26.3 has $5 \times 4 = 20$ boxes[7] or cells of observed data, in each of which there is but a single entry. We shall see later that it is desirable to have more than one entry in a box, if that is possible. However, there are some situations, such as the present one, in which only one entry is possible. We could include more pencils or we could test each pencil

---

[7] The term "box" is used in this text, since we have already used $\overline{X}_c$ to indicate the mean of a column and shall later use $\overline{X}_b$ to indicate the mean of a box.

TABLE 26.3

Computation of Values Required for Analysis of Variance of Data of Strength of Lead in Number 2 Pencils Manufactured by "Company D"

A. Observed data, in kilograms, and sums.

Location of test on pencil	Pencil 1 X_1	Pencil 2 X_2	Pencil 3 X_3	Pencil 4 X_4	Pencil 5 X_5	$\sum_1^{N_r} X$	$\left(\sum_1^{N_r} X\right)^2$
I	1.82	1.70	1.70	1.82	1.92	8.96	80.2816
II	1.56	1.36	1.68	1.98	1.86	8.44	71.2336
III	1.78	1.54	2.02	1.82	1.64	8.80	77.4400
IV	1.74	1.92	1.92	1.64	1.75	8.97	80.4609
$\sum_1^{N_c} X$	6.90	6.52	7.32	7.26	7.17	35.17 $\sum X$	309.4161 $\sum_1^{k_r}\left(\sum_1^{N_r} X\right)^2$

Data from tests of pencils of various brands conducted for the Eagle Pencil Co.

B. Squares of observed data and sum.

Location of test on pencil	X_1^2	X_2^2	X_3^2	X_4^2	X_5^2	Total
I	3.3124	2.8900	2.8900	3.3124	3.6864	16.0912
II	2.4336	1.8496	2.8224	3.9204	3.4596	14.4856
III	3.1684	2.3716	4.0804	3.3124	2.6896	15.6224
IV	3.0276	3.6864	3.6864	2.6896	3.0625	16.1525
Total	11.9420	10.7976	13.4792	13.2348	12.8981	62.3517 $= \sum X^2$

$$N_c = 4, \quad N_r = 5, \quad N = 20.$$
$$(\sum X)^2 = (35.17)^2 = 1,236.9289.$$
$$\sum_1^{k_c}\left(\sum_1^{N_c} X\right)^2 = (6.90)^2 + (6.52)^2 + (7.32)^2 + (7.26)^2 + (7.17)^2 = 247.8193.$$

at more locations, but we could not have more than one test at a given location on a pencil.

For the data of Table 26.3, we have variation between column means and total variation, as before. However, there is no variation within columns, but instead, there is variation between row means and a residual variation representing a difference between (1) total variation and (2) variation between column means plus variation between row means. We shall first compute each of these variations.

Total variation. The expression is the same as that previously used, and for the data of 26.3, we have

$$\sum X^2 - \frac{(\sum X)^2}{N} = 62.3517 - \frac{1,236.9289}{20} = 0.505255.$$

Variation between column means may also be obtained by use of the expression used before, but, as pointed out in footnote 5, it may be slightly simplified when the number of items in the columns is the same. For the pencil data,

$$\frac{\overset{k_c}{\underset{1}{\Sigma}}\left(\overset{N_c}{\underset{1}{\Sigma}X}\right)^2}{N_c} - \frac{(\Sigma X)^2}{N} = \frac{247.8193}{4} - \frac{1,236.9289}{20} = 0.108380.$$

Variation between row means. This concept is the exact parallel of that just given. Using the following symbols,

$\bar{X}_r$, the mean of a row,
N_r, the number of items in a row,
k_r, the number of rows,
$\overset{N_r}{\underset{1}{\Sigma}}$, a sum over the N_r items in a row, and
$\overset{k_r}{\underset{1}{\Sigma}}$, a sum over the k_r rows,

and remembering that the number of items in the rows is the same, we have

$$\frac{\overset{k_r}{\underset{1}{\Sigma}}\left(\overset{N_r}{\underset{1}{\Sigma}X}\right)^2}{N_r} - \frac{(\Sigma X)^2}{N} = \frac{309.4161}{5} - \frac{1,236.9289}{20} = 0.036775.$$

Residual variation. The sum of the variation between column means and the variation between row means is less than total variation. This difference, which is

$$(0.505255) - (0.108380 + 0.036775) = 0.360100,$$

is ordinarily referred to as "residual variation," since it is usually computed as a residual. It is possible to compute this value directly by means of the expression

$$\Sigma(X + \bar{X} - \bar{X}_r - \bar{X}_c)^2.$$

For the data of Table 26.3, this time-consuming computation gives 0.360100, the same value as was obtained as a residual.

Estimated variances. Table 26.4 summarizes the foregoing results and shows also the number of degrees of freedom and the estimated variances. Since there are five column means, the variation of which was computed around $\bar{X}$, variation between column means has four degrees of freedom. Variation between row means involved four means, the variation of which was in relation to $\bar{X}$, so variation between row means has three degrees

TABLE 26.4

*Summary of Computations for Analysis of Variance of Data of
Strength of Lead in Pencils*

Source of variation	Amount of variation	Degrees of freedom	Estimated variance
Between column means.........	0.108380	4	0.027095
Between row means............	0.036775	3	0.012258
Residual.....................	0.360100	12	0.030008
Total.......................	0.505255	19	...

of freedom. Since total variation has $N - 1 = 20 - 1 = 19$ degrees of freedom, residual variation has $19 - (4 + 3) = 12$ degrees of freedom.

From the estimated variances of Table 26.4, we may now make two F tests, one for column means:

$$F = \frac{0.027095}{0.030008} = 0.903; \; n_1 = 4, \, n_2 = 12,$$

and the other for row means:

$$F = \frac{0.012258}{0.030008} = 0.408; \; n_1 = 3, \, n_2 = 12.$$

Since neither of these F values exceeds 1.0, it is clear that neither the estimated variance between column means (that is, between pencils) nor the estimated variance between row means (that is, between locations) exceeds our estimate of chance variance. Therefore, no significance test is needed.[8] If the reader is interested in knowing whether either F value is significantly less than 1.0, he may proceed as indicated earlier: compute $\frac{1}{F}$ and look up this value in Appendix M with the degrees of freedom reversed. He will find that neither of the F values is significantly less than 1.0.

The denominator for both of the F values computed above was estimated residual variance; that was our measure of chance variance, since it was the only one of the four sources of variation which would not be affected by heterogeneity. The fact that there was but one entry in a box in Table 26.3 makes it impossible to evaluate two elements which are present and separable when there is more than one entry in a box. These are: (1) interaction between the two criteria of classification and (2) variation within boxes.

---

[8] If we ignore the locations on the pencils where the tests were made, the data of Table 26.3 form a problem with one criterion of classification. On this basis, also, variance between column means (that is, between pencils) is not significant. See the first edition of this text, pp. 356–359.

Two criteria of classification, more than one entry in a box.
Part I of Table 26.5 shows data of life in minutes of nine brands of flash-light cells when in new condition and after 6–12 months' storage. Here there are two criteria of classification, as before, but there are five entries in each box. Total variation is now made up of four components: variation between column means, variation between row means, inter-action between column and row means, and variation within boxes. Using the sums shown in Table 26.5, we shall proceed to obtain the numerical values of all of these.

Total variation. The expression for total variation is the same as previously used.

$$\Sigma X^2 - \frac{(\Sigma X)^2}{N} = 34,325,736 - \frac{2,874,460,996}{90},$$

$$= 2,387,280.49.$$

Variation between column means employs the same formula as in the preceding illustration, since the number of items in the two columns of Part I of Table 26.5 is the same.

$$\frac{\sum\limits_{1}^{k_c}\left(\sum\limits_{1}^{N_c} X\right)^2}{N_c} - \frac{(\Sigma X)^2}{N} = \frac{1,454,015,716}{45} - \frac{2,874,460,996}{90},$$

$$= 373,004.85.$$

Variation between row means also uses the same expression as in the preceding example, since the number of items in the nine rows of Part I of Table 26.5 is the same.

$$\frac{\sum\limits_{1}^{k_r}\left(\sum\limits_{1}^{N_r} X\right)^2}{N_r} - \frac{(\Sigma X)^2}{N} = \frac{333,359,050}{10} - \frac{2,874,460,996}{90},$$

$$= 1,397,449.49.$$

Variation within boxes. This is the variation of the items in the boxes around the means of the boxes. Symbolically it is

$$\sum\limits_{1}^{k_b}\left[\sum\limits_{1}^{N_b}(X - \bar{X}_b)^2\right],$$

where

$\bar{X}_b$ is the mean of a box,
N_b is the number of items in a box,

TABLE 26.5

Computation of Values Required for Analysis of Variance of Data of Life of Type D Flashlight Cells*

I. Observed data and sums for columns and rows

II. Squares and sums for columns and rows

Brand	New	After storage	$\sum_{1}^{N_r} X$	Brand	New	After storage	$\sum_{1}^{N_r} X^2$
A	696	612		A	484,416	374,544	
	728	513			529,984	263,169	
	730	558	6,214		532,900	311,364	3,955,732
	683	479			466,489	229,441	
	720	495			518,400	245,025	
B	661	643		B	436,921	413,449	
	646	642			417,316	412,164	
	693	636	6,597		480,249	404,496	4,355,555
	674	678			454,276	459,684	
	678	646			459,684	417,316	
C	749	722		C	561,001	521,284	
	757	670			573,049	448,900	
	832	649	7,092		692,224	421,201	5,130,856
	787	718			619,369	515,524	
	760	448			577,600	200,704	
D	840	706		D	705,600	498,436	
	734	657			538,756	431,649	
	845	728	7,515		714,025	529,984	5,726,771
	798	576			636,804	331,776	
	885	746			783,225	556,516	
E	690	628		E	476,100	394,384	
	733	648			537,289	419,904	
	736	602	6,649		541,696	362,404	4,440,023
	691	622			477,481	386,884	
	659	640			434,281	409,600	
F	733	672		F	537,289	451,584	
	757	604			573,049	364,816	
	714	622	6,637		509,796	386,884	4,438,071
	608	576			369,664	331,776	
	693	658			480,249	432,964	
G	478	296		G	228,484	87,616	
	734	455			538,756	207,025	
	635	320	4,752		403,225	102,400	2,491,574
	672	272			451,584	73,984	
	410	480			168,100	230,400	
H	470	413		H	220,900	170,569	
	586	543			343,396	294,849	
	395	138	3,669		156.025	19,044	1,624,223
	414	38			171,396	1,444	
	438	234			191,844	54,756	
I	680	352		I	462,400	123,904	
	507	408			257,049	166,464	
	362	544	4,489		131,044	295,936	2,162,931
	458	227			209,764	51,529	
	555	396			308,025	156,816	
$\sum_{1}^{N_c} X$	29,704	23,910	53,614 $= \sum X$	$\sum_{1}^{N_c} X^2$	20,361,174	13,964,562	34,325,736 $= \sum X^2$

TABLE 26.5 (*Continued*)

III. Sums and squares of sums for boxes

Box	$\overset{N_b}{\underset{1}{\Sigma}} X$	$\left(\overset{N_b}{\underset{1}{\Sigma}} X\right)^2$
Row 1, Col. 1	3,557	12,652,249
Col. 2	2,657	7,059,649
Row 2, Col. 1	3,352	11,235,904
Col. 2	3,245	10,530,025
Row 3, Col. 1	3,885	15,093,225
Col. 2	3,207	10,284,849
Row 4, Col. 1	4,102	16,826,404
Col. 2	3,413	11,648,569
Row 5, Col. 1	3,509	12,313,081
Col. 2	3,140	9,859,600
Row 6, Col. 1	3,505	12,285,025
Col. 2	3,132	9,809,424
Row 7, Col. 1	2,929	8,579,041
Col. 2	1,823	3,323,329
Row 8, Col. 1	2,303	5,303,809
Col. 2	1,366	1,865,956
Row 9, Col. 1	2,562	6,563,844
Col. 2	1,927	3,713,329
Total	53,614	$168,947,312 = \overset{k_b}{\underset{1}{\Sigma}}\left(\overset{N_b}{\underset{1}{\Sigma}} X\right)^2$

* Life of a cell is the time in minutes for cell voltage to drop to 0.90 volts when tested as in Federal Specification W-B-101b.   Type D cells are the largest flashlight size.

Data in part I furnished through the courtesy of Consumers' Research, Washington, New Jersey, from its tests of flashlight batteries reported in CR's August 1953 Bulletin.

$$(\Sigma X)^2 = (53,614)^2 = 2,874,460,996.$$

$$\overset{k_c}{\underset{1}{\Sigma}}\left(\overset{N_c}{\underset{1}{\Sigma}} X\right)^2 = (29,704)^2 + (23,910)^2 = 1,454,015,716.$$

$$\overset{k_r}{\underset{1}{\Sigma}}\left(\overset{N_r}{\underset{1}{\Sigma}} X\right)^2 = (6,214)^2 + (6,597)^2 + (7,092)^2 + (7,515)^2$$
$$+ (6,649)^2 + (6,637)^2 + (4,752)^2 + (3,669)^2$$
$$+ (4,489)^2 = 333,359,050.$$

k_b is the number of boxes,

$\overset{N_b}{\underset{1}{\Sigma}}$ is a sum over the N_b items in a box, and

$\overset{k_b}{\underset{1}{\Sigma}}$ is a sum over the k_b boxes.

By a process similar to that shown in Appendix S, section 26.2, this expression becomes

$$\Sigma X^2 - \sum_{1}^{k_b} \left[\frac{\left(\sum\limits_{1}^{N_b} X \right)^2}{N_b} \right].$$

However, there is the same number of items in each of the boxes of Table 26.5, Part I; so we can write

$$\Sigma X^2 - \frac{\sum\limits_{1}^{k_b} \left(\sum\limits_{1}^{N_b} X \right)^2}{N_b} = 34{,}325{,}736 - \frac{168{,}947{,}312}{5},$$

$$= 34{,}325{,}736 - 33{,}789{,}462.4,$$

$$= 536{,}273.6.$$

Interaction. The numerical value for total variation exceeds the sum of the three variations last obtained. This difference is the variation due to interaction between column means and row means. Its numerical value is

$$2{,}387{,}280.49 - (373{,}004.85 + 1{,}397{,}449.49 + 536{,}273.6) = 80{,}552.55.$$

Alternatively, but much more laboriously, interaction may be computed directly from

$$\sum_{1}^{k_b} [N_b(\overline{X}_b + \overline{X} - \overline{X}_r - \overline{X}_c)^2].$$

Estimated variances. Table 26.6 shows the amount of variation, the degrees of freedom, and the estimated variance for each source of variation; total variation and the degrees of freedom for total variation are also

TABLE 26.6
Summary of Computations for Analysis of Variance of Data of Life of Type D Flashlight Cells

Source of variation	Amount of variation	Degrees of freedom	Estimated variance
Between column means.......	373,004.85	1	373,004.85
Between row means..........	1,397,449.49	8	174,681.19
Interaction..................	80,552.55	8	10,069.07
Within boxes	536,273.6	72	7,448.24
Total...................	2,387,280.49	89	...

shown. The number of degrees of freedom for variation within boxes is $k_b(N_b - 1) = 72$, since the deviation of each item in a box was taken from the mean of the box. Degrees of freedom for interaction are obtained by subtracting the degrees of freedom for the other three sources of variation from the degrees of freedom for total variation. Thus, the number of degrees of freedom for interaction is

$$89 - (1 + 8 + 72) = 8.$$

We are now ready to test the estimated variance between column means and the estimated variance between row means. However, we must first decide which of the other two variances is to be the denominator of the F test. It is true that the variation within boxes is the only one of the four sources of variation which would be unaffected by heterogeneity among column, row, or box means. It would therefore appear that estimated variance within boxes should be our measure of chance. But there is another point to consider: if the difference between row (or column) means is not greater than the interaction between row and column means, the difference can hardly be considered meaningful.[9] Consequently, the usual procedure is as follows: first test the estimated variance of interaction against the estimated variance within boxes; if the estimated variance of interaction is significantly larger than the estimated variance within boxes, test each of the other two estimated variances against the estimated variance of interaction; if the estimated variance of interaction is smaller than, or is not significantly larger than, the estimated variance within boxes, pool the variation and the degrees of freedom from these two sources and compute a new estimated variance to be used as the denominator for the F test.[10]

Testing first the estimated variance of interaction against estimated variance within boxes, we have

$$F = \frac{10,069.07}{7,448.24} = 1.35. \quad (n_1 = 8; n_2 = 72.)$$

From Appendix M it is seen that this value of F is not significantly greater than 1.0, so estimated variance of interaction does not significantly exceed the estimated variance within boxes.

Since interaction is not significant, we pool the variation of interaction

---

[9] This point is not so easy to grasp from the data of Table 26.5 as it is from an illustration given by Mood. His example, for which no data are given, deals with five men (columns) operating four machines (rows) and has three observations in each box. He notes that one man may do better on one machine than another man, but the first man may not do as much better or may even do worse on a second machine. To be meaningful, the differences between machines should exceed the interaction; otherwise, one might install what appeared to be the best machine but find that the man assigned to operate that machine is not as productive on it as he would have been on another machine. See A. M. Mood, *Introduction to the Theory of Statistics*, McGraw-Hill Book Company, New York, 1950, pp. 334–337.

[10] Some authorities recommend using the larger of the two variances attributable to interaction or within boxes. If estimated variances of interaction is the larger, but not significantly so, this procedure allows for possible small effects of interaction not revealed when estimated variance of interaction was tested. It also tends to increase the number of Type II errors.

and within boxes, and divide this value by the degrees of freedom for these two sources of variation, giving

$$616,826.15 \div 80 = 7,710.33.$$

This is the denominator of F for testing estimated variance between column means and estimated variance between row means.

For column means,

$$F = \frac{373,004.85}{7,710.33} = 48.38. \quad (n_1 = 1; n_2 = 80.)$$

From Appendix M it is seen that this value of F is far beyond the 0.001 point, so the difference between column means (between fresh and stored cells) is real.

For row means,

$$F = \frac{174,681.19}{7,710.33} = 22.66. \quad (n_1 = 8; n_2 = 80.)$$

This F value, too, is beyond the 0.001 point, and the difference between row means (between brands of cells) is significant.

Situations in which there are two criteria of classification with unequal numbers of items in the boxes, and those involving three or more criteria of classification, are beyond the scope of this book.

Interrelationships Between $\frac{x}{\sigma}$, t, χ^2, and F

In Chapter 24 it was noted that the t distribution approaches the normal distribution as n approaches infinity. The normal distribution is therefore a special case of the t distribution, as shown in the last row of Appendix I.

In Chapter 25 it was pointed out that, for the same set of data, normal deviates yield the same probabilities as do χ^2 values when $n = 1$ for χ^2. More specifically, we found, upon comparing Appendices H and J, that for a given probability $\left(\dfrac{x}{\sigma}\right)^2 = \chi^2$ when $n = 1$ for χ^2.

In this chapter it was noted that, for any given probability, $\dfrac{\chi^2}{n} = F$, when n for χ^2 equals n_1 for F and when $n_2 = \infty$ for F. This may be seen by comparing Appendices J and M.

In this chapter, also, it was pointed out that for any given probability, $t^2 = F$ when n for t equals n_2 for F and when n_1 for F is 1. This is apparent from an examination of Appendices I and M.

What has been said in the preceding four paragraphs has been brought together in Chart 26.2. From this chart it is clear that F is an inclusive distribution in that the other three distributions are merely special cases of F.

MEASURES OF SKEWNESS AND KURTOSIS

Skewness. In Chapter 10 the skewness of the distribution of the grades of 409 students, as measured by β_1, was found to be 0.16. Using 0.05 as a criterion, is this value of β_1 significantly greater than 0? Egon S. Pearson has prepared tables of the 0.10 and 0.02 limits of β_1 when based on samples drawn from a normal population. This table is shown as Appendix O, and the small chart included with that appendix shows the

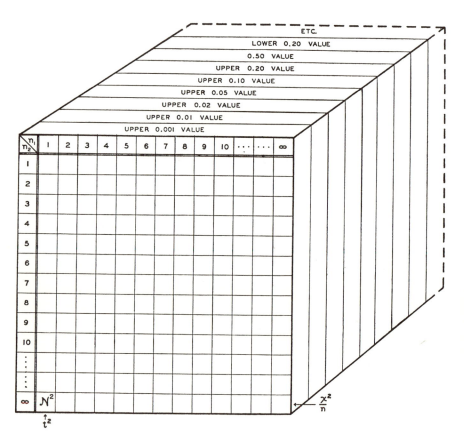

Chart 26.2. Relationship Between the Normal, t, χ^2, and F Distributions. Each box within the double rules may be thought of as the end of a drawer which, when pulled out, reveals the F values and, in some instances, the squared normal (N^2), t^2, and $\frac{\chi^2}{n}$ values for the indicated probabilities. The entire diagram is F. The box at the extreme lower left is N^2. The left column is t^2. The bottom row is $\frac{\chi^2}{n}$.

This chart is an elaboration of one given in K. Mather, *Statistical Analysis in Biology*, Interscience Publishers, New York, p. 47.

shape of the distribution of β_1. Appendix O does not show the values of β_1 for $N = 409$, but for either $N = 400$ or $N = 450$ the value $\beta_1 = 0.16$ is beyond the 0.02 point. Significant skewness is present.

In Chapter 10 the value of β_1 for the distribution of ages at death of 371 American inventors was found to be 0.16. From Appendix O this value, also, is seen to be significantly greater than zero.

In Chapter 23 a normal curve was fitted to the distribution of baseball throws for distance by 303 first-year high school girls. β_1 was found to be 0.0104. The value for β_1 does not differ significantly from 0, as may be seen from Appendix O.

Kurtosis. Table 10.9 showed a leptokurtic distribution, the cost of building five-room wood houses, with $\beta_2 = 4.46$ and $N = 82$. With 0.05 as our criterion, is this value of 4.46 significantly different from 3.0, the value of β_2 for a normal distribution? Appendix P shows the upper and lower 0.01 and 0.05 limits of β_2 when based on random samples from a normal distribution. Since Appendix P shows no entries for values of N below 100, we cannot be sure whether or not $\beta_2 = 4.46$ is beyond the upper 0.01 point, but it is probably beyond 0.05.

In Table 10.10 a distribution of the length of life of a group of electric lamps was found to have $\beta_2 = 2.22$. We cannot make a test to determine whether 2.22 is significantly less than 3.0, since the data of Table 10.10 were in terms of percentage frequencies and we do not know the number of lamps involved. However, if we look at Appendix P, we may note that $\beta_2 = 2.18$ is at the lower 0.01 limit and $\beta_2 = 2.35$ is at the lower 0.05 limit when the sample consists of but 100 items. For samples of 125 items or more, $\beta_2 = 2.22$ is beyond the 0.01 point. If the data of Table 10.10 include 100 or more lamps (and they should, or percentages should not have been shown), the distribution is significantly platykurtic.

CORRELATION COEFFICIENTS

Simple correlation. When a correlation analysis has been made for a sample, a number of questions may be raised. Among them are: Does the value of r differ significantly from zero? Does the value of r differ significantly from a specified value other than zero? Do two r values differ significantly from each other? What are the confidence limits of the correlation in the population? What single estimate of the correlation in the population may be made? We shall consider each of these in turn.

Does the value of r differ significantly from zero? Here we test the hypothesis that there is no correlation in the population. That is, that r_ϕ^2 or $r_\phi = 0$. If the hypothesis is discredited, the correlation is considered significant. The procedure involves the t-test with which the reader is already familiar. The value of t is obtained from

$$t = r\sqrt{\frac{(N-2)}{1-r^2}} \quad \text{or} \quad \sqrt{\frac{r^2(N-2)}{1-r^2}},$$

after which we ascertain P from Appendix I with $n = N - 2$. (Two degrees of freedom are lost because of the two constants in the estimating equation.)[11]   For the data of height growth and diameter growth of trees, N was 20 and r was $+0.758$.   These give

$$t = 0.758 \sqrt{\frac{(20 - 2)}{1 - 0.574}} = 4.93.$$

When $n = 20 - 2 = 18$, Appendix I shows that $t = 4.93$ has $P < 0.001$. Consequently, the value of r is significant.

It is of interest that this test is the same as the test to ascertain whether b differs significantly from zero.   The expression to use is[12]

$$t = b \sqrt{\frac{\Sigma x^2 (N - 2)}{\Sigma y_s^2}}.$$

For the tree data, we found $b = +1.677$, $\Sigma x^2 = 42.6055$, and $\Sigma y_s^2 = 88.74$.   Consequently,

$$t = 1.677 \sqrt{\frac{42.6055 (20 - 2)}{88.74}} = 4.93,$$

the same as obtained before.

Does the value of r *differ significantly from a specified value other than zero?*   When $r_\wp = 0$, the distribution of values of r from random samples is symmetrical about 0, ranging from -1.0 to $+1.0$.   When $r_\wp \neq 0$, the distribution of values of r from random samples is not symmetrical around $r_\wp$, and the t-test is inappropriate.   To test whether r differs significantly

---

[11] A more complete statement is this: We know that $t^2 = F$ when n_1 for F is 1 and when n for t equals n_2 for F.   The F test corresponding to the above t test is

$$F = \frac{\Sigma y_c^2 \div (2 - 1)}{\Sigma y_s^2 \div (N - 2)}.$$

Explained variation has $2 - 1 = 1$ degree of freedom, since it is based upon the deviations of the Y_c values ($Y_c = a + bX$) from $\bar{Y}$.   Unexplained variation has $N - 2$ degrees of freedom, since it is based upon the deviations of the N values from $Y_c = a + bX$.

[12] For proof of the equality, see Appendix S, section 26.3.   A number of alternative formulas for testing r or b are available.   Among these are:

$$t = \sqrt{\frac{b \Sigma xy (N - 2)}{\Sigma y_s^2}} = \sqrt{\frac{(\Sigma xy)^2 (N - 2)}{\Sigma x^2 \Sigma y^2 - (\Sigma xy)^2}},$$

$$= \sqrt{\frac{\Sigma y_c^2 (N - 2)}{\Sigma y_s^2}}.$$

from a value of $r_\wp \neq 0$, we transform r into[13]

$$z = 1.15129 \log \frac{1+r}{1-r},$$

the distribution of which is approximately normal around

$$z_\wp = 1.15129 \log \frac{1+r_\wp}{1-r_\wp},$$

with the standard error of z being[14]

$$\sigma_z = \frac{1}{\sqrt{N - 2.6667}}.$$

Suppose that we wish to know whether our r of $+0.758$ for the tree-growth data differs significantly from a hypothetical $r_\wp$ of $+0.750$. We compute

$$z = 1.15129 \log \frac{1+0.758}{1-0.758} = 0.992;$$

$$z_\wp = 1.15129 \log \frac{1+0.750}{1-0.750} = 0.973;$$

$$\sigma_z = \frac{1}{\sqrt{20 - 2.6667}} = 0.240; \text{ and}$$

$$\frac{x}{\sigma} = \frac{z - z_\wp}{\sigma_z} = \frac{0.992 - 0.973}{0.240} = \frac{0.019}{0.240} = 0.08.$$

Appendix H tells us that we may expect a difference this large or larger owing to chance causes about 94 times in 100. The hypothesis that $r = +0.758$ is the correlation of a random sample from a population having $r_\wp = +0.750$ is not impugned. The difference is not significant.

Do two values of r *differ significantly from each other?* If we were interested in testing the significance of the difference between the value of $r = +0.758$ ($z_1 = 0.992$) for our sample and that of another *sample* r of

---

[13] See R. A. Fisher, *Statistical Methods for Research Workers, op. cit.*, pp. 197–204.

[14] The usual expression is $\sigma_z = \dfrac{1}{\sqrt{N-3}}$. For an explanation of that given here, see

"New Light on the Correlation Coefficient and its Transforms," by Harold Hotelling, *Journal of the Royal Statistical Society*, Series B, Vol. XV, No. 2, 1953, p. 220. On pages 223–224, Hotelling suggests two modifications of z which may be more nearly normal than the form given above.

$+0.750$ $(z_2 = 0.973)$, obtained from 20 pairs of items, we would compute

$$\sigma_{z_1} = \frac{1}{\sqrt{20 - 2.6667}} = 0.240;$$

$$\sigma_{z_2} = \frac{1}{\sqrt{20 - 2.6667}} = 0.240;$$

$$\sigma_{z_1 - z_2} = \sqrt{\sigma_{z_1}^2 + \sigma_{z_2}^2} = \sqrt{(0.240)^2 + (0.240)^2},$$
$$= 0.339; \text{ and}$$

$$\frac{x}{\sigma} = \frac{z_1 - z_2}{\sigma_{z_1 - z_2}} = \frac{0.992 - 0.973}{0.339} = \frac{0.019}{0.339} = 0.06.$$

The table of normal areas (Appendix H) gives $P = 0.95$, and we conclude that the difference is not significant.

Confidence limits of $r_\wp$. As in the case of $\overline{X}_\wp$, π, and σ, we may wish to know the confidence limits of $r_\wp$. These are obtained by use of the expression

$$z = z_\wp \pm \frac{x}{\sigma} \sigma_z.$$

This will give us two values for $z_\wp$, which are then converted to $r_\wp$ values. If we wish the 95 per cent confidence limits $\left(\frac{x}{\sigma} = 1.960\right)$ for the tree-growth data, where r was $+0.758$ and $z = 0.992$, we have

$$0.992 = z_\wp \pm (1.960)(0.240).$$
$$z_\wp = 0.992 \pm 0.4704.$$
$$z_{\wp_1} = 0.5216 \text{ and}$$
$$z_{\wp_2} = 1.4624.$$

Converting $z_{\wp_1}$ to $r_{\wp_1}$ and $z_{\wp_2}$ to $r_{\wp_2}$ gives

$$r_{\wp_1} = +0.479 \text{ and}$$
$$r_{\wp_2} = +0.898,$$

which are the 95 per cent confidence limits.

Single estimate of $r_\wp$. When discussing variances, we noted that a single estimate of σ^2 might be made from a sample by means of

$$\hat{\sigma}^2 = \frac{\Sigma x^2}{N - 1}.$$

In somewhat similar fashion, an estimate may be made of $r_\wp^2$. We shall refer to it as $\hat{r}^2$. We use $\hat{r}^2$, rather than the more logical $\hat{r}_\wp^2$, to indicate an estimate of the coefficient of determination in the population, in order to avoid complicated subscripts in later sections of this chapter.

We already know, from footnote 8 in Chapter 19, that

$$r^2 = 1 - \frac{\Sigma y_s^2}{\Sigma y^2} = 1 - \frac{\Sigma y_s^2 \div N}{\Sigma y^2 \div N},$$

$$= 1 - \frac{s_{Y.X}^2}{s_Y^2}.$$

Now, $s_{Y.X}^2$ is a biased estimate of $\sigma_{Y.X}^2$, and s_Y^2 is a biased estimate of σ_Y^2. Unbiased estimates are obtained by dividing the measures of variation by the appropriate number of degrees of freedom, rather than by N. Thus,

$$\hat{\sigma}_Y^2 = \frac{\Sigma y^2}{N - 1};$$

$$\hat{\sigma}_{Y.X}^2 = \frac{\Sigma y_s^2}{N - 2}; \text{ and}$$

$$\hat{r}^2 = 1 - \frac{\hat{\sigma}_{Y.X}^2}{\hat{\sigma}_Y^2} = 1 - \frac{\Sigma y_s^2 \div (N - 2)}{\Sigma y^2 \div (N - 1)},$$

$$= 1 - \frac{\Sigma y_s^2}{\Sigma y^2} \cdot \frac{N - 1}{N - 2}.$$

Since

$$\frac{\Sigma y_s^2}{\Sigma y^2} = 1 - r^2,$$

we may write

$$\hat{r}^2 = 1 - (1 - r^2) \frac{N - 1}{N - 2}.$$

For the tree-growth data, where $r^2 = 0.574$ and $r = +0.758$:

$$\hat{r}^2 = 1 - (1 - 0.574) \frac{20 - 1}{20 - 2},$$

$$= 0.550.$$

$$\hat{r} = +0.742.$$

When r^2 is very low, $\hat{r}^2$ may be negative. In such a case, the correlation in the population should be considered to be zero.

Non-linear correlation. When dealing with a second-degree curve, a third-degree curve, or a curve of higher order, we may wish to know: (1) whether the non-linear coefficient of determination is significantly larger than a coefficient based upon a curve of lower order, or (2) whether the non-linear coefficient is significantly greater than zero. We may also occasionally wish to make an estimate of the correlation in the population.

Second-degree curve. For the data of diameter and volume of ponderosa pine trees, we found, in Chapter 20, that

$$r^2 = \frac{\text{Variation explained by straight line}}{\text{Total variation}},$$

$$= \frac{\Sigma y_c^2}{\Sigma y^2} = \frac{152{,}259.2}{159{,}698} = 0.953,$$

and

$$r_{Y.XX^2}^2 = \frac{\text{Variation explained by second-degree curve}}{\text{Total variation}},$$

$$= \frac{\Sigma y_{cY.XX^2}^2}{\Sigma y^2} = \frac{156{,}235.5}{159{,}698} = 0.978.$$

The simplest method of ascertaining whether $r_{Y.XX^2}^2$ is significantly larger than r^2 is to compute the measure $r_{YX^2.X}^2$ mentioned in footnote 2 of Chapter 20, and make a t-test of $r_{YX^2.X}^2$ with $n = N - 3$. (Explanation of the use of $N - 3$ is given on the next page.) This coefficient of partial determination, $r_{YX^2.X}^2$, which tells us the proportion that (1) the added variation explained by the use of X^2 constitutes of (2) the variation unexplained by the straight line, is

$$r_{YX^2.X}^2 = \frac{r_{Y.XX^2}^2 - r^2}{1 - r^2},$$

$$= \frac{0.978 - 0.953}{1 - 0.953} = 0.532.$$

The t test is exactly the same as the t test for r, except that we use $N - 3$ instead of $N - 2$.

$$t = \sqrt{\frac{r_{YX^2.X}^2 (N - 3)}{1 - r_{YX^2.X}^2}},$$

$$= \sqrt{\frac{0.532(20 - 3)}{0.468}} = 4.4.$$

When $n = 17$, a value of $t = 4.4$ is beyond the 0.001 level (see Appendix I), so we conclude that the use of X^2 has explained a significantly larger amount of variation.

The foregoing is a simpler equivalent of the usual F test[15] in which

$$F = \frac{\left[\left(\begin{array}{c}\text{Variation explained by} \\ \text{second-degree curve}\end{array}\right) - \left(\begin{array}{c}\text{Variation explained} \\ \text{by straight line}\end{array}\right)\right] \div \begin{array}{c}\text{Degrees of} \\ \text{freedom}\end{array}}{\left[\left(\begin{array}{c}\text{Total} \\ \text{variation}\end{array}\right) - \left(\begin{array}{c}\text{Variation explained by} \\ \text{second-degree curve}\end{array}\right)\right] \div \text{Degrees of freedom}},$$

$$= \frac{(\Sigma y^2_{cY.XX^2} - \Sigma y^2_c) \div 1}{(\Sigma y^2 - \Sigma y^2_{cY.XX^2}) \div (N - 3)},$$

with $N_1 = 1$ and $N_2 = N - 3$. The number of degrees of freedom in the numerator is $2 - 1 = 1$, because it is the difference between the number of degrees of freedom for explained variation computed from the second-degree curve (which is two) and the number of degrees of freedom for explained variation computed from the straight line (which is one). Explained variation obtained from the second-degree curve has $3 - 1 = 2$ degrees of freedom because the equation has three constants and the variation of the computed values was taken around $\overline{Y}$; explained variation gotten from the straight line has $2 - 1 = 1$ degree of freedom because the equation has two constants and the variation of the computed values was taken around $\overline{Y}$. The number of degrees of freedom for $\Sigma y^2_{sY.XX^2} = \Sigma y^2 - \Sigma y^2_{cY.XX^2}$, in the denominator, is $N - 3$ because the unexplained variation was obtained from the squared differences of the Y values (of which there are N) from a second-degree curve, which has three constants. Alternatively, we may note that total variation has $N - 1$ degrees of freedom and that explained variation has $3 - 1$ degrees of freedom; therefore, their difference, which is unexplained variation, has $(N - 1) - (3 - 1) = N - 3$ degrees of freedom.

If the numerator and denominator of the expression given above for F are each divided by Σy^2, we have the alternative form

$$F = \frac{(r^2_{Y.XX^2} - r^2) \div 1}{(1 - r^2_{Y.XX^2}) \div (N - 3)},$$

with $n_1 = 1$ and $n_2 = N - 3$.

To ascertain whether $r^2_{Y.XX^2} = 0.978$ is significantly greater than 0, we use the F-test, computing either[16]

$$F = \frac{r^2_{Y.XX^2} \div (3 - 1)}{(1 - r^2_{Y.XX^2}) \div (N - 3)}$$

---

[15] The equivalence of the t test and the F test for this and other coefficients of partial determination is shown in Appendix S, section 26.4.

[16] If both numerator and denominator of the second expression are divided by Σy^2, the first expression is obtained.

or

$$F = \frac{\Sigma y_{cY.XX^2}^2 \div (3 - 1)}{(\Sigma y^2 - \Sigma y_{cY.XX^2}^2) \div (N - 3)},$$

with $n_1 = 3 - 1$ and $n_2 = N - 3$. We use $(3 - 1)$ degrees of freedom in the numerator because the second-degree curve has three constants and explained variation computed from that curve was taken around $\bar{Y}$; more generally, the degrees of freedom for explained variation are $(m - 1)$, where m is the number of constants in the estimating equation. The number of degrees of freedom in the denominator was explained in the preceding paragraph; in general, the number of degrees of freedom for unexplained variation is $(N - m)$.

Using the first expression for the data of ponderosa pine trees, we get

$$F = \frac{0.978 \div (3 - 1)}{(1 - 0.978) \div (20 - 3)},$$
$$= 379.1 \text{ (only two digits are significant)},$$

with $n_1 = 2$ and $n_2 = 17$. Referring to the F table of Appendix M, it is clear that this F value significantly exceeds 1.0, since it has a probability of much less than 0.001, and that, therefore, $r_{Y.XX^2}^2$ significantly exceeds zero.

The procedure for making an estimate of the correlation in the population is similar to that previously given for linear correlation. That is

$$\hat{r}_{Y.XX^2}^2 = 1 - \frac{\Sigma y_{sY.XX^2}^2 \div (N - 3)}{\Sigma y^2 \div (N - 1)},$$
$$= 1 - (1 - r_{Y.XX^2}^2)\frac{N - 1}{N - 3},$$
$$= 1 - (1 - 0.978)\tfrac{19}{17} = 0.975.$$

Third-degree curve. To ascertain whether the use of X^3 in a curve of the type

$$Y_c = a + bX + cX^2 + dX^3$$

explains a significant additional amount of variation, compute

$$r_{YX^3.XX^2}^2 = \frac{r_{Y.XX^2X^3}^2 - r_{Y.XX^2}^2}{1 - r_{Y.XX^2}^2}$$

and then make a t test using

$$t = \sqrt{\frac{r_{YX^3.XX^2}^2(N - 4)}{1 - r_{YX^3.XX^2}^2}}$$

with $n = N - 4$. The equivalent F test is

$$F = \frac{(\Sigma y_{cY.XX^2X^3}^2 - \Sigma y_{cY.XX^2}^2) \div 1}{(\Sigma y^2 - \Sigma y_{cY.XX^2X^3}^2) \div (N - 4)},$$

$$= \frac{(r_{Y.XX^2X^3}^2 - r_{Y.XX^2}^2) \div 1}{(1 - r_{Y.XX^2X^3}^2) \div (N - 4)},$$

with $n_1 = 1$ and $n_2 = N - 4$.

To test the hypothesis that the population correlation is zero, compute

$$F = \frac{r_{Y.XX^2X^3}^2 \div (4 - 1)}{(1 - r_{Y.XX^2X^3}^2) \div (N - 4)} \quad \text{or}$$

$$F = \frac{\Sigma y_{cY.XX^2X^3}^2 \div (4 - 1)}{\Sigma y_{sY.XX^2X^3}^2 \div (N - 4)},$$

with $n_1 = 4 - 1$ and $n_2 = N - 4$. Remember that $\Sigma y_{sY.XX^2X^3}^2 = \Sigma y^2 - \Sigma y_{cY.XX^2X^3}^2$.

The estimate of the correlation in the population is

$$\hat{r}_{Y.XX^2X^3}^2 = 1 - \frac{\Sigma y_{sY.XX^2X^3}^2 \div (N - 4)}{\Sigma y^2 \div (N - 1)},$$

$$= 1 - (1 - r_{Y.XX^2X^3}^2) \frac{N - 1}{N - 4}.$$

The reader can readily adapt these expressions for curves of a higher order. That, however, should rarely be necessary, since third-degree curves are not often used and curves of higher order are even more infrequently employed.

The correlation ratio. For the data of yield per acre of broom corn and man hours per ton, we found in Chapter 20 that

$$\eta_{Y.x}^2 = \frac{\text{Variation explained by column means}}{\text{Total variation of the series}},$$

$$= \frac{148.115}{217.515} = 0.681.$$

If a second-degree curve is fitted to the same data, we get[17]

$$r_{Y.XX^2}^2 = \frac{\Sigma y_{cY.XX^2}^2}{\Sigma y^2},$$

$$= \frac{140.743}{217.515} = 0.647.$$

---

[17] For the correlation analysis of these data using a second-degree curve, see the first edition of this text, pp. 721–727.

To ascertain whether $\eta_{Y.X}^2$ is significantly larger than $r_{Y.XX^2}^2$, we compute

$$
\begin{aligned}
F &= \frac{(\eta_{Y.X}^2 - r_{Y.XX^2}^2) \div \text{Degrees of freedom}}{(1 - \eta_{Y.X}^2) \div \text{Degrees of freedom}} \\[2mm]
&= \frac{(0.681 - 0.647) \div (11 - 2)}{(1 - 0.681) \div (103 - 12)} = \frac{0.00378}{0.00351} = 1.1,
\end{aligned}
$$

with $n_1 = 9$ and $n_2 = 91$.   Or, we may use

$$
F = \frac{\left[\left(\begin{array}{c}\text{Variation explained}\\ \text{by column means}\end{array}\right) - \left(\begin{array}{c}\text{Variation explained by}\\ \text{second-degree curve}\end{array}\right)\right] \div \begin{array}{c}\text{Degrees of}\\ \text{freedom}\end{array}}{\left[\left(\begin{array}{c}\text{Total variation}\\ \text{of the } Y \text{ series}\end{array}\right) - \left(\begin{array}{c}\text{Variation explained}\\ \text{by column means}\end{array}\right)\right] \div \begin{array}{c}\text{Degrees of}\\ \text{freedom}\end{array}},
$$

$$
= \frac{(148.115 - 140.743) \div (11 - 2)}{(217.515 - 148.115) \div (103 - 12)} = \frac{0.8191}{0.7626} = 1.1,
$$

with $n_1 = 9$ and $n_2 = 91$.   The degrees of freedom in the numerator represent the difference between the degrees of freedom for explained variation using the column means (which is 11) and the degrees of freedom for explained variation using the second-degree curve (which is 2).   The number of degrees of freedom for explained variation using the column means is $12 - 1 = 11$ because there were 12 column means and the variation of those means was computed in relation to $\overline{Y}$.   The number of degrees of freedom for explained variation using the second-degree curve is $3 - 1 = 2$ because the equation has three constants and the variation of the computed values was taken around $\overline{Y}$.   The degrees of freedom in the denominator, for the variation unexplained by the column means, are N minus the number of column means, that is, $103 - 12 = 91$.

Referring to Appendix M to ascertain the probability of $F = 1.1$ when $n_1 = 9$ and $n_2 = 91$, we find that neither $n_1 = 9$ nor $n_2 = 91$ is shown in the table.   However, it is not necessary to interpolate.   By looking at the F values when $n_1 = 8$ and 12 and $n_2 = 60$ and 120, it is clear that the probability is greater than 0.10 and that $\eta_{Y.X}^2$ is not significantly larger than $r_{Y.XX^2}^2$.

To determine whether $\eta_{Y.X}^2$ is significantly greater than zero, we use expressions for F similar to those previously employed for the same purpose for non-linear coefficients.   They are

$$F = \frac{\eta_{Y.x}^2 \div (\text{Degrees of freedom} = \text{Number of column means} - 1)}{(1 - \eta_{Y.x}^2) \div \left(\begin{array}{l}\text{Degrees of freedom} = \\ N - \text{Number of column means}\end{array}\right)},$$

$$= \frac{0.681 \div (12 - 1)}{(1 - 0.681) \div (103 - 12)} = \frac{0.0619}{0.00351} = 17.6, \text{ or,}$$

$$F = \frac{\left(\begin{array}{l}\text{Variation explained} \\ \text{by column means}\end{array}\right) \div \left(\begin{array}{l}\text{Degrees of freedom} = \text{Number} \\ \text{of column means} - 1\end{array}\right)}{\left[\left(\begin{array}{l}\text{Total} \\ \text{variation of} \\ \text{the } Y \text{ series}\end{array}\right) - \left(\begin{array}{l}\text{Variation} \\ \text{explained by} \\ \text{column means}\end{array}\right)\right] \div \left(\begin{array}{l}\text{Degrees of freedom} = \\ N - \text{Number of} \\ \text{column means}\end{array}\right)}$$

$$= \frac{148.115 \div (12 - 1)}{(217.515 - 148.115) \div (103 - 12)} = \frac{13.46}{0.763} = 17.6.$$

For this value of F, $n_1 = 11$ and $n_2 = 91$. Neither of these is tabled in Appendix M; but, looking up $n_1 = 8$ or 12 and $n_2 = 60$ or 120, it is clear that $F = 17.7$ is far beyond the upper 0.001 point. $\eta_{Y.x}^2$ is significantly greater than zero.

The value of $\hat{\eta}_{Y.x}^2$, an estimate for the population, is

$$\hat{\eta}_{Y.x}^2 = 1 - \frac{\left[\left(\begin{array}{l}\text{Total varia-} \\ \text{tion of the} \\ Y \text{ series}\end{array}\right) - \left(\begin{array}{l}\text{Variation} \\ \text{explained by} \\ \text{column means}\end{array}\right)\right] \div \left(\begin{array}{l}N - \text{Number} \\ \text{of column} \\ \text{means}\end{array}\right)}{(\text{Total variation of the } Y \text{ series}) \div (N - 1)},$$

or

$$\hat{\eta}_{Y.x}^2 = 1 - (1 - \eta_{Y.x}^2) \frac{N - 1}{N - \text{Number of column means}},$$

$$= 1 - (1 - 0.681)\tfrac{102}{91} = 0.642.$$

Multiple correlation. When dealing with multiple correlation coefficients, we are primarily interested in knowing whether a given R^2 (or R) value is significant. We shall not use the example of Chapter 21 as an illustration, because the data used there were not a sample. Instead we shall consider a four-variable problem dealing with the physical measurements of 27 boys who were 12, 13, or 14 weeks old.[18]

---

[18] These and other data for boys and girls of various ages were supplied by the New York Foundling Hospital, courtesy of Dr. Alfred J. Vignec. Miss Marion C. Gentile kindly transcribed the figures.

The variables were:

X_1, weight in kilograms,
X_2, height in centimeters,
X_3, head circumference in centimeters, and
X_4, chest circumference in centimeters.

We shall test $R^2_{1.23}$ and $R^2_{1.234}$, and, to do that, we need the following values:

$$N = 27.$$
$$\Sigma x_1^2 = 11.6258.$$
$$\Sigma x_{c1.23}^2 = 9.1085;$$
$$\Sigma x_{s1.23}^2 = 2.5173;$$
$$R^2_{1.23} = 0.783.$$
$$\Sigma x_{c1.234}^2 = 10.0152;$$
$$\Sigma x_{s1.234}^2 = 1.6106;$$
$$R^2_{1.234} = 0.861.$$

To ascertain whether a multiple coefficient of determination significantly exceeds zero, we employ an F test, similar to those used for the same purpose for non-linear coefficients. In general form, we may use either[19]

$$F = \frac{R^2_{1.234\cdots m} \div (m - 1)}{(1 - R^2_{1.234\cdots m}) \div (N - m)},$$

or,

$$F = \frac{\Sigma x_{c1.234\cdots m}^2 \div (m - 1)}{\Sigma x_{s1.234\cdots m}^2 \div (N - m)},$$

with $n_1 = m - 1$ and $N_2 = N - m$.

Using the first expression to test $R^2_{1.23}$ gives

$$F = \frac{0.783 \div (3 - 1)}{(1 - 0.783) \div (27 - 3)} = 43.4,$$

with $n_1 = 2$ and $n_2 = 24$. From Appendix M, the value obtained for F is seen to be far beyond the upper 0.001 point, and $R^2_{1.23}$ is clearly significant.

---

[19] The equivalence of the two expressions is fairly obvious: in the denominator of the second expression, write $\Sigma x_1^2 - \Sigma x_{c1.234\cdots m}^2$ in place of $\Sigma x_{s1.234\cdots m}^2$; then divide the numerator and the denominator by Σx_1^2; the result is the first expression.

Again using the first of the two expressions, but this time to test $R^2_{1.234}$, we obtain

$$F = \frac{0.861 \div (4-1)}{(1-0.861) \div (27-4)} = 47.5,$$

with $n_1 = 3$ and $n_2 = 23$. $R^2_{1.234}$ is also significant.

Occasionally one may wish the value of $\hat{R}^2_{1.234\cdots m}$, the estimated coefficient of multiple determination in the population. This is

$$\hat{R}^2_{1.234\cdots m} = 1 - \frac{\Sigma x^2_{s1.234\cdots m} \div (N-m)}{\Sigma x^2_1 \div (N-1)},$$

$$= 1 - \frac{\Sigma x^2_{s1.234\cdots m}}{\Sigma x^2_1} \cdot \frac{N-1}{N-m},$$

$$= 1 - (1 - R^2_{1.234\cdots m}) \frac{N-1}{N-m}.$$

Computing only $\hat{R}^2_{1.234}$ for the data of the 27 boys, we obtain

$$\hat{R}^2_{1.234} = 1 - (1 - R^2_{1.234}) \frac{N-1}{N-m},$$

$$= 1 - (1 - 0.861) \frac{27-1}{27-4},$$

$$= 0.843.$$

Partial correlation. Since a coefficient of partial determination tells us the proportion that (1) the additional explained variation attributable to a given independent variable is of (2) the unexplained variation before the use of that independent variable, we are often interested in knowing whether the coefficient differs significantly from zero. The test involves computing

$$t = \sqrt{\frac{r^2_{1m.23\cdots(m-1)}(N-m)}{1 - r^2_{1m.23\cdots(m-1)}}},$$

with $n = N - m$.

For the data of the physical measurements of the 27 boys,

$$r^2_{14.23} = \frac{R^2_{1.234} - R^2_{1.23}}{1 - R^2_{1.23}} \quad \text{or} \quad \frac{\Sigma x^2_{c1.234} - \Sigma x^2_{c1.23}}{\Sigma x^2_1 - \Sigma x^2_{c1.23}}.$$

Using the first expression gives

$$r_{14.23}^2 = \frac{0.861 - 0.783}{1 - 0.783} = 0.359.$$

Variable X_4 explained 36 per cent of the variation which X_2 and X_3 had failed to explain.

For the value of t, we get

$$t = \sqrt{\frac{0.359(27 - 4)}{1 - 0.359}} = 3.59,$$

with $n = 23$. From the t table of Appendix I, it is seen that $0.001 < P < 0.01$, and we consider $r_{14.23}^2$ to be significant.

In similar fashion, it may be ascertained whether $r_{13.24}^2$ and $r_{12.34}^2$ are significant. Without making the tests here, we shall merely note that $r_{12.34}^2$ is significant at the 0.01 level and that $r_{13.24}^2$ is not significant, even at the 0.05 level, since P for $r_{13.24}^2$ is between 0.30 and 0.40. This does not tell us that we should necessarily exclude X_3 from our analysis, since X_3 may contribute some useful information even though we have not been able to demonstrate its significance. However, if we desired to use but two independent variables, they should, of course, be X_2 and X_4.

As noted on page 627, the t test is an alternative to the F test for testing the significance of a partial coefficient of determination. The F test, in general terms, is

$$F = \frac{(\Sigma x_{c1.234\cdots m}^2 - \Sigma x_{c1.234\cdots(m-1)}^2) \div [m - (m - 1)]}{(\Sigma x_1^2 - \Sigma x_{c1.234\cdots m}^2) \div (N - m)},$$

where $m - (m - 1)$ is, of course, always 1. That this expression for F and the square of that given above for t are the same is demonstrated in Appendix S, section 26.4.

In rare instances one may wish to know whether a coefficient of partial determination differs significantly from a population value which is not zero. Such a test may be made in exactly the same fashion as for the simple linear correlation coefficient (see pages 621–622), with the standard error of z being

$$\sigma_z = \frac{1}{\sqrt{N - 2.6667 - (m - 2)}} = \frac{1}{\sqrt{N - m - 0.6667}},$$

where m is the number of variables involved, which is the same as the number of constants in the multiple estimating equation, since we are considering only linear multiple correlation.

If one wishes the value of $\hat{r}^2_{1m.23\cdots(m-1)}$, the estimate for the population, it may be obtained from

$$\hat{r}^2_{1m.23\cdots(m-1)} = 1 - \frac{\Sigma x^2_{s1.234\cdots m} \div (N - m)}{\Sigma x^2_{s1.234\cdots(m-1)} \div [N - (m - 1)]},$$

or, if we divide the numerator and denominator each by Σx^2_1, from

$$\hat{r}^2_{1m.23\cdots(m-1)} = 1 - \frac{1 - \hat{R}^2_{1.234\cdots m}}{1 - \hat{R}^2_{1.234\cdots(m-1)}},$$

$$= \frac{\hat{R}^2_{1.234\cdots m} - \hat{R}^2_{1.234\cdots(m-1)}}{1 - \hat{R}^2_{1.234\cdots(m-1)}}.$$

APPENDICES

APPENDIX A

Symbols Used in Each Chapter

Symbols Used in Chapter 9

β_1: lower-case Greek beta, a measure of skewness. See Chapter 10.

β_2: lower-case Greek beta, a measure of kurtosis. See Chapter 10.

d: deviation of an X value from $\overline{X}_d$.

d': deviation, in terms of class intervals, of an X value from $\overline{X}_d$.

Δ_1: upper-case Greek delta, the difference between the frequency of the modal class and the frequency of the class graphically to the left of the modal class.

Δ_2: upper-case Greek delta, the difference between the frequency of the modal class and the frequency of the class graphically to the right of the modal class.

f: a frequency.

$f_1, f_2, f_3, \cdots$: the frequencies associated with $X_1, X_2, X_3, \cdots$.

G: the geometric mean.

H: the harmonic mean.

i: the class interval.

l_1: the lower limit of a class.

l_2: the upper limit of a class.

Med: the median.

Mo: the mode.

n: as used in the "compound interest formula," the number of years (or other time units) from the beginning to the end of the period.

N: the number of items in a sample.

P_o and P_n: as used in the "compound interest formula," respectively, the value at the beginning and at the end of the period.

Q_1, Q_2, Q_3: the quartiles. $Q_2 = $ Med.

Σ: upper-case Greek sigma, meaning "take the sum of."

r: as used in the "compound interest formula," the ratio of increase or decrease per year (or other time unit).

s: the standard deviation of a sample. See Chapter 10.

x: the deviation of a value from $\bar{X}$.

x_1, x_2, x_3, $\cdots$: deviations of X_1, X_2, X_3, $\cdots$ from $\bar{X}$.

X: a value in a series; also, the mid-value of a class in a frequency distribution.

X_1, X_2, X_3, $\cdots$: the values in a series; also, the mid-values of the classes of a frequency distribution.

$\bar{X}_d$: a designated mean used as a first approximation to facilitate the computation of $\bar{X}$ of a frequency distribution.

$\bar{X}$: the arithmetic mean. In later chapters, we shall distinguish between the arithmetic mean of a sample, $\bar{X}$, and the arithmetic mean of the population, $\bar{X}_\wp$.

∞ : infinity.

Symbols Used in Chapter 10

AD: the average (or mean) deviation.

α_3: lower-case Greek alpha, a measure of skewness using the third powers of the x values.

α_4: lower-case Greek alpha, a measure of kurtosis using the fourth powers of the x values.

β_1: lower-case Greek beta, a measure of skewness using the third powers of the x values.

β_2: lower-case Greek beta, a measure of kurtosis using the fourth powers of the x values.

d: deviation of an X value from $\bar{X}_d$.

d': deviation, in terms of class intervals, of an X value from $\bar{X}_d$.

f: a frequency.

h^2: a measure of uniformity, the reciprocal of $2s^2$.

i: the class interval.

M: used with s to indicate a specified multiple of s.

Med: the median.

Mo: the mode.

μ_1, μ_2, μ_3, μ_4: lower-case Greek mu; respectively, the first, second, third, and fourth moments about $\bar{X}$, with Sheppard's corrections. $\mu_1 = \pi_1 = 0$ and $\mu_3 = \pi_3$.

N: the number of items in a sample.

ν_1, ν_2, ν_3, ν_4: lower-case Greek nu; respectively, the first, second, third, and fourth moments about $\bar{X}_d$.

P_1, P_2, $\cdots$, P_{99}: the percentiles.

π_1, π_2, π_3, π_4: lower-case Greek pi; respectively, the first, second, third, and fourth moments about $\bar{X}$. $\pi_1 = 0$.

Q: the semi-interquartile range.

Q_1, Q_2, Q_3: the quartiles. $Q_2 = $ Med.

s: the standard deviation of a sample.

s^2: the variance of a sample.

Sk: the Pearsonian measure of skewness.

Sk_Q: a measure of skewness based on the quartiles.

$\hat{\sigma}$: lower-case Greek sigma, "sigma caret" or "sigma hat," estimate of the standard deviation of a population.

σ: lower-case Greek sigma, the standard deviation of a population.

Σ: upper-case Greek sigma, meaning "take the sum of."

V: the coefficient of variation.

x: deviation of X from $\overline{X}$.

X: a value in a series; also, the mid-value of a class in a frequency distribution.

$\overline{X}$: the arithmetic mean.   In later chapters we shall distinguish between the arithmetic mean of a sample, $\overline{X}$, and the arithmetic mean of the population, $\overline{X}_{\wp}$.

$\overline{X}_d$: a designated mean.

| |: disregard signs; thus, $\Sigma|x|$ means "take the sum of the x values without regard to signs."

Symbols Used in Chapter 12

a: a constant in the equation $Y_c = a + bX$; the value of Y_c when $X = 0$; the Y intercept.

b: a constant in the equation $Y_c = a + bX$; the slope.

N: the number of items in a series.

Σ: upper-case Greek sigma, meaning "take the sum of."

X: a value of the X series.

X_1, X_2, X_3, $\cdots$, X_N: specific values of the X series.

$\overline{X}$: the arithmetic mean of the X values.

Y: an observed value of the Y series.

Y_c: a computed value of the Y series.

Y_1, Y_2, Y_3, $\cdots$, Y_N: specific values of the Y series.

$\overline{Y}$: the arithmetic mean of the Y values.

Symbols Used in Chapter 13

a: a constant in various trend equations.

b: a constant in various trend equations.

c: a constant in a polynomial of the second, or higher, degree.   As a subscript, c distinguishes a computed value from an observed value; see Y_c.

d: a constant in a polynomial of the third, or higher, degree.

e: a constant in a polynomial of the fourth, or higher, degree.

f: a constant in a polynomial of the fifth, or higher, degree.

k: the asymptote of an asymptotic growth curve.

k_0, k_1, k_2: When one logistic curve is built upon part of another, k_0 is the upper asymptote of the first logistic curve and k_1 and k_2 are, respectively, the lower and upper asymptotes of the second logistic curve.

μ: lower-case Greek mu, used to assist in determining the trend values for a logistic curve. $\mu = 10^{a+bX}$.

n: for a modified exponential or a Gompertz curve, the number of years in each third of the series; for a logistic curve, the number of time units between x_0 and x_1, or between x_1 and x_2.

N: the number of items in a series.

Σ: upper-case Greek sigma, meaning "take the sum of."

Σ_1, Σ_2, Σ_3: respectively, the sums of values for the first, second, and third equal parts of a series.

x_0, x_1, x_2: when fitting a logistic curve, the years associated with y_0, y_1, and y_2.

X: a value of the *X* series.

y_0, y_1, y_2: the three selected *Y* values used for fitting a logistic curve.

Y: an observed value of the *Y* series.

Y_c: a computed value of the *Y* series.

!: factorial. $5! = 1 \times 2 \times 3 \times 4 \times 5$.

Symbols Used in Chapter 16

β_1: lower-case Greek beta, a measure of skewness. See Chapter 10.

β_2: lower-case Greek beta, a measure of kurtosis. See Chapter 10.

C: cyclical.

I: irregular.

N: the number of items in a series.

s: standard deviation. See Chapter 10.

S: seasonal.

Σ: upper-case Greek sigma, meaning "take the sum of."

T: trend.

X: a value of the *X* series.

y: a cyclical deviation; after irregular movements have been smoothed, the deviation of a value in a time series from the combined estimate of trend and seasonal.

Y_c: a computed value of the *Y* series.

Symbols Used in Chapter 17 and in Chapter 18

p: price of a commodity.

P: price index number.

q: quantity of a commodity.

Q: quantity index number.

n: a subscript indicating a given period or the current period.

o: a subscript indicating the base period.

Σ: upper-case Greek sigma, meaning "take the sum of."

Numerical subscripts written 59,64, for example, may accompany either P or Q (p or q) and indicate a 1964 index on a 1959 base. When written 64 or 59-61, for example, such subscripts may appear with p or q and indicate that the price or quantity referred to is for the year specified or is the average (or total) for the years separated by the hyphen.

u: units of purchasing power per dollar.

Symbols Used in Chapter 19

a: the value of Y_c when $X = 0$ in the equation $Y_c = a + bX$.

a': the value of X_c when $Y = 0$ in the equation $X_c = a' + b'Y$.

a_1: number of observed frequencies in the upper left cell of a 2×2 table.

a_2: number of observed frequencies in the lower left cell of a 2×2 table.

b: the slope of the estimating equation $Y_c = a + bX$.

b': the slope of the estimating equation $X_c = a' + b'Y$.

b_1: number of observed frequencies in the upper right cell of a 2×2 table.

b_2: number of observed frequencies in the lower right cell of a 2×2 table.

C: coefficient of mean square contingency.

d'_X: deviation of a cell, in terms of classes, from $\overline{X}_d$.

d'_Y: deviation of a cell, in terms of classes, from $\overline{Y}_d$.

D: difference between the ranks of paired values.

f: a frequency; in grouped correlation, a frequency in a cell.

f_X: a frequency of the X series; in grouped correlation, a column frequency.

f_Y: a frequency of the Y series; in grouped correlation, a row frequency.

k: coefficient of alienation.

k^2: coefficient of non-determination.

N: the number of items in a sample. In two-variable correlation, N is the number of pairs of items.

r: coefficient of correlation.

r^2: coefficient of determination.

r_{rank}: coefficient of rank correlation.

s_X: standard deviation of the X series.

s_Y: standard deviation of the Y series.

$s_{Y.x}$: standard error of estimate for the estimating equation $Y_c = a + bX$.

Σ: upper-case Greek sigma, meaning "take the sum of."

Σy^2: total variation of the Y values.

Σy_c^2: variation of Y explained by use of the estimating equation $Y_c = a + bX$.

Σy_s^2: variation of Y unexplained by use of the estimating equation $Y_c = a + bX$.

x: $X - \bar{X}$.

X: the X series; also, an observed value in the X series. Thus, we refer to correlating X and Y, but ΣX means "sum the values in the X series."

X axis: the horizontal axis.

X_c: a computed X value.

$\bar{X}$: the arithmetic mean of the X series.

χ^2: chi-square. The symbol is a lower-case Greek chi.

y: $Y - \bar{Y}$. Σy^2 is the total variation in the Y series.

y_c: $Y_c - \bar{Y}$. Σy_c^2 is the explained variation in the Y series.

y_s: $Y - Y_c$. Σy_s^2 is the unexplained variation in the Y series.

Y: the Y series, also an observed value in the Y series. Thus, we refer to correlating X and Y, but ΣY means "sum the values in the Y series."

Y axis: the vertical axis.

Y_c: a computed Y value.

$\bar{Y}$: the arithmetic mean of the Y series.

$\bar{Y}_c$: the arithmetic mean of the Y_c values; $\bar{Y}_c = \bar{Y}$.

Symbols Used in Chapter 20

a: value of Y_c when $X = 0$ in the estimating equations $Y_c = a + bX$, $Y_c = a + bX + cX^2$, and $Y_c = a + bX + cX^2 + dX^3$; value of $(\sqrt{Y})_c$ when $X = 0$ in the estimating equation $(\sqrt{Y})_c = a + bX$; value of $\left(\dfrac{1}{Y}\right)_c$ when $X = 0$ in the estimating equation $\left(\dfrac{1}{Y}\right)_c = a + bX$.

Log a is the value of $(\log Y)_c$ when $X = 0$ in the estimating equation $(\log Y)_c = \log a + X \log b$ and when $X = 1$ in the estimating equation $(\log Y)_c = \log a + b \log X$.

b: b, or $\log b$, is a constant in the various estimating equations mentioned above for a.

c: a constant in the estimating equations $Y_c = a + bX + cX^2$ and $Y_c = a + bX + cX^2 + dX^3$.

d: a constant in the estimating equation $Y_c = a + bX + cX^2 + dX^3$.

η: lower-case Greek eta, the correlation ratio.

k: the number of columns in a correlation table.

N: the number of items in a sample. In two-variable linear or non-linear correlation, N is the number of pairs of items.

N_c: the number of items in a column in a correlation table.

$r_{Y.X}^2$: coefficient of determination for X and Y.

$r_{Y.XX^2}^2$: coefficient of determination for X and Y, the estimating equation $Y_c = a + bX + cX^2$ having been used.

$r_{Y.XX^2X^3}^2$: coefficient of determination for X and Y, the estimating equation $Y_c = a + bX + cX^2 + dX^3$ having been used.

$r_{YX^2.X}^2$: a measure of (1) the increased variation attributable to the use of X^2, expressed as a ratio of (2) the amount of variation unexplained by the use of X alone. See the coefficient of partial determination, explained in Chapter 21.

$r_{\log Y.X}^2$: coefficient of determination for X and log Y.

$r_{\log Y.\log X}^2$: coefficient of determination for log X and log Y.

$r_{\frac{1}{Y}.X}^2$: coefficient of determination for X and $\dfrac{1}{Y}$.

$r_{\sqrt{Y}.X}^2$: coefficient of determination for X and $\sqrt{Y}$.

$s_{Y.X}$: standard error of estimate for the estimating equation $Y_c = a + bX$.

$s_{Y.XX^2}$: standard error of estimate for the estimating equation $Y_c = a + bX + cX^2$.

$s_{Y.XX^2X^3}$: standard error of estimate for the estimating equation $Y_c = a + bX + cX^2 + dX^3$.

$s_{\log Y.X}$: standard error of estimate for the estimating equation $(\log Y)_c = \log a + X \log b$.

$s_{\log Y.\log X}$: standard error of estimate for the estimating equation $(\log Y)_c = \log a + b \log X$.

$s_{\frac{1}{Y}.X}$: standard error of estimate for the estimating equation $\left(\dfrac{1}{Y}\right)_c = a + bX$.

$s_{\sqrt{Y}.X}$: standard error of estimate for the estimating equation $(\sqrt{Y})_c = a + bX$.

Σ: upper-case Greek sigma, meaning "take the sum of."

$\overset{k}{\underset{1}{\Sigma}}$: a summation over the k columns in a correlation table.

$\overset{N_c}{\underset{1}{\Sigma}}$: a summation over the N_c items in a column in a correlation table.

Σy^2: total variation of the Y values.

$\Sigma(\log y)^2$: total variation of the log Y values. See footnotes 10 and 11.

$\Sigma\left(\dfrac{1}{y}\right)^2$: total variation of the $\left(\dfrac{1}{Y}\right)$ values. See footnote 15.

$\Sigma(\sqrt{y})^2$: total variation of the $\sqrt{Y}$ values. See footnote 12.

Σy_c^2: explained variation for the estimating equation $Y_c = a + bX$.

$\Sigma y_{c Y.XX^2}^2$: explained variation for the estimating equation $Y_c = a + bX + cX^2$.

$\Sigma y_{cr.xx^2x^3}^2$: explained variation for the estimating equation $Y_c = a + bX + cX^2 + dX^3$.

$\Sigma(\log y)_c^2$: explained variation for the estimating equation $(\log Y)_c = \log a + b \log X$ or for the estimating equation $(\log Y)_c = \log a + X \log b$. See footnote 11.

$\Sigma\left(\dfrac{1}{y}\right)_c^2$: explained variation for the estimating equation $\left(\dfrac{1}{Y}\right)_c = a + bX$.

$\Sigma(\sqrt{y})_c^2$: explained variation for the estimating equation $(\sqrt{Y})_c = a + bX$.

Σy_s^2: unexplained variation for the estimating equation $Y_c = a + bX$.

$\Sigma y_{sr.xx^2}^2$: unexplained variation for the estimating equation $Y_c = a + bX + cX^2$.

$\Sigma y_{sr.xx^2x^3}^2$: unexplained variation for the estimating equation $Y_c = a + bX + cX^2 + dX^3$.

$\Sigma(\log y)_s^2$: unexplained variation for the estimating equation $(\log Y)_c = \log a + b \log X$ or for the estimating equation $(\log Y)_c = \log a + X \log b$. See footnote 11.

$\Sigma\left(\dfrac{1}{y}\right)_s^2$: unexplained variation for the estimating equation $\left(\dfrac{1}{Y}\right)_c = a + bX$.

$\Sigma(\sqrt{y})_s^2$: unexplained variation for the estimating equation $(\sqrt{Y})_c = a + bX$.

X: the X series, also an observed value in the X series. Thus, we refer to correlating X and Y, but ΣX means "sum the values in the X series."

y: see Σy^2; $y = Y - \bar{Y}$.

y_c: see Σy_c^2 and Σy_c^2 with various additional subscripts. In general, y_c (with or without additional subscripts) is the difference between the appropriate computed Y, or computed transformed Y, value and the corresponding arithmetic mean.

y_s: see Σy_s^2 and Σy_s^2 with various additional subscripts. In general, y_s (with or without additional subscripts) is the difference between an observed Y, or transformed observed Y, value and the corresponding computed value.

Y: the Y series, also an observed value in the Y series. Thus, we refer to correlating X and Y, but ΣY means "sum the values in the Y series."

$\bar{Y}$: the arithmetic mean of the Y values.

$\bar{Y}_c$: when used in connection with the correlation ratio, the arithmetic mean of a column. (This symbol was used in the preceding chapter to mean the arithmetic mean of the computed Y values, but it is not so used in this chapter.)

$\overline{\log Y}$: the arithmetic mean of the log Y values.

$\left(\dfrac{\overline{1}}{Y}\right)$: the arithmetic mean of the $\dfrac{1}{Y}$ values.

$\overline{\sqrt{Y}}$: the arithmetic mean of the $\sqrt{Y}$ values.

Y_c: a computed Y value.

$(\log Y)_c$: a computed $\log Y$ value:

$\left(\dfrac{1}{Y}\right)_c$: a computed $\dfrac{1}{Y}$ value:

$(\sqrt{Y})_c$: a computed $\sqrt{Y}$ value.

Symbols Used in Chapter 21

For the symbols used in the first paragraph of this chapter, see the list for Chapter 19.

$a_{1.2}$: value of $X_{c1.2}$ when $X_2 = 0$ in the estimating equation $X_{c1.2} = a_{1.2} + b_{12}X_2$. Same as a in the estimating equation $Y_c = a + bX$ used in Chapter 19.

$a_{1.3}$: value of $X_{c1.3}$ when $X_3 = 0$ in the estimating equation $X_{c1.3} = a_{1.3} + b_{13}X_3$.

$a_{1.23}$: value of $X_{c1.23}$ when $X_2 = 0$ and $X_3 = 0$ in the estimating equation $X_{c1.23} = a_{1.23} + b_{12.3}X_2 + b_{13.2}X_3$.

$a_{1.24}$: value of $X_{c1.24}$ when $X_2 = 0$ and $X_4 = 0$ in the estimating equation $X_{c1.24} = a_{1.24} + b_{12.4}X_2 + b_{14.2}X_4$.

$a_{1.34}$: value of $X_{c1.34}$ when $X_3 = 0$ and $X_4 = 0$ in the estimating equation $X_{c1.34} = a_{1.34} + b_{13.4}X_3 + b_{14.3}X_4$.

$a_{1.22'3}$: value of $X_{c1.22'3}$ when X_2, X_2^2, and X_3 equal zero in the estimating equation $X_{c1.22'3} = a_{1.22'3} + b_{12.2'3}X_2 + b_{12'.23}X_2^2 + b_{13.22'}X_3$.

b_{12}: coefficient of X_2 in the estimating equation $X_{c1.2} = a_{1.2} + b_{12}X_2$. Same as b in Chapter 19.

b_{13}: coefficient of X_3 in the estimating equation $X_{c1.3} = a_{1.3} + b_{13}X_3$.

$b_{12.3}$: coefficient of X_2 in the estimating equation $X_{c1.23} = a_{1.23} + b_{12.3}X_2 + b_{13.2}X_3$.

$b_{13.2}$: coefficient of X_3 in the estimating equation $X_{c1.23} = a_{1.23} + b_{12.3}X_2 + b_{13.2}X_3$.

$b_{12.4}$, $b_{14.2}$: coefficients, respectively, of X_2 and X_4 in the estimating equation shown above for $a_{1.24}$.

$b_{13.4}$, $b_{14.3}$: coefficients, respectively, of X_3 and X_4 in the estimating equation shown above for $a_{1.34}$.

$b_{12.34}$: coefficient of X_2 in the estimating equation $X_{c1.234} = a_{1.234} + b_{12.34}X_2 + b_{13.24}X_3 + b_{14.23}X_4$.

$b_{13.24}$: coefficient of X_3 in the estimating equation $X_{c1.234} = a_{1.234} + b_{12.34}X_2 + b_{13.24}X_3 + b_{14.23}X_4$.

$b_{14.23}$: coefficient of X_4 in the estimating equation $X_{c1.234} = a_{1.234} + b_{12.34}X_2 + b_{13.24}X_3 + b_{14.23}X_4$.

$b_{12.34\cdots m}$, $b_{13.24\cdots m}$, $b_{14.23\cdots m}$, $\cdots$, $b_{1m.23\cdots(m-1)}$: coefficients, respectively, of X_2, X_3, X_4, $\cdots$, X_m in the estimating equation for $X_{c1.234\cdots m}$

$b_{12.2'3}$, $b_{12'.23}$, $b_{13.22'}$: coefficients, respectively, of X_2, X_2^2, and X_3 in the estimating equation given above for $a_{1.22'3}$.

b_{21}: coefficient of X_1 in the estimating equation $X_{c2.1} = a_{2.1} + b_{21}X_1$. Used in this chapter only to assist in the computation of $d_{12.34}^2$.

N: the number of items in a sample. In multiple or partial correlation, N is the number of sets of observations.

r_{12}^2: coefficient of determination for X_1 and X_2.

r_{13}^2: coefficient of determination for X_1 and X_3.

r_{14}^2: coefficient of determination for X_1 and X_4.

r_{23}^2: coefficient of determination for X_2 and X_3.

r_{24}^2: coefficient of determination for X_2 and X_4.

r_{34}^2: coefficient of determination for X_3 and X_4.

$r_{12.3}^2$: coefficient of partial determination; the *additional* variation in X_1 explained by X_2, expressed as a proportion of the variation in X_1 which was *unexplained* by X_3.

$r_{13.2}^2$: coefficient of partial determination; the *additional* variation in X_1 explained by X_3, expressed as a proportion of the variation in X_1 which was *unexplained* by X_2.

$r_{12.4}$, $r_{13.4}$, $r_{14.2}$, $r_{14.3}$, $r_{24.3}$, $r_{34.2}$: coefficients of partial correlation, used in this chapter to assist in computing various other measures.

$r_{12.34}^2$: coefficient of partial determination; the *additional* variation in X_1 explained by X_2, expressed as a proportion of the variation in X_1 which was *unexplained* by X_3 and X_4.

$r_{13.24}^2$: coefficient of partial determination; the *additional* variation in X_1 explained by X_3, expressed as a proportion of the variation in X_1 which was *unexplained* by X_2 and X_4.

$r_{14.23}^2$: coefficient of partial determination; the *additional* variation in X_1, explained by X_4, expressed as a proportion of the variation in X_1 which was *unexplained* by X_2 and X_3.

$r_{12.34\cdots m}^2$: a general form of the coefficient of partial determination; the *additional* variation in X_1 explained by X_2, expressed as a proportion of the variation in X_1 which was *unexplained* by X_3, X_4, $\cdots$, X_m.

$r_{1m.23\cdots(m-1)}^2$: a general form of the coefficient of partial determination; the *additional* variation in X_1 explained by X_m, expressed as a proportion of the variation in X_1 which was *unexplained* by X_2, X_3, $\cdots$, $X_{(m-1)}$.

$r_{1m.23\cdots(m-2)}$, $r_{1(m-1).23\cdots(m-2)}$, $r_{m(m-1).23\cdots(m-2)}$: general forms of coefficients of partial correlation used in this chapter to compute

$r_{1m.23\cdots(m-1)}$. Note that the three coefficients are one order below the one being computed; the first excludes $X_{(m-1)}$, the second excludes X_m, and the third excludes X_1.

$R^2_{1.23}$: coefficient of multiple determination; the proportion of variation in X_1 which was explained by X_2 and X_3.

$R^2_{1.24}$: coefficient of multiple determination; the proportion of variation in X_1 which was explained by X_2 and X_4.

$R^2_{1.34}$: coefficient of multiple determination; the proportion of variation in X_1 which was explained by X_3 and X_4.

$R^2_{1.234}$: coefficient of multiple determination; the proportion of variation in X_1 which was explained by X_2, X_3, and X_4.

$R^2_{1.234\cdots m}$: a general form of the coefficient of multiple determination; the proportion of variation in X_1 which was explained by X_2, X_3, X_4, $\cdots$, X_m.

$R^2_{1.234\cdots(m-1)}$: a general form of the coefficient of multiple determination used to assist in the computation of $r^2_{1m.23\cdots(m-1)}$; the proportion of variation in X_1 which was explained by X_2, X_3, X_4, $\cdots$, $X_{(m-1)}$.

$R^2_{1.34\cdots m}$: a general form of the coefficient of multiple determination used to assist in the computation of $r^2_{12.34\cdots m}$; the proportion of variation in X_1 which was explained by X_3, X_4, $\cdots$, X_m.

s_1, s_2, s_3, s_4, $\cdots$: respectively, the standard deviations of the X_1, X_2, X_3, X_4, $\cdots$ series.

$s_{1.2}$: standard error of estimate for the estimating equation $X_{c1.2} = a_{1.2} + b_{12}X_2$. Same as $s_{Y.X}$ in Chapter 19.

$s_{1.3}$: standard error of estimate for the estimating equation $X_{c1.3} = a_{1.3} + b_{13}X_3$.

$s_{1.23}$: standard error of estimate for the estimating equation $X_{c1.23} = a_{1.23} + b_{12.3}X_2 + b_{13.2}X_3$.

$s_{1.24}$: standard error of estimate for the estimating equation $X_{c1.24} = a_{1.24} + b_{12.4}X_2 + b_{14.2}X_4$.

$s_{1.34}$: standard error of estimate for the estimating equation $X_{c1.34} = a_{1.34} + b_{13.4}X_3 + b_{14.3}X_4$.

$s_{1.234}$: standard error of estimate for the estimating equation $X_{c1.234} = a_{1.234} + b_{12.34}X_2 + b_{13.24}X_3 + b_{14.23}X_4$.

$s_{1.234\cdots m}$: a general form of the standard error of estimate

$s_{m.123\cdots(m-1)}$: a general form of the standard error of estimate used to assist in computing $b_{1m.23\cdots(m-1)}$.

Σ: upper-case Greek sigma, meaning "take the sum of."

Σx_1^2: total variation of the X_1 values.

$\Sigma x_{c1.2}^2$, $\Sigma x_{c1.3}^2$, $\Sigma x_{c1.4}^2$: variation of X_1 explained, respectively, by X_2, by X_3, and by X_4.

$\Sigma x_{c1.23}^2$, $\Sigma x_{c1.24}^2$, $\Sigma x_{c1.34}^2$: variation of X_1 explained, respectively, by X_2 and X_3, by X_2 and X_4, and by X_3 and X_4.

$\Sigma x^2_{c1.234}$: variation of X_1 explained by X_2, X_3, and X_4.

$\Sigma x^2_{s1.2}$, $\Sigma x^2_{s1.3}$, $\Sigma x^2_{s1.4}$: variation of X_1 unexplained, respectively, by X_2, by X_3, and by X_4.

$\Sigma x^2_{s1.23}$, $\Sigma x^2_{s1.24}$, $\Sigma x^2_{s1.34}$: variation of X_1 unexplained, respectively, by X_2 and X_3, by X_2 and X_4, and by X_3 and X_4.

$\Sigma x^2_{s1.234}$: variation of X_1 unexplained by X_2, X_3, and X_4.

x_1, x_2, x_3, x_4, $\cdots$, x_m: values in the X_1, X_2, X_3, X_4, $\cdots$, X_m series expressed as deviations from their respective arithmetic means.

x_{c1}: see Σx^2_{c1} with various additional subscripts.

x_{s1}: see Σx^2_{s1} with various additional subscripts.

X_1: the X_1 series, also an observed value in the X_1 series. Thus, we refer to correlating X_1 with X_2, X_3, and X_4, but ΣX_1 means "take the sum of the values in the X_1 series."

X_2, X_3, X_4, $\cdots$, X_m: respectively, the X_2, X_3, X_4, $\cdots$, X_m series; also observed values in those series. See X_1.

$\overline{X}_1$, $\overline{X}_2$, $\overline{X}_3$, $\overline{X}_4$, $\cdots$, $\overline{X}_m$: respectively, the arithmetic means of the X_1, X_2, X_3, X_4, $\cdots$, X_m series.

$X_{c1.2}$: a computed value of the X_1 series when the estimating equation $X_{c1.2} = a_{1.2} + b_{12}X_2$ is used. Same as Y_c in Chapter 19.

$X_{c1.3}$: a computed value of the X_1 series when the estimating equation $X_{c1.3} = a_{1.3} + b_{13}X_3$ is used.

$X_{c1.23}$: a computed value of the X_1 series when the estimating equation $X_{c1.23} = a_{1.23} + b_{12.3}X_2 + b_{13.2}X_3$ is used.

$X_{c1.24}$: a computed value of the X_1 series when the estimating equation shown above for $a_{1.24}$ is used.

$X_{c1.34}$: a computed value of the X_1 series when the estimating equation shown above for $a_{1.34}$ is used.

$X_{c1.234}$: a computed value of the X_1 series when the estimating equation $X_{c1.234} = a_{1.234} + b_{12.34}X_2 + b_{13.24}X_3 + b_{14.23}X_4$ is used.

$X_{c1.22'3}$: a computed value of the X_1 series when the estimating equation shown above for $a_{1.22'3}$ is used.

Symbols Used in Chapter 22

a: the value of Y_c when $X = 0$ in the equation $Y_c = a + bX$.

$a_{1.23}$: value of $X_{c1.23}$ when $X_2 = 0$ and $X_3 = 0$ in the estimating equation $X_{c1.23} = a_{1.23} + b_{12.3}X_2 + b_{13.2}X_3$.

$a_{2.13}$: value of $X_{c2.13}$ when $X_1 = 0$ and $X_3 = 0$ in the estimating equation $X_{c2.13} = a_{2.13} + b_{21.3}X_1 + b_{23.1}X_3$.

b: coefficient of X in the equation $Y_c = a + bX$.

$b_{12.3}$: coefficient of X_2 in the estimating equation shown above for $a_{1.23}$.

$b_{13.2}$: coefficient of X_3 in the estimating equation shown above for $a_{1.23}$.

$b_{21.3}$: coefficient of X_1 in the estimating equation shown above for $a_{2.13}$.

$b_{23.1}$: coefficient of X_3 in the estimating equation shown above for $a_{2.13}$.

N: the number of pairs of items for two-variable correlation; the number of sets of items for multiple and partial correlation.

r: coefficient of correlation. r_{12}, r_{13}, r_{23} are coefficients referring, respectively, to X_1 and X_2, to X_1 and X_3, and to X_2 and X_3.

$r_{12.3}$: coefficient of partial correlation, the values of X_3 being held constant.

s_x: the standard deviation of the x values.

s_y: the standard deviation of the y values.

Σ: upper-case Greek sigma, meaning "take the sum of."

x: deviation of an X value from the trend line for the X values.

X: the X series, also an observed value in the X series.   Thus, we refer to correlating X and Y, but ΣX means "sum the values in the X series."

X_1: the X_1 series; also, an observed value in the X_1 series.   Thus, we refer to correlating X_1 with X_2 or with X_3, or with both X_2 and X_3, but ΣX_1 means "sum the values in the X_1 series."

X_2, X_3: respectively, the X_2 series and the X_3 series; also, observed values in those series.   See X_1.

$X_{c1.23}$: a computed value of the X_1 series when the estimating equation shown above for $a_{1.23}$ is used.

$X_{c2.13}$: a computed value of the X_2 series when the estimating equation shown above for $a_{2.13}$ is used.

y: deviation of a Y value from the trend line for the Y values.

Y: the Y series; also, an observed value in the Y series.   Thus, we refer to correlating X and Y, but ΣY means "sum the values in the Y series."

Y_c: a computed value of the Y series.

Symbols Used in Chapter 23

A: when tossing a die, the occurrence of a white side. A has no numerical value.

α_3: lower-case Greek alpha, a measure of skewness, $\sqrt{\beta_1}$.   See Chapter 10.

B: when tossing a die, the non-occurrence of a white side. B has no numerical value.

β_1, β_2: lower-case Greek beta; respectively, measures of skewness and kurtosis.   See Chapter 10.

c: a correction for skewness sometimes used in fitting a logarithmic normal curve.

C_0, C_1, C_2, $\cdots$: the binomial coefficients.

d': deviation, in terms of class intervals, of an X value from $\overline{X}_d$.

e: 2.71828; the limit of the series $1 + 1 + \dfrac{1}{2!} + \dfrac{1}{3!} + \dfrac{1}{4!} + \cdots$.

f: a frequency.

$F_1\left(\dfrac{x}{s}\right)$: in fitting the second-approximation curve, the normal-curve areas of Appendix E.

$F_2\left(\dfrac{x}{s}\right)$: in fitting the second-approximation curve, the tabled values of Appendix F which, when multiplied by α_3, give the modification for skewness.

h: in coin tossing, the occurrence of a head.

i: the class interval.

k: the number of samples.

N: the number of items in a sample.

ν_1, ν_2, ν_3: lower-case Greek nu; the first, second, and third moments about a selected origin. See Chapter 10.

p: the proportion of occurrences in a sample.

π: lower-case Greek pi, in the expression for the normal curve; the constant 3.14159; in the binomial, the proportion of occurrences in a population.

π_2, π_3: lower-case Greek pi; the second and third movements about $\overline{X}$. See Chapter 10.

q: the proportion of non-occurrences in a sample.

Q: the quartile deviation or semi-interquartile range. See Chapter 10.

Q_1, Q_2, Q_3: the quartiles. See Chapter 9.

s: the standard deviation of a sample. See Chapter 10.

$s_{\log}$: the standard deviation of the logarithms of a series of sample values.

$\text{Sk}_{\log}$: a coefficient of skewness based on the logarithms of the quartiles.

σ: lower-case Greek sigma. The standard deviation of a population.

$\hat{\sigma}$: the estimated standard deviation of a population, computed from a single sample. Referred to as "sigma caret" or "sigma hat." See Chapter 24.

t: in coin tossing, the occurrence of a tail or the non-occurrence of a head.

τ: lower-case Greek tau; the proportion of non-occurrences in a population.

x: $X - \overline{X}$.

X: a value of the X-series.

$\overline{X}$: the arithmetic mean. See Chapter 9.

$\overline{X}_d$: a designated mean. See Chapter 9.

$\overline{X}_{\log}$: the arithmetic mean of a series of logarithms.

$x_{\log}$: $\log X - \overline{X}_{\log}$.

Y_c: a computed ordinate of a fitted curve.

Y_0: the computed ordinate of the normal curve at $\overline{X}$.

$\int_0^x f(x)\,dx$: proportionate area under a curve from $\overline{X}$ to X.

Symbols Used in Chapter 24

$\beta_{1_{\mathcal{P}}}$: lower-case Greek beta; skewness in a population.

$\beta_{1_{\bar{X}}}$: skewness of the distribution of sample $\bar{X}$ values.

$\beta_{2_{\mathcal{P}}}$: kurtosis in a population.

$\beta_{2_{\bar{X}}}$: kurtosis of the distribution of sample $\bar{X}$ values.

D: a difference between paired values.

d': deviation, in terms of class intervals, of X from $\bar{X}_d$.

F: $\dfrac{\hat{\sigma}_1^2}{\hat{\sigma}_2^2}$; see Chapter 26.

f: frequency.

k: number of samples. k will ordinarily be much smaller than K.

K: the number of possible samples of a given size from a population.

n: degrees of freedom in a sample.   When two samples are under consideration, $n = n_1 + n_2$.

N: the number of items in a sample.

P: probability; varies from 0 to 1.

$\mathcal{P}$: the number of items in a population.   As a subscript, $\mathcal{P}$ means "population," thus $\bar{X}_{\mathcal{P}}$ is the arithmetic mean of a population.

r: the correlation coefficient.

s: the standard deviation of a sample.

σ: lower-case Greek sigma; the standard deviation of a population.

$\hat{\sigma}$: the estimated standard deviation of a population, computed from a single sample.   Referred to as "sigma caret" or "sigma hat."

   $\hat{\sigma}_1$ is an estimate based on sample 1.

   $\hat{\sigma}_2$ is an estimate based on sample 2.

   $\hat{\sigma}_{1+2}$ is an estimate computed by pooling x^2 values and degrees of freedom from two samples.

$\hat{\sigma}_D$: the estimated population standard error for a series of D values.

$\sigma_{\bar{X}}$: the standard error of $\bar{X}$.   When two samples are under consideration, we use $\sigma_{\bar{X}_1}$ and $\sigma_{\bar{X}_2}$.

$\hat{\sigma}_{\bar{X}}$: the estimated standard error of $\bar{X}$.

$\hat{\sigma}_{\bar{X}_1-\bar{X}_2}$: the estimated standard error of the difference between two sample arithmetic means.

$\hat{\sigma}_{\bar{X}_D}$: the estimated standard error of $\bar{X}_D$.

Σ: upper-case Greek sigma, meaning "take the sum of."

t: $\dfrac{\bar{X} - \bar{X}_{\mathcal{P}}}{\hat{\sigma}_{\bar{X}}}$, $\dfrac{\bar{X}_1 - \bar{X}_2}{\hat{\sigma}_{\bar{X}_1-\bar{X}_2}}$, or $\dfrac{\bar{X}_D}{\hat{\sigma}_{\bar{X}_D}}$.

x: $X - \bar{X}$; also, $\bar{X} - \bar{X}_{\mathcal{P}}$ in the expression $\dfrac{x}{\sigma}$, which see.

x_1: a deviation of a value in series 1 from $\bar{X}_1$; $\Sigma x_1^2 = \Sigma(X_1 - \bar{X}_1)^2$.

x_2: a deviation of a value in series 2 from $\overline{X}_2$; $\Sigma x_2^2 = \Sigma(X_2 - \overline{X}_2)^2$.

X: an observed value in a sample.

X_1: an observed value in sample 1.

X_2: an observed value in sample 2.

$\overline{X}$: the arithmetic mean of a sample.

$\overline{X}_1$: the arithmetic mean of sample 1.

$\overline{X}_2$: the arithmetic mean of sample 2.

$\overline{X}_D$: the arithmetic mean of a series of D values.

$\overline{X}_\wp$: the arithmetic mean of a population.

$\overline{X}_{\wp_1}$: the lower confidence limit of $\overline{X}_\wp$.

$\overline{X}_{\wp_2}$: the upper confidence limit of $\overline{X}_\wp$.

$\dfrac{x}{\sigma}$: a deviation divided by its standard error, for example, $\dfrac{\overline{X} - \overline{X}_\wp}{\sigma_{\overline{X}}}$.

χ^2: lower-case Greek chi.   See Chapter 25.

Symbols Used in Chapter 25

Part 1: Proportions

a: number of occurrences in a sample.

a_1: number of occurrences in sample 1.

a_2: number of occurrences in sample 2.

α: lower-case Greek alpha; number of occurrences in a population.

A: indicating an occurrence; A has no numerical value.

b: number of non-occurrences in a sample.

β: lower-case Greek beta; number of non-occurrences in a population.

B: indicating a non-occurrence; B has no numerical value.

k: number of samples.

N: the number of items in a sample.

N_1: number of items in sample 1.

N_2: number of items in sample 2.

p: proportion of occurrences in a sample.

p_k: proportion of occurrences in the k'th sample.

p_1: proportion of occurrences in sample 1.

p_2: proportion of occurrences in sample 2.

$\bar{p}$: an estimate of π based on two samples; a weighted average of p_1 and p_2.

P: probability; varies from 0 to 1.

π: lower-case Greek pi; proportion of occurrences in a population.

π_1: the lower confidence limit of π.

π_2: the upper confidence limit of π.

q: proportion of non-occurrences in a sample. $q = 1 - p$.

q_1: proportion of non-occurrences in sample 1.

q_2: proportion of non-occurrences in sample 2.

$\bar{q}$: $1 - \bar{p}$.

σ_a: the standard error of a.

σ_p: the standard error of p.

$\hat{\sigma}_{p_1-p_2}$: estimated standard error of the difference between p_1 and p_2.

τ: lower-case Greek tau; proportion of non-occurrences in a population. $\tau = 1 - \pi$.

$\dfrac{x}{\sigma}$: a deviation divided by its standard error; for example, $\dfrac{p - \pi}{\sigma_p}$ and $\dfrac{a - \pi N}{\sigma_a}$.

Part 2: The Chi-Square Test

a: number of occurrences in a sample.

a_1: number of observed frequencies in the upper left cell of a 2×2 table or, in general, in any $2 \times R$ table.

a_2: number of observed frequencies in the second row of the first column of a $2 \times R$ table; in the lower left cell of a 2×2 table.

a_3: number of observed frequencies in the third row of the first column of a $2 \times R$ table.

A: indicating an occurrence; A has no numerical value.

b: number of non-occurrences in a sample.

b_1: number of observed frequencies in the upper right cell of a 2×2 table or, in general, in any $2 \times R$ table.

b_2: number of observed frequencies in the second row of the second column of a $2 \times R$ table; in the lower right cell of a 2×2 table.

b_3: number of observed frequencies in the third row of the second column of a $2 \times R$ table.

B: indicating a non-occurrence; B has no numerical value.

C: number of columns of observed frequencies (exclusive of totals) in a chi-square table which has its marginal totals set.

f: an observed frequency.

f_c: a computed frequency.

n: degrees of freedom.

N: number of items in a sample. For 2×2 and larger tables, N is the number of items in the entire table.

N_a: number of frequencies (items) in the first column of a $2 \times R$ table.

N_b: number of frequencies (items) in the second column of a $2 \times R$ table.

$N_1, N_2, N_3, \cdots$: respectively, number of frequencies (items) in the first, second, third, $\cdots$ row of a $2 \times R$ table.

p: proportion of occurrences in a sample.

p_1: proportion of occurrences in sample 1.

p_2: proportion of occurrences in sample 2.

P: probability, varies from 0 to 1.

π: lower-case Greek pi; proportion of occurrences in a population.

R: number of rows of observed frequencies (exclusive of totals) in a chi-square table which has its marginal totals set.

σ^2: the variance of a population.

$\hat{\sigma}^2$: the estimated variance of a population.

σ_a: the standard error of a.

σ_p: the standard error of p.

Σ: upper-case Greek sigma; meaning "take the sum of."

$\dfrac{x}{\sigma}$: a deviation divided by its standard error, for example, $\dfrac{p - \pi}{\sigma_p}$.

χ^2: chi-square. The symbol is a lower-case Greek chi.

!: factorial. For example, $4! = 1 \times 2 \times 3 \times 4$.

Symbols Used in Chapter 26

Variances

$F: \dfrac{\hat{\sigma}_1^2}{\hat{\sigma}_2^2}$.

G: the geometric mean.

k: number of samples.

L: the ratio of the geometric mean of several variances to their arithmetic mean.

n: degrees of freedom.

$n_1, n_2, n_3, \cdots$: respectively, degrees of freedom in samples $1, 2, 3, \cdots$.
n_k refers to the number of degrees of freedom in the k'th sample.

N: number of items in a sample.

$N_1, N_2, N_3, \cdots$: respectively, number of items in samples $1, 2, 3, \cdots$.
N_k refers to the number of items in the k'th sample.

N_i: used in connection with L to indicate the number of items in any one of several samples of equal size.

P: probability; varies from 0 to 1.

s^2: the variance of a sample.

s_1^2: the variance of sample 1.

s_2^2: the variance of sample 2.

σ^2: population variance.

σ_1^2: the lower confidence limit of σ^2.

σ_2^2: the upper confidence limit of σ^2.

$\hat{\sigma}^2$: the estimated variance of a population obtained from a sample.

$\hat{\sigma}_1^2, \hat{\sigma}_2^2, \hat{\sigma}_3^2, \cdots$: respectively, estimates of population variance from samples $1, 2, 3, \cdots$. $\hat{\sigma}_k^2$ refers to the estimate from the k'th sample.

Σ: upper-case Greek sigma, meaning "take the sum of."

$x: X - \overline{X}$.

x_1: a deviation of a value in sample 1 from $\overline{X}_1$; $\Sigma x_1^2 = \Sigma(X_1 - \overline{X}_1)^2$.

x_2: a deviation of a value in sample 2 from $\overline{X}_2$; $\Sigma x_2^2 = \Sigma(X_2 - \overline{X}_2)^2$.

$\overline{X}_1$: the arithmetic mean of sample 1.

$\overline{X}_2$: the arithmetic mean of sample 2.

χ^2: see Chapter 25. The symbol is a lower-case Greek chi.

∞ : infinity sign.

Analysis of Variance

F: the ratio of two estimates of σ^2.

k_b: the number of boxes.

k_c: the number of columns.

k_r: the number of rows.

n: degrees of freedom.

n_1: degrees of freedom associated with the numerator of F.

n_2: degrees of freedom associated with the denominator of F.

N: number of items in all rows, all columns, or all boxes.

N_b: number of items in a box.

N_c: number of items in a column.

N_r: number of items in a row.

N_1, N_2, N_3, $\cdots$: respectively, the number of items in Columns 1, 2. 3, $\cdots$.

P: probability; varies from 0 to 1.

$\hat{\sigma}^2$: estimate of population variance using $\sum\limits_{1}^{N}(X - \overline{X})^2$.

Σ: upper-case Greek sigma, meaning "take the sum of."

$\sum\limits_{1}^{k_b}$: a summation over the k_b boxes.

$\sum\limits_{1}^{k_c}$: a summation over the k_c columns.

$\sum\limits_{1}^{k_r}$: a summation over the k_r rows.

$\sum\limits_{1}^{N}$: a summation over all items.   Same as Σ.

$\sum\limits_{1}^{N_b}$: a summation over the N_b items in a box.

$\sum\limits_{1}^{N_c}$: a summation over the N_c items in a column.

$\sum\limits_{1}^{N_r}$: a summation over the N_r items in a row.

t: see Chapter 24. $t = \sqrt{F}$ when $n_1 = 1$.

X: an observed value.

$\overline{X}$: the arithmetic mean of all the items, the "grand mean."

$\overline{X}_b$: the arithmetic mean of a box.

$\overline{X}_c$: the arithmetic mean of a column.

$\overline{X}_r$: the arithmetic mean of a row.

$\overline{X}_1$, $\overline{X}_2$, $\overline{X}_3$, $\cdots$: respectively, the arithmetic means of Columns 1, 2, 3, $\cdots$.

χ^2: chi-square; see Chapter 25. $\dfrac{\chi^2}{n} = F$ when $N_2 = \infty$.

Skewness and Kurtosis

β_1: lower-case Greek beta; measure of skewness in a sample. See Chapter 10.

β_2: lower-case Greek beta; measure of kurtosis in a sample. See Chapter 10.

N: number of items in a sample.

Correlation Coefficients

b: slope of the estimating equation $Y_c = a + bX$.

F: a ratio between two estimated variances.

$\eta^2_{Y.x}$: lower-case Greek eta; the square of the correlation ratio based on column means (see Chapter 20); sometimes referred to as the "ratio of determination."

$\hat{\eta}^2_{Y.x}$: lower-case Greek eta; population estimate of $\eta^2_{Y.x}$.

m: number of constants in an estimating equation. For the correlation ratio $\eta_{Y.x}$, m is the number of columns.

n: degrees of freedom.

n_1 and n_2: respectively, degrees of freedom associated with the numerator and the denominator of F.

N: number of items in a sample. In two-variable linear or non-linear correlation, N is the number of pairs of items. In multiple or partial correlation, N is the number of sets of observations.

N_1 and N_2: respectively, the number of pairs of items from which r_1 and r_2 were computed.

P: probability; varies from 0 to 1.

r: sample coefficient of correlation, linear correlation of two variables. When two samples are under consideration, we use r_1 and r_2.

$r_\wp$: population coefficient of correlation, linear correlation of two variables.

$r_{\wp_1}$: lower confidence limit of $r_\wp$.

$r_{\wp_2}$: upper confidence limit of $r_\wp$.

$\hat{r}^2$: estimated value of $r_\wp^2$; obtained from a sample.

$r^2_{13.2}$: coefficient of partial determination. See Chapter 21.

$r^2_{1m.23\cdots(m-1)}$: a general form of the coefficient of partial determination for m variables.

$\hat{r}^2_{1m.23\cdots(m-1)}$: estimated population value of $r^2_{1m.23\cdots(m-1)}$.

$r^2_{12.34}$, $r^2_{13.24}$, $r^2_{14.23}$: the three forms of the coefficient of partial determination for four variables, when X_1 is the dependent variable.

$r^2_{YX^2.x}$: coefficient of partial determination; the additional variation in Y explained by X^2, expressed as a proportion of the variation in Y which was unexplained by X.

$r_{Y.XX^2}^2$: coefficient of determination for X and Y, the estimating equation $Y_c = a + bX + cX^2$ having been used.

$\hat{r}_{Y.XX^2}^2$: population estimate of $r_{Y.XX^2}^2$.

$r_{YX^3.XX^2}^2$: coefficient of partial determination; the additional variation in Y explained by X^3, expressed as a proportion of the variation in Y which was unexplained by X and X^2.

$r_{Y.XX^2X^3}^2$: coefficient of determination for X and Y, the estimating equation $Y_c = a + bX + cX^2 + dX^3$ having been used.

$\hat{r}_{Y.XX^2X^3}^2$: population estimate of $r_{Y.XX^2X^3}^2$.

$R_{1.23}^2$: coefficient of multiple determination; the proportion of variation in X_1 which was explained by X_2 and X_3.

$R_{1.234}^2$: coefficient of multiple determination; the proportion of variation in X_1 which was explained by X_2, X_3, and X_4.

$R_{1.234\ldots m}^2$: a general form of the coefficient of multiple determination for m variables.

$\hat{R}_{1.234\ldots m}^2$: estimated population value of $R_{1.234\ldots m}^2$.

s_Y^2: total variance of the Y series.

$s_{Y.X}^2$: the square of the standard error of estimate for the estimating equation $Y_c = a + bX$; unexplained variance.

$\hat{\sigma}^2$: estimated variance in a population.

$\hat{\sigma}_Y^2$: estimated population variance (total variance) of the Y series.

$\hat{\sigma}_{Y.X}^2$: population estimate of the unexplained variance resulting from use of the estimating equation $Y_c = a + bX$.

σ_z: standard error of z.

$\sigma_{z_1-z_2}$: standard error of $z_1 - z_2$.

Σ: upper-case Greek sigma, meaning "take the sum of."

Σx_1^2: total variation in the X_1 series.

$\Sigma x_{c1.23}^2$: explained variation resulting from use of the estimating equation $X_{c1.23} = a_{1.23} + b_{12.3}X_2 + b_{13.2}X_3$.

$\Sigma x_{c1.234}^2$: explained variation resulting from use of the estimating equation $X_{c1.234} = a_{1.234} + b_{12.34}X_2 + b_{13.24}X_3 + b_{14.23}X_4$.

$\Sigma x_{c1.234\ldots m}^2$: a general form, explained variation resulting from use of the estimating equation $X_{c1.234\ldots m} = a_{1.234\ldots m}b_{12.34\ldots m}X_2 + b_{13.24\ldots m}X_3 + b_{14.23\ldots m}X_4 + \cdots + b_{1m.23\ldots(m-1)}X_m$.

$\Sigma x_{c1.234\ldots(m-1)}^2$: explained variation resulting from use of the estimating equation $X_{c1.234\ldots(m-1)} = a_{1.234\ldots(m-1)} + b_{12.34\ldots(m-1)}X_2 + b_{13.24\ldots(m-1)}X_3 + b_{14.23\ldots(m-1)}X_4 + \cdots + b_{1(m-1).23\ldots(m-2)}X_{(m-1)}$.

$\Sigma x_{s1.23}^2$: unexplained variation resulting from use of the estimating equation shown for $\Sigma x_{c1.23}^2$.

$\Sigma x_{s1.234}^2$: unexplained variation resulting from use of the estimating equation shown for $\Sigma x_{c1.234}^2$.

$\Sigma x_{s1.234\ldots m}^2$: a general form; unexplained variation resulting from use of the estimating equation shown for $\Sigma x_{c1.234\ldots m}^2$.

$\Sigma x_{s1.234\cdots(m-1)}^2$: unexplained variation resulting from use of the estimating equation shown for $\Sigma x_{c1.234\cdots(m-1)}^2$.

Σy^2: total variation of the Y series.

Σy_c^2: explained variation resulting from use of the estimating equation $Y_c = a + bX$.

$\Sigma y_{cY.XX^2}^2$: explained variation resulting from use of the estimating equation $Y_c = a + bX + cX^2$.

$\Sigma y_{cY.XX^2X^3}^2$: explained variation resulting from use of the estimating equation $Y_c = a + bX + cX^2 + dX^3$.

Σy_s^2: unexplained variation resulting from use of the estimating equation $Y_c = a + bX$.

$\Sigma y_{sY.XX^2}^2$: unexplained variation resulting from use of the estimating equation $Y_c = a + bX + cX^2$.

$\Sigma y_{sY.XX^2X^3}^2$: unexplained variation resulting from use of the estimating equation $Y_c = a + bX + cX^2 + dX^3$.

t: $\sqrt{\dfrac{r^2(N - m)}{1 - r^2}}$, or an equivalent expression (see note 15). r^2 may be either a two-variable linear coefficient of determination or a partial coefficient of determination.

$\dfrac{x}{\sigma}$: a deviation divided by its standard error; for example, $\dfrac{z - 0}{\sigma_z}$ or $\dfrac{z_1 - z_2}{\sigma_{z_1-z_2}}$.

X: an observed value in the X series; also, the X series.

$X_1, X_2, X_3, X_4, \cdots$: respectively, the $X_1, X_2, X_3, X_4, \cdots$ series; also, observed values in those series. Thus, we may refer to correlating X_1 with X_2, X_3, and X_4, but ΣX_1 means "take the sum of the values in the X_1 series."

$\bar{X}$: the arithmetic mean of the X series.

y: $Y - \bar{Y}$.

y_c: $Y_c - \bar{Y}$. See also Σy_c^2 and Σy_c^2 with additional subscripts.

y_s: $Y - Y_c$. See also Σy_s^2 and Σy_s^2 with additional subscripts.

Y: an observed value in the Y series; also, the Y series.

$\bar{Y}$: the arithmetic mean of the Y series.

Y_c: a computed Y value.

z: $1.15129 \log \dfrac{1 + r}{1 - r}$. When two samples are under consideration, we use z_1 and z_2 to correspond to r_1 and r_2.

$z_\wp$: $1.15129 \log \dfrac{1 + r_\wp}{1 - r_\wp}$.

$z_{\wp_1}$: lower confidence limit of $z_\wp$.

$z_{\wp_2}$: upper confidence limit of $z_\wp$.

APPENDIX B

Sums of the First Six Powers of the First 50 Natural Numbers

The following table, giving the sums of the first six powers of the first M natural numbers from $M = 1$ to $M = 50$ will be most frequently used in connection with the fitting of a trend line to time series. For that type of problem, M is the highest value of X used in the computation table. When

M	$\sum\limits_{1}^{M} X$	$\sum\limits_{1}^{M} X^2$	$\sum\limits_{1}^{M} X^3$	$\sum\limits_{1}^{M} X^4$	$\sum\limits_{1}^{M} X^5$	$\sum\limits_{1}^{M} X^6$
1	1	1	1	1	1	1
2	3	5	9	17	33	65
3	6	14	36	98	276	794
4	10	30	100	354	1 300	4 890
5	15	55	225	979	4 425	20 515
6	21	91	441	2 275	12 201	67 171
7	28	140	784	4 676	29 008	184 820
8	36	204	1 296	8 772	61 776	446 964
9	45	285	2 025	15 333	120 825	978 405
10	55	385	3 025	25 333	220 825	1 978 405
11	66	506	4 356	39 974	381 874	3 749 966
12	78	650	6 084	60 710	630 708	6 735 950
13	91	819	8 281	89 271	1 002 001	11 562 759
14	105	1 015	11 025	127 687	1 539 825	19 092 295
15	120	1 240	14 400	178 312	2 299 200	30 482 920
16	136	1 496	18 496	243 848	3 347 776	47 260 136
17	153	1 785	23 409	327 369	4 767 633	71 397 705
18	171	2 109	29 241	432 345	6 657 201	105 409 929
19	190	2 470	36 100	562 666	9 133 300	152 455 810
20	210	2 870	44 100	722 666	12 333 300	216 455 810
21	231	3 311	53 361	917 147	16 417 401	302 221 931
22	253	3 795	64 009	1 151 403	21 571 033	415 601 835
23	276	4 324	76 176	1 431 244	28 007 376	563 637 724
24	300	4 900	90 000	1 763 020	35 970 000	754 740 700
25	325	5 525	105 625	2 153 645	45 735 625	998 881 325
26	351	6 201	123 201	2 610 621	57 617 001	1 307 797 101
27	378	6 930	142 884	3 142 062	71 965 908	1 695 217 590
28	406	7 714	164 836	3 756 718	89 176 276	2 177 107 894
29	435	8 555	189 225	4 463 999	109 687 425	2 771 931 215
30	465	9 455	216 225	5 273 999	133 987 425	3 500 931 215
31	496	10 416	246 016	6 197 520	162 616 576	4 388 434 896
32	528	11 440	278 784	7 246 096	196 171 008	5 462 176 720
33	561	12 529	314 721	8 432 017	235 306 401	6 753 644 689
34	595	13 685	354 025	9 768 353	280 741 825	8 298 449 105
35	630	14 910	396 900	11 268 978	333 263 700	10 136 714 730
36	666	16 206	443 556	12 948 594	393 729 876	12 313 497 066
37	703	17 575	494 209	14 822 755	463 073 833	14 879 223 475
38	741	19 019	549 081	16 907 891	542 309 001	17 890 159 859
39	780	20 540	608 400	19 221 332	632 533 200	21 408 903 620
40	820	22 140	672 400	21 781 332	734 933 200	25 504 903 620
41	861	23 821	741 321	24 607 093	850 789 401	30 255 007 861
42	903	25 585	815 409	27 718 789	981 480 633	35 744 039 605
43	946	27 434	894 916	31 137 590	1 128 489 076	42 065 402 654
44	990	29 370	980 100	34 885 686	1 293 405 300	49 321 716 510
45	1 035	31 395	1 071 225	38 986 311	1 477 933 425	57 625 482 135
46	1 081	33 511	1 168 561	43 463 767	1 683 896 401	67 099 779 031
47	1 128	35 720	1 272 384	48 343 448	1 913 241 408	77 878 994 360
48	1 176	38 024	1 382 976	53 651 864	2 168 045 376	90 109 584 824
49	1 225	40 425	1 500 625	59 416 665	2 450 520 625	103 950 872 025
50	1 275	42 925	1 625 625	65 666 665	2 763 020 625	119 575 872 025

the X origin has been taken at the center of the X values, it is necessary to multiply the summations shown in this table by two. When the origin has been taken at the first X value in a time series, N as used in the normal equations is $M + 1$; when the origin has been taken at the center of the X values in a time series, N is $2M + 1$.

The sums of the first six powers of the first M natural numbers may be obtained from the following expressions:

$$\sum_1^M X = \frac{M(M + 1)}{2} \qquad \sum_1^M X^4 = \left(\frac{3M^2 + 3M - 1}{5}\right) \sum_1^M X^2$$

$$\sum_1^M X^2 = \left(\frac{2M + 1}{3}\right) \sum_1^M X \qquad \sum_1^M X^5 = \left(\frac{2M^2 + 2M - 1}{3}\right) \sum_1^M X^3$$

$$\sum_1^M X^3 = \left(\sum_1^M X\right)^2 \qquad \sum_1^M X^6 = \left(\frac{3M^4 + 6M^3 - 3M + 1}{7}\right) \sum_1^M X^2$$

A table of the sums of the first 7 powers of the first 100 natural numbers may be found in E. S. Pearson and H. O. Hartley, *Biometrika Tables for Statisticians*, Vol. I, Cambridge University Press, London, 1954, pp. 224–225, and in Karl Pearson, *Tables for Statisticians and Biometricians*, third edition, Part I, Cambridge University Press, London, 1948, pp. 40–41. It appears also on the same pages in earlier editions.

APPENDIX C

Sums of the First Six Powers of the First 50 Odd Natural Numbers

This table shows the sums of the first six powers of the first M_o odd natural numbers from $M_o = 1$ to $M_o = 50$. Note that, when $M_o = 2$, we have the odd natural numbers 1 and 3; when $M_o = 3$, reference is to 1, 3, and 5; when $M_o = 4$, the numbers 1, 3, 5, and 7 are involved; and so

(Highest odd natural number)	M_o	$\sum_1^{M_o} X_o$	$\sum_1^{M_o} X_o^2$	$\sum_1^{M_o} X_o^3$	$\sum_1^{M_o} X_o^4$	$\sum_1^{M_o} X_o^5$	$\sum_1^{M_o} X_o^6$
1	1	1	1	1	1	1	1
3	2	4	10	28	82	244	730
5	3	9	35	153	707	3 369	16 355
7	4	16	84	496	3 108	20 176	134 004
9	5	25	165	1 225	9 669	79 225	665 445
11	6	36	286	2 556	24 310	240 276	2 437 006
13	7	49	455	4 753	52 871	611 569	7 263 815
15	8	64	680	8 128	103 496	1 370 944	18 654 440
17	9	81	969	13 041	187 017	2 790 801	42 792 009
19	10	100	1 330	19 900	317 338	5 266 900	89 837 890
21	11	121	1 771	29 161	511 819	9 351 001	175 604 011
23	12	144	2 300	41 328	791 660	15 787 344	323 639 900
25	13	169	2 925	56 953	1 182 285	25 552 969	567 780 525
27	14	196	3 654	76 636	1 713 726	39 901 876	955 201 014
29	15	225	4 495	101 025	2 421 007	60 413 025	1 550 024 335
31	16	256	5 456	130 816	3 344 528	89 042 176	2 437 528 016
33	17	289	6 545	166 753	4 530 449	128 177 569	3 728 995 985
35	18	324	7 770	209 628	6 031 074	180 699 444	5 567 261 610
37	19	361	9 139	260 281	7 905 235	250 043 401	8 132 988 019
39	20	400	10 660	319 600	10 218 676	340 267 600	11 651 731 780
41	21	441	12 341	388 521	13 044 437	456 123 801	16 401 836 021
43	22	484	14 190	468 028	16 463 238	603 132 244	22 723 199 070
45	23	529	16 215	559 153	20 563 863	787 660 369	31 026 964 695
47	24	576	18 424	662 976	25 443 544	1 017 005 376	41 806 180 024
49	25	625	20 825	780 625	31 208 345	1 299 480 625	55 647 467 225
51	26	676	23 426	913 276	37 973 546	1 644 505 876	73 243 755 026
53	27	729	26 235	1 062 153	45 864 027	2 062 701 369	95 408 116 155
55	28	784	29 260	1 228 528	55 014 652	2 565 985 744	123 088 756 780
57	29	841	32 509	1 413 721	65 570 653	3 167 677 801	157 385 204 029
59	30	900	35 990	1 619 100	77 688 014	3 882 602 100	199 565 737 670
61	31	961	39 711	1 846 081	91 533 855	4 727 198 401	251 086 112 031
63	32	1 024	43 680	2 096 128	107 286 816	5 719 634 944	313 609 614 240
65	33	1 089	47 905	2 370 753	125 137 441	6 879 925 569	389 028 504 865
67	34	1 155	52 394	2 671 516	145 288 562	8 230 050 676	479 486 887 034
69	35	1 225	57 155	3 000 025	167 955 683	9 794 082 025	587 405 050 115
71	36	1 296	62 196	3 357 936	193 367 364	11 598 311 376	715 505 334 036
73	37	1 369	67 525	3 746 953	221 765 605	13 671 382 969	866 839 560 325
75	38	1 444	73 150	4 168 828	253 406 230	16 044 429 844	1 044 818 075 950
77	39	1 521	79 079	4 625 361	288 559 271	18 751 214 001	1 253 240 456 039
79	40	1 600	85 320	5 118 400	327 509 352	21 828 270 400	1 496 327 911 560
81	41	1 681	91 881	5 649 841	370 556 073	25 315 054 801	1 778 757 448 041
83	42	1 764	98 770	6 221 628	418 014 394	29 254 095 444	2 105 697 821 410
85	43	1 849	105 995	6 835 753	470 215 019	33 691 148 569	2 482 847 337 035
87	44	1 936	113 564	7 494 256	527 504 780	38 675 357 776	2 916 473 538 044
89	45	2 025	121 485	8 199 225	590 247 021	44 259 417 225	3 413 454 829 005
91	46	2 116	129 766	8 952 796	658 821 982	50 499 738 676	3 981 324 081 046
93	47	2 209	138 415	9 757 153	733 627 183	57 456 622 369	4 628 314 264 495
95	48	2 304	147 440	10 614 528	815 077 808	65 194 431 744	5 363 406 155 120
97	49	2 401	156 849	11 527 201	903 607 089	73 781 772 001	6 196 378 160 049
99	50	2 500	166 650	12 497 500	999 666 690	83 291 672 500	7 137 858 309 450

on. For convenience, the table shows both the highest odd natural number and M_o. The sums shown here will be used almost exclusively in connection with the fitting of a trend line to a time series having an even number of years (or other periods) and where the origin is taken between the two center X values. Under these conditions: (1) the largest X value shown in the computation table is the highest odd natural number and M_o = (highest odd natural number + 1) ÷ 2; (2) the sums read from the table must be multiplied by 2; and (3) N as used in the normal equations is $2M_o$. X_o means "odd value of X."

The sums of the first six powers of the first M_o odd natural numbers may be obtained from the following:

$$\sum_{1}^{M_o} X_o = M_o^2$$

$$\sum_{1}^{M_o} X_o^2 = \frac{4M_o^3 - M_o}{3}$$

$$\sum_{1}^{M_o} X_o^3 = (2M_o^2 - 1)\sum_{1}^{M_o} X_o$$

$$\sum_{1}^{M_o} X_o^4 = \left(\frac{12M_o^2 - 7}{5}\right)\sum_{1}^{M_o} X_o^2$$

$$\sum_{1}^{M_o} X_o^5 = \left(\frac{16M_o^4 - 20M_o^2 + 7}{3}\right)\sum_{1}^{M_o} X_o$$

$$\sum_{1}^{M_o} X_o^6 = \left(\frac{48M_o^4 - 72M_o^2 + 31}{7}\right)\sum_{1}^{M_o} X_o^2$$

A table of the sums of the first six powers of the first 100 odd natural numbers is given in "Formulae for Facilitating Computations in Time Series Analysis," by Frank A. Ross, *Journal of The American Statistical Association*, March 1925, pp. 75–79.

APPENDIX D

Ordinates of the Normal Curve

Erected at Distances $\dfrac{x}{s}$ from $\overline{X}$, Expressed as Decimal Fractions of the

Maximum Ordinate Y_0

The maximum ordinate is computed from the expression $Y_0 = \dfrac{Ni}{s\sqrt{2\pi}} = \dfrac{Ni}{2.5066s}$.

The values tabled below result from solving the expression $e^{\frac{-x^2}{2s^2}}$.

The proportional height of an ordinate to be erected at any given value on the X axis can be read from the table by determining x (the deviation of the given value from the mean) and computing $\dfrac{x}{s}$. Thus, if $\overline{X} = \$25.00$, $s = \$4.00$, $Y_0 = 1950$, and it is desired to ascertain the height of an ordinate to be erected at $\$23.00$; $x = \$2.00$ and $\dfrac{x}{s} = \dfrac{\$2.00}{\$4.00} = 0.50$. From the table the ordinate is found to be 0.88250 of the maximum ordinate Y_0, or $0.88250 \times 1950 = 1721$.

Ordinates of the Normal Curve

$\frac{x}{s}$	0	.01	.02	.03	.04	.05	.06	.07	.08	.09
0.0	1.00000	.99995	.99980	.99955	.99920	.99875	.99820	.99755	.99685	.99596
0.1	.99501	.99396	.99283	.99158	.99025	.98881	.98728	.98565	.98393	.98211
0.2	.98020	.97819	.97609	.97390	.97161	.96923	.96676	.96420	.96156	.95882
0.3	.95600	.95309	.95010	.94702	.94387	.94055	.93723	.93382	.93024	.92677
0.4	.92312	.91939	.91558	.91169	.90774	.90371	.89961	.89543	.89119	.88688
0.5	.88250	.87805	.87353	.86896	.86432	.85962	.85488	.85006	.84519	.84025
0.6	.83527	.83023	.82514	.82000	.81481	.80957	.80429	.79896	.79359	.78817
0.7	.78270	.77721	.77167	.76610	.76048	.75484	.74916	.74342	.73769	.73193
0.8	.72615	.72033	.71448	.70861	.70272	.69681	.69087	.68493	.67896	.67298
0.9	.66698	.66097	.65494	.64891	.64287	.63683	.63077	.62472	.61865	.61259
1.0	.60653	.60047	.59440	.58834	.58228	.57623	.57017	.56414	.55810	.55209
1.1	.54607	.54007	.53409	.52812	.52214	.51620	.51027	.50437	.49848	.49260
1.2	.48675	.48092	.47511	.46933	.46357	.45783	.45212	.44644	.44078	.43516
1.3	.42956	.42399	.41845	.41294	.40747	.40202	.39661	.39123	.38589	.38058
1.4	.37531	.37007	.36487	.35971	.35459	.34950	.34445	.33944	.33447	.32954
1.5	.32465	.31980	.31500	.31023	.30550	.30082	.29618	.29158	.28702	.28251
1.6	.27804	.27361	.26923	.26489	.26059	.25634	.25213	.24797	.24385	.23978
1.7	.23575	.23176	.22782	.22392	.22008	.21627	.21251	.20879	.20511	.20148
1.8	.19790	.19436	.19086	.18741	.18400	.18064	.17732	.17404	.17081	.16762
1.9	.16448	.16137	.15831	.15530	.15232	.14939	.14650	.14364	.14083	.13806
2.0	.13534	.13265	.13000	.12740	.12483	.12230	.11981	.11737	.11496	.11259
2.1	.11025	.10795	.10570	.10347	.10129	.09914	.09702	.09495	.09290	.09090
2.2	.08892	.08698	.08507	.08320	.08136	.07956	.07778	.07604	.07433	.07265
2.3	.07100	.06939	.06780	.06624	.06471	.06321	.06174	.06029	.05888	.05750
2.4	.05614	.05481	.05350	.05222	.05096	.04973	.04852	.04734	.04618	.04505
2.5	.04394	.04285	.04179	.04074	.03972	.03873	.03775	.03680	.03586	.03494
2.6	.03405	.03317	.03232	.03148	.03066	.02986	.02908	.02831	.02757	.02684
2.7	.02612	.02542	.02474	.02408	.02343	.02280	.02218	.02157	.02098	.02040
2.8	.01984	.01929	.01876	.01823	.01772	.01723	.01674	.01627	.01581	.01536
2.9	.01492	.01449	.01408	.01367	.01328	.01288	.01252	.01215	.01179	.01145

$\frac{x}{s}$	0	.1	.2	.3	.4	.5	.6	.7	.8	.9
3.	.01111	.00819	.00598	.00432	.00309	.00219	.00153	.00106	.00073	.00050
4.	.00034	.00022	.00015	.00010	.00006	.00004	.00003	.00002	.00001	.00001
5.	.00000									

Largely from Rugg's *Statistical Methods Applied to Education*, by arrangement with the publishers, Houghton Mifflin Company. More detailed tables of normal-curve ordinates may be found in E. S. Pearson and H. O. Hartley, *Biometrika Tables for Statisticians*, Volume I, Cambridge University Press, London, 1954, pp. 104–110; in Karl Pearson, *Tables for Statisticians and Biometricians*, third edition, Part I, The University Press, London, 1948, pp. 2–8; and in Federal Works Agency, Work Projects Administration for the City of New York, *Tables of Probability Functions*, National Bureau of Standards, New York, 1942, Vol. II, pp. 2–238. The values shown in these tables should be multiplied by $\sqrt{2\pi} = 2.5066$ to agree with those shown above.

APPENDIX E

Areas Under the Normal Curve

From the Arithmetic Mean to Distances* $\frac{x}{s}$ or $\frac{x}{\sigma}$ from the Arithmetic Mean, Expressed as Decimal Fractions of the Total Area 1.0000

This table shows the black area:

$\frac{x}{s}$ or $\frac{x}{\sigma}$	.00	.01	.02	.03	.04	.05	.06	.07	.08	.09
0.0	.0000	.0040	.0080	.0120	.0160	.0199	.0239	.0279	.0319	.0359
0.1	.0398	.0438	.0478	.0517	.0557	.0596	.0636	.0675	.0714	.0753
0.2	.0832	.0871	.0910	.0948	.0987	.1026	.1064	.1103	.1141
0.3	.1179	.1217	.1255	.1293	.1331	.1368	.1406	.1443	.1480	.1517
0.4	.1554	.1591	.1628	.1664	.1700	.1736	.1772	.1808	.1844	.1879
0.5	.1915	.1950	.1985	.2019	.2054	.2088	.2123	.2157	.2190	.2224
0.6	.2257	.2291	.2324	.2357	.2389	.2422	.2454	.2486	.2518	.2549
0.7	.2580	.2612	.2642	.2673	.2704	.2734	.2764	.2794	.2823	.2852
0.8	.2881	.2910	.2939	.2967	.2995	.3023	.3051	.3078	.3106	.3133
0.9	.3159	.3186	.3212	.3238	.3264	.3289	.3315	.3340	.3365	.3389
1.0	.3413	.3438	.3461	.3485	.3508	.3531	.3554	.3577	.3599	.3621
1.1	.3643	.3665	.3686	.3708	.3729	.3749	.3770	.3790	.3810	.3830
1.2	.3849	.3869	.3888	.3907	.3925	.3944	.3962	.3980	.3997	.4015
1.3	.4032	.4049	.4066	.4082	.4099	.4115	.4131	.4147	.4162	.4177
1.4	.4192	.4207	.4222	.4236	.4251	.4265	.4279	.4292	.4306	.4319
1.5	.4332	.4345	.4357	.4370	.4382	.4394	.4406	.4418	.4429	.4441
1.6	.4452	.4463	.4474	.4484	.4495	.4505	.4515	.4525	.4535	.4545
1.7	.4554	.4564	.4573	.4582	.4591	.4599	.4608	.4616	.4625	.4633
1.8	.4641	.4649	.4656	.4664	.4671	.4678	.4686	.4693	.4699	.4706
1.9	.4713	.4719	.4726	.4732	.4738	.4744	.4750	.4756	.4761	.4767
2.0	.4772	.4778	.4783	.4788	.4793	.4798	.4803	.4808	.4812	.4817
2.1	.4821	.4826	.4830	.4834	.4838	.4842	.4846	.4850	.4854	.4857
2.2	.4861	.4864	.4868	.4871	.4875	.4878	.4881	.4884	.4887	.4890
2.3	.4893	.4896	.4898	.4901	.4904	.4906	.4909	.4911	.4913	.4916
2.4	.4918	.4920	.4922	.4925	.4927	.4929	.4931	.4932	.4934	.4936
2.5	.4938	.4940	.4941	.4943	.4945	.4946	.4948	.4949	.4951	.4952
2.6	.4953	.4955	.4956	.4957	.4959	.4960	.4961	.4962	.4963	.4964
2.7	.4965	.4966	.4967	.4968	.4969	.4970	.4971	.4972	.4973	.4974
2.8	.4974	.4975	.4976	.4977	.4977	.4978	.4979	.4979	.4980	.4981
2.9	.4981	.4982	.4982	.4983	.4984	.4984	.4985	.4985	.4986	.4986
3.0	.49865	.4987	.4987	.4988	.4988	.4989	.4989	.4989	.4990	.4990
3.1	.49903	.4991	.4991	.4991	.4992	.4992	.4992	.4992	.4993	.4993
3.2	.4993129									
3.3	.4995106									
3.4	.4996631									
3.5	.4997674									
3.6	.4998409									
3.7	.4998922									
3.8	.4999277									
3.9	.4999519									
4.0	.4999683									
4.5	.4999966									
5.0	.4999997133									

* The expression $\frac{x}{s}$ is used when fitting a normal curve; $\frac{x}{\sigma}$ is employed when making a test of significance involving the standard deviation of the population and the normal curve.

Largely from Rugg's *Statistical Methods Applied to Education* (with corrections), by arrangement with the publishers, Houghton Mifflin Company. A more detailed table of normal-curve areas, but in two directions from the arithmetic mean, is given in Federal Works Agency, Work Projects Administration for the City of New York, *Tables of Probability Functions*, National Bureau of Standards, New York, 1942, Vol. II, pp. 2–338.

APPENDIX F

Values of $F_2\left(\dfrac{x}{s}\right)$

For Use in Fitting Curves of the Type

$$Y_c = \frac{Ni}{s\sqrt{2\pi}}\, e^{\frac{-x^2}{2s^2}} - \left\{\frac{Ni}{s\sqrt{2\pi}}\, e^{\frac{-x^2}{2s^2}}\left[\frac{\alpha_3}{2}\left(\frac{x}{s}-\frac{x^3}{3s^3}\right)\right]\right\} = \frac{Ni}{s\sqrt{2\pi}}\, e^{\frac{-x^2}{2s^2}}\left[1 - \frac{\alpha_3}{2}\left(\frac{x}{s}-\frac{x^3}{3s^3}\right)\right]$$

$\dfrac{x}{s}$	.00	.01	.02	.03	.04	.05	.06	.07	.08	.09
.0	.00000	.00001	.00004	.00009	.00016	.00025	.00036	.00049	.00064	.00081
.1	.00099	.00120	.00143	.00167	.00194	.00222	.00253	.00285	.00319	.00355
.2	.00392	.00432	.00473	.00516	.00561	.00607	.00656	.00705	.00757	.00810
.3	.00865	.00921	.00979	.01038	.01099	.01161	.01225	.01290	.01356	.01424
.4	.01493	.01564	.01635	.01708	.01782	.01857	.01933	.02011	.02089	.02168
.5	.02248	.02329	.02411	.02494	.02578	.02662	.02748	.02833	.02920	.03007
.6	.03095	.03183	.03272	.03361	.03450	.03540	.03631	.03721	.03812	.03904
.7	.03995	.04086	.04178	.04270	.04362	.04453	.04545	.04637	.04728	.04820
.8	.04911	.05002	.05093	.05183	.05274	.05363	.05453	.05542	.05631	.05719
.9	.05806	.05894	.05980	.06066	.06152	.06236	.06320	.06404	.06486	.06568
1.0	.06649	.06729	.06809	.06887	.06965	.07042	.07118	.07193	.07267	.07340
1.1	.07412	.07483	.07552	.07621	.07689	.07756	.07822	.07886	.07950	.08012
1.2	.08073	.08133	.08192	.08250	.08306	.08361	.08416	.08468	.08520	.08571
1.3	.08620	.08668	.08715	.08760	.08805	.08848	.08890	.08930	.08970	.09008
1.4	.09045	.09080	.09115	.09148	.09180	.09211	.09241	.09269	.09296	.09322
1.5	.09347	.09371	.09394	.09415	.09435	.09454	.09472	.09489	.09505	.09519
1.6	.09533	.09546	.09557	.09567	.09577	.09585	.09592	.09599	.09604	.09608
1.7	.09612	.09614	.09616	.09616	.09616	.09615	.09613	.09610	.09606	.09602
1.8	.09597	.09590	.09584	.09576	.09568	.09559	.09549	.09539	.09527	.09516
1.9	.09503	.09490	.09477	.09463	.09448	.09433	.09417	.09401	.09384	.09366
2.0	.09349	.09330	.09312	.09293	.09273	.09253	.09233	.09213	.09192	.09170
2.1	.09149	.09127	.09105	.09082	.09060	.09037	.09014	.08991	.08967	.08943
2.2	.08919	.08895	.08871	.08847	.08823	.08798	.08774	.08749	.08724	.08699
2.3	.08674	.08650	.08625	.08600	.08575	.08550	.08525	.08500	.08475	.08450
2.4	.08426	.08401	.08376	.08352	.08327	.08303	.08279	.08255	.08231	.08207
2.5	.08183	.08159	.08136	.08112	.08089	.08066	.08043	.08020	.07998	.07975
2.6	.07953	.07931	.07909	.07888	.07866	.07845	.07824	.07803	.07782	.07762
2.7	.07742	.07722	.07702	.07682	.07663	.07644	.07625	.07606	.07588	.07569
2.8	.07551	.07534	.07516	.07499	.07482	.07465	.07448	.07432	.07416	.07400
2.9	.07384	.07369	.07354	.07339	.07324	.07309	.07295	.07281	.07267	.07254
3.0	.07240									
3.1	.07118									
3.2	.07016									
3.3	.06933									
3.4	.06866									
3.5	.06813									
3.6	.06771									
3.7	.06739									
3.8	.06714									
3.9	.06696									
4.0	.06683									

From W. A. Shewhart, *Economic Control of Quality of Manufactured Product*, D. Van Nostrand Co., Princeton, N. J., 1931, p. 91. Courtesy of D. Van Nostrand Company, Inc., and The Bell Telephone Laboratories.

For values of $F_2\left(\dfrac{x}{s}\right)$ beyond the range shown above, use the expression $F_2\left(\dfrac{x}{s}\right)$

$$= \frac{1}{6\sqrt{2\pi}}\left\{1 - \left[1 - \left(\frac{x}{s}\right)^2\right]e^{\frac{-x^2}{2s^2}}\right\} = \frac{1}{15.036}\left\{1 - \left[1 - \left(\frac{x}{s}\right)^2\right]e^{\frac{-x^2}{2s^2}}\right\}.$$ The values

of $e^{\frac{-x^2}{2s^2}}$ may be conveniently read from the table of ordinates of the normal curve, Appendix D, or from a more extensive table in E. S. Pearson and H. O. Hartley, *Biometrika Tables for Statisticians*, Vol. I, Cambridge University Press, London, 1954, pp. 104–110, and in Karl Pearson, *Tables for Statisticians and Biometricians*, third edition, Part I, The University Press, London, 1948, pp. 2–8. The values for z shown in the last two tables yield $e^{\frac{-x^2}{2s^2}}$ when multiplied by 2.5066.

APPENDIX G

Areas in One Tail of the Normal Curve at Selected Values* of $\frac{x}{s}$ or $\frac{x}{\sigma}$ from the Arithmetic Mean

This table shows the black area:

or

$\frac{x}{s}$ or $\frac{x}{\sigma}$	.00	.01	.02	.03	.04	.05	.06	.07	.08	.09
0.0	.5000	.4960	.4920	.4880	.4840	.4801	.4761	.4721	.4681	.4641
0.1	.4602	.4562	.4522	.4483	.4443	.4404	.4364	.4325	.4286	.4247
0.2	.4207	.4168	.4129	.4090	.4052	.4013	.3974	.3936	.3897	.3859
0.3	.3821	.3783	.3745	.3707	.3669	.3632	.3594	.3557	.3520	.3483
0.4	.3446	.3409	.3372	.3336	.3300	.3264	.3228	.3192	.3156	.3121
0.5	.3085	.3050	.3015	.2981	.2946	.2912	.2877	.2843	.2810	.2776
0.6	.2743	.2709	.2676	.2643	.2611	.2578	.2546	.2514	.2483	.2451
0.7	.2420	.2389	.2358	.2327	.2296	.2266	.2236	.2206	.2177	.2148
0.8	.2119	.2090	.2061	.2033	.2005	.1977	.1949	.1922	.1894	.1867
0.9	.1841	.1814	.1788	.1762	.1736	.1711	.1685	.1660	.1635	.1611
1.0	.1587	.1562	.1539	.1515	.1492	.1469	.1446	.1423	.1401	.1379
1.1	.1357	.1335	.1314	.1292	.1271	.1251	.1230	.1210	.1190	.1170
1.2	.1151	.1131	.1112	.1093	.1075	.1056	.1038	.1020	.1003	.0985
1.3	.0968	.0951	.0934	.0918	.0901	.0885	.0869	.0853	.0838	.0823
1.4	.0808	.0793	.0778	.0764	.0749	.0735	.0721	.0708	.0694	.0681
1.5	.0668	.0655	.0643	.0630	.0618	.0606	.0594	.0582	.0571	.0559
1.6	.0548	.0537	.0526	.0516	.0505	.0495	.0485	.0475	.0465	.0455
1.7	.0446	.0436	.0427	.0418	.0409	.0401	.0392	.0384	.0375	.0367
1.8	.0359	.0351	.0344	.0336	.0329	.0322	.0314	.0307	.0301	.0294
1.9	.0287	.0281	.0274	.0268	.0262	.0256	.0250	.0244	.0239	.0233
2.0	.0228	.0222	.0217	.0212	.0207	.0202	.0197	.0192	.0188	.0183
2.1	.0179	.0174	.0170	.0166	.0162	.0158	.0154	.0150	.0146	.0143
2.2	.0139	.0136	.0132	.0129	.0125	.0122	.0119	.0116	.0113	.0110
2.3	.0107	.0104	.0102	.00990	.00964	.00939	.00914	.00889	.00866	.00842
2.4	.00820	.00798	.00776	.00755	.00734	.00714	.00695	.00676	.00657	.00639
2.5	.00621	.00604	.00587	.00570	.00554	.00539	.00523	.00508	.00494	.00480
2.6	.00466	.00453	.00440	.00427	.00415	.00402	.00391	.00379	.00368	.00357
2.7	.00347	.00336	.00326	.00317	.00307	.00298	.00289	.00280	.00272	.00264
2.8	.00256	.00248	.00240	.00233	.00226	.00219	.00212	.00205	.00199	.00193
2.9	.00187	.00131	.00175	.00169	.00164	.00159	.00154	.00149	.00144	.00139

$\frac{x}{s}$ or $\frac{x}{\sigma}$	.0	.1	.2	.3	.4	.5	.6	.7	.8	.9
3	.00135	$.0^3968$	$.0^3687$	$.0^3483$	$.0^3337$	$.0^3233$	$.0^3159$	$.0^3108$	$.0^4723$	$.0^4481$
4	$.0^4317$	$.0^4207$	$.0^4133$	$.0^5854$	$.0^5541$	$.0^5340$	$.0^5211$	$.0^5130$	$.0^6793$	$.0^6479$
5	$.0^6287$	$.0^6170$	$.0^7996$	$.0^7579$	$.0^7333$	$.0^7190$	$.0^7107$	$.0^8599$	$.0^8332$	$.0^8182$
6	$.0^9987$	$.0^9530$	$.0^9282$	$.0^9149$	$.0^{10}777$	$.0^{10}402$	$.0^{10}206$	$.0^{10}104$	$.0^{11}523$	$.0^{11}260$

* See note to Appendix E.

From *Tables of Areas in Two Tails and in One Tail of the Normal Curve*, by Frederick E. Croxton. Copyright, 1949, by permission of Prentice-Hall, Inc.

APPENDIX H

Areas in Two Tails of the Normal Curve at Selected Values* of $\frac{x}{s}$ or $\frac{x}{\sigma}$ from the Arithmetic Mean

This table shows the black areas:

$\frac{x}{s}$ or $\frac{x}{\sigma}$	.00	.01	.02	.03	.04	.05	.06	.07	.08	.09
0.0	1.0000	.9920	.9840	.9761	.9681	.9601	.9522	.9442	.9362	.9283
0.1	.9203	.9124	.9045	.8966	.8887	.8808	.8729	.8650	.8572	.8493
0.2	.8415	.8337	.8259	.8181	.8103	.8026	.7949	.7872	.7795	.7718
0.3	.7642	.7566	.7490	.7414	.7339	.7263	.7188	.7114	.7039	.6965
0.4	.6892	.6818	.6745	.6672	.6599	.6527	.6455	.6384	.6312	.6241
0.5	.6171	.6101	.6031	.5961	.5892	.5823	.5755	.5687	.5619	.5552
0.6	.5485	.5419	.5353	.5287	.5222	.5157	.5093	.5029	.4965	.4902
0.7	.4839	.4777	.4715	.4654	.4593	.4533	.4473	.4413	.4354	.4295
0.8	.4237	.4179	.4122	.4065	.4009	.3953	.3898	.3843	.3789	.3735
0.9	.3681	.3628	.3576	.3524	.3472	.3421	.3371	.3320	.3271	.3222
1.0	.3173	.3125	.3077	.3030	.2983	.2937	.2891	.2846	.2801	.2757
1.1	.2713	.2670	.2627	.2585	.2543	.2501	.2460	.2420	.2380	.2340
1.2	.2301	.2263	.2225	.2187	.2150	.2113	.2077	.2041	.2005	.1971
1.3	.1936	.1902	.1868	.1835	.1802	.1770	.1738	.1707	.1676	.1645
1.4	.1615	.1585	.1556	.1527	.1499	.1471	.1443	.1416	.1389	.1362
1.5	.1336	.1310	.1285	.1260	.1236	.1211	.1188	.1164	.1141	.1118
1.6	.1096	.1074	.1052	.1031	.1010	.0989	.0969	.0949	.0930	.0910
1.7	.0891	.0873	.0854	.0836	.0819	.0801	.0784	.0767	.0751	.0735
1.8	.0719	.0703	.0688	.0672	.0658	.0643	.0629	.0615	.0601	.0588
1.9	.0574	.0561	.0549	.0536	.0524	.0512	.0500	.0488	.0477	.0466
2.0	.0455	.0444	.0434	.0424	.0414	.0404	.0394	.0385	.0375	.0366
2.1	.0357	.0349	.0340	.0332	.0324	.0316	.0308	.0300	.0293	.0285
2.2	.0278	.0271	.0264	.0257	.0251	.0244	.0238	.0232	.0226	.0220
2.3	.0214	.0209	.0203	.0198	.0193	.0188	.0183	.0178	.0173	.0168
2.4	.0164	.0160	.0155	.0151	.0147	.0143	.0139	.0135	.0131	.0128
2.5	.0124	.0121	.0117	.0114	.0111	.0108	.0105	.0102	.00988	.00960
2.6	.00932	.00905	.00879	.00854	.00829	.00805	.00781	.00759	.00736	.00715
2.7	.00693	.00673	.00653	.00633	.00614	.00596	.00578	.00561	.00544	.00527
2.8	.00511	.00495	.00480	.00465	.00451	.00437	.00424	.00410	.00398	.00385
2.9	.00373	.00361	.00350	.00339	.00328	.00318	.00308	.00298	.00288	.00279

$\frac{x}{s}$ or $\frac{x}{\sigma}$	.0	.1	.2	.3	.4	.5	.6	.7	.8	.9
3	.00270	.00194	.00137	$.0^3967$	$.0^3674$	$.0^3465$	$.0^3318$	$.0^3216$	$.0^3145$	$.0^4962$
4	$.0^4633$	$.0^4413$	$.0^4267$	$.0^4171$	$.0^4108$	$.0^5680$	$.0^5422$	$.0^5260$	$.0^4159$	$.0^6958$
5	$.0^6573$	$.0^6340$	$.0^6199$	$.0^6116$	$.0^7666$	$.0^7380$	$.0^7214$	$.0^7120$	$.0^8663$	$.0^8364$
6	$.0^8197$	$.0^8106$	$.0^9565$	$.0^9298$	$.0^9155$	$.0^{10}803$	$.0^{10}411$	$.0^{10}208$	$.0^{10}105$	$.0^{11}520$

* See note to Appendix E.

From *Tables of Areas in Two Tails and in One Tail of the Normal Curve*, by Frederick E. Croxton. Copyright, 1949, by permission of Prentice-Hall, Inc.

Values

For Given Degrees of Freedom (*n*) and

This table shows the black

	Level of significance (*P*)							
n	.90	.80	.70	.60	.50	.40	.30	.25
1	.158	.325	.510	.727	1.000	1.376	1.963	2.414
2	.142	.289	.445	.617	.816	1.061	1.386	1.604
3	.137	.277	.424	.584	.765	.978	1.250	1.423
4	.134	.271	.414	.569	.741	.941	1.190	1.344
5	.132	.267	.408	.559	.727	.920	1.156	1.301
6	.131	.265	.404	.553	.718	.906	1.134	1.273
7	.130	.263	.402	.549	.711	.896	1.119	1.254
8	.130	.262	.399	.546	.706	.889	1.108	1.240
9	.129	.261	.398	.543	.703	.883	1.100	1.230
10	.129	.260	.397	.542	.700	.879	1.093	1.221
11	.129	.260	.396	.540	.697	.876	1.088	1.214
12	.128	.259	.395	.539	.695	.873	1.083	1.209
13	.128	.259	.394	.538	.694	.870	1.079	1.204
14	.128	.258	.393	.537	.692	.868	1.076	1.200
15	.128	.258	.393	.536	.691	.866	1.074	1.197
16	.128	.258	.392	.535	.690	.865	1.071	1.194
17	.128	.257	.392	.534	.689	.863	1.069	1.191
18	.127	.257	.392	.534	.688	.862	1.067	1.189
19	.127	.257	.391	.533	.688	.861	1.066	1.187
20	.127	.257	.391	.533	.687	.860	1.064	1.185
21	.127	.257	.391	.532	.686	.859	1.063	1.183
22	.127	.256	.390	.532	.686	.858	1.061	1.182
23	.127	.256	.390	.532	.685	.858	1.060	1.180
24	.127	.256	.390	.531	.685	.857	1.059	1.179
25	.127	.256	.390	.531	.684	.856	1.058	1.178
26	.127	.256	.390	.531	.684	.856	1.058	1.177
27	.127	.256	.389	.531	.684	.855	1.057	1.176
28	.127	.256	.389	.530	.683	.855	1.056	1.175
29	.127	.256	.389	.530	.683	.854	1.055	1.174
30	.127	.256	.389	.530	.683	.854	1.055	1.173
40	.126	.255	.388	.529	.681	.851	1.050	1.167
60	.126	.254	.387	.527	.679	.848	1.046	1.162
120	.126	.254	.386	.526	.677	.845	1.041	1.156
∞	.126	.253	.385	.524	.674	.842	1.036	1.150

The values in this table were taken, by permission, from *Statistical Tables for Biological, Agricultural, and Medical Research*, by R. A. Fisher and F. Yates, published by Oliver and Boyd, Edinburgh, and from *Biometrika*, Vol. XXXII, April 1942, p. 300, "Table of Percentage Points of the *t*-distribution," by Maxine Merrington. A table of *t*, similar in

I

of t

at Specified Levels of Significance (P)

areas:

Level of significance (P)								n
.20	.10	.05	.025	.02	.01	.005	.001	
3.078	6.314	12.706	25.452	31.821	63.657	127.32	636.619	1
1.886	2.920	4.303	6.205	6.965	9.925	14.089	31.598	2
1.638	2.353	3.182	4.176	4.541	5.841	7.453	12.941	3
1.533	2.132	2.776	3.495	3.747	4.604	5.598	8.610	4
1.476	2.015	2.571	3.163	3.365	4.032	4.773	6.859	5
1.440	1.943	2.447	2.969	3.143	3.707	4.317	5.959	6
1.415	1.895	2.365	2.841	2.998	3.499	4.029	5.405	7
1.397	1.860	2.306	2.752	2.896	3.355	3.832	5.041	8
1.383	1.833	2.262	2.685	2.821	3.250	3.690	4.781	9
1.372	1.812	2.228	2.634	2.764	3.169	3.581	4.587	10
1.363	1.796	2.201	2.593	2.718	3.106	3.497	4.437	11
1.356	1.782	2.179	2.560	2.681	3.055	3.428	4.318	12
1.350	1.771	2.160	2.533	2.650	3.012	3.372	4.221	13
1.345	1.761	2.145	2.510	2.624	2.977	3.326	4.140	14
1.341	1.753	2.131	2.490	2.602	2.947	3.286	4.073	15
1.337	1.746	2.120	2.473	2.583	2.921	3.252	4.015	16
1.333	1.740	2.110	2.458	2.567	2.898	3.222	3.965	17
1.330	1.734	2.101	2.445	2.552	2.878	3.197	3.922	18
1.328	1.729	2.093	2.433	2.539	2.861	3.174	3.883	19
1.325	1.725	2.086	2.423	2.528	2.845	3.153	3.850	20
1.323	1.721	2.080	2.414	2.518	2.831	3.135	3.819	21
1.321	1.717	2.074	2.406	2.508	2.819	3.119	3.792	22
1.319	1.714	2.069	2.398	2.500	2.807	3.104	3.767	23
1.318	1.711	2.064	2.391	2.492	2.797	3.090	3.745	24
1.316	1.708	2.060	2.385	2.485	2.787	3.078	3.725	25
1.315	1.706	2.056	2.379	2.479	2.779	3.067	3.707	26
1.314	1.703	2.052	2.373	2.473	2.771	3.056	3.690	27
1.313	1.701	2.048	2.368	2.467	2.763	3.047	3.674	28
1.311	1.699	2.045	2.364	2.462	2.756	3.038	3.659	29
1.310	1.697	2.042	2.360	2.457	2.750	3.030	3.646	30
1.303	1.684	2.021	2.329	2.423	2.704	2.971	3.551	40
1.296	1.671	2.000	2.299	2.390	2.660	2.915	3.460	60
1.289	1.658	1.980	2.270	2.358	2.617	2.860	3.373	120
1.282	1.645	1.960	2.241	2.326	2.576	2.807	3.291	∞

arrangement to that of Appendix E, giving areas of the t distribution from the mean to t (in one direction) and for $n = 1$ to $n = 20$ may be found in "New Tables for Testing the Significance of Observations," by "Student," *Metron*. Vol. V. No. 3 (1925), pages 114–118.

This table shows
the black area:

for $n = 1$ and $n = 2$,

n	Value of P										
	.999	.995	.99	.98	.975	.95	.90	.80	.75	.70	.50
1	.05157	.04393	.03157	.03628	.03982	.00393	.0158	.0642	.102	.148	.455
2	.00200	.0100	.0201	.0404	.0506	.103	.211	.446	.575	.713	1.386
3	.0243	.0717	.115	.185	.216	.352	.584	1.005	1.213	1.424	2.366
4	.0908	.207	.297	.429	.484	.711	1.064	1.649	1.923	2.195	3.357
5	.210	.412	.554	.752	.831	1.145	1.610	2.343	2.675	3.000	4.351
6	.381	.676	.872	1.134	1.237	1.635	2.204	3.070	3.455	3.828	5.348
7	.598	.989	1.239	1.564	1.690	2.167	2.833	3.822	4.255	4.671	6.346
8	.857	1.344	1.646	2.032	2.180	2.733	3.490	4.594	5.071	5.527	7.344
9	1.152	1.735	2.088	2.532	2.700	3.325	4.168	5.380	5.899	6.393	8.343
10	1.479	2.156	2.558	3.059	3.247	3.940	4.865	6.179	6.737	7.267	9.342
11	1.834	2.603	3.053	3.609	3.816	4.575	5.578	6.989	7.584	8.148	10.341
12	2.214	3.074	3.571	4.178	4.404	5.226	6.304	7.807	8.438	9.034	11.340
13	2.617	3.565	4.107	4.765	5.009	5.892	7.042	8.634	9.299	9.926	12.340
14	3.041	4.075	4.660	5.368	5.629	6.571	7.790	9.467	10.165	10.821	13.339
15	3.483	4.601	5.229	5.985	6.262	7.261	8.547	10.307	11.036	11.721	14.339
16	3.942	5.142	5.812	6.614	6.908	7.962	9.312	11.152	11.912	12.624	15.338
17	4.416	5.697	6.408	7.255	7.564	8.672	10.085	12.002	12.792	13.531	16.338
18	4.905	6.265	7.015	7.906	8.231	9.390	10.865	12.857	13.675	14.440	17.338
19	5.407	6.844	7.633	8.567	8.907	10.117	11.651	13.716	14.562	15.352	18.338
20	5.921	7.434	8.260	9.237	9.591	10.851	12.443	14.578	15.452	16.266	19.337
21	6.447	8.034	8.897	9.915	10.283	11.591	13.240	15.445	16.344	17.182	20.337
22	6.983	8.643	9.542	10.600	10.982	12.338	14.041	16.314	17.240	18.101	21.337
23	7.529	9.260	10.196	11.293	11.688	13.091	14.848	17.187	18.137	19.021	22.337
24	8.085	9.886	10.856	11.992	12.401	13.848	15.659	18.062	19.037	19.943	23.337
25	8.649	10.520	11.524	12.697	13.120	14.611	16.473	18.940	19.939	20.867	24.337
26	9.222	11.160	12.198	13.409	13.844	15.379	17.292	19.820	20.843	21.792	25.336
27	9.803	11.808	12.879	14.125	14.573	16.151	18.114	20.703	21.749	22.719	26.336
28	10.391	12.461	13.565	14.847	15.308	16.928	18.939	21.588	22.657	23.647	27.336
29	10.986	13.121	14.256	15.574	16.047	17.708	19.768	22.475	23.567	24.577	28.336
30	11.588	13.787	14.953	16.306	16.791	18.493	20.599	23.364	24.478	25.508	29.336

For values of $n > 30$, approximate values for χ^2 may be obtained from the expression

$$n\left[1 - \frac{2}{9n} \pm \frac{x}{\sigma}\sqrt{\frac{2}{9n}}\right]^3,$$

where $\frac{x}{\sigma}$ is the normal deviate cutting off the corresponding tails of a normal distribution. If $\frac{x}{\sigma}$ is taken at the 0.02 level, so that 0.01 of the normal distribution is in each tail, the expression yields χ^2 at the 0.99 and 0.01 points. For very large values of n, it is sufficiently accurate to compute $\sqrt{2\chi^2}$, the distribution of which is approximately normal around a mean of $\sqrt{2n-1}$ and with a standard deviation of 1.

J

of χ^2

(n) and for Specified Values of P

and

for $n \geq 3$.

Value of P										n
.30	.25	.20	.10	.05	.025	.02	.01	.005	.001	
1.074	1.323	1.642	2.706	3.841	5.024	5.412	6.635	7.879	10.827	1
2.408	2.773	3.219	4.605	5.991	7.378	7.824	9.210	10.597	13.815	2
3.665	4.108	4.642	6.251	7.815	9.348	9.837	11.345	12.838	16.268	3
4.878	5.385	5.989	7.779	9.488	11.143	11.668	13.277	14.860	18.465	4
6.064	6.626	7.289	9.236	11.070	12.832	13.388	15.086	16.750	20.517	5
7.231	7.841	8.558	10.645	12.592	14.449	15.033	16.812	18.548	22.457	6
8.383	9.037	9.803	12.017	14.067	16.013	16.622	18.475	20.278	24.322	7
9.524	10.219	11.030	13.362	15.507	17.535	18.168	20.090	21.955	26.125	8
10.656	11.389	12.242	14.684	16.919	19.023	19.679	21.666	23.589	27.877	9
11.781	12.549	13.442	15.987	18.307	20.483	21.161	23.209	25.188	29.588	10
12.899	13.701	14.631	17.275	19.675	21.920	22.618	24.725	26.757	31.264	11
14.011	14.845	15.812	18.549	21.026	23.337	24.054	26.217	28.300	32.909	12
15.119	15.984	16.985	19.812	22.362	24.736	25.472	27.688	29.819	34.528	13
16.222	17.117	18.151	21.064	23.685	26.119	26.873	29.141	31.319	36.123	14
17.322	18.245	19.311	22.307	24.996	27.488	28.259	30.578	32.801	37.697	15
18.418	19.369	20.465	23.542	26.296	28.845	29.633	32.000	34.267	39.252	16
19.511	20.489	21.615	24.769	27.587	30.191	30.995	33.409	35.718	40.790	17
20.601	21.605	22.760	25.989	28.869	31.526	32.346	34.805	37.156	42.312	18
21.689	22.718	23.900	27.204	30.144	32.852	33.687	36.191	38.582	43.820	19
22.775	23.828	25.038	28.412	31.410	34.170	35.020	37.566	39.997	45.315	20
23.858	24.935	26.171	29.615	32.671	35.479	36.343	38.932	41.401	46.797	21
24.939	26.039	27.301	30.813	33.924	36.781	37.659	40.289	42.796	48.268	22
26.018	27.141	28.429	32.007	35.172	38.076	38.968	41.638	44.181	49.728	23
27.096	28.241	29.553	33.196	36.415	39.364	40.270	42.980	45.558	51.179	24
28.172	29.339	30.675	34.382	37.652	40.646	41.566	44.314	46.925	52.620	25
29.246	30.434	31.795	35.563	38.885	41.923	42.856	45.642	48.290	54.052	26
30.319	31.528	32.912	36.741	40.113	43.194	44.140	46.963	49.645	55.476	27
31.391	32.620	34.027	37.916	41.337	44.461	45.419	48.278	50.993	56.893	28
32.461	33.711	35.139	39.087	42.557	45.722	46.693	49.588	52.336	58.302	29
33.530	34.800	36.250	40.256	43.773	46.979	47.962	50.892	53.672	59.703	30

This table is taken by consent from Table IV of *Statistical Tables for Biological, Agricultural, and Medical Research*, by R. A. Fisher and F. Yates, published by Oliver and Boyd, Edinburgh; from *Biometrika*, Vol. 32, pp. 187–191, "Table of Percentage Points of the χ^2 Distribution," by Catherine M. Thompson; and from *Biometrika*, Vol. 40, p. 421, "99.9 and 0.1 % Points of the χ^2 Distribution," by T. Lewis. The values shown in Miss Thompson's table (and the values at the 0.001 point as well) may also be found in E. S. Pearson and H. O. Hartley, *Biometrika Tables for Statisticians*, Vol. I, Cambridge University Press, London, 1954, pp. 130–131.

Values of $\dfrac{\hat{\sigma}^2}{\sigma^2}$ for Use in Determining

This table shows
the black areas:

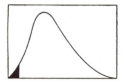

n	Lower points							.50
	.001	.005	.01	.025	.05	.10	.25	
1	$.0^5157$	$.0^43927$	$.0^31571$	$.0^29821$	.003932	.01579	.1015	.4549
2	.001000	.005013	.01005	.02532	.05129	.1054	.2877	.6931
3	.008099	.02391	.03828	.07193	.1173	.1948	.4042	.7887
4	.02270	.05175	.07428	.1211	.1777	.2659	.4806	.8392
5	.04204	.08235	.1109	.1662	.2291	.3221	.5349	.8703
6	.06351	.1126	.1453	.2062	.2726	.3674	.5758	.8914
7	.08550	.1413	.1770	.2414	.3096	.4047	.6078	.9065
8	.1071	.1681	.2058	.2725	.3416	.4362	.6338	.9180
9	.1280	.1928	.2320	.3000	.3695	.4631	.6554	.9270
10	.1479	.2156	.2558	.3247	.3940	.4865	.6737	.9342
11	.1667	.2367	.2776	.3469	.4159	.5071	.6895	.9401
12	.1845	.2562	.2975	.3670	.4355	.5253	.7032	.9450
13	.2013	.2742	.3159	.3853	.4532	.5417	.7153	.9492
14	.2172	.2910	.3329	.4021	.4693	.5564	.7261	.9528
15	.2322	.3067	.3486	.4175	.4841	.5698	.7358	.9559
16	.2464	.3214	.3633	.4317	.4976	.5820	.7445	.9587
17	.2598	.3351	.3769	.4450	.5101	.5932	.7525	.9611
18	.2725	.3480	.3897	.4573	.5217	.6036	.7597	.9632
19	.2846	.3602	.4017	.4688	.5325	.6132	.7664	.9651
20	.2961	.3717	.4130	.4795	.5425	.6221	.7726	.9669
21	.3070	.3826	.4237	.4897	.5520	.6305	.7783	.9684
22	.3174	.3929	.4337	.4992	.5608	.6382	.7836	.9699
23	.3274	.4026	.4433	.5082	.5692	.6456	.7886	.9712
24	.3369	.4119	.4524	.5167	.5770	.6524	.7932	.9724
25	.3460	.4208	.4610	.5248	.5845	.6589	.7976	.9735
26	.3547	.4292	.4692	.5325	.5915	.6651	.8017	.9745
27	.3631	.4373	.4770	.5398	.5982	.6709	.8055	.9754
28	.3711	.4450	.4845	.5467	.6046	.6764	.8092	.9763
29	.3788	.4525	.4916	.5533	.6106	.6816	.8126	.9771
30	.3863	.4596	.4984	.5597	.6164	.6866	.8159	.9779
40	.4479	.5177	.5541	.6108	.6627	.7263	.8415	.9834
50	.4935	.5598	.5941	.6471	.6953	.7538	.8588	.9867
60	.5290	.5922	.6247	.6747	.7198	.7743	.8716	.9889
70	.5577	.6182	.6492	.6965	.7391	.7904	.8814	.9905
80	.5815	.6396	.6692	.7144	.7549	.8035	.8893	.9917
90	.6017	.6577	.6862	.7294	.7681	.8143	.8958	.9926
100	.6192	.6733	.7006	.7422	.7793	.8236	.9013	.9933
∞	1.0000	1.0000	1.0000	1.0000	1.0000	1.0000	1.0000	1.0000
$\dfrac{x}{\sigma}$*	-3.0902	-2.5758	-2.3263	-1.9600	-1.6449	-1.2816	$-.6745$	0

* When $n > 30$, values of $\dfrac{\hat{\sigma}^2}{\sigma^2}$ may be approximated by use of the expression

$$\left(\frac{9n - 2 + \frac{x}{\sigma} \sqrt{18n}}{9n} \right)^3,$$

674

K

Sampling Limits of $\hat{\sigma}^2$

and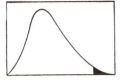

Upper points								n
.25	.10	.05	.025	.01	.005	.001		
1.323	2.706	3.841	5.024	6.635	7.879	10.827	1
1.386	2.303	2.996	3.689	4.605	5.298	6.908	2
1.369	2.084	2.605	3.116	3.782	4.279	5.423	3
1.346	1.945	2.372	2.786	3.319	3.715	4.616	4
1.325	1.847	2.214	2.566	3.017	3.350	4.103	5
1.307	1.774	2.099	2.408	2.802	3.091	3.743	6
1.291	1.717	2.010	2.288	2.639	2.897	3.475	7
1.277	1.670	1.938	2.192	2.511	2.744	3.266	8
1.265	1.632	1.880	2.114	2.407	2.621	3.097	9
1.255	1.599	1.831	2.048	2.321	2.519	2.959	10
1.246	1.570	1.789	1.993	2.248	2.432	2.842	11
1.237	1.546	1.752	1.945	2.185	2.358	2.742	12
1.230	1.524	1.720	1.903	2.130	2.294	2.656	13
1.223	1.505	1.692	1.866	2.082	2.237	2.580	14
1.216	1.487	1.666	1.833	2.039	2.187	2.513	15
1.211	1.471	1.644	1.803	2.000	2.142	2.453	16
1.205	1.457	1.623	1.776	1.965	2.101	2.399	17
1.200	1.444	1.604	1.751	1.934	2.064	2.351	18
1.196	1.432	1.586	1.729	1.905	2.031	2.306	19
1.191	1.421	1.571	1.708	1.878	2.000	2.266	20
1.187	1.410	1.556	1.689	1.854	1.971	2.228	21
1.184	1.401	1.542	1.672	1.831	1.945	2.194	22
1.180	1.392	1.529	1.655	1.810	1.921	2.162	23
1.177	1.383	1.517	1.640	1.791	1.898	2.132	24
1.174	1.375	1.506	1.626	1.773	1.877	2.105	25
1.171	1.368	1.496	1.612	1.755	1.857	2.079	26
1.168	1.361	1.486	1.600	1.739	1.839	2.055	27
1.165	1.354	1.476	1.588	1.724	1.821	2.032	28
1.162	1.348	1.467	1.577	1.710	1.805	2.010	29
1.160	1.342	1.459	1.566	1.696	1.789	1.990	30
1.140	1.295	1.394	1.484	1.592	1.669	1.835	40
1.127	1.263	1.350	1.428	1.523	1.590	1.733	50
1.116	1.240	1.318	1.388	1.473	1.533	1.660	60
1.108	1.222	1.293	1.357	1.435	1.489	1.605	70
1.102	1.207	1.273	1.333	1.404	1.454	1.560	80
1.096	1.195	1.257	1.313	1.379	1.426	1.525	90
1.091	1.185	1.243	1.296	1.358	1.402	1.494	100
1.000	1.000	1.000	1.000	1.000	1.000	1.000	∞
$+ .6745$	$+1.2816$	$+1.6449$	$+1.9600$	$+2.3263$	$+2.5758$	$+3.0902$	$\frac{x}{\sigma}*$

where $\frac{x}{\sigma}$ is the normal deviate cutting off the corresponding tail of a normal distribution.

The values in this table were computed from values of χ^2 given in the references mentioned in Appendix J

by use of the expression $\hat{\sigma}^2 = \frac{\chi^2}{n} \sigma^2$.

Values of $\frac{\sigma^2}{\hat{\sigma}^2}$ for Use in Determining

This table shows
the black areas:

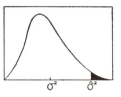

$\sigma^2 \qquad \hat{\sigma}^2$

n	Lower limits							.50
	.001	.005	.01	.025	.05	.10	.25	
1	.0924	.1269	.1507	.1990	.2603	.3696	.7557	2.198
2	.1448	.1887	.2171	.2711	.3338	.4343	.7213	1.443
3	.1844	.2337	.2644	.3209	.3839	.4799	.7302	1.268
4	.2166	.2692	.3013	.3590	.4216	.5142	.7428	1.192
5	.2437	.2985	.3314	.3896	.4517	.5413	.7546	1.149
6	2672	.3235	.3569	.4152	.4765	.5637	.7652	1.122
7	.2878	.3452	.3789	.4372	.4976	.5825	.7746	1.103
8	.3062	.3644	.3982	.4562	.5159	.5987	.7829	1.089
9	.3228	.3815	.4154	.4731	.5319	.6129	.7903	1.079
10	.3380	.3970	.4309	.4882	.5462	.6255	.7969	1.070
11	.3518	.4111	.4449	.5018	.5591	.6368	.8029	1.064
12	.3646	.4240	.4577	.5142	.5707	.6469	.8083	1.058
13	.3765	.4360	.4695	.5256	.5813	.6562	.8133	1.054
14	.3876	.4470	.4804	.5360	.5911	.6646	.8179	1.050
15	.3979	.4573	.4906	.5457	.6001	.6724	.8221	1.046
16	.4076	.4669	.5000	.5547	.6085	.6796	.8261	1.043
17	.4168	.4759	.5088	.5631	.6162	.6863	.8297	1.041
18	.4254	.4844	.5172	.5710	.6235	.6926	.8331	1.038
19	.4336	.4925	.5250	.5783	.6303	.6984	.8363	1.036
20	.4414	.5000	.5324	.5853	.6367	.7039	.8394	1.034
21	.4487	.5072	.5394	.5919	.6428	.7091	.8422	1.033
22	.4558	.5141	.5460	.5981	.6485	.7140	.8449	1.031
23	.4625	.5206	.5524	.6041	.6539	.7186	.8474	1.030
24	.4689	.5268	.5584	.6097	.6591	.7230	.8498	1.028
25	.4751	.5327	.5642	.6151	.6640	.7271	.8521	1.027
26	.4810	.5384	.5697	.6202	.6686	.7311	.8543	1.026
27	.4867	.5439	.5749	.6251	.6731	.7349	.8564	1.025
28	.4922	.5491	.5800	.6298	.6774	.7385	.8584	1.024
29	.4974	.5542	.5848	.6343	.6814	.7419	.8603	1.023
30	.5025	.5590	.5895	.6386	.6854	.7452	.8621	1.023
40	.5449	.5991	.6280	.6741	.7174	.7721	.8769	1.017
50	.5770	.6290	.6566	.7001	.7407	.7916	.8876	1.013
60	.6024	.6525	.6789	.7203	.7587	.8065	.8958	1.011
70	.6232	.6717	.6970	.7367	.7732	.8185	.9023	1.010
80	.6408	.6878	.7122	.7503	.7852	.8283	.9077	1.008
90	.6559	.7015	.7251	.7618	.7954	.8367	.9123	1.007
100	.6691	.7134	.7363	.7718	.8042	.8439	.9162	1.007
∞	1.0000	1.0000	1.0000	1.0000	1.0000	1.0000	1.0000	1.000
$\frac{x}{\sigma}$*	+3.0902	+2.5758	+2.3263	+1.9600	+1.6449	+1.2816	+ .6745	0

* When $n > 30$, values of $\frac{\sigma^2}{\hat{\sigma}^2}$ may be approximated by use of the expression

$$1 \div \left(\frac{9n - 2 + \frac{x}{\sigma}\sqrt{18n}}{9n} \right)^3,$$

L

Confidence Limits of σ^2

and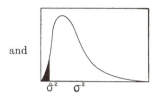

Upper limits							
.25	.10	.05	.025	.01	.005	.001	n
9.849	63.328	254.32	1,018.3	6,366.0	25,465	637,000	1
3.476	9.491	19.496	39.498	99.501	199.51	999.50	2
2.474	5.134	8.526	13.902	26.125	41.829	123.47	3
2.081	3.761	5.628	8.257	13.463	19.325	44.051	4
1.869	3.105	4.365	6.015	9.020	12.144	23.785	5
1.737	2.722	3.669	4.849	6.880	8.879	15.745	6
1.645	2.471	3.230	4.142	5.650	7.076	11.696	7
1.578	2.293	2.928	3.670	4.859	5.951	9.334	8
1.526	2.159	2.707	3.333	4.311	5.188	7.813	9
1.484	2.055	2.538	3.080	3.909	4.639	6.762	10
1.450	1.972	2.404	2.883	3.602	4.226	5.998	11
1.422	1.904	2.296	2.725	3.361	3.904	5.420	12
1.398	1.846	2.206	2.595	3.165	3.647	4.967	13
1.377	1.797	2.131	2.487	3.004	3.436	4.604	14
1.359	1.755	2.066	2.395	2.868	3.260	4.307	15
1.343	1.718	2.010	2.316	2.753	3.111	4.059	16
1.329	1.686	1.960	2.247	2.653	2.984	3.850	17
1.316	1.657	1.917	2.187	2.566	2.873	3.670	18
1.305	1.631	1.878	2.133	2.489	2.776	3.514	19
1.294	1.607	1.843	2.085	2.421	2.690	3.378	20
1.285	1.586	1.812	2.042	2.360	2.614	3.257	21
1.276	1.567	1.783	2.003	2.305	2.545	3.151	22
1.268	1.549	1.757	1.968	2.256	2.484	3.055	23
1.261	1.533	1.733	1.935	2.211	2.428	2.969	24
1.254	1.518	1.711	1.906	2.169	2.376	2.890	25
1.247	1.504	1.691	1.878	2.131	2.330	2.819	26
1.241	1.491	1.672	1.853	2.097	2.287	2.754	27
1.236	1.478	1.654	1.829	2.064	2.247	2.695	28
1.231	1.467	1.638	1.807	2.034	2.210	2.640	29
1.226	1.456	1.622	1.787	2.006	2.176	2.589	30
1.188	1.377	1.509	1.637	1.805	1.932	2.233	40
1.164	1.327	1.438	1.545	1.683	1.786	2.026	50
1.147	1.291	1.389	1.482	1.601	1.688	1.890	60
1.135	1.265	1.353	1.436	1.540	1.618	1.793	70
1.124	1.245	1.325	1.400	1.494	1.563	1.720	80
1.116	1.228	1.302	1.371	1.457	1.520	1.662	90
1.109	1.214	1.283	1.347	1.427	1.485	1.615	100
1.000	1.000	1.000	1.000	1.000	1.000	1.000	∞
.6745	-1.2816	-1.6449	-1.9600	-2.3263	-2.5758	-3.0902	$\frac{x}{\sigma}$*

where $\frac{x}{\sigma}$ is the corresponding normal deviate.

The values in this table were computed from values of χ^2 given in the references mentioned in Appendix J, by use of the expression $\sigma^2 = \frac{n}{\chi^2} \hat{\sigma}^2$.

APPENDIX M

Values of *F*

For Given Degrees of Freedom (n_1 and n_2) and at Selected Upper Points

Values of F for corresponding lower points may be obtained by transposing the values of n_1 and n_2 and computing $\frac{1}{F}$.

This table shows the black areas:
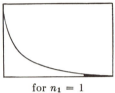 and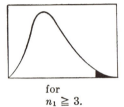

for $n_1 = 1$
and $n_1 = 2$

for $n_1 \geqq 3.$

n_2	$n_1 = 1$					$n_1 = 2$				
	.10	.05	.025	.01	.001	.10	.05	.025	.01	.001
1	39.864	161.45	647.79	4,052.2	405,284	49.500	199.50	799.50	4,999.5	500,000
2	8.526	18.513	38.506	98.503	998.5	9.000	19.000	39.000	99.000	999.0
3	5.538	10.128	17.443	34.116	167.0	5.462	9.552	16.044	30.817	148.5
4	4.545	7.709	12.218	21.198	74.14	4.325	6.944	10.649	18.000	61.25
5	4.060	6.608	10.007	16.258	47.18	3.780	5.786	8.434	13.274	37.12
6	3.776	5.987	8.813	13.745	35.51	3.463	5.143	7.260	10.925	27.00
7	3.589	5.591	8.073	12.246	29.25	3.257	4.737	6.542	9.547	21.69
8	3.458	5.318	7.571	11.259	25.42	3.113	4.459	6.060	8.649	18.49
9	3.360	5.117	7.209	10.561	22.86	3.006	4.256	5.715	8.022	16.39
10	3.285	4.965	6.937	10.044	21.04	2.924	4.103	5.456	7.559	14.91
11	3.225	4.844	6.724	9.646	19.69	2.860	3.982	5.256	7.206	13.81
12	3.176	4.747	6.554	9.330	18.64	2.807	3.885	5.096	6.927	12.97
13	3.136	4.667	6.414	9.074	17.81	2.763	3.806	4.965	6.701	12.31
14	3.102	4.600	6.298	8.862	17.14	2.726	3.739	4.857	6.515	11.78
15	3.073	4.543	6.200	8.683	16.59	2.695	3.682	4.765	6.359	11.34
16	3.048	4.494	6.115	8.531	16.12	2.668	3.634	4.687	6.226	10.97
17	3.026	4.451	6.042	8.400	15.72	2.645	3.592	4.619	6.112	10.66
18	3.007	4.414	5.978	8.285	15.38	2.624	3.555	4.560	6.013	10.39
19	2.990	4.381	5.922	8.185	15.08	2.606	3.522	4.508	5.926	10.16
20	2.975	4.351	5.872	8.096	14.82	2.589	3.493	4.461	5.849	9.95
21	2.961	4.325	5.827	8.017	14.59	2.575	3.467	4.420	5.780	9.77
22	2.949	4.301	5.786	7.945	14.38	2.561	3.443	4.383	5.719	9.61
23	2.937	4.279	5.750	7.881	14.19	2.549	3.422	4.349	5.664	9.47
24	2.927	4.260	5.717	7.823	14.03	2.538	3.403	4.319	5.614	9.34
25	2.918	4.242	5.686	7.770	13.88	2.528	3.385	4.291	5.568	9.22
26	2.909	4.225	5.659	7.721	13.74	2.519	3.369	4.266	5.526	9.12
27	2.901	4.210	5.633	7.677	13.61	2.511	3.354	4.242	5.488	9.02
28	2.894	4.196	5.610	7.636	13.50	2.503	3.340	4.220	5.453	8.93
29	2.887	4.183	5.588	7.598	13.39	2.496	3.328	4.201	5.421	8.85
30	2.881	4.171	5.568	7.563	13.29	2.489	3.316	4.182	5.390	8.77
40	2.835	4.085	5.424	7.314	12.61	2.440	3.232	4.051	5.178	8.25
60	2.791	4.001	5.286	7.077	11.97	2.393	3.150	3.925	4.977	7.76
120	2.748	3.920	5.152	6.851	11.38	2.347	3.072	3.805	4.786	7.32
∞	2.706	3.841	5.024	6.635	10.83	2.303	2.996	3.689	4.605	6.91

Values of F at the 0.10, 0.05, 0.025, and 0.01 points were taken, by permission, from *Biometrika*, Vol. XXXIII,

Values of *F*

For Given Degrees of Freedom (n_1 and n_2) and at Selected Upper Points

Values of *F* for corresponding lower points may be obtained by transposing the values of n_1 and n_2 and computing $\frac{1}{F}$.

n_2	$n_1 = 3$					$n_1 = 4$				
	.10	.05	.025	.01	.001	.10	.05	.025	.01	.001
1	53.593	215.71	864.16	5,403.3	540,379	55.833	224.58	899.58	5,624.6	562,500
2	9.162	19.164	39.165	99.166	999.2	9.243	19.247	39.248	99.249	999.2
3	5.391	9.277	15.439	29.457	141.1	5.343	9.117	15.101	28.710	137.1
4	4.191	6.591	9.979	16.694	56.18	4.107	6.388	9.604	15.977	53.44
5	3.620	5.410	7.764	12.060	33.20	3.520	5.192	7.388	11.392	31.09
6	3.289	4.757	6.599	9.779	23.70	3.181	4.534	6.227	9.148	21.92
7	3.074	4.347	5.890	8.451	18.77	2.960	4.120	5.523	7.847	17.19
8	2.924	4.066	5.416	7.591	15.83	2.806	3.838	5.053	7.006	14.39
9	2.813	3.863	5.078	6.992	13.90	2.693	3.633	4.718	6.422	12.56
10	2.728	3.708	4.826	6.552	12.55	2.605	3.478	4.468	5.994	11.28
11	2.660	3.587	4.630	6.217	11.56	2.536	3.357	4.275	5.668	10.35
12	2.606	3.490	4.474	5.953	10.80	2.480	3.259	4.121	5.412	9.63
13	2.560	3.410	4.347	5.739	10.21	2.434	3.179	3.996	5.205	9.07
14	2.522	3.344	4.242	5.564	9.73	2.395	3.112	3.892	5.035	8.62
15	2.490	3.287	4.153	5.417	9.34	2.361	3.056	3.804	4.893	8.25
16	2.462	3.239	4.077	5.292	9.00	2.333	3.007	3.729	4.773	7.94
17	2.437	3.197	4.011	5.185	8.73	2.308	2.965	3.665	4.669	7.68
18	2.416	3.160	3.954	5.092	8.49	2.286	2.928	3.608	4.579	7.46
19	2.397	3.127	3.903	5.010	8.28	2.266	2.895	3.559	4.500	7.26
20	2.380	3.098	3.859	4.938	8.10	2.249	2.866	3.515	4.431	7.10
21	2.365	3.072	3.819	4.874	7.94	2.233	2.840	3.475	4.369	6.95
22	2.351	3.049	3.783	4.817	7.80	2.219	2.817	3.440	4.313	6.81
23	2.339	3.028	3.750	4.765	7.67	2.206	2.795	3.408	4.264	6.69
24	2.327	3.009	3.721	4.718	7.55	2.195	2.776	3.379	4.218	6.59
25	2.317	2.991	3.694	4.676	7.45	2.184	2.759	3.353	4.177	6.49
26	2.308	2.975	3.670	4.637	7.36	2.174	2.743	3.329	4.140	6.41
27	2.299	2.960	3.647	4.601	7.27	2.166	2.728	3.307	4.106	6.33
28	2.291	2.947	3.626	4.568	7.19	2.157	2.714	3.286	4.074	6.25
29	2.283	2.934	3.607	4.538	7.12	2.149	2.701	3.267	4.045	6.19
30	2.276	2.922	3.589	4.510	7.05	2.142	2.690	3.250	4.018	6.12
40	2.226	2.839	3.463	4.313	6.60	2.091	2.606	3.126	3.828	5.70
60	2.177	2.758	3.342	4.126	6.17	2.041	2.525	3.008	3.649	5.31
120	2.130	2.680	3.227	3.949	5.79	1.992	2.447	2.894	3.480	4.95
∞	2.084	2.605	3.116	3.782	5.42	1.945	2.372	2.786	3.319	4.62

April 1943, pp. 73–78, "Tables of Percentage Points of the Inverted Beta (*F*) Distribution," by Maxine Merrington and Catherine M. Thompson. Values of *F* at the 0.001 point were taken from Table V of R. A. Fisher and F. Yates, *Statistical Tables for Biological, Agricultural, and Medical Research,* Oliver and Boyd, Ltd., Edinburgh, 1949, by permission of the authors and publishers. The tables which originally appeared in *Biometrika* may be found also in E. S. Pearson and H. O. Hartley, *Biometrika Tables for Statisticians,* Vol. I, Cambridge University Press, London 1954, pp. 157–163. This source provided fourteen corrections for the values at the 0.001 point.

Values of F

For Given Degrees of Freedom (n_1 and n_2) and at Selected Upper Points

Values of F for corresponding lower points may be obtained by transposing the values of n_1 and n_2 and computing $\frac{1}{F}$.

n_2	$n_1 = 5$					$n_1 = 6$				
	.10	.05	.025	.01	.001	.10	.05	.025	.01	.001
1	57.241	230.16	921.85	5,763.7	576,405	58.204	233.99	937.11	5,859.0	585,937
2	9.293	19.296	39.298	99.299	999.3	9.326	19.333	39.331	99.332	999.3
3	5.309	9.014	14.885	28.237	134.6	5.285	8.941	14.735	27.911	132.8
4	4.051	6.256	9.364	15.522	51.71	4.910	6.163	9.197	15.207	50.53
5	3.453	5.050	7.146	10.967	29.75	3.404	4.950	6.978	10.672	28.84
6	3.108	4.387	5.988	8.746	20.81	3.055	4.284	5.820	8.466	20.03
7	2.883	3.972	5.285	7.460	16.21	2.827	3.866	5.119	7.191	15.52
8	2.726	3.688	4.817	6.632	13.49	2.668	3.581	4.652	6.371	12.86
9	2.611	3.482	4.484	6.057	11.71	2.551	3.374	4.320	5.802	11.13
10	2.522	3.326	4.236	5.636	10.48	2.461	3.217	4.072	5.386	9.92
11	2.451	3.204	4.044	5.316	9.58	2.389	3.095	3.881	5.069	9.05
12	2.394	3.106	3.891	5.064	8.89	2.331	2.996	3.728	4.821	8.38
13	2.347	3.025	3.767	4.862	8.35	2.283	2.915	3.604	4.620	7.86
14	2.307	2.958	3.663	4.695	7.92	2.243	2.848	3.501	4.456	7.43
15	2.273	2.901	3.576	4.556	7.57	2.208	2.790	3.415	4.318	7.09
16	2.244	2.852	3.502	4.437	7.27	2.178	2.741	3.341	4.202	6.81
17	2.218	2.810	3.438	4.336	7.02	2.152	2.699	3.277	4.102	6.56
18	2.196	2.773	3.382	4.248	6.81	2.130	2.661	3.221	4.015	6.35
19	2.176	2.740	3.333	4.171	6.62	2.109	2.628	3.172	3.939	6.18
20	2.158	2.711	3.289	4.103	6.46	2.091	2.599	3.128	3.871	6.02
21	2.142	2.685	3.250	4.042	6.32	2.075	2.573	3.090	3.812	5.88
22	2.128	2.661	3.215	3.988	6.19	2.060	2.549	3.055	3.758	5.76
23	2.115	2.640	3.184	3.939	6.08	2.047	2.528	3.023	3.710	5.65
24	2.103	2.621	3.155	3.895	5.98	2.035	2.508	2.995	3.667	5.55
25	2.092	2.603	3.129	3.855	5.88	2.024	2.490	2.969	3.627	5.46
26	2.082	2.587	3.105	3.818	5.80	2.014	2.474	2.945	3.591	5.38
27	2.073	2.572	3.083	3.785	5.73	2.004	2.459	2.923	3.558	5.31
28	2.064	2.558	3.062	3.754	5.66	1.996	2.445	2.903	3.528	5.24
29	2.057	2.545	3.044	3.725	5.59	1.988	2.432	2.884	3.499	5.18
30	2.049	2.534	3.026	3.699	5.53	1.980	2.421	2.867	3.474	5.12
40	1.997	2.450	2.904	3.514	5.13	1.927	2.336	2.744	3.291	4.73
60	1.946	2.368	2.786	3.339	4.76	1.875	2.254	2.627	3.119	4.37
120	1.896	2.290	2.674	3.174	4.42	1.824	2.175	2.515	2.956	4.04
∞	1.847	2.214	2.566	3.017	4.10	1.774	2.099	2.408	2.802	3.74

Values of F

For Given Degrees of Freedom (n_1 and n_2) and at Selected Upper Points

Values of F for corresponding lower points may be obtained by transposing the values of n_1 and n_2 and computing $\frac{1}{F}$.

n_2	$n_1 = 8$					$n_1 = 12$				
	.10	.05	.025	.01	.001	.10	.05	.025	.01	.001
1	59.439	238.88	956.66	5,981.6	598,144	60.705	243.91	976.71	6,106.3	610,667
2	9.367	19.371	39.373	99.374	999.4	9.408	19.413	39.415	99.416	999.4
3	5.252	8.845	14.540	27.489	130.6	5.216	8.745	14.337	27.052	128.3
4	3.955	6.041	8.980	14.799	49.00	3.896	5.912	8.751	14.374	47.41
5	3.339	4.818	6.757	10.289	27.64	3.268	4.678	6.525	9.888	26.42
6	2.983	4.147	5.600	8.102	19.03	2.905	4.000	5.366	7.718	17.99
7	2.752	3.726	4.899	6.840	14.63	2.668	3.575	4.666	6.469	13.71
8	2.589	3.438	4.433	6.029	12.04	2.502	3.284	4.200	5.667	11.19
9	2.469	3.230	4.102	5.467	10.37	2.379	3.073	3.868	5.111	9.57
10	2.377	3.072	3.855	5.057	9.20	2.284	2.913	3.621	4.706	8.45
11	2.304	2.948	3.664	4.745	8.35	2.209	2.788	3.430	4.397	7.63
12	2.245	2.849	3.512	4.499	7.71	2.147	2.687	3.277	4.155	7.00
13	2.195	2.767	3.388	4.302	7.21	2.097	2.604	3.153	3.960	6.52
14	2.154	2.699	3.285	4.140	6.80	2.054	2.534	3.050	3.800	6.13
15	2.118	2.641	3.199	4.004	6.47	2.017	2.475	2.963	3.666	5.81
16	2.088	2.591	3.125	3.890	6.19	1.985	2.425	2.889	3.553	5.55
17	2.061	2.548	3.061	3.791	5.96	1.958	2.381	2.825	3.455	5.32
18	2.038	2.510	3.005	3.705	5.76	1.933	2.342	2.769	3.371	5.13
19	2.017	2.477	2.956	3.631	5.59	1.912	2.308	2.720	3.296	4.97
20	1.998	2.447	2.913	3.564	5.44	1.892	2.278	2.676	3.231	4.82
21	1.982	2.421	2.874	3.506	5.31	1.875	2.250	2.637	3.173	4.70
22	1.967	2.397	2.839	3.453	5.19	1.859	2.226	2.602	3.121	4.58
23	1.953	2.375	2.808	3.406	5.09	1.845	2.204	2.570	3.074	4.48
24	1.941	2.355	2.779	3.363	4.99	1.832	2.183	2.541	3.032	4.39
25	1.929	2.337	2.753	3.324	4.91	1.820	2.165	2.515	2.993	4.31
26	1.919	2.321	2.729	3.288	4.83	1.809	2.148	2.491	2.958	4.24
27	1.909	2.305	2.707	3.256	4.76	1.799	2.132	2.469	2.926	4.17
28	1.900	2.291	2.687	3.226	4.69	1.790	2.118	2.448	2.896	4.11
29	1.892	2.278	2.669	3.198	4.64	1.781	2.104	2.430	2.869	4.05
30	1.884	2.266	2.651	3.173	4.58	1.773	2.092	2.412	2.843	4.00
40	1.829	2.180	2.529	2.993	4.21	1.715	2.004	2.288	2.665	3.64
60	1.775	2.097	2.412	2.823	3.87	1.657	1.917	2.169	2.496	3.31
120	1.722	2.016	2.299	2.663	3.55	1.601	1.834	2.055	2.336	3.02
∞	1.670	1.938	2.102	2.511	3.27	1.546	1.752	1.945	2.185	2.74

Values of F

For Given Degress of Freedon (n_1 and n_2) and at Selected Upper Points

Values of F for corresponding lower points may be obtained by transposing the values of n_1 and n_2 and computing $\frac{1}{F}$.

n_2	\multicolumn{5}{c}{$n_1 = 24$}	\multicolumn{5}{c}{$n_1 = \infty$}
	.10	.05	.025	.01	.001	.10	.05	.025	.01	.001
1	62.002	249.05	997.25	6,234.6	623,497	63.328	254.32	1,018.3	6,366.0	636,619
2	9.450	19.454	39.456	99.458	999.5	9.491	19.496	39.498	99.501	999.5
3	5.176	8.638	14.124	26.598	125.9	5.134	8.527	13.902	26.125	123.5
4	3.831	5.774	8.511	13.929	45.77	3.761	5.628	8.257	13.463	44.05
5	3.190	4.527	6.278	9.467	25.14	3.105	4.365	6.015	9.020	23.79
6	2.818	3.841	5.117	7.313	16.89	2.722	3.669	4.849	6.880	15.75
7	2.575	3.410	4.415	6.074	12.73	2.471	3.230	4.142	5.650	11.70
8	2.404	3.115	3.947	5.279	10.30	2.293	2.928	3.670	4.859	9.33
9	2.277	2.900	3.614	4.729	8.72	2.159	2.707	3.333	4.311	7.81
10	2.178	2.737	3.365	4.327	7.64	2.055	2.538	3.080	3.909	6.76
11	2.100	2.609	3.172	4.021	6.85	1.972	2.405	2.883	3.602	6.00
12	2.036	2.505	3.019	3.780	6.25	1.904	2.296	2.725	3.361	5.42
13	1.983	2.420	2.893	3.587	5.78	1.846	2.206	2.596	3.165	4.97
14	1.938	2.349	2.789	3.427	5.41	1.797	2.131	2.487	3.004	4.60
15	1.899	2.288	2.701	3.294	5.10	1.755	2.066	2.395	2.868	4.31
16	1.866	2.235	2.625	3.181	4.85	1.718	2.010	2.316	2.753	4.06
17	1.836	2.190	2.560	3.083	4.63	1.686	1.960	2.247	2.653	3.85
18	1.810	2.150	2.503	2.999	4.45	1.657	1.917	2.187	2.566	3.67
19	1.787	2.114	2.452	2.925	4.29	1.631	1.878	2.133	2.489	3.51
20	1.767	2.083	2.408	2.859	4.15	1.607	1.843	2.085	2.421	3.38
21	1.748	2.054	2.368	2.801	4.03	1.586	1.812	2.042	2.360	3.26
22	1.731	2.028	2.332	2.749	3.92	1.567	1.783	2.003	2.305	3.15
23	1.716	2.005	2.299	2.702	3.82	1.549	1.757	1.968	2.256	3 05
24	1.702	1.984	2.269	2.659	3.74	1.533	1.733	1.935	2.211	2 97
25	1.689	1.964	2.242	2.620	3.66	1.518	1.711	1.906	2.169	2.89
26	1.677	1.946	2.217	2.585	3.59	1.504	1.691	1.878	2.132	2.82
27	1.666	1.930	2.195	2.552	3.52	1.491	1.672	1.853	2.096	2.75
28	1.656	1.915	2.174	2.522	3.46	1.478	1.654	1.829	2.064	2.69
29	1.646	1.901	2.154	2.495	3.41	1.467	1.638	1.807	2.034	2 64
30	1.638	1.887	2.136	2.469	3.36	1.456	1.622	1.787	2.006	2.59
40	1.574	1.793	2.007	2.288	3.01	1.377	1.509	1.637	1.805	2.23
60	1.511	1.700	1.882	2.115	2.69	1.292	1.389	1.482	1.601	1.89
120	1.447	1.608	1.760	1.950	2.40	1.193	1.254	1.310	1.380	1.54
∞	1.383	1.517	1.640	1.791	2.13	1.000	1.000	1.000	1.000	1.00

APPENDIX N

Values of L at the 0.05 and 0.01 Points for Specified Values of N_i and k, when $N_1 = N_2 = \cdots = N_k = N_i$

If L has been computed from samples of varying size, take N_i equal to $\dfrac{N_1 + N_2 + \cdots + N_k}{k}$, provided that no sample consists of fewer than 15 or 20 items.

This table shows the black area:

k	$N_i = 3$		$N_i = 4$		$N_i = 5$		$N_i = 6$		$N_i = 7$		$N_i = 8$		$N_i = 9$	
	.05	.01	.05	.01	.05	.01	.05	.01	.05	.01	.05	.01	.05	.01
2	.312	.141	.478	.284	.585	.398	.656	.485	.708	.551	.745	.603	.775	.645
3	.304	.162	.470	.314	.576	.429	.648	.514	.700	.578	.739	.628	.769	.667
4	.315	.188	.480	.345	.585	.459	.656	.542	.707	.604	.744	.652	.774	.689
5	.328	.210	.491	.370	.595	.484	.665	.565	.714	.624	.751	.670	.780	.706
6	.339	.230	.502	.391	.604	.504	.673	.583	.721	.641	.757	.685	.785	.720
7	.350	.246	.512	.409	.612	.520	.680	.597	.727	.654	.763	.697	.790	.730
8	.359	.260	.520	.424	.620	.534	.686	.610	.733	.665	.768	.707	.795	.740
9	.367	.273	.527	.437	.626	.545	.691	.620	.738	.674	.772	.715	.798	.747
10	.374	.284	.534	.448	.631	.555	.696	.629	.742	.682	.776	.722	.802	.753
12	.387	.303	.545	.467	.641	.572	.704	.644	.749	.696	.782	.734	.807	.764
14	.397	.318	.554	.481	.649	.585	.711	.655	.755	.706	.787	.744	.812	.773
16	.405	.331	.561	.493	.655	.596	.716	.665	.759	.714	.791	.751	.816	.779
18	.412	.342	.567	.504	.660	.605	.721	.672	.763	.721	.795	.756	.819	.784
20	.418	.352	.573	.512	.665	.613	.725	.679	.767	.727	.798	.761	.822	.788
22	.424	.360	.577	.520	.669	.619	.728	.684	.770	.732	.800	.765	.824	.792
24	.428	.367	.581	.526	.672	.624	.731	.688	.772	.736	.802	.768	.826	.795
26	.433	.373	.585	.532	.675	.629	.734	.693	.775	.740	.805	.772	.828	.798
28	.437	.379	.589	.537	.678	.634	.736	.697	.777	.744	.807	.776	.829	.802
30	.441	.386	.592	.543	.681	.639	.739	.703	.779	.748	.809	.781	.831	.806

k	$N_i = 10$		$N_i = 12$		$N_i = 15$		$N_i = 20$		$N_i = 30$		$N_i = 60$		$N_i = \infty$	
	.05	.01	.05	.01	.05	.01	.05	.01	.05	.01	.05	.01	.05	.01
2	.798	.678	.833	.730	.868	.783	.902	.836	.935	.890	.968	.945	1.000	1.000
3	.792	.699	.828	.748	.863	.798	.898	.848	.933	.898	.967	.949	1.000	1.000
4	.797	.719	.832	.765	.866	.812	.900	.859	.934	.906	.967	.953	1.000	1.000
5	.802	.735	.836	.779	.870	.823	.903	.867	.936	.911	.968	.956	1.000	1.000
6	.808	.748	.841	.789	.873	.832	.906	.874	.938	.916	.969	.958	1.000	1.000
7	.812	.757	.844	.798	.876	.839	.908	.879	.939	.920	.970	.960	1.000	1.000
8	.816	.766	.848	.805	.879	.844	.910	.884	.941	.923	.971	.962	1.000	1.000
9	.819	.773	.851	.811	.881	.849	.912	.887	.942	.925	.971	.963	1.000	1.000
10	.822	.779	.853	.816	.883	.853	.913	.890	.943	.927	.972	.964	1.000	1.000
12	.828	.789	.857	.824	.887	.860	.916	.896	.944	.931	.973	.966	1.000	1.000
14	.832	.796	.861	.831	.890	.865	.918	.900	.946	.933	.973	.967	1.000	1.000
16	.835	.802	.863	.836	.892	.870	.920	.903	.947	.936	.974	.968	1.000	1.000
18	.838	.807	.866	.840	.894	.873	.921	.905	.948	.937	.974	.969	1.000	1.000
20	.840	.811	.868	.844	.896	.876	.922	.908	.949	.939	.975	.970	1.000	1.000
22	.843	.814	.870	.847	.897	.878	.924	.909	.950	.940	.975	.970	1.000	1.000
24	.844	.817	.872	.850	.898	.880	.924	.911	.950	.941	.975	.971	1.000	1.000
26	.846	.820	.873	.852	.899	.882	.925	.912	.951	.942	.976	.971	1.000	1.000
28	.848	.823	.874	.854	.900	.884	.926	.914	.951	.943	.976	.972	1.000	1.000
30	.849	.827	.876	.856	.901	.886	.927	.915	.952	.944	.976	.972	1.000	1.000

Based on a table in "An Investigation Into the Application of Neyman and Pearson's L_1 Test, with Tables of Percentage Limits," by P. P. N. Nayer, *Statistical Research Memoirs*, Vol. I (1936), pp. 38–51, by permission of the author. An earlier table of the same nature is given in "Tables for the Application of L-Tests," by P. C. Mahalanobis, *Sankhya: The Indian Journal of Statistics*, Vol. I, Part 1 (June 1933), pp. 109–122.

APPENDIX O

Upper 0.10 and 0.02 Limits of β_1 When Computed from Random Samples from a Normal Population

This table shows the black area:

N	0.10	0.02
50	.285	.619
75	.198	.424
100	.152	.321
125	.123	.258
150	.103	.216
175	.089	.185
200	.078	.162
250	.063	.130
300	.053	.108
350	.045	.093
400	.040	.081
450	.035	.072
500	.032	.065
550	.029	.059
600	.027	.054
650	.025	.050
700	.023	.046
750	.021	.043
800	.020	.041
850	.019	.038
900	.018	.036
950	.017	.034
1000	.016	.032
1200	.013	.027
1400	.012	.023
1600	.010	.020
1800	.009	.018
2000	.008	.016
2500	.006	.013
3000	.005	.011
3500	.005	.009
4000	.004	.008
4500	.004	.007
5000	.003	.006

Taken, by permission, from a table given by Egon S. Pearson in his article "A Further Development of Tests of Normality," *Biometrika*, Vol. XXII, pages 239 ff. A similar table for $\sqrt{\beta_1}$ is given in E. S. Pearson and H. O. Hartley, *Biometrika Tables for Statisticians*, Vol. I, Cambridge University Press, London, 1954, p. 183.

APPENDIX P

Upper and Lower 0.05 and 0.01 Limits of β_2 When Computed from Random Samples from a Normal Population

This table shows the black areas:

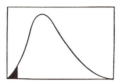 and

N	Lower limits		Upper limits	
	0.01	0.05	0.05	0.01
100	2.18	2.35	3.77	4.39
125	2.24	2.40	3.70	4.24
150	2.29	2.45	3.65	4.14
175	2.33	2.48	3.61	4.05
200	2.37	2.51	3.57	3.98
250	2.42	2.55	3.52	3.87
300	2.46	2.59	3.47	3.79
350	2.50	2.62	3.44	3.72
400	2.52	2.64	3.41	3.67
450	2.55	2.66	3.39	3.63
500	2.57	2.67	3.37	3.60
550	2.58	2.69	3.35	3.57
600	2.60	2.70	3.34	3.54
650	2.61	2.71	3.33	3.52
700	2.62	2.72	3.31	3.50
750	2.64	2.73	3.30	3.48
800	2.65	2.74	3.29	3.46
850	2.66	2.74	3.28	3.45
900	2.66	2.75	3.28	3.43
950	2.67	2.76	3.27	3.42
1000	2.68	2.76	3.26	3.41
1200	2.71	2.78	3.24	3.37
1400	2.72	2.80	3.22	3.34
1600	2.74	2.81	3.21	3.32
1800	2.76	2.82	3.20	3.30
2000	2.77	2.83	3.18	3.28
2500	2.79	2.85	3.16	3.25
3000	2.81	2.86	3.15	3.22
3500	2.82	2.87	3.14	3.21
4000	2.83	2.88	3.13	3.19
4500	2.84	2.88	3.12	3.18
5000	2.85	2.89	3.12	3.17

Taken, by permission, from a table given by Egon S. Pearson in his article "A Further Development of Tests of Normality," *Biometrika*, Vol. XXII, pages 239 ff.   A similar table is given in E. S. Pearson and H. O. Hartley, *Biometrika Tables for Statisticians*, Volume I, Cambridge University Press, London, 1954, p. 184.

APPENDIX Q

Squares, Square Roots, and Reciprocals, 1–1,000

No.	Square	Square Root	Reciprocal	No.	Square	Square Root	Reciprocal
1	1	1.0000000	1.000000000	51	26 01	7.1414284	.019607843
2	4	1.4142136	0.500000000	52	27 04	7.2111026	.019230769
3	9	1.7320508	.333333333	53	28 09	7.2801099	.018867925
4	16	2.0000000	.250000000	54	29 16	7.3484692	.018518519
5	25	2.2360680	.200000000	55	30 25	7.4161985	.018181818
6	36	2.4494897	.166666667	56	31 36	7.4833148	.017857143
7	49	2.6457513	.142857143	57	32 49	7.5498344	.017543860
8	64	2.8284271	.125000000	58	33 64	7.6157731	.017241379
9	81	3.0000000	.111111111	59	34 81	7.6811457	.016949153
10	1 00	3.1622777	.100000000	60	36 00	7.7459667	.016666667
11	1 21	3.3166248	.090909091	61	37 21	7.8102497	.016393443
12	1 44	3.4641016	.083333333	62	38 44	7.8740079	.016129032
13	1 69	3.6055513	.076923077	63	39 69	7.9372539	.015873016
14	1 96	3.7416574	.071428571	64	40 96	8.0000000	.015625000
15	2 25	3.8729833	.066666667	65	42 25	8.0622577	.015384615
16	2 56	4.0000000	.062500000	66	43 56	8.1240384	.015151515
17	2 89	4.1231056	.058823529	67	44 89	8.1853528	.014925373
18	3 24	4.2426407	.055555556	68	46 24	8.2462113	.014705882
19	3 61	4.3588989	.052631579	69	47 61	8.3066239	.014492754
20	4 00	4.4721360	.050000000	70	49 00	8.3666003	.014285714
21	4 41	4.5825757	.047619048	71	50 41	8.4261498	.014084507
22	4 84	4.6904158	.045454545	72	51 84	8.4852814	.013888889
23	5 29	4.7958315	.043478261	73	53 29	8.5440037	.013698630
24	5 76	4.8989795	.041666667	74	54 76	8.6023253	.013513514
25	6 25	5.0000000	.040000000	75	56 25	8.6602540	.013333333
26	6 76	5.0990195	.038461538	76	57 76	8.7177979	.013157895
27	7 29	5.1961524	.037037037	77	59 29	8.7749644	.012987013
28	7 84	5.2915026	.035714286	78	60 84	8.8317609	.012820513
29	8 41	5.3851648	.034482759	79	62 41	8.8881944	.012658228
30	9 00	5.4772256	.033333333	80	64 00	8.9442719	.012500000
31	9 61	5.5677644	.032258065	81	65 61	9.0000000	.012345679
32	10 24	5.6568542	.031250000	82	67 24	9.0553851	.012195122
33	10 89	5.7445626	.030303030	83	68 89	9.1104336	.012048193
34	11 56	5.8309519	.029411765	84	70 56	9.1651514	.011904762
35	12 25	5.9160798	.028571429	85	72 25	9.2195445	.011764706
36	12 96	6.0000000	.027777778	86	73 96	9.2736185	.011627907
37	13 69	6.0827625	.027027027	87	75 69	9.3273791	.011494253
38	14 44	6.1644140	.026315789	88	77 44	9.3808315	.011363636
39	15 21	6.2449980	.025641026	89	79 21	9.4339811	.011235955
40	16 00	6.3245553	.025000000	90	81 00	9.4868330	.011111111
41	16 81	6.4031242	.024390244	91	82 81	9.5393920	.010989011
42	17 64	6.4807407	.023809524	92	84 64	9.5916630	.010869565
43	18 49	6.5574385	.023255814	93	86 49	9.6436508	.010752688
44	19 36	6.6332496	.022727273	94	88 36	9.6953597	.010638298
45	20 25	6.7082039	.022222222	95	90 25	9.7467943	.010526316
46	21 16	6.7823300	.021739130	96	92 16	9.7979590	.010416667
47	22 09	6.8556546	.021276596	97	94 09	9.8488578	.010309278
48	23 04	6.9282032	.020833333	98	96 04	9.8994949	.010204082
49	24 01	7.0000000	.020408163	99	98 01	9.9498744	.010101010
50	25 00	7.0710678	.020000000	100	1 00 00	10.0000000	.010000000

No.	Square	Square Root	Reciprocal .00	No.	Square	Square Root	Reciprocal .00
101	1 02 01	10.0498756	9900990	151	2 28 01	12.2882057	6622517
102	1 04 04	10.0995049	9803922	152	2 31 04	12.3288280	6578947
103	1 06 09	10.1488916	9708738	153	2 34 09	12.3693169	6535948
104	1 08 16	10.1980390	9615385	154	2 37 16	12.4096736	6493506
105	1 10 25	10.2469508	9523810	155	2 40 25	12.4498996	6451613
106	1 12 36	10.2956301	9433962	156	2 43 36	12.4899960	6410256
107	1 14 49	10.3440804	9345794	157	2 46 49	12.5299641	6369427
108	1 16 64	10.3923048	9259259	158	2 49 64	12.5698051	6329114
109	1 18 81	10.4403065	9174312	159	2 52 81	12.6095202	6289308
110	1 21 00	10.4880885	9090909	160	2 56 00	12.6491106	6250000
111	1 23 21	10.5356538	9009009	161	2 59 21	12.6885775	6211180
112	1 25 44	10.5830052	8928571	162	2 62 44	12.7279221	6172840
113	1 27 69	10.6301458	8849558	163	2 65 69	12.7671453	6134969
114	1 29 96	10.6770783	8771930	164	2 68 96	12.8062485	6097561
115	1 32 25	10.7238053	8695652	165	2 72 25	12.8452326	6060606
116	1 34 56	10.7703296	8620690	166	2 75 56	12.8840987	6024096
117	1 36 89	10.8166538	8547009	167	2 78 89	12.9228480	5988024
118	1 39 24	10.8627805	8474576	168	2 82 24	12.9614814	5952381
119	1 41 61	10.9087121	8403361	169	2 85 61	13.0000000	5917160
120	1 44 00	10.9544512	8333333	170	2 89 00	13.0384048	5882353
121	1 46 41	11.0000000	8264463	171	2 92 41	13.0766968	5847953
122	1 48 84	11.0453610	8196721	172	2 95 84	13.1148770	5813953
123	1 51 29	11.0905365	8130081	173	2 99 29	13.1529464	5780347
124	1 53 76	11.1355287	8064516	174	3 02 76	13.1909060	5747126
125	1 56 25	11.1803399	8000000	175	3 06 25	13.2287566	5714286
126	1 58 76	11.2249722	7936508	176	3 09 76	13.2664992	5681818
127	1 61 29	11.2694277	7874016	177	3 13 29	13.3041347	5649718
128	1 63 84	11.3137085	7812500	178	3 16 84	13.3416641	5617978
129	1 66 41	11.3578167	7751938	179	3 20 41	13.3790882	5586592
130	1 69 00	11.4017543	7692308	180	3 24 00	13.4164079	5555556
131	1 71 61	11.4455231	7633588	181	3 27 61	13.4536240	5524862
132	1 74 24	11.4891253	7575758	182	3 31 24	13.4907376	5494505
133	1 76 89	11.5325626	7518797	183	3 34 89	13.5277493	5464481
134	1 79 56	11.5758369	7462687	184	3 38 56	13.5646600	5434783
135	1 82 25	11.6189500	7407407	185	3 42 25	13.6014705	5405405
136	1 84 96	11.6619038	7352941	186	3 45 96	13.6381817	5376344
137	1 87 69	11.7046999	7299270	187	3 49 69	13.6747943	5347594
138	1 90 44	11.7473401	7246377	188	3 53 44	13.7113092	5319149
139	1 93 21	11.7898261	7194245	189	3 57 21	13.7477271	5291005
140	1 96 00	11.8321596	7142857	190	3 61 00	13.7840488	5263158
141	1 98 81	11.8743422	7092199	191	3 64 81	13.8202750	5235602
142	2 01 64	11.9163753	7042254	192	3 68 64	13.8564065	5208333
143	2 04 49	11.9582607	6993007	193	3 72 49	13.8924440	5181347
144	2 07 36	12.0000000	6944444	194	3 76 36	13.9283883	5154639
145	2 10 25	12.0415946	6896552	195	3 80 25	13.9642400	5128205
146	2 13 16	12.0830460	6849315	196	3 84 16	14.0000000	5102041
147	2 16 09	12.1243557	6802721	197	3 88 09	14.0356688	5076142
148	2 19 04	12.1655251	6756757	198	3 92 04	14.0712473	5050505
149	2 22 01	12.2065556	6711409	199	3 96 01	14.1067360	5025126
150	2 25 00	12.2474487	6666667	200	4 00 00	14.1421356	5000000

No.	Square	Square Root	Reciprocal .00	No.	Square	Square Root	Reciprocal .00
201	4 04 01	14.1774469	4975124	251	6 30 01	15.8429795	3984064
202	4 08 04	14.2126704	4950495	252	6 35 04	15.8745079	3968254
203	4 12 09	14.2478068	4926108	253	6 40 09	15.9059737	3952569
204	4 16 16	14.2828569	4901961	254	6 45 16	15.9373775	3937008
205	4 20 25	14.3178211	4878049	255	6 50 25	15.9687194	3921569
206	4 24 36	14.3527001	4854369	256	6 55 36	16.0000000	3906250
207	4 28 49	14.3874946	4830918	257	6 60 49	16.0312195	3891051
208	4 32 64	14.4222051	4807692	258	6 65 64	16.0623784	3875969
209	4 36 81	14.4568323	4784689	259	6 70 81	16.0934769	3861004
210	4 41 00	14.4913767	4761905	260	6 76 00	16.1245155	3846154
211	4 45 21	14.5258390	4739336	261	6 81 21	16.1554944	3831418
212	4 49 44	14.5602198	4716981	262	6 86 44	16.1864141	3816794
213	4 53 69	14.5945195	4694836	263	6 91 69	16.2172747	3802281
214	4 57 96	14.6287388	4672897	264	6 96 96	16.2480768	3787879
215	4 62 25	14.6628783	4651163	265	7 02 25	16.2788206	3773585
216	4 66 56	14.6969385	4629630	266	7 07 56	16.3095064	3759398
217	4 70 89	14.7309199	4608295	267	7 12 89	16.3401346	3745318
218	4 75 24	14.7648231	4587156	268	7 18 24	16.3707055	3731343
219	4 79 61	14.7986486	4566210	269	7 23 61	16.4012195	3717472
220	4 84 00	14.8323970	4545455	270	7 29 00	16.4316767	3703704
221	4 88 41	14.8660687	4524887	271	7 34 41	16.4620776	3690037
222	4 92 84	14.8996644	4504505	272	7 39 84	16.4924225	3676471
223	4 97 29	14.9331845	4484305	273	7 45 29	16.5227116	3663004
224	5 01 76	14.9666295	4464286	274	7 50 76	16.5529454	3649635
225	5 06 25	15.0000000	4444444	275	7 56 25	16.5831240	3636364
226	5 10 76	15.0332964	4424779	276	7 61 76	16.6132477	3623188
227	5 15 29	15.0665192	4405286	277	7 67 29	16.6433170	3610108
228	5 19 84	15.0996689	4385965	278	7 72 84	16.6733320	3597122
229	5 24 41	15.1327460	4366812	279	7 78 41	16.7032931	3584229
230	5 29 00	15.1657509	4347826	280	7 84 00	16.7332005	3571429
231	5 33 61	15.1986842	4329004	281	7 89 61	16.7630546	3558719
232	5 38 24	15.2315462	4310345	282	7 95 24	16.7928556	3546099
233	5 42 89	15.2643375	4291845	283	8 00 89	16.8226038	3533569
234	5 47 56	15.2970585	4273504	284	8 06 56	16.8522995	3521127
235	5 52 25	15.3297097	4255319	285	8 12 25	16.8819430	3508772
236	5 56 96	15.3622915	4237288	286	8 17 96	16.9115345	3496503
237	5 61 69	15.3948043	4219409	287	8 23 69	16.9410743	3484321
238	5 66 44	15.4272486	4201681	288	8 29 44	16.9705627	3472222
239	5 71 21	15.4596248	4184100	289	8 35 21	17.0000000	3460208
240	5 76 00	15.4919334	4166667	290	8 41 00	17.0293864	3448276
241	5 80 81	15.5241747	4149378	291	8 46 81	17.0587221	3436426
242	5 85 64	15.5563492	4132231	292	8 52 64	17.0880075	3424658
243	5 90 49	15.5884573	4115226	293	8 58 49	17.1172428	3412969
244	5 95 36	15.6204994	4098361	294	8 64 36	17.1464282	3401361
245	6 00 25	15.6524758	4081633	295	8 70 25	17.1755640	3389831
246	6 05 16	15.6843871	4065041	296	8 76 16	17.2046505	3378378
247	6 10 09	15.7162336	4048583	297	8 82 09	17.2336879	3367003
248	6 15 04	15.7480157	4032258	298	8 88 04	17.2626765	3355705
249	6 20 01	15.7797338	4016064	299	8 94 01	17.2916165	3344482
250	6 25 00	15.8113883	4000000	300	9 00 00	17.3205081	3333333

No.	Square	Square Root	Reciprocal .00	No.	Square	Square Root	Reciprocal .00
301	9 06 01	17.3493516	3322259	351	12 32 01	18.7349940	2849003
302	9 12 04	17.3781472	3311258	352	12 39 04	18.7616630	2840909
303	9 18 09	17.4068952	3300330	353	12 46 09	18.7882942	2832861
304	9 24 16	17.4355958	3289474	354	12 53 16	18.8148877	2824859
305	9 30 25	17.4642492	3278689	355	12 60 25	18.8414437	2816901
306	9 36 36	17.4928557	3267974	356	12 67 36	18.8679623	2808989
307	9 42 49	17.5214155	3257329	357	12 74 49	18.8944436	2801120
308	9 48 64	17.5499288	3246753	358	12 81 64	18.9208879	2793296
309	9 54 81	17.5783958	3236246	359	12 88 81	18.9472953	2785515
310	9 61 00	17.6068169	3225806	360	12 96 00	18.9736660	2777778
311	9 67 21	17.6351921	3215434	361	13 03 21	19.0000000	2770083
312	9 73 44	17.6635217	3205128	362	13 10 44	19.0262976	2762431
313	9 79 69	17.6918060	3194888	363	13 17 69	19.0525589	2754821
314	9 85 96	17.7200451	3184713	364	13 24 96	19.0787840	2747253
315	9 92 25	17.7482393	3174603	365	13 32 25	19.1049732	2739726
316	9 98 56	17.7763888	3164557	366	13 39 56	19.1311265	2732240
317	10 04 89	17.8044938	3154574	367	13 46 89	19.1572441	2724796
318	10 11 24	17.8325545	3144654	368	13 54 24	19.1833261	2717391
319	10 17 61	17.8605711	3134796	369	13 61 61	19.2093727	2710027
320	10 24 00	17.8885438	3125000	370	13 69 00	19.2353841	2702703
321	10 30 41	17.9164729	3115265	371	13 76 41	19.2613603	2695418
322	10 36 84	17.9443584	3105590	372	13 83 84	19.2873015	2688172
323	10 43 29	17.9722008	3095975	373	13 91 29	19.3132079	2680965
324	10 49 76	18.0000000	3086420	374	13 98 76	19.3390796	2673797
325	10 56 25	18.0277564	3076923	375	14 06 25	19.3649167	2666667
326	10 62 76	18.0554701	3067485	376	14 13 76	19.3907194	2659574
327	10 69 29	18.0831413	3058104	377	14 21 29	19.4164878	2652520
328	10 75 84	18.1107703	3048780	378	14 28 84	19.4422221	2645503
329	10 82 41	18.1383571	3039514	379	14 36 41	19.4679223	2638522
330	10 89 00	18.1659021	3030303	380	14 44 00	19.4935887	2631579
331	10 95 61	18.1934054	3021148	381	14 51 61	19.5192213	2624672
332	11 02 24	18.2208672	3012048	382	14 59 24	19.5448203	2617801
333	11 08 89	18.2482876	3003003	383	14 66 89	19.5703858	2610966
334	11 15 56	18.2756669	2994012	384	14 74 56	19.5959179	2604167
335	11 22 25	18.3030052	2985075	385	14 82 25	19.6214169	2597403
336	11 28 96	18.3303028	2976190	386	14 89 96	19.6468827	2590674
337	11 35 69	18.3575598	2967359	387	14 97 69	19.6723156	2583979
338	11 42 44	18.3847763	2958580	388	15 05 44	19.6977156	2577320
339	11 49 21	18.4119526	2949853	389	15 13 21	19.7230829	2570694
340	11 56 00	18.4390889	2941176	390	15 21 00	19.7484177	2564103
341	11 62 81	18.4661853	2932551	391	15 28 81	19.7737199	2557545
342	11 69 64	18.4932420	2923977	392	15 36 64	19.7989899	2551020
343	11 76 49	18.5202592	2915452	393	15 44 49	19.8242276	2544529
344	11 83 36	18.5472370	2906977	394	15 52 36	19.8494332	2538071
345	11 90 25	18.5741756	2898551	395	15 60 25	19.8746069	2531646
346	11 97 16	18.6010752	2890173	396	15 68 16	19.8997487	2525253
347	12 04 09	18.6279360	2881844	397	15 76 09	19.9248588	2518892
348	12 11 04	18.6547581	2873563	398	15 84 04	19.9499373	2512563
349	12 18 01	18.6815417	2865330	399	15 92 01	19.9749844	2506266
350	12 25 00	18.7082869	2857143	400	16 00 00	20.0000000	2500000

No.	Square	Square Root	Reciprocal .00	No	Square	Square Root	Reciprocal .00
401	16 08 01	20.0249844	2493766	451	20 34 01	21.2367606	2217295
402	16 16 04	20.0499377	2487562	452	20 43 04	21.2602916	2212389
403	16 24 09	20.0748599	2481390	453	20 52 09	21.2837967	2207506
404	16 32 16	20.0997512	2475248	454	20 61 16	21.3072758	2202643
405	16 40 25	20.1246118	2469136	455	20 70 25	21.3307290	2197802
406	16 48 36	20.1494417	2463054	456	20 79 36	21.3541565	2192982
407	16 56 49	20.1742410	2457002	457	20 88 49	21.3775583	2188184
408	16 64 64	20.1990099	2450980	458	20 97 64	21.4009346	2183406
409	16 72 81	20.2237484	2444988	459	21 06 81	21.4242853	2178649
410	16 81 00	20.2484567	2439024	460	21 16 00	21.4476106	2173913
411	16 89 21	20.2731349	2433090	461	21 25 21	21.4709106	2169197
412	16 97 44	20.2977831	2427184	402	21 34 44	21.4941853	2164502
413	17 05 69	20.3224014	2421308	463	21 43 69	21.5174348	2159827
414	17 13 96	20.3469899	2415459	464	21 52 96	21.5406592	2155172
415	17 22 25	20.3715488	2409639	465	21 62 25	21.5638587	2150538
416	17 30 56	20.3960781	2403846	466	21 71 56	21.5870331	2145923
417	17 38 89	20.4205779	2398082	467	21 80 89	21.6101828	2141328
418	17 47 24	20.4450483	2392344	468	21 90 24	21.6333077	2136752
419	17 55 61	20.4694895	2386635	469	21 99 61	21.6564078	2132196
420	17 64 00	20.4939015	2380952	470	22 09 00	21.6794834	2127660
421	17 72 41	20.5182845	2375297	471	22 18 41	21.7025344	2123142
422	17 80 84	20.5426386	2369668	472	22 27 84	21.7255610	2118644
423	17 89 29	20.5669638	2364066	473	22 37 29	21.7485632	2114165
424	17 97 76	20.5912603	2358491	474	22 46 76	21.7715411	2109705
425	18 06 25	20.6155281	2352941	475	22 56 25	21.7944947	2105263
426	18 14 76	20.6397674	2347418	476	22 65 76	21.8174242	2100840
427	18 23 29	20.6639783	2341920	477	22 75 29	21.8403297	2096436
428	18 31 84	20.6881609	2336449	478	22 84 84	21.8632111	2092050
429	18 40 41	20.7123152	2331002	479	22 94 41	21.8860686	2087683
430	18 49 00	20.7364414	2325581	480	23 04 00	21.9089023	2083333
431	18 57 61	20.7605395	2320186	481	23 13 61	21.9317122	2079002
432	18 66 24	20.7846097	2314815	482	23 23 24	21.9544984	2074689
433	18 74 89	20.8086520	2309469	483	23 32 89	21.9772610	2070393
434	18 83 56	20.8326667	2304147	484	23 42 56	22.0000000	2066116
435	18 92 25	20.8566536	2298851	485	23 52 25	22.0227155	2061856
436	19 00 96	20.8806130	2293578	486	23 61 96	22.0454077	2057613
437	19 09 69	20.9045450	2288330	487	23 71 69	22.0680765	2053388
438	19 18 44	20.9284495	2283105	488	23 81 44	22.0907220	2049180
439	19 27 21	20.9523268	2277904	489	23 91 21	22.1133444	2044990
440	19 36 00	20.9761770	2272727	490	24 01 00	22.1359436	2040816
441	19 44 81	21.0000000	2267574	491	24 10 81	22.1585198	2036660
442	19 53 64	21.0237960	2262443	492	24 20 64	22.1810730	2032520
443	19 62 49	21.0475652	2257336	493	24 30 49	22.2036033	2028398
444	19 71 36	21.0713075	2252252	494	24 40 36	22.2261108	2024291
445	19 80 25	21.0950231	2247191	495	24 50 25	22.2485955	2020202
446	19 89 16	21.1187121	2242152	496	24 60 16	22.2710575	2016129
447	19 98 09	21.1423745	2237136	497	24 70 09	22.2934968	2012072
448	20 07 04	21.1660105	2232143	498	24 80 04	22.3159136	2008032
449	20 16 01	21.1896201	2227171	499	24 90 01	22.3383079	2004008
450	20 25 00	21.2132034	2222222	500	25 00 00	22.3606798	2000000

No.	Square	Square Root	Reciprocal .00	No.	Square	Square Root	Reciprocal .00
501	25 10 01	22.3830293	1996008	551	30 36 01	23.4733892	1814882
502	25 20 04	22.4053565	1992032	552	30 47 04	23.4946802	1811594
503	25 30 09	22.4276615	1988072	553	30 58 09	23.5159520	1808318
504	25 40 16	22.4499443	1984127	554	30 69 16	23.5372046	1805054
505	25 50 25	22.4722051	1980198	555	30 80 25	23.5584380	1801802
506	25 60 36	22.4944438	1976285	556	30 91 36	23.5796522	1798561
507	25 70 49	22.5166605.	1972387	557	31 02 49	23.6008474	1795332
508	25 80 64	22.5388553	1968504	558	31 13 64	23.6220236	1792115
509	25 90 81	22.5610283	1964637	559	31 24 81	23.6431808	1788909
510	26 01 00	22.5831796	1960784	560	31 36 00	23.6643191	1785714
511	26 11 21	22.6053091	1956947	561	31 47 21	23.6854386	1782531
512	26 21 44	22.6274170	1953125	562	31 58 44	23.7065392	1779359
513	26 31 69	22.6495033	1949318	563	31 69 69	23.7276210	1776199
514	26 41 96	22.6715681	1945525	564	31 80 96	23.7486842	1773050
515	26 52 25	22.6936114	1941748	565	31 92 25	23.7697286	1769912
516	26 62 56	22.7156334	1937984	566	32 03 56	23.7907545	1766784
517	26 72 89	22.7376340	1934236	567	32 14 89	23.8117618	1763668
518	26 83 24	22.7596134	1930502	568	32 26 24	23.8327506	1760563
519	26 93 61	22.7815715	1926782	569	32 37 61	23.8537209	1757469
520	27 04 00	22.8035085	1923077	570	32 49 00	23.8746728	1754386
521	27 14 41	22.8254244	1919386	571	32 60 41	23.8956063	1751313
522	27 24 84	22.8473193	1915709	572	32 71 84	23.9165215	1748252
523	27 35 29	22.8691933	1912046	573	32 83 29	23.9374184	1745201
524	27 45 76	22.8910463	1908397	574	32 94 76	23.9582971	1742160
525	27 56 25	22.9128785	1904762	575	33 06 25	23.9791576	1739130
526	27 66 76	22.9346899	1901141	576	33 17 76	24.0000000	1736111
527	27 77 29	22.9564806	1897533	577	33 29 29	24.0208243	1733102
528	27 87 84	22.9782506	1893939	578	33 40 84	24.0416306	1730104
529	27 98 41	23.0000000	1890359	579	33 52 41	24.0624188	1727116
530	28 09 00	23.0217289	1886792	580	33 64 00	24.0831891	1724138
531	28 19 61	23.0434372	1883239	581	33 75 61	24.1039416	1721170
532	28 30 24	23.0651252	1879699	582	33 87 24	24.1246762	1718213
533	28 40 89	23.0867928	1876173	583	33 98 89	24.1453929	1715266
534	28 51 56	23.1084400	1872659	584	34 10 56	24.1660919	1712329
535	28 62 25	23.1300670	1869159	585	34 22 25	24.1867732	1709402
536	28 72 96	23.1516738	1865672	586	34 33 96	24.2074369	1706485
537	28 83 69	23.1732605	1862197	587	34 45 69	24.2280829	1703578
538	28 94 44	23.1948270	1858736	588	34 57 44	24.2487113	1700680
539	29 05 21	23.2163735	1855288	589	34 69 21	24.2693222	1697793
540	29 16 00	23.2379001	1851852	590	34 81 00	24.2899156	1694915
541	29 26 81	23.2594067	1848429	591	34 92 81	24.3104916	1692047
542	29 37 64	23.2808935	1845018	592	35 04 64	24.3310501	1689189
543	29 48 49	23.3023604	1841621	593	35 16 49	24.3515913	1686341
544	29 59 36	23.3238076	1838235	594	35 28 36	24.3721152	1683502
545	29 70 25	23.3452351	1834862	595	35 40 25	24.3926218	1680672
546	29 81 16	23.3666429	1831502	596	35 52 16	24.4131112	1677852
547	29 92 09	23.3880311	1828154	597	35 64 09	24.4335834	1675042
548	30 03 04	23.4093998	1824818	598	35 76 04	24.4540385	1672241
549	30 14 01	23.4307490	1821494	599	35 88 01	24.4744765	1669449
550	30 25 00	23.4520788	1818182	600	36 00 00	24.4948974	1666667

No.	Square	Square Root	Reciprocal .00	No.	Square	Square Root	Reciprocal .00
601	36 12 01	24.5153013	1663894	651	42 38 01	25.5147016	1536098
602	36 24 04	24.5356883	1661130	652	42 51 04	25.5342907	1533742
603	36 36 09	24.5560583	1658375	653	42 64 09	25.5538647	1531394
604	36 48 16	24.5764115	1655629	654	42 77 16	25.5734237	1529052
605	36 60 25	24.5967478	1652893	655	42 90 25	25.5929678	1526718
606	36 72 36	24.6170673	1650165	656	43 03 36	25.6124969	1524390
607	36 84 49	24.6373700	1647446	657	43 16 49	25.6320112	1522070
608	36 96 64	24.6576560	1644737	658	43 29 64	25.6515107	1519757
609	37 08 81	24.6779254	1642036	659	43 42 81	25.6709953	1517451
610	37 21 00	24.6981781	1639344	660	43 56 00	25.6904652	1515152
611	37 33 21	24.7184142	1636661	661	43 69 21	25.7099203	1512859
612	37 45 44	24.7386338	1633987	662	43 82 44	25.7293607	1510574
613	37 57 69	24.7588368	1631321	663	43 95 69	25.7487864	1508296
614	37 69 96	24.7790234	1628664	664	44 08 96	25.7681975	1506024
615	37 82 25	24.7991935	1626016	665	44 22 25	25.7875939	1503759
616	37 94 56	24.8193473	1623377	666	44 35 56	25.8069758	1501502
617	38 06 89	24.8394847	1620746	667	44 48 89	25.8263431	1499250
618	38 19 24	24.8596058	1618123	668	44 62 24	25.8456960	1497006
619	38 31 61	24.8797106	1615509	669	44 75 61	25.8650343	1494768
620	38 44 00	24.8997992	1612903	670	44 89 00	25.8843582	1492537
621	38 56 41	24.9198716	1610306	671	45 02 41	25.9036677	1490313
622	38 68 84	24.9399278	1607717	672	45 15 84	25.9229628	1488095
623	38 81 29	24.9599679	1605136	673	45 29 29	25.9422435	1485884
624	38 93 76	24.9799920	1602564	674	45 42 76	25.9615100	1483680
625	39 06 25	25.0000000	1600000	675	45 56 25	25.9807621	1481481
626	39 18 76	25.0199920	1597444	676	45 69 76	26.0000000	1479290
627	39 31 29	25.0399681	1594896	677	45 83 29	26.0192237	1477105
628	39 43 84	25.0599282	1592357	678	45 96 84	26.0384331	1474926
629	39 56 41	25.0798724	1589825	679	46 10 41	26.0576284	1472754
630	39 69 00	25.0998008	1587302	680	46 24 00	26.0768096	1470588
631	39 81 61	25.1197134	1584786	681	46 37 61	26.0959767	1468429
632	39 94 24	25.1396102	1582278	682	46 51 24	26.1151297	1466276
633	40 06 89	25.1594913	1579779	683	46 64 89	26.1342687	1464129
634	40 19 56	25.1793566	1577287	684	46 78 56	26.1533937	1461988
635	40 32 25	25.1992063	1574803	685	46 92 25	26.1725047	1459854
636	40 44 96	25.2190404	1572327	686	47 05 96	26.1916017	1457726
637	40 57 69	25.2388589	1569859	687	47 19 69	26.2106848	1455604
638	40 70 44	25.2586619	1567398	688	47 33 44	26.2297541	1453488
639	40 83 21	25.2784493	1564945	689	47 47 21	26.2488095	1451379
640	40 96 00	25.2982213	1562500	690	47 61 00	26.2678511	1449275
641	41 08 81	25.3179778	1560062	691	47 74 81	26.2868789	1447178
642	41 21 64	25.3377189	1557632	692	47 88 64	26.3058929	1445087
643	41 34 49	25.3574447	1555210	693	48 02 49	26.3248932	1443001
644	41 47 36	25.3771551	1552795	694	48 16 36	26.3438797	1440922
645	41 60 25	25.3968502	1550388	695	48 30 25	26.3628527	1438849
646	41 73 16	25.4165301	1547988	696	48 44 16	26.3818119	1436782
647	41 86 09	25.4361947	1545595	697	48 58 09	26.4007576	1434720
648	41 99 04	25.4558441	1543210	698	48 72 04	26.4196896	1432665
649	42 12 01	25.4754784	1540832	699	48 86 01	26.4386081	1430615
650	42 25 00	25.4950976	1538462	700	49 00 00	26.4575131	1428571

No.	Square	Square Root	Reciprocal .00	No.	Square	Square Root	Reciprocal .00
701	49 14 01	26.4764046	1426534	751	56 40 01	27.4043792	1331558
702	49 28 04	26.4952826	1424501	752	56 55 04	27.4226184	1329787
703	49 42 09	26.5141472	1422475	753	56 70 09	27.4408455	1328021
704	49 56 16	26.5329983	1420455	754	56 85 16	27.4590604	1326260
705	49 70 25	26.5518361	1418440	755	57 00 25	27.4772633	1324503
706	49 84 36	26.5706605	1416431	756	57 15 36	27.4954542	1322751
707	49 98 49	26.5894716	1414427	757	57 30 49	27.5136330	1321004
708	50 12 64	26.6082694	1412429	758	57 45 64	27.5317998	1319261
709	50 26 81	26.6270539	1410437	759	57 60 81	27.5499546	1317523
710	50 41 00	26.6458252	1408451	760	57 76 00	27.5680975	1315789
711	50 55 21	26.6645833	1406470	761	57 91 21	27.5862284	1314060
712	50 69 44	26.6833281	1404494	762	58 06 44	27.6043475	1312336
713	50 83 69	26.7020598	1402525	763	58 21 69	27.6224546	1310616
714	50 97 96	26.7207784	1400560	764	58 36 96	27.6405499	1308901
715	51 12 25	26.7394839	1398601	765	58 52 25	27.6586334	1307190
716	51 26 56	26.7581763	1396648	766	58 67 56	27.6767050	1305483
717	51 40 89	26.7768557	1394700	767	58 82 89	27.6947648	1303781
718	51 55 24	26.7955220	1392758	768	58 98 24	27.7128129	1302083
719	51 69 61	26.8141754	1390821	769	59 13 61	27.7308492	1300390
720	51 84 00	26.8328157	1388889	770	59 29 00	27.7488739	1298701
721	51 98 41	26.8514432	1386963	771	59 44 41	27.7668868	1297017
722	52 12 84	26.8700577	1385042	772	59 59 84	27.7848880	1295337
723	52 27 29	26.8886593	1383126	773	59 75 29	27.8028775	1293661
724	52 41 76	26.9072481	1381215	774	59 90 76	27.8208555	1291990
725	52 56 25	26.9258240	1379310	775	60 06 25	27.8388218	1290323
726	52 70 76	26.9443872	1377410	776	60 21 76	27.8567766	1288660
727	52 85 29	26.9629375	1375516	777	60 37 29	27.8747197	1287001
728	52 99 84	26.9814751	1373626	778	60 52 84	27.8926514	1285347
729	53 14 41	27.0000000	1371742	779	60 68 41	27.9105715	1283697
730	53 29 00	27.0185122	1369863	780	60 84 00	27.9284801	1282051
731	53 43 61	27.0370117	1367989	781	60 99 61	27.9463772	1280410
732	53 58 24	27.0554985	1366120	782	61 15 24	27.9642629	1278772
733	53 72 89	27.0739727	1364256	783	61 30 89	27.9821372	1277139
734	53 87 56	27.0924344	1362398	784	61 46 56	28.0000000	1275510
735	54 02 25	27.1108834	1360544	785	61 62 25	28.0178515	1273885
736	54 16 96	27.1293199	1358696	786	61 77 96	28.0356915	1272265
737	54 31 69	27.1477439	1356852	787	61 93 69	28.0535203	1270648
738	54 46 44	27.1661554	1355014	788	62 09 44	28.0713377	1269036
739	54 61 21	27.1845544	1353180	789	62 25 21	28.0891438	1267427
740	54 76 00	27.2029410	1351351	790	62 41 00	28.1069386	1265823
741	54 90 81	27.2213152	1349528	791	62 56 81	28.1247222	1264223
742	55 05 64	27.2396769	1347709	792	62 72 64	28.1424946	1262626
743	55 20 49	27.2580263	1345895	793	62 88 49	28.1602557	1261034
744	55 35 36	27.2763634	1344086	794	63 04 36	28.1780056	1259446
745	55 50 25	27.2946881	1342282	795	63 20 25	28.1957444	1257862
746	55 65 16	27.3130006	1340483	796	63 36 16	28.2134720	1256281
747	55 80 09	27.3313007	1338688	797	63 52 09	28.2311884	1254705
748	55 95 04	27.3495887	1336898	798	63 68 04	28.2488938	1253133
749	56 10 01	27.3678644	1335113	799	63 84 01	28.2665881	1251564
750	56 25 00	27.3861279	1333333	800	64 00 00	28.2842712	1250000

No.	Square	Square Root	Reciprocal .00	No.	Square	Square Root	Reciprocal 00
801	64 16 01	28:3019434	1248439	851	72 42 01	29.1719043	1175088
802	64 32 04	28.3196045	1246883	852	72 59 04	29.1890390	1173709
803	64 48 09	28.3372546	1245330	853	72 76 09	29.2061637	1172333
804	64 64 16	28.3548938	1243781	854	72 93 16	29.2232784	1170960
805	64 80 25	28.3725219	1242236	855	73 10 25	29 2403830	1169591
806	64 96 36	28.3901391	1240695	856	73 27 36	29.2574777	1168224
807	65 12 49	28.4077454	1239157	857	73 44 49	29.2745623	1166861
808	65 28 64	28.4253408	1237624	858	73 61 64	29.2916370	1165501
809	65 44 81	28.4429253	1236094	859	73 78 81	29.3087018	1164144
810	65 61 00	28.4604989	1234568	860	73 96 00	29.3257566	1162791
811	65 77 21	28.4780617	1233046	861	74 13 21	29.3428015	1161440
812	65 93 44	28.4956137	1231527	862	74 30 44	29.3598365	1160093
813	66 09 69	28.5131549	1230012	863	74 47 69	29.3768616	1158749
814	66 25 96	28.5306852	1228501	864	74 64 96	29.3938769	1157407
815	66 42 25	28.5482048	1226994	865	74 82 25	29.4108823	1156069
816	66 58 56	28.5657137	1225490	866	74 99 56	29.4278779	1154734
817	66 74 89	28.5832119	1223990	867	75 16 89	29.4448637	1153403
818	66 91 24	28.6006993	1222494	868	75 34 24	29.4618397	1152074
819	67 07 61	28.6181760	1221001	869	75 51 61	29.4788059	1150748
820	67 24 00	28.6356421	1219512	870	75 69 00	29.4957624	1149425
821	67 40 41	28.6530976	1218027	871	75 86 41	29.5127091	1148106
822	67 56 84	28.6705424	1216545	872	76 03 84	29.5296461	1146789
823	67 73 29	28.6879766	1215067	873	76 21 29	29.5465734	1145475
824	67 89 76	28.7054002	1213592	874	76 38 76	29.5634910	1144165
825	68 06 25	28.7228132	1212121	875	76 56 25	29.5803989	1142857
826	68 22 76	28.7402157	1210654	876	76 73 76	29.5972972	1141553
827	68 39 29	28.7576077	1209190	877	76 91 29	29.6141858	1140251
828	68 55 84	28.7749891	1207729	878	77 08 84	29.6310648	1138952
829	68 72 41	28.7923601	1206273	879	77 26 41	29.6479342	1137656
830	68 89 00	28.8097206	1204819	880	77 44 00	29.6647939	1136364
831	69 05 61	28.8270706	1203369	881	77 61 61	29.6816442	1135074
832	69 22 24	28.8444102	1201923	882	77 79 24	29.6984848	1133787
833	69 38 89	28.8617394	1200480	883	77 96 89	29.7153159	1132503
834	69 55 56	28.8790582	1199041	884	78 14 56	29.7321375	1131222
835	69 72 25	28.8963666	1197605	885	78 32 25	29.7489496	1129944
836	69 88 96	28.9136646	1196172	886	78 49 96	29.7657521	1128668
837	70 05 69	28.9309523	1194743	887	78 67 69	29.7825452	1127396
838	70 22 44	28.9482297	1193317	888	78 85 44	29.7993289	1126126
839	70 39 21	28.9654967	1191895	889	79 03 21	29.8161030	1124859
840	70 56 00	28.9827535	1190476	890	79 21 00	29.8328678	1123596
841	70 72 81	29.0000000	1189061	891	79 38 81	29.8496231	1122334
842	70 89 64	29.0172363	1187648	892	79 56 64	29.8663690	1121076
843	71 06 49	29.0344623	1186240	893	79 74 49	29.8831056	1119821
844	71 23 36	29.0516781	1184834	894	79 92 36	29.8998328	1118568
845	71 40 25	29.0688837	1183432	895	80 10 25	29.9165506	1117318
846	71 57 16	29.0860791	1182033	896	80 28 16	29.9332591	1116071
847	71 74 09	29.1032644	1180638	897	80 46 09	29.9499583	1114827
848	71 91 04	29.1204396	1179245	898	80 64 04	29.9666481	1113586
849	72 08 01	29.1376046	1177856	899	80 82 01	29.9833287	1112347
850	72 25 00	29.1547595	1176471	900	81 00 00	30.0000000	1111111

No.	Square	Square Root	Reciprocal .00	No.	Square	Square Root	Reciprocal .00
901	81 18 01	30.0166620	1109878	951	90 44 01	30.8382879	1051525
902	81 36 04	30.0333148	1108647	952	90 63 04	30.8544972	1050420
903	81 54 09	30.0499584	1107420	953	90 82 09	30.8706981	1049318
904	81 72 16	30.0665928	1106195	954	91 01 16	30.8868904	1048218
905	81 90 25	30.0832179	1104972	955	91 20 25	30.9030743	1047120
906	82 08 36	30.0998339	1103753	956	91 39 36	30.9192497	1046025
907	82 26 49	30.1164407	1102536	957	91 58 49	30.9354166	1044932
908	82 44 64	30.1330383	1101322	958	91 77 64	30.9515751	1043841
909	82 62 81	30.1496269	1100110	959	91 96 81	30.9677251	1042753
910	82 81 00	30.1662063	1098901	960	92 16 00	30.9838668	1041667
911	82 99 21	30.1827765	1097695	961	92 35 21	31.0000000	1040583
912	83 17 44	30.1993377	1096491	962	92 54 44	31.0161248	1039501
913	83 35 69	30.2158899	1095290	963	92 73 69	31.0322413	1038422
914	83 53 96	30.2324329	1094092	964	92 92 96	31.0483494	1037344
915	83 72 25	30.2489669	1092896	965	93 12 25	31.0644491	1036269
916	83 90 56	30.2654919	1091703	966	93 31 56	31.0805405	1035197
917	84 08 89	30.2820079	1090513	967	93 50 89	31.0966236	1034126
918	84 27 24	30.2985148	1089325	968	93 70 24	31.1126984	1033058
919	84 45 61	30.3150128	1088139	969	93 89 61	31.1287648	1031992
920	84 64 00	30.3315018	1086957	970	94 09 00	31.1448230	1030928
921	84 82 41	30.3479818	1085776	971	94 28 41	31.1608729	1029866
922	85 00 84	30.3644529	1084599	972	94 47 84	31.1769145	1028807
923	85 19 29	30.3809151	1083424	973	94 67 29	31.1929479	1027749
924	85 37 76	30.3973683	1082251	974	94 86 76	31.2089731	1026694
925	85 56 25	30.4138127	1081081	975	95 06 25	31.2249900	1025641
926	85 74 76	30.4302481	1079914	976	95 25 76	31.2409987	1024590
927	85 93 29	30.4466747	1078749	977	95 45 29	31.2569992	1023541
928	86 11 84	30.4630924	1077586	978	95 64 84	31.2729915	1022495
929	86 30 41	30.4795013	1076426	979	95 84 41	31.2889757	1021450
930	86 49 00	30.4959014	1075269	980	96 04 00	31.3049517	1020408
931	86 67 61	30.5122926	1074114	981	96 23 61	31.3209195	1019368
932	86 86 24	30.5286750	1072961	982	96 43 24	31.3368792	1018330
933	87 04 89	30.5450487	1071811	983	96 62 89	31.3528308	1017294
934	87 23 56	30.5614136	1070664	984	96 82 56	31.3687743	1016260
935	87 42 25	30.5777697	1069519	985	97 02 25	31.3847097	1015228
936	87 60 96	30.5941171	1068376	986	97 21 96	31.4006369	1014199
937	87 79 69	30.6104557	1067236	987	97 41 69	31.4165561	1013171
938	87 98 44	30.6267857	1066098	988	97 61 44	31.4324673	1012146
939	88 17 21	30.6431069	1064963	989	97 81 21	31.4483704	1011122
940	88 36 00	30.6594194	1063830	990	98 01 00	31.4642654	1010101
941	88 54 81	30.6757233	1062699	991	98 20 81	31.4801525	1009082
942	88 73 64	30.6920185	1061571	992	98 40 64	31.4960315	1008065
943	88 92 49	30.7083051	1060445	993	98 60 49	31.5119025	1007049
944	89 11 36	30.7245830	1059322	994	98 80 36	31.5277655	1006036
945	89 30 25	30.7408523	1058201	995	99 00 25	31.5436206	1005025
946	89 49 16	30.7571130	1057082	996	99 20 16	31.5594677	1004016
947	89 68 09	30.7733651	1055966	997	99 40 09	31.5753068	1003009
948	89 87 04	30.7896086	1054852	998	99 60 04	31.5911380	1002004
949	90 06 01	30.8058436	1053741	999	99 80 01	31.6069613	1001001
950	90 25 00	30.8220700	1052632	1000	1 00 00 00	31.6227766	1000000

APPENDIX R

Common Logarithms of Numbers

The common logarithm of a number (N in the table) is the power to which 10 must be raised to produce N. The adjective "common" indicates that a logarithm is to the base 10 rather than to some other base—for example, $e = 2.71828$, the base of "natural" logarithms. When the unmodified term "logarithm" is used, it is generally understood that common logarithms are meant. A logarithm is composed of two parts, the *characteristic* and the *mantissa*.

The characteristic, which is always an integer or zero, is determined by the following rule:

If $N \geqq 1$, the characteristic is positive and its value is one less than the number of digits in N which are to the left of the decimal point. For example,

N	Characteristic
4568	3
456.8	2
45.68	1
4.568	0

If $N < 1$, the characteristic is negative and its value is one more than the number of zeros just to the right of the decimal point. For example,

N	Characteristic
0.4568	−1 or 9 − 10
0.04568	−2 or 8 − 10
0.004568	−3 or 7 − 10
0.0004568	−4 or 6 − 10

The mantissa, which is always a decimal or zero, is obtained from a table such as that which follows. The mantissa is the same for any given combination of digits no matter where the decimal point may be placed. Thus, for all of the eight N's just listed, the mantissa is 0.659726.

Combining the characteristic and the mantissa gives the logarithm. For the eight values of N given above,

N	Logarithm
4568	3.659726
456.8	2.659726
45.68	1.659726
4.568	0.659726
0.4568	9.659726 − 10
0.04568	8.659726 − 10
0.004568	7.659726 − 10
0.0004568	6.659726 − 10

N.	0	1	2	3	4	5	6	7	8	9	D.
100	000000	000434	000868	001301	001734	002166	002598	003029	003461	003891	432
1	4321	4751	5181	5609	6038	6466	6894	7321	7748	8174	428
2	8600	9026	9451	9876	010300	010724	011147	011570	011993	012415	424
3	012837	013259	013680	014100	4521	4940	5360	5779	6197	6616	420
4	7033	7451	7868	8284	8700	9116	9532	9947	020361	020775	416
105	021189	021603	022016	022428	022841	023252	023664	024075	4486	4896	412
6	5306	5715	6125	6533	6942	7350	7757	8164	8571	8978	408
7	9384	9789	030195	030600	031004	031408	031812	032216	032619	033021	404
8	033424	033826	4227	4628	5029	5430	5830	6230	6629	7028	400
9	7426	7825	8223	8620	9017	9414	9811	040207	040602	040998	397
110	041393	041787	042182	042576	042969	043362	043755	044148	044540	044932	393
1	5323	5714	6105	6495	6885	7275	7664	8053	8442	8830	390
2	9218	9606	9993	050380	050766	051153	051538	051924	052309	052694	386
3	053078	053463	053846	4230	4613	4996	5378	5760	6142	6524	383
4	6905	7286	7666	8046	8426	8805	9185	9563	9942	060320	379
115	060698	061075	061452	061829	062206	062582	062958	063333	063709	4083	376
6	4458	4832	5206	5580	5953	6326	6699	7071	7443	7815	373
7	8186	8557	8928	9298	9668	070038	070407	070776	071145	071514	370
8	071882	072250	072617	072985	073352	3718	4085	4451	4816	5182	366
9	5547	5912	6276	6640	7004	7368	7731	8094	8457	8819	363
120	079181	079543	079904	080266	080626	080987	081347	081707	082067	082426	360
1	082785	083144	083503	3861	4219	4576	4934	5291	5647	6004	357
2	6360	6716	7071	7426	7781	8136	8490	8845	9198	9552	355
3	9905	090258	090611	090963	091315	091667	092018	092370	092721	093071	352
4	093422	3772	4122	4471	4820	5169	5518	5866	6215	6562	349
125	6910	7257	7604	7951	8298	8644	8990	9335	9681	100026	346
6	100371	100715	101059	101403	101747	102091	102434	102777	103119	3462	343
7	3804	4146	4487	4828	5169	5510	5851	6191	6531	6871	341
8	7210	7549	7888	8227	8565	8903	9241	9579	9916	110253	338
9	110590	110926	111263	111599	111934	112270	112605	112940	113275	3609	335
130	113943	114277	114611	114944	115278	115611	115943	116276	116608	116940	333
1	7271	7603	7934	8265	8595	8926	9256	9536	9915	120245	330
2	120574	120903	121231	121560	121888	122216	122544	122871	123198	3525	328
3	3852	4178	4504	4830	5156	5481	5806	6131	6456	6781	325
4	7105	7429	7753	8076	8399	8722	9045	9368	9690	130012	323
135	130334	130655	130977	131298	131619	131939	132260	132580	132900	3219	321
6	3539	3858	4177	4496	4814	5133	5451	5769	6086	6403	318
7	6721	7037	7354	7671	7987	8303	8618	8934	9249	9564	316
8	9879	140194	140508	140822	141136	141450	141763	142076	142389	142702	314
9	143015	3327	3639	3951	4263	4574	4885	5196	5507	5818	311
140	146128	146438	146748	147058	147367	147676	147985	148294	148603	148911	309
1	9219	9527	9835	150142	150449	150756	151063	151370	151676	151982	307
2	152288	152594	152900	3205	3510	3815	4120	4424	4728	5032	305
3	5336	5640	5943	6246	6549	6852	7154	7457	7759	8061	303
4	8362	8664	8965	9266	9567	9868	160168	160469	160769	161068	301
145	161368	161667	161967	162266	162564	162863	3161	3460	3758	4055	299
6	4353	4650	4947	5244	5541	5838	6134	6430	6726	7022	297
7	7317	7613	7908	8203	8497	8792	9086	9380	9674	9968	295
8	170262	170555	170848	171141	171434	171726	172019	172311	172603	172895	293
9	3186	3478	3769	4060	4351	4641	4932	5222	5512	5802	291
150	176091	176381	176670	176959	177248	177536	177825	178113	178401	178689	289
1	8977	9264	9552	9839	180126	180413	180699	180986	181272	181558	287
2	181844	182129	182415	182700	2985	3270	3555	3839	4123	4407	285
3	4691	4975	5259	5542	5825	6108	6391	6674	6956	7239	283
4	7521	7803	8084	8366	8647	8928	9209	9490	9771	190051	281
155	190332	190612	190892	191171	191451	191730	192010	192289	192567	2846	279
6	3125	3403	3681	3959	4237	4514	4792	5069	5346	5623	278
7	5900	6176	6453	6729	7005	7281	7556	7832	8107	8382	276
8	8657	8932	9206	9481	9755	200029	200303	200577	200850	201124	274
9	201397	201670	201943	202216	202488	2761	3033	3305	3577	3848	272
N.	0	1	2	3	4	5	6	7	8	9	D.

Log e = 0.434295; log π = 0.497150; log $\sqrt{\pi}$ = 0.248575.

N.	0	1	2	3	4	5	6	7	8	9	D.
160	204120	204391	204663	204934	205204	205475	205746	206016	206286	206556	271
1	6826	7096	7365	7634	7904	8173	8441	8710	8979	9247	269
2	9515	9783	210051	210319	210586	210853	211121	211388	211654	211921	267
3	212188	212454	2720	2986	3252	3518	3783	4049	4314	4579	266
4	4844	5109	5373	5638	5902	6166	6430	6694	6957	7221	264
165	7484	7747	8010	8273	8536	8798	9060	9323	9585	9846	262
6	220108	220370	220631	220892	221153	221414	221675	221936	222196	222456	261
7	2716	2976	3236	3496	3755	4015	4274	4533	4792	5051	259
8	5309	5568	5826	6084	6342	6600	6858	7115	7372	7630	258
9	7887	8144	8400	8657	8913	9170	9426	9682	9938	230193	256
170	230449	230704	230960	231215	231470	231724	231979	232234	232488	232742	255
1	2996	3250	3504	3757	4011	4264	4517	4770	5023	5276	253
2	5528	5781	6033	6285	6537	6789	7041	7292	7544	7795	252
3	8046	8297	8548	8799	9049	9299	9550	9800	240050	240300	250
4	240549	240799	241048	241297	241546	241795	242044	242293	2541	2790	249
175	3038	3286	3534	3782	4030	4277	4525	4772	5019	5266	248
6	5513	5759	6006	6252	6499	6745	6991	7237	7482	7728	246
7	7973	8219	8464	8709	8954	9198	9443	9687	9932	250176	245
8	250420	250664	250908	251151	251395	251638	251881	252125	252358	2610	243
9	2853	3096	3338	3580	3822	4064	4306	4548	4790	5031	242
180	255273	255514	255755	255996	256237	256477	256718	256958	257198	257439	241
1	7679	7918	8158	8398	8637	8877	9116	9355	9594	9833	239
2	260071	260310	260548	260787	261025	261263	261501	261739	261976	262214	238
3	2451	2688	2925	3162	3399	3636	3873	4109	4346	4582	237
4	4818	5054	5290	5525	5761	5996	6232	6467	6702	6937	235
185	7172	7406	7641	7875	8110	8344	8578	8812	9046	9279	234
6	9513	9746	9980	270213	270446	270679	270912	271144	271377	271609	233
7	271842	272074	272306	2538	2770	3001	3233	3465	3696	3927	232
8	4158	4389	4620	4850	5081	5311	5542	5772	6002	6232	230
9	6462	6692	6921	7151	7380	7609	7838	8067	8296	8525	229
190	278754	278982	279211	279439	279667	279895	280123	280351	280578	280806	228
1	281033	281261	281488	281715	281942	282169	2396	2622	2849	3075	227
2	3301	3527	3753	3979	4205	4431	4657	4882	5107	5332	226
3	5557	5782	6007	6232	6456	6681	6905	7130	7354	7578	225
4	7802	8026	8249	8473	8696	8920	9143	9366	9589	9812	223
195	290035	290257	290480	290702	290925	291147	291369	291591	291813	292034	222
6	2256	2478	2699	2920	3141	3363	3584	3804	4025	4246	221
7	4466	4687	4907	5127	5347	5567	5787	6007	6226	6446	220
8	6665	6884	7104	7323	7542	7761	7979	8198	8416	8635	219
9	8853	9071	9289	9507	9725	9943	300161	300378	300595	300813	218
200	301030	301247	301464	301681	301898	302114	302331	302547	302764	302980	217
1	3196	3412	3628	3844	4059	4275	4491	4706	4921	5136	216
2	5351	5566	5781	5996	6211	6425	6639	6854	7068	7282	215
3	7496	7710	7924	8137	8351	8564	8778	8991	9204	9417	213
4	9630	9843	310056	310268	310481	310693	310906	311118	311330	311542	212
205	311754	311966	2177	2389	2600	2812	3023	3234	3445	3656	211
6	3867	4078	4289	4499	4710	4920	5130	5340	5551	5760	210
7	5970	6180	6390	6599	6809	7018	7227	7436	7646	7854	209
8	8063	8272	8481	8689	8898	9106	9314	9522	9730	9938	208
9	320146	320354	320562	320769	320977	321184	321391	321598	321805	322012	207
210	322219	322426	322633	322839	323046	323252	323458	323665	323871	324077	206
1	4282	4488	4694	4899	5105	5310	5516	5721	5926	6131	205
2	6336	6541	6745	6950	7155	7359	7563	7767	7972	8176	204
3	8380	8583	8787	8991	9194	9398	9601	9805	330008	330211	203
4	330414	330617	330819	331022	331225	331427	331630	331832	2034	2236	202
215	2438	2640	2842	3044	3246	3447	3649	3850	4051	4253	202
6	4454	4655	4856	5057	5257	5458	5658	5859	6059	6260	201
7	6460	6660	6860	7060	7260	7459	7659	7858	8058	8257	200
8	8456	8656	8855	9054	9253	9451	9650	9849	340047	340246	199
9	340444	340642	340841	341039	341237	341435	341632	341830	2028	2225	198
N.	0	1	2	3	4	5	6	7	8	9	D.

N.	0	1	2	3	4	5	6	7	8	9	D.
220	342423	342620	342817	343014	343212	343409	343606	343802	343999	344196	197
1	4392	4589	4785	4981	5178	5374	5570	5766	5962	6157	196
2	6353	6549	6744	6939	7135	7330	7525	7720	7915	8110	195
3	8305	8500	8694	8889	9083	9278	9472	9666	9860	350054	194
4	350248	350442	350636	350829	351023	351216	351410	351603	351796	1989	193
225	2183	2375	2568	2761	2954	3147	3339	3532	3724	3916	193
6	4108	4301	4493	4685	4876	5068	5260	5452	5643	5834	192
7	6026	6217	6408	6599	6790	6981	7172	7363	7554	7744	191
8	7935	8125	8316	8506	8696	8886	9076	9266	9456	9646	190
9	9835	360025	360215	360404	360593	360783	360972	361161	361350	361539	189
230	361728	361917	362105	362294	362482	362671	362859	363048	363236	363424	188
1	3612	3800	3988	4176	4363	4551	4739	4926	5113	5301	188
2	5488	5575	5862	6049	6236	6423	6610	6796	6983	7169	187
3	7356	7542	7729	7915	8101	8287	8473	8659	8845	9030	186
4	9216	9401	9587	9772	9958	370143	370328	370513	370698	370883	185
235	371068	371253	371437	371622	371806	1991	2175	2360	2544	2728	184
6	2912	3096	3280	3464	3647	3831	4015	4198	4382	4565	184
7	4748	4932	5115	5298	5481	5664	5846	6029	6212	6394	183
8	6577	6759	6942	7124	7306	7488	7670	7852	8034	8216	182
9	8398	8580	8761	8943	9124	9306	9487	9668	9849	380030	181
240	380211	380392	380573	380754	380934	381115	381296	381476	381656	381837	181
1	2017	2197	2377	2557	2737	2917	3097	3277	3456	3636	180
2	3815	3995	4174	4353	4533	4712	4891	5070	5249	5428	179
3	5606	5785	5964	6142	6321	6499	6677	6856	7034	7212	178
4	7390	7568	7746	7923	8101	8279	8456	8634	8811	8989	178
245	9166	9343	9520	9698	9875	390051	390228	390405	390582	390759	177
6	390935	391112	391288	391464	391641	1817	1993	2169	2345	2521	176
7	2697	2873	3048	3224	3400	3575	3751	3926	4101	4277	176
8	4452	4627	4802	4977	5152	5326	5501	5676	5850	6025	175
9	6199	6374	6548	6722	6896	7071	7245	7419	7592	7766	174
250	397940	398114	398287	398461	398634	398808	398981	399154	399328	399501	173
1	9674	9847	400020	400192	400365	400538	400711	400883	401056	401228	173
2	401401	401573	1745	1917	2089	2261	2433	2605	2777	2949	172
3	3121	3292	3464	3635	3807	3978	4149	4320	4492	4663	171
4	4834	5005	5176	5346	5517	5688	5858	6029	6199	6370	171
255	6540	6710	6881	7051	7221	7391	7561	7731	7901	8070	170
6	8240	8410	8579	8749	8918	9087	9257	9426	9595	9764	169
7	9933	410102	410271	410440	410609	410777	410964	411114	411283	411451	169
8	411620	1788	1956	2124	2293	2461	2629	2796	2964	3132	168
9	3300	3467	3635	3803	3970	4137	4305	4472	4639	4806	167
260	414973	415140	415307	415474	415641	415808	415974	416141	416308	416474	167
1	6641	6807	6973	7139	7306	7472	7638	7804	7970	8135	166
2	8301	8467	8633	8798	8964	9129	9295	9460	9625	9791	165
3	9956	420121	420286	420451	420616	420781	420945	421110	421275	421439	165
4	421604	1768	1933	2097	2261	2426	2590	2754	2918	3082	164
265	3246	3410	3574	3737	3901	4065	4228	4392	4555	4718	164
6	4882	5045	5208	5371	5534	5697	5860	6023	6186	6349	163
7	6511	6674	6836	6999	7161	7324	7486	7648	7811	7973	162
8	8135	8297	8459	8621	8783	8944	9106	9268	9429	9591	162
9	9752	9914	430075	430236	430398	430559	430720	430881	431042	431203	161
270	431364	431525	431685	431846	432007	432167	432328	432488	432649	432809	161
1	2959	3130	3290	3450	3610	3770	3930	4090	4249	4409	160
2	4569	4729	4888	5048	5207	5367	5526	5685	5844	6004	159
3	6163	6322	6481	6640	6799	6957	7116	7275	7433	7592	159
4	7751	7909	8067	8226	8384	8542	8701	8859	9017	9175	158
275	9333	9491	9648	9806	9964	440122	440279	440437	440594	440752	158
6	440909	441066	441224	441381	441538	1695	1852	2009	2166	2323	157
7	2480	2637	2793	2950	3106	3263	3419	3576	3732	3889	157
8	4045	4201	4357	4513	4669	4825	4981	5137	5293	5449	156
9	5604	5760	5915	6071	6226	6382	6537	6692	6848	7003	155
N.	0	1	2	3	4	5	6	7	8	9	D.

N.	0	1	2	3	4	5	6	7	8	9	D.
280	447158	447313	447468	447623	447778	447933	448088	448242	448397	448552	155
1	8706	8861	9015	9170	9324	9478	9633	9787	9941	450095	154
2	450249	450403	450557	450711	450865	451018	451172	451326	451479	1633	154
3	1786	1940	2093	2247	2400	2553	2706	2859	3012	3165	153
4	3318	3471	3624	3777	3930	4082	4235	4387	4540	4692	153
285	4845	4997	5150	5302	5454	5606	5758	5910	6062	6214	152
6	6366	6518	6670	6821	6973	7125	7276	7428	7579	7731	152
7	7882	8033	8184	8336	8487	8638	8789	8940	9091	9242	151
8	9392	9543	9694	9845	9995	460146	460296	460447	460597	460748	151
9	460898	461048	461198	461348	461499	1649	1799	1948	2098	2248	150
290	462398	462548	462697	462847	462997	463146	463296	463445	463594	463744	150
1	3893	4042	4191	4340	4490	4639	4788	4936	5035	5234	149
2	5383	5532	5680	5829	5977	6126	6274	6423	6571	6719	149
3	6868	7016	7164	7312	7460	7608	7756	7904	8052	8200	148
4	8347	8495	8643	8790	8938	9085	9233	9380	9527	9675	148
295	9822	9969	470116	470263	470410	470557	470704	470851	470998	471145	147
6	471292	471438	1585	1732	1878	2025	2171	2318	2464	2610	146
7	2756	2903	3049	3195	3341	3487	3633	3779	3925	4071	146
8	4216	4362	4508	4653	4799	4944	5090	5235	5381	5526	146
9	5671	5816	5962	6107	6252	6397	6542	6687	6832	6976	145
300	477121	477266	477411	477555	477700	477844	477989	478133	478278	478422	145
1	8566	8711	8855	8999	9143	9287	9431	9575	9719	9863	144
2	480007	480151	480294	480438	480582	480725	480869	481012	481156	481299	144
3	1443	1586	1729	1872	2016	2159	2302	2445	2588	2731	143
4	2874	3016	3159	3302	3445	3587	3730	3872	4015	4157	143
305	4300	4442	4585	4727	4869	5011	5153	5295	5437	5579	142
6	5721	5863	6005	6147	6289	6430	6572	6714	6855	6997	142
7	7138	7280	7421	7563	7704	7845	7986	8127	8259	8410	141
8	8551	8692	8833	8974	9114	9255	9396	9537	9677	9818	141
9	9958	490099	490239	490380	490520	490661	490801	490941	491081	491222	140
310	491362	491502	491642	491782	491922	492062	492201	492341	492481	492621	140
1	2760	2900	3040	3179	3319	3458	3597	3737	3876	4015	139
2	4155	4294	4433	4572	4711	4850	4989	5128	5267	5406	139
3	5544	5683	5822	5960	6099	6238	6376	6515	6653	6791	139
4	6930	7068	7206	7344	7483	7621	7759	7897	8035	8173	138
315	8311	8448	8586	8724	8862	8999	9137	9275	9412	9550	138
6	9687	9824	9962	500099	500236	500374	500511	500648	500785	500922	137
7	501059	501196	501333	1470	1607	1744	1880	2017	2154	2291	137
8	2427	2564	2700	2837	2973	3109	3246	3382	3518	3655	136
9	3791	3927	4063	4199	4335	4471	4607	4743	4878	5014	136
320	505150	505286	505421	505557	505693	505828	505964	506099	506234	506370	136
1	6505	6640	6776	6911	7046	7181	7316	7451	7586	7721	135
2	7856	7991	8126	8260	8395	8530	8664	8799	8934	9068	135
3	9203	9337	9471	9606	9740	9874	510009	510143	510277	510411	134
4	510545	510679	510813	510947	511081	511215	1349	1482	1616	1750	134
325	1883	2017	2151	2284	2418	2551	2684	2818	2951	3084	133
6	3218	3351	3484	3617	3750	3883	4016	4149	4282	4415	133
7	4548	4681	4813	4946	5079	5211	5344	5476	5609	5741	133
8	5874	6006	6139	6271	6403	6535	6668	6800	6932	7064	132
9	7196	7328	7460	7592	7724	7855	7987	8119	8251	8382	132
330	518514	518646	518777	518909	519040	519171	519303	519434	519566	519697	131
1	9828	9959	520090	520221	520353	520484	520615	520745	520876	521007	131
2	521138	521269	1400	1530	1661	1792	1922	2053	2183	2314	131
3	2444	2575	2705	2835	2966	3096	3226	3356	3486	3616	130
4	3746	3876	4006	4136	4266	4396	4526	4656	4785	4915	130
335	5045	5174	5304	5434	5563	5693	5822	5951	6081	6210	129
6	6339	6469	6598	6727	6856	6985	7114	7243	7372	7501	129
7	7630	7759	7888	8016	8145	8274	8402	8531	8660	8788	129
8	8917	9045	9174	9302	9430	9559	9687	9815	9943	530072	128
9	530200	530328	530456	530584	530712	530840	530968	531096	531223	1351	128
N.	0	1	2	3	4	5	6	7	8	9	D.

N.	0	1	2	3	4	5	6	7	8	9	D.
340	531479	531607	531734	531862	531990	532117	532245	532372	532500	532627	128
1	2754	2882	3009	3136	3264	3391	3518	3645	3772	3899	127
2	4026	4153	4280	4407	4534	4661	4787	4914	5041	5167	127
3	5294	5421	55*7	5674	5800	5927	6053	6180	6306	6432	126
4	6558	6685	6811	6937	7063	7189	7315	7441	7567	7693	126
345	7819	7945	8071	8197	8322	8448	8574	8699	8825	8951	126
6	9076	9202	9327	9452	9578	9703	9829	9954	540079	540204	125
7	540329	540455	540580	540705	540830	540955	541080	541205	1330	1454	125
8	1579	1704	1829	1953	2078	2203	2327	2452	2576	2701	125
9	2825	2950	3074	3199	3323	3447	3571	3696	3820	3944	124
350	544068	544192	544316	544440	544564	544688	544812	544936	545060	545183	124
1	5307	5431	5555	5678	5802	5925	6049	6172	6296	6419	124
2	6543	6666	6789	6913	7036	7159	7282	7405	7529	7652	123
3	7775	7898	8021	8144	8267	8389	8512	8635	8758	8881	123
4	9003	9126	9249	9371	9494	9616	9739	9861	9984	550106	123
355	550228	550351	550473	550595	550717	550840	550962	551084	551206	1328	122
6	1450	1572	1694	1816	1938	2060	2181	2303	2425	2547	122
7	2668	2790	2911	3033	3155	3276	3398	3519	3640	3762	122
8	3883	4004	4126	4247	4368	4489	4610	4731	4852	4973	121
9	5094	5215	5336	5457	5578	5699	5820	5940	6061	6182	121
360	556303	556423	556544	556664	556785	556905	557026	557146	557267	557387	120
1	7507	7627	7748	7868	7988	8108	8228	8349	8469	8589	120
2	8709	8829	8948	9068	9188	9308	9428	9548	9667	9787	120
3	9907	560026	560146	560265	560385	560504	560624	560743	560863	560982	119
4	561101	1221	1340	1459	1578	1698	1817	1936	2055	2174	119
365	2293	2412	2531	2650	2769	2887	3006	3125	3244	3362	119
6	3481	3600	3718	3837	3955	4074	4192	4311	4429	4548	119
7	4666	4784	4903	5021	5139	5257	5376	5494	5612	5730	118
8	5848	5966	6084	6202	6320	6437	6555	6673	6791	6909	118
9	7026	7144	7262	7379	7497	7614	7732	7849	7967	8084	118
370	568202	568319	568436	568554	568671	568788	568905	569023	569140	569257	117
1	9374	9491	9608	9725	9842	9959	570076	570193	570309	570426	117
2	570543	570660	570776	570893	571010	571126	1243	1359	1476	1592	117
3	1709	1825	1942	2058	2174	2291	2407	2523	2639	2755	116
4	2872	2988	3104	3220	3336	3452	3568	3684	3800	3915	116
375	4031	4147	4263	4379	4494	4610	4726	4841	4957	5072	116
6	5188	5303	5419	5534	5650	5765	5880	5996	6111	6226	115
7	6341	6457	6572	6687	6802	6917	7032	7147	7252	7377	115
8	7492	7607	7722	7836	7951	8066	8181	8295	8410	8525	115
9	8639	8754	8868	8983	9097	9212	9326	9441	9555	9669	114
380	579784	579898	580012	580126	580241	580355	580469	580583	580697	580811	114
1	580925	581039	1153	1267	1381	1495	1608	1722	1836	1950	114
2	2063	2177	2291	2404	2518	2631	2745	2858	2972	3085	114
3	3199	3312	3426	3539	3652	3765	3879	3992	4105	4218	113
4	4331	4444	4557	4670	4783	4896	5009	5122	5235	5348	113
385	5461	5574	5686	5799	5912	6024	6137	6250	6362	6475	113
6	6587	6700	6812	6925	7037	7149	7262	7374	7486	7599	112
7	7711	7823	7935	8047	8160	8272	8384	8496	8608	8720	112
8	8832	8944	9056	9167	9279	9391	9503	9615	9726	9838	112
9	9950	590061	590173	590284	590396	590507	590619	590730	590842	590953	112
390	591065	591176	591287	591399	591510	591621	591732	591843	591955	592066	111
1	2177	2288	2399	2510	2621	2732	2843	2954	3064	3175	111
2	3286	3397	3508	3618	3729	3840	3950	4061	4171	4282	111
3	4393	4503	4614	4724	4834	4945	5055	5165	5276	5380	110
4	5496	5606	5717	5827	5937	6047	6157	6267	6377	6487	110
395	6597	6707	6817	6927	7037	7146	7256	7366	7476	7586	110
6	7695	7805	7914	8024	8134	8243	8353	8462	8572	8681	110
7	8791	8900	9009	9119	9228	9337	9446	9556	9665	9774	109
8	9883	9992	600101	600210	600319	600428	600537	600646	600755	600864	109
9	600973	601082	1191	1299	1408	1517	1625	1734	1843	1951	109
N.	0	1	2	3	4	5	6	7	8	9	D.

N.	0	1	2	3	4	5	6	7	8	9	D.
400	602060	602169	602277	602386	602494	602603	602711	602819	602928	603036	108
1	3144	3253	3361	3469	3577	3686	3794	3902	4010	4118	108
2	4226	4334	4442	4550	4658	4766	4874	4982	5089	5197	108
3	5305	5413	5521	5628	5736	5844	5951	6059	6166	6274	108
4	6381	6489	6596	6704	6811	6919	7026	7133	7241	7348	107
405	7455	7562	7669	7777	7884	7991	8098	8205	8312	8419	107
6	8526	8633	8740	8847	8954	9061	9167	9274	9381	9488	107
7	9594	9701	9808	9914	610021	610128	610234	610341	610447	610554	107
8	610660	610767	610873	610979	1086	1192	1298	1405	1511	1617	106
9	1723	1829	1936	2042	2148	2254	2360	2466	2572	2678	106
410	612784	612890	612996	613102	613207	613313	613419	613525	613630	613736	106
1	3842	3947	4053	4159	4264	4370	4475	4581	4686	4792	106
2	4897	5003	5108	5213	5319	5424	5529	5634	5740	5845	105
3	5950	6055	6160	6265	6370	6476	6581	6686	6790	6895	105
4	7000	7105	7210	7315	7420	7525	7629	7734	7839	7943	105
415	8048	8153	8257	8362	8466	8571	8676	8780	8884	8989	105
6	9093	9198	9302	9406	9511	9615	9719	9824	9928	620032	104
7	620136	620240	620344	620448	620552	620656	620760	620864	620968	1072	104
8	1176	1280	1384	1488	1592	1695	1799	1903	2007	2110	104
9	2214	2318	2421	2525	2628	2732	2835	2939	3042	3146	104
420	623249	623353	623456	623559	623663	623766	623869	623973	624076	624179	103
1	4282	4385	4488	4591	4695	4798	4901	5004	5107	5210	103
2	5312	5415	5518	5621	5724	5827	5929	6032	6135	6238	103
3	6340	6443	6546	6648	6751	6853	6956	7058	7161	7263	103
4	7366	7468	7571	7673	7775	7878	7980	8082	8185	8287	102
425	8389	8491	8593	8695	8797	8900	9002	9104	9206	9308	102
6	9410	9512	9613	9715	9817	9919	630021	630123	630224	630326	102
7	630428	630530	630631	630733	630835	630936	1038	1139	1241	1342	102
8	1444	1545	1647	1748	1849	1951	2052	2153	2255	2356	101
9	2457	2559	2660	2761	2862	2963	3064	3165	3266	3367	101
430	633468	633569	633670	633771	633872	633973	634074	634175	634276	634376	101
1	4477	4578	4679	4779	4880	4981	5081	5182	5283	5383	101
2	5484	5584	5685	5785	5886	5986	6087	6187	6287	6388	100
3	6488	6588	6688	6789	6889	6989	7089	7189	7290	7390	100
4	7490	7590	7690	7790	7890	7990	8090	8190	8290	8389	100
435	8489	8589	8689	8789	8888	8988	9088	9188	9287	9387	100
6	9486	9586	9686	9785	9889	9984	640084	640183	640283	640382	99
7	640481	640581	640680	640779	640879	640978	1077	1177	1276	1375	99
8	1474	1573	1672	1771	1871	1970	2069	2168	2267	2366	99
9	2465	2563	2662	2761	2860	2959	3058	3156	3255	3354	99
440	643453	643551	643650	643749	643847	643946	644044	644143	644242	644340	98
1	4439	4537	4636	4734	4832	4931	5029	5127	5226	5324	98
2	5422	5521	5619	5717	5815	5913	6011	6110	6208	6306	98
3	6404	6502	6600	6698	6796	6894	6992	7089	7187	7285	98
4	7383	7481	7579	7676	7774	7872	7969	8067	8165	8262	98
445	8360	8458	8555	8653	8750	8848	8945	9043	9140	9237	97
6	9335	9432	9530	9627	9724	9821	9919	650016	650113	650210	97
7	650308	650405	650502	650599	650696	650793	650890	0987	1084	1181	97
8	1278	1375	1472	1569	1666	1762	1859	1956	2053	2150	97
9	2246	2343	2440	2536	2633	2730	2826	2923	3019	3116	97
450	653213	653309	653405	653502	653598	653695	653791	653888	653984	654080	96
1	4177	4273	4369	4465	4562	4658	4754	4850	4946	5042	96
2	5138	5235	5331	5427	5523	5619	5715	5810	5906	6002	96
3	6098	6194	6290	6386	6482	6577	6673	6769	6864	6960	96
4	7056	7152	7247	7343	7438	7534	7629	7725	7820	7916	96
455	8011	8107	8202	8298	8393	8488	8584	8679	8774	8870	95
6	8965	9060	9155	9250	9346	9441	9536	9631	9726	9821	95
7	9916	660011	660106	660201	660296	660391	660486	660581	660676	660771	95
8	660865	0960	1055	1150	1245	1339	1434	1529	1623	1718	95
9	1813	1907	2002	2096	2191	2286	2380	2475	2569	2663	95
N.	0	1	2	3	4	5	6	7	8	9	D.

N.	0	1	2	3	4	5	6	7	8	9	D.
460	662758	662852	662947	663041	663135	663230	663324	663418	663512	663607	94
1	3701	3795	3889	3983	4078	4172	4266	4360	4454	4548	94
2	4642	4736	4830	4924	5018	5112	5206	5299	5393	5487	94
3	5581	5675	5769	5862	5956	6050	6143	6237	6331	6424	94
4	6518	6612	6705	6799	6892	6986	7079	7173	7266	7360	94
465	7453	7546	7640	7733	7826	7920	8013	8106	8199	8293	93
6	8386	8479	8572	8665	8759	8852	8945	9038	9131	9224	93
7	9317	9410	9503	9596	9689	9782	9875	9967	670060	670153	93
8	670246	670339	670431	670524	670617	670710	670802	670895	0988	1080	93
9	1173	1265	1358	1451	1543	1636	1728	1821	1913	2005	93
470	672098	672190	672283	672375	672467	672560	672652	672744	672836	672929	92
1	3021	3113	3205	3297	3390	3482	3574	3666	3758	3850	92
2	3942	4034	4126	4218	4310	4402	4494	4586	4677	4769	92
3	4861	4953	5045	5137	5228	5320	5412	5503	5595	5687	92
4	5778	5870	5962	6053	6145	6236	6328	6419	6511	6602	92
475	6694	6785	6876	6968	7059	7151	7242	7333	7424	7516	91
6	7607	7698	7789	7881	7972	8063	8154	8245	8336	8427	91
7	8518	8609	8700	8791	8882	8973	9064	9155	9246	9337	91
8	9428	9519	9610	9700	9791	9882	9973	680063	680154	680245	91
9	680336	680426	680517	680607	680698	680789	680879	0970	1060	1151	91
480	681241	681332	681422	681513	681603	681693	681784	681874	681964	682055	90
1	2145	2235	2326	2416	2506	2596	2686	2777	2867	2957	90
2	3047	3137	3227	3317	3407	3497	3587	3677	3767	3857	90
3	3947	4037	4127	4217	4307	4396	4486	4576	4666	4756	90
4	4845	4935	5025	5114	5204	5294	5383	5473	5563	5652	90
485	5742	5831	5921	6010	6100	6189	6279	6368	6458	6547	89
6	6636	6726	6815	6904	6994	7033	7172	7261	7351	7440	89
7	7529	7618	7707	7796	7886	7975	8064	8153	8242	8331	89
8	8420	8509	8598	8687	8776	8865	8953	9042	9131	9220	89
9	9309	9398	9486	9575	9664	9753	9841	9930	690019	690107	89
490	690196	690285	690373	690462	690550	690639	690728	690816	690905	690993	89
1	1081	1170	1258	1347	1435	1524	1612	1700	1789	1877	88
2	1965	2053	2142	2230	2318	2406	2494	2583	2671	2759	88
3	2847	2935	3023	3111	3199	3287	3375	3463	3551	3639	88
4	3727	3815	3903	3991	4078	4166	4254	4342	4430	4517	88
495	4605	4693	4781	4868	4956	5044	5131	5219	5307	5394	88
6	5482	5569	5657	5744	5832	5919	6007	6094	6182	6269	87
7	6356	6444	6531	6618	6706	6793	6880	6968	7055	7142	87
8	7229	7317	7404	7491	7578	7665	7752	7839	7926	8014	87
9	8101	8188	8275	8362	8449	8535	8622	8709	8796	8883	87
500	698970	699057	699144	699231	699317	699404	699491	699578	699664	699751	87
1	9338	9924	700011	700098	700184	700271	700358	700444	700531	700617	87
2	700704	700790	0877	0963	1050	1136	1222	1309	1395	1482	86
3	1568	1654	1741	1827	1913	1999	2086	2172	2258	2344	86
4	2431	2517	2603	2689	2775	2861	2947	3033	3119	3205	86
505	3291	3377	3463	3549	3635	3721	3807	3893	3979	4065	86
6	4151	4236	4322	4408	4494	4579	4665	4751	4837	4922	86
7	5008	5094	5179	5265	5350	5436	5522	5607	5693	5778	86
8	5864	5949	6035	6120	6206	6291	6376	6462	6547	6632	85
9	6718	6803	6888	6974	7059	7144	7229	7315	7400	7485	85
510	707570	707655	707740	707826	707911	707996	708081	708166	708251	708336	85
1	8421	8506	8591	8676	8761	8846	8931	9015	9100	9185	85
2	9270	9355	9440	9524	9609	9694	9779	9863	9948	710033	85
3	710117	710202	710287	710371	710456	710540	710625	710710	710794	0879	85
4	0963	1048	1132	1217	1301	1385	1470	1554	1639	1723	84
515	1807	1892	1976	2060	2144	2229	2313	2397	2481	2566	84
6	2650	2734	2818	2902	2986	3070	3154	3238	3323	3407	84
7	3491	3575	3659	3742	3826	3910	3994	4078	4162	4246	84
8	4330	4414	4497	4581	4665	4749	4833	4916	5000	5084	84
9	5167	5251	5335	5418	5502	5586	5669	5753	5836	5920	84
N.	0	1	2	3	4	5	6	7	8	9	D.

N.	0	1	2	3	4	5	6	7	8	9	D.
520	716003	716087	716170	716254	716337	716421	716504	716588	716671	716754	83
1	6838	6921	7004	7088	7171	7254	7338	7421	7504	7587	83
2	7671	7754	7837	7920	8003	8086	8169	8253	8336	8419	83
3	8502	8585	8668	8751	8834	8917	9000	9083	9165	9248	83
4	9331	9414	9497	9580	9663	9745	9828	9911	9994	720077	83
525	720159	720242	720325	720407	720490	720573	720655	720738	720821	0903	83
6	0986	1068	1151	1233	1316	1398	1481	1563	1646	1728	82
7	1811	1893	1975	2058	2140	2222	2305	2387	2469	2552	82
8	2634	2716	2798	2881	2963	3045	3127	3209	3291	3374	82
9	3456	3538	3620	3702	3784	3866	3948	4030	4112	4194	82
530	724276	724358	724440	724522	724604	724685	724767	724849	724931	725013	82
1	5095	5176	5258	5340	5422	5503	5585	5667	5748	5830	82
2	5912	5993	6075	6156	6238	6320	6401	6483	6564	6646	82
3	6727	6809	6890	6972	7053	7134	7216	7297	7379	7460	81
4	7541	7623	7704	7785	7866	7948	8029	8110	8191	8273	81
535	8354	8435	8516	8597	8678	8759	8841	8922	9003	9084	81
6	9165	9246	9327	9408	9489	9570	9651	9732	9813	9893	81
7	9974	730055	730136	730217	730298	730378	730459	730540	730621	730702	81
8	730782	0863	0944	1024	1105	1186	1266	1347	1428	1508	81
9	1589	1669	1750	1830	1911	1991	2072	2152	2233	2313	81
540	732394	732474	732555	732635	732715	732796	732876	732956	733037	733117	80
1	3197	3278	3358	3438	3518	3598	3679	3759	3839	3919	80
2	3999	4079	4160	4240	4320	4400	4480	4560	4640	4720	80
3	4800	4880	4960	5040	5120	5200	5279	5359	5439	5519	80
4	5599	5679	5759	5838	5918	5998	6078	6157	6237	6317	80
545	6397	6476	6556	6635	6715	6795	6874	6954	7034	7113	80
6	7193	7272	7352	7431	7511	7590	7670	7749	7829	7908	79
7	7987	8057	8146	8225	8305	8384	8463	8543	8622	8701	79
8	8781	8860	8939	9018	9097	9177	9256	9335	9414	9493	79
9	9572	9651	9731	9810	9889	9968	740047	740126	740205	740284	79
550	740363	740442	740521	740600	740678	740757	740836	740915	740994	741073	79
1	1152	1230	1309	1388	1467	1546	1624	1703	1782	1860	79
2	1939	2018	2096	2175	2254	2332	2411	2489	2568	2647	79
3	2725	2804	2882	2961	3039	3118	3196	3275	3353	3431	78
4	3510	3588	3667	3745	3823	3902	3980	4058	4136	4215	78
555	4293	4371	4449	4528	4606	4684	4762	4840	4919	4997	78
6	5075	5153	5231	5309	5387	5465	5543	5621	5699	5777	78
7	5855	5933	6011	6089	6167	6245	6323	6401	6479	6556	78
8	6634	6712	6790	6868	6945	7023	7101	7179	7256	7334	78
9	7412	7489	7567	7645	7722	7800	7878	7955	8033	8110	78
560	748188	748266	748343	748421	748498	748576	748653	748731	748808	748885	77
1	8963	9040	9118	9195	9272	9350	9427	9504	9582	9659	77
2	9736	9814	9891	9968	750045	750123	750200	750277	750354	750431	77
3	750508	750586	750663	750740	0817	0894	0971	1048	1125	1202	77
4	1279	1356	1433	1510	1587	1664	1741	1818	1895	1972	77
565	2048	2125	2202	2279	2356	2433	2509	2586	2663	2740	77
6	2816	2893	2970	3047	3123	3200	3277	3353	3430	3506	77
7	3583	3660	3736	3813	3889	3966	4042	4119	4195	4272	77
8	4348	4425	4501	4578	4654	4730	4807	4883	4960	5036	76
9	5112	5189	5265	5341	5417	5494	5570	5646	5722	5799	76
570	755875	755951	756027	756103	756180	756256	756332	756408	756484	756560	76
1	6636	6712	6788	6864	6940	7016	7092	7168	7244	7320	76
2	7396	7472	7548	7624	7700	7775	7851	7927	8003	8079	76
3	8155	8230	8306	8382	8458	8533	8609	8685	8761	8836	76
4	8912	8988	9063	9139	9214	9290	9366	9441	9517	9592	76
575	9668	9743	9819	9894	9970	760045	760121	760196	760272	760347	75
6	760422	760498	760573	760649	760724	0799	0875	0950	1025	1101	75
7	1176	1251	1326	1402	1477	1552	1627	1702	1778	1853	75
8	1928	2003	2078	2153	2228	2303	2378	2453	2529	2604	75
9	2679	2754	2829	2904	2978	3053	3128	3203	3278	3353	75
N.	0	1	2	3	4	5	6	7	8	9	D.

N.	0	1	2	3	4	5	6	7	8	9	D.
580	763428	763503	763578	763653	763727	763802	763877	763952	764027	764101	75
1	4176	4251	4326	4400	4475	4550	4624	4699	4774	4848	75
2	4923	4998	5072	5147	5221	5296	5370	5445	5520	5594	75
3	5669	5743	5818	5892	5966	6041	6115	6190	6264	6338	74
4	6413	6487	6562	6636	6710	6785	6859	6933	7007	7082	74
585	7156	7230	7304	7379	7453	7527	7601	7675	7749	7823	74
6	7898	7972	8046	8120	8194	8268	8342	8416	8490	8564	74
7	8638	8712	8786	8860	8934	9008	9082	9156	9230	9303	74
8	9377	9451	9525	9599	9673	9746	9820	9894	9968	770042	74
9	770115	770189	770263	770336	770410	770484	770557	770631	770705	0778	74
590	770852	770926	770999	771073	771146	771220	771293	771367	771440	771514	74
1	1587	1661	1734	1808	1881	1955	2028	2102	2175	2248	73
2	2322	2395	2468	2542	2615	2688	2762	2835	2908	2981	73
3	3055	3128	3201	3274	3348	3421	3494	3567	3640	3713	73
4	3786	3860	3933	4006	4079	4152	4225	4298	4371	4444	73
595	4517	4590	4663	4736	4809	4882	4955	5028	5100	5173	73
6	5246	5319	5392	5465	5538	5610	5683	5756	5829	5902	73
7	5974	6047	6120	6193	6265	6338	6411	6483	6556	6629	73
8	6701	6774	6846	6919	6992	7064	7137	7209	7282	7354	73
9	7427	7499	7572	7644	7717	7789	7862	7934	8006	8079	72
600	778151	778224	778296	778368	778441	778513	778585	778658	778730	778802	72
1	8874	8947	9019	9091	9163	9236	9308	9380	9452	9524	72
2	9596	9669	9741	9813	9885	9957	780029	780101	780173	780245	72
3	780317	780389	780461	780533	780605	780677	0749	0821	0893	0965	72
4	1037	1109	1181	1253	1324	1396	1468	1540	1612	1684	72
605	1755	1827	1899	1971	2042	2114	2186	2258	2329	2401	72
6	2473	2544	2616	2688	2759	2831	2902	2974	3046	3117	72
7	3189	3260	3332	3403	3475	3546	3618	3689	3761	3832	71
8	3904	3975	4046	4118	4189	4261	4332	4403	4475	4546	71
9	4617	4689	4760	4831	4902	4974	5045	5116	5187	5259	71
610	785330	785401	785472	785543	785615	785686	785757	785828	785899	785970	71
1	6041	6112	6183	6254	6325	6396	6467	6538	6609	6680	71
2	6751	6822	6893	6964	7035	7106	7177	7248	7319	7390	71
3	7460	7531	7602	7673	7744	7815	7885	7956	8027	8098	71
4	8168	8239	8310	8381	8451	8522	8593	8663	8734	8804	71
615	8875	8946	9016	9087	9157	9228	9299	9369	9440	9510	71
6	9581	9651	9722	9792	9863	9933	790004	790074	790144	790215	70
7	790285	790356	790426	790496	790567	790637	0707	0778	0848	0918	70
8	0988	1059	1129	1199	1269	1340	1410	1480	1550	1620	70
9	1691	1761	1831	1901	1971	2041	2111	2181	2252	2322	70
620	792392	792462	792532	792602	792672	792742	792812	792882	792952	793022	70
1	3092	3162	3231	3301	3371	3441	3511	3581	3651	3721	70
2	3790	3860	3930	4000	4070	4139	4209	4279	4349	4418	70
3	4488	4558	4627	4697	4767	4836	4906	4976	5045	5115	70
4	5185	5254	5324	5393	5463	5532	5602	5672	5741	5811	70
625	5880	5949	6019	6088	6158	6227	6297	6366	6436	6505	69
6	6574	6644	6713	6782	6852	6921	6990	7060	7129	7198	69
7	7268	7337	7406	7475	7545	7614	7683	7752	7821	7890	69
8	7960	8029	8098	8167	8236	8305	8374	8443	8513	8582	69
9	8651	8720	8789	8858	8927	8996	9065	9134	9203	9272	69
630	799341	799409	799478	799547	799616	799685	799754	799823	799892	799961	69
1	800029	800098	800167	800236	800305	800373	800442	800511	800580	800648	69
2	0717	0786	0854	0923	0992	1061	1129	1198	1266	1335	69
3	1404	1472	1541	1609	1678	1747	1815	1884	1952	2021	69
4	2089	2158	2226	2295	2363	2432	2500	2568	2637	2705	68
635	2774	2842	2910	2979	3047	3116	3184	3252	3321	3389	68
6	3457	3525	3594	3662	3730	3798	3867	3935	4003	4071	68
7	4139	4208	4276	4344	4412	4480	4548	4616	4685	4753	68
8	4821	4809	4957	5025	5093	5161	5229	5297	5365	5433	68
9	5501	5569	5637	5705	5773	5841	5908	5976	6044	6112	68
N.	0	1	2	3	4	5	6	7	8	9	D.

N.	C	1	2	3	4	5	6	7	8	9	D.
640	806180	806248	806316	806384	806451	806519	806587	806655	806723	806790	68
1	6858	6926	6994	7061	7129	7197	7264	7332	7400	7467	68
2	7535	7603	7670	7738	7806	7873	7941	8008	8076	8143	68
3	8211	8279	8346	8414	8481	8549	8616	8684	8751	8818	67
4	8886	8953	9021	9088	9156	9223	9290	9358	9425	9492	67
645	9560	9627	9694	9762	9829	9896	9964	810031	810098	810165	67
6	810233	810300	810367	810434	810501	810569	810636	0703	0770	0837	67
7	0904	0971	1039	1106	1173	1240	1307	1374	1441	1508	67
8	1575	1642	1709	1776	1843	1910	1977	2044	2111	2178	67
9	2245	2312	2379	2445	2512	2579	2646	2713	2780	2847	67
650	812913	812980	813047	813114	813181	813247	813314	813381	813448	813514	67
1	3581	3648	3714	3781	3848	3914	3981	4048	4114	4181	67
2	4248	4314	4381	4447	4514	4581	4647	4714	4780	4847	67
3	4913	4980	5046	5113	5179	5246	5312	5378	5445	5511	66
4	5578	5644	5711	5777	5843	5910	5976	6042	6109	6175	66
655	6241	6308	6374	6440	6506	6573	6639	6705	6771	6838	66
6	6904	6970	7036	7102	7169	7235	7301	7367	7433	7499	66
7	7565	7631	7698	7764	7830	7896	7962	8028	8094	8160	66
8	8226	8292	8358	8424	8490	8556	8622	8688	8754	8820	66
9	8885	8951	9017	9083	9149	9215	9281	9346	9412	9478	66
660	819544	819610	819676	819741	819807	819873	819939	820004	820070	820136	66
1	820201	820267	820333	820399	820464	820530	820595	0661	0727	0792	66
2	0858	0924	0989	1055	1120	1186	1251	1317	1382	1448	66
3	1514	1579	1645	1710	1775	1841	1905	1972	2037	2103	65
4	2168	2233	2299	2364	2430	2495	2560	2626	2691	2756	65
665	2822	2887	2952	3018	3083	3148	3213	3279	3344	3409	65
6	3474	3539	3605	3670	3735	3800	3865	3930	3996	4061	65
7	4126	4191	4256	4321	4386	4451	4516	4581	4646	4711	65
8	4776	4841	4906	4971	5036	5101	5166	5231	5296	5361	65
9	5426	5491	5556	5621	5686	5751	5815	5880	5945	6010	65
670	826075	826140	826204	826269	826334	826399	826464	826528	826593	826658	65
1	6723	6787	6852	6917	6981	7046	7111	7175	7240	7305	65
2	7369	7434	7499	7563	7628	7692	7757	7821	7886	7951	65
3	8015	8080	8144	8209	8273	8338	8402	8467	8531	8595	64
4	8660	8724	8789	8853	8918	8982	9046	9111	9175	9239	64
675	9304	9368	9432	9497	9561	9625	9690	9754	9818	9882	64
6	9947	830011	830075	830139	830204	830268	830332	830396	830460	830525	64
7	830589	0653	0717	0781	0845	0909	0973	1037	1102	1166	64
8	1230	1294	1358	1422	1486	1550	1614	1678	1742	1806	64
9	1870	1934	1998	2062	2126	2189	2253	2317	2381	2445	64
680	832509	832573	832637	832700	832764	832828	832892	832956	833020	833083	64
1	3147	3211	3275	3338	3402	3466	3530	3593	3657	3721	64
2	3784	3848	3912	3975	4039	4103	4166	4230	4294	4357	64
3	4421	4484	4548	4611	4675	4739	4802	4866	4929	4993	64
4	5056	5120	5183	5247	5310	5373	5437	5500	5564	5627	63
685	5691	5754	5817	5881	5944	6007	6071	6134	6197	6261	63
6	6324	6387	6451	6514	6577	6641	6704	6767	6830	6894	63
7	6957	7020	7083	7146	7210	7273	7336	7399	7462	7525	63
8	7588	7652	7715	7778	7841	7904	7967	8030	8093	8156	63
9	8219	8282	8345	8408	8471	8534	8597	8660	8723	8786	63
690	838849	838912	838975	839038	839101	839164	839227	839289	839352	839415	63
1	9478	9541	9604	9667	9729	9792	9855	9918	9981	840043	63
2	840106	840169	840232	840294	840357	840420	840482	840545	840608	0671	63
3	0733	0796	0859	0921	0984	1046	1109	1172	1234	1297	63
4	1359	1422	1485	1547	1610	1672	1735	1797	1860	1922	63
695	1985	2047	2110	2172	2235	2297	2360	2422	2484	2547	62
6	2609	2672	2734	2796	2859	2921	2983	3046	3108	3170	62
7	3233	3295	3357	3420	3482	3544	3606	3669	3731	3793	62
8	3855	3918	3930	4042	4104	4166	4229	4291	4353	4415	62
9	4477	4539	4601	4664	4726	4788	4850	4912	4974	5036	62
N.	0	1	2	3	4	5	6	7	8	9	D.

N.	0	1	2	3	4	5	6	7	8	9	D.
700	845098	845160	845222	845284	845346	845408	845470	845532	845594	845656	62
1	5718	5780	5842	5904	5966	6028	6090	6151	6213	6275	62
2	6337	6399	6461	6523	6585	6646	6708	6770	6832	6894	62
3	6955	7017	7079	7141	7202	7264	7326	7388	7449	7511	62
4	7573	7634	7696	7758	7819	7881	7943	8004	8066	8128	62
705	8189	8251	8312	8374	8435	8497	8559	8620	8682	8743	62
6	8805	8866	8928	8989	9051	9112	9174	9235	9297	9358	61
7	9419	9481	9542	9604	9665	9726	9788	9849	9911	9972	61
8	850033	850095	850156	850217	850279	850340	850401	850462	850524	850585	61
9	0646	0707	0769	0830	0891	0952	1014	1075	1136	1197	61
710	851258	851320	851381	851442	851503	851564	851625	851686	851747	851809	61
1	1870	1931	1992	2053	2114	2175	2236	2297	2358	2419	61
2	2480	2541	2602	2663	2724	2785	2846	2907	2968	3029	61
3	3090	3150	3211	3272	3333	3394	3455	3516	3577	3637	61
4	3698	3759	3820	3881	3941	4002	4063	4124	4185	4245	61
715	4306	4367	4428	4488	4549	4610	4670	4731	4792	4852	61
6	4913	4974	5034	5095	5156	5216	5277	5337	5398	5459	61
7	5519	5580	5640	5701	5761	5822	5882	5943	6003	6064	61
8	6124	6185	6245	6306	6366	6427	6487	6548	6608	6668	60
9	6729	6789	6850	6910	6970	7031	7091	7152	7212	7272	60
720	857332	857393	857453	857513	857574	857634	857694	857755	857815	857875	60
1	7935	7995	8056	8116	8176	8236	8297	8357	8417	8477	60
2	8537	8597	8657	8718	8778	8838	8898	8958	9018	9078	60
3	9138	9198	9258	9318	9379	9439	9499	9559	9619	9679	60
4	9739	9799	9859	9918	9978	860038	860098	860158	860218	860278	60
725	860338	860398	860458	860518	860578	0637	0697	0757	0817	0877	60
6	0937	0996	1056	1116	1176	1236	1295	1355	1415	1475	60
7	1534	1594	1654	1714	1773	1833	1893	1952	2012	2072	60
8	2131	2191	2251	2310	2370	2430	2489	2549	2608	2668	60
9	2728	2787	2847	2906	2966	3025	3085	3144	3204	3263	60
730	863323	863382	863442	863501	863561	863620	863680	363739	863799	863858	59
1	3917	3977	4036	4096	4155	4214	4274	4333	4392	4452	59
2	4511	4570	4630	4689	4748	4808	4867	4926	4985	5045	59
3	5104	5163	5222	5282	5341	5400	5459	5519	5578	5637	59
4	5696	5755	5814	5874	5933	5992	6051	6110	6169	6228	59
735	6287	6346	6405	6465	6524	6583	6642	6701	6760	6819	59
6	6878	6937	6996	7035	7114	7173	7232	7291	7350	7409	59
7	7467	7526	7585	7644	7703	7762	7821	7880	7939	7998	59
8	8056	8115	8174	8233	8292	8350	8409	8468	8527	8586	59
9	8644	8703	8762	8821	8879	8938	8997	9056	9114	9173	59
740	869232	869290	869349	869408	869466	869525	869584	869642	869701	869760	59
1	9818	9377	9935	9994	870053	870111	870170	870228	870287	870345	59
2	870404	870462	870521	870579	0538	0596	0755	0813	0872	0930	58
3	0989	1047	1106	1164	1223	1281	1339	1398	1456	1515	58
4	1573	1631	1690	1748	1806	1865	1923	1981	2040	2098	58
745	2156	2215	2273	2331	2389	2448	2506	2564	2622	2681	58
6	2739	2797	2855	2913	2972	3030	3088	3146	3204	3262	58
7	3321	3379	3437	3495	3553	3611	3669	3727	3785	3844	58
8	3902	3960	4018	4076	4134	4192	4250	4308	4366	4424	58
9	4482	4540	4598	4656	4714	4772	4830	4888	4945	5003	58
750	875061	875119	875177	875235	875293	875351	875409	875466	875524	875582	58
1	5640	5698	5756	5813	5871	5929	5987	6045	6102	6160	58
2	6218	6276	6333	6391	6449	6507	6564	6622	6680	6737	58
3	6795	6853	6910	6968	7026	7083	7141	7199	7256	7314	58
4	7371	7429	7487	7544	7602	7659	7717	7774	7832	7889	58
755	7947	8004	8062	8119	8177	8234	8292	8349	8407	8464	57
6	8522	8579	8637	8694	8752	8809	8866	8924	8981	9039	57
7	9096	9153	9211	9268	9325	9383	9440	9497	9555	9612	57
8	9669	9726	9784	9841	9898	9956	880013	880070	880127	880185	57
9	880242	880299	880356	880413	880471	880528	0585	0642	0699	0756	57

| N. | 0 | 1 | 2 | 3 | 4 | 5 | 6 | 7 | 8 | 9 | D. |

N.	0	1	2	3	4	5	6	7	8	9	D.
760	880814	880871	880928	880985	881042	881099	881156	881213	881271	881328	57
1	1385	1442	1499	1556	1613	1670	1727	1784	1841	1898	57
2	1955	2012	2069	2126	2183	2240	2297	2354	2411	2468	57
3	2525	2581	2638	2695	2752	2809	2866	2923	2980	3037	57
4	3093	3150	3207	3264	3321	3377	3434	3491	3548	3605	57
765	3661	3718	3775	3832	3888	3945	4002	4059	4115	4172	57
6	4229	4285	4342	4399	4455	4512	4569	4625	4682	4739	57
7	4795	4852	4909	4965	5022	5078	5135	5192	5248	5305	57
8	5361	5418	5474	5531	5587	5644	5700	5757	5813	5870	57
9	5926	5983	6039	6096	6152	6209	6265	6321	6378	6434	56
770	886491	886547	886604	886660	886716	886773	886829	886885	886942	886998	56
1	7054	7111	7167	7223	7280	7336	7392	7449	7505	7561	56
2	7617	7674	7730	7786	7842	7898	7955	8011	8067	8123	56
3	8179	8236	8292	8348	8404	8460	8516	8573	8629	8685	56
4	8741	8797	8853	8909	8965	9021	9077	9134	9190	9246	56
775	9302	9358	9414	9470	9526	9582	9638	9694	9750	9806	56
6	9862	9918	9974	890030	890086	890141	890197	890253	890309	890365	56
7	890421	890477	890533	0589	0645	0700	0756	0812	0868	0924	56
8	0980	1035	1091	1147	1203	1259	1314	1370	1426	1482	56
9	1537	1593	1649	1705	1760	1816	1872	1928	1983	2039	56
780	892095	892150	892206	892262	892317	892373	892429	892484	892540	892595	56
1	2651	2707	2762	2818	2873	2929	2985	3040	3096	3151	56
2	3207	3262	3318	3373	3429	3484	3540	3595	3651	3706	56
3	3762	3817	3873	3928	3984	4039	4094	4150	4205	4261	55
4	4316	4371	4427	4482	4538	4593	4648	4704	4759	4814	55
785	4870	4925	4980	5036	5091	5146	5201	5257	5312	5367	55
6	5423	5478	5533	5588	5644	5699	5754	5809	5864	5920	55
7	5975	6030	6085	6140	6195	6251	6306	6361	6416	6471	55
8	6526	6581	6636	6692	6747	6802	6857	6912	6967	7022	55
9	7077	7132	7187	7242	7297	7352	7407	7462	7517	7572	55
790	897627	897682	897737	897792	897847	897902	897957	898012	898067	898122	55
1	8176	8231	8286	8341	8396	8451	8506	8561	8615	8670	55
2	8725	8780	8835	8890	8944	8999	9054	9109	9164	9218	55
3	9273	9328	9383	9437	9492	9547	9602	9656	9711	9766	55
4	9821	9875	9930	9985	900039	900094	900149	900203	900258	900312	55
795	900367	900422	900476	900531	0586	0640	0695	0749	0804	0859	55
6	0913	0968	1022	1077	1131	1186	1240	1295	1349	1404	55
7	1458	1513	1567	1622	1676	1731	1785	1840	1894	1948	54
8	2003	2057	2112	2166	2221	2275	2329	2384	2438	2492	54
9	2547	2601	2655	2710	2764	2818	2873	2927	2981	3036	54
800	903090	903144	903199	903253	903307	903361	903416	903470	903524	903578	54
1	3633	3687	3741	3795	3849	3904	3958	4012	4066	4120	54
2	4174	4229	4283	4337	4391	4445	4499	4553	4607	4661	54
3	4716	4770	4824	4878	4932	4986	5040	5094	5148	5202	54
4	5256	5310	5364	5418	5472	5526	5580	5634	5688	5742	54
805	5796	5850	5904	5958	6012	6066	6119	6173	6227	6281	54
6	6335	6389	6443	6497	6551	6604	6658	6712	6766	6820	54
7	6874	6927	6981	7035	7089	7143	7196	7250	7304	7358	54
8	7411	7465	7519	7573	7626	7680	7734	7787	7841	7895	54
9	7949	8002	8056	8110	8163	8217	8270	8324	8378	8431	54
810	908485	908539	908592	908646	908699	908753	908807	908860	908914	908967	54
1	9021	9074	9128	9181	9235	9289	9342	9396	9449	9503	54
2	9556	9610	9663	9716	9770	9823	9877	9930	9984	910037	53
3	910091	910144	910197	910251	910304	910358	910411	910464	910518	0571	53
4	0624	0678	0731	0784	0838	0891	0944	0998	1051	1104	53
815	1158	1211	1264	1317	1371	1424	1477	1530	1584	1637	53
6	1690	1743	1797	1850	1903	1956	2009	2063	2116	2169	53
7	2222	2275	2328	2381	2435	2488	2541	2594	2647	2700	53
8	2753	2806	2859	2913	2966	3019	3072	3125	3178	3231	53
9	3284	3337	3390	3443	3496	3549	3602	3655	3708	3761	53
N.	0	1	2	3	4	5	6	7	8	9	D.

N.	0	1	2	3	4	5	6	7	8	9	D.
820	913814	913867	913920	913973	914026	914079	914132	914184	914237	914290	53
1	4343	4396	4449	4502	4555	4608	4660	4713	4766	4819	53
2	4872	4925	4977	5030	5083	5136	5189	5241	5294	5347	53
3	5400	5453	5505	5558	5611	5664	5716	5769	5822	5875	53
4	5927	5980	6033	6085	6138	6191	6243	6296	6349	6401	53
825	6454	6507	6559	6612	6664	6717	6770	6822	6875	6927	53
6	6980	7033	7085	7138	7190	7243	7295	7348	7400	7453	53
7	7506	7558	7611	7663	7716	7768	7820	7873	7925	7978	52
8	8030	8083	8135	8188	8240	8293	8345	8397	8450	8502	52
9	8555	8607	8659	8712	8764	8816	8869	8921	8973	9026	52
830	919078	919130	919183	919235	919287	919340	919392	919444	919496	919549	52
1	9601	9653	9706	9758	9810	9862	9914	9967	920019	920071	52
2	920123	920176	920228	920280	920332	920384	920436	920489	0541	0593	52
3	0645	0697	0749	0801	0853	0906	0958	1010	1062	1114	52
4	1166	1218	1270	1322	1374	1426	1478	1530	1582	1634	52
835	1686	1738	1790	1842	1894	1946	1998	2050	2102	2154	52
6	2206	2258	2310	2362	2414	2466	2518	2570	2622	2674	52
7	2725	2777	2829	2881	2933	2985	3037	3089	3140	3192	52
8	3244	3296	3348	3399	3451	3503	3555	3607	3658	3710	52
9	3762	3814	3865	3917	3969	4021	4072	4124	4176	4228	52
840	924279	924331	924383	924434	924486	924538	924589	924641	924693	924744	52
1	4796	4848	4899	4951	5003	5054	5106	5157	5209	5261	52
2	5312	5364	5415	5467	5518	5570	5621	5673	5725	5776	52
3	5828	5879	5931	5902	6034	6085	6137	6188	6240	6291	51
4	6342	6394	6445	6497	6548	6600	6651	6702	6754	6805	51
845	6857	6908	6959	7011	7062	7114	7165	7216	7268	7319	51
6	7370	7422	7473	7524	7576	7627	7678	7730	7781	7832	51
7	7883	7935	7986	8037	8088	8140	8191	8242	8293	8345	51
8	8396	8447	8498	8549	8601	8652	8703	8754	8805	8857	51
9	8908	8959	9010	9061	9112	9163	9215	9266	9317	9368	51
850	929419	929470	929521	929572	929623	929674	929725	929776	929827	929879	51
1	9930	9981	930032	930083	930134	930185	930236	930287	930338	930389	51
2	930440	930491	0542	0592	0643	0694	0745	0796	0847	0898	51
3	0949	1000	1051	1102	1153	1204	1254	1305	1356	1407	51
4	1458	1509	1560	1610	1661	1712	1763	1814	1865	1915	51
855	1966	2017	2068	2118	2169	2220	2271	2322	2372	2423	51
6	2474	2524	2575	2626	2677	2727	2778	2829	2879	2930	51
7	2981	3031	3082	3133	3183	3234	3285	3335	3386	3437	51
8	3487	3538	3589	3639	3690	3740	3791	3841	3892	3943	51
9	3993	4044	4094	4145	4195	4246	4296	4347	4397	4448	51
860	934498	934549	934599	934650	934700	934751	934801	934852	934902	934953	50
1	5003	5054	5104	5154	5205	5255	5306	5356	5406	5457	50
2	5507	5558	5608	5658	5709	5759	5809	5860	5910	5960	50
3	6011	6061	6111	6162	6212	6262	6313	6363	6413	6463	50
4	6514	6564	6614	6665	6715	6765	6815	6865	6916	6966	50
865	7016	7066	7117	7167	7217	7267	7317	7367	7418	7468	50
6	7518	7568	7618	7668	7718	7769	7819	7869	7919	7969	50
7	8019	8069	8119	8169	8219	8269	8320	8370	8420	8470	50
8	8520	8570	8620	8670	8720	8770	8820	8870	8920	8970	50
9	9020	9070	9120	9170	9220	9270	9320	9369	9419	9469	50
870	939519	939569	939619	939669	939719	939769	939819	939869	939918	939968	50
1	940018	940068	940118	940168	940218	940267	940317	940367	940417	940467	50
2	0516	0566	0616	0666	0716	0765	0815	0865	0915	0964	50
3	1014	1064	1114	1163	1213	1263	1313	1362	1412	1462	50
4	1511	1561	1611	1660	1710	1760	1809	1859	1909	1958	50
875	2008	2058	2107	2157	2207	2256	2306	2355	2405	2455	50
6	2504	2554	2603	2653	2702	2752	2801	2851	2901	2950	50
7	3000	3049	3099	3148	3198	3247	3297	3346	3396	3445	49
8	3495	3544	3593	3643	3692	3742	3791	3841	3890	3939	49
9	3989	4038	4088	4137	4186	4236	4285	4335	4384	4433	49
N.	0	1	2	3	4	5	6	7	8	9	D.

N.	0	1	2	3	4	5	6	7	8	9	D.
880	944483	944532	944581	944631	944680	944729	944779	944828	944877	944927	49
1	4976	5025	5074	5124	5173	5222	5272	5321	5370	5419	49
2	5469	5518	5567	5616	5665	5715	5764	5813	5862	5912	49
3	5961	6010	6059	6108	6157	6207	6256	6305	6354	6403	49
4	6452	6501	6551	6600	6649	6698	6747	6796	6845	6894	49
885	6943	6992	7041	7090	7140	7189	7238	7287	7336	7385	49
6	7434	7483	7532	7581	7630	7679	7728	7777	7826	7875	49
7	7924	7973	8022	8070	8119	8168	8217	8266	8315	8364	49
8	8413	8462	8511	8560	8609	8657	8706	8755	8804	8853	49
9	8902	8951	8999	9048	9097	9146	9195	9244	9292	9341	49
890	949390	949439	949488	949536	949585	949634	949683	949731	949780	949829	49
1	9878	9926	9975	950024	950073	950121	950170	950219	950267	950316	49
2	950365	950414	950462	0511	0560	0608	0657	0706	0754	0803	49
3	0851	0900	0949	0997	1046	1095	1143	1192	1240	1289	49
4	1338	1386	1435	1483	1532	1580	1629	1677	1726	1775	49
895	1823	1872	1920	1969	2017	2066	2114	2163	2211	2260	48
6	2308	2356	2405	2453	2502	2550	2599	2647	2696	2744	48
7	2792	2841	2889	2938	2986	3034	3083	3131	3180	3228	48
8	3276	3325	3373	3421	3470	3518	3566	3615	3663	3711	48
9	3760	3808	3856	3905	3953	4001	4049	4098	4146	4194	48
900	954243	954291	954339	954387	954435	954484	954532	954580	954628	954677	48
1	4725	4773	4821	4869	4918	4966	5014	5062	5110	5158	48
2	5207	5255	5303	5351	5399	5447	5495	5543	5592	5640	48
3	5688	5736	5784	5832	5880	5928	5976	6024	6072	6120	48
4	6168	6216	6265	6313	6361	6409	6457	6505	6553	6601	48
905	6649	6697	6745	6793	6840	6888	6936	6984	7032	7080	48
6	7128	7176	7224	7272	7320	7368	7416	7464	7512	7559	48
7	7607	7655	7703	7751	7799	7847	7894	7942	7990	8038	48
8	8086	8134	8181	8229	8277	8325	8373	8421	8468	8516	48
9	8564	8612	8659	8707	8755	8803	8850	8898	8946	8994	48
910	959041	959089	959137	959185	959232	959280	959328	959375	959423	959471	48
1	9518	9566	9614	9661	9709	9757	9804	9852	9900	9947	48
2	9995	960042	960090	960138	960185	960233	960280	960328	960376	960423	48
3	960471	0518	0566	0613	0661	0709	0756	0804	0851	0899	48
4	0946	0994	1041	1089	1136	1184	1231	1279	1326	1374	48
915	1421	1469	1516	1563	1611	1658	1706	1753	1801	1848	47
6	1895	1943	1990	2038	2085	2132	2180	2227	2275	2322	47
7	2369	2417	2464	2511	2559	2606	2653	2701	2748	2795	47
8	2843	2890	2937	2985	3032	3079	3126	3174	3221	3268	47
9	3316	3363	3410	3457	3504	3552	3599	3646	3693	3741	47
920	963788	963835	963882	963929	963977	964024	964071	964118	964165	964212	47
1	4260	4307	4354	4401	4448	4495	4542	4590	4637	4684	47
2	4731	4778	4825	4872	4919	4966	5013	5061	5108	5155	47
3	5202	5249	5296	5343	5390	5437	5484	5531	5578	5625	47
4	5672	5719	5766	5813	5860	5907	5954	6001	6048	6095	47
925	6142	6189	6236	6283	6329	6376	6423	6470	6517	6564	47
6	6611	6658	6705	6752	6799	6845	6892	6939	6986	7033	47
7	7080	7127	7173	7220	7267	7314	7361	7408	7454	7501	47
8	7548	7595	7642	7688	7735	7782	7829	7875	7922	7969	47
9	8016	8062	8109	8156	8203	8249	8296	8343	8390	8436	47
930	968483	968530	968576	968623	968670	968716	968763	968810	968856	968903	47
1	8950	8996	9043	9090	9136	9183	9229	9276	9323	9369	47
2	9416	9463	9509	9556	9602	9649	9695	9742	9789	9835	47
3	9882	9928	9975	970021	970068	970114	970161	970207	970254	970300	47
4	970347	970393	970440	0486	0533	0579	0626	0672	0719	0765	46
935	0812	0858	0904	0951	0997	1044	1090	1137	1183	1229	46
6	1276	1322	1369	1415	1461	1508	1554	1601	1647	1693	46
7	1740	1786	1832	1879	1925	1971	2018	2064	2110	2157	46
8	2203	2249	2295	2342	2388	2434	2481	2527	2573	2619	46
9	2666	2712	2758	2804	2851	2897	2943	2989	3035	3082	46
N.	0	1	2	3	4	5	6	7	8	9	D.

N.	0	1	2	3	4	5	6	7	8	9	D.
940	973128	973174	973220	973266	973313	973359	973405	973451	973497	973543	46
1	3590	3636	3682	3728	3774	3820	3866	3913	3959	4005	46
2	4051	4097	4143	4189	4235	4281	4327	4374	4420	4466	46
3	4512	4558	4604	4650	4696	4742	4788	4834	4880	4926	46
4	4972	5018	5064	5110	5156	5202	5248	5294	5340	5386	46
945	5432	5478	5524	5570	5616	5662	5707	5753	5799	5845	46
6	5891	5937	5983	6029	6075	6121	6167	6212	6258	6304	46
7	6350	6396	6442	6488	6533	6579	6625	6671	6717	6763	46
8	6808	6854	6900	6946	6992	7037	7083	7129	7175	7220	46
9	7266	7312	7358	7403	7449	7495	7541	7586	7632	7678	46
950	977724	977769	977815	977861	977906	977952	977998	978043	978089	978135	46
1	8181	8226	8272	8317	8363	8409	8454	8500	8546	8591	46
2	8637	8683	8728	8774	8819	8865	8911	8956	9002	9047	46
3	9093	9138	9184	9230	9275	9321	9366	9412	9457	9503	46
4	9548	9594	9639	9685	9730	9776	9821	9867	9912	9958	46
955	980003	980049	980094	980140	980185	980231	980276	980322	980367	980412	45
6	0458	0503	0549	0594	0640	0685	0730	0776	0821	0867	45
7	0912	0957	1003	1048	1093	1139	1184	1229	1275	1320	45
8	1366	1411	1456	1501	1547	1592	1637	1683	1728	1773	45
9	1819	1864	1909	1954	2000	2045	2090	2135	2181	2226	45
960	982271	982316	982362	982407	982452	982497	982543	982588	982633	982678	45
1	2723	2769	2814	2859	2904	2949	2994	3040	3085	3130	45
2	3175	3220	3265	3310	3356	3401	3446	3491	3536	3581	45
3	3626	3671	3716	3762	3807	3852	3897	3942	3987	4032	45
4	4077	4122	4167	4212	4257	4302	4347	4392	4437	4482	45
965	4527	4572	4617	4662	4707	4752	4797	4842	4887	4932	45
6	4977	5022	5067	5112	5157	5202	5247	5292	5337	5382	45
7	5426	5471	5516	5561	5606	5651	5696	5741	5786	5830	45
8	5875	5920	5965	6010	6055	6100	6144	6189	6234	6279	45
9	6324	6369	6413	6458	6503	6548	6593	6637	6682	6727	45
970	986772	986817	986861	986906	986951	986996	987040	987085	987130	987175	45
1	7219	7264	7309	7353	7398	7443	7488	7532	7577	7622	45
2	7666	7711	7756	7800	7845	7890	7934	7979	8024	8068	45
3	8113	8157	8202	8247	8291	8336	8381	8425	8470	8514	45
4	8559	8604	8648	8693	8737	8782	8826	8871	8916	8960	45
975	9005	9049	9094	9138	9183	9227	9272	9316	9361	9405	45
6	9450	9494	9539	9583	9628	9672	9717	9761	9806	9850	44
7	9395	9939	9983	990028	990072	990117	990161	990206	990250	990294	44
8	990339	990383	990428	0472	0516	0561	0605	0650	0694	0738	44
9	0783	0827	0871	0916	0960	1004	1049	1093	1137	1182	44
980	991226	991270	991315	991359	991403	991448	991492	991536	991580	991625	44
1	1669	1713	1758	1802	1846	1890	1935	1979	2023	2067	44
2	2111	2156	2200	2244	2288	2333	2377	2421	2465	2509	44
3	2554	2598	2642	2686	2730	2774	2819	2863	2907	2951	44
4	2995	3039	3083	3127	3172	3216	3260	3304	3348	3392	44
985	3436	3480	3524	3568	3613	3657	3701	3745	3789	3833	44
6	3877	3921	3965	4009	4053	4097	4141	4185	4229	4273	44
7	4317	4361	4405	4449	4493	4537	4581	4625	4669	4713	44
8	4757	4801	4845	4889	4933	4977	5021	5065	5108	5152	44
9	5196	5240	5284	5328	5372	5416	5460	5504	5547	5591	44
990	995635	995679	995723	995767	995811	995854	995898	995942	995986	996030	44
1	6074	6117	6161	6205	6249	6293	6337	6380	6424	6468	44
2	6512	6555	6599	6643	6687	6731	6774	6818	6862	6906	44
3	6949	6993	7037	7080	7124	7168	7212	7255	7299	7343	44
4	7386	7430	7474	7517	7561	7605	7648	7692	7736	7779	44
995	7823	7867	7910	7954	7998	8041	8085	8129	8172	8216	44
6	8259	8303	8347	8390	8434	8477	8521	8564	8608	8652	44
7	8695	8739	8782	8826	8869	8913	8956	9000	9043	9087	44
8	9131	9174	9218	9261	9305	9348	9392	9435	9479	9522	44
9	9565	9609	9652	9696	9739	9783	9826	9870	9913	9957	43
N.	0	1	2	3	4	5	6	7	8	9	D.

APPENDIX S

Demonstrations

Section 9.1

To prove that $\Sigma x = 0$.

Let $\quad x_1 = X_1 - \bar{X}, x_2 = X_2 - \bar{X}, \cdots, x_N = X_N - \bar{X}.$

Then $\quad \Sigma x = \Sigma(X - \bar{X})$

$\qquad = \Sigma X - N\bar{X}.$

But $\qquad \bar{X} = \dfrac{\Sigma X}{N}.$

Therefore, $\qquad \Sigma x = \Sigma X - N\dfrac{\Sigma X}{N} = 0.$

Section 9.2

To prove that $\bar{X} = \bar{X}_d + \dfrac{\Sigma d}{N}.$

$$\bar{X} = \frac{X_1 + X_2 + \cdots + X_N}{N}.$$

Adding and subtracting $\bar{X}_d$,

$$\bar{X} = \bar{X}_d + \frac{(X_1 - \bar{X}_d) + (X_2 - \bar{X}_d) + \cdots + (X_N - \bar{X}_d)}{N}.$$

But, by definition,

$$d_1 = X_1 - \bar{X}_d, d_2 = X_2 - \bar{X}_d, \cdots, d_N = X_N - \bar{X}_d.$$

Then

$$\bar{X} = \bar{X}_d + \frac{d_1 + d_2 + \cdots + d_N}{N}$$

$$= \bar{X}_d + \frac{\Sigma d}{N}.$$

If each item is weighted by its frequency, the expression is

$$\bar{X} = \bar{X}_d + \frac{\Sigma f d}{N}.$$

Section 9.3

To prove that $\overline{X} > G$ for a series of positive values not all the same.

X_1 and X_N are the smallest and largest values of the series. For these two values,

$$(X_1 - X_N)^2 > 0;$$
$$X_1^2 - 2X_1X_N + X_N^2 > 0.$$

Adding $4X_1X_N$ to both sides of the inequality gives

$$X_1^2 + 2X_1X_N + X_N^2 > 4X_1X_N.$$

Taking the square root, we have

$$X_1 + X_N > 2\sqrt{X_1X_N} \text{ and}$$
$$\frac{X_1 + X_N}{2} > \sqrt{X_1X_N}.$$

If X_1 and X_N are each replaced by $\dfrac{X_1 + X_N}{2}$, the value of $\overline{X}$ for the entire series is not changed. However, such a replacement *increases* the value of G, since $\dfrac{X_1 + X_N}{2} > \sqrt{X_1X_N}$ and the contribution of $\left(\dfrac{X_1 + X_N}{2}\right)^2$ to the geometric mean *exceeds* the original contribution of X_1X_N. Continually repeating this process for the smallest and largest remaining values results in continually increasing the value of G, which approaches $\overline{X}$, and equals it following the last substitution, since the individual values are then all the same.

Section 9.4

To prove that $G > H$ for a series of positive values not all the same.

X_1 and X_N are the smallest and largest values of the series. In the preceding section, it was shown that

$$X_1 + X_N > 2\sqrt{X_1X_N}.$$

Therefore,

$$\sqrt{X_1X_N}\,(X_1 + X_N) > 2X_1X_N \text{ and}$$
$$\sqrt{X_1X_N} > \frac{2X_1X_N}{X_1 + X_N}.$$

But $\dfrac{2X_1X_N}{X_1 + X_N} = \dfrac{2}{\dfrac{X_1 + X_N}{X_1X_N}} = \dfrac{2}{\dfrac{1}{X_1} + \dfrac{1}{X_N}}$, which is H.

If X_1 and X_N are each replaced by their harmonic mean, $\dfrac{2X_1X_N}{X_1 + X_N}$, the value of H for the entire series is unchanged.   However, such a replacement *decreases* the value of G, since $\dfrac{2X_1X_N}{X_1 + X_N} < \sqrt{X_1X_N}$ and the contribution of $\left(\dfrac{2X_1X_N}{X_1 + X_N}\right)^2$ to the geometric mean would be *less* than the contribution of X_1X_N.   Continually repeating this process for the smallest and largest remaining values results in continually decreasing the value of G, which approaches H, and equals it following the last substitution, since the individual values are then all the same.

Section 10.1

To prove that Σd^2 is smallest when $\bar{X}_d = \bar{X}$; that is, that Σx^2 is a minimum.   Where $x = X - \bar{X}$, $d = X - \bar{X}_d$, and $\bar{X}_d$ may be any designated value, which may or may not be $\bar{X}$.   Then

$$\Sigma d^2 = \Sigma(X - \bar{X}_d)^2,$$
$$= \Sigma X^2 - 2\bar{X}_d\Sigma X + N\bar{X}_d^2.$$

But $\bar{X} = \dfrac{\Sigma X}{N}$ and $\Sigma X = N\bar{X}$, so

$$\Sigma d^2 = \Sigma X^2 - 2\bar{X}_dN\bar{X} + N\bar{X}_d^2.$$

Adding and subtracting $N\bar{X}^2$ gives

$$\Sigma d^2 = \Sigma X^2 - N\bar{X}^2 + (N\bar{X}^2 - 2\bar{X}_dN\bar{X} + N\bar{X}_d^2),$$
$$= \Sigma X^2 - N\bar{X}^2 + N(\bar{X}^2 - 2\bar{X}_d\bar{X} + \bar{X}_d^2),$$
$$= \Sigma X^2 - N\bar{X}^2 + N(\bar{X} - \bar{X}_d)^2.$$

If $\bar{X}_d$ is either larger or smaller than $\bar{X}$, the third term, $N(\bar{X} - \bar{X}_d)^2$, is positive, and therefore Σd^2 is smallest when $\bar{X}_d = \bar{X}$, in which case $\Sigma d^2 = \Sigma x^2$.

Section 10.2

To show that $\sqrt{\dfrac{\Sigma x^2}{N}} = \sqrt{\dfrac{\Sigma d^2}{N} - \left(\dfrac{\Sigma d}{N}\right)^2}.$

Since $x = X - \bar{X},$

$$\sqrt{\dfrac{\Sigma x^2}{N}} = \sqrt{\dfrac{\Sigma(X - \bar{X})^2}{N}}$$

$$= \sqrt{\dfrac{\Sigma(X^2 - 2X\bar{X} + \bar{X}^2)}{N}}$$

$$= \sqrt{\dfrac{\Sigma X^2 - 2\bar{X}\Sigma X + N\bar{X}^2}{N}}.$$

But since $\dfrac{\Sigma X}{N} = \overline{X},$

$$\sqrt{\frac{\Sigma x^2}{N}} = \sqrt{\frac{\Sigma X^2}{N} - 2\overline{X}^2 + \overline{X}^2}$$

$$= \sqrt{\frac{\Sigma X^2}{N} - \overline{X}^2}$$

$$= \sqrt{\frac{\Sigma X^2}{N} - \left(\frac{\Sigma X}{N}\right)^2}.$$

By definition, $d = X - \overline{X}_d$, or $X = d + \overline{X}_d$.
Therefore:

$$\sqrt{\frac{\Sigma X^2}{N} - \left(\frac{\Sigma X}{N}\right)^2} = \sqrt{\frac{\Sigma(d + \overline{X}_d)^2}{N} - \left[\frac{\Sigma(d + \overline{X}_d)}{N}\right]^2}$$

$$= \sqrt{\frac{\Sigma(d^2 + 2d\overline{X}_d + \overline{X}_d^2)}{N} - \left(\frac{\Sigma d + N\overline{X}_d}{N}\right)^2}$$

$$= \sqrt{\frac{\Sigma d^2 + 2\overline{X}_d \Sigma d + N\overline{X}_d^2}{N} - \frac{(\Sigma d)^2 + 2N\overline{X}_d \Sigma d + N^2\overline{X}_d^2}{N^2}}$$

$$= \sqrt{\frac{\Sigma d^2}{N} + 2\overline{X}_d \frac{\Sigma d}{N} + \overline{X}_d^2 - \frac{(\Sigma d)^2}{N^2} - 2\overline{X}_d \frac{\Sigma d}{N} - \overline{X}_d^2}$$

$$= \sqrt{\frac{\Sigma d^2}{N} - \left(\frac{\Sigma d}{N}\right)^2}.$$

For a frequency distribution.

$$s = \sqrt{\frac{\Sigma f x^2}{N}}, \text{ and } \sqrt{\frac{\Sigma f x^2}{N}} = \sqrt{\frac{\Sigma f d^2}{N} - \left(\frac{\Sigma f d}{N}\right)^2}.$$

Or, with deviations in terms of class intervals,

$$\sqrt{\frac{\Sigma f x^2}{N}} = i \sqrt{\frac{\Sigma f(d')^2}{N} - \left(\frac{\Sigma f d'}{N}\right)^2}.$$

Section 10.3

To prove that $\pi_3 = \dfrac{\Sigma f(d')^3}{N} - 3\dfrac{\Sigma f d'}{N} \dfrac{\Sigma f(d')^2}{N} + 2\left(\dfrac{\Sigma f d'}{N}\right)^3.$

It was shown in Section 9.2 that

$$\overline{X} = \overline{X}_d + \frac{\Sigma d}{N}.$$

For any selected X value, say X_1, $\quad x_1 = X_1 - \bar{X} = X_1 - \bar{X}_d - \dfrac{\Sigma d}{N}$.

But $X_1 - \bar{X}_d = d_1$; therefore, $x_1 = d_1 - \dfrac{\Sigma d}{N}$.

Similarly, $\quad x_2 = d_2 - \dfrac{\Sigma d}{N}$, $\quad x_3 = d_3 - \dfrac{\Sigma d}{N}$, etc.

Thus, $\qquad \dfrac{\Sigma x^3}{N} = \dfrac{\Sigma\left(d - \dfrac{\Sigma d}{N}\right)^3}{N}$,

$$= \frac{\Sigma\left[d^3 - 3\dfrac{\Sigma d}{N}d^2 + 3\left(\dfrac{\Sigma d}{N}\right)^2 d - \left(\dfrac{\Sigma d}{N}\right)^3\right]}{N},$$

$$= \frac{\Sigma d^3 - 3\dfrac{\Sigma d}{N}\Sigma d^2 + 3\left(\dfrac{\Sigma d}{N}\right)^2\Sigma d - N\left(\dfrac{\Sigma d}{N}\right)^3}{N},$$

$$= \frac{\Sigma d^3}{N} - 3\frac{\Sigma d}{N}\frac{\Sigma d^2}{N} + 3\left(\frac{\Sigma d}{N}\right)^2\frac{\Sigma d}{N} - \left(\frac{\Sigma d}{N}\right)^3,$$

$$= \frac{\Sigma d^3}{N} - 3\frac{\Sigma d}{N}\frac{\Sigma d^2}{N} + 3\left(\frac{\Sigma d}{N}\right)^3 - \left(\frac{\Sigma d}{N}\right)^3,$$

$$= \frac{\Sigma d^3}{N} - 3\frac{\Sigma d}{N}\frac{\Sigma d^2}{N} + 2\left(\frac{\Sigma d}{N}\right)^3.$$

For a frequency distribution this becomes

$$\frac{\Sigma f x^3}{N} = \frac{\Sigma f d^3}{N} - 3\frac{\Sigma f d}{N}\frac{\Sigma f d^2}{N} + 2\left(\frac{\Sigma f d}{N}\right)^3$$

or, in terms of class intervals cubed,

$$\pi_3 = \frac{\Sigma f (d')^3}{N} - 3\frac{\Sigma f d'}{N}\frac{\Sigma f (d')^2}{N} + 2\left(\frac{\Sigma f d'}{N}\right)^3.$$

Section 12.1

The Least-Squares Criterion

The following discussion assumes that the distribution of chance errors follows the normal curve, and that the best central value from which to measure such accidental deviations is therefore that value which makes it most probable that the deviations are distributed normally.

Let a series of such deviations, or errors, and the interval within which they fall be designated by the following symbols:

x_1 is an item falling at the mid-point of a very small interval, Δx_1;
x_2 " " " " " " " " " " " " Δx_2;
.
.
.
x_N " " " " " " " " " " " " Δx_N.

Now the probability that a deviation will fall within a certain interval is

$$P = \frac{\text{Area of frequency curve within boundaries of that interval}}{\text{Area of entire frequency curve}}.$$

Thus the probability of obtaining an error x_1 which falls within the interval Δx_1 is approximately the ratio of the area of a rectangle, with base of Δx_1 and height the ordinate at the mid-point of the interval, to the area of the entire frequency curve.

If this curve is the normal curve, this probability is

$$\frac{i}{\sigma \sqrt{2\pi}} e^{-\frac{x_1^2}{2\sigma^2}} \Delta x_1,$$

since the expression for the ordinate of a normal curve as a ratio to the entire number of frequencies is $Y_c = \dfrac{i}{\sigma \sqrt{2\pi}} e^{-\frac{x^2}{2\sigma^2}}$.

The probability of obtaining errors x_2, x_3, etc., falling within specified intervals is similarly obtained.

The probability that several independent events will occur is the product of the individual probabilities of the separate events. Therefore, the probability that the particular *set* of errors will occur which we have assumed (that is, a normal distribution of errors) is as follows:

$$P = \left(\frac{i}{\sigma \sqrt{2\pi}} e^{-\frac{x_1^2}{2\sigma^2}} \Delta x_1 \right) \times \left(\frac{i}{\sigma \sqrt{2\pi}} e^{-\frac{x_2^2}{2\sigma^2}} \Delta x_2 \right)$$

$$\times \cdots \times \left(\frac{i}{\sigma \sqrt{2\pi}} e^{-\frac{x_N^2}{2\sigma^2}} \Delta x_N \right)$$

$$= \frac{i^N}{\sigma^N (2\pi)^{\frac{N}{2}}} e^{-\frac{x_1^2 + x_2^2 + \cdots + x_N^2}{2\sigma^2}} \times \Delta x_1 \times \Delta x_2 \times \cdots \times \Delta x_N.$$

Since any number raised to a negative power will be greatest when that exponent is least, P is greatest when $x_1^2 + x_2^2 + \cdots + x_N^2$ is least. Therefore, the probability that accidental deviations from some central value will follow the normal curve is greatest when the sum of the squared deviations from that central value is at a minimum.

Section 12.2

Derivation of the Normal Equations for a Straight Line Fitted by the Method of Least Squares

If Y_c is a trend, or computed, value, $Y - Y_c$ is a deviation from trend. To satisfy the least-squares criterion, $\Sigma(Y - Y_c)^2$ must be a minimum. Since the straight-line equation type is $Y_c = a + bX$,

$$\Sigma(Y - Y_c)^2 = \Sigma[Y - (a + bX)]^2 = \Sigma(Y - a - bX)^2.$$

Expanding, this expression becomes

$$\Sigma Y^2 - 2a\Sigma Y - 2b\Sigma XY + Na^2 + 2ab\Sigma X + b^2\Sigma X^2.\ldots\ldots(1)$$

If this expression is solved for a and b, we shall obtain the two normal equations. Rewriting expression (1) according to descending powers of a gives

$$Na^2 + 2a(b\Sigma X - \Sigma Y) + \Sigma Y^2 - 2b\Sigma XY + b^2\Sigma X^2.$$

This is a quadratic of the type $pm^2 + qm + r$, where p is N, m is a, q is $2(b\Sigma X - \Sigma Y)$, and r is $\Sigma Y^2 - 2b\Sigma XY + b^2\Sigma X^2$. If p is positive (as it must always be for statistical problems when $p = N$), such a quadratic has a minimum value when $m = \dfrac{-q}{2p}.$ Therefore.

$$a = \frac{-2(b\Sigma X - \Sigma Y)}{2N} = \frac{\Sigma Y - b\Sigma X}{N}\ldots\ldots\ldots\ldots(2)$$

Rewriting (2) gives

$$\Sigma Y = Na + b\Sigma X. \ldots\ , \text{ the first normal equation.}$$

Rearranging expression (1) according to descending powers of b gives

$$b^2\Sigma X^2 + 2b(a\Sigma X - \Sigma XY) + \Sigma Y^2 - 2a\Sigma Y + Na^2\ldots\ldots(3)$$

In this quadratic, p is ΣX^2, m is b, q is $2(a\Sigma X - \Sigma XY)$, and r is $\Sigma Y^2 - 2a\Sigma Y + Na^2$. Since ΣX^2 is positive, expression (3) will have a minimum value when $m = \dfrac{-q}{2p}$, so

$$b = \frac{-2(a\Sigma X - \Sigma XY)}{2\Sigma X^2} = \frac{\Sigma XY - a\Sigma X}{\Sigma X^2}\ldots\ldots\ldots\ldots(4)$$

Rewriting (4) gives

$$\Sigma XY = a\Sigma X + b\Sigma X^2 \ldots \ldots, \text{ the second normal equation.}$$

Section 13.1

Derivation of the Equations for Fitting Growth Curve of the Type $Y_c = k + ab^x$

Designating by n the number of years in each third of the data, the first equation (see Equation I, p. **266**) is:

$$\Sigma_1 Y = nk + a + ab + ab^2 + ab^3 + \cdots + ab^{(n-1)}$$
$$= nk + a[1 + b + b^2 + b^3 + \cdots + b^{(n-1)}].$$

If now the expression inside the brackets be multiplied by $\dfrac{b-1}{b-1}$, we have

$$\frac{[1 + b + b^2 + b^3 + \cdots + b^{(n-1)}](b-1)}{b-1} \quad\ldots\ldots\ldots\ldots\ldots\ldots\ldots(1)$$

$$= \frac{b + b^2 + b^3 + \cdots + b^{(n-1)} + b^n - 1 - b - b^2 - b^3 - \cdots - b^{(n-1)}}{b-1} \quad\ldots(2)$$

$$= \frac{b^n - 1}{b-1}.$$

The fourth term shown in the numerator of expression (2) is $b^{(n-1)}$. This follows from the fact that the next-to-the-last term within the brackets of expression (1) may also be designated as $b^{(n-2)}$; and $b^{(n-2)} \times b = b^{(n-1)}$. All three equations are obtained in a similar fashion. They are:

$$\text{I. } \Sigma_1 Y = nk + a\left(\frac{b^n - 1}{b-1}\right).$$

$$\text{II. } \Sigma_2 Y = nk + ab^n\left(\frac{b^n - 1}{b-1}\right).$$

$$\text{III. } \Sigma_3 Y = nk + ab^{2n}\left(\frac{b^n - 1}{b-1}\right).$$

Equations A, B, and C now are:

$$\text{A. } \Sigma_2 Y - \Sigma_1 Y = a\left(\frac{b^n - 1}{b-1}\right)(b^n - 1) = a\frac{(b^n - 1)^2}{b-1}.$$

$$\text{B. } \Sigma_3 Y - \Sigma_2 Y = ab^n\frac{(b^n - 1)^2}{b-1}.$$

$$C. \quad \frac{\Sigma_3 Y - \Sigma_2 Y}{\Sigma_2 Y - \Sigma_1 Y} = ab^n \frac{(b^n - 1)^2}{b - 1} \div a \frac{(b^n - 1)^2}{b - 1} = b^n.$$

Therefore, $b = \sqrt[n]{\dfrac{\Sigma_3 Y - \Sigma_2 Y}{\Sigma_2 Y - \Sigma_1 Y}}.$

Equation A gives us the formula for a:

$$\Sigma_2 Y - \Sigma_1 Y = a \frac{(b^n - 1)^2}{b - 1}.$$

$$a = (\Sigma_2 Y - \Sigma_1 Y) \frac{b - 1}{(b^n - 1)^2}.$$

From Equation I we find:

$$\Sigma_1 Y = nk + \left(\frac{b^n - 1}{b - 1} \right) a.$$

$$k = \frac{1}{n} \left[\Sigma_1 Y - \left(\frac{b^n - 1}{b - 1} \right) a \right].$$

Section 19.1

To prove that $\bar{Y}_c = \bar{Y}$.

$$Y_c = a + bX.$$
$$\Sigma Y_c = \Sigma(a + bX)$$
$$= Na + b\Sigma X.$$

But $Na + b\Sigma X = \Sigma Y$ (Normal equation I).

Therefore, $\Sigma Y_c = \Sigma Y$ ....(1)

$$\frac{\Sigma Y_c}{N} = \frac{\Sigma Y}{N}, \text{ and}$$

$$\bar{Y}_c = \bar{Y} \text{ ....(2)}$$

To prove that $\Sigma Y_c^2 = a\Sigma Y + b\Sigma XY$.

$$\Sigma Y_c^2 = \Sigma(a + bX)^2$$
$$= \Sigma(a^2 + 2abX + b^2 X^2)$$
$$= Na^2 + 2ab\Sigma X + b^2\Sigma X^2$$
$$= a(Na + b\Sigma X) + b(a\Sigma X + b\Sigma X^2).$$

But $Na + b\Sigma X = \Sigma Y$ (Normal equation I), and
$a\Sigma X + b\Sigma X^2 = \Sigma XY$ (Normal equation II).
Therefore,

$$\Sigma Y_c^2 = a\Sigma Y + b\Sigma XY \text{ ....(3)}$$

To prove that $\Sigma y_c^2 = \Sigma Y_c^2 - \bar{Y}\Sigma Y$.

By the procedure shown in footnote 3 of Chapter 21 for Σx^2 it may be shown that

$$\Sigma y^2 = \Sigma Y^2 - \bar{Y}\Sigma Y.$$

Similarly, it is true that $\Sigma y_c^2 = \Sigma Y_c^2 - \bar{Y}_c\Sigma Y_c$.

But $\bar{Y}_c = \bar{Y}$ (Equation 2) and $\Sigma Y_c = \Sigma Y$ (Equation 1).

Therefore, $\Sigma y_c^2 = \Sigma Y_c^2 - \bar{Y}\Sigma Y$ . . . . (4)

To prove that $\Sigma y_s^2 = \Sigma Y^2 - \Sigma Y_c^2$.

$$\Sigma y_s^2 = \Sigma(Y - Y_c)^2$$
$$= \Sigma Y^2 - 2\Sigma Y Y_c + \Sigma Y_c^2.$$

But $Y_c = a + bX$; hence, $\Sigma Y Y_c = \Sigma[Y(a + bX)] = \Sigma(aY + bXY)$
$$= a\Sigma Y + b\Sigma XY.$$

Now $a\Sigma Y + b\Sigma XY = \Sigma Y_c^2$ (Equation 3).

Therefore, $\Sigma y_s^2 = \Sigma Y^2 - 2\Sigma Y_c^2 + \Sigma Y_c^2$
$$= \Sigma Y^2 - \Sigma Y_c^2 . . . . (5)$$

To prove that $\Sigma y_c^2 = b\Sigma xy$.

$$\Sigma y_c^2 = \Sigma(bx)^2 = b^2\Sigma x^2 = b\frac{\Sigma xy}{\Sigma x^2}\Sigma x^2 = b\Sigma xy . . . . (6)$$

To prove that $\Sigma y_s^2 = \Sigma y^2 - \Sigma y_c^2$.
$$\Sigma y_s^2 = \Sigma Y^2 - \Sigma Y_c^2. \quad \text{(Equation 5)}$$

But

$$\Sigma Y^2 = \Sigma y^2 + \bar{Y}\Sigma Y, \text{ and}$$
$$\Sigma Y_c^2 = \Sigma y_c^2 + \bar{Y}\Sigma Y. \quad \text{(Equation 4)}$$

Therefore,

$$\Sigma y_s^2 = (\Sigma y^2 + \bar{Y}\Sigma Y) - (\Sigma y_c^2 + \bar{Y}\Sigma Y)$$
$$= \Sigma y^2 - \Sigma y_c^2 . . . . (7)$$

Section 19.2

Derivation of Constants for Straight-Line Equation when Origin Is at $\bar{X}$, $\bar{Y}$

The normal equations for fitting a straight line by the method of least squares are

$$\Sigma Y = Na + b\Sigma X;$$
$$\Sigma XY = a\Sigma X + b\Sigma X^2.$$

If the origin be taken at $\bar{X}, \bar{Y}$ instead of 0,0, we have

$$\Sigma y = Na + b\Sigma x;$$
$$\Sigma xy = a\Sigma x + b\Sigma x^2.$$
$$\text{But } \Sigma y = 0, \text{ and } \Sigma x = 0.$$
$$\text{Therefore, } a = 0, \text{ and } b = \frac{\Sigma xy}{\Sigma v^2}.$$

The estimating equation becomes $y_c = bx$ instead of $Y_c = a + bX$.

Section 19.3

To prove that $\dfrac{\Sigma y_c^2}{\Sigma y^2} = \dfrac{(\Sigma xy)^2}{\Sigma x^2 \Sigma y^2}$.

Since $y_c = bx$, we may write

$$\frac{\Sigma y_c^2}{\Sigma y^2} = \frac{\Sigma (bx)^2}{\Sigma y^2} = \frac{b^2 \Sigma x^2}{\Sigma y^2}.$$

From the second normal equation, $b = \dfrac{\Sigma xy}{\Sigma x^2}$.   Therefore,

$$\frac{\Sigma y_c^2}{\Sigma y^2} = \frac{\left(\dfrac{\Sigma xy}{\Sigma x^2}\right)^2 \Sigma x^2}{\Sigma y^2} = \frac{(\Sigma xy)^2}{\Sigma x^2 \Sigma y^2}.$$

Section 19.4

To prove that $\dfrac{\Sigma xy}{N s_x s_y} = \dfrac{N\Sigma XY - (\Sigma X)(\Sigma Y)}{\sqrt{[N\Sigma X^2 - (\Sigma X)^2][N\Sigma Y^2 - (\Sigma Y)^2]}}$.

$$\Sigma xy = \Sigma[(X - \bar{X})(Y - \bar{Y})] = \Sigma(XY - \bar{X}Y - X\bar{Y} + \bar{X}\bar{Y}),$$
$$= \Sigma XY - \bar{X}\Sigma Y - \bar{Y}\Sigma X + N\bar{X}\bar{Y}$$
$$= \Sigma XY - N\bar{X}\bar{Y} - N\bar{X}\bar{Y} + N\bar{X}\bar{Y}$$
$$= \Sigma XY - N\bar{X}\bar{Y}.$$

$$s_x = \sqrt{\frac{\Sigma X^2}{N} - \left(\frac{\Sigma X}{N}\right)^2}, \text{ and } s_y = \sqrt{\frac{\Sigma Y^2}{N} - \left(\frac{\Sigma Y}{N}\right)^2}.$$

Therefore,

$$\frac{\Sigma xy}{N s_X s_Y} = \frac{\Sigma XY - N\bar{X}\bar{Y}}{N\sqrt{\frac{\Sigma X^2}{N} - \left(\frac{\Sigma X}{N}\right)^2}\sqrt{\frac{\Sigma Y^2}{N} - \left(\frac{\Sigma Y}{N}\right)^2}}$$

$$= \frac{N(\Sigma XY - N\bar{X}\bar{Y})}{\left[N\sqrt{\frac{\Sigma X^2}{N} - \left(\frac{\Sigma X}{N}\right)^2}\right]\left[N\sqrt{\frac{\Sigma Y^2}{N} - \left(\frac{\Sigma Y}{N}\right)^2}\right]}$$

$$= \frac{N\Sigma XY - (\Sigma X)(\Sigma Y)}{\sqrt{[N\Sigma X^2 - (\Sigma X)^2][N\Sigma Y^2 - (\Sigma Y)^2]}}.$$

Section 19.5

Given that $X_1, X_2, \cdots, X_N$ can take values only of the integers 1 through N, without duplication or omission, and that the same is true of $Y_1, Y_2, \cdots, Y_N$.

To prove that $r_{\text{rank}} = 1 - \dfrac{6\Sigma D^2}{N(N^2 - 1)}$.

Paralleling the proof given in Section 24.4 for arithmetic means, it may be shown that

$$s_D^2 = s_X^2 + s_Y^2 - 2r s_X s_Y,$$

where $D = X - Y$. From this relationship it follows that

$$r = \frac{s_X^2 + s_Y^2 - \dfrac{\Sigma D^2}{N}}{2 s_X s_Y}.$$

But $\Sigma X^2 = \Sigma Y^2$ when we are dealing with ranks. Therefore,

$$r_{\text{rank}} = \frac{2 s_X^2 - \dfrac{\Sigma D^2}{N}}{2 s_X^2} = 1 - \frac{\Sigma D^2}{2 N s_X^2}.$$

Now ΣX is the sum of the first N natural numbers, or $\dfrac{N(N + 1)}{2}$;

$$\bar{X} = \frac{N + 1}{2},$$

and ΣX^2 is the sum of the squares of the first N natural numbers, or $\dfrac{N(N + 1)(2N + 1)}{6}$. Therefore,

$$Ns_x^2 = \Sigma(X - \bar{X})^2 = \Sigma X^2 - \bar{X}\Sigma X,$$
$$= \frac{N(N + 1)(2N + 1)}{6} - \frac{N + 1}{2} \cdot \frac{N(N + 1)}{2},$$
$$= \frac{2N(N + 1)(2N + 1) - 3N(N + 1)^2}{12},$$
$$= \frac{N(N^2 - 1)}{12}.$$

Substituting in the expression for r, we have

$$r_{rank} = 1 - \frac{\Sigma D^2}{\dfrac{N(N^2 - 1)}{6}} = 1 - \frac{6\Sigma D^2}{N(N^2 - 1)}.$$

Section 20.1

The point of diminishing absolute returns is the highest point in the total returns curve. At this point the slope is zero. The slope of a curve at any point may be found by taking the first derivative of the equation. The first derivative of the equation $Y_c = a + bX + cX^2 + dX^3$ is

$$\frac{dY_c}{dX} = b + 2cX + 3dX^2.$$

Setting $\dfrac{dY_c}{dX} = 0$, we have $X = \dfrac{-c \pm \sqrt{c^2 - 3bd}}{3d}$.

For the total returns equation $Y_c = 890.32 + 78.264X + 20.324X^2 - 4.4649X^3$, the above equation yields $X = -1.337$ and 4.371. When the slope is zero, we have a maximum or a minimum point. Only positive values of X are of interest, and inspection of Chart 20.3 indicates that a maximum is reached when X is close to 4. Or, if the reader will compute Y_c values in the neighborhood of $X = -1.337$ and $X = 4.371$, he will discover that the former is a minimum and the latter a maximum. When $X = 4.371$, the computed total returns $Y_c = 1,247.85$. The point of diminishing total returns is reached when the input of nitrogen is 4.371 per cent. At this point the estimated yield is 1,247.85 pounds.

The point of diminishing marginal returns is the point of inflection in the curve. It is the point where the change in the slope is zero. The change in the slope is the second derivative of the estimating equation.

Thus,

$$\frac{d^2Y_c}{dX^2} = 2c + 6dX.$$

Setting $\frac{d^2Y_c}{dX^2} = 0$, we have $X = -\frac{c}{3d}$.

For the total returns equation, the point of inflection is $X = 1.517$. Thus the point of diminishing marginal returns is reached when the input of nitrogen is 1.517 per cent. At this point the estimated yield is $Y_c = 1{,}040.23$ pounds.

Section 21.1

Proof that

$$\left(\frac{r_{12} - r_{13}r_{23}}{\sqrt{1 - r_{13}^2}\,\sqrt{1 - r_{23}^2}}\right)^2 = \frac{\Sigma x_{c1.23}^2 - \Sigma x_{c1.3}^2}{\Sigma x_1^2 - \Sigma x_{c1.3}^2}.$$

A demonstration for the other formulas of these types would proceed along similar lines.

If $r_{12.3} = \dfrac{r_{12} - r_{13}r_{23}}{\sqrt{1 - r_{13}^2}\,\sqrt{1 - r_{23}^2}}$, ... (1)

$$r_{12.3}^2 = \frac{r_{12}^2 - 2r_{12}r_{13}r_{23} + r_{13}^2 r_{23}^2}{1 - r_{13}^2 - r_{23}^2 + r_{13}^2 r_{23}^2}.$$

But $r_{12}^2 = \dfrac{(\Sigma x_1 x_2)^2}{\Sigma x_1^2 \Sigma x_2^2}$, $r_{12} = \dfrac{\Sigma x_1 x_2}{\sqrt{\Sigma x_1^2 \Sigma x_2^2}}$, and similar formulas obtain for the other r's. Therefore:

$$r_{12.3}^2 = \frac{\dfrac{(\Sigma x_1 x_2)^2}{\Sigma x_1^2 \Sigma x_2^2} - 2\left[\dfrac{\Sigma x_1 x_2}{\sqrt{\Sigma x_1^2 \Sigma x_2^2}} \times \dfrac{\Sigma x_1 x_3}{\sqrt{\Sigma x_1^2 \Sigma x_3^2}} \times \dfrac{\Sigma x_2 x_3}{\sqrt{\Sigma x_2^2 \Sigma x_3^2}}\right] + \left[\dfrac{(\Sigma x_1 x_3)^2}{\Sigma x_1^2 \Sigma x_3^2} \times \dfrac{(\Sigma x_2 x_3)^2}{\Sigma x_2^2 \Sigma x_3^2}\right]}{1 - \dfrac{(\Sigma x_1 x_3)^2}{\Sigma x_1^2 \Sigma x_3^2} - \dfrac{(\Sigma x_2 x_3)^2}{\Sigma x_2^2 \Sigma x_3^2} + \left[\dfrac{(\Sigma x_1 x_3)^2}{\Sigma x_1^2 \Sigma x_3^2} \times \dfrac{(\Sigma x_2 x_3)^2}{\Sigma x_2^2 \Sigma x_3^2}\right]}$$

Multiplying numerator and denominator by $\Sigma x_1^2 \Sigma x_2^2 (\Sigma x_3^2)^2$, this simplifies to the following equation:

$$r_{12.3}^2 = \frac{(\Sigma x_3^2)^2 (\Sigma x_1 x_2)^2 - 2\Sigma x_3^2 \Sigma x_1 x_2 \Sigma x_1 x_3 \Sigma x_2 x_3 + (\Sigma x_1 x_3)^2 (\Sigma x_2 x_3)^2}{\Sigma x_1^2 \Sigma x_2^2 (\Sigma x_3^2)^2 - \Sigma x_2^2 \Sigma x_3^2 (\Sigma x_1 x_3)^2 - \Sigma x_1^2 \Sigma x_3^2 (\Sigma x_2 x_3)^2 + (\Sigma x_1 x_3)^2 (\Sigma x_2 x_3)^2} . \quad (2)$$

We know that $r_{12.3}^2 = \dfrac{\Sigma x_{c1.23}^2 - \Sigma x_{c1.3}^2}{\Sigma x_1^2 - \Sigma x_{c1.3}^2}$ . . . . (3)

But $\Sigma x_{c1.3}^2 = b_{13} \Sigma x_1 x_3 = \dfrac{\Sigma x_1 x_3}{\Sigma x_3^2} \Sigma x_1 x_3 = \dfrac{(\Sigma x_1 x_3)^2}{\Sigma x_3^2}$.

Also, $\Sigma x_{c1.23}^2 = b_{12.3}\Sigma x_1 x_2 + b_{13.2}\Sigma x_1 x_3.$

Now, the normal equations for obtaining $b_{12.3}$ and $b_{13.2}$ are:

$$\text{II. } \Sigma x_1 x_2 = b_{12.3}\Sigma x_2^2 + b_{13.2}\Sigma x_2 x_3;$$

$$\text{III. } \Sigma x_1 x_3 = b_{12.3}\Sigma x_2 x_3 + b_{13.2}\Sigma x_3^2.$$

In order to solve for $b_{13.2}$, we may multiply Equation II by $\Sigma x_2 x_3$, and Equation III by Σx_2^2, and subtract Equation II from Equation III. Thus,

II. $\qquad \Sigma x_1 x_2 \Sigma x_2 x_3 = b_{12.3}\Sigma x_2^2 \Sigma x_2 x_3 + b_{13.2}(\Sigma x_2 x_3)^2$

III. $\qquad \dfrac{\Sigma x_1 x_3 \Sigma x_2^2 = b_{12.3}\Sigma x_2^2 \Sigma x_2 x_3 + b_{13.2}\Sigma x_2^2 \Sigma x_3^2}{}$

$$\Sigma x_1 x_3 \Sigma x_2^2 - \Sigma x_1 x_2 \Sigma x_2 x_3 = b_{13.2}\Sigma x_2^2 \Sigma x_3^2 - b_{13.2}(\Sigma x_2 x_3)^2$$

$$b_{13.2} = \frac{\Sigma x_1 x_3 \Sigma x_2^2 - \Sigma x_1 x_2 \Sigma x_2 x_3}{\Sigma x_2^2 \Sigma x_3^2 - (\Sigma x_2 x_3)^2}.$$

In a similar fashion, we may solve for $b_{12.3}$. This involves multiplying Equation II by Σx_3^2 and Equation III by $\Sigma x_2 x_3$. By such a process we find that

$$b_{12.3} = \frac{\Sigma x_1 x_3 \Sigma x_2 x_3 - \Sigma x_1 x_2 \Sigma x_3^2}{(\Sigma x_2 x_3)^2 - \Sigma x_2^2 \Sigma x_3^2}.$$

Substituting these expressions for $b_{13.2}$ and $b_{12.3}$ in the equation for $\Sigma x_{c1.23}^2$, we have

$$\Sigma x_{c1.23}^2 = \frac{\Sigma x_1 x_3 \Sigma x_2 x_3 - \Sigma x_1 x_2 \Sigma x_3^2}{(\Sigma x_2 x_3)^2 - \Sigma x_2^2 \Sigma x_3^2}\,\Sigma x_1 x_2 + \frac{\Sigma x_1 x_3 \Sigma x_2^2 - \Sigma x_1 x_2 \Sigma x_2 x_3}{\Sigma x_2^2 \Sigma x_3^2 - (\Sigma x_2 x_3)^2}\,\Sigma x_1 x_3.$$

This simplifies to

$$\Sigma x_{c1.23}^2 = \frac{(\Sigma x_1 x_3)^2 \Sigma x_2^2 + (\Sigma x_1 x_2)^2 \Sigma x_3^2 - 2\Sigma x_1 x_2 \Sigma x_1 x_3 \Sigma x_2 x_3}{\Sigma x_2^2 \Sigma x_3^2 - (\Sigma x_2 x_3)^2}.$$

Now substituting our expressions for $\Sigma x_{c1.23}^2$ and $\Sigma x_{c1.3}^2$ in Formula (3), we have

$$r_{12.3}^2 = \frac{\dfrac{(\Sigma x_1 x_3)^2 \Sigma x_2^2 + (\Sigma x_1 x_2)^2 \Sigma x_3^2 - 2\Sigma x_1 x_2 \Sigma x_1 x_3 \Sigma x_2 x_3}{\Sigma x_2^2 \Sigma x_3^2 - (\Sigma x_2 x_3)^2} - \dfrac{(\Sigma x_1 x_3)^2}{\Sigma x_3^2}}{\Sigma x_1^2 - \dfrac{(\Sigma x_1 x_3)^2}{\Sigma x_3^2}}.$$

Expanding and simplifying, this expression becomes Equation (2). Therefore,

$$\left(\frac{r_{12} - r_{13}r_{23}}{\sqrt{1 - r_{13}^2}\,\sqrt{1 - r_{23}^2}}\right)^2 = \frac{\Sigma x_{c1.23}^2 - \Sigma x_{c1.3}^2}{\Sigma x_1^2 - \Sigma x_{c1.3}^2}.$$

Section 24.1

To prove that $\dfrac{\bar{X}_1 + \bar{X}_2 + \cdots + \bar{X}_K}{K} = \bar{X}_\wp$, when $N_1 = N_2 = \cdots = N_K = N$.

$$\frac{\bar{X}_1 + \bar{X}_2 + \cdots + \bar{X}_K}{K} = \frac{\dfrac{\Sigma X_1}{N_1} + \dfrac{\Sigma X_2}{N_2} + \cdots + \dfrac{\Sigma X_K}{N_K}}{K},$$

$$= \frac{\Sigma X_1 + \Sigma X_2 + \cdots + \Sigma X_K}{NK}.$$

Each random sample of N items contains $\dfrac{N}{\wp}$ of the population, and each item will occur $\dfrac{N}{\wp} K$ times. Therefore,

$$\frac{\Sigma X_1 + \Sigma X_2 + \cdots + \Sigma X_K}{NK} = \frac{\dfrac{N}{\wp} K \overset{\wp}{\underset{1}{\Sigma}} X}{NK},$$

where $\overset{\wp}{\underset{1}{\Sigma}}$ indicates a summation over the items in the population.

$$\frac{\dfrac{N}{\wp} K \overset{\wp}{\underset{1}{\Sigma}} X}{NK} = \frac{1}{\wp} \overset{\wp}{\underset{1}{\Sigma}} X,$$

$$= \bar{X}_\wp.$$

Section 24.2

To prove that $\sigma_{\bar{x}} = \dfrac{\sigma}{\sqrt{N}}$, when $N_1 = N_2 = \cdots = N_K = N$.

The scheme of the random samples appears as follows:

Item	Sample 1	Sample 2	Sample 3
a	X_{a1}	X_{a2}	X_{a3}
b	X_{b1}	X_{b2}	X_{b3}
c	X_{c1}	X_{c2}	X_{c3}
$\cdot$	$\cdot$	$\cdot$	$\cdot$
$\cdot$	$\cdot$	$\cdot$	$\cdot$
$\cdot$	$\cdot$	$\cdot$	$\cdot$
N	X_{N1}	X_{N2}	X_{N3}

There are K samples. The individual items are replaced after each sample has been drawn.

We shall use

$\overset{K}{\underset{1}{\Sigma}}$ to indicate a summation over the K samples;

$\overset{\wp}{\underset{1}{\Sigma}}$ to indicate a summation over the items in the population;

Σ to indicate a summation over a sample—over a particular sample if a subscript follows X; thus, ΣX_1 is the sum of the X values in sample 1; and

x to mean $X - \overline{X}_\wp$, a usage of x employed only in this proof.

The deviations of the items from the population mean are $x_{a1} = X_{a1} - \overline{X}_\wp$, $x_{b1} = X_{b1} - X_\wp$, $\cdots$, $x_{N1} = X_{N1} - \overline{X}_\wp$, $x_{a2} = X_{a2} - \overline{X}_\wp$, etc. We can therefore write the various items as $\overline{X}_\wp + x_{a1}$, $\overline{X}_\wp + x_{b1}$, $\cdots$, $\overline{X}_\wp + x_{N1}$, $\overline{X}_\wp + x_{a2}$, etc.

$$\text{For Sample 1: } \Sigma X_1 = N\overline{X}_\wp + \Sigma x_1,$$
$$\text{For Sample 2: } \Sigma X_2 = N\overline{X}_\wp + \Sigma x_2,$$
$$\text{and so forth,}$$

where $\Sigma x_1 \neq 0$, $\Sigma x_2 \neq 0$, etc., since $x = X - \overline{X}_\wp$.

Adding a constant to (or subtracting a constant from) a series of values does not alter the value of the standard deviation of those values, so that

$$\sigma_{\Sigma X} = \sigma_{\Sigma x}.$$

For the K samples,

$$\sigma_{\Sigma x}^2 = \frac{\overset{K}{\underset{1}{\Sigma}}(\Sigma x)^2}{K} - \left[\frac{\overset{K}{\underset{1}{\Sigma}}(\Sigma x)}{K}\right]^2,$$

$$= \frac{\overset{K}{\underset{1}{\Sigma}}(\Sigma x)^2}{K},$$

since

$$\overset{K}{\underset{1}{\Sigma}}(\Sigma x) = \Sigma x_1 + \Sigma x_2 + \cdots + \Sigma x_K = 0,$$

and

$$K\sigma_{\Sigma x}^2 = \overset{K}{\underset{1}{\Sigma}}(\Sigma x)^2 = \overset{K}{\underset{1}{\Sigma}}(x_a + x_b + x_c + \cdots + x_N)^2.$$

For any one sample,

$$(x_a + x_b + x_c + \cdots + x_N)^2 = x_a^2 + x_ax_b + x_ax_c + \cdots + x_ax_N$$
$$+ x_ax_b + x_b^2 + x_bx_c + \cdots + x_bx_N$$
$$+ x_ax_c + x_bx_c + x_c^2 + \cdots + x_cx_N$$
$$+ \cdots$$
$$+ x_ax_N + x_bx_N + x_cx_N + \cdots + x_N^2,$$
$$= \Sigma x_i^2 + 2\Sigma x_ix_j,$$

where x_i represents any item and $x_i x_j$ represents the product resulting from each combination of two different items. Therefore, for the K samples,

$$K\sigma^2_{\Sigma x} = \sum_1^K (\Sigma x_i^2 + 2\Sigma x_i x_j),$$

$$= \sum_1^K (\Sigma x_i^2) + 2\sum_1^K (\Sigma x_i x_j).$$

Each sample of N items contains $\dfrac{N}{\mathcal{P}}$ of the population, and each item will occur in $\dfrac{N}{\mathcal{P}}$ of the samples, or $\dfrac{N}{\mathcal{P}} K$ times. If a given item (x_i) occurs in $\dfrac{N}{\mathcal{P}}$ of the samples, a second item (x_j) will occur in $\dfrac{N-1}{\mathcal{P}-1}$ of the samples in which the first item occurs, and both items will occur in $\dfrac{N}{\mathcal{P}} \cdot \dfrac{N-1}{\mathcal{P}-1}$ of the samples, or $\dfrac{N(N-1)}{\mathcal{P}(\mathcal{P}-1)} K$ times. Thus, each $x_i x_j$ will occur $\dfrac{N(N-1)}{\mathcal{P}(\mathcal{P}-1)} K$ times.

Therefore,

$$K\sigma^2_{\Sigma x} = \frac{N}{\mathcal{P}} K \sum_1^{\mathcal{P}} x_i^2 + 2 \frac{N(N-1)}{\mathcal{P}(\mathcal{P}-1)} K \sum_1^{\mathcal{P}} x_i x_j$$

and

$$\sigma^2_{\Sigma x} = \frac{N}{\mathcal{P}} \sum_1^{\mathcal{P}} x_i^2 + 2 \frac{N(N-1)}{\mathcal{P}(\mathcal{P}-1)} \sum_1^{\mathcal{P}} x_i x_j.$$

By a development similar to that shown above for $(\Sigma x)^2$ for one sample, we have

$$2\sum_1^{\mathcal{P}} x_i x_j = \left(\sum_1^{\mathcal{P}} x_i\right)^2 - \sum_1^{\mathcal{P}} x_i^2.$$

But $\sum_1^{\mathcal{P}} x_i = 0$. Therefore, $2\sum_1^{\mathcal{P}} x_i x_j = -\sum_1^{\mathcal{P}} x_i^2$, and

$$\sigma^2_{\Sigma x} = \frac{N}{\mathcal{P}} \sum_1^{\mathcal{P}} x_i^2 - \frac{N(N-1)}{\mathcal{P}(\mathcal{P}-1)} \sum_1^{\mathcal{P}} x_i^2,$$

$$= \frac{N}{\mathcal{P}} \mathcal{P}\sigma^2 - \frac{N(N-1)}{\mathcal{P}(\mathcal{P}-1)} \mathcal{P}\sigma^2,$$

$$= N\sigma^2 - \frac{N(N-1)}{\mathcal{P}-1} \sigma^2,$$

$$= N\sigma^2\left(1 - \frac{N-1}{\mathcal{P}-1}\right),$$

$$= N\sigma^2\left[\frac{(\mathcal{P}-1)-(N-1)}{\mathcal{P}-1}\right],$$

$$= N\sigma^2\frac{\mathcal{P}-N}{\mathcal{P}-1}.$$

$$\sigma_{\Sigma x} = \sqrt{N}\,\sigma\,\sqrt{\frac{\mathcal{P}-N}{\mathcal{P}-1}}.$$

Since each sample consists of N items, each deviation of a sample sum from the arithmetic mean of the sample sums is N times as large as each corresponding deviation of a sample mean from the arithmetic mean of the sample means, $\overline{X}_\mathcal{P}$, and each squared deviation of a sample sum is N^2 times the squared deviation of each sample mean.   Therefore, the standard deviation of the sample sums is N times the standard deviation of the sample means.   Dividing each side of the last equation by N gives

$$\sigma_{\bar{x}} = \frac{\sigma}{\sqrt{N}}\sqrt{\frac{\mathcal{P}-N}{\mathcal{P}-1}}.$$

If $\mathcal{P}$ is infinite, or, if $\mathcal{P}$ is finite but large in relation to N, so that the value of $\sqrt{\dfrac{\mathcal{P}-N}{\mathcal{P}-1}}$ is effectively 1, the expression may be written

$$\sigma_{\bar{x}} = \frac{\sigma}{\sqrt{N}}.$$

Section 24.3

To show that $\dfrac{\hat{\sigma}_1^2 + \hat{\sigma}_2^2 + \cdots + \hat{\sigma}_K^2}{K} = \sigma^2$, when $N_1 = N_2 = \cdots = N_K = N$.

The variation of a single sample from $\overline{X}_\mathcal{P}$ is $\sum_1^N (X - \overline{X}_\mathcal{P})^2$.   This may be divided into two parts

$$\sum_1^N (X - \overline{X}_\mathcal{P})^2 = \sum_1^N [(X - \overline{X}) + (\overline{X} - \overline{X}_\mathcal{P})]^2,$$

where $\overline{X}$ represents the mean of a sample,

$$= \sum_1^N [(X - \overline{X})^2 + 2(X - \overline{X})(\overline{X} - \overline{X}_\mathcal{P}) + (\overline{X} - \overline{X}_\mathcal{P})^2],$$

$$= \sum_1^N (X - \overline{X})^2 + 2(\overline{X} - \overline{X}_\mathcal{P})\sum_1^N (X - \overline{X}) + N(\overline{X} - \overline{X}_\mathcal{P})^2.$$

But $\sum_1^N (X - \bar{X}) = 0$, and, therefore,

$$\sum_1^N (X - \bar{X}_\wp)^2 = \sum_1^N (X - \bar{X})^2 + N(\bar{X} - \bar{X}_\wp)^2.$$

Summing for the K samples,

$$\sum_1^K \left[\sum_1^N (X - \bar{X}_\wp)^2 \right] = \sum_1^K \left[\sum_1^N (X - \bar{X})^2 \right] + \sum_1^K [N(\bar{X} - \bar{X}_\wp)^2].$$

Each random sample of N items contains $\dfrac{N}{\wp}$ of the population, and each item will occur $\dfrac{N}{\wp} K$ times. Considering each of the three parts of the preceding expression separately, we have

$$\sum_1^K \left[\sum_1^N (X - \bar{X}_\wp)^2 \right] = \frac{N}{\wp} K \sum_1^\wp (X - \bar{X}_\wp)^2,$$

$$= NK \frac{\sum_1^\wp (X - \bar{X}_\wp)^2}{\wp},$$

$$= NK\sigma^2.$$

$$\sum_1^K \left[\sum_1^N (X - \bar{X})^2 \right] = \sum_1^K (Ns^2),$$

$$= N \sum_1^K s^2,$$

where s^2 is the variance, $s^2 = \dfrac{\sum x^2}{N}$, of a sample.

$$\sum_1^K [N(\bar{X} - \bar{X}_\wp)^2] = N \sum_1^K (\bar{X} - \bar{X}_\wp)^2,$$

$$= NK\sigma_{\bar{x}}^2.$$

We may now write

$$NK\sigma^2 = N \sum_1^K s^2 + NK\sigma_{\bar{x}}^2,$$

and, dividing by K,

$$N\sigma^2 = N\overline{s^2} + N\sigma_{\bar{x}}^2,$$

where $\overline{s^2}$ is the arithmetic mean of the s^2 values.

$$N\sigma^2 = N\overline{s^2} + N \frac{\sigma^2}{N},$$

$$= N\overline{s^2} + \sigma^2.$$

$$N\sigma^2 - \sigma^2 = N\overline{s^2}.$$

$$\sigma^2(N - 1) = N\overline{s^2}.$$

$$\sigma^2 = \frac{N}{N-1} \overline{s^2},$$

$$= \frac{N}{N-1} \frac{\dfrac{\Sigma x_1^2}{N} + \dfrac{\Sigma x_2^2}{N} + \cdots + \dfrac{\Sigma x_K^2}{N}}{K},$$

$$= \frac{\dfrac{\Sigma x_1^2}{N-1} + \dfrac{\Sigma x_2^2}{N-1} + \cdots + \dfrac{\Sigma x_K^2}{N-1}}{K},$$

$$= \frac{\hat{\sigma}_1^2 + \hat{\sigma}_2^2 + \cdots + \hat{\sigma}_K^2}{K}.$$

Section 24.4

To prove that $\sigma_{\bar{x}_1 - \bar{x}_2} = \sqrt{\sigma_{\bar{x}_1}^2 + \sigma_{\bar{x}_2}^2}$ for independent samples.

Given two independent series of paired arithmetic means, the means being for random samples of the same size, and each series consisting of K means, as follows:

Sample	Series 1	Series 2	Difference
1	$\bar{X}_{1,1}$	$\bar{X}_{2,1}$	$\bar{X}_{1,1} - \bar{X}_{2,1}$
2	$\bar{X}_{1,2}$	$\bar{X}_{2,2}$	$\bar{X}_{1,2} - \bar{X}_{2,2}$
3	$\bar{X}_{1,3}$	$\bar{X}_{2,3}$	$\bar{X}_{1,3} - \bar{X}_{2,3}$
.	.	.	.
.	.	.	.
.	.	.	.
K	$\bar{X}_{1,K}$	$\bar{X}_{2,K}$	$\bar{X}_{1,K} - \bar{X}_{2,K}$

The variance of the differences is

$$\sigma_{\bar{X}_1 - \bar{X}_2}^2 = \frac{\overset{K}{\underset{1}{\Sigma}}[(\bar{X}_1 - \bar{X}_2) - (\bar{\bar{X}}_1 - \bar{\bar{X}}_2)]^2}{K}$$

where $(\bar{\bar{X}}_1 - \bar{\bar{X}}_2)$ is the arithmetic mean of the differences and may be written

$$\frac{\overset{K}{\underset{1}{\Sigma}}(\bar{X}_1 - \bar{X}_2)}{K} = \frac{\overset{K}{\underset{1}{\Sigma}}\bar{X}_1}{K} - \frac{\overset{K}{\underset{1}{\Sigma}}\bar{X}_2}{K} = \bar{\bar{X}}_1 - \bar{\bar{X}}_2,$$

where $\bar{\bar{X}}_1$ and $\bar{\bar{X}}_2$ are the arithmetic means of series 1 and series 2,

so that

$$\sigma_{\bar{X}_1 - \bar{X}_2}^2 = \frac{\overset{K}{\underset{1}{\Sigma}}[(\bar{X}_1 - \bar{X}_2) - (\bar{\bar{X}}_1 - \bar{\bar{X}}_2)]^2}{K},$$

$$= \frac{\overset{K}{\underset{1}{\Sigma}}[(\bar{X}_1 - \bar{\bar{X}}_1) - (\bar{X}_2 - \bar{\bar{X}}_2)]^2}{K}$$

Writing $\bar{x}_1 = \bar{X}_1 - \bar{\bar{X}}_1$ and $\bar{x}_2 = \bar{X}_2 - \bar{\bar{X}}_2$, we have

$$\sigma^2_{\bar{X}_1 - \bar{X}_2} = \frac{\sum\limits_1^K (\bar{x}_1 - \bar{x}_2)^2}{K} = \frac{\sum\limits_1^K (\bar{x}_1^2 - 2\bar{x}_1\bar{x}_2 + \bar{x}_2^2)}{K},$$

$$= \frac{\sum\limits_1^K \bar{x}_1^2}{K} - 2\frac{\sum\limits_1^K \bar{x}_1\bar{x}_2}{K} + \frac{\sum\limits_1^K \bar{x}_2^2}{K}.$$

Now, $\dfrac{\sum\limits_1^K \bar{x}_1\bar{x}_2}{K}$ is a portion of the expression for the correlation coefficient

for the two series of means, which may be written $r_{\bar{x}_1\bar{x}_2} = \dfrac{\sum\limits_1^K \bar{x}_1\bar{x}_2}{K\sigma_{\bar{x}_1}\sigma_{\bar{x}_2}}$ (see

page 403 for the product-moment formula for r for a sample), so that

$$2\frac{\sum\limits_1^K \bar{x}_1\bar{x}_2}{K} = 2r_{\bar{x}_1\bar{x}_2}\sigma_{\bar{x}_1}\sigma_{\bar{x}_2}. \quad \text{Also, } \frac{\sum\limits_1^K \bar{x}_1^2}{K} = \sigma^2_{\bar{x}_1}, \text{ and } \frac{\sum\limits_1^K \bar{x}_2^2}{K} = \sigma^2_{\bar{x}_2}.$$

Therefore,

$$\sigma^2_{\bar{X}_1 - \bar{X}_2} = \sigma^2_{\bar{x}_1} - 2r_{\bar{x}_1\bar{x}_2}\sigma_{\bar{x}_1}\sigma_{\bar{x}_2} + \sigma^2_{\bar{x}_2}, \text{ and}$$

$$\sigma_{\bar{X}_1 - \bar{X}_2} = \sqrt{\sigma^2_{\bar{x}_1} - 2r_{\bar{x}_1\bar{x}_2}\sigma_{\bar{x}_1}\sigma_{\bar{x}_2} + \sigma^2_{\bar{x}_2}}.$$

Since the two series of means are independent, $r_{\bar{x}_1\bar{x}_2} = 0$ and

$$\sigma_{\bar{X}_1 - \bar{X}_2} = \sqrt{\sigma^2_{\bar{x}_1} + \sigma^2_{\bar{x}_2}}.$$

Section 24.5

$\dfrac{\hat{\sigma}_1^2 + \hat{\sigma}_2^2}{2}$ is an equally weighted average of $\hat{\sigma}_1^2$ and $\hat{\sigma}_2^2$. Using weights

equal to the number of degrees of freedom ($N_1 - 1$ and $N_2 - 1$) in each
of the two samples, we have

$$\hat{\sigma}_{1+2}^2 = \frac{(N_1 - 1)\hat{\sigma}_1^2 + (N_2 - 1)\hat{\sigma}_2^2}{N_1 - 1 + N_2 - 1},$$

$$= \frac{(N_1 - 1)\dfrac{\Sigma x_1^2}{N_1 - 1} + (N_2 - 1)\dfrac{\Sigma x_2^2}{N_2 - 1}}{N_1 - 1 + N_2 - 1},$$

$$= \frac{\Sigma x_1^2 + \Sigma x_2^2}{N_1 - 1 + N_2 - 1}.$$

Section 24.6

To prove that $\hat{\sigma}_{1+2} \sqrt{\dfrac{1}{N_1} + \dfrac{1}{N_2}} = \sqrt{\dfrac{\hat{\sigma}_1^2}{N_1} + \dfrac{\hat{\sigma}_2^2}{N_2}}$ when $N_1 = N_2 = N$,

$$\hat{\sigma}_{1+2} \sqrt{\frac{1}{N_1} + \frac{1}{N_2}} = \sqrt{\frac{\hat{\sigma}_{1+2}^2}{N} + \frac{\hat{\sigma}_{1+2}^2}{N}},$$

$$= \sqrt{\frac{\dfrac{(N-1)\hat{\sigma}_1^2 + (N-1)\hat{\sigma}_2^2}{N-1+N-1}}{N} + \frac{\dfrac{(N-1)\hat{\sigma}_1^2 + (N-1)\hat{\sigma}_2^2}{N-1+N-1}}{N}}$$

$$= \sqrt{\frac{\dfrac{(N-1)(\hat{\sigma}_1^2 + \hat{\sigma}_2^2)}{2N-2}}{N} + \frac{\dfrac{(N-1)(\hat{\sigma}_1^2 + \hat{\sigma}_2^2)}{2N-2}}{N}},$$

$$= \sqrt{\frac{\dfrac{\hat{\sigma}_1^2 + \hat{\sigma}_2^2}{2}}{N} + \frac{\dfrac{\hat{\sigma}_1^2 + \hat{\sigma}_2^2}{2}}{N}},$$

$$= \sqrt{\frac{\hat{\sigma}_1^2 + \hat{\sigma}_2^2}{N}} = \sqrt{\frac{\hat{\sigma}_1^2}{N} + \frac{\hat{\sigma}_2^2}{N}},$$

$$= \sqrt{\frac{\hat{\sigma}_1^2}{N_1} + \frac{\hat{\sigma}_2^2}{N_2}}.$$

Section 25.1

To prove that $\sigma_p = \sqrt{\dfrac{\pi\tau}{N}}$.

A proportion p is the arithmetic mean of a series of values where each occurrence equals 1 and each non-occurrence equals zero.

For a sample, we have:

	Number	Proportion
Occurrences.........................	a	p
Non-occurrences....................	b	q
Total........................	N	1.0

It is obvious that $a = Np$ and $b = Nq$.

Since an occurrence equals 1 and a non-occurrence equals zero, we have

$$\bar{X} = \frac{a(1) + b(0)}{N} = \frac{a}{N} = p,$$

and it follows that $\sigma_{\bar{x}} = \sigma_p = \dfrac{\sigma}{\sqrt{N}}.$

To obtain an expression for σ, we use the following population symbols:

	Number	Proportion
Occurrences	α	π
Non-occurrences	β	τ
Total	$\mathcal{P}$	1.0

It is clear that $\pi = \dfrac{\alpha}{\mathcal{P}}$ and $\tau = \dfrac{\beta}{\mathcal{P}}$.

Again, each occurrence equals 1 and each non-occurrence equals zero, so that

$$\sigma = \sqrt{\frac{\alpha(1)^2 + \beta(0)^2}{\mathcal{P}} - \left[\frac{\alpha(1) + \beta(0)}{\mathcal{P}}\right]^2},$$

$$= \sqrt{\frac{\alpha}{\mathcal{P}} - \left(\frac{\alpha}{\mathcal{P}}\right)^2} = \sqrt{\pi - \pi^2} = \sqrt{\pi(1 - \pi)},$$

$$= \sqrt{\pi\tau}.$$

We may now write

$$\sigma_p = \frac{\sigma}{\sqrt{N}} = \frac{\sqrt{\pi\tau}}{\sqrt{N}} = \sqrt{\frac{\pi\tau}{N}}.$$

Since $a = Np$, we may also write

$$\sigma_a = N\sigma_p = N\sqrt{\frac{\pi\tau}{N}} = \sqrt{N\pi\tau}.$$

Section 26.1

To prove that

$$\sum_{1}^{k_c}[N_c(\bar{X}_c - \bar{X})^2] = \sum_{1}^{k_c}\left[\frac{\left(\sum_{1}^{N_c}X\right)^2}{N_c}\right] - \frac{(\sum X)^2}{N}.$$

The expression on the left says: "For each column, square the deviation of the column mean from the grand mean, multiply by the number of items in the column, and sum these products for all columns."

$$\sum_{1}^{k_c}[N_c(\bar{X}_c - \bar{X})^2] = \sum_{1}^{k_c}[N_c(\bar{X}_c^2 - 2\bar{X}\bar{X}_c + \bar{X}^2)],$$

$$= \sum_{1}^{k_c}(N_c\bar{X}_c^2 - 2N_c\bar{X}\bar{X}_c + N_c\bar{X}^2),$$

$$= \sum_{1}^{k_c}(N_c\bar{X}_c^2) - 2\bar{X}\sum_{1}^{k_c}(N_c\bar{X}_c) + \sum_{1}^{k_c}(N_c\bar{X}^2).$$

But $\quad \sum\limits_{1}^{k_c}(N_c\bar{X}_c^2) = \sum\limits_{1}^{k_c}\left[N_c\left(\dfrac{\sum\limits_{1}^{N_c}X}{N_c}\right)^2\right] = \sum\limits_{1}^{k_c}\left[\dfrac{\left(\sum\limits_{1}^{N_c}X\right)^2}{N_c}\right];$

$\sum\limits_{1}^{k_c}(N_c\bar{X}_c) = \sum\limits_{1}^{k_c}\left(N_c\dfrac{\sum\limits_{1}^{N_c}X}{N_c}\right) = \sum\limits_{1}^{k_c}\left(\sum\limits_{1}^{N_c}X\right) = \sum X;$ and

$\sum\limits_{1}^{k_c}(N_c\bar{X}^2) = N\bar{X}^2 = \dfrac{(\sum X)^2}{N}.$

Therefore,

$$\sum\limits_{1}^{k_c}[N_c(\bar{X}_c - \bar{X})^2] = \sum\limits_{1}^{k_c}\left[\dfrac{\left(\sum\limits_{1}^{N_c}X\right)^2}{N_c}\right] - 2\bar{X}\sum X + \dfrac{(\sum X)^2}{N},$$

$$= \sum\limits_{1}^{k_c}\left[\dfrac{\left(\sum\limits_{1}^{N_c}X\right)^2}{N_c}\right] - \dfrac{(\sum X)^2}{N}.$$

Section 26.2

To prove that

$$\sum\limits_{1}^{k_c}\left[\sum\limits_{1}^{N_c}(X - \bar{X}_c)^2\right] = \sum X^2 - \sum\limits_{1}^{k_c}\left[\dfrac{\left(\sum\limits_{1}^{N_c}X\right)^2}{N_c}\right].$$

The expression on the left says: "For each column, total the squared deviations from the mean of that column and sum these totals for all columns."

$$\sum\limits_{1}^{k_c}\left[\sum\limits_{1}^{N_c}(X - \bar{X}_c)^2\right] = \sum\limits_{1}^{k_c}\left[\sum\limits_{1}^{N_c}(X^2 - 2\bar{X}_cX + \bar{X}_c^2)\right],$$

$$= \sum\limits_{1}^{k_c}\left(\sum\limits_{1}^{N_c}X^2 - 2\bar{X}_c\sum\limits_{1}^{N_c}X + N_c\bar{X}_c^2\right),$$

$$= \sum\limits_{1}^{k_c}\left[\sum\limits_{1}^{N_c}X^2 - 2\dfrac{\left(\sum\limits_{1}^{N_c}X\right)^2}{N_c} + \dfrac{\left(\sum\limits_{1}^{N_c}X\right)^2}{N_c}\right],$$

$$= \sum\limits_{1}^{k_c}\left[\sum\limits_{1}^{N_c}X^2 - \dfrac{\left(\sum\limits_{1}^{N_c}X\right)^2}{N_c}\right],$$

$$= \sum X^2 - \sum\limits_{1}^{k_c}\left[\dfrac{\left(\sum\limits_{1}^{N_c}X\right)^2}{N_c}\right].$$

Section 26.3

To prove that $\sqrt{\dfrac{r^2(N-2)}{1-r^2}} = \sqrt{\dfrac{b^2\Sigma x^2(N-2)}{\Sigma y_s^2}}.$

$$\sqrt{\frac{r^2(N-2)}{1-r^2}} = \sqrt{\frac{\dfrac{(\Sigma xy)^2}{\Sigma x^2\Sigma y^2}(N-2)}{\dfrac{\Sigma y_s^2}{\Sigma y^2}}} = \sqrt{\frac{\dfrac{(\Sigma xy)^2}{\Sigma x^2}(N-2)}{\Sigma y_s^2}}.$$

Since $b = \dfrac{\Sigma xy}{\Sigma x^2},$ $\quad \dfrac{(\Sigma xy)^2}{\Sigma x^2} = b^2\Sigma x^2,$ and

$$\sqrt{\frac{r^2(N-2)}{1-r^2}} = \sqrt{\frac{b^2\Sigma x^2(N-2)}{\Sigma y_s^2}}.$$

Section 26.4

To prove that $t^2 = F$ for coefficients of partial correlation. That is, that

$$\frac{r^2_{1m.23\cdots(m-1)}(N-m)}{1-r^2_{1m.23\cdots(m-1)}} = \frac{(\Sigma x^2_{c1.234\cdots m} - \Sigma x^2_{c1.234\cdots(m-1)})(N-m)}{\Sigma x^2_1 - \Sigma x^2_{c1.234\cdots m}}.$$

Since $r^2_{1m.23\cdots(m-1)} = \dfrac{\Sigma x^2_{c1.234\cdots m} - \Sigma x^2_{c1.234\cdots(m-1)}}{\Sigma x^2_1 - \Sigma x^2_{c1.234\cdots(m-1)}},$ we may write

$$\frac{r^2_{1m.23\cdots(m-1)}(N-m)}{1-r^2_{1m.23\cdots(m-1)}}$$

$$= \frac{\dfrac{\Sigma x^2_{c1.234\cdots m} - \Sigma x^2_{c1.234\cdots(m-1)}}{\Sigma x^2_1 - \Sigma x^2_{c1.234\cdots(m-1)}}(N-m)}{\dfrac{\Sigma x^2_1 - \Sigma x^2_{c1.234\cdots(m-1)}}{\Sigma x^2_1 - \Sigma x^2_{c1.234\cdots(m-1)}} - \dfrac{\Sigma x^2_{c1.234\cdots m} - \Sigma x^2_{c1.234\cdots(m-1)}}{\Sigma x^2_1 - \Sigma x^2_{c1.234\cdots(m-1)}}}$$

$$= \frac{(\Sigma x^2_{c1.234\cdots m} - \Sigma x^2_{c1.234\cdots(m-1)})(N-m)}{\Sigma x^2_1 - \Sigma x^2_{c1.234\cdots m}}.$$

APPENDIX T

Rounding Numbers[1]

Terminology

Original data result from measurements (which can never be exact) **or** from counting. Measurements will therefore always be rounded; counts may be rounded. A number which is the result of rounding always represents a range of possible values rather than a single value. Thus, if such a number is recorded as 78 pounds, we know that the true value is not lower than 77.5 pounds nor higher than 78.5 pounds.

A digit is significant if the error in the next position to the right does not exceed ± 5. Thus, if a measurement is recorded as 172.3 pounds, we assume that the correct value does not lie beyond the limits of 172.3 ± 0.05, or 172.25 pounds and 172.35 pounds, and there are four significant digits. It is sometimes difficult to ascertain the number of significant digits, even in an enumeration. Thus, it is extremely unlikely that there were exactly 178,464,236 persons in the continental United States on April 1, 1960, as reported by the Bureau of the Census.

Below are given three illustrations of correct terminology for measurements that have been accurately made and properly recorded, or for rounded enumerations:

127.34 is said to contain five significant digits. It has been rounded to five significant digits, or to two significant decimal places.

4,125 thousand or 4.125 million or $4,125 \times 10^3$ or 4,125,000, is significant to four digits. If occurring in a table, usually 4,125 is recorded, with a prefatory note or column heading specifying thousands. The number of significant digits in 4,125,000 is ambiguous, since it may range from four to seven. The context, however, often indicates the number of significant digits. There is no ambiguity if a number ends in zero after

---

[1] This discussion of rounding numbers is from F. E. Croxton and D. J. Cowden, *Practical Business Statistics*, third edition, Prentice-Hall, Inc., Englewood Cliffs, N. J., 1960, pp. 52–57.

a decimal point. Thus 4,125.0 and 4.1250 each have five significant digits.

0.00031 contains two rather than five significant digits (though 0.10031 contains five and 1.00031 contains six). This is because the choice of a unit of measurement is arbitrary. For instance, 0.031 meters is also 31 millimeters. The importance of this concept will be apparent when rules for multiplying and dividing rounded numbers are given.

Rules for Rounding

1. If the leftmost of the digits discarded is less than 5, the preceding digit is not affected. Thus 113.746 becomes 113.7 when rounded to four digits.

2. If the leftmost of the digits discarded is greater than 5, or is 5 followed by digits not all of which are zero if carried out to a sufficient number of digits, the preceding digit is increased by one. Thus, 129.673 becomes 129.7 when rounded to four digits. Also, 87.2500001 becomes 87.3 when rounded to three digits.

3. If the leftmost of the digits discarded is 5, followed by zeros, the preceding digit is increased by one if it is odd, and left unchanged if it is even. The number is thus rounded in such a manner that the last digit retained is even. For example, 103.55 becomes 103.6 and 103.45 becomes 103.4 when rounded to four digits. (However, 103.5499 becomes 103.5 as explained in paragraph 1, and 103.4501 becomes 103.5 as explained in paragraph 2.) This rule is adopted in order to avoid the cumulation of errors in summations, which could result if the preceding digit were always raised or always left unchanged. The rule (making the last digit even) is more generally used than its reverse (making the last digit odd). It is more convenient than alternately adding and dropping the half, since one is spared the trouble of remembering which was done last.

Products and Quotients Obtained from Rounded Numbers

1. In multiplication (including squaring), division, or extraction of square root, one should not record as a *final answer* more digits than there are in the original number with the fewest significant digits.[2] The follow-

---

[2] In special circumstances an exception may be made to this rule, provided the number of digits that are significant in the answer is clearly indicated.

Where several computations involving multiplication, division, or extracting a square root are involved in working with one set of data, it is sometimes advisable to record *one more* digit in *intermediate* computations than there are in the original number with the fewest significant digits. Sometimes more than one nonsignificant digit may be desirable. In this volume we have sometimes carried more than one nonsignificant digit in order to obtain a formal check on the accuracy of our computations. While the extra digits may not be absolutely accurate, they are sufficiently close to contribute something to the final answer. For instance, if we want

ing illustrations thus indicate the maximum number of digits which it is good practice to record:

$$358 \times 412 = 147 \text{ thousand.}$$
$$14 \times 427 = 6.0 \text{ thousand.}$$
$$3,194 \times 25 \times 427 = 34 \text{ million.}$$
$$4,831 \times 0.00412 = 19.9$$
$$5,673 \times 8 \text{ (exactly)} = 45.38 \text{ thousand.}$$
$$25 \div 23 = 1.1$$
$$42.7 \div 52 = 0.82$$
$$52 \div 42.7 = 1.2$$
$$\sqrt{0.354} = 0.595$$

In the above illustrations the maximum number of digits that may be significant is recorded; in some instances the number significant will be fewer than the number recorded.[3]

2. If a given number of significant digits is required in the final answer, each of the original numbers and each of the intermediate results should have one more significant digit than the number of digits required in the answer. If any of the original data contain more digits than called for by this rule, the excess digits may be rounded off. Thus, if three digits are required in the final answer, we may proceed as follows:

$$\sqrt{\frac{(2.7608)^2}{(13.195)(0.87367)}} = \sqrt{\frac{(2.761)^2}{(13.20)(0.8737)}} = \sqrt{\frac{7.623}{11.53}} = \sqrt{0.6611} = 0.813.$$

As is almost always the case, the final answer is the same as if we had retained all of the original digits and also one more digit in each intermediate step:

$$\sqrt{\frac{(2.7608)^2}{(13.195)(0.87367)}} = \sqrt{\frac{7.6220}{11.528}} = \sqrt{0.66117} = 0.813.$$

The rounding of the original data is justified because of the small probability that most of the numbers involved will be in error close to

---

three digits in our final answer and have $(4.137 \times 0.684) \div (0.316 \times 7.831)$ we would employ $2.830 \div 2.475 = 1.14$ rather than $2.83 \div 2.47 = 1.15$.

[3] In the case of the seventh illustration there is, strictly speaking, only one significant digit in the answer. Remembering that a rounded number recorded as 42.7 may vary between 42.65 and 42.75, while one recorded as 52 may vary between 51.5 and 52.5, we may compute:

$$42.75 \div 51.5 = .830 \text{ to three digits, the largest possible result;}$$
$$42.7 \div 52 = .821 \text{ to three digits;}$$
$$42.65 \div 52.5 = .812 \text{ to three digits, the smallest possible result.}$$

Since .830 and .812 are not included within $.821 \pm .005$, it is apparent that the second digit in .821 is not significant.

the maximum possible amount, and the large probability that there will be considerable offsetting of errors.

3. When the correct product or quotient is known in advance, it should be recorded rather than the approximate product or quotient resulting from use of the rounded original numbers. Thus, although $0.125 \times 0.333 = 0.0416$, if it is known that the actual operation is $\frac{1}{8} \times \frac{1}{3} = \frac{1}{24} = 0.0417$, the answer should be recorded as 0.0417 rather than 0.0416.

Sums and Differences Obtained from Rounded Numbers

Rules for addition and subtraction substantially parallel those for multiplication and division, except that it is the number of significant decimal places, rather than the number of significant digits, that must be considered.

1. In addition or subtraction, one should never record as a *final answer* more decimal places than there are in the original number with the fewest significant decimal places. The following illustrations thus indicate the maximum number of digits which it is good practice to record:

$$2{,}156.2 + 39 = 2{,}195.$$
$$2{,}156.2 - 39 = 2{,}117.$$
$$13 + 12 = 25.$$
$$13 - 12 = 1.$$

In the above illustrations the maximum number of significant decimal places is recorded; in some instances the number significant will be fewer than the number recorded.[4]

2. If a given number of significant decimal places is required in the final answer, it is desirable that each of the original numbers have one more significant decimal place than the number of decimal places required in the answer. If any of the original data contain more digits than called for by this rule, the excess digits may be rounded off. Thus, if no decimal place (no digit to the right of the decimal point) is required in the final answer, we may proceed as follows:

$$\left.\begin{array}{r} 122.34 \\ 81.7 \\ 293.826 \end{array}\right\} \text{may be rounded to} \left\{\begin{array}{r} 122.3 \\ 81.7 \\ 293.8 \end{array}\right.$$

$$\underline{497.866497.8,}$$

both of which round to 498.

The rounding of the original data is justified because of the small proba-

---

[4] If the student will check the last two results by a procedure similar to that described in footnote 3, he will find that the last digit recorded is not significant, since the limits of error are ± 1.0, instead of the permissible ± 0.5.

bility that most of the numbers involved will be in error close to the maximum possible amount, and the large probability that there will be considerable offsetting of errors.

3. When the correct total is known in advance, it should be recorded, rather than the approximate total resulting from addition of the rounded numbers. Thus:

	Dollars	Thousands of dollars	Per cent of total*
	507,334	507.3	66.67
	126,832	126.8	16.67
	126,834	126.8	16.67
Total of recorded numbers................	761,000	760.9	100.01
Record the total known to be correct........	761,000	761.0	100.00

* Computed from column 1. Total would not be exactly 100, even if 7 digits were recorded for each percentage.

Index